# NUMERICA

*[For B.E., B.Tech., B.Sc. (Applied Sciences) M.C.A. and B.Sc., M.Sc. (Mathematics Main)]*

**(Includes all portions of Anna University Syllabus)**


**P. KANDASAMY**

M.A., Ph.D.

*Professor of Mathematics (Retd.)*

*P.S.G. College of Technology*

*COIMBATORE*

*&*

*Visiting Professor*

*Amrita Institute of Technology and Science (Deemed University)*

*COIMBATORE*

**K. THILAGAVATHY**

M.Sc., M.Phil, Ph.D.

*Reader in Mathematics*

*Kongunadu Arts and Science College*

*COIMBATORE*

**K. GUNAVATHY**

M.E., Ph.D.

*Professor, Department of*

*Electronics and Communication Engineering*

*P.S.G. College of Technology*

*COIMBATORE*

**S. CHAND & COMPANY PVT. LTD.**

**(An ISO 9001 : 2008 Company)**

**RAM NAGAR, NEW DELHI - 110 055**

**S. CHAND & COMPANY PVT. LTD.**
**(An ISO 9001 : 2008 Company)**
*Head Office*: 7361, RAM NAGAR, NEW DELHI - 110 055
Phone: 23672080-81-82, 9899107446, 9911310888 Fax: 91-11-23677446
www.schandpublishing.com; e-mail: helpdesk@schandpublishing.com

**Branches**

| | | |
|---|---|---|
| Ahmedabad | : | Ph: 27541965, 27542369, ahmedabad@schandpublishing.com |
| Bengaluru | : | Ph: 22268048, 22354008, bangalore@schandpublishing.com |
| Bhopal | : | Ph: 4274723, 4209587, bhopal@schandpublishing.com |
| Chandigarh | : | Ph: 2725443, 2725446, chandigarh@schandpublishing.com |
| Chennai | : | Ph. 28410027, 28410058, chennai@schandpublishing.com |
| Coimbatore | : | Ph: 2323620, 4217136, coimbatore@schandpublishing.com (Marketing Office) |
| Cuttack | : | Ph: 2332580; 2332581, cuttack@schandpublishing.com |
| Dehradun | : | Ph: 2711101, 2710861, dehradun@schandpublishing.com |
| Guwahati | : | Ph: 2738811, 2735640, guwahati@schandpublishing.com |
| Hyderabad | : | Ph: 27550194, 27550195, hyderabad@schandpublishing.com |
| Jaipur | : | Ph: 2219175, 2219176, jaipur@schandpublishing.com |
| Jalandhar | : | Ph: 2401630, 5000630, jalandhar@schandpublishing.com |
| Kochi | : | Ph: 2378740, 2378207-08, cochin@schandpublishing.com |
| Kolkata | : | Ph: 22367459, 22373914, kolkata@schandpublishing.com |
| Lucknow | : | Ph: 4026791, 4065646 lucknow@schandpublishing.com |
| Mumbai | : | Ph: 22690881, 22610885, mumbai@schandpublishing.com |
| Nagpur | : | Ph: 6451311, 2720523, 2777666, nagpur@schandpublishing.com |
| Patna | : | Ph: 2300489, 2302100, patna@schandpublishing.com |
| Pune | : | Ph: 64017298, pune@schandpublishing.com |
| Raipur | : | Ph: 2443142, raipur@schandpublishing.com (Marketing Office) |
| Ranchi | : | Ph: 2361178, ranchi@schandpublishing.com |
| Siliguri | : | Ph: 2520750, siliguri@schandpublishing.com (Marketing Office) |
| Visakhapatnam | : | Ph: 2782609 visakhapatnam@schandpublishing.com (Marketing Office) |



*First Edition 1997*
*Subsequent Editions and Reprints 1997, 99 (Twice), 2000, 2001, 2002, 2003 (Twice), 2005 (Twice), 2006, 2007, 2008, 2009 (Twice), 2010 (Thrice), 2012 (Twice), 2013 (Twice), 2014, 2015*
*Reprint 2016*

**ISBN :** 978-81-219-1438-3 **Code :** 1010B 175

**This book is for Sale in India & other SAARC Countries only.**

PRINTED IN INDIA

*By Vikas Publishing House Pvt. Ltd., Plot 20/4, Site-IV, Industrial Area Sahibabad, Ghaziabad-201010 and Published by S.Chand & Company Pvt. Ltd., 7361, Ram Nagar, New Delhi -110 055.*

## THIRD REVISED EDITION

Cubic spline interpolation is added in this Revised Edition.

**AUTHORS**

## PREFACE TO THE FIRST EDITION

We are very happy to present to our readers, students and teachers alike, this book on "Numerical Methods". Actually this is in continuation to other three Volumes of our book "Text book on Engineering Mathematics" for B.E. course, which cater to the needs of the first and the second year students. The present book is to meet the requirements of the students of the fifth semester, the need of which was being felt very anxiously.

In the treatment, we have tried to maintain the same style, as used in the other three Volumes. All the topics have been covered comprehensively, but with clarity in lucid and easy way to grasp. There is a good number of fully solved examples with exercises to be worked out, at the end of each chapter. Besides there are short answer questions, model question papers and a few University question papers at the end of the book. We are sure that this book will receive the same warm welcome by its users, as in the case of other three Volumes of the series.

We shall feel highly obliged for any suggestions and constructive criticisms for the improvement of the book.

Lastly, we thank our Publishers, M/s S. Chand & Company Ltd., New Delhi, specially the Managing Director, Sh. Rajendra Kumar Gupta and the Director, Sh. Ravindra Kumar Gupta for their kind cooperation at every stage, without which it would not have been possible to bring out this book in such a fine format and that too in a record time.

**AUTHORS**

For suggestions, write to
P. Kandasamy,
66, Thirty feet Road
Krishnasamy Nagar
Ramanathapuram
Coimbatore-641045

# ANNA UNIVERSITY
# SYLLABUS

*(June 2004 onwards)*
*(B.E./B. Tech. Courses)*

## MA 1251 Numerical Methods

### OBJECTIVES

With the present development of the computer technology, it is necessary to develop efficient algorithms for solving problems in science, engineering and technology. This course gives a complete procedure for solving different kinds of problems that occur in engineering numerically. At the end of the course the students would be acquainted with the basic concepts in numerical methods and their uses.

1. **Solution of Equations and Eigne Value Problems** **9**

   Linear interpolation methods (method of false position)—Newton's method—Statement of Fixed Point Theorem—Fixed pointer iteration $x = g(x)$ method—Solution of liner system of Gaussian elimination and Gauss-Jordan methods—Iterative methods : Gausss Jacobi and Gauss—Seidel methods—Inverse of a matrix by Gauss-Jordan method. Eigen value of a matrix by power methods.

2. **Interpolation and Approximation** **9**

   Lagrangian Polynomials—Divided difference—Interpolaticn with a cubic spline—Newton forward and backward difference formulae.

3. **Numerical Differentiation and Integration** **9**

   Derivatives from difference table—Divided difference and finite difference—Numerical integration by Trapezoidal and Simpson's 1/3 and 3/8 rules—Romberg's method—Two and three point Gaussian quadrature formulas—Double integrals using trapezoidal and Simpson's rules

4. **Initial Value Problems for Ordinary Differential Equations** **9**

   Single step Methods : Taylor Series and methods—Euler and Modified Euler methods—Fourth order Runge-Kutta method for solving first and second order equations—Multistep methods—Milne's and Adam's predictor and corrector methods.

5. **Boundary Value Problems** **9**

   Finite difference solution for the second order ordinary differential equations. Finite difference solution for one dimensional heat equation by implict and explict methods—one dimensional wave equation and two dimensional Laplace and Poisson equations.

**TUTORIAL** **15**

**Total : 60**

## TEXT BOOKS

1. Gerald, C.F., and Wheatley, P.O., "Applied Numerical Analysis", Sixth Edition, Pearson Education Asia, New Delhi 2002.
2. Balagurusamy, E., "Numerical Methods", Tata McGraw-Hill Pub. Co. Ltd., New Delhi 1999.

## REFERENCES

1. Kandasamy, P. Thilakavthy, K and Gunavathy, K. Numerical Methods. S. Chand and Co. New Delhi 1999.
2. Burden, R.L. and Faries, T.D., "Numerical Analysis", Seventh Edition, Thomson Asia Pvt. Ltd, Singapore 2002.
3. Venkatraman M.K., "Numerical Methods" National Pub. Company, Chennai, 1991.
4. Sankara Rao K., "Numerical Methods for Scientists and Engineers", 2nd Ed. Prentice Hall India 2004.

# CONTENTS

# 1

# *Empirical Laws and Curve Fittings*

## 1.1. Introduction

In practical life and also in Engineering and Science, we come across experiments which involve two quantities. An anxiety arises in us to know the relationship which connects the two quantities. For example, we measure the heights and weights of students in our class and represent those values by $x_i$ and $y_i$, $i = 1, 2, ..., n$ (assume there are $n$ students). Now, we would like to know whether there is any relation between $x$ and $y$. This relation, when written as an equation $y = f(x)$, is called an emperical equation. Many times we may not be able to get an exact relation but we may get only an approximate curve. This approximating curve is an empirical equation and the method of finding such an approximating curve is called curve fitting. The constants occuring in the equation of the approximating curve can be found by various methods If $(x_i, y_i)$, $i = 1, 2, ..., n$ are the n paired data which are plotted on the graph sheet, it is possible to draw a number of smooth curves passing through the points. So, the approximating curve is not unique.

## 1.2. The linear law

Suppose that the relationship between the variables $x$ and $y$ is linear.

Assume it to be $y = ax + b$ ...(1)

That is, if the points $(x_i, y_i)$ are plotted in the graph-sheet, they should lie on a straight line. '$a$' is the slope of the straight and $b$ is the $y$-intercept. Taking any two points $(x_1, y_1)$ and $(x_2, y_2)$ which are apart, slope of the straight line $a = \dfrac{y_2 - y_1}{x_2 - x_1}$ ; $b$ can be found by knowing the $y$-intercept or by substituting any point on the line. Substituting $a$ and $b$ in (1), we get the straight line required.

## 1.3. Laws reducible to linear law

(1) Law of the pattern $y = ax^n$ where $a$ and $n$ are constants.

Let $y = ax^n$ be the law.

Taking logarithm on both sides,

$\log_{10} y = \log_{10} a + n \log_{10} x$

*i.e.*, $Y = A + n X$ where $Y = \log_{10} y$, $A = \log_{10} a$ and $X = \log_{10} x$

Now $A$ and $n$ can be found as explained earlier.

Hence, $a$ and $n$ are known.

(2) Law of the pattern $y = a e^{bx}$ where $a$, $b$ are constants.

Taking logarithm on both sides,

$\log_{10} y = \log_{10} a + bx$

*i.e.*, $Y = A + bx$ where $\log_{10} y = Y$, $A = \log_{10} a$

After getting $A$, $b$ we get again $a$ and $b$.

Hence, $y = a e^{bx}$ is known.

(3) Law of the pattern $y = a + bx^n$ where $n$ is known and $a$, $b$ are unknown constants.

Setting $x^n = u$, we have $y = a + bu$, which is linear in $y$ and $u$. Since $x$ is given, $u$ can be found out. The linear fit $y = a + bu$ can be got as explained earlier.

The forms $y = a + bx^2$, $y = a + b\sqrt{x}$, $y = a + \dfrac{b}{x}$ are all of this type explained above.

In general, getting an emperical equation, depends upon :

(*i*) the determination of the form of the equation, and

(*ii*) the evaluation of the constants in the equation.

Normally, the form of the equation is agreed upon from the data and then the constants are evaluated.

In this chapter, given the form of the equation, we will try to evaluate the constants.

**Example 1.** *Plot the points on the graph and obtain a relation of the form $y = ax + b$ given the following data. Find $y$ at $x$ = 500.*

| $x$ | 225 | 300 | 430 | 560 | 600 |
|---|---|---|---|---|---|
| $y$ | 60 | 75 | 100 | 125 | 145 |

**Solution.** Since the form is already accepted to be linear, we plot the points on the graph-sheet and draw a smooth straight line which is only approximate.

$$\text{Slope} = \frac{75-60}{300-225} = 0{\cdot}2$$

Hence $y = 0{\cdot}2x + b$

Substituting, $60 = 0{\cdot}2(225) + b \quad \therefore \quad b = 15$

Hence the rough form is $y = 0{\cdot}2x + 15$

Value of $y$ at $x = 500$ is 115.

**Note.** The equation is not unique since the answer depends upon our approach. One can give a number approximating straight lines. Hence, graphical approach is not accurate. Hence we will go to analytical approach rather than graphical approach.

## EXERCISE 1.1

**1.** Find the relation of the form $y = \frac{a}{x} + b$ from the data using the graph:

| $x$ | : | 1·95 | 2·46 | 3 | 3·44 | 3·96 |
|---|---|---|---|---|---|---|
| $y$ | : | 67 | 63 | 59·6 | 58 | 56 |

**2.** Find the relation of the form $y = a + \frac{b}{x}$ given

| $x$ | : | 36·8 | 31·5 | 26·3 | 21·0 | 15·8 | 12·6 | 8·4 |
|---|---|---|---|---|---|---|---|---|
| $y$ | : | 12·5 | 12·9 | 13·1 | 13·3 | 14·1 | 14·5 | 16·3 |

**3.** Plot the points and obtain a st. line fit from the graph.

| $x$ | : | 1 | 2 | 3 | 4 | 5 | 6 |
|---|---|---|---|---|---|---|---|
| $y$ | : | 1200 | 900 | 600 | 200 | 110 | 50 |

**4.** For the following data, fit a curve of the form, $yx^n = k$ from the data given below:

| $y$ | : | 15 | 30 | 60 | 100 | 200 | 400 |
|---|---|---|---|---|---|---|---|
| $x$ | : | 10 | 5·6 | 3·2 | 2·1 | 1·2 | 0·7 |

### 1.4. Evaluation of constants by the method of group averages (To fit a straight line)

Let $(x_i, y_i)$, $i = 1, 2, \ldots, n$ be $n$ sets of observations and the law relating $x$ and $y$ be

$$y = a + bx \qquad \ldots(1)$$

We assume that the law is a linear one (we do not prove it is linear). We want to determine $a$ and $b$. By assumption $y = a + bx$ is the law, it does not mean the points lie on the st. line. It is only an approximating st. line and it is possible that no point may lie on the line.

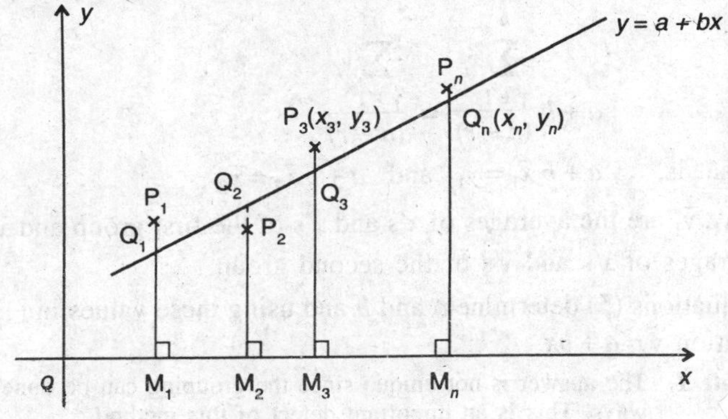

We plot the points $(x_i, y_i)$ by $P_i$, $i = 1, 2, ..., n$. The ordinates at $x = x_i$, meets the straight line at $Q_i$, $i = 1, 2, ..., n$.

At $x = x_i$, $P_i M_i = y_i$, and $Q_i M_i = a + bx_i$

$P_i M_i = y_i =$ observed value of $y$ at $x = x_i$

$Q_i M_i = a + bx_i =$ expected value of $y$ at $x = x_i$

$d_i = Q_i P_i = M_i P_i - M_i Q_i = y_i - (a + bx_i)$ which is the difference between the observed value $y$ and the expected value of $y$ is called the residual at $x = x_i$. In general, $d_i$'s may be positive or negative.

*Principle*: The method of group averages is based on the *principle* (assumption) that the sum of the residuals at all points is ***Zero***.

*i.e.,* $$\Sigma d_i = 0 \qquad ...(2)$$

Since we require two equations to find two unknowns $a$ and $b$, we divide the given data into two groups, first one containing $\gamma$ sets of values and the other containing $(n - \gamma)$ sets of values. We apply the principle $\Sigma d_i = 0$ for each group. Hence

$$\sum_{i=1}^{\gamma} [y_i - (a + bx_i)] = 0 \quad \text{and} \quad \sum_{i=r+1}^{n} [y_i - (a + bx_i)] = 0$$

$$\therefore \quad \sum_{1}^{\gamma} y_i = \sum_{1}^{\gamma} (a + bx_i) \quad \text{and} \quad \sum_{r+1}^{n} y_i = \sum_{r+1}^{n} (a + bx_i)$$

*i.e.,* $$\gamma a + b \sum_{1}^{\gamma} x_i = \sum_{1}^{\gamma} y_i \quad \text{and} \quad (n - \gamma) a + b \sum_{r+1}^{n} x_i = \sum_{r+1}^{n} y_i$$

Hence, $$a + b \frac{\sum_{1}^{\gamma} x_i}{r} = \frac{\sum_{1}^{\gamma} y_i}{r} \qquad ...(3)$$

and $$a + b \frac{\sum_{\gamma+1}^{n} x_i}{(n - r)} = \frac{\sum_{\gamma+1}^{n} y_i}{(n - r)} \qquad ...(4)$$

That is, $$a + b\bar{x}_1 = \bar{y}_1 \quad \text{and} \quad a + b\bar{x}_2 = \bar{y}_2 \qquad ...(5)$$

where $\bar{x}_1, \bar{y}_1$ are the averages of $x$'s and $y$'s of the first group and $\bar{x}_2, \bar{y}_2$ are the averages of $x$'s and $y$'s of the second group.

Equations (5) determine $a$ and $b$ and using these values in (1) we get the relation $y = a + bx$.

**Note 1.** The answer is not unique since the grouping can be done in many ways. This is an important defect of this method.

**2.** The straight line passes through the two points $(\bar{x}_1, \bar{y}_1)$ and $(\bar{x}_2, \bar{y}_2)$. Hence its equation is

$$\frac{y-\bar{y}_1}{x-\bar{x}_1} = \frac{\bar{y}_1-\bar{y}_2}{\bar{x}_1-\bar{x}_2}.$$

**3.** In practice, we shall divide the data into two groups so that both contain the same number of points.

**4.** The equations got is only an approximate fit to the data given.

**Example 2.** *Find a straight line fit of the form $y = a + bx$, by the method of group averages for the following data :*

| | | | | | | | |
|---|---|---|---|---|---|---|---|
| $x$ | : | 0 | 5 | 10 | 15 | 20 | 25 |
| $y$ | : | 12 | 15 | 17 | 22 | 24 | 30 |

(M.K.U., 1973)

**Solution.** Let us divide the data into two groups each containing three sets of data.

| | Group I : $x$ | $y$ | Group II : $x$ | $y$ |
|---|---|---|---|---|
| | 0 | 12 | 15 | 22 |
| | 5 | 15 | 20 | 24 |
| | 10 | 17 | 25 | 30 |
| Sum : | 15 | 44 | 60 | 76 |

$$\therefore \quad \bar{x}_1 = \frac{15}{3} = 5\,; \qquad \bar{y}_1 = \frac{44}{3} = 14{\cdot}6666$$

$$\bar{x}_2 = \frac{60}{3} = 20\,; \qquad \bar{y}_2 = \frac{76}{3} = 25{\cdot}3333$$

Substituting the average values $\bar{x}$ in $\bar{y} = a + b\,\bar{x}$, we get

$$a + 5b = 14{\cdot}6666 \qquad \ldots(1)$$

$$a + 20b = 25{\cdot}3333 \qquad \ldots(2)$$

(2) – (1) gives, $\quad 15b = 10{\cdot}6667$

$$\therefore \quad b = 0{\cdot}71111$$

$$a = 14{\cdot}6666 - 5\,(0{\cdot}71111) = 11{\cdot}11105$$

Hence, the straight is $y = 11{\cdot}11105 + 0{\cdot}71111\,x$

**Aliter:** The required equation is the straight line joining the points (5, 14·6666) and (20, 25·3333). Its equation is,

$$\frac{y - 14{\cdot}6666}{x-5} = \frac{25{\cdot}3333 - 14{\cdot}6666}{20-5} = \frac{10{\cdot}6667}{15} = 0{\cdot}71111$$

*i.e.,* $\quad y = 14{\cdot}6666 + 0{\cdot}71111\,x - 5 \times (0{\cdot}71111)$

$$y = 0{\cdot}71111\,x + 11{\cdot}11105$$

**Example 3.** *The following table gives corresponding values of x and y. Obtain an equation of the form $y = ax + bx^2$.*

| | | | | | | | |
|---|---|---|---|---|---|---|---|
| $x$ | : | 1·1 | 2·0 | 3·2 | 4·0 | 5·5 | 6·3 |
| $y$ | : | 5·3 | 14·2 | 30·1 | 43·8 | 77·3 | 97·8 |

**Solution.** Rewriting the equation as $\frac{y}{x} = a + bx$, put $\frac{y}{x} = Y$ ; $x = X$

Hence the equation is $Y = a + bX$

| | Group I | | Group II | |
|---|---|---|---|---|
| | $x = X$ | $Y = \frac{y}{x}$ | $x = X$ | $Y = \frac{y}{x}$ |
| | 1·1 | 4·82 | 4·0 | 10·95 |
| | 2·0 | 7·10 | 5·5 | 14·05 |
| | 3·2 | 9·41 | 6·3 | 15·52 |
| Sum : | 6·3 | 21·33 | 15·8 | 40·52 |

$$\bar{X}_1 = \frac{6\cdot3}{3} = 2\cdot1, \qquad \bar{Y}_1 = \frac{21\cdot33}{3} = 7\cdot11$$

$$\bar{X}_2 = \frac{15\cdot8}{3} = 5\cdot2666, \qquad \bar{Y}_2 = \frac{40\cdot52}{3} = 13\cdot5066$$

$\therefore$ The line joining $(\bar{X}_1, \bar{Y}_1)$ and $(\bar{X}_2, \bar{Y}_2)$ is

$$\frac{Y - 7\cdot11}{X - 2\cdot1} = \frac{13\cdot5066 - 7\cdot11}{5\cdot2666 - 2\cdot1} = \frac{6\cdot3966}{3\cdot1666} = 2\cdot02002$$

*i.e.,*
$$Y = 7\cdot11 + 2\cdot02X - 2\cdot02 \times 2\cdot1$$
$$Y = 2\cdot02X + 2\cdot868$$
$$\frac{y}{x} = 2\cdot02X + 2\cdot868$$

*i.e.,* $y = 2\cdot02x^2 + 2\cdot868x$ is the required equation.

(Here $a = 2\cdot868,\ b = 2\cdot02$)

**Example 4.** *The following numbers relate to the flow of water over a triangular notch.*

| $H$ : | 1·2 | 1·4 | 1·6 | 1·8 | 2·0 | 2·4 |
|---|---|---|---|---|---|---|
| $Q$ : | 4·2 | 6·1 | 8·5 | 11·5 | 14·9 | 23·5 |

*If the law is* $Q = C\,H^n$, *find C and n by the method of group averages.*

**Solution.** $Q = CH^n$

$$\log_{10} Q = \log_{10} C + n \log_{10} H$$

$y = a + nx$ where $\log_{10} Q = y$, $\log_{10} H = x$ and $a = \log_{10} C$

| | Group I | | Group II | |
|---|---|---|---|---|
| | $x = \log_{10} H$, | $y = \log_{10} Q$ | $x = \log_{10} H$, | $y = \log_{10} Q$ |
| | 0·07918 | 0·62325 | 0·25527 | 1·06070 |
| | 0·14163 | 0·78533 | 0·30103 | 1·17319 |
| | 0·20412 | 0·92942 | 0·38021 | 1·37107 |
| Sum : | 0·42493 | 2·33800 | 0·93651 | 3·60496 |

$$\bar{x}_1 = \frac{0\cdot42493}{3} = 0\cdot141643\ ; \qquad \bar{y}_1 = \frac{2\cdot3380}{3} = 0\cdot77933$$

$$\bar{x}_2 = \frac{0\cdot93651}{3} = 0\cdot31217\ ; \qquad \bar{y}_2 = \frac{3\cdot60496}{3} = 1\cdot20165$$

The equations are

$$0{\cdot}77933 = a + n\,(0{\cdot}14164)$$

$$1{\cdot}20165 = a + n\,(0{\cdot}31217)$$

$$n\,(0{\cdot}31217 - 0{\cdot}14164) = 1{\cdot}20165 - 0{\cdot}77933$$

$$0{\cdot}17053\,n = 0{\cdot}42232$$

$$\therefore \quad n = 2{\cdot}47651$$

$$a = 0{\cdot}77933 - 2{\cdot}47651 \times 0{\cdot}14164 = 0{\cdot}428557$$

Hence $C = 10^a = 10^{0{\cdot}428557} = 2{\cdot}68261$

Law is $\mathbf{Q = 2{\cdot}68261\, H^{2{\cdot}47651}}$

**Example 5.** *Using the following table, fit a curve of the form $y = ax^b$. Find a and b and find the formula by the method of group averages.*

| | | | | | | | | |
|---|---|---|---|---|---|---|---|---|
| $x$ : | *10* | *20* | *30* | *40* | *50* | *60* | *70* | *80* |
| $y$ : | *1·06* | *1·33* | *1·52* | *1·68* | *1·81* | *1·91* | *2·01* | *2·11* |

(*M.K.U.*)

**Solution.** $\log y = \log a + b \log x$

Let $Y = \log_{10} y, \quad A = \log_{10} a, \quad X = \log_{10} x$

We get $$Y = A + bx \qquad ...(1)$$

Divide into two groups each containing 4 data.

| | Group I | | Group II | |
|---|---|---|---|---|
| | $X$ | $Y$ | $X$ | $Y$ |
| | 1·0 | 0·0253 | 1·6990 | 0·2577 |
| | 1·3010 | 0·1239 | 1·7782 | 0·2810 |
| | 1·4771 | 0·1818 | 1·8451 | 0·3032 |
| | 1·6020 | 0·22531 | 1·9031 | 0·3243 |
| Sum : | 5·3801 | 0·5563 | 7·2254 | 1·1662 |

$$\overline{X}_1 = \frac{5{\cdot}3801}{4} = 1{\cdot}3450, \quad \overline{Y}_1 = \frac{0{\cdot}5563}{4} = 0{\cdot}1391$$

$$\overline{X}_2 = \frac{7{\cdot}2254}{4} = 1{\cdot}8064, \quad \overline{Y}_2 = \frac{1{\cdot}1662}{4} = 0{\cdot}2916$$

$$\therefore \quad 0{\cdot}1391 = A + b\,(1{\cdot}3450)$$

$$0{\cdot}2916 = A + b\,(1{\cdot}8064)$$

$$\therefore \quad b\,(1{\cdot}3450 - 1{\cdot}8064) = 0{\cdot}1391 - 0{\cdot}2916$$

$$b = \frac{0{\cdot}1525}{0{\cdot}4614} = 0{\cdot}3305$$

$$A = 0{\cdot}1391 - 0{\cdot}3305 \times 1{\cdot}3450 = -0{\cdot}3054$$

$$a = 10^{-0{\cdot}3054} = 0{\cdot}4950 \quad \therefore \quad \mathbf{y = 0{\cdot}495\, x^{0{\cdot}3305}}$$

**Example 6.** *Convert the equation $y = \dfrac{b}{x\,(x-a)}$ to a linear form and hence determine a and b. Which will best fit the following data :*

| | | | | | | | |
|---|---|---|---|---|---|---|---|
| $x$ : | 3·6 | 4·8 | 6·0 | 7·2 | 8·4 | 9·6 | 10·8 |
| $y$ : | 0·83 | 0·31 | 0·17 | 0·10 | 0·07 | 0·05 | 0·04 |

**Solution.** Here, $y = \dfrac{b}{x(x-a)}$ $\quad\therefore\quad xy = \dfrac{b}{x-a}$

$$\therefore \quad x - a = \frac{b}{xy}, \quad i.e., \quad x = a + \frac{b}{xy} \qquad ...(1)$$

Take $\quad x = Y, \ \dfrac{1}{xy} = X$

Hence $\quad Y = a + bX$

We form the table.

| | Group I | | Group II | |
|---|---|---|---|---|
| | $X = \frac{1}{xy}$ | $Y = x$ | $X = \frac{1}{xy}$ | $Y = x$ |
| | 0·3347 | 3·6 | 1·7007 | 8·4 |
| | 0·6720 | 4·8 | 2·0833 | 9·6 |
| | 0·9804 | 6·0 | 2·3148 | 10·8 |
| | 1·3889 | 7·2 | | |
| Sum : | 3·3760 | 21·6 | 6·0988 | 28·8 |

$$\bar{X}_1 = \frac{3.3760}{4} = 0.8440 \qquad \bar{Y}_1 = \frac{21.6}{4} = 5.4$$

$$\bar{X}_2 = \frac{6.0988}{3} = 2.0329 \qquad \bar{Y}_2 = \frac{28.8}{3} = 9.6$$

$$\therefore \qquad 5.4 = a + b\,(0.8440)$$

$$9.6 = a + b\,(2.0329)$$

$$b\,(2.0329 - 0.8440) = 9.6 - 5.4$$

$$\therefore \qquad b = 3.5327, \ a = 2.4185$$

$\therefore$ the equation is $\mathbf{y = \dfrac{3.5327}{x\,(x - 2.4185)}}$

**Example 7.** *Fit a curve of the form* $y = a + bx^3$ *by the method of group averages given that*

| | | | | | |
|---|---|---|---|---|---|
| $x$ : | 5 | 7 | 9 | 11 | 12 |
| $y$ : | 290 | 560 | 1144 | 1810 | 2300 |

**Solution.** Put $x^3 = X$. Then $y = a + b\,X$ is the form required

| | Group I | | Group II | |
|---|---|---|---|---|
| | $X = x^3$ | $y$ | $X = x^3$ | $y$ |
| | 125 | 290 | 1331 | 1810 |
| | 343 | 560 | | |
| | 729 | 1144 | 1728 | 2300 |
| Sum : | 1197 | 1994 | 3059 | 4110 |

$$\bar{X}_1 = \frac{1197}{3} = 399 \qquad \bar{Y}_1 = \frac{1994}{3} = 664.66$$

$$\overline{X}_2 = \frac{3059}{2} = 1529 \qquad \overline{Y}_2 = \frac{4110}{2} = 2055$$

Hence, $\overline{Y}_1 = a + b\,\overline{x}_1$ implies $664{\cdot}66 = a + b\,(399)$ ...(1)

Similarly, $2055 = a + b\,(1529)$ ...(2)

$$b\,(1529 - 399) = 2055 - 664{\cdot}6$$

$$b = \frac{1390{\cdot}4}{1130} = 1{\cdot}2304$$

$$a = 664{\cdot}66 - 399\,b$$

$$= 664{\cdot}66 - 399 \times 1{\cdot}2304$$

$$= 173{\cdot}73$$

$\therefore$ the equation is $y = 173{\cdot}73 + 1{\cdot}2304\,x^3$

## 1.5. Equations involving three constants

If, for a given set of data, a straight line fit is not correct, we may have to fit a parabola or other types of curves which involve three constants. We will see below some of these cases and discuss how the unknowns could be estimated.

**TYPE 1. (i) The equation of the form $y = a + bx + cx^2$ (Parabola).**

We shall reduce this equation to a linear graph from which two unknowns can be found as in the previous article.

Assume that a *particular point* $(x_1, y_1)$ satisfies the given equation. That is

$$y_1 = a + bx_1 + cx_1^2$$

Hence, $$y - y_1 = b\,(x - x_1) + c\,(x^2 - x_1^2)$$

*i.e.*, $$\frac{y - y_1}{x - x_1} = b + c\,(x + x_1)$$

Set $$\frac{y - y_1}{x - x_1} = Y \quad \text{and} \quad x + x_1 = X$$

Hence, the equation becomes,

$$Y = b + cX \text{ which is linear in } X \text{ and } Y.$$

Now, $b$ and $c$ can be found out by the previous method of group averages.

**Example 8.** *The data given below will fit a formula of the type $y = a + bx + cx^2$. Find the formula.*

| | | | | | | | |
|---|---|---|---|---|---|---|---|
| *x* : | *87·5* | *84·0* | *77·8* | *63,·7* | *46·7* | *36·9* | |
| *y* : | *292* | *283* | *270* | *235* | *197* | *181* | (*M.K.U.*) |

**Solution.** Take the point (87·5, 292) as the particular point on the curve

$$y = a + bx + cx^2 \quad \text{...(1)}$$

$$\therefore \quad 292 = a + (87{\cdot}5)\,b + (87{\cdot}5)^2.c \quad \text{...(2)}$$

(1) – (2) gives

$$y-292=b\,(x-87\cdot5)+c[x^2-(87\cdot5)^2]$$

$$\frac{y-292}{x-87\cdot5}=b+c\,(x+87\cdot5)$$

*i.e.,* $Y=b+c\,X$ where $Y=\dfrac{y-292}{x-87\cdot5}$ and $X=x+87\cdot5$

Now we will do this by the method of group averages dividing the given data into two groups each containing three data.

| *Group I* | | | | *Group II* | | | |
|---|---|---|---|---|---|---|---|
| $x$ | $y$ | $X=x+87\cdot5$ | $Y=\dfrac{y-292}{x-87\cdot5}$ | $x$ | $y$ | $x$ | $y$ |
| 87·5 | 292 | — | — | 63·7 | 235 | 151·2 | 2·3950 |
| 84·0 | 283 | 171·5 | 2·5714 | 46·7 | 197 | 134·2 | 2·3284 |
| 77·8 | 270 | 165·3 | 2·2680 | 36·9 | 181 | 124·4 | 2·1937 |
| | | 336·8 | 4·8394 | | | 409·8 | 6·9171 |

$$\overline{X}_1=\frac{336\cdot8}{2}=168\cdot4 \qquad \overline{Y}_1=\frac{4\cdot8394}{2}=2\cdot4197$$

$$\overline{X}_2=\frac{409\cdot8}{3}=136\cdot6 \qquad \overline{Y}_2=\frac{6\cdot9171}{3}=2\cdot3057$$

Substituting in $Y=b+cX$, we have

$$2\cdot4197=b+168\cdot4\,c \qquad ...(3)$$

$$2\cdot3057=b+136\cdot6\,c \qquad ...(4)$$

$$c\,(168\cdot4-136\cdot6)=2\cdot4197-2\cdot3057$$

$$31\cdot8\,c=11\cdot4 \qquad \therefore \quad c=\mathbf{0\cdot00358}$$

$$b=2\cdot4197-168\cdot4\,c=\mathbf{1\cdot8168}$$

$$Y=\frac{y-292}{x-87\cdot5}=1\cdot8168+0\cdot00358\,X$$

$$\frac{y-292}{x-87\cdot5}=1\cdot8168+(x+87\cdot5)\times0\cdot00358$$

$$=0\cdot00358\,x+2\cdot13$$

$$\therefore \quad y=0\cdot00358\,x^2+1\cdot81675\,x+105\cdot62$$

**Example 9.** *Fit a parabola of the pattern* $y=a+bx+cx^2$ *to the data given below* :

| $x$ : | 20 | 40 | 60 | 80 | 100 | 120 |
|---|---|---|---|---|---|---|
| $y$ : | 5·5 | 9·1 | 14·9 | 22·8 | 33·3 | 46·0 |

**Solution.** Assume that the point (20, 5·5) lies on the parabola.

$$\therefore \quad 5\cdot5=a+20b+400c \qquad ...(1)$$

$$y=a+bx+cx^2 \qquad ...(2)$$

Subtracting,

$$y-5\cdot5=b\,(x-20)+c\,(x^2-20^2)$$

$$\frac{y-5\cdot5}{x-20}=b+c\,(x+20)$$

*i.e.,* $$Y=B+cx \qquad ...(3)$$

where $Y=\dfrac{y-5\cdot5}{x-20}$ and $X=x+20$ and $B=b+20c$

Let us form the tables dividing the given set into two sets.

| | $x$ | $y$ | $y-5\cdot5$ | $x-20$ | $Y=\dfrac{y-5\cdot5}{x-20}$ |
|---|---|---|---|---|---|
| | 20 | 5·5 | 0 | 0 | — |
| *Group I* : | | | | | |
| | 40 | 9·1 | 3·6 | 20 | 0·18 |
| | 60 | 14·9 | 9·4 | 40 | 0·235 |
| | 80 | 22·8 | 17·3 | 60 | 0·288 |
| Total | 180 | | | | 0·703 |
| *Group II* : | | | | | |
| | 100 | 33·3 | 27·8 | 80 | 0·348 |
| | 120 | 46·0 | 40·5 | 10 | 0·405 |
| Total | 220 | | | | 0·753 |

$$\therefore\quad \bar{x}_1=\frac{180}{3}=60,\qquad \bar{Y}_1=\frac{0\cdot703}{3}=0\cdot234$$

$$\bar{x}_2=\frac{220}{2}=110,\qquad \bar{Y}_2=\frac{0\cdot753}{2}=0\cdot3765$$

Using in (3),

$$0\cdot234=B+60c \qquad ...(4)$$

$$0\cdot3765=B+110c \qquad ...(5)$$

Subtracting, $50c=0\cdot1425,\quad c=0\cdot00285$

$\therefore\quad B=0\cdot234-60c=0\cdot063$

Putting in (3), we get

$$\frac{y-5\cdot5}{x-20}=0\cdot063+0\cdot00285x$$

$$y=5\cdot5+0\cdot00285x^2+(0\cdot063-20\times0\cdot00285)\,x-0\cdot063\times20$$

$$\mathbf{y=0\cdot00285x^2+0\cdot006x+4\cdot24}$$

This is more or less a straight line.

**TYPE 2. Equation of the pattern $\mathbf{y=a\,x^b+c}$**

First, we will get the value of $c$ so that the points $(x_1, y_1), (x_2, y_2), (x_3, y_3)$ be three points on the curve where $x_1, x_2, x_3$ are in geometric progression. (*i.e.,* $x_2^2=x_1x_3$).

Substituting these points on the curve,

$$y_1=a\,x_1^{\,b}+c$$

$\therefore \quad y_1 - c = a\,x_1^{\,b}\ ;\ \ y_2 - c = a\,x_2^{\,b}\ ;\ \ y_3 - c = a\,x_3^{\,b}$

Hence $\quad (y_1 - c)(y_3 - c) = a^2(x_1x_3)^b = a^2\,(x_2^{\,2})^b = (ax_2^{\,b})^2 = (y_2 - c)^2$

*i.e.,* $\quad y_1y_3 - c\,(y_1 + y_3) + c^2 = y_2^{\,2} + c^2 - 2cy_2$

$$c = \frac{y_1y_3 - y_2^{\,2}}{y_1 + y_3 - 2y_2}$$

Using this value of $c$ in $y - c = ax^b$ we have only 2 unknowns left out.

$\log_{10}(y - c) = \log_{10}a + b\log_{10}x$

$$Y = A + b\,X,\ \text{where}\ Y = \log_{10}(y - c),\ A = \log_{10}a\ \text{and}\ X = \log_{10}x$$

This being linear is $X$ and $Y$, we get the equation and also $A$ and $b$. Knowing $A$, we get $a$.

Hence the equation $y = c + ax^b$ is found out.

**Example 10.** *A curve given by the equation of the form $y = ax^b + c$ is to be fitted to the following data. Determine the values of a, b and c.*

| $x$ : | 0·2 | 0·5 | 1·0 | 2·0 | 3·0 | 4·0 |
|---|---|---|---|---|---|---|
| $y$ : | 3·2 | 3·2 | 4·1 | 8·1 | 13·7 | 22·6 |

**Solution.** Let us search for three points whose abscissae are in G.P.

$\therefore \quad x_1 = 0{\cdot}5, \quad x_2 = 1{\cdot}0, \quad x_3 = 2{\cdot}0 \quad \text{since} \quad x_1x_3 = x_2^{\,2}$

$$\therefore \qquad c = \frac{y_1y_3 - y_2^{\,2}}{y_1 + y_3 - 2y_2} = \frac{3{\cdot}2 \times 8{\cdot}1 - (4{\cdot}1)^2}{3{\cdot}2 + 8{\cdot}1 - 2(4{\cdot}1)} = 2{\cdot}9387$$

$$\therefore \qquad y - 2{\cdot}9387 = ax^b \qquad \text{...(1)}$$

$$\log\,(y - 2{\cdot}9387) = \log a + b\log x$$

$$Y = A + b\,X \qquad \text{...(2)}$$

where $\quad X = \log x, \quad Y = \log\,(y - 2{\cdot}9387), \quad A = \log a$

We write down the table required for us. We divide into two groups each containing three data.

| $x$ | $y$ | $y - 2{\cdot}9387$ | $Y = \log\,(y - 2{\cdot}9387)$ | $X$ |
|---|---|---|---|---|
| 0·2 | 3·2 | 0·2613 | − 0·5829 | − 0·6989 |
| 0·5 | 3·2 | 0·2613 | − 0·5829 | − 0·3010 |
| 1·0 | 4·1 | 1·1613 | 0·0649 | 0 |
| | | | − 1·1009 | − 0·9999 |
| 2·0 | 8·1 | 5·1613 | 0·7128 | 0·3010 |
| 3·0 | 13·7 | 10·7613 | 1·0319 | 0·4771 |
| 4·0 | 22·6 | 19·6613 | 1·2936 | 0·6021 |
| | | | 3·0383 | 1·3802 |

$$\overline{X}_1 = \frac{-\,0{\cdot}9999}{3} = -\,0{\cdot}3333,\ \overline{Y}_1 = \frac{-\,1{\cdot}1009}{3} = -\,0{\cdot}3670$$

$$\bar{X}_2 = \frac{1\cdot3802}{3} = 0\cdot4601, \quad \bar{Y}_2 = \frac{3\cdot0383}{3} = 1\cdot0128$$

Using in (2),

$$-0\cdot3670 = A + b\,(-0\cdot3333) \quad ...(3)$$

$$1\cdot0128 = A + b\,(0\cdot4601) \quad ...(4)$$

$$0\cdot7934\,b = 1\cdot3798\;;\; b = \mathbf{1\cdot7390}$$

$$\therefore \quad A = 0\cdot3333\,b - 0\cdot3670 = 0\cdot2126$$

$$\log a = A\;; \quad a = 10^A = 1\cdot6315$$

$\therefore$ The equation is $\mathbf{y = 1\cdot6315\,x^{1\cdot7390} + 2\cdot9387}$

**Example 11.** *Fit a curve of the form $y = ax^b + c$ to the following data.*

| $x$ | : | 2 | 4 | 6 | 8 | 10 |
|---|---|---|---|---|---|---|
| $y$ | : | 5·0 | 8·6 | 13·9 | 25·3 | 35·6 |

**Solution.** We search for three values of $x$'s which are in G.P.

$\therefore \quad x_1 = 2,\ x_2 = 4,\ x_3 = 8$ so that $x_1x_3 = x_2^2$

Hence $c = \dfrac{y_1y_3 - y_2^2}{y_1 + y_3 - 2y_2} = \dfrac{5 \times 25\cdot3 - (8\cdot6)^2}{5 + 25\cdot3 - 2(8\cdot6)} = 4\cdot01$

$$\therefore \quad y = ax^b + 4\cdot01$$

$$y - 4\cdot01 = ax^b \quad ...(1)$$

Taking logarithm,

$$\log_{10}(y - 4\cdot01) = \log_{10}a + b\log_{10}x$$

*i.e.,* $\quad Y = A + b\,X \quad ...(2)$

where $\quad Y = \log_{10}(y - 4\cdot01),\ A = \log_{10}a,\ X = \log_{10}x$

We form the table for working.

| $x$ | $y$ | $y - 4\cdot01$ | | $Y = \log_{10}(y - 4\cdot01)$ | $x = \log_{10}x$ |
|---|---|---|---|---|---|
| 2 | 5·0 | 0·99 | | – 0·0044 | 0·3010 |
| 4 | 8·6 | 4·59 | | 0·6618 | 0·6020 |
| 6 | 13·9 | 9·89 | | 0·9952 | 0·7782 |
| | | | Total | 1·6526 | 1·6812 |
| 8 | 25·3 | 21·29 | | 1·3281 | 0·9031 |
| 10 | 35·6 | 31·59 | | 1·4995 | 1·0000 |
| | | | Total | 2·8276 | 1·9031 |

$$\bar{X}_1 = \frac{1\cdot6812}{3} = 0\cdot5604\;; \quad \bar{Y}_1 = \frac{1\cdot6526}{3} = 0\cdot5509$$

$$\bar{X}_2 = \frac{1\cdot9031}{2} = 0\cdot9516\;; \quad \bar{Y}_2 = \frac{2\cdot8276}{2} = 1\cdot4138$$

Using in (2), $\quad 0\cdot5509 = A + 0\cdot5604\,b$

$$1\cdot4138 = A + 0\cdot9516\,b$$

Solving we get $\quad b = 2\cdot2057, \quad A = -0\cdot6852$

$$a = 10^A = 0\cdot2064$$

Hence the equation is $\quad \mathbf{y = 0\cdot2064 \times x^{2\cdot2057} + 4\cdot01}$

**TYPE 3. The equation of the form $y = ab^x + c$**

If the curve is of the form $y = ab^x + c$, we select three points $(x_1, y_1)$, $(x_2, y_2)$, $(x_3, y_3)$ on this curve so that $x_1, x_2, x_3$ are in arithmetical progression. *i.e.,* $x_1 + x_3 = 2x_2$

Substituting these points on the curve,

$$y_1 = ab^{x_1} + c$$

$$\therefore \quad y_1 - c = a\,b^{x_1}\ ; \quad y_2 - c = a\,b^{x_2}\ ; \quad y_3 - c = a\,b^{x_3}$$

$$(y_1 - c)(y_3 - c) = a^2\, b^{x_1 + x_3} = a^2\, b^{2x_2} = (a\,b^{x_2})^2 = (y_2 - c)^2$$

$$\therefore \quad c = \frac{y_1 y_3 - {y_2}^2}{y_1 + y_3 - 2y_2} \qquad \text{(same as in previous work)}$$

If this $c$ is found out, $y - c$ is known.

Now $\quad y - c = a\,b^x$

$\therefore \quad \log_{10}(y - c) = \log a + x \log_{10} b$

*i.e.,* $\quad Y = A + Bx$

This is linear in $x$ and $Y$. Hence $A$, $B$ can be found out. Therefore $a$, $b$ can be got using $A$, $B$. Thus the curve is got.

**TYPE 4. The equation of the form $y = a\,e^{bx} + c$**

This is nothing but $y = a\,(e^b)^x + c = a.k^x + c$ where $k = e^b$. Hence, it is same as Type 3.

**Example 12.** *The values of x and y are related by the law $y = ab^x + c$. Corresponding values of x and y are given below. Find the best values of a, b and c.*

| $x$ : | 2 | 4 | 6 | 8 | 10 | 12 |
|---|---|---|---|---|---|---|
| $y$ : | 24 | 41 | 69 | 126·5 | 219 | 404 |

**Solution.** Select three values of abscissae which are in arithmetical progression.

Let $x_1 = 8$, $x_2 = 10$, $x_3 = 12$ since $x_1 + x_3 = 2x_2$

(In fact, all $x$'s are in A.P. Hence, you can select these values in number of ways:

2, 4, 6 or 4, 6, 8 or 6, 8, 10 or 8, 10, 12 or 2, 6, 10 etc.)

$$\therefore \quad c = \frac{y_1 y_3 - {y_2}^2}{y_1 + y_3 - 2y_2} = \frac{126{\cdot}5 \times 404 - (219)^2}{126{\cdot}5 + 404 - 2(219)} = \frac{3145}{92{\cdot}5} = 34$$

$$\therefore \quad y - 34 = ab^x$$

Taking logarithm

$$\log_{10}(y - 34) = \log_{10}a + x \log_{10}b$$

*i.e.,* $Y = A + x.B$ where $Y = \log_{10}(y - 34)$, $A = \log_{10}a$, $B = \log_{10}b$

We will use the method of group averages taking 3 sets in each group.

| | $x$ | $y$ | $y-34$ | $Y=\log_{10}(y-34)$ |
|---|---|---|---|---|
| | 2 | 24 | $-10$ | – |
| | 4 | 41 | 7 | 0·8451 |
| | 6 | 69 | 35 | 1·5441 |
| Total | 10 | | | 2·3892 |
| | 8 | 126·5 | 92·5 | 1·9661 |
| | 10 | 219 | 185 | 2·2671 |
| | 12 | 404 | 370 | 2·5682 |
| | 30 | | | 6·8014 |

$$\bar{x}_1 = \frac{10}{2} = 5\,; \qquad \bar{Y}_1 = \frac{2\cdot3892}{2} = 1\cdot1946$$

$$\bar{x}_2 = \frac{30}{3} = 10\,; \qquad \bar{Y}_2 = \frac{6\cdot8014}{3} = 2\cdot2671$$

Using in $Y = A + Bx$,

$$1\cdot1946 = A + 5B \qquad \text{...(3)}$$

$$2\cdot2671 = A + 10B \qquad \text{...(4)}$$

Solving $B = 0\cdot2145$; $A = 0\cdot1221$; $a = 10^A = 1\cdot3246$; $b = 10^B = 1\cdot6387$

$$\therefore \qquad y = (1\cdot3246) \times (1\cdot6387)^x + 34$$

**Example 13.** *The temperature* $\theta$ *of a vessel of cooling water and the time t in minutes since the beginning of observation are connected by the law of the form* $\theta = ae^{bt} + c$. *The corresponding values of* $\theta$ *and t are given by*

| $t$ : | 0 | 1 | 2 | 3 | 5 | 7 | 10 | 15 | 20 |
|---|---|---|---|---|---|---|---|---|---|
| $\theta$ : | 52·2 | 48·8 | 46·0 | 43·5 | 39·7 | 36·5 | 33·0 | 28·7 | 26·0 |

Find the best values of $a$, $b$, $c$.

**Solution.** Search for values of $t$ which are in A.P.

Take $t_1 = 0$, $t_2 = 10$, $t_3 = 20$ which are in A.P.

$$\therefore \qquad \theta_1 = 52\cdot2, \quad \theta_2 = 33\cdot0, \quad \theta_3 = 26\cdot0$$

$$\therefore \qquad c = \frac{\theta_1\,\theta_3 - \theta_2^{\,2}}{\theta_1 + \theta_3 - 2\theta_2} = \frac{52\cdot2 \times 26\cdot0 - (33)^2}{52\cdot2 + 26\cdot0 - 2(33)} = 21\cdot98$$

$$\therefore \qquad \theta - 21\cdot98 = a\,e^{bt} \qquad \text{...(1)}$$

Taking logarithm,

$$\log_{10}(\theta - 21\cdot98) = \log_{10}a + bt.\log_{10}e$$

*i.e.*, $$Y = A + Bt \qquad \text{...(2)}$$

which is linear and $Y = \log_{10}(\theta - 21\cdot98)$, $A = \log_{10}a$, $B = b\log_{10}e$.

We will form the table :

*Group I*

| | $t$ | $\theta$ | $\theta - 21{\cdot}98$ | $Y = \log_{10}(\theta - 21{\cdot}98)$ |
|---|---|---|---|---|
| | 0 | 52·2 | 30·22 | 1·4803 |
| | 1 | 48·8 | 26·82 | 1·4284 |
| | 2 | 46·0 | 24·02 | 1·3806 |
| | 3 | 43·5 | 21·52 | 1·3328 |
| Total | 6 | .... | | 5·6221 |

*Group II*

| | $t$ | $\theta$ | $\theta - 21{\cdot}98$ | $Y$ |
|---|---|---|---|---|
| | 5 | 39·7 | 17·72 | 1·2485 |
| | 7 | 36·5 | 14·52 | 1·1620 |
| | 10 | 33·0 | 11·02 | 1·0422 |
| | 15 | 28·7 | 6·72 | 0·8274 |
| | 20 | 26·0 | 4·02 | 0·6042 |
| Total | 57 | | | 4·8843 |

$$\bar{t}_1 = \frac{6}{4} = 1{\cdot}5, \qquad \bar{Y}_1 = \frac{5{\cdot}6221}{4} = 1{\cdot}4055$$

$$\bar{t}_2 = \frac{57}{5} = 11{\cdot}4, \qquad \bar{Y}_2 = \frac{4{\cdot}8843}{5} = 0{\cdot}9769$$

Using equation (2),

$$1{\cdot}4055 = A + B\,(1{\cdot}5) \qquad \text{...(3)}$$

$$0{\cdot}9769 = A + B\,(11{\cdot}4) \qquad \text{...(4)}$$

Solving (3) and (4), we get $B = -0{\cdot}04329,\ A = 1{\cdot}4704$

$$\therefore\ a = 10^A = 29{\cdot}5393\ ;\quad b = \frac{B}{\log_{10}e} = -0{\cdot}09968$$

Substituting in the equation

$$\boldsymbol{\theta = (29{\cdot}5393)\, e^{-0{\cdot}09968\,t} + 21{\cdot}98}$$

## EXERCISE 1.2

By the method of group averages, solve the following problems :

**1.** Fit a straight line to the following data :

| $x$ | : | 0 | 5 | 10 | 15 | 20 | 25 |
|---|---|---|---|---|---|---|---|
| $y$ | : | 12 | 15 | 17 | 22 | 24 | 30 |

**2.** The latent heat of vaporisation of steam $\gamma$ is given by the following table at different times $t$.

If the relation is of the from $r = A + Bt$, determine values of $A$ and $B$.

| $t$ | : | 40 | 50 | 60 | 70 | 80 | 90 | 100 | 110 |
|---|---|---|---|---|---|---|---|---|---|
| $\gamma$ | : | 1069·1 | 1063·6 | 1058·2 | 1052·7 | 1049·3 | 1041·8 | 1036·3 | 1030·8 |

**3.** Fit a st. line to the following data :

| $x$ | : | 1 | 2 | 3 | 4 | 5 | 6 | 7 | 8 | 9 | 10 |
|---|---|---|---|---|---|---|---|---|---|---|---|
| $y$ | : | 52·5 | 58·7 | 65·0 | 70·2 | 75·4 | 81·1 | 87·2 | 95·5 | 102·2 | 108·4 |

4. Fit a curve of the form $y = ax^n$ from the following data :

| | | | | | | | | |
|---|---|---|---|---|---|---|---|---|
| $y$ | : | 1·68 | 2·45 | 3·08 | 4·09 | 4·97 | 5·95 | 7·39 | 9·00 |
| $x$ | : | 0·013 | 0·027 | 0·042 | 0·073 | 0·108 | 0·151 | 0·233 | 0·341 |

5. From the following table fit a curve of the form $y = ab^x$

| | | | | | | |
|---|---|---|---|---|---|---|
| $x$ | : | $\pi/2$ | $\pi$ | $3\pi/2$ | $2\pi$ | $5\pi/2$ |
| $y$ | : | 2·9 | 4·0 | 5·7 | 8·9 | 12·4 |

6. Find the best values of $a$ and $b$ if the following data given are related by $y = ax + bx^2$

| | | | | | | | |
|---|---|---|---|---|---|---|---|
| $x$ | : | 1 | 2 | 3 | 4 | 5 | 6 |
| $y$ | : | 2·6 | 5·4 | 8·7 | 12·1 | 16 | 20·2 |

7. The following pairs of values were found for the potential difference $V$ volts and the current $A$ amperes in an electric circuit and are given below:

| | | | | | | |
|---|---|---|---|---|---|---|
| $V$ | : | 50·3 | 47·3 | 46·8 | 45·1 | 43·6 |
| $A$ | : | 1·96 | 2·98 | 3·96 | 5·96 | 9·57 |

Find the curve of the form $V = a + \dfrac{b}{A}$ [*M.K.U., 1976*]

8. If $p$ is the pull required to lift a weight $w$ by means of a pully block, find a law of the form $p = a + bw$ from the following data :

| | | | | | |
|---|---|---|---|---|---|
| $w$ | : | 50 | 70 | 100 | 120 |
| $p$ | : | 12 | 15 | 21 | 25 |

[*M.S. 1965*]

9. Fit a straight line to the data if the relation is of the form $y = kx^n$ given

| | | | | | |
|---|---|---|---|---|---|
| $x$ | : | 25·9 | 259 | 2590 | 25900 |
| $y$ | : | 0·308 | 0·209 | 0·148 | 0·098 |

[*M.K.U.*]

10. Fit a curve of the form $y = ax^2 + bx + c$ given

| | | | | | | | |
|---|---|---|---|---|---|---|---|
| $x$ | : | 10 | 20 | 30 | 40 | 50 | 60 |
| $y$ | : | 4·5 | 7·1 | 10·5 | 15·5 | 20·5 | 27·1 |

11. The pressure and volume of a quantity of gas when subjected to compression are given below.
If the law governed is $pv^n = k$, find the law.

| | | | | | | | |
|---|---|---|---|---|---|---|---|
| $p$ | : | 15 | 30 | 60 | 100 | 200 | 400 |
| $v$ | : | 10 | 5·61 | 3·15 | 2·06 | 1·15 | 0·65 |

12. Fit a curve of the form $v = at^2 + bt + c$ given the following data :

| | | | | | | | |
|---|---|---|---|---|---|---|---|
| $t$ | : | 1 | 2 | 3 | 4 | 5 | 6 |
| $v$ | : | 3 | 4 | 7 | 12 | 21 | 32 |

13. Fit a curve of the form $y = ax^b + c$ from the data :

| | | | | | | | |
|---|---|---|---|---|---|---|---|
| $x$ | : | 0·5 | 1 | 2 | 4 | 8 | 12 |
| $y$ | : | 160 | 120 | 94 | 75 | 62 | 56 |

14. The following data represent test values got while testing a centrifugal pump. Assuming the relation to be $H = A + BQ + CQ^2$, where $Q$ is the discharge in litre per second and $H$, head in metre of water, find the relation by the method of group averages.

| | | | | | | | | | | |
|---|---|---|---|---|---|---|---|---|---|---|
| $Q$ | : | 2 | 2·5 | 3 | 3·5 | 4 | 4·5 | 5 | 5·5 | 6 |
| $H$ | : | 18 | 17·8 | 17·5 | 17 | 15·8 | 14·8 | 13·3 | 11·7 | 9 |

[*M.S., 1971*]

**15.** Fit a curve of the form $y = a + bx^n$ given the data :

| $x$ : | 20 | 40 | 60 | 80 | 100 |
|---|---|---|---|---|---|
| $y$ : | 5·0 | 8·6 | 13·9 | 25·3 | 35·6 |

**16.** Fit a curve of the form $y = ab^{-x}$ from the data given below :

| $x$ : | 0·1 | 0·2 | 0·4 | 0·6 | 1·0 | 1·5 | 2·0 |
|---|---|---|---|---|---|---|---|
| $y$ : | 350 | 316 | 120 | 63 | 12·86 | 2·57 | 0·425 |

**17.** Fit a straight line $x = ay + b$ given the data :

| $x$ : | 3 | 4 | 5 | 6 | 7 |
|---|---|---|---|---|---|
| $y$ : | 6 | 9 | 10 | 11 | 12 |

**18.** Obtain a curve of the form $v = a\,e^{bt} + c$ to the data given below :

| $t$ : | 11 | 8 | 6 | 2 | 1 |
|---|---|---|---|---|---|
| $v$ : | 10·99 | 11·34 | 11·65 | 12·46 | 12·71 |

**19.** Fit a curve of the form $y = a\,e^{bx}$ given :

| $x$ : | 58 | 86 | 148 | 166 | 188 | 202 | 210 |
|---|---|---|---|---|---|---|---|
| $y$ : | 0 | 0·004 | 0·018 | 0·029 | 0·051 | 0·073 | 0·090 |

**20.** Determine the relation $y = ax^b$ given :

| $x$ : | 25 | 20 | 12 | 9 | 7 | 5 |
|---|---|---|---|---|---|---|
| $y$ : | 0·22 | 0·20 | 0·15 | 0·13 | 0·12 | 0·10 |

**21.** Fit a curve of the form $\frac{1}{x} = a + by$ given the data :

| $y$ : | 0 | 1 | 2·5 | 5 | 10 |
|---|---|---|---|---|---|
| $x$ : | 1·02 | 0·08 | 0·62 | 0·46 | 0·32 |

**22.** Fit a curve of the from $y = ab^x + c$ given :

| $x$ : | 1·0 | 1·7 | 2·2 | 2·8 | 3·4 |
|---|---|---|---|---|---|
| $y$ : | 3·47 | 4·96 | 7·11 | 12·13 | 22·45 |

**23.** Fit a curve of the from $y = a + bx^n$ given :

| $x$ : | 0·2 | 0·5 | 1·0 | 2·0 | 3·0 | 4·0 |
|---|---|---|---|---|---|---|
| $y$ : | 3·22 | 3·22 | 4·15 | 8·2 | 13·9 | 23·5 |

**24.** The following figures give the exports in Rs. lakhs of an Engineering Industry. Fit a straight line trend by the method of group averages.

| *Year* : | 1956-57 | 57-58 | 58-59 | 59-60 | 60-61 | 61-62 |
|---|---|---|---|---|---|---|
| *Exports* : | 341 | 393 | 390 | 505 | 847 | 992 |

**25.** Fit a curve of the form $y = ab^x + c$ to the following data :

| $x$ : | 0 | 1 | 2 | 3 | 4 | 5 | 6 | 7 | 8 |
|---|---|---|---|---|---|---|---|---|---|
| $y$ : | 2·4 | 3·2 | 3·7 | 5·1 | 7·8 | 13·2 | 23·6 | 44·8 | 87·0 |

**26.** Fit a curve of the form $y = ax^b + c$ to the data :

| $x$ : | 2 | 3 | 4 | 5 | 6 | 7 | 8 | 9 |
|---|---|---|---|---|---|---|---|---|
| $y$ : | 18 | 33 | 52 | 80 | 112 | 153 | 197 | 248 |

**27.** Determine a curve of the form $y = c + ax^n$ that fits the data :

| $x$ : | 0·5 | 1·0 | 1·5 | 2·0 | 2·5 | 3·0 |
|---|---|---|---|---|---|---|
| $y$ : | 4·5 | 8·0 | 14·0 | 23·4 | 34·0 | 49·0 |

**28.** Fit a curve of the form $y = a + bc^x$ to the following data :

| $x$ : | 1 | 2 | 3 | 4 | 5 |
|---|---|---|---|---|---|
| $y$ : | 14 | 48 | 194 | 775 | 3076 |

**29.** Fit a curve of the form $y = c + ax^b$ to the data given below :

| $x$ : | 1 | 2 | 3 | 4 | 5 | 6 |
|---|---|---|---|---|---|---|
| $y$ : | 3 | 17 | 55 | 129 | 251 | 433 |

## 1.6. The principle of least squares

In the previous articles, we have seen two methods of fitting curve, *viz.*, (*i*) the graphical method and (*ii*) the method of group averages. The first one is a rough method and in the second method, the evaluation of constants vary from one grouping to another grouping of data. So, we adopt another method, called *the method of least squares* which gives a unique set of values to the constants in the equation of the fitting curve.

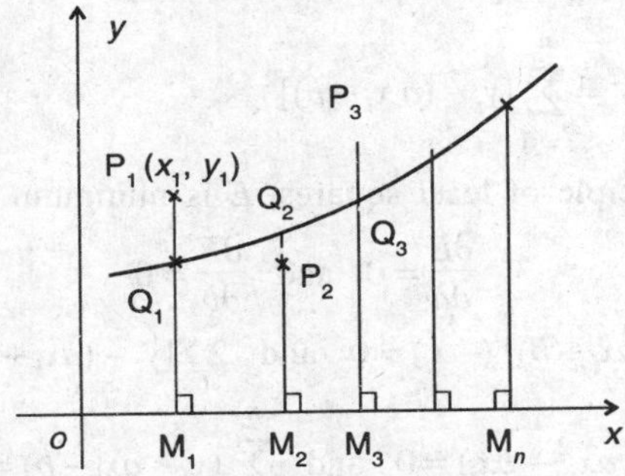


Let $(x_i, y_i)$, $i = 1, 2, ..., n$ be the $n$ sets of observations and let

$$y = f(x) \quad ...(1)$$

be the relation suggested between $x$ and $y$.

Let $(x_i, y_i)$ be represented by the point $P_i$. Let the ordinate at $P_i$ meet $y = f(x)$ at $Q_i$ and the $x$-axis at $M_i$.

$$M_iQ_i = f(x_i) \text{ and } M_iP_i = y_i$$

$$Q_iP_i = M_iP_i - M_iQ_i = y_i - f(x_i), \; i = 1, 2, ..., n$$

$d_i = y_i - f(x_i)$ is called the residual at $x = x_i$. Some of the $d_i$'s may be positive and some may be negative.

$E = \sum_{i=1}^{n} d_i^2 = \sum_{i=1}^{n} [y_i - f(x_i)]^2$ is the sum of the squares of the residuals.

If $E = 0$, *i.e.*, each $d_i = 0$, then all the $n$ points $P_i$ will lie on $y = f(x)$.

If not, we will choose $f(x)$ such that $E$ is minimum. That is, the best fitting curve to the set of points is that for which $E$ is minimum. This principle is known as the *principle of least squares* or the *least square criterion.*

This principle *does not suggest* to determine the *form of the curve* $y = f(x)$ but it *determines the values of the parameters* or constants of the equation of the curve.

We will consider some of the best fitting curves of the type :

(*i*) a straight line (*ii*) a second degree curve (*ii*) the exponential curve $y = ae^{bx}$ (*iv*) the curve $y = ax^n$.

**1.7. Fitting a straight line by the method of least squares**

Let $(x_i, y_i)$, $i = 1, 2, ..., n$ be the $n$ sets of observations and let the related relation by $y = ax + b$. Now we have to select $a$ and $b$ so that the straight line is the best fit to the data.

As explained earlier, the residual at $x = x_i$ is

$$d_i = y_i - f(x_i) = y_i - (ax_i + b),\ i = 1, 2, ..., n$$

$$E = \sum_{i=1}^{n} d_i^2 = \sum_{i=1}^{n} [y_i - (a\, x_i + b)]^2$$

By the principle of least squares, $E$ is minimum.

$$\therefore \qquad \frac{\partial E}{\partial a} = 0 \text{ and } \frac{\partial E}{\partial b} = 0$$

*i.e.,* $\qquad 2\Sigma[y_i - (ax_i + b)]\,(-x_i) = 0 \text{ and } 2\,\Sigma[y_i - (ax_i + b)](-1) = 0$

*i.e.,* $\qquad \sum_{i=1}^{n} (x_i y_i - ax_i^2 - bx_i) = 0 \text{ and } \sum_{i=1}^{n} (y_i - ax_i - b) = 0$

*i.e.,*
$$a\sum_{i=1}^{n} x_i^2 + b\sum_{i=1}^{n} x_i = \sum_{i=1}^{n} x_i y_i \qquad ...(1)$$

and
$$a\sum_{i=1}^{n} x_i + nb = \sum_{i=1}^{n} y_i \qquad ...(2)$$

Since, $x_i$, $y_i$ are known, equations (1) and (2) give two equations in $a$ and $b$. Solve for $a$ and $b$ from (1) and (2) and obtain the best fit $y = ax + b$.

**Note 1.** Equations (1) and (2) are called *normal equations.*

**2.** Dropping suffix $i$ from (1) and (2), the normal equations are

$$a\Sigma x + nb = \Sigma y \text{ and } a\Sigma x^2 + b\Sigma x = \Sigma xy$$

which are got by taking $\Sigma$ on both sides of $y = ax + b$ and also taking $\Sigma$ on both sides after multiplying by $x$ both sides of $y = ax + b$.

**3.** Transformations like $X = \dfrac{x - a}{h}$, $Y = \dfrac{y - b}{k}$ reduce the linear equation $y = \alpha x + \beta$ to the form $Y = AX + B$. Hence, a linear fit is another linear fit in both systems of coordinates.

**Example 14.** *By the method of least squares find the best fitting straight line to the data given below :*

| $x$ : | 5 | 10 | 15 | 20 | 25 |
|---|---|---|---|---|---|
| $y$ : | 15 | 19 | 23 | 26 | 30 |

**Solution.** Let the straight line be $y = ax + b$

The normal equations are $a\Sigma x + 5b = \Sigma y$ ...(1)

$$a\,\Sigma x^2 + b\Sigma x = \Sigma xy \quad ...(2)$$

To calculate $\Sigma x$, $\Sigma x^2$, $\Sigma y$, $\Sigma xy$ we form below the table.

| | $x$ | $y$ | $x^2$ | $xy$ |
|---|---|---|---|---|
| | 5 | 16 | 25 | 80 |
| | 10 | 19 | 100 | 190 |
| | 15 | 23 | 225 | 345 |
| | 20 | 26 | 400 | 520 |
| | 25 | 30 | 625 | 750 |
| Total | 75 | 114 | 1375 | 1885 |

The normal equations are $75a + 5b = 114$ ...(1)

$$1375a + 75b = 1885 \quad ...(2)$$

Eliminate $b$; multiply (1) by 15

$$1125a + 75b = 1710 \quad ...(3)$$

(2) – (3) gives, $250a = 175$ or $a = 0{\cdot}7$

Hence $b = 12{\cdot}3$

Hence, the best fitting line is $\mathbf{y = 0{\cdot}7x + 12{\cdot}3}$

**Aliter.** Let $X = \dfrac{x-15}{5}$, $Y = y - 23$

Let the line in the new variable be $Y = AX + B$ ...(1)

| $x$ | $y$ | $X$ | $X^2$ | $Y$ | $XY$ |
|---|---|---|---|---|---|
| 5 | 16 | – 2 | 4 | – 7 | 14 |
| 10 | 19 | – 1 | 1 | – 4 | 4 |
| 15 | 23 | 0 | 0 | 0 | 0 |
| 20 | 26 | 1 | 1 | 3 | 3 |
| 25 | 30 | 2 | 4 | 7 | 14 |
| Total : Σ | | 0 | 10 | – 1 | 35 |

The normal equations are $A\Sigma X + 5B = \Sigma Y$ ...(4)

$$A\Sigma X^2 + B\Sigma X = \Sigma XY \quad ...(5)$$

Therefore, $5B = -1$ $\therefore$ $B = -0{\cdot}2$

$\therefore$ $10A = 35$ $A = 3{\cdot}5$

The equations $Y = 3{\cdot}5X - 0{\cdot}2$

*i.e.,* $$y - 23 = 3{\cdot}5\left(\frac{x-15}{5}\right) - 0{\cdot}2 = 0{\cdot}7x - 10{\cdot}5 - 0{\cdot}2$$

*i.e.,* $$\mathbf{Y = 0{\cdot}7x + 12{\cdot}3}$$

which is the same equation as seen before.

**Example 15.** *Fit a straight line to the data given below. Also estimate the value of y at x = 2·5.*

| x : | 0 | 1 | 2 | 3 | 4 |
|---|---|---|---|---|---|
| y : | 1 | 1·8 | 3·3 | 4·5 | 6·3 |

**Solution.** Let the best fit be $y = ax + b$ ...(1)

The normal equations are

$$a\Sigma x + 5b = \Sigma y \qquad ...(2)$$

$$a\Sigma x^2 + b\Sigma x = \Sigma xy \qquad ...(3)$$

We prepare the table for easy use.

| | $x$ | $y$ | $x^2$ | $xy$ |
|---|---|---|---|---|
| | 0 | 1·0 | 0 | 0 |
| | 1 | 1·8 | 1 | 1·8 |
| | 2 | 3·3 | 4 | 6·6 |
| | 3 | 4·5 | 9 | 13·5 |
| | 4 | 6·3 | 16 | 25·2 |
| Total | 10 | 16·9 | 30 | 47·1 |

Substituting in (2) and (3), we get,

$$10a + 5b = 16{\cdot}9$$

$$30a + 10b = 47{\cdot}1$$

Solving, we get, $a = 1{\cdot}33, \quad b = 0{\cdot}72$

Hence, the equation is $y = 1{\cdot}33x + 0{\cdot}72$

$$y\ (at\ x = 2{\cdot}5) = 1{\cdot}33 \times 2{\cdot}5 + 0{\cdot}72 = 4{\cdot}045$$

**Example 16.** *Fit a straight line to the following data. Also estimate the value of y at x = 70.*

| x : | 71 | 68 | 73 | 69 | 67 | 65 | 66 | 67 |
|---|---|---|---|---|---|---|---|---|
| y : | 69 | 72 | 70 | 70 | 68 | 67 | 68 | 64 |

**Solution.** Since the values of $x$ and $y$ are larger, we choose the origins for $x$ and $y$ at 69 and 67 respectively. In other words, we transform $x$ and $y$.

Let $X = x - 69$, and $Y = y - 67$

Let $Y = aX + b$ be the best fit. ...(1)

The normal equations are

$$a\Sigma X + 8b = \Sigma Y \qquad ...(2)$$

$$a\Sigma X^2 + b\Sigma X = \Sigma XY \qquad ...(3)$$

*Calculations* :

| $x$ | $y$ | $X$ | $Y$ | $X^2$ | $XY$ |
|---|---|---|---|---|---|
| 71 | 69 | 2 | 2 | 4 | 4 |
| 68 | 72 | − 1 | 5 | 1 | − 5 |
| 73 | 70 | 4 | 3 | 16 | 12 |
| 69 | 70 | 0 | 3 | 0 | 0 |
| 67 | 68 | − 2 | 1 | 4 | − 2 |
| 65 | 67 | − 4 | 0 | 16 | 0 |
| 66 | 68 | − 3 | 1 | 9 | − 3 |
| 67 | 64 | − 2 | − 3 | 4 | 6 |
| Total: | | − 6 | 12 | 54 | 12 |

Substituting in (2) and (3),

$$-6a+8b=12 \qquad \text{...(4)}$$

$$54a-6b=12$$

Solving, we get, $a=0{\cdot}424242,\ b=0{\cdot}181818$

Therefore, $\qquad Y=0{\cdot}4242X+0{\cdot}1818$

*i.e.,* $\qquad y-67=0{\cdot}4242\,(x-69)+0{\cdot}1818$

$$y=0{\cdot}4242x+37{\cdot}909$$

$$y\,(x=70)=0{\cdot}4242\times 70+37{\cdot}909=\mathbf{67{\cdot}6030}$$

**Example 17.** *By proper transformation, convert the relation $y=a+bxy$ to a linear form and find the equation to fit the data.*

| $x$ : | − 4 | 1 | 2 | 3 |
|---|---|---|---|---|
| $y$ : | 4 | 6 | 10 | 8 |

[*MS. BE 1972*]

**Solution.** Let $X=xy$ $\therefore$ The equation becomes $y=a+bx$.

The normal equations are

$$a\Sigma X+b\Sigma X^2=\Sigma Xy \qquad \text{...(1)}$$

and $$4a+b\Sigma X=\Sigma y \qquad \text{...(2)}$$

| | $x$ | $y$ | $X$ | $X^2$ | $XY$ |
|---|---|---|---|---|---|
| | − 4 | 4 | − 16 | 256 | − 64 |
| | 1 | 6 | 6 | 36 | 36 |
| | 2 | 10 | 20 | 400 | 200 |
| | 3 | 8 | 24 | 576 | 192 |
| Total: | | 28 | 34 | 1268 | 364 |

Using (1) and (2),

$$34a+1268b=364$$

$$4a+34b=28$$

Solving we get, $b=0{\cdot}1286,\ a=5{\cdot}9069$

Therefore, the equation is $y=5{\cdot}9069+0{\cdot}1286\,X$

*i.e.,* $\qquad y=5{\cdot}9069+0{\cdot}1286\,xy.$

Using this equation we get $y\,(1-0{\cdot}1286x)=5{\cdot}9069$

*i.e.,* $$y=\frac{5{\cdot}9069}{1-0{\cdot}1286x}$$

We tabulate the values to verify:

| $x$ : | $-4$ | 1 | 2 | 3 |
|---|---|---|---|---|
| $y$ : | 5·23 | 6·78 | 7·95 | 9·62 |

**Note.** If we take $u = \frac{1}{xy}$, $v = \frac{1}{x}$ we get

$v = au + b$. Taking this as linear, we get

$a = 10{\cdot}5,\ b = -0{\cdot}13$

That is $y = 10{\cdot}5 - 0{\cdot}13xy$

*i.e.*, $$y = \frac{10{\cdot}5}{1 + 0{\cdot}13x}$$

Now tabulating, we get

| $x$ : | $-4$ | 1 | 2 | 3 |
|---|---|---|---|---|
| $y$ : | 21·87 | 92·92 | 0·12 | 7·55 |

The values of $y$ are far away from the given values. Perhaps, the *selection of the form* is not correct.

## 1.8. Fitting a parabola or fitting a second degree curve (by the method of least squares)

Let $(x_i, y_i), i = 1, 2, ..., n$ be $n$ sets of observations of two related variables $x$ and $y$. Let $y = ax^2 + bx + c$ be the equation which fits them best.

Now, we have to find the constants $a, b, c$.

For any $x = x_i$, the expected value of $y$ is $ax_i^2 + bx_i + c$ and the corresponding observed value is $y_i$.

The residual $d_i = y_i - (ax_i^2 + bx_i + c)$

Let $E$ denote the sum of the squares of the residuals.

That is, $$E = \sum_{i=1}^{n} [y_i - (ax_i^2 + bx_i + c)]^2$$

By the principle of least squares, $E$ is minimum for best values $a, b, c$.

$$\therefore \quad \frac{\partial E}{\partial a} = 0, \quad \frac{\partial E}{\partial b} = 0 \text{ and } \frac{\partial E}{\partial c} = 0$$

$\therefore$ Differentiating $E$, partially w.r.t. $a, b, c$ and equating to zero, we get,

$$\sum_{i=1}^{n} 2\,[y_i - (ax_i^2 + bx_i + c)]\,(-x_i^2) = 0$$

$$\sum_{i=1}^{n} 2\,[y_i - (ax_i^2 + bx_i + c)]\,(-x_i) = 0$$

$$\sum_{i=1}^{n} 2\,[y_i - (a\,x_i + bx_i + c)]\,(-1) = 0$$

Simplifying, we get

$$a\Sigma\, x_i^4 + b\Sigma x_i^3 + c\Sigma x_i^2 = \Sigma x_i^2 y_i$$

$$a\Sigma x_i^3 + b\Sigma x_i^2 + c\Sigma x_i = \Sigma x_i y_i$$

$$a\Sigma x_i^2 + b\Sigma x_i + nc = \Sigma y_i$$

Dropping the suffices, the *normal equations* are

$$a\Sigma x^4 + b\Sigma x^3 + c\Sigma x^2 = \Sigma\, x^2 y \qquad ...(1)$$

$$a\Sigma x^3 + b\Sigma x^2 + c\Sigma x = \Sigma xy \qquad ...(2)$$

$$a\Sigma x^2 + b\Sigma x + nc = \Sigma y \qquad ...(3)$$

The three equations (1), (2), (3) give the values of $a$, $b$, $c$. Substituting these values of $a$, $b$, $c$ in $y = ax^2 + bx + c$, we get the result.

**Note.** To obtain the normal equations, we remember the following :

(*i*) In $y = ax^2 + bx + c$, take $\Sigma$ on both sides.

(*ii*) Multiply by $x$ both sides and then take $\Sigma$ on both sides.

(*iii*) Multiply both sides by $x^2$ and then take $\Sigma$ on both sides.

**Example 18.** *Fit a parabola, by the method of least squares, to the following data; also estimate y at x = 6.*

| $x$ : | 1 | 2 | 3 | 4 | 5 |
|---|---|---|---|---|---|
| $y$ : | 5 | 12 | 26 | 60 | 97 |

**Solution.** Let $y = ax^2 + bx + c$ be the best fit.

Then, the normal equations are

$$a\Sigma x^2 + b\Sigma x + 5c = \Sigma y \qquad ...(1)$$

$$a\Sigma x^3 + b\Sigma x^2 + c\Sigma x = \Sigma xy \qquad ...(2)$$

$$a\Sigma x^4 + b\Sigma x^3 + c\Sigma x^2 = \Sigma x^2 y \qquad ...(3)$$

We form the table.

| | $x$ | $y$ | $x^2$ | $x^3$ | $x^4$ | $xy$ | $x^2y$ |
|---|---|---|---|---|---|---|---|
| | 1 | 5 | 1 | 1 | 1 | 5 | 5 |
| | 2 | 12 | 4 | 8 | 16 | 24 | 48 |
| | 3 | 26 | 9 | 27 | 81 | 78 | 234 |
| | 4 | 60 | 16 | 64 | 256 | 240 | 960 |
| | 5 | 97 | 25 | 125 | 625 | 485 | 2425 |
| Total: | 15 | 200 | 55 | 225 | 979 | 832 | 3672 |

Hence the equations (1), (2), (3) become,

$$55a + 15b + 5c = 200 \qquad ...(4)$$

$$225a + 55b + 15c = 832 \qquad ...(5)$$

$$979a + 225b + 55c = 3672 \qquad ...(6)$$

Solving we get, $a = 5{\cdot}7143$, $b = -11{\cdot}0858$ and $c = 10{\cdot}4001$

Hence, the parabola is, $y = 5{\cdot}7143x^2 - 11{\cdot}0858x + 10{\cdot}4001$

$$y\,(x=6) = \mathbf{149{\cdot}6001}$$

**Example 19.** *Fit a second degree parabola to the data.*

| $x$ : | 1929 | 1930 | 1931 | 1932 | 1933 | 1934 | 1935 |
|---|---|---|---|---|---|---|---|
| $y$ : | 352 | 356 | 357 | 358 | 360 | 361 | 361 |

Let $X = x - 1932$, $Y = y - 357$

Let $Y = aX^2 + bX + C$ be the best fit.

The normals equations are

$$a\Sigma x^2 + b\Sigma X + 7c = \Sigma Y \quad \text{...(1)}$$

$$a\Sigma X^3 + b\Sigma X^2 + c\Sigma X = \Sigma XY \quad \text{...(2)}$$

$$a\Sigma X^4 + b\Sigma X^3 + c\Sigma X^2 = \Sigma X^2 Y \quad \text{...(3)}$$

*Calculation Table :*

| | $x$ | $y$ | $X$ | $Y$ | $X^2$ | $X^3$ | $X^4$ | $XY$ | $X^2Y$ |
|---|---|---|---|---|---|---|---|---|---|
| | 1929 | 352 | – 3 | – 5 | 9 | – 27 | 81 | 15 | – 45 |
| | 1930 | 356 | – 2 | – 1 | 4 | – 8 | 16 | 2 | – 4 |
| | 1931 | 357 | – 1 | 0 | 1 | – 1 | 1 | 0 | 0 |
| | 1932 | 358 | 0 | 1 | 0 | 0 | 0 | 0 | 0 |
| | 1933 | 360 | 1 | 3 | 1 | 1 | 1 | 3 | 3 |
| | 1934 | 361 | 2 | 4 | 4 | 8 | 16 | 8 | 16 |
| | 1935 | 361 | 3 | 4 | 9 | 27 | 81 | 12 | 36 |
| Total | | | 0 | 6 | 28 | 0 | 196 | 40 | 6 |

Hence the normal equations become,

$$28a + 7c = 6 \quad \text{...(4)}$$

$$28b = 40 \quad \text{...(5)}$$

$$196a + 28c = 6 \quad \text{...(6)}$$

$\therefore$ $b = 1{\cdot}4286$, $a = -0{\cdot}21429$, $c = 1{\cdot}7143$

$\therefore$ The equation is $Y = -0{\cdot}21429\,X^2 + 1{\cdot}4286\,X + 1{\cdot}7143$

*i.e.,* $y - 357 = -0{\cdot}21429\,(x - 1932)^2 + 1{\cdot}7143 + 1{\cdot}4286\,(x - 1932)$

*i.e.,* $y = -0{\cdot}21429\,x^2 + 829{\cdot}445\,x - 802265{\cdot}33$

**Example 20.** *Fit a second degree parabola to the following data, taking y as dependent variable.*

| $x$ : | 1 | 2 | 3 | 4 | 5 | 6 | 7 | 8 | 9 |
|---|---|---|---|---|---|---|---|---|---|
| $y$ : | 2 | 6 | 7 | 8 | 10 | 11 | 11 | 10 | 9 |

**Solution.** Let $X = x - \bar{x} = x - 5$ and $Y = y - 7$

Let $Y = aX^2 + bX + c$ be the best fit.

| $x$ | $y$ | $X$ | $Y$ | $X^2$ | $X^3$ | $X^4$ | $XY$ | $X^2Y$ |
|---|---|---|---|---|---|---|---|---|
| 1 | 2 | – 4 | – 5 | 16 | – 64 | 256 | 20 | – 80 |
| 2 | 6 | – 3 | – 1 | 9 | – 27 | 81 | 3 | – 9 |
| 3 | 7 | – 2 | 0 | 4 | – 8 | 16 | 0 | 0 |

| | | | | | | | | |
|---|---|---|---|---|---|---|---|---|
| 4 | 8 | − 1 | 1 | 1 | − 1 | 1 | − 1 | 1 |
| 5 | 10 | 0 | 3 | 0 | 0 | 0 | 0 | 0 |
| 6 | 11 | 1 | 4 | 1 | 1 | 1 | 4 | 4 |
| 7 | 11 | 2 | 4 | 4 | 8 | 16 | 8 | 16 |
| 8 | 10 | 3 | 3 | 9 | 27 | 81 | 9 | 27 |
| 9 | 9 | 4 | 2 | 16 | 64 | 256 | 8 | 32 |
| Total | | 0 | 11 | 60 | 0 | 708 | 51 | − 9 |

The normal equations are

$$708a + 60c = -9$$

$$60b = 51$$

$$60a + 9c = 11$$

Solving we get, $b = 0{\cdot}85,\ a = -0{\cdot}2673,\ c = 3{\cdot}0042$

Hence the equation is

$$Y = -0{\cdot}2673\,X^2 + 0{\cdot}85\,X + 3{\cdot}0042$$

$$\therefore \quad y - 7 = -0{\cdot}2673\,(x-5)^2 + 0{\cdot}85\,(x-5) + 3{\cdot}0042$$

*i.e.,* $$\mathbf{y = -0{\cdot}2673\,x^2 + 3{\cdot}523\,x - 0{\cdot}9283}$$

**1.9. Fitting an exponential curve**

Let $(x_i, y_i), i = 1, 2, ..., n$ be the $n$ sets of observations of related data and let $y = ab^x$ be the best fit for the data. Then taking logarithm on both sides,

$$\log_{10} y = \log_{10} a + x \log_{10} b$$

*i.e.,* $Y = A + Bx$ where $Y = \log_{10} y,\ A = \log_{10} a,\ B = \log_{10} b$

This being linear in $x$ and $Y$, *we can find* $A$, $B$ since $x$ and $Y = \log_{10} y$ are known. From $A$, $B$, we can get $a$, $b$ and hence $y = ab^x$ is found out.

**1.10. Fitting a curve of the form $\mathbf{y = ax^b}$**

Since $y = ax^b$, $\log_{10} y = \log_{10} a + b \log_{10} x$

*i.e.,* $Y = A + bX$ where $Y = \log_{10} y,\ X = \log_{10} x$ and $A = \log_{10} a$

Again using this linear fit, we find $A$, $b$.

Hence $a$, $b$ are known. Thus $y = ab^x$ is found out.

**Example 21.** *From the table given below, find the best values of a and b in the law $y = ae^{bx}$ by the method of least squares.*

| | | | | | |
|---|---|---|---|---|---|
| *x* : | *0* | *5* | *8* | *12* | *20* |
| *y* : | *3·0* | *1·5* | *1·0* | *0·55* | *0·18* |

**Solution.** $y = ae^{bx}$

$$\therefore \quad \log_{10} y = \log_{10} a + bx \log_{10} e$$

*i.e.,* $$Y = A + Bx \qquad \text{...(1)}$$

The normal equations are

$$B\Sigma x + 5A = \Sigma Y \qquad \text{...(2)}$$

$$B\Sigma x^2 + A\Sigma x = \Sigma xY \quad ...(3)$$

| | $x$ | $y$ | $Y$ | $x^2$ | $xY$ |
|---|---|---|---|---|---|
| | 0 | 3·0 | 0·4771 | 0 | 0 |
| | 5 | 1·5 | 0·1761 | 25 | 0·8805 |
| | 8 | 1·0 | 0 | 64 | 0 |
| | 12 | 0·55 | – 0·2596 | 144 | – 3·1152 |
| | 20 | 0·18 | – 0·7447 | 400 | – 14·894 |
| Total | 45 | | – 0·3511 | 633 | – 17·1287 |

Using equations (2) and (3),

$$5A + 45B = -0{\cdot}3511$$

$$45A + 633B = -17{\cdot}1287$$

Solving we get $A = 0{\cdot}4815,\ B = -0{\cdot}0613$

$$a = 10^A = 3{\cdot}0304$$

$$b \log_{10} e = B = -0{\cdot}0613$$

$$\therefore \quad b = -0{\cdot}0613 \times \log_e 10 = -0{\cdot}1411$$

Hence, the curve is $\mathbf{y = 3{\cdot}0304\, e^{-0{\cdot}1411x}}$

**Example 22.** *Fit a curve of the form* $y = ab^x$ *to the data*

| $x$ : | *1* | *2* | *3* | *4* | *5* | *6* |
|---|---|---|---|---|---|---|
| $y$ : | *151* | *100* | *61* | *50* | *20* | *8* |

**Solution.** $y = ab^x$

$$\therefore \quad \log_{10} y = \log_{10} a + x \log_{10} b$$

*i.e.,* $$Y = A + Bx \quad ...(1)$$

The normal equations are

$$B\Sigma x + 6A = \Sigma Y \quad ...(2)$$

$$B\Sigma x^2 + A\Sigma x = \Sigma xY \quad ...(3)$$

| | $x$ | $y$ | $Y$ | $x^2$ | $xY$ |
|---|---|---|---|---|---|
| | 1 | 151 | 2·1790 | 1 | 2·1790 |
| | 2 | 100 | 2·0 | 4 | 4·0 |
| | 3 | 61 | 1·7853 | 9 | 5·3559 |
| | 4 | 50 | 1·6990 | 16 | 6·7960 |
| | 5 | 20 | 1·3010 | 25 | 6·5050 |
| | 6 | 8 | 0·9031 | 36 | 5·4186 |
| Total | 21 | | 9·8674 | 91 | 30·2545 |

Using (2) and (3), we get

$$6A + 21B = 9{\cdot}8674 \quad ...(4)$$

$$21A + 91B = 30{\cdot}2545 \quad ...(5)$$

Solving, $A = 2{\cdot}5010,\ B = -0{\cdot}2447$

Since $\log_{10} a = A,\ a = 10^A = 316{\cdot}9568$

$$b = 10^B = 0{\cdot}5692$$

$\therefore$ the equation is $\mathbf{y = 316{\cdot}9568\,(0{\cdot}5692)^x}$

**Example 23.** *It is known that the curve $y = ax^b$ fits in the data given below. Find the best values of a and b.*

| x : | 1 | 2 | 3 | 4 | 5 | 6 |
|---|---|---|---|---|---|---|
| y : | 1200 | 900 | 600 | 200 | 110 | 50 |

**Solution.** $y = ax^b$

Taking logarithm, $\log_{10} y = \log_{10} a + b \log_{10} x$

*i.e.,* $$Y = A + bX \quad ...(1)$$

where $Y = \log_{10} y$, $X = \log_{10} x$, $A = \log_{10} a$

The normal equations are

$$b\Sigma X + 6A = \Sigma Y \quad ...(2)$$

$$b\Sigma X^2 + A\Sigma X = \Sigma XY \quad ...(3)$$

| | x | y | X | Y | $X^2$ | XY |
|---|---|---|---|---|---|---|
| | 1 | 1200 | 0·0 | 3·0792 | 0·0 | 0·0 |
| | 2 | 900 | 0·3010 | 2·9542 | 0·0906 | 0·8892 |
| | 3 | 600 | 0·4771 | 2·7782 | 0·2276 | 1·3255 |
| | 4 | 200 | 0·6021 | 2·3010 | 0·3625 | 1·3854 |
| | 5 | 110 | 0·6990 | 2·0414 | 0·4886 | 1·4269 |
| | 6 | 50 | 0·7781 | 1·6990 | 0·6054 | 1·3220 |
| Total | | | 2·8573 | 14·8530 | 1·7747 | 6·3490 |

Using (2) and (3), we have,

$$6A + 2{\cdot}8573b = 14{\cdot}8530$$

$$2{\cdot}8573A + 1{\cdot}7747b = 6{\cdot}3490$$

Solving, $A = 3{\cdot}3086$, $b = -1{\cdot}7494$

$\therefore$ $a = 10^A = 2035$

Hence, the equation is $\mathbf{y = 2035\, x^{-1{\cdot}7494}}$

## 1.11. Calculation of the sum of the squares of the residuals in the case of straight line fit

In fitting a straight line, we have seen that the sum of the squares of the residuals $E$ is given by

$$E = \Sigma[y - (ax + b)]^2$$
$$= \Sigma[y - (ax + b)]\,[y - (ax + b)]$$
$$= \Sigma\{y\,[y - (ax + b)] - ax\,[y - (ax + b)] - b\,[y - (ax + b)]\}$$
$$= \Sigma y\,[y - (ax + b)] - a\Sigma x\,[y - (ax + b)] - b\Sigma[y - (ax + b)]$$
$$= \Sigma y\,[y - (ax + b)]$$

since the last two sums vanish due to normal equations $\Sigma x\,[y - (ax + b)] = 0$ ; $\Sigma[y - (ax + b)] = 0$

$$\therefore \quad E = \Sigma y^2 - a\Sigma xy - b\Sigma y$$

when we fit a straight line by the method of least squares, the error committed (which is minimum) is given by

$$\boxed{E = \Sigma y^2 - a\Sigma xy - b\Sigma y}$$

## 1.12. Calculation of the sum of the squares of the residuals in the case of parabola fit

In fitting a parabola, we have seen that the sum of the squares of residuals $E$ is given by

$$E = \Sigma[y - (ax^2 + bx + c)]^2$$
$$= \Sigma[y - (ax^2 + bx + c)]\,[y - (ax^2 + bx + c)]$$
$$= \Sigma y\,[y - (ax^2 + bx + c)] - a\Sigma x^2[y - (ax^2 + bx + c)]$$
$$- b\Sigma x\,[y - (ax^2 + bx + c)] - c\Sigma[y - (ax^2 + bx + c)]$$

$= \Sigma y\,[y - (ax^2 + bx + c)]$ since the last three summations vanish due to normal equations.

$$= \Sigma y^2 - a\Sigma x^2 y - b\Sigma xy - c\Sigma y$$

When we fit a parabola by the method of least squares, the error committed (which is minimum) is given by

$$\boxed{E = \Sigma y^2 - a\Sigma x^2 y - b\Sigma xy - c\Sigma y}$$

**Note.** To remember this formula, multiply $y - (ax^2 + bx + c)$ by $y$ and take $\Sigma$.

**Example 24.** *Fit a straight line and a parabola to the following data and find out which one is most appropriate. Reason out for your conclusion.*

| $x$ : | 0 | 1 | 2 | 3 | 4 |
|---|---|---|---|---|---|
| $y$ : | 1 | 1·8 | 1·3 | 2·5 | 6·3 |

**Solution.** *Stage 1* : Let $y = ax + b$ be the best fit.

Then the normal equations are

$$a\Sigma x + 5b = \Sigma y \qquad ...(1)$$

and

$$a\Sigma x^2 + b\Sigma x = \Sigma xy \qquad ...(2)$$

| | $x$ | $y$ | $x^2$ | $x^3$ | $x^4$ | $xy$ | $x^2y$ | $y^2$ |
|---|---|---|---|---|---|---|---|---|
| | 0 | 1 | 0 | 0 | 0 | 0 | 0 | 1 |
| | 1 | 1·8 | 1 | 1 | 1 | 1·8 | 1·8 | 3·24 |
| | 2 | 1·3 | 4 | 8 | 16 | 2·6 | 5·2 | 1·69 |
| | 3 | 2·5 | 9 | 27 | 81 | 7·5 | 22·5 | 6·25 |
| | 4 | 6·3 | 16 | 64 | 256 | 25·2 | 100·8 | 39·69 |
| Total | 10 | 12·9 | 30 | 100 | 354 | 37·1 | 130·3 | 51·87 |

Using (1) and (2), $10a + 5b = 12·9$

and $30a + 10b = 37·1$

Solving, we get, $b = 0·32$, $a = 1·33$

The best straight line fit is $\mathbf{y = 1·33x + 0·32}$

Error in this case $= E_1 = \Sigma y^2 - a\Sigma xy - b\Sigma y$

$$= 51·87 - 1·33\,(37·1) - 0·32(12·9)$$
$$= \mathbf{-\,1·60}$$

*Stage 2* : Let $y = Ax^2 + Bx + c$ be the parabola fit.

The normal equations are

$$A\Sigma x^2 + B\Sigma x + 5c = \Sigma y$$
$$A\Sigma x^3 + B\Sigma x^2 + c\Sigma x = \Sigma xy$$
$$A\Sigma x^4 + B\Sigma x^3 + c\Sigma x^2 = \Sigma x^2 y$$

*i.e.,*

$$30A + 10B + 5c = 12{\cdot}9 \quad ...(3)$$
$$100A + 30B + 10c = 37{\cdot}1 \quad ...(4)$$
$$354A + 100B + 30c = 130{\cdot}3 \quad ...(5)$$

Solving, $A = 0{\cdot}55$, $B = -1{\cdot}07$, $c = 1{\cdot}42$

The best fitting curve is $\mathbf{y = 0{\cdot}55x^2 - 1{\cdot}07x + 1{\cdot}42}$

Error in this case is $E_2 = \Sigma y^2 - A\Sigma x^2 y - B\Sigma xy - c\Sigma y$

$$= 51{\cdot}87 - (0{\cdot}55)(130{\cdot}3) + 1{\cdot}07\,(37{\cdot}1) - 1{\cdot}42\,(12{\cdot}9)$$
$$= \mathbf{1{\cdot}584}$$

The error in the case of straight line fit is $= |E_1| = 1{\cdot}60$

The error in the case of parabola fit is $|E_2| = 1{\cdot}584$

$$|E_2| = 1{\cdot}584 < 1{\cdot}60 = |E_1|$$

$\therefore$ the parabola fit is better.

But both errors are more or less equal since $1{\cdot}584 \approx 1{\cdot}6$

Hence, we may even say both are of same status.

Though total errors are same, there may be different deviations as the table below exhibits.

| $x$ | | 0 | 1 | 2 | 3 | 4 |
|---|---|---|---|---|---|---|
| $y$ by data given | : | 1 | 1·8 | 1·3 | 2·5 | 6·3 |
| $y$ by st. line fit | : | 0·32 | 1·65 | 2·98 | 4·31 | 5·64 |
| $y$ by parabola fit | : | 1·42 | 0·90 | 1·48 | 3·16 | 5·94 |

## EXERCISE 1.3

Use the *method of least squares* and do the following problems :

**1.** Fit a straight line to the following data. Hence find $y(x = 25)$.

| $x$ | : | 0 | 5 | 10 | 15 | 20 |
|---|---|---|---|---|---|---|
| $y$ | : | 7 | 11 | 16 | 20 | 26 |

**2.** Fit a straight line to the following data :

| $x$ | : | 0·0 | 0·2 | 0·4 | 0·6 | 0·8 | 1·0 |
|---|---|---|---|---|---|---|---|
| $y$ | : | −1·85 | −1·20 | −0·55 | 0·15 | 0·80 | 1·35 |

**3.** The weights of a calf taken at weekly intervals are supplied below. Fit a straight line and calculate the average rate of growth per week.

| Age $x$ | : | 1 | 2 | 3 | 4 | 5 | 6 | 7 | 8 | 9 | 10 |
|---|---|---|---|---|---|---|---|---|---|---|---|
| Weight $y$ | : | 52·5 | 58·7 | 65·0 | 70·2 | 75·4 | 81·1 | 87·2 | 95·5 | 102·2 | 106·4 |

**4.** Fit a straight line to the data given below :

| $x$ : | 1 | 2 | 3 | 4 | 5 | 6 |
|---|---|---|---|---|---|---|
| $y$ : | 1200 | 900 | 600 | 200 | 110 | 50 |

**5.** Fit a straight line to the following data :

| $u$ : | 6 | 8 | 10 | 12 | 14 | 16 | 18 | 20 | 22 | 24 |
|---|---|---|---|---|---|---|---|---|---|---|
| $v$ : | 3·8 | 3·7 | 4·0 | 3·9 | 4·3 | 4·2 | 4·2 | 4·4 | 4·5 | 4·5 |

**6.** Fit a st. line to the data.

| $x$ : | – 3 | – 1 | 1 | 4 | 5 | 7 | 10 |
|---|---|---|---|---|---|---|---|
| $y$ : | – 2 | – 1 | 0 | 1·5 | 2 | 3 | 4·5 |

**7.** Find the best fit of straight line to the data.

| $t$ : | 6 | 7 | 7 | 8 | 8 | 8 | 9 | 9 | 10 |
|---|---|---|---|---|---|---|---|---|---|
| $\theta$ : | 5 | 5 | 4 | 5 | 4 | 3 | 4 | 3 | 3 |

**8.** Obtain a st. line fit to the data below :

| $x$ : | 1 | 2 | 3 | 4 | 5 |
|---|---|---|---|---|---|
| $y$ : | 4 | 3 | 6 | 7 | 11 |

**9.** Find the best fitting straight line to the data.

(*a*)

| $x$ : | 75 | 80 | 93 | 65 | 87 | 71 | 98 | 68 | 84 | 77 |
|---|---|---|---|---|---|---|---|---|---|---|
| $y$ : | 82 | 78 | 86 | 72 | 91 | 80 | 95 | 72 | 89 | 74 |

[*MKU*]

(*b*)

| $x$ : | 0 | 5 | 10 | 15 | 20 | 25 | 30 |
|---|---|---|---|---|---|---|---|
| $y$ : | 10 | 14 | 19 | 25 | 31 | 36 | 39 |

[*MS.BE*]

(*c*)

| $x$ : | 1 | 2 | 3 | 4 | 5 |
|---|---|---|---|---|---|
| $y$ : | 16 | 19 | 23 | 26 | 30 |

[*MS. BE 72*]

(*d*)

| $x$ : | 1 | 2 | 3 | 4 | 5 | 6 |
|---|---|---|---|---|---|---|
| $y$ : | 14 | 27 | 41 | 56 | 68 | 75 |

[*MS. M.Sc.*]

**10.** Fit a curve of the form $y = ax + b$ to the data.

| $x$ : | 1 | 2 | 3 | 4 | 5 |
|---|---|---|---|---|---|
| $y$ : | 14 | 27 | 40 | 55 | 68 |

[*MS. BE*]

**11.** A rubber band stretched under a force $F$ is found to increase in length $l$. The following observations were got.

| $F$ : | 2 | 3 | 4 | 5 | 6 | 7 | 8 | 9 | 10 | 11 | 12 |
|---|---|---|---|---|---|---|---|---|---|---|---|
| $l$ : | 10 | 17 | 21 | 28 | 36 | 43 | 51 | 60 | 70 | 83 | 93 |

Fit a straight line. [*MS.BE*]

**12.** Fit a straight line to the data.

| x : | 0·5 | 1·0 | 1·5 | 2·0 | 2·5 | 3·0 |
|---|---|---|---|---|---|---|
| $y$ : | 0·31 | 0·82 | 1·29 | 1·85 | 2·51 | 3·02 |

**13.** Fit a parabola to the data.

| $x$ : | 0 | 0·1 | 0·2 | 0·3 | 04 | 0·5 | 0·6 | 0·7 | 0·8 | 0·9 |
|---|---|---|---|---|---|---|---|---|---|---|
| $y$ : | 3·1950 | 3·2299 | 3·2532 | 3·2611 | 3·2516 | 3·2282 | 3·1807 | 3·1266 | 3·0594 | 2·9759 |

**14.** Fit a parabola to the data.

| $x$ : | 1 | 2 | 3 | 4 | 5 |
|---|---|---|---|---|---|
| $y$ : | 2 | 3 | 5 | 8 | 10 |

**15.** Fit a st. line to the data :

| $x$ : | 3 | 4 | 5 | 6 | 7 |
|---|---|---|---|---|---|
| $y$ : | 6 | 9 | 10 | 11 | 12 |

**16.** The variables $x$ and $y$ are related by $y = Ax^B$. Find the curve from the following data :

| $x$ : | 1 | 2 | 3 | 4 | 5 |
|---|---|---|---|---|---|
| $y$ : | 7·1 | 27·8 | 62·1 | 110 | 161 |

**17.** Fit a parabola to the data given below :

| $x$ : | 1 | 2 | 3 | 4 | 5 |
|---|---|---|---|---|---|
| $y$ : | 90 | 220 | 390 | 625 | 915 |

**18.** The following table gives the levels of prices in certain years. Fit a second degree parabola to the data.

| Year : | 1875 | 76 | 77 | 78 | 79 | 80 | 81 | 82 | 83 | 84 | 85 |
|---|---|---|---|---|---|---|---|---|---|---|---|
| Price : | 88 | 87 | 81 | 78 | 74 | 79 | 85 | 84 | 90 | 92 | 100 |

[*MS. BE 1970*]

**19.** Fit a second degree curve to the data.

| $x$ : | 1929 | 1930 | 1931 | 1932 | 1933 | 1934 | 1935 | 1936 | 1937 |
|---|---|---|---|---|---|---|---|---|---|
| $y$ : | 352 | 356 | 357 | 358 | 360 | 361 | 361 | 360 | 359 |

**20.** Fit a curve of the form $y = ax + bx^2$ to the data.

| $x$ : | 1 | 2 | 3 | 4 | 5 |
|---|---|---|---|---|---|
| $y$ : | 1·8 | 5·1 | 8·9 | 14·1 | 19·8 |

**21.** Fit a parabola to the data given below :

| $x$ : | 1 | 2 | 3 | 4 | 5 |
|---|---|---|---|---|---|
| $y$ : | 1250 | 1400 | 1650 | 1950 | 2300 |

**22.** Fit a parabola to the data.

| $x$ : | 1·0 | 1·5 | 2·0 | 2·5 | 3·0 | 3·5 | 4·0 |
|---|---|---|---|---|---|---|---|
| $y$ : | 1·1 | 1·3 | 1·6 | 2·6 | 2·7 | 3·4 | 4·1 |

**23.** Fit a curve of the form $y = ax^2 + b$ for the following data.

| $x$ : | 1 | 2 | 3 | 4 | 5 |
|---|---|---|---|---|---|
| $y$ : | 20·9 | 24·1 | 28·9 | 36·1 | 44·7 |

**24.** Fit a curve of the form $y = ax^2 + bx + c$ given the table.

| $x$ : | 10 | 20 | 30 | 40 | 50 | 60 |
|---|---|---|---|---|---|---|
| $y$ : | 157 | 179 | 210 | 252 | 302 | 361 |

**25.** Fit a law of the type $y = ae^{bx}$ to the data.

| $x$ : | 0 | 1 | 2 | 3 |
|---|---|---|---|---|
| $y$ : | 1·05 | 2·10 | 3·85 | 8·30 |

**26.** Fit a curve of the form $y = ae^{bx}$ to the data given below :

| $x$ : | 0 | 2 | 4 |
|---|---|---|---|
| $y$ : | 5·012 | 10 | 31·62 |

[*BE. 1971*]

**27.** Fit a curve of the form $y = ae^{bx}$ to the data.

| $x$ : | 1 | 2 | 3 | 4 | 5 | 6 | 7 | 8 |
|---|---|---|---|---|---|---|---|---|
| $y$ : | 15·3 | 20·5 | 27·4 | 36·6 | 49·1 | 65·6 | 87·8 | 117·6 |

**28.** The following table gives the number of petals on a certain species of flower. Fit an exponential curve to the data.

| | | | | | | | |
|---|---|---|---|---|---|---|---|
| No. of petals | $x$ : | 5 | 6 | 7 | 8 | 9 | 10 |
| No. of flowers having a specified no. of petals | $y$ : | 133 | 55 | 23 | 7 | 2 | 2 |

**29.** Fit a curve of the form $y = ab^x$ to the data given below :

| $x$ : | 1 | 2 | 3 | 4 | 5 | 6 |
|---|---|---|---|---|---|---|
| $y$ : | 151 | 100 | 61 | 50 | 20 | 8 |

**30.** Fit the curve $pv^\gamma = k$ to the following data.

| $p$ : | 0·5 | 1·0 | 1·5 | 2·0 | 2·5 | 3·0 |
|---|---|---|---|---|---|---|
| $v$ : | 1·62 | 1·00 | 0·75 | 0·62 | 0·52 | 0·46 |

**31.** Fit a curve of the form $y = ab^x$ to the data.

| $x$ : | 2 | 3 | 4 | 5 | 6 |
|---|---|---|---|---|---|
| $y$ : | 144 | 172·8 | 207·4 | 248·8 | 298·5 |

**32.** Fit the curve of the form $y = ae^{bx}$ to the data given below:

| $x$ : | 1 | 2 | 3 | 4 |
|---|---|---|---|---|
| $y$ : | 1·65 | 2·70 | 4·50 | 7·35 |

**33.** An experiment on the life of a cutting tool at different cutting speeds are given below :

| | | | | |
|---|---|---|---|---|
| Speed $v$ units : | 350 | 400 | 500 | 600 |
| Life $T$ in min. : | 61 | 26 | 7 | 2·6 |

Fit a relation of the form $v = aT^b$ [BE'67]

**34.** The horse power $I$, required to drive a ship of displacement $D$ tons at a ten-knob speed is given by the table below. Find a formula of the form $I = aD^n$ to fit the data.

| $D$ : | 1720 | 2300 | 3200 | 4100 |
|---|---|---|---|---|
| $I$ : | 655 | 789 | 1000 | 1164 |

**35.** For the following data, fit a straight line and a parabola and show that the parabola fits the data significantly better than the straight line.

| $x$ : | 0·00 | 0·25 | 0·50 | 0·75 | 1·00 |
|---|---|---|---|---|---|
| $y$ : | 0·00 | 0·06 | 0·20 | 0·60 | 0·90 |

**36.** Given the following data:

| $x$ : | 0 | 1 | 2 | 3 | 4 |
|---|---|---|---|---|---|
| $y$ : | 1 | 5 | 10 | 22 | 38 |

find the straight line and the parabola of best fit and calculate the sum of the squares of the residuals in both cases. Which curve is more appropriate and why ?

**37.** Fit the parabola and the straight line of best fit to the following data and out of them which is more reliable ?

| $x$ : | – 2 | 1 | 4 | 7 | 10 |
|---|---|---|---|---|---|
| $y$ : | 10·8 | 1·9 | 29·2 | 92 | 190 |

**38.** It is known that $x, y$ are related by $y = \frac{a}{x} + bx$ and the experimental values are given below.

| $x$ : | 1 | 2 | 4 | 6 | 8 |
|---|---|---|---|---|---|
| $y$ : | 5·43 | 6·28 | 10·32 | 14·86 | 19·5 |

Obtain the best values of $a$ and $b$.

**39.** Growth of bacteria ($y$) in a culture after $x$ hours is given below. Estimate the growth when $x = 7$ hours.

| Hours $x$ : | 0 | 1 | 2 | 3 | 4 | 5 | 6 |
|---|---|---|---|---|---|---|---|
| Growth (Number) $y$ : | 32 | 47 | 65 | 92 | 132 | 190 | 275 |

**40.** Fit the straight and the parabola of best fit to the following data and explain which is more preferable.

| $x$ : | 0 | 1 | 2 | 3 | 4 | 5 |
|---|---|---|---|---|---|---|
| $y$ : | 14 | 18 | 22 | 28 | 35 | 39 |

**41.** Fit the straight line and the parabola of best fit to the following data and explain which is more reliable.

| $x$ : | 1 | 2 | 3 | 4 | 5 |
|---|---|---|---|---|---|
| $y$ : | 10 | 12 | 8 | 10 | 14 |

**42.** Find the most plausible values of $x, y, z$ from the equations,
$3x + 2y - 5z = 5$, $x - y + 2z = 3$, $4x + y + 4z = 21$ and $-x + 3y + 3z = 14$

[**Hint** : Let $S = (3x + 2y - 5z - 5)^2 + (x - y + 2z - 3)^2 + (4x + y + 4z - 21)^2 + (-x + 3y + 3z - 14)^2$

$\frac{\partial S}{\partial x} = 0$, $\frac{\partial S}{\partial y} = 0$, $\frac{\partial S}{\partial z} = 0$ give respectively $27x + 6y = 88$, $6x + 15y + z = 70$, $y + 54z = 107$

Solving $x = 2{\cdot}47$, $y = 3{\cdot}55$, $z = 1{\cdot}92$ are the most plausible values of $x, y, z$).

**43.** Fit a st. line to the following data showing the production of a commodity in different areas in Coimbatore.

| Year $x$ : | 1911 | 1912 | 1913 | 1914 | 1915 |
|---|---|---|---|---|---|
| Production in (1000 tons) $y$ : | 10 | 12 | 8 | 10 | 14 |

## 1.13. Method of moments

We will see below another method of curve fitting called *the method of moments.*

Let $(x_i, y_i)$, $i = 1, 2, \ldots, n$ be $n$ sets of observations of related data so that the $x$'s are equally spaced. That is, $x_i - x_{i-1} = \Delta x = h$ (constant), $i = 2, 3, \ldots n$. For such a set of $n$ points, we define,

the first moment $= \mu_1 = \Sigma y \Delta x = \Delta x \Sigma y$

the second moment $= \mu_2 = \Sigma xy \Delta x = \Delta x \Sigma xy$

the third moment $= \mu_3 = \Sigma x^2 y \Delta x = \Delta x \Sigma x^2 y$

and so on. These are known as the moments of the *observed* values of $y$.

Let $y = f(x)$ be a curve which fits the data best.

The first moment $= \gamma_1 = \int y dx$

The second moment $= \gamma_2 = \int xy dx$

The third moment $= \gamma_3 = \int x^2 y dx$ and so on.

These moments are called *moments of the computed values of* $y$ or *moments of the expected values of* $y$. This method of moments is based on the principles that the moments of the observed values of $y$ and the moments of the expected values of $y$ are equal, *i.e.*, $\mu_i = \gamma_i$, $i = 1, 2, 3...$ .

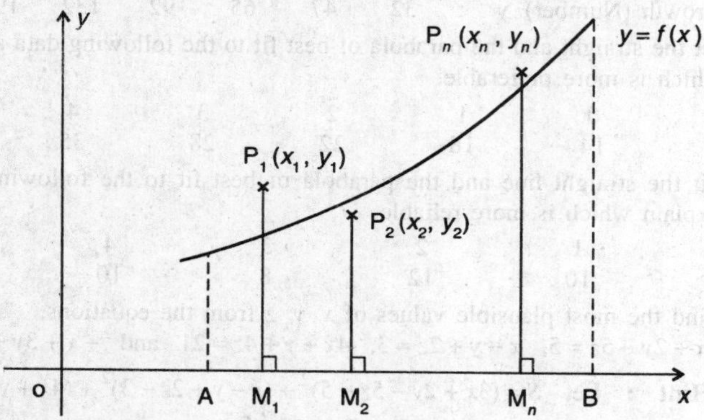


In the figure, $P_i$ is $(x_i, y_i)$, $i = 1, 2, ..., n$.

$P_iM_i$ is the ordinate of $P_i$.

$$M_iM_{i-1} = \Delta x, \quad i = 1, 2, ..., n.$$

Since $y_1$ is the ordinate at $x = x_1$, we will take it as the mid ordinate of the interval of breadth $\Delta x$, *i.e.*, $A$ is a point on the $x$-axis such that $AM_1 = \dfrac{\Delta x}{2}$.

$y_1 \Delta x$ is the area of the rectangle of breadth $\Delta x$ whose middle ordinate is $y_1$

$\therefore \ \mu_1 = \Delta x \sum_{i=1}^{n} y_i =$ sum of areas of such $n$ rectangles where the last rectangle goes beyond $M_n$ to $B$ such that $M_nB = \dfrac{\Delta x}{2}$

This area is approximately equal to area enclosed by the curve, the $x$-axis and $x = x_1 - \dfrac{\Delta x}{2}$, $x = x_n + \dfrac{\Delta x}{2}$ which is $\displaystyle\int_{x_1 - \frac{\Delta x}{2}}^{x_n + \frac{\Delta x}{2}} y\, dx = \gamma_1$

$\therefore$ Since $\mu_1 = \gamma_1$,

$$\Delta x \Sigma y = \int_{x_1 - \frac{\Delta x}{2}}^{x_n + \frac{\Delta x}{2}} y\, dx \qquad ...(1)$$

Similarly, $$\Delta x \Sigma xy = \int_{x_1 - \frac{1}{2}\Delta x}^{x_n + \frac{1}{2}\Delta x} x\, y\, dx \qquad ...(2)$$

..................................................

$$\Delta x \Sigma x^r y = \int_{x_1 - \frac{1}{2}\Delta x}^{x_n + \frac{1}{2}\Delta x} x^r\, y\, dx \qquad ...(r+1)$$

These equations, called, *observation equations* will give equations in the unknowns involved in $y = f(x)$. We will solve for the unknowns of $f(x)$ from these equations.

**Case 1.** If $f(x)$ is a linear expression, *i.e.*, $y = f(x)$ is a linear fit such as $y = ax + b$,

$$\Delta x \Sigma y = \int_\alpha^\beta y\, dx = \int_\alpha^\beta (ax + b)\, dx = \left( \frac{ax^2}{2} + bx \right)_\alpha^\beta = \frac{a}{2} (\beta^2 - \alpha^2) + b\, (\beta - \alpha)$$

Similarly, $$\Delta x \Sigma xy = \int_\alpha^\beta x\, (ax + b)\, dx = \left( \frac{ax^3}{3} + \frac{bx^2}{2} \right)_\alpha^\beta$$

$$= \frac{a}{3} (\beta^3 - \alpha^3) + \frac{b}{2} (\beta^2 - \alpha^2)$$

where $\alpha = x_1 - \frac{1}{2} \Delta x$, $\beta = x_n + \frac{1}{2} \Delta x$.

Since two equations are sufficient to solve for two constants $a$ and $b$, we have, *two observation equations*, namely,

$$\frac{a}{2} (\beta^2 - \alpha^2) + b\, (\beta - \alpha) = \Delta x \Sigma y \qquad ...(I)$$

$$\frac{a}{3} (\beta^3 - \alpha^3) + \frac{b}{2} (\beta^2 - \alpha^2) = \Delta x \Sigma xy \qquad ...(II)$$

Solving for $a$ and $b$ from (I) and (II), we get $a$, $b$. Knowing $a$ and $b$, the best linear fit is $y = ax + b$.

**Case 2.** If the best fitting curve is a parabola, *i.e.*, $y = ax^2 + bx + c$ is the curve, we have

$$\Delta x \Sigma y = \int_\alpha^\beta y\, dx = \int_\alpha^\beta (ax^2 + bx + c)\, dx$$

$$= \frac{a}{3} (\beta^3 - \alpha^3) + \frac{b}{2} (\beta^2 - \alpha^2) + c\, (\beta - \alpha)$$

Similarly,

$$\Delta x \Sigma xy = \int_{\alpha}^{\beta} xy\, dx = \int_{\alpha}^{\beta} x\,(ax^2 + bx + c)\, dx$$

$$= \frac{1}{4}(\beta^4 - \alpha^4) + \frac{b}{3}(\beta^3 - \alpha^3) + \frac{c}{2}(\beta^2 - \alpha^2)$$

and so on where $\alpha = x_1 - \frac{1}{2}\Delta x, \quad \beta = x_n + \frac{1}{2}\Delta x$

To solve for three unknowns *a, b, c* we require three equations. Hence, the three observation equations are

$$\frac{a}{3}(\beta^3 - \alpha^3) + \frac{b}{2}(\beta^2 - \alpha^2) + c\,(\beta - \alpha) = \Delta x \Sigma y \qquad \text{...(III)}$$

$$\frac{a}{4}(\beta^4 - \alpha^4) + \frac{b}{3}(\beta^3 - \alpha^3) + \frac{c}{2}(\beta^2 - \alpha^2) = \Delta x \Sigma xy \qquad \text{...(IV)}$$

$$\frac{a}{5}(\beta^5 - \alpha^5) + \frac{b}{4}(\beta^4 - \alpha^4) + \frac{c}{3}(\beta^3 - \alpha^3) = \Delta x \Sigma x^2 y \qquad \text{...(V)}$$

These equations (III), (IV) and (V) give us the values of *a, b, c* which when substituted in the curve $y = ax^2 + bx + c$, we get the curve required.

**Note.** *To apply this method, x's should be equally spaced.*

**Example 25.** *By using the method of moments, obtain a straight line fit to the data:*

| | | | | | |
|---|---|---|---|---|---|
| x : | 1 | 2 | 3 | 4 | |
| y : | 0·30 | 0·64 | 1·32 | 5·40 | [MKU 1969] |

**Solution.** Here $\Delta x = 2 - 1 = 1$

$$\therefore \quad \alpha = x_1 - \frac{\Delta x}{2} = 1 - \frac{1}{2} = 1/2 \;;\; \beta = x_n + \frac{1}{2}\Delta x = 4{\cdot}5$$

Let $y = ax + b$ be the best fit.

The two observation equations are

$$\frac{a}{2}(\beta^2 - \alpha^2) + b\,(\beta - \alpha) = \Delta x \Sigma y \qquad \text{...(1)}$$

$$\frac{a}{3}(\beta^3 - \alpha^3) + \frac{b}{2}(\beta^2 - \alpha^2) = \Delta x \Sigma xy \qquad \text{...(2)}$$

As we require $\Sigma y$ and $\Sigma xy$, we calculate them

$$\Sigma y = 0{\cdot}30 + 0{\cdot}64 + 1{\cdot}32 + 5{\cdot}40 = 7{\cdot}66$$

$$\Sigma xy = 0{\cdot}30 + 1{\cdot}28 + 3{\cdot}96 + 21{\cdot}60 = 27{\cdot}14$$

Substituting in (1) and (2), we get,

$$\frac{a}{2}[(4{\cdot}5)^2 - (0{\cdot}5)^2] + b\,[4{\cdot}5 - 0{\cdot}5] = 1\,(7{\cdot}66)$$

$$\frac{a}{3}[(4{\cdot}5)^3 - (0{\cdot}5)^3] + \frac{b}{2}[(4{\cdot}5)^2 - (0{\cdot}5)^2] = 1\,(27{\cdot}14)$$

*i.e.,* $10a + 4b = 7{\cdot}66$ ...(3)

$30{\cdot}333a + 10b = 27{\cdot}14$ ...(4)

Solving, $a = 1{\cdot}4981$; $b = -1{\cdot}8303$

Hence the best straight line fit is $\mathbf{y = 1{\cdot}4981x - 1{\cdot}8303}$

**Example 26.** *By using the method of moments, obtain a second degree curve which fits best to the following data :*

| *x* : | *1* | *2* | *3* | *4* |
|---|---|---|---|---|
| *y* : | *0·30* | *0·64* | *1·32* | *5·40* |

**Solution.** This is exactly the same data as in the previous problem.

Here, $\Delta x = 1$, $\alpha = 0{\cdot}5$, $\beta = 4{\cdot}5$. The best fit is $y = ax^2 + bx + c$.

The three observation equations are,

$$\frac{a}{3}(\beta^3 - \alpha^3) + \frac{b}{2}(\beta^2 - \alpha^2) + c(\beta - \alpha) = \Delta x \Sigma y \quad ...(4)$$

$$\frac{a}{4}(\beta^4 - \alpha^4) + \frac{b}{3}(\beta^3 - \alpha^3) + \frac{c}{2}(\beta^2 - \alpha^2) = \Delta x \Sigma xy \quad ...(5)$$

$$\frac{a}{5}(\beta^5 - \alpha^5) + \frac{b}{4}(\beta^4 - \alpha^4) + \frac{c}{3}(\beta^3 - \alpha^3) = \Delta x \Sigma x^2 y \quad ...(6)$$

We calculate the R.H. sides.

$$\Sigma y = 7{\cdot}66, \quad \Sigma xy = 27{\cdot}14$$

$$\Sigma x^2 y = 0{\cdot}30 + 4\,(0{\cdot}64) + 9\,(1{\cdot}32) + 16\,(5{\cdot}40) = 101{\cdot}14$$

Also, $\beta - \alpha = 4{\cdot}5 - 0{\cdot}5 = 4$

$$\beta^2 - \alpha^2 = 20, \ \beta^3 - \alpha^3 = 91, \ \beta^4 - \alpha^4 = 410, \ \beta^5 - \alpha^5 = 1845{\cdot}25$$

Using in (4), (5), (6), we get,

$30{\cdot}333a + 10b + 4c = 7{\cdot}66$ ...(7)

$102{\cdot}5a + 30{\cdot}333b + 10c = 27{\cdot}14$ ...(8)

$369{\cdot}05a + 102{\cdot}5b + 30{\cdot}333c = 101{\cdot}14$ ...(9)

Solving, we get $a = 0{\cdot}6567$, $b = -1\,7856$, $c = 1{\cdot}399$

Hence, the curve is $\mathbf{y = 0{\cdot}6567x^2 - 1{\cdot}7856x + 1{\cdot}399}$

**Example 27.** *By the method of moments, fit a st. line and a parabola to the data*

| *x* : | *1* | *2* | *3* | *4* |
|---|---|---|---|---|
| *y* : | *1·7* | *1·8* | *2·3* | *3·2* |

**Solution.** (*i*) Let $y = ax + b$ be the st. line which fits best.

$$\Delta x = 1, \ \alpha = 0{\cdot}5, \ \beta = 4{\cdot}5$$

$$\beta - \alpha = 4; \ \beta^2 - \alpha^2 = 20; \ \beta^3 - \alpha^3 = 91; \ \Sigma y = 9{\cdot}0; \ \Sigma xy = 25; \ \Sigma x^2 y = 80{\cdot}8$$

As in the problem 25,

$$\frac{a}{2}(20) + b\,(4) = 1\,(\Sigma y) = 9$$

*i.e.,* $10a + 4b = 9$ ...(1)

$$\frac{a}{3}(91)+\frac{b}{2}(20)=25$$

*i.e.,* $$91a+30b=75 \quad ...(2)$$

Solving for $a$, $b$ from (1) and (2), $a=0{\cdot}49$, $b=1{\cdot}025$

Hence, the curve is $\mathbf{y=(0{\cdot}49)\,x+1{\cdot}025}$

(*ii*) Let $y=ax^2+bx+c$ be the best parabola fit. Here $\Sigma x^2y=80{\cdot}8$.

The observation equations are

$$4a+10b+\frac{91}{3}c=9 \quad ...(1)$$

$$10a+\frac{91}{3}b+102{\cdot}5c=25 \quad ...(2)$$

$$\frac{91}{3}a+102{\cdot}5b+\frac{1845{\cdot}25}{5}c=80{\cdot}8 \quad ...(3)$$

Solving $a=0{\cdot}01$, $b=0{\cdot}45$, $c=1{\cdot}09$

Hence the equation is $\mathbf{y=0{\cdot}01x^2+0{\cdot}45x+1{\cdot}09}$

## EXERCISE 1.4

**1.** By the method of moments, fit a st. line and parabola to the data given below:

| $x$ : | 1 | 2 | 3 | 4 |
|---|---|---|---|---|
| $y$ : | 0·17 | 0·18 | 0·23 | 0·32 |

[*MS BE 71*]

**2.** Fit a parabola by the method of moments to the data given below :

| $x$ : | – 2 | – 1 | 0 | 1 | 2 |
|---|---|---|---|---|---|
| $y$ : | – 72 | – 46 | – 12 | 35 | 93 |

**3.** Fit a st. line by the method of moments to the data.

| $x$ : | 2 | 4 | 6 | 8 | 10 | 12 | 14 | 16 |
|---|---|---|---|---|---|---|---|---|
| $y$ : | 1 | 2 | 4 | 7 | 8 | 10 | 6 | 8 |

**4.** Use the method of moments to fit a st. line to the data given below :

| $x$ : | 1 | 3 | 5 | 7 | 9 |
|---|---|---|---|---|---|
| $y$ : | 1·5 | 2·8 | 4·0 | 4·7 | 6·0 |

[*MKU 1976*]

**5.** Fit a straight line by the method of moments to the data.

| $x$ : | 1 | 2 | 3 | 4 |
|---|---|---|---|---|
| $y$ : | 16 | 19 | 23 | 26 |

[*MKU 1977*]

**6.** In the previous exercises, wherever, $x$'s are equally spaced, work out such problems by this method.

# ANSWERS

## EXERCISE 1.1 Page 3

**1.** $y=\frac{42}{x}+45{\cdot}5$ **2.** $y=11{\cdot}4+\frac{41{\cdot}9}{x}$ **3.** $y=1362-243{\cdot}2x$

**4.** $y\,x^{-1{\cdot}22}=251{\cdot}2$

## EXERCISE 1.2 Page 16

**1.** $y = 0{\cdot}7x + 11{\cdot}1$ **2.** $A = 1090{\cdot}93, B = -0{\cdot}546$ **3.** $y = 6{\cdot}104x + 46{\cdot}048$

**4.** $a = 15{\cdot}49, n = 0{\cdot}51$ **5.** $y = 1{\cdot}936\,(1{\cdot}264)^x$ **6.** $y = 2{\cdot}42x + 0{\cdot}16x^2$

**7.** $V = 42{\cdot}1115 + \dfrac{16{\cdot}44}{A}$ **8.** $p = 2{\cdot}1 + 0{\cdot}19w$ **9.** $y = 0{\cdot}267\,x^{0{\cdot}331}$

**10.** $y = 0{\cdot}005x^2 + 0{\cdot}105x + 3{\cdot}95$ **12.** $v = 1{\cdot}375t^2 - 3{\cdot}875t + 5{\cdot}875$

**13.** $y = (97{\cdot}66)\,x^{-0{\cdot}4477} + 23{\cdot}4$ **14.** $A = 15{\cdot}8, B = 2{\cdot}1, c = -0{\cdot}5$

**15.** $a = 4{\cdot}01, b = 0{\cdot}0013, c = 2{\cdot}207$ **18.** $a = 3{\cdot}1, b = -0{\cdot}1, c = 10$

**24.** $y = 239{\cdot}2 + 135{\cdot}5x$ **25.** $y = 2{\cdot}26 + (0{\cdot}2992)\,(2{\cdot}07)^x$

**26.** $y = 7{\cdot}6 + 2{\cdot}528\,.\,x^{2{\cdot}079}$ **27.** $y = 3{\cdot}5 + 4{\cdot}447\,x^{2{\cdot}123}$

**28.** $y = 2 + 2{\cdot}909\,(4{\cdot}033)^x$ **29.** $y = 1 + 2x^3$

## EXERCISE 1.3 Page 31

**1.** $y = 0{\cdot}94x + 6{\cdot}6$; $30{\cdot}1$ **2.** $y = 3{\cdot}24x - 1{\cdot}84$

**3.** $y = 6{\cdot}16x + 45{\cdot}74$; rate of growth = $6{\cdot}16$ **4.** $y = 1361{\cdot}97 - 243{\cdot}42x$

**5.** $v = 0{\cdot}09u + 3{\cdot}76$ **6.** $x = 2y + 1$

**7.** $\theta = 8 - 0{\cdot}5t$ **8.** $y = 5{\cdot}909x + 0{\cdot}965$

**9.** (*a*) $y = 0{\cdot}66x + 29{\cdot}13$ (*b*) $y = 1{\cdot}02x + 9{\cdot}54$ (*c*) $y = 12{\cdot}3 + 3{\cdot}5x$

(*d*) $y = 12{\cdot}66x + 2{\cdot}53$ **10.** $y = 13{\cdot}6x$ **12.** $y = 1{\cdot}1x - 0{\cdot}285$

**13.** $y = 3{\cdot}1951 + 0{\cdot}4425x - 0{\cdot}7653x^2$ **14.** $y = 0{\cdot}403 + 0{\cdot}388x - 2{\cdot}790x^2$

**15.** $x = \dfrac{5}{7}y - \dfrac{13}{7}$ **16.** $y = 7{\cdot}173x^{1{\cdot}952}$

**17.** $y = 393 + 205{\cdot}5\,(x - 3) + 27{\cdot}5\,(x - 3)^2$

**18.** $y = 0{\cdot}62\,(x - 1880)^2 + 1{\cdot}18\,(x - 1880) + 79{\cdot}1$

**19.** $y = 349 + 3{\cdot}55x - 0{\cdot}27x^2$ **20.** $y = 1{\cdot}521x + 0{\cdot}49x^2$

**22.** $y = 1{\cdot}04 - 0{\cdot}20x + 0{\cdot}24x^2$

**23.** $y = 20{\cdot}04 + 0{\cdot}99x^2$ **24.** $y = 0{\cdot}466x^2 + 0{\cdot}826x + 143{\cdot}9$

**25.** $y = 0{\cdot}7386\,e^{0{\cdot}6808x}$ **26.** $y = 4{\cdot}642\,e^{0{\cdot}46x}$

**27.** $y = 12{\cdot}50\,e^{0{\cdot}28x}$ **28.** $y = 12630\,e^{-0{\cdot}92x}$

**29.** $y = 309{\cdot}0\,(0{\cdot}5754)^x$ **30.** $pv^{1{\cdot}4} = 16980$

**31.** $y = 100\,(1{\cdot}2)^x$ **32.** $y = e^{0{\cdot}4994x}$ **33.** $v = 682{\cdot}3\,T^{-0{\cdot}1558}$

**34.** $I = 3{\cdot}98\,D^{0{\cdot}70}$ **36.** $Y = 9{\cdot}1x - 3$; $y = 2{\cdot}2x^2 + 0{\cdot}3x + 1{\cdot}4$

$E_1 = 70{\cdot}7, E_2 = 2{\cdot}5$ parabola is better.

**38.** $y = 32{\cdot}14\,(1{\cdot}427)^x$; 387 numbers.

## EXERCISE 1.4 Page 40

**1.** $y = 0{\cdot}047x + 0{\cdot}12$ **2.** $y = -9{\cdot}6 + 39{\cdot}5x + 4{\cdot}4x^2$

**3.** $y = 1{\cdot}116 + 0{\cdot}515x$ **4.** $y = 1{\cdot}1845 + 0{\cdot}5231x$

2

# Theory of Equations

**An expression of the form**

$f(x) = a_0 x^n + a_1 x^{n-1} + a_2 x^{n-2} + \ldots + a_n$, where $n$ is a positive integer and $a_0, a_1, a_2, \ldots a_n$ are constants, is called a polynomial in $x$ of the $n$th degree, if $a_0 \neq 0$.

$f(x) = a_0 x^n + a_1 x^{n-1} + a_2 x^{n-2} + \ldots + a_n = 0$ is called an *algebraic equation* or *polynomial equation* of the $n$th degree, if $a_0 \neq 0$

**Fundamental Theorem of Algebra**

*Every equation has a root, real or imaginary*

As the proof of this theorm is outside the scope of this book, we assume the truth of this theorem.

1. *Every polynomial equation of the nth degree has n and only n roots.*

Let the equation be $f(x) = 0$. By fundamental theorem of algebra, this has a root, say $\alpha_1$. i.e., $f(\alpha_1) = 0$

Therefore, $x - \alpha_1$ is a factor of $f(x)$.

*i.e.*, $f(x) = (x - \alpha_1)\, \phi_1(x)$ where $\phi_1(x)$ is an algebraic equation of $(n-1)$ th degree.

Now $\phi_1(x) = 0$ has a root, say $\alpha_2$.

$\therefore$ $\phi_1(\alpha_2) = 0$ and hence $(x - \alpha_2)$ is a factor of $\phi_1(x)$.

$\therefore$ $\phi_1(x) = (x - \alpha_2)\, \phi_2(x)$ where $\phi_2(x)$ is a polynomial of degree $(n - 2)$.

$\therefore$ $f(x) = (x - \alpha_1)(x - \alpha_2)\, \phi_2(x)$

By continuing the process, we get

$$f(x) = (x - \alpha_1)\,(x - \alpha_2) \ldots (x - \alpha_n)\, \phi_n(x)$$

where $\phi_n(x)$ is of degree $(n - n)$ *i.e.*, zero. *i.e.*, $\phi_n(x)$ is a constant only.

$\therefore$ $f(x) = a_0 (x - \alpha_1)(x - \alpha_2) \ldots (x - \alpha_n)$

Hence, $f(x) = 0$ has $n$ roots $\alpha_1, \alpha_2, \ldots \alpha_n$.

Since $f(x) \neq 0$ for any other value of x except $\alpha_1, \alpha_2, \ldots \alpha_n$ the equation has only $n$ roots. (Of course, may be real or comple or may be distinct or equal)

*If $f(x) = 0$ is a polynomial equation and if $f(a)$ and $f(b)$ are of different signs, then at least one root of the equation $f(x) = 0$ must lie between a and b.*

Using the above simple theorem, we can show easily the following theorems.

3. *If $f(x) = 0$ is an equation of odd degree then it has at least one real root whose sign is opposite to that of the last term.*

4. If *$f(x) = 0$ is of even degree and the constant term is negative, the equation has at least one positive root and atleast one negative root.*

5. *If $f(x) = 0$ has no real root between a and b ($a < b$), then $f(a)$ and $f(b)$ are of same sign.*

**Theorem :** *In a polynomial equation with real coefficients, imaginary roots occur in conjugate pairs.*

Let $\alpha + i\beta$ be a root of $f(x) = 0$ where $\beta \neq 0$ and $\alpha, \beta$ are real

We assert that $\alpha - i\beta$ is also a root of $f(x) = 0$.

$[x - (\alpha + i\beta)]\,[x - (\alpha - i\beta)] = (x - \alpha)^2 + \beta^2$

When $f(x)$ is divided by $(x - \alpha)^2 + \beta^2$, let the quotient be $\phi(x)$ and remainder be $Ax + B$.

$\therefore \quad f(x) = [(x - \alpha)^2 + \beta^2]\,\phi(x) + Ax + B.$

Since $f(\alpha + i\beta) = 0$, we get $A(\alpha + i\beta) + B = 0$

*i.e.*, $A\alpha + B = 0$ and $A\beta = 0$.

$\beta \neq 0$ implies $A = 0$ and hence $B = 0. \therefore\ f(x) = [(x - \alpha)^2 + \beta^2]\,\phi(x)$

$f(\alpha - i\beta) = [(\alpha - i\beta - \alpha)^2 + \beta^2]\,\phi(\alpha - i\beta) = 0$

$\therefore \quad \alpha - i\beta$ is also a root of $f(x) = 0$.

**Example 1.** *Solve $x^4 + 4x^3 + 5x^2 + 2x - 2 = 0$, given $-1 + i$ is a root.*

**Sol.** Since $-1 + i$ is a root, $-1 - i$ is also a root.

$[x - (-1 + i)]\,[x - (-1 - i)] = (x + 1)^2 + 1 = x^2 + 2x + 2.$

When the polynomial is divided by $x^2 + 2x + 2$, the remainder is zero.

$\therefore \quad x^4 + 4x^3 + 5x^2 + 2x - 2 = (x^2 + 2x + 2)(x^2 + ax - 1)$

Equating coefficient of $x^3$ on both sides, $a + 2 = 4 \therefore\ a = 2$

$\therefore \quad f(x) = (x^2 + 2x + 2)(x^2 + 2x - 1)$

Solving $x^2 + 2x - 1 = 0$ we get $x = \dfrac{-2 \pm \sqrt{8}}{2} = -1 \pm \sqrt{2}$

$\therefore$ The four roots are $-1 \pm i, -1 \pm \sqrt{2}$.

**6. Theorem.** *In an equation with rational coefficients, irrational roots in the form of quadratic surds, occur in conjugate pairs.*

Let $a + \sqrt{b}$ be a root of $f(x) = 0$ where $b \neq 0$ and $b$ is not a perfect square and $a$, $b$ are rational. We assert then $a - \sqrt{b}$ is also a root of $f(x) = 0$

$[x - (a + \sqrt{b})]\,[x - (a - \sqrt{b})] = (x - a)^2 - b$

Therefore, when $f(x)$ is divided by $(x - a)^2 - b$, let the quotient be $\phi(x)$ and remainder be $Ax + B$.

$\therefore \quad f(x) = [(x - a)^2 - b]\,\phi(x) + Ax + B.$

$f(a + \sqrt{b}) = 0$ implies $A(a + \sqrt{b}) + B = 0$

Equating rational and irrational parts, we get, $Aa + B = 0$ and $A = 0 \therefore B = 0$

$\therefore \quad f(x) = [(x - a)^2 - b]\,\phi(x)$

$\therefore \quad f(a - \sqrt{b}) = [(a - \sqrt{b} - a)^2 - b]\,\phi(a - \sqrt{b}) = 0$

Hence, $a - \sqrt{b}$ is also a root of $f(x) = 0$.

**Example 2.** *Solve* $x^4 - 10x^3 + 26x^2 - 10x + 1 = 0$ *given that* $2 + \sqrt{3}$ *is a root of the equation.*

**Sol.** Since $2 + \sqrt{3}$ is a root, $2 - \sqrt{3}$ is also a root of the equation.

$\therefore \quad [x - (2 + \sqrt{3})]\,[x - (2 - \sqrt{3})] = (x - 2)^2 - 3 = x^2 - 4x + 1$

When $f(x)$ is divided by $(x^2 - 4x + 1)$, the remainder is zero.

$\therefore \quad x^4 - 10x^3 + 26x^2 - 10x + 1 = (x^2 - 4x + 1)(x^2 + ax + 1)$

Equating coefficients of $x^3$ on both sides, $a - 4 = -10 \quad \therefore \quad a = -6$

Hence $\quad f(x) = (x^2 - 4x + 1)(x^2 - 6x + 1)$

**Solving** $\quad x^2 - 6x + 1 = 0$, we get, $x = \dfrac{6 \pm \sqrt{32}}{2} = 3 \pm 2\sqrt{2}$

The four roots are $2 \pm \sqrt{3}, 3 \pm 2\sqrt{2}$,

**7. Theorem.** *Relations between the roots and the coefficients of equation.*

Let the roots of $f(x) = a_0 x^n + a_1 x^{n-1} + a_2 x^{n-2} + \ldots + a_n = 0$

be $\alpha_1, \alpha_2, \ldots \alpha_n$.

Then $f(x) = a_0 x^n + a_1 x^{n-1} + a_2 x^{n-2} + \ldots + a_n = a_0 (x - \alpha_1)$

$(x - \alpha_2) \ldots (x - \alpha_n)$

$= a_0 [x^n - (\Sigma \alpha_1) x^{n-1} + (\Sigma \alpha_1 \alpha_2) x^{n-2} + \ldots + (-1)^n \alpha_1 \alpha_2 \ldots \alpha_n]$

where $\Sigma\,\alpha_1\,\alpha_2 \dots \alpha_r$ denotes the sum of the products of $\alpha_1, \alpha_2, \dots \alpha_r$ taken $r$ at a time.

Equating the coefficients of like powers on both sides, $-a_0\,\Sigma\,\alpha_1 = a_1$

$$+a_0\,\Sigma\,\alpha_1\alpha_2 = a_2\,;\quad a_0\,\Sigma\,\alpha_1\,\alpha_2\,\alpha_3 = a_3$$

$$a_0\,[\,(-1)^n\,\alpha_1\,\alpha_2 \dots \alpha_n\,] = a_n$$

$$\therefore \quad S_1 = \Sigma\,\alpha_1 = -\frac{a_1}{a_0}\,;\; S_2 = \Sigma\,\alpha_1\,\alpha_2 = +\frac{a_2}{a_0}$$

$$S_3 = \Sigma\,\alpha_1\,\alpha_2\,\alpha_3 = -\frac{a_3}{a_0}\,;\;\cdots\; S_n = \alpha_1\,\alpha_2 \dots \alpha_n = (-1)^n\,\frac{a_n}{a_0}$$

**Example 3.** *Find the condition that the roots of the equation $x^3 + px^2 + qx + r = 0$ may be in*

(*i*) *arithmetical progression* **(*M.S. Ap. 94*)**

(*ii*) *geometrical progression,* and

(*iii*) *harmonic progression.*

**Sol.** (*i*) Let the roots in *A.P.* be $\alpha - d, \alpha, \alpha + d$.

Sum of the roots $= \alpha - d + \alpha + \alpha + d = \frac{-p}{1} = -p \;\therefore\; 3\alpha = -p \;\therefore\; \alpha = -\frac{p}{3}$

Now $x = \alpha$ is a root of the given equation.

$\therefore \quad \alpha = -\frac{p}{3}$ should satisfy the equation

$$\therefore \quad \left(-\frac{p}{3}\right)^3 + P\left(-\frac{p}{3}\right)^2 + q\left(-\frac{p}{3}\right) + r = 0$$

$$\text{or} \quad \frac{-p^3}{27} + \frac{p^3}{9} - \frac{pq}{3} + r = 0 \qquad i.e., \quad 2p^3 - 9\,pq + 27\,r = 0$$

(*ii*) Let the roots in G.P. be $\frac{\alpha}{\beta}$, $\alpha$, $\alpha\beta$ where $\beta$ is the common ratio.

$$\text{Product of the root} = \frac{\alpha}{\beta}\cdot\alpha.\,\alpha\beta = -r \;i.e.,\; \alpha^3 = -r \qquad \dots(1)$$

$$x = \alpha \text{ is a root of } f(x) = 0 \qquad \therefore\; \alpha^3 + p\alpha^2 + q\alpha + r = 0$$

$$-r + \alpha\,(p\alpha + q) + r = 0 \;\therefore\; \alpha\,(p\alpha + q) = 0\,;\; \alpha = \neq 0 \;\therefore\; \alpha = -\frac{q}{p}.$$

Putting in (1), we get $\frac{-q^3}{p^3} = -r \;\therefore\; p^3\,r = q^3$.

(*iii*) Let the roots of the equation be in H.P.

Put $x = \frac{1}{y}$. Then the equation becomes,

$$\left(\frac{1}{y}\right)^3 + p\left(\frac{1}{y}\right)^2 + q\left(\frac{1}{y}\right) + r = 0 \quad i.e., \; ry^3 + qy^2 + py + 1 = 0 \qquad ...(1)$$

The roots of the equation (1) are in A.P.

$\therefore$ Let $\alpha - d, \alpha, \alpha + d$ be the roots of (1).

Sum of the roots $= \alpha - d + \alpha + \alpha + d = -\frac{q}{r} \;\therefore\; 3\alpha = -\frac{q}{r} \therefore\; \alpha = -\frac{q}{3r}$.

$\alpha$ satisfies the equation (1)

$$\therefore \qquad r\left(-\frac{q}{3r}\right)^3 + q\left(-\frac{q}{3r}\right)^2 + p\left(-\frac{q}{3r}\right) + 1 = 0$$

*i.e.,* $-q^3 + 3q^3 - 9pqr + 27r^2 = 0$ *i.e.,* $2q^3 - 9pqr + 27r^2 = 0$

**Example 4.** *Solve* $x^3 - 15x^2 + 71x - 105 = 0$ *given that the roots of the equation are in A.P.*

**Sol.** Let the roots be $\alpha - d, \alpha, \alpha + d$.

Sum of the roots $= \alpha - d + \alpha + \alpha + d = 15$

$\therefore \qquad 3\alpha = 15 \;;\; \alpha = 5$

Since $x = 5$ is a root, $x - 5$ is a factor of $f(x)$.

$\therefore \quad x^3 - 15x^2 + 71x - 105 = (x - 5)(x^2 + ax + 21)$

$\therefore\; a - 5 = -15 \quad \therefore\; a = -10$

$\therefore \quad$ *Solving,* $x^2 - 10x + 21 = 0$, we get $x = 3, 7$

The roots are 3, 5, 7.

*Aliter*

Product of roots $= 105$

$(5 - d) \cdot 5 \cdot (5 + d) = 105$

$25 - d^2 = 21$

$d^2 = 4$

$d = \pm 2$

The roots are

3, 5, 7.

**Example 5.** *Solve* $x^3 - 19x^2 + 114x - 216 = 0$, *given that the roots are in G.P.*

**Sol.** Let the roots be $\frac{\alpha}{r}, \alpha, \alpha r$.

Product of roots $= \alpha^3 = 216. \quad \therefore\; \alpha = 6 \quad \therefore\; x - 6$ is a root of $f(x)$

$\therefore \quad x^3 - 19x^2 + 114x - 216 = (x - 6)(x^2 + ax + 36)$

Equating coefficients of $x^2$, $\quad a - 6 = -19 \;\;\therefore\; a = -13$

Solving $x^2 - 13x + 36 = 0$ we get $x = 4$ or $9 \;\therefore$ The roots are 4, 6, 9.

**Example 6.** *Solve $6x^3 - 11x^2 + 6x - 1 = 0$ given that the roots are in H.P.*

**Sol.** Put $x = \frac{1}{y}$. Then the given equation becomes,

$$6\left(\frac{1}{y}\right)^3 - 11\left(\frac{1}{y}\right)^2 + 6\left(\frac{1}{y}\right) - 1 = 0 \quad i.e., \quad y^3 - 6y^2 + 11y - 6 = 0 \quad ...(1)$$

The roots of (1) are in A.P.

Let the roots of (1) be $\alpha - d, \alpha, \alpha + d$. $\therefore$ Sum of roots $= 3\alpha = 6 \;\therefore\; \alpha = 2$

$\therefore \quad y - 2$ is a factor of $y^3 - 6y^2 + 11y - 6$

$\therefore \; y^3 - 6y^2 + 11y - 6 = (y-2)(y^2 + ay + 3) \;\therefore\; a - 2 = -6 \;\; i.e., \; a = -4$

Solving $y^2 - 4y + 3 = 0$, we get $y = 1$ or $3$. The roots of (1) are 1, 2, 3.

Hence the roots of given equation are $1, \frac{1}{2}, \frac{1}{3}$

**Example 7.** *Find the condition that the equation*

$x^4 + px^3 + qx^2 + rx + s = 0$

(*i*) *may have a pair of roots whose sum is zero.*

(*ii*) *be such that the sum of two roots equals the sum of the other two roots.*

(*iii*) *may have roots such that the product of two roots equals the product of the other two roots.*

**Sol.** Let the four roots of the equation be $\alpha, \beta, \gamma, \delta$

(*i*) Let $\alpha + \beta = 0$.

We have $x^4 + px^3 + qx^2 + rx + s = (x - \alpha)(x - \beta)(x - \gamma)(x - \delta)$

$$= [x^2 - (\alpha + \beta)x + \alpha\beta][x^2 - (\gamma + \delta)x + \gamma\delta] \quad ...(1)$$

$$= [x^2 + \alpha\beta][x^2 - (\gamma + \delta)x + \gamma\delta] \quad \because \; \alpha + \beta = 0$$

$$= (x^2 + a)(x^2 - bx + c).$$

Equating the coefficients on both sides, $-b = p$ ...(2) $\quad a + c = q$ ...(3)

$-ab = r$ ...(4) $\qquad ac = s$ ...(5)

$\therefore \qquad b = -p, \; a = \frac{r}{p}$, using (4), $c = \frac{s}{a} = \frac{sp}{r}$

Using (3), we get, $\frac{r}{p} + \frac{sp}{r} = q \quad i.e., \quad r^2 + p^2 s = pqr$

(*ii*) Let $\alpha + \beta = \gamma + \delta = a \;\therefore$ Equation (1) becomes,

$$x^4 + px^3 + qx^2 + rx + s = (x^2 - ax + b)(x^2 - ax + c)$$

Equating coefficients, $\quad -2a = p \quad \therefore a = -\dfrac{p}{2}$

$$a^2 + b + c = q\,; \qquad b + c = q - a^2 = q - \frac{p^2}{4}$$

$$-ab - ac = r\,; \qquad b + c = \frac{r}{(-a)} = \frac{2r}{p}\,; \quad bc = s$$

$$\therefore \qquad q - \frac{p^2}{4} = \frac{2r}{p} \qquad \text{(Equating } b + c\text{)}$$

*i.e.*, $\quad 4pq - p^3 = 8r \quad$ *ie.*, $p^3 - 4pq + 8r = 0$

(*iii*) Let $\alpha\,\beta = \gamma\,\delta = \widehat{B} \quad \therefore$ Equation (1) becomes,

$$x^4 + px^3 + qx^2 + rx + s = (x^2 - Ax + B)\,(x^2 - Cx + B)$$

$$\therefore \qquad -(A + C) = p\,; \;\; 2B + AC = q\,; \;\; -B\,(A + C) = r\,; \;\; B^2 = s$$

$$\therefore \qquad r^2 = B^2\,(A + C)^2 = sp^2 \quad \therefore \;\; p^2 s = x^2$$

**Example 8.** *Solve* $x^4 - 2x^3 + 4x^2 + 6x - 21 = 0$; *given that two of its roots are equal in magnitude but opposite in sign.*

**Sol.** Let the roots be $\alpha, \beta, \gamma, \delta$.

Here, $\alpha = -\beta \quad \therefore \quad \alpha + \beta = 0$

$$\therefore \quad x^4 - 2x^3 + 4x^2 + 6x - 21 = (x - \alpha)\,(x - \beta)\,(x - \gamma)\,(x - \delta)$$

$$= [x^2 - (\alpha + \beta)\,x + \alpha\,\beta\,]\,[x^2 - (\gamma + \delta)\,x + \gamma\,\delta)$$

$$= (x^2 + a)\,(x^2 - bx + c)$$

Equating the coefficients on both sides,

$$-b = -2\,; \;\; a + c = 4\,; \;\; -at = 6\,; \;\; ac = -21$$

$$\therefore \quad b = 2, \;\; a = -3, \;\; c = 7$$

$$\therefore \quad x^4 - 2x^3 + 4x^2 + 6x - 21 = (x^2 - 3)\,(x^2 - 2x + 7).$$

Solving $x^2 - 3 = 0$, we get $x = \pm\sqrt{3}$

Solving $x^2 - 2x + 7 = 0$, $x = \dfrac{2 \pm \sqrt{4 - 28}}{2} = 1 \pm \sqrt{6}\,i$

$\therefore \quad$ The four roots are $\pm\sqrt{3}$, $1 \pm \sqrt{6}\,i$

**Example 9.** *If* $\alpha_1, \alpha_2, \ldots \alpha_n$ *are the roots of the equation* $(x - a_2)\ldots(x - a_n) + b = 0$, *then prove that* $a_1, a_2 \ldots a_n$ *are the roots of* $(x - \alpha_1)\,(x - \alpha_2)\ldots(x - \alpha_n) - b = 0$

**Sol .** Since $\alpha_1, \alpha_2 \ldots \alpha_n$ are the roots of

$(x - a_1)\,(x - a_2)\ldots(x - a_n) + b = 0$, we have

$$(x - a_1)(x - a_2) \dots (x - a_n) + b = (x - \alpha_1)(x - \alpha_2) \dots (x - \alpha_n)$$

(**Hint :** Check that the coefficient of $x^n$ on both sides are equal)

Hence,

$$(x - \alpha_1)(x - \alpha_2) \dots (x - \alpha_n) - b \equiv (x - a_1)(x - a_2) \dots (x - a_n)$$

So, $(x - \alpha_1)(x - \alpha_2) \dots (x - \alpha_n) - b = 0$ implies

$(x - a_1)(x - a_2) \dots (x - a_n) = 0$ which means

$a_1, a_2 \dots a_n$ are the roots of

$$(x - \alpha_1)(x - \alpha_2) \dots (x - \alpha_n) - b = 0$$

**Example 10.** *Solve $2x^3 - x^2 - 22x - 24 = 0$ given that two of its roots are in the ratio 3 : 4.* **(Ms. A.S. Nov 91)**

**Sol.** Let the roots be $3k$, $4k$ and $\gamma$

Sum of the roots $= 7k + \gamma = \frac{1}{2}$ ..(1)

and "$\Sigma \alpha \beta$" $= 12k^2 + 4k\gamma + 3k\gamma = \frac{-22}{2} = -11$ ...(2)

Using $\gamma = \frac{1}{2} - 7k$ in (2), we get

$$12k^2 + 4k\left(\frac{1}{2} - 7k\right) + 3k\left(\tfrac{1}{2} - 7k\right) = -11$$

*i.e.,* $74k^2 - 7k - 22 = 0$

*i.e.,* $(37k - 22)(2k + 1) = 0 \quad \therefore \quad k = -1/2$ or $22/37$

Taking $k = -1/2$, the roots are $-\frac{3}{2}, -2, \frac{1}{2} + \frac{7}{2}$ *i.e.,* $\frac{-3}{2}, -2, 4$

Taking $k = \frac{22}{37}$, $3k = \frac{66}{37}$ does not satisfy the equation.

**Example 11.** *Form the third degree equation, two of whose roots are $1 - i$ and 2*

**Sol.** Since, $1 - i$ is a root $1 + i$ is also a root. Therefore, the equation of degree three is

$$[x - (1 - i)][x - (1 + i)][x - 2] = 0; \quad [(x - 1)^2 - i^2](x - 2) = 0$$

$$(x^2 - 2x + 2)(x - 2) = 0 \quad i.e., \quad x^3 - 4x^2 + 6x - 4 = 0.$$

**Example 12.** *Solve $x^4 + 2x^3 - 21x^2 - 22x + 40 = 0$ whose roots are in A.P.*

**Sol.** Let the roots be $a - 3d, a - d, a + d, a + 3d$.

Sum of roots $= 4a = -2 \therefore a = -1/2$

Product of roots $= (a^2 - 9d^2)(a^2 - d^2) = 40$

or $\left(\frac{1}{4} - 9d^2\right)\left(\frac{1}{4} - d^2\right) = 40$

Set $d^2 = k \therefore \left(\frac{1}{4} - 9k\right)\left(\frac{1}{4} - k\right) = 40$

$$9k^2 - \frac{5}{2}k + \frac{1}{16} = 40 \text{ or } 144k^2 - 40k - 639 = 0$$

$$(4k - 9)(36k + 71) = 0 \quad \therefore \quad k = 9/4 \text{ or } -71/36$$

*i.e.*, $d^2 = \frac{9}{4}$ or $-\frac{71}{36}$ $\therefore d = \pm 3/2$

$\therefore$ The roots are –5, –2, 1, 4

**Example 13.** *If* $\alpha, \beta, \gamma$ *are the roots of* $x^3 + px^2 + qx + r = 0$ *find the condition if (i)* $\alpha + \beta = 0$ *(ii)* $\alpha\beta = -1$

**Sol.** (*i*) Since $\alpha + \beta + \gamma = -p$, $\quad 0 + \gamma = -p \quad \therefore \gamma = -p$

$\gamma$ satisfies the equation

$\therefore \quad -p^3 + p^3 - pq + r \equiv 0 \quad \therefore r = pq.$

(*ii*) Since $\alpha\beta\gamma = -r$

$-\gamma = -r \quad \therefore \gamma = r$ satisfies the equation

$\therefore$ Substituting, $r^3 + pr^2 + qr + r = 0$ i.e., $r^2 + pr + q + 1 = 0$

## Exercises 1

1. If $\alpha, \beta, \gamma$ are the roots of the equation $(x + a)(x + b)(x + c) = d$ prove that $a, b, c$ are the roots of the equation $(x + \alpha)(x + \beta)(x + \gamma) = d$.
2. If $\alpha_1, \alpha_2, \ldots\ldots \alpha_n$ are the roots of the equation.
   $(a_1 - x)(a_2 - x) \ldots\ldots (a_n - x) + b = 0$, then prove that
   $a_1, a_2, \ldots\ldots a_n$ are the roots of the equation
   $(\alpha_1 - x)(\alpha_2 - x) \ldots\ldots (\alpha_n - x) - b = 0.$
3. If $a, b, c$ are all positive, show that the roots of
   $\frac{1}{x-a} + \frac{1}{x-b} + \frac{1}{x-c} = \frac{1}{x}$ are all real
4. Solve the equation $x^4 + 2x^3 - 16x^2 - 22x + 7 = 0$ given that $2 + \sqrt{3}$ is a root.
5. Solve $x^3 - 11x^2 + 37x - 35 = 0$ given that $3 + \sqrt{2}$ is a root.
6. Solve $x^4 - 6x^3 + 11x^2 - 10x + 2 = 0$ given that $2 + \sqrt{3}$ is a root.
7. Solve $6x^4 - 13x^3 - 35x^2 - x + 3 = 0$ given that $2 - \sqrt{3}$ is a root.
8. Solve the equation $3x^3 - 4x^2 + x + 88 = 0$ given that $2 + i\sqrt{7}$ is a root.
9. Solve $x^4 - 4x^2 + 8x + 35 = 0$ given that $2 + i\sqrt{3}$ is a root.

**10.** Solve $x^4 + 2x^2 + 77 = 16x$ given that $-2 + i\sqrt{7}$ is a root.

**11.** Solve $x^4 - 8x^3 + 34x^2 - 72x + 45 = 0$ given that $2 + i\sqrt{11}$ is a root.

**12.** Solve $x^4 + 2x^3 - 5x^2 + 6x + 2 = 0$ given that $1 - i$ is a root.

**13.** Solve the equation $x^5 - 3x^4 + 4x^3 + 4x^2 - 21x + 15 = 0$ given that $1 + 2i$ and $\sqrt{3}$ are two roots.

**14.** Solve $x^4 + 4x^3 + 6x^2 + 4x + 5 = 0$ given that $i$ is a root.

Solve the following equations (15 to 18).

**15.** $x^3 - 9x^2 + 26x - 24 = 0$ given that the roots are in A.P. ***(BE Ap 94)***

**16.** $x^3 - 6x^2 + 13x - 10 = 0$ given that the roots are in A.P.

**17.** $x^3 - 12x^2 + 39x - 28 = 0$ whose roots are in A.P.

**18.** $x^4 + 2x^3 - 21x^2 - 22x + 40 = 0$ whose roots are in A.P.
(**Hint :** Assume the roots to be $a - 3d, a - d, a + d, a + 3d$)

**19.** Solve the equations given that the roots are in Geometrical Progression

(*i*) $8x^3 - 14x^2 + 7x - 1 = 0$ (*ii*) $27x^3 + 42x^2 - 28x - 8 = 0$

(*iii*) $x^3 - 7x^2 + 14x - 8 = 0$ (*iv*) $3x^3 - 26x^2 + 52x = 24$

(*v*) $x^4 - 15x^3 + 70x^2 - 120x + 64 = 0$

**20.** Solve the equations given that the roots are in Harmonical Progression

(*i*) $6x^3 - 11x^2 - 3x + 2 = 0$ (*ii*) $15x^3 - 13x^2 - 3x + 1 = 0$

(*iii*) $6x^3 - 11x^2 + 6x - 1 = 0$ (*iv*) $40x^4 - 22x^3 - 21x^2 + 2x + 1 = 0$

**21.** Find the condition that the equation $x^4 + px^3 + qx^2 + rx + s = 0$ may have two pairs of equal roots

**22.** If $\alpha, \beta, \gamma, \delta$ are the roots of the equation $x^4 + px^3 + qx^2 + rx + s = 0$ such that $\alpha\beta + \gamma\delta = 0$, find the condition.

**23.** If $\alpha, \beta, \gamma$, are the roots of $x^3 + px^2 + qx + r = 0$ find the condition if (*i*) $\alpha + \beta = 0$. (*ii*) $\alpha\beta = -1$.

**24.** Solve $6x^4 - 11x^3 + 11x^2 - 5x + 2 = 0$ if the product of two roots is unity.

**25.** Solve $x^3 - 3x^2 - 10x + 24 = 0$ if one root is double another.

**26.** If the equation $x^4 - 4x^3 - 2x^2 + 12x + 9 = 0$ has two pairs of equal roots, find them

**27.** The equation $4x^3 - 32x^2 - x + 8 = 0$ is such that the sum of two of its roots is zero. Find them.

**28.** Solve $x^4 + 4x^3 - 5x^2 - 8x + 6 = 0$ given that the sum of two of its roots is zero.

**29.** Solve $3x^3 - 32x^2 + 33x + 108 = 0$ given that one root is square of another.

**30.** Form the fourth degree equation two of whose roots are $1 + i$ and $2 + \sqrt{3}$.

**31.** Form the third degree equation two of whose roots are $1 + i$ and 5

**32.** Frame an equation with rational coefficients, one of whose roots is $\sqrt{2}+\sqrt{5}$.

**33.** Solve $8x^4+4x^3-18x^2+11x-2=0$ given that if has three equal roots.

**34.** Solve $3x^4-40x^3+130x^2-120x+27=0$ given that the roots are in G.P.

**35.** Solve $x^4+4x^3-2x^2-12x+9=0$ given that it has two pairs of equal roots.

**36.** Solve $x^4-4x^3-17x^2+24x+36=0$ given that the product of two of the roots is 12.

**Symmetric function of the roots**

**Example 1.** *If $\alpha, \beta, \gamma$ are the roots of the equation $x^3+px^2+qx+r=0$ find the value of* (*i*) $\Sigma\alpha^2\beta$ (*ii*) $\Sigma\alpha^2$ (*iii*) $\Sigma\alpha^3$

**Sol.** (*i*) $\Sigma\alpha=-p, \Sigma\alpha\beta=q, \alpha\beta\gamma=-r$

$\therefore \quad \Sigma\alpha^2\beta\equiv(\Sigma\alpha\beta)(\Sigma\alpha)-3\alpha\beta\gamma=q(-p)-3(-r)=3r-pq$

(*ii*) $\Sigma\alpha^2\equiv(\Sigma\alpha)^2-2\Sigma\alpha\beta=p^2-2q$

(*iii*) $\Sigma\alpha^3\equiv(\Sigma\alpha)^3-3(\Sigma\alpha)(\Sigma\alpha\beta)+3\alpha\beta\gamma=-p^3+3pq-3r.$

**Example 2.** *If $\alpha, \beta, \gamma, \delta$ are the roots of $x^4+px^3+qx^2+rx+s=0$ find the value of* (*i*) $\Sigma\alpha^2$ (*ii*) $\Sigma\alpha^2\beta\gamma$ (*iii*) $\Sigma\alpha^2\beta^2$

**Sol.** We know, $\Sigma\alpha=-p$ ; $\Sigma\alpha\beta=q$ ; $\Sigma\alpha\beta\gamma=-r$ ; $\alpha\beta\gamma\delta=s$

(*i*) $\Sigma\alpha^2\equiv(\Sigma\alpha)^2-2\Sigma\alpha\beta=p^2-2q$

(*ii*) $\Sigma\alpha^2\beta\gamma\equiv(\Sigma\alpha\beta\gamma)(\Sigma\alpha)-4\alpha\beta\gamma\delta=pr-4s$

(*iii*) $\Sigma\alpha^2\beta^2\equiv(\Sigma\alpha\beta)^2-2\Sigma\alpha^2\beta\gamma-6\alpha\beta\gamma\delta$

$=q^2-2(pr-4s)-6s=q^2-2pr+2s.$

**Formation of Equations**

**Example 1.** *If $\alpha, \beta, \gamma$ are the roots of $x^3+px^2+qx+r=0.$ ; form the equation whose roots are* (*i*) $\alpha+\beta, \beta+\gamma, \gamma+\alpha$.

(*ii*) $\dfrac{1}{\alpha^2}, \dfrac{1}{\beta^2}, \dfrac{1}{\gamma^2}$ (*iii*) $\dfrac{\alpha}{\beta+\gamma}, \dfrac{\beta}{\gamma+\alpha}, \dfrac{\gamma}{\alpha+\beta}$.

Given : $\Sigma\alpha=-p$ ; $\Sigma\alpha\beta=q$ ; $\alpha\beta\gamma=-r$

**Sol.** (*i*) Let the new root be denoted by $y$.

$\therefore \quad y=\alpha+\beta=-p-\gamma=-p-x \qquad \because \gamma=x.$

$\therefore \quad x=-p-y$ satisfies the given equation.

$\because \quad (-p-y)^3+p(-p-y)^2+q(-p-y)+r=0$

$-(p+y)^3+p(p+y)^2-q(p+y)+r=0$

$y^3+2y^2p+y(p^2+q)+pq-r=0$ is the required equation.

Hence, $(\alpha+\beta)(\beta+\gamma)(\gamma+\alpha)=$ product of the roots of equation (*ii*) $$= \frac{-(pq-r)}{1} = r - pq.$$

Let $y = \frac{1}{\alpha^2} = \frac{1}{x^2}$ $\therefore$ $x = \frac{1}{\sqrt{y}}$. Substituting in the given equation we get

$$\frac{1}{y\sqrt{y}} + \frac{p}{y} + \frac{q}{\sqrt{y}} + r = 0$$

*i.e.,* $1 + p\sqrt{y} + qy + ry\sqrt{y} = 0$ *i.e.,* $\sqrt{y}\,(p + ry) = -(1 + qy)$

Squaring, $y\,(p + ry)^2 = (1 + qy)^2$

*i.e.,* $r^2 y^3 + y^2 (2pr - q^2) + y\,(p^2 - 2q) - 1 = 0$ ...(3)

Hence, $\sum \frac{1}{\alpha^2}$ = sum of the roots of (3) $= \frac{q^2 - 2pr}{r^2}$.

(*iii*) Let $y = \frac{\alpha}{\beta + \gamma} = \frac{\alpha}{-p - \alpha}$ $\because$ $\alpha + \beta + \gamma = -p$ $\therefore$ $y = \frac{-x}{p + x}$

$\therefore$ $-py - xy = x$ *i.e.,* $x = \frac{-py}{1 + y}$.

Substituting in the given equation,

$$\frac{-p^3 y^3}{(1+y)^3} + p \,.\, \frac{p^2 y^2}{(1+y)^2} - \frac{pqy}{1+y} + r = 0$$

*i.e.,* $r\,(1 + y)^3 - pq\,y\,(1 + y)^2 + p^3 y^2 (1 + y) - p^3 y^3 = 0$

$(r - pq)\,y^3 + (3r - 2pq + p^3)\,y^2 + (3r - pq)\,y + r = 0$

Hence, $$\sum \frac{\alpha}{\beta + \gamma} = \frac{2pq - p^3 - 3r}{r - pq}$$

**Example 2.** *If a, b, c are the roots of* $x^3 + px^2 + qx + r = 0$; *find the equation whose roots are (i) ab, bc, ca (ii)* $a^2$, $b^2$, $c^2$ *(iii)* $a\,(b + c)$, $b\,(c + a)$, $c\,(a + b)$

**Sol.** We have, $\Sigma a = -p$, $\Sigma ab = q$, $abc = -r$.

(*i*) Let $y = ab = \frac{abc}{c} = \frac{-r}{c} = \frac{-r}{x}$

$\therefore$ $x = -\frac{r}{y}$ satisfies the given equation

$$\therefore \quad \left(-\frac{r}{y}\right)^3 + p\left(-\frac{r}{y}\right)^2 + q\left(-\frac{r}{y}\right) + r = 0$$

*i.e.,* $y^3 - qy^2 + pry - r^2 = 0$ is the required equation

(*ii*) $x^3 + px^2 + qx + r = 0$ *i.e.,* $x\,(x^2 + q) = -(r + px^2)$

Squaring, $x^2 (x^2 + q)^2 = (r + px^2)^2$. Putting $x^2 = y$,

$$y(y+q)^2 = (r+py)^2$$

*i.e.,* $y^3 + (2q - p^2)y^2 + (q^2 - 2pr)y - r^3 = 0$ has roots $a^2, b^2, c^2$.

$\therefore$ $\Sigma a^2 = p^2 - 2q$ and $\Sigma a^2 b^2 = q^2 - 2pr$.

(*iii*) Let $y = a(b+c) = a(a+b+c-a) = a(-p-a)$

$\therefore$ $y = x(-p-x)$ *i.e.,* $x^2 + px + y = 0$ ...(2)

But $x^3 + px^2 + qx + r = 0$ ...(1)

Eliminating $x$ between (1) and (2), we get the required equation.

(2) $\times x -$ (1) gives. $x(y-q) = r$ $\therefore$ $x = \dfrac{r}{y-q}$

Substituting in (1), we get

$$y^3 - 2qy^2 + (pr + q^2)y + r^3 - pqr = 0 \qquad \therefore \quad \Sigma a(b+c) = 2q.$$

**Example 3.** *If* α, β, γ *are the roots* $x^3 - x - 1 = 0$, *show that*

$$\frac{1+\alpha}{1-\alpha} + \frac{1+\beta}{1-\beta} + \frac{1+\gamma}{1-\gamma} = -7.$$

**Sol.** Let $y = \dfrac{1+\alpha}{1-\alpha} = \dfrac{1+x}{1+x}$ $\therefore$ $y - xy = 1 + x$

or $x(1+y) = y - 1$ $\therefore$ $x = \dfrac{y-1}{y+1}$

Substituting $\left(\dfrac{y-1}{y+1}\right)^3 - \dfrac{y-1}{y+1} - 1 = 0$

*i.e.,* $(y-1)^3 - (y-1)(y+1)^2 - (y+1)^3 = 0$

*i.e.,* $y^3 + 7y^2 + y + 1 = 0$ (1)

$\sum \dfrac{1+\alpha}{1-\alpha} =$ sum of roots of (1) $= -7$.

**Example 4.** *Prove that the sum of the cubes of the roots of* $x^3 - 6x^2 + 11x - 6 = 0$ *is 36.*

**Sol.** Let the roots be α, β, γ; $\therefore$ $\Sigma\alpha = 6, \Sigma\alpha\beta = 11, \alpha\beta\gamma = 6$.

$\alpha^3 - 6\alpha^2 + 11\alpha - 6 = 0 \therefore \alpha^3 = 6\alpha^2 - 11\alpha + 6$

$$\begin{aligned}\Sigma\alpha^3 &= 6\Sigma\alpha^2 - 11\Sigma\alpha + \Sigma 6 \\ &= 6[(\Sigma\alpha)^2 - 2\Sigma\alpha\beta] - 11\Sigma\alpha + 18 \\ &= 6[36 - 22] - 11(6) + 18 = 84 - 66 + 18 = 36.\end{aligned}$$

*Aliter* : $\Sigma\alpha^3 = (\Sigma\alpha)^3 - 3(\Sigma\alpha)(\Sigma\alpha\beta) + 3\alpha\beta r$

$$= (6)^3 - 3(6)(11) + 3(6) = 216 - 198 + 18 = 36$$

**Example 5.** *If* $\alpha, \beta, \gamma$ *are the roots of* $x^3 - 3ax + b = 0$; *show that* $\Sigma (\alpha - \beta)(\alpha - \gamma) = 9a$. **(*BR. University*)**

**Sol.** We have, $\Sigma \alpha = 0$ ; $\Sigma \alpha \beta = -3a$, ; $\alpha \beta \gamma = -b$

$$\Sigma \alpha^2 = (\Sigma \alpha)^2 - 2 \Sigma \alpha \beta = 0 - 2(-3a) = 6a$$

$$\Sigma (\alpha - \beta)(\alpha - \gamma) = \Sigma [\alpha^2 - (\alpha \beta + \alpha \gamma - \beta \gamma)]$$

$$= \Sigma \alpha^2 - \Sigma \alpha \beta - \Sigma \alpha \gamma + \Sigma \beta \gamma$$

$$= 6a - (-3a) - (-3a) + (-3a) = 9a$$

(**Note :** $\Sigma \alpha \beta = \Sigma \beta \gamma = \Sigma \alpha \gamma$)

**Example 6.** *If* $\alpha, \beta, \gamma$ *are the roots of* $x^3 - 14x + 8 = 0$, *find* $\Sigma \alpha^2$ and $\Sigma \alpha^3$.

**Sol.** We have, $\Sigma \alpha = 0, \Sigma \alpha \beta = -14, \alpha \beta \gamma = -8$

$$\Sigma \alpha^2 = (\Sigma \alpha)^2 - 2 \Sigma \alpha \beta = 0 - 2(-14) = 28$$

$$\alpha^3 = 14\alpha - 8 \quad \text{(since } \alpha \text{ satisfies } x^3 - 14x + 8 = 0\text{)}$$

$$\therefore \quad \Sigma \alpha^3 = 14 \Sigma \alpha - 24 = 14(0) - 24 = -24.$$

*Aliter* : Use the identity for $\Sigma \alpha^3$

$$\Sigma \alpha^3 = (\Sigma \alpha)^3 - 3(\Sigma \alpha)(\Sigma \alpha \beta) + 3\alpha \beta \gamma$$

$$= 0 - 3(0) + 3(-8) = -24.$$

$$\left\{ \begin{array}{l} \text{OR} \quad \text{If } \alpha + \beta + \gamma = 0 \\ \alpha^3 + \beta^3 + \gamma^3 = 3\alpha \beta \gamma = -24 \end{array} \right.$$

**Certain standard transformations :**

If $\alpha_1, \alpha_2 \ldots \alpha_n$ be the roots of the equation $a_0 x^n + a_1 x^{n-1} + a_2 x^{n-2} + \ldots + a_n = 0$, then form the equation whose roots are

(*i*) $-\alpha_1, -\alpha_2, \ldots -\alpha_n$ (*ii*) $k\alpha_1, k\alpha_2 \ldots k\alpha_n$

(*iii*) $\dfrac{1}{\alpha_1}, \dfrac{1}{\alpha_2}, \ldots, \dfrac{1}{\alpha_n}$ and hence find the value of $\sum \dfrac{1}{\alpha_1}$.

**Sol.** (*i*) Let $y = -\alpha_1 = -x \quad \therefore \quad x = -y$.

Substituting in the given equation, we get

$$a_0 (-y)^n + a_1 (-y)^{n-1} + \ldots a_n = 0$$

*i.e.*, $$(-1)^n a_0 y^n + a_1 (-1)^{n-1} y^{n-1} + \ldots + a_n = 0$$

*i.e.*, $$a_0 y^n - a_1 y^{n-1} + a_2 y^{n-2} - \ldots + (-1)^n a_n = 0$$

(*ii*) Let $y = k\alpha_1 = kx \quad \therefore \quad x = y/k$.

Substituting in the given equation, we get

$$a_0 y^n + a_1 ky^{n-1} + a_2 k^2 y^{n-2} + \ldots + a_n k^n = 0$$

(*iii*) Let $y = \frac{1}{\alpha_1} = \frac{1}{x} \quad \therefore \quad x = \frac{1}{y}$

Substituting in the given equation, we get,

$$a_n y^n + a_{n-1} y^{n-1} + \ldots + a_1 y + a_0 = 0 \text{ whose roots are}$$

$$\frac{1}{\alpha_1}, \frac{1}{\alpha_2}, \ldots \frac{1}{\alpha_n}$$

Hence, sum of the roots $= \sum \frac{1}{\alpha_1} = -\frac{a_{n-1}}{a_n}$.

## Exercises 2

**1.** If $\alpha, \beta, \gamma$ are the roots $x^3 + p_1 x^2 + p_2 x + p_3 = 0$ find the value of

(*i*) $(a^2 - \beta\gamma)(\beta^2 - \gamma\alpha)(\gamma^2 - \alpha\beta)$ (*ii*) $(a^2 + 1)(\beta^2 + 1)(\gamma^2 + 1)$

(*iii*) $\frac{1}{\alpha} + \frac{1}{\beta} + \frac{1}{\gamma}$ (*iv*) $\sum \frac{1}{\alpha\beta}$ (*v*) $\Sigma\alpha^3$.

**2.** If $\alpha, \beta, \gamma$ are the roots of $x^3 + qx + r = 0$, find the value of

(*i*) $\sum \frac{1}{\alpha + \beta}$ (*ii*) $\Sigma \alpha^4$ (*iii*) $\sum \frac{\alpha\beta}{\gamma}$ (*iv*) $\Sigma \alpha^2$

(*v*) $(\alpha + \beta)(\beta + \gamma)(\gamma + \alpha)$ (*vi*) $(\alpha + \beta - 2\gamma)(\beta + \gamma - 2\alpha)(\gamma + \alpha - 2\beta)$

(*vii*) $\Sigma \alpha^3$ (*viii*) $\Sigma \alpha^2 \beta$ (*ix*) $\Sigma \alpha^2 \beta^2$

**3.** If $\alpha, \beta, \gamma$ are the roots of $x^3 - 3ax + b = 0$, show that $\Sigma(\alpha - \beta)(\alpha - \gamma) = 9a$.

**4.** If $\alpha, \beta, \gamma, \delta$ are the roots of the equation $x^4 + px^3 + qx^2 + rx + s = 0$ find the value of (*i*) $\Sigma \alpha^2 \beta\gamma$ (*ii*) $\sum \frac{1}{\alpha^2}$.

**5.** If $\alpha, \beta, \gamma$ are the roots of the equation $x^3 + px^2 + qx + r = 0$ form the equation whose roots are (i)$\alpha + \beta - \gamma, \beta + \gamma - \alpha, \gamma + \alpha - \beta$ (ii)$\alpha^2 + \beta^2, \beta^2 + \gamma^2, \gamma^2 + \alpha^2$ (iii) $\beta\gamma - \alpha^2, \gamma\alpha - \beta^2, \alpha\beta - \gamma^2$.

**6.** Find the sum of the squares and the sum of the cubes of the roots of (i) $x^3 = 14x - 8$ (ii) $x^4 = 22x^2 - 84x + 49$.

**7.** Find the equation whose roots are squares of the roots of $x^3 + px^2 + qx + r = 0$

**8.** Find the equation each of whose roots exceeds by 2 the roots of the equation $x^3 - 4x^2 + 3x - 1 = 0$.

**9.** Find the equation whose roots are squares of the roots of $x^3 - x^2 + 8x - 6 = 0$

**10.** Prove that the sum of the cubes of the roots of $x^3 - 6x^2 + 11x - 6 = 0$ is 36.

**11.** Find the equation whose roots are the roots of $x^5 + 6x^4 + 6x^3 - 7x^2 + 2x - 1 = 0$ with the signs changed.

**12.** If $\alpha, \beta, \gamma$ are the roots of $x^3 + px^2 + qx + r = 0$ form the equation whose roots are

(i) $\alpha - \frac{1}{\beta\gamma}, \beta - \frac{1}{\alpha\gamma}, \gamma - \frac{1}{\alpha\beta}$ (ii) $\alpha + \frac{1}{\beta\gamma}, \beta + \frac{1}{\alpha\gamma}, \gamma + \frac{1}{\alpha\beta}$

**13.** If $\alpha, \beta, \gamma$ are the roots of $x^3 - px^2 + qx - r = 0$, find the equation whose roots are

(i) $\alpha\beta + \frac{1}{\gamma}, \beta\gamma + \frac{1}{\alpha}, \gamma\alpha + \frac{1}{\beta}$ (ii) $\frac{\alpha}{\beta+\gamma-\alpha}, \frac{\beta}{\gamma+\alpha-\beta}, \frac{\gamma}{\alpha+\beta-\gamma}$

**14.** If $\alpha, \beta, \gamma$ are the roots of $x^3 + px + q = 0$, form the equation whose roots are $(\alpha - \beta)^2, (\beta - \gamma)^2, (\gamma - \alpha)^2$. hence evaluate

(i) $\Sigma (\alpha - \beta)^2$ (ii) $(\alpha - \beta)^2 (\beta - \gamma)^2 (\gamma - \alpha)^2$

**15.** If $\alpha$ is a root of $x^7 - 1 = 0$ show that the equation whose roots are $\alpha + \alpha^6, a^2 + \alpha^5, \alpha^3 + \alpha^4$ is $y^3 + y^2 - 2y - 1 = 0$.

**16.** If $\alpha, \beta, \gamma, \delta$ are the roots of the equation $x^4 - 7x^3 + 8x^2 - 5x + 10 = 0$, frame the equation whose roots are

(i) $\alpha^2, \beta^2, \gamma^2, \delta^2$ (ii) $\alpha^2 + 2, \beta^2 + 2, \gamma^2 + 2, \delta^2 + 2$

**17.** If $\alpha, \beta, \gamma$ are the roots of $x^3 = x + 1$, show that $\frac{1+\alpha}{1-\alpha} + \frac{1+\beta}{1-\beta} + \frac{1+\gamma}{1-\gamma} = -7.$

**18.** If $\alpha$ is a root of $x^2 (x+1)^2 - k(x-1)(2x^2 + x + 1) = 0$, prove that $\frac{\alpha+1}{\alpha-1}$ is also a root.

**19.** If $\alpha$ is a root of $x^3 = 3x - 1$, show that $\alpha^2 - 2$ is also a root and find the third root.

**20.** If $\alpha, \beta, \gamma$ are the root of $x^3 + 2x^2 + 3x + 3 = 0$, prove that $\sum \frac{\alpha^2}{(\alpha+1)^2} = 13.$

**To diminish the roots of an equation by h**

Suppose $\alpha_1, \alpha_2, \ldots, \alpha_n$ are the roots of $f(x) = 0$. Now, we require the equation whose roots are $\alpha_1 - h, \alpha_2 - h, \ldots\ldots, \alpha_n - h$.

Let $y = \alpha_i - h = x - h$.

$\therefore$ $x = y + h$. Substituting in the given equation,

$f(y + h) = 0$ is the required equation.

If $f(x) \equiv a_0 x^n + a_1 x^{n-1} + \ldots + a_n = 0$, then the required equation is

$$a_0 (y + h)^n + a_1 (y + h)^{n-1} + \ldots + a_n = 0$$

*i.e.,* $$a_0 y^n + (a_0 nh + a_1) y^{n-1} + (\ldots) y^{n-2} + \ldots = 0$$

If the term in $y^{n-1}$ is to be absent (i.e., the second term should vanish) then $a_0 nh + a_1 = 0$

*i.e.,* $$h = \frac{-a_1}{na_0} = \frac{1}{n}\left(-\frac{a_1}{a_0}\right) = \frac{\text{Sum of the roots}}{\text{degree}}$$

In other words, if the roots of the given equation are diminished by $h$ where $h = \frac{-a_1}{na_0} = \frac{\text{Sum of the roots}}{\text{degree}}$ then the second term of the resulting equation will be absent.

**Note.** To increase the roots by $h$, decrease the roots by $(-h)$.

**Example 1.** *Diminish by 3 the roots of $x^4 + 3x^3 - 2x^2 - 4x - 3 = 0$.*

**Sol.** Let $y = x - 3$. $\therefore x = y + 3$

Hence the required equation is

$$(y+3)^4 + 3(y+3)^3 - 2(y+3)^2 - 4(y+3) - 3 = 0$$

*i.e.,* $y^4 + 15y^3 + 79y^2 + 173y + 129 = 0.$

**Aliter :** We can do the same problem by synthetic division, as detailed below :

| | | | | | |
|---|---|---|---|---|---|
| 3 | 1 | 3 | –2 | –4 | –3 |
| | | 3 | 18 | 48 | 132 |
| 3 | 1 | 6 | 16 | 44 | 129 |
| | | 3 | 27 | 129 | |
| 3 | 1 | 9 | 43 | 173 | |
| | | 3 | 36 | | |
| 3 | 1 | 12 | 79 | | |
| | | 3 | | | |
| | 1 | 15 | | | |

$\therefore$ The required equation is $x^4 + 15x^3 + 79x^2 + 173x + 129 = 0$

**Example 2.** *Inerease by 2 the roots of $x^4 - x^3 - 10x^2 + 4x + 24 = 0$ and hence solve the equation.*

**Sol.** By synthetic division process,

| | | | | | |
|---|---|---|---|---|---|
| – 2 | 1 | – 1 | – 10 | 4 | 24 |
| | | – 2 | 6 | 8 | – 24 |
| – 2 | 1 | – 3 | – 4 | 12 | 0 |
| | | – 2 | 10 | –12 | |
| – 2 | 1 | – 5 | 6 | 0 | |
| | | – 2 | 14 | | |
| – 2 | 1 | – 7 | 20 | | |
| | | – 2 | | | |
| | 1 | – 9 | | | |

Hence the required equation is $x^4 - 9x^3 + 20x^2 = 0$ ...(2)

$\therefore \quad x^2(x^2 - 9x + 20) = 0 \quad i.e., \; x^2(x-4)(x-5) = 0$

$\therefore$ the roots of (2) are 0, 0, 4, 5

Hence the roots of the given equation are (subtract 2)

$$-2, -2, 2, 3.$$

**Example 3.** *Transform the equation $x^4 - 8x^3 - x^2 + 68x + 60 = 0$ into one which does not contain the term in $x^3$. Hence solve the equation.*

Take $h = \dfrac{-a_1}{na_0} = \dfrac{8}{4} = 2$ Diminish the roots by 2.

| | | | | | |
|---|---|---|---|---|---|
| 2 | 1 | −8 | −1 | 68 | 60 |
| | | 2 | −12 | −26 | 84 |
| 2 | 1 | −6 | −13 | 42 | 144 |
| | | 2 | −8 | −42 | |
| 2 | 1 | −4 | −21 | 0 | |
| | | 2 | −4 | | |
| 2 | 1 | −2 | −25 | | |
| | | 2 | | | |
| | 1 | 0 | | | |

$\therefore$ Transformed equation is $x^4 - 25x^2 + 144 = 0$ ...(2)

*i.e.*, $(x^2 - 9)(x^2 - 16) = 0$ *i.e.*, $x = \pm 3, \pm 4$ are the roots of (2)

Hence the roots of the given equation are

$$-1, -2, 5, 6.$$

**Example 4.** *Diminish by one the roots of $x^4 - 4x^3 - 7x^2 + 22x + 24 = 0$ and hence solve it.*

**Sol.** To diminish :

| | | | | | |
|---|---|---|---|---|---|
| 1 | 1 | −4 | −7 | 22 | 24 |
| | | 1 | −3 | −10 | 12 |
| 1 | 1 | −3 | −10 | 12 | 36 |
| | | 1 | −2 | −12 | |
| 1 | 1 | −2 | −12 | 0 | |
| | | 1 | −1 | | |
| 1 | 1 | −1 | −13 | | |
| | | 1 | | | |
| | 1 | 0 | | | |

The reduced equation is $x^4 - 13x^2 + 36 = 0$ *i.e.*, $(x^2 - 4)(x^2 - 9) = 0$

$\therefore \qquad x^2 = 4$ or $9$ *i.e.*, $x = \pm 2, \pm 3$

Hence the roots of the given equation are (Add 1) 3, –1, 4, –2

**Example 5.** *The equation whose roots are the roots of* $x^4 - 5x^3 + 7x^2 - 117x + 11 = 0$ *each diminished by h is* $x^4 + 3x^3 + x^2 - 17x - 19 = 0$ *; Find the value of h.*

**Sol.** Let $\alpha, \beta, \gamma, \delta$ be the roots of $x^4 - 5x^3 + 7x^2 - 17x + 11 = 0$

Then $\alpha - h, \beta - h, \gamma - h, \delta - h$ are roots of $x^4 + 3x^3 + x^2 - 17x - 19 = 0$

$\therefore \qquad \Sigma\alpha = 5$ and $\Sigma\alpha - 4h = -3 \quad \therefore \quad 5 - 4h = -3 \quad \therefore \quad h = 2$

**Exercises 3**

1. Transform the equation $x^3 + px^2 + qx + r = 0$ into another, lacking the second degree term
2. Diminish the roots of $3x^3 + 8x^2 + 8x + 12 = 0$ by 4.
3. Diminish the roots of $x^4 - 8x^3 + 19x^2 - 12x + 2 = 0$ by 2 and hence solve the equation.
4. Transform the equation $x^4 - 4x^3 - 7x^2 + 22x + 24 = 0$ into one in which the term in $x^3$ is missing and hence solve the equation.
5. Increase by 7 the roots of the equation $3x^4 + 7x^3 - 15x^2 + x - 2 = 0$.
6. Remove the second term in $x^4 + 20x^3 + 143x^2 + 430x + 462 = 0$ and hence solve the equation.
7. Remove the second term in $x^4 - 12x^3 + 48x^2 - 72x + 35 = 0$ and hence solve it.

**Multiple Roots**

*If* $f(x) = 0$ *has a multiple root* $\alpha$ *of multiplicity r, then* $f'(x) = 0$ *has a multiple root* $\alpha$ *of multiplicity* $(r - 1)$.

Let the degree of $f(x) = 0$ be $n$.

Then $\qquad f(x) = (x - \alpha)^r \phi(x)$ where $\phi(\alpha) \neq 0$

$$\therefore \qquad f'(x) = (x - \alpha)^r \phi'(x) + r(x - \alpha)^{r-1} \phi(x)$$

$$= (x - \alpha)^{r-1} [r\phi(x) + (x - \alpha)\phi'(x)] = (x - \alpha)^{r-1} \psi(x)$$

Evidently, $\psi(\alpha) = r\phi(\alpha) \neq 0$

$\therefore \qquad f'(x) = 0$ has a root $\alpha$ of multiplicity $(r - 1)$

**Example 1.** *Solve* $x^3 - 4x^2 + 5x - 2 = 0$ given that it has a double root.

**Sol.** Let $f(x) = x^3 - 4x^2 + 5x - 2 = 0$ possess a double root $\alpha$.

Then $\qquad f'(x) = 3x^2 - 8x + 5 = 0$ has a root $\alpha$.

$$3x^2 - 8x + 5 = (x-1)(3x-5) = 0 \quad \therefore \; x = 1 \text{ or } \frac{5}{3}$$

$$f(1) = 1 - 4 + 5 - 2 = 0 \;\; \therefore \; x = 1 \text{ is the double root}$$

$f(x) = (x-1)^2(x-2)$ $\therefore$ The roots are 1, 1, 2.

**Example 2.** *Solve* $8x^4 + 4x^3 - 18x^2 + 11x - 2 = 0$ *given that it has three equal roots.*

**Sol.** $f(x) = 8x^4 + 4x^3 - 18x^2 + 11x - 2 = 0$ has roots $\alpha, \alpha, \alpha, \beta$.

$$f' = 32x^3 + 12x^2 - 36x + 11 = 0 \text{ has roots } \alpha, \alpha, \gamma$$

$$f'' = 96x^2 + 24x - 36 = 0 \text{ has roots } \alpha, \delta$$

Solve $96x^2 + 24x - 36 = 0$ or $8x^2 + 2x - 3 = 0$

*i.e.*, $(4x+3)(2x-1) = 0 \quad \therefore \quad x = \frac{1}{2}$ or $-3/4$

$$f\left(\frac{1}{2}\right) = 8\left(\frac{1}{16}\right) + 4\left(\frac{1}{8}\right) - 18\left(\frac{1}{4}\right) + \frac{11}{2} - 2$$

$$= \frac{1}{2} + \frac{1}{2} - \frac{9}{2} + \frac{11}{2} - 2 = 0$$

$\therefore \quad \frac{1}{2}$ is the repeated root.

Product of roots $= \alpha^3 \beta = \frac{1}{8}\beta = \frac{-2}{8} \quad \therefore \beta = -2$

$\therefore$ Roots are $\frac{1}{2}, \frac{1}{2}, \frac{1}{2}$, and $-2$.

**Example 3.** *Solve* $x^4 + 4x^3 - 2x^2 - 12x + 9 = 0$ *given that it has two pairs of equal roots.*

**Sol.** Let the equation possess the roots $\alpha, \alpha, \beta, \beta$.

Sum of roots $= 2(\alpha + \beta) = -4 \quad \therefore \; \alpha + \beta = -2$

$f'(x) = 4x^3 + 12x^2 - 4x - 12 = 0$ has roots $\alpha, \beta, \gamma$

Sum of roots $= \alpha + \beta + \gamma = -\frac{12}{4} = -3 \quad \therefore \; -2 + \gamma = -3 \quad \therefore \; \gamma = -1$

Now solve $f'(x) = 0$ knowing one root $\gamma = -1$

| –1 | 4 | 12 | –4 | –12 |
|---|---|---|---|---|
| | | –4 | –8 | 12 |
| | 4 | 8 | –12 | 0 |

Solve $4x^2 + 8x - 12 = 0$ or $x^2 + 2x - 3 = 0$

$\therefore \quad (x+3)(x-1) = 0$ i.e., $x = 1$ or $-3$

The four roots are $1, 1, -3, -3$.

**Note :** We can do this problem by number of ways.

**Example 4.** *Find k so that the equation $2x^3 - 9x^2 + 12x + k = 0$ may have a double root.*

**Sol.** Let $f(x) = 2x^3 - 9x^2 + 12x + k$

If $f(x) = 0$ has a double root , then $f'(x) = 0$ has that root.

$f'(x) = 0$ implies $6x^2 - 18x + 12 = 0 \quad$ *i.e.,* $x^2 - 3x + 2 = 0$

*i.e.,* $(x-1)(x-2) = 0 \quad \therefore\ x = 1$ or $2$

If $x = 1$ is a double root then $f(1) = 0$

i.e., $2 - 9 + 12 + k = 0 \quad \therefore\ k = -5$

If $x = 2$ is a double root, then $f(2) = 0$

*i.e.* $16 - 36 + 24 + k = 0 \quad \therefore\ k = -4.$

## Exercise 4

1. Solve $4x^3 + 8x^2 + 5x + 1 = 0$; given that it has a double root.
2. Solve $8x^4 + 4x^3 - 18x^2 + 11x - 2 = 0$; given that it has three equal roots. [**Hint :** Solve $f''(x) = 0$ and proceed.]
3. Solve $x^4 - 6x^3 + 13x^2 - 12x + 4 = 0$; given that it has two sets of equal roots.
4. Solve $x^4 - 14x^3 + 73x^2 - 168x + 144 = 0$; given that it has two pairs of equal roots.
5. Solve $2x^3 - 9x^2 + 12x - 4 = 0$; given that it has two equal roots.
6. Solve $x^4 + 4x^3 - 2x^2 - 12x + 9 = 0$; given that it has two pairs of equal roots.
7. If the equation $x^3 - 3px^2 + 3qx - r = 0$ has a pair of equal roots, show that the third root is $\dfrac{3p^3 - 4pq + r}{p^2 - q}$.
8. Find $k$, if the equation $2x^3 - 9x^2 + 12x + k = 0$ has a double root.
9. If the equation $x^4 + px^3 + qx^2 + rx + s = 0$ has three equal roots, show that each of them is $\dfrac{6s - pq}{3p^2 - 8q}$
10. Show that the condition that $x^3 + 3px + q = 0$ should have repeated roots is $4p^3 + q^2 = 0$.

## Reciprocal Equation

If an equation $f(x) = 0$ remains unaltered when $x$ is changed to $\dfrac{1}{x}$, then it is called a *reciprocal equation i.e.*, if $f(x) = 0$ has a root $\alpha$, then $\frac{1}{\alpha}$ is also a root of $f(x) = 0$ if it is *reciprocal.*

Let $a_0x^n + a_1x^{n-1} + a_2x^{n-2} + \ldots + a_{n-1}x + a_n = 0$ ...(1)

be a reciprocal equation. Then, changing $x$ to $\frac{1}{x}$, we get,

$a_nx^n + a_{n-1}x^{n-1} + a_{n-2}x^{n-2} + \ldots\ldots + a_1x + a_0 = 0$ ...(2)

Equations (1) and (2) are identical.

$$\therefore \quad \frac{a_0}{a_n} = \frac{a_1}{a_{n-1}} = \frac{a_2}{a_{n-2}} = \ldots = \frac{a_{n-1}}{a_1} = \frac{a_n}{a_0}$$

$$\therefore \quad a_0^2 = a_n^2\ ;\ a_1^2 = a_{n-1}^2\ ;\ a_2^2 = a_{n-2}^2\ ;\ \text{etc.}$$

$$\therefore \quad a_0 = \pm\, a_n,\ a_1 = \pm\, a_{n-1},\ a_2 = \pm\, a_{n-2}, \ldots$$

**Case 1.** $a_0 = a_n,\ \ a_1 = a_{n-1},\ a_2 = a_{n-2}, \ldots$

**Case 2.** $a_0 = -\,a_n,\ a_1 = -\,a_{n-1},\ a_2 = -\,a_{n-2}, \ldots$

In case 1, we say that it is a reciprocal equation with like signs for its coefficients and in case 2, it is a reciprocal equation with unlike signs for its coefficients.

In case 1, the coefficients of the corresponding terms taken from the beginning and end are equal.

In case 2, the coefficients of the corresponding terms taken from the beginning and end are equal in magnitude but opposite in signs.

**Type I.** *Reciprocal equation of even degree with like signs for its coefficients.*

**Example 1.** Solve $4x^4 - 20x^3 + 33x^2 - 20x + 4 = 0$

**Sol.** This is a reciprocal equation of even degree with like signs for its coefficients.

Divide by $x^2$ throughout. Then the equation becomes,

$$4x^2 - 20x + 33 - 20\frac{1}{x} + \frac{4}{x^2} = 0$$

*i.e.*, $$4\left(x^2 + \frac{1}{x^2}\right) - 20\left(x + \frac{1}{x}\right) + 33 = 0 \quad \text{...(1)}$$

Put $y = x + \frac{1}{x}\cdot$ Then $x^2 + \frac{1}{x^2} = \left(x + \frac{1}{x}\right)^2 - 2 = y^2 - 2$

and $$x^3+\frac{1}{x^3}=\left(x+\frac{1}{x}\right)^3-3x\frac{1}{x}\left(x+\frac{1}{x}\right)=y^3-3y$$

Hence (1) becomes, $4(y^2-2)-20y+33=0$

*i.e.*, $4y^2-20y+25=0$ *i.e.*, $(2y-5)(2y-5)=0$

$\therefore\ y=\frac{5}{2}$ twice $\therefore\ x+\frac{1}{x}=\frac{5}{2}$ *i.e.*, $2x^2-5x+2=0$ $\therefore\ x=2$ or $\frac{1}{2}$

Hence the roots are $\frac{1}{2}, 2, \frac{1}{2}, 2$.

**Type II.** *Reciprocal equation of odd degree with like signs for its coefficients.*

**Example 2.** *Solve* $x^5+4x^4+x^3+x^2+4x+1=0$

**Sol.** This is evidently a reciprocal equation of odd degree with like signs for its coefficients.

In this case, we can easily verify that $x=-1$ is *always* a root.

$\therefore x+1$ is a factor of L.H.S. of the equation.

Factorize the L.H.S. by synthetic division.

| | | | | | | |
|---|---|---|---|---|---|---|
| $-1$ | 1 | 4 | 1 | 1 | 4 | 1 |
| | | $-1$ | $-3$ | 2 | $-3$ | $-1$ |
| | 1 | 3 | $-2$ | 3 | 1 | 0 |

$\therefore\quad x^5+4x^4+x^3+x^2+4x+1=(x+1)(x^4+3x^3-2x^2+3x+1)$

Now, solve : $x^4+3x^3-2x^2+3x+1=0$

This is also a reciprocal equation of type I. Therefore, divide by $x^2$.

Hence $$\left(x^2+\frac{1}{x^2}\right)+3\left(x+\frac{1}{x}\right)-2=0 \qquad ...(2)$$

put $x+\frac{1}{x}=y$. Hence (2) becomes, $(y^2-2)+3y-2=0$

*i.e.*, $y^2+3y-4=0$ *i.e.*, $(y+4)(y-1)=0$ $\therefore y=1$ or $-4$

Taking $x+\frac{1}{x}=1$,

$$x^2-x+1=0$$

$$\therefore\quad x=\frac{1\pm\sqrt{-3}}{2}=\frac{1\pm i\sqrt{3}}{2}$$

Taking $x+\frac{1}{x}=-4$.

$$x^2+4x+1=0$$

$$\therefore\quad x=\frac{-4\pm\sqrt{12}}{2}=-2\pm\sqrt{3}$$

Hence the roots are $-1, \frac{1 \pm i\sqrt{3}}{2}, -2 \pm \sqrt{3}$

**Type III.** *Reciprocal equation of odd degree with unlike signs for its coefficients.*

**Example 3.** *Solve* $x^5 - 5x^4 + 9x^3 - 9x^2 + 5x - 1 = 0$.

**Sol.** In this case, evidently $x = 1$ is *always* a root, since it satisfies the equation. (Verify it).

$\therefore (x - 1)$ is a factor of L.H.S. of the equation.

Factorizing by synthetic division, we see,

| | | | | | | |
|---|---|---|---|---|---|---|
| 1 | 1 | −5 | 9 | −9 | 5 | −1 |
| | | 1 | −4 | 5 | −4 | 1 |
| | 1 | −4 | 5 | −4 | 1 | 0 |

$$x^5 - 5x^4 + 9x^3 - 9x^2 + 5x - 1 = (x-1)(x^4 - 4x^3 + 5x^2 - 4x + 1)$$

Now solve, $x^4 - 4x^3 + 5x^2 - 4x + 1 = 0$

This is again a reciprocal equation of type I.

Dividing by $x^2$, $\left(x^2 + \frac{1}{x^2}\right) - 4\left(x + \frac{1}{x}\right) + 5 = 0$

*i.e.*, $(y^2 - 2) - 4y + 5 = 0$ where $y = x + \frac{1}{x}$ *i.e.*, $y^2 - 4x + 3 = 0 \therefore y = 1$ or 3

$$x + \frac{1}{x} = 1 \text{ yields } x = \frac{1 \pm i\sqrt{3}}{2}; \; x + \frac{1}{x} = 3 \text{ yields } x = \frac{3 \pm \sqrt{5}}{2}$$

Hence the roots are $1, \frac{1 \pm i\sqrt{3}}{2}, \frac{3 \pm \sqrt{5}}{2}$.

**Type IV.** *Reciprocal equation of even degree with unlike signs for its coefficients.*

**Example 4.** *Solve*: $6x^6 - 25x^5 + 31x^4 - 31x^2 + 25x - 6 = 0$

**(*MM Ap 94*)**

**Sol.** (Note the middle term is missing)

In this case $x = \pm 1$ are both roots (verify).

Dividing the L.H.S. of equation by $x - 1$ and $x + 1$, we see

| | | | | | | | |
|---|---|---|---|---|---|---|---|
| 1 | 6 | −25 | 31 | 0 | −31 | 25 | − 6 |
| | | 6 | −19 | 12 | 12 | −19 | 6 |
| −1 | 6 | −19 | 12 | 12 | −19 | 6 | 0 |
| | | − 6 | 25 | −37 | 25 | − 6 | |
| | 6 | −25 | 37 | −25 | 6 | 0 | |

$\therefore \quad f(x) = (x^2 - 1)(6x^4 - 25x^3 + 37x^2 - 25x + 6)$

Now solve : $6x^4 - 25x^3 + 37x^2 - 25x + 6 = 0$

This is again a reciprocal equation of type I.

Hence solving, we get $x = 2, \frac{1}{2}, \frac{1}{6}(5 \pm i\sqrt{11})$

$\therefore$ The roots of the given equation are $\pm 1, 2, \frac{1}{2}, \frac{1}{6}(5 \pm i\sqrt{11})$.

**Descarte's Rule of Signs**

We state below the rules without proof :

1. An equation $f(x) = 0$ cannot have more number of *positive roots* than there are changes of sign in the terms of the polynomial $f(x)$.

2. An equation $f(x) = 0$ cannot have more number of *negative roots* than there are changes of sign in the terms of the polynomial $f(-x)$.

**Example.** *Determine the nature of the roots of* $x^6 + 3x^5 + 5x - 1 = 0$.

**Sol.** The series of the signs of the terms in $f(x)$ are + + + −

Hence, there is only one change of sign.

Therefore, there cannot be *more than* one positive root ... (1)

$$f(0) = -1 = -\text{ ve and } f(\infty) = +\infty = +\text{ ve}$$

$\therefore$ There is *at least* one root lying between 0 and $\infty$

*i.e.*, one positive root (at least) ... (2)

Combining (1) and (2), there is exactly one positive root.

The series of signs of the terms in $f(-x)$ are + − − −

Hence there is at most one negative root since there is only one change of sign in the terms of $f(-x)$. $f(0) = -$ ve and $f(-\infty) = +$ ve

$\therefore$ There is *at least* one negative root for $f(x) = 0$

Hence, there is exactly one negative root of $f(x) = 0$

The remaining four roots are complex roots.

**EXERCISE 5**

Discuss the nature of roots of the equation :

**1.** $x^5 + x^4 + x^3 + x^2 + 1 = 0$ **2.** $x^6 - 3x^4 + 2x^3 - 1 = 0$

**3.** $x^5 + 5x - 9 = 0$ **4.** $x^5 + x^2 - 1 = 0$

**5.** $x^5 + 27 = 0$ **6.** $x^5 - 6x^2 - 4x + 7 = 0$.

**EXERCISE 6**

Solve the following equations.

**1.** $6x^4 - 25x^3 + 37x^2 - 25x + 6 = 0$ **2.** $x^4 - 10x^3 + 26x^2 - 10x + 1 = 0$

**3.** $6x^4 - 35x^3 + 62x^2 - 35x + 6 = 0$ **4.** $3x^6 + x^5 - 27x^4 + 27x^2 - x - 3 = 0$

**5.** $6x^6 - 25x^5 + 31x^4 - 31x^2 + 25x - 6 = 0$

**6.** $6x^6 - 35x^5 + 56x^4 - 56x^2 + 35x - 6 = 0$

**7.** $2x^6 - 9x^5 + 10x^4 - 3x^3 + 10x^2 - 9x + 2 = 0$

**8.** $x^6 + 2x^5 + 2x^4 - 2x^2 - 2x - 1 = 0$

**9.** $6x^5 + 11x^4 - 33x^3 - 33x^2 + 11x + 6 = 0$

**10.** $6x^5 - 41x^4 + 97x^3 - 97x^2 + 41x - 6 = 0$

**11.** $6x^5 - x^4 - 43x^3 + 43x^2 + x - 6 = 0$ **12.** $x^5 + x^4 + x^3 + x^2 + x + 1 = 0$

**13.** $x^5 - x^4 + x^3 - x^2 + x - 1 = 0$ **14.** $x^5 + 4x^4 + 3x^3 + 3x^2 + 4x + 1 = 0$

**15.** Show that $x^4 - 3x^3 + 4x^2 - 2x + 1 = 0$ can be transformed into a eciprocal equation by diminishing the roots by unity. Hence solve the equation.

**16.** Transform $x^4 - 5x^3 + 9x^2 - 5x - 1 = 0$ by diminishing the roots by 2 and hence solve it.

**17.** Increase the roots of $6x^4 + 29x^3 + 13x^2 - 32x - 16 = 0$ by 1 and hence solve it.

## ANSWERS

### EXERCISE 1 Page 50

**4.** $2 \pm \sqrt{3}, -3 \pm \sqrt{2}$ **5.** $5, 3 \pm \sqrt{2}$ **6.** $2 \pm \sqrt{3}, 1 \pm i$

**7.** $2 \pm \sqrt{3}, -\frac{3}{2}, -\frac{1}{3}$ **8.** $2 \pm i\sqrt{7}, -8/3$ **9.** $2 \pm i\sqrt{3}, -2 \pm i$

**10.** $-2 \pm i\sqrt{7}, 2 \pm i\sqrt{3}$ **11.** $2 \pm i\sqrt{11}, 1, 3$ **12.** $1 \pm i, -2 \pm \sqrt{3}$

**13.** $1 \pm 2i, \pm\sqrt{3}, 1$ **14.** $2 \pm i, \pm i$ **15.** 2, 3, 4.

**16.** $2 \pm i, 2$ **17.** 1 4, 7, **18.** 1, 4, –5, –2 **19.** (*i*) $\frac{1}{4}, \frac{1}{2}, 1$

(*ii*) $-2, \frac{2}{3}, -\frac{2}{9}$ (*iii*) 1, 2, 4 (*iv*) $\frac{2}{3}, 2, 6$ (*v*) 1, 2, 4, 8

**20.** (*i*) $-\frac{1}{2}, 2, \frac{1}{3}$ (*ii*) $-\frac{1}{3}, 1, \frac{1}{5}$ (*iii*) $1, \frac{1}{2}, \frac{1}{3}$ (*iv*) $-\frac{1}{5}, -\frac{1}{2}, 1, \frac{1}{4}$

**21.** $p^2 s = r^2$ **22.** $p^2 s + r^2 = 4qs$ **23.** (*i*) $pq = r$ (*ii*) $r^2 + pr + q + 1 = 0$

**24.** $\frac{3 \pm i\sqrt{7}}{4}, \frac{1 \pm i\sqrt{11}}{6}$ **25.** $-3, 2, 4$ **26.** $-1, -1, 3, 3$

**27.** $8, \frac{1}{2}, -\frac{1}{2}$ **28.** $\pm\sqrt{2}, -2 \pm \sqrt{7}$ **29.** $3, 9, -\frac{4}{3}$

**30.** $x^4 - 6x^3 + 11x^2 - 10x + 2 = 0$ **31.** $x^3 - 7x^2 + 12x - 10 = 0$

**32.** $x^4 - 14x^2 + 9 = 0$ **33.** $\frac{1}{2}, \frac{1}{2}, \frac{1}{2}, -2$

**34.** $\pm\frac{1}{\sqrt{3}}, \pm\sqrt{3}$ **35.** 1, 1 – 3, –3 **36.** – 1, – 3, 2, 6

### EXERCISE 2 Page 56

**1.** (*i*) $p_1^3 p_3 - p_2^3$ (*ii*) $(p_3 - p_1)^2 + (p_2 - 1)^2$ (*iii*) $-q_2/q_3$

(*iv*) $p_1/p_3$ (*v*) $3p_1 p_2 - p_1^3 - 3p_3$ **2.** (*i*) $q/r$

(*ii*) $2q^2$ (*iii*) $-q^2/r$ (*iv*) $-2q$ (*v*) $r$ (*vi*) $27r$

(*vii*) $-3r$ (*viii*) $3r$ (*ix*) $q^2$ **4.** (*i*) $pr - 4s$ (*ii*) $\frac{r^2 - 2qs}{s^2}$

**5.** (*i*) $(y + p)^3 - 2p(y + p)^2 + 4q(y + p)\ 8r = 0$

(*ii*) Eliminate $x$ between the given equation and $xy = (p + x)^2 x + 2r$

(*iii*) $y^3 - (3q - p^2)y^2 + (3q^2 - p^2 q)y + rp^3 - q^3 = 0$

**6.** (*i*) 28, – 24 (*ii*) 44, –252 **7.** $y^3 + (2q - p^2)y^2 + (q^2 - 2pr)y - r^2 = 0$

**8.** $x^3 - 10x^2 + 31x - 31 = 0$ **9.** $y^3 + 15y^2 + 52y - 36 = 0$

**10.** $y^3 + 15y^2 + 52y - 36 = 0$ **11.** $x^5 - 6x^4 + 6x^3 + 7x^2 + 2x + 1 = 0$

**12.** (*i*) $r^2y^3 + pr(1+r)y^2 + q(1+r)^2 y = (1+r)^3 = 0$

(*ii*) $y^3 + 2py^2 + (p^2 + q)y + pq - r = 0$

**13.** (*i*) $ry^3 - q(1+r)y^2 + p(1+r)^2 y - (1+r)^3 = 0$

(*ii*) $(p^3 - 4pq + 8r)y^3 + (p^3 - 4pq + 12r)y^2 + (6r - pq)y + r = 0$

**14.** $y^3 + 6qp^2 + 9q^2 y + (4q^3 + 27r^2) = 0$ (*i*) $-6q$ (*ii*) $-(4q^3 + 27r^2)$

**16.** (*i*) $x^4 - 33x^3 + 14x^2 + 135x + 100 = 0$

(*ii*) $x^4 - 41x^3 + 236x^2 - 349x + 166 = 0$

## EXERCISE 3 page 60

1. $x^3 + \frac{1}{3}(3q - p^2)x + \frac{1}{27}(2p^3 - 9pq + 27r) = 0$

2. $3x^3 + 44x^2 + 216x + 364 = 0$ **3.** $x^4 - 5x^2 + 6 = 0$ ; $2 \pm \sqrt{2}, 2 \pm \sqrt{3}$

4. $x^4 - 13x^2 + 36 = 0; -1, -2, 3, 4$

5. $3x^4 - 77x^3 + 720x^2 - 2876x + 4058 = 0$

6. $x^4 - 7x^2 + 12 = 0$: $-5 \pm \sqrt{3}, -3, -7$. **7.** $3 \pm \sqrt{2}$ , 1, 5

## EXERCISE 4 page 62

**1.** $x = -\frac{1}{2}, -\frac{1}{2}, -1$ **2.** $\frac{1}{2}, \frac{1}{2}, \frac{1}{2}, -2$ **3.** 1, 1, 2, 2

**4.** 3, 3, 4, 4 **5.** $2, 2, \frac{1}{2}$ **6.** 1, 1, 3, – 3 **8.** – 5, – 4

## EXERCISE 5 page 66

1. No positive root, atmost 3 –ve roots, at least 2 complex roots.
2. atmost 3 +ve, one –ve root, at least 2 complex.
3. one +ve, no –ve, exactly 4 complex.
4. one +ve, 2 –ve atmost 2 complex. **5.** no +ve, one –ve, exactly 4 complex. **6.** 2 +ve, atmost one –ve, atleast 2 complex.

## EXERCISE 6 page 66-67.

**1.** $\frac{1}{2}, 2, \frac{5 \pm i\sqrt{11}}{6}$ **2.** $3 \pm 3\sqrt{2},\ 2 \pm \sqrt{3}$ **3.** $2, \frac{1}{2}, \frac{1}{3}, 3$

**4.** $\pm 1, -\frac{1}{3}, -3, \frac{3 \pm \sqrt{5}}{2}$ **5.** $\pm 1, 2, \frac{1}{2}, \frac{5 + i\sqrt{11}}{6}$

**6.** $\pm 1, 2, \frac{1}{2}, \frac{1}{3}, 3$ **7.** $2, \frac{1}{2}, \frac{3 \pm \sqrt{5}}{2}, \frac{-1 \pm i\sqrt{3}}{2}$

**8.** $\pm 1, \frac{-1 \pm i\sqrt{3}}{2}, \frac{-1 \pm i\sqrt{3}}{2}$ **9.** $-1, 2, \frac{1}{2}, -3, -\frac{1}{3}$ **10.** $1, \frac{1}{2}, 2, 3, \frac{1}{3}$

**11.** $1, \frac{1}{2}, 2, -3, -\frac{1}{3}$ **12.** $-1, \frac{-1 \pm \sqrt{3}\,i}{2}, \frac{1 \pm \sqrt{3}\,i}{2}$ **13.** $1, \frac{1 + \sqrt{3}\,i}{2}, \frac{-1 \pm \sqrt{3}\,i}{2}$

**14.** $x = -1, x + \frac{1}{x} = \frac{-3 \pm \sqrt{17}}{2}$, **15.** $y^4 + y^3 + y^2 + y + 1 = 0$

**16.** $1.809 \pm 0.981\,i, -0.153, 1.536$ **17.** $1, -\frac{1}{2}, -4, \frac{-4}{3}$

# 3

# The Solution of Numerical Algebraic and Transcendental Equations

**3·1.** In the field of Science and Engineering, the solution of equations of the form $f(x)=0$ occurs in many applications. If $f(x)$ is a polynomial of degree two or three or four, exact formulae are available. But, if $f(x)$ is a transcendental function like $a+be^x+c\sin x+d\log x$ etc., the solution is not exact and we do not have formulae to get the solutions. When the coefficients are numerical values, we can adopt various numerical approximate methods to solve such algebraic and transcendental equations. We will see below some methods of solving such numerical equations. From the theory of equations, we recall to our memory the following theorem:

*If $f(x)$ is continuous in the interval $(a, b)$ and if $f(a)$ and $f(b)$ are of opposite signs, then the equation $f(x)=0$ will have atleast one real root between $a$ and $b$.*

### 3.1.1. The Bisection method (or BOLZANO's method) (or Interval halving method)

**AIM**: Suppose we have an equation of the form $f(x)=0$ whose solution in the range $(a, b)$ is to be searched. We also assume that $f(x)$ is continuous and it can be algebraic or transcendental. If $f(a)$ and $f(b)$ are of opposite signs, atleast one real root between $a$ and $b$ should exist. For convenience, let $f(a)$ be positive and $f(b)$ be negative. Then atleast one root exists between $a$ and $b$. As a first approximation, we assume that root to be $x_0=\dfrac{a+b}{2}$ (mid point of the ends of the range). Now, find the sign of $f(x_0)$. If $f(x_0)$ is negative, the root lies between $a$ and $x_0$. If $f(x_0)$ is positive, the root lies between $x_0$ and $b$. Any one of this is true. Suppose $f(x_0)$ is positive as shown in the Fig. 3·1, then the root lies between $x_0$ and

$b$ and take the root as $x_1 = \dfrac{x_0 + b}{2}\cdot$ Now $f(x_1)$ is negative (as in the Fig. 3·1). Hence the root lies between $x_0$ and $x_1$ and let the root be (approximate) $x_2 = \dfrac{x_0 + x_1}{2}\cdot$ Now $f(x_2)$ is negative as in the Fig. 3·1, then the root lies between $x_0$ and $x_2$ and let $x_3 = \dfrac{x_0 + x_2}{2}$ and so on. In this way, taking the mid-point of the range as the approximate root, we form a sequence of approximate roots $x_0, x_1, x_2, \ldots$ whose limit of convergence is the exact root. However, depending on the precision required, we stop the process after some steps. Though simple, the convergence of this method is *slow but sure.*

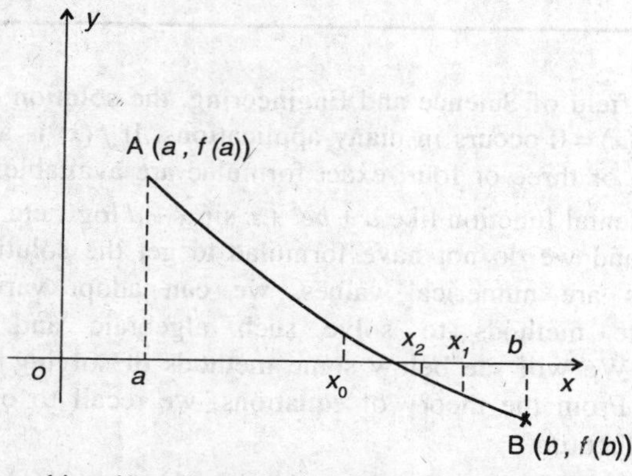


**Note.** After $n$ bisections, the length of the subinterval which contains $x_n$ is $\dfrac{b-a}{2^n}\cdot$ If the error is to be made less than a small quantity $\varepsilon$, say,

$$\frac{b-a}{2^n} < \varepsilon. \text{ That is, } 2^n > \frac{b-a}{\varepsilon}$$

The number of iterations $n$ should be greater than $\dfrac{\log\left(\dfrac{b-a}{\varepsilon}\right)}{\log 2}$.

**Example 1.** *Find the positive root of $x^3 - x = 1$ correct to four decimal places by bisection method.*

**Solution.** Let $f(x) = x^3 - x - 1$

Here, $f(0) = -1 = -ve$ and $f(1) = -ve$

$f(2) = 5 = +ve$. Hence a root lies between 1 and 2. We can take the range as (1, 2) and proceed. We can still shorten the range.

$$f(1{\cdot}5) = 0{\cdot}8750 = +ve$$

and

$$f(1) = -1 = -ve$$

Hence, the root lies between 1 and 1·5 ...(1)

Let $$x_0 = \frac{1 + 1{\cdot}5}{2} = 1{\cdot}2500$$

$$f(x_0) = f(1{\cdot}25) = -0{\cdot}29688$$

Hence the root lies between 1·25 and 1·5 ...(2)

Now, $$x_1 = \frac{1{\cdot}25 + 1{\cdot}5}{2} = 1{\cdot}3750$$

$$f(1{\cdot}3750) = 0{\cdot}22461 = +ve$$

The root lies between 1·2500 and 1·3750.

Now $$x_2 = \frac{1{\cdot}2500 + 1{\cdot}3750}{2} = 1{\cdot}3125$$

$$f(1{\cdot}3125) = -0{\cdot}051514$$

Therefore, root lies between 1·3750 and 1·3125

Now $$x_3 = \frac{1{\cdot}3125 + 1{\cdot}3750}{2} = 1{\cdot}3438$$

$$f(x_3) = f(1{\cdot}3438) = 0{\cdot}082832 = +ve$$

The root lies between 1·3125 and 1·3438

Hence $$x_4 = \frac{1{\cdot}3125 + 1{\cdot}3438}{2} = 1{\cdot}3282$$

$$f(1{\cdot}3282) = 0{\cdot}014898$$

Therefore the root lies between 1·3125 and 1·3282

$$x_5 = \tfrac{1}{2}(1{\cdot}3125 + 1{\cdot}3282) = 1{\cdot}3204$$

$$f(1{\cdot}3204) = -0{\cdot}0183{\cdot}40$$

The root lies between 1·3204 and 1·3282

$$x_6 = \frac{1}{2}(1{\cdot}3204 + 1{\cdot}3282) = 1{\cdot}3243$$

$$f(1{\cdot}3243) = -ve$$

Hence, the root lies between 1·3243 and 1·3282

$\therefore$ $$x_7 = \tfrac{1}{2}(1{\cdot}3243 + 1{\cdot}3282) = 1{\cdot}3263$$

$$f(1{\cdot}3263) = +ve$$

$\therefore$ The root lies between 1·3243 and 1·3263

$$x_8 = \tfrac{1}{2}(1{\cdot}3243 + 1{\cdot}3263) = 1{\cdot}3253$$

$$f(1{\cdot}3253) = +ve$$

The root lies between 1·3243 and 1·3253

$\therefore$ $$x_9 = \tfrac{1}{2}(1{\cdot}3243 + 1{\cdot}3253) = 1{\cdot}3248$$

$$f(1{\cdot}3248) = +ve$$

$\therefore$ The root lies between 1·3243 and 1·3248

$$x_{10} = \frac{1}{2}(1{\cdot}3243 + 1{\cdot}3248) = 1{\cdot}32455$$

$$f(1{\cdot}32455) = -\,ve$$

The root lies between 1·3248 and 1·32455

$$\therefore \quad x_{11} = \frac{1}{2}(1{\cdot}3248 + 1{\cdot}32455) = 1{\cdot}3247$$

$$f(1{\cdot}3247) = -\,ve$$

∴ The root lies between 1·3247 and 1·3248

Hence, $\quad x_{12} = \frac{1}{2}(1{\cdot}3247 + 1{\cdot}3248) = 1{\cdot}32475$

Therefore, the approximate root is 1·32475
(This is not correct to 5 decimal places).

**Example 2.** *Assuming that a root of $x^3 - 9x + 1 = 0$ lies in the interval (2, 4), find that root by bisection method.*

**Solution.** Let $\quad f(x) = x^3 - 9x + 1$

$$f(2) = -ve \text{ and } f(4) = +\,ve$$

Therefore, a root lies between 2 and 4

Let $\quad x_0 = \frac{2+4}{2} = 3$

Now $f(3) = +\,ve$; hence the root lies between 2 and 3

$$x_1 = \frac{2+3}{2} = 2{\cdot}5$$

$$f(x_1) = f(2{\cdot}5) = -\,ve$$

The root lies between 2·5 and 3.

$$x_2 = \frac{2{\cdot}5 + 3}{2} = 2{\cdot}75$$

$$f(2{\cdot}75) = -\,ve$$

The root lies between 2·75 and 3

$$x_3 = \frac{1}{2}(2{\cdot}75 + 3) = 2{\cdot}875$$

$$f(x_3) = f(2{\cdot}875) = -\,ve$$

Therefore, the root lies between 2·875 and 3

$$x_4 = \frac{1}{2}(2{\cdot}875 + 3) = 2{\cdot}9375$$

$$f(2{\cdot}9375) = -\,ve$$

∴ The root lies between 2·9375 and 3

$$x_5 = \frac{1}{2}(2{\cdot}9375 + 3) = 2{\cdot}9688$$

$$f(2{\cdot}9688) = +\,ve$$

The root lies between 2·9688 and 2·9375

$$x_6 = \frac{1}{2}(2{\cdot}9375 + 2{\cdot}9688) = 2{\cdot}9532$$

$$f(2{\cdot}9532) = +\,ve$$

$\therefore$ The root lies between 2·9375 and 2·9532

$$x_7 = \frac{1}{2}(2{\cdot}9375 + 2{\cdot}9532) = 2{\cdot}9454$$

$$f(2{\cdot}9454) = +ve$$

The root lies between 2·9375 and 2·9454

$$x_8 = \frac{1}{2}(2{\cdot}9375 + 2{\cdot}9454) = 2{\cdot}9415$$

$$f(2{\cdot}9415) = -ve$$

The root lies between 2·9415 and 2·9454.

$$x_9 = \frac{1}{2}(2{\cdot}9415 + 2{\cdot}9454) = 2{\cdot}9435$$

$$f(2{\cdot}9435) = +ve$$

The root lies between 2·9415 and 2·9435.

$$x_{10} = 2{\cdot}9425$$

$$f(2{\cdot}9425) = -ve$$

The root lies between 2·9425 and 2·9435.

$$x_{11} = 2{\cdot}9430$$

$$f(2{\cdot}9430) = +ve$$

$$x_{12} = 2{\cdot}94275$$

$$x_{13} = 2{\cdot}942875$$

Approximate root is 2·9429.

**Example 3.** *Find the positive root of $x - \cos x = 0$ by bisection method.*

**Solution.** Let $\quad f(x) = x - \cos x$

$$f(0) = -ve,\ f(0{\cdot}5) = 0{\cdot}5 - \cos(0{\cdot}5) = -0{\cdot}37758$$

$$f(1) = 1 - \cos 1 = 0{\cdot}45970$$

Hence, the root lies between 0·5 and 1.

$$x_0 = \frac{0{\cdot}5 + 1}{2} = 0{\cdot}75$$

$$f(0{\cdot}75) = 0{\cdot}75 - \cos(0{\cdot}75) = 0{\cdot}018311 = +ve$$

$\therefore$ The root lies between 0·5 and 0·75.

$$x_1 = \frac{0{\cdot}5 + 0{\cdot}75}{2} = 0{\cdot}625$$

$$f(0{\cdot}625) = 0{\cdot}625 - \cos(0{\cdot}625) = -0{\cdot}18596$$

The root lies between 0·625 and 0·750.

$$x_2 = \frac{1}{2}(0{\cdot}625 + 0{\cdot}750) = 0{\cdot}6875$$

$$f(0{\cdot}6875) = -0{\cdot}085335$$

$\therefore$ The root lies between 0·6875 and 0·75.

$$x_3 = \frac{1}{2}(0{\cdot}6875 + 0{\cdot}75) = 0{\cdot}71875$$

$$f(0{\cdot}71875) = 0{\cdot}71875 - \cos(0{\cdot}71875) = -0{\cdot}033879$$

The root lies between 0·71875 and 0·75

$$x_4 = \frac{1}{2}(0{\cdot}71875 + 0{\cdot}75) = 0{\cdot}73438$$

$$f(0{\cdot}73438) = -0{\cdot}0078664 = -ve$$

∴ The root lies between 0·73438 and 0·75

$$x_5 = 0{\cdot}742190$$

$$f(0{\cdot}74219) = 0{\cdot}0051999 = +ve$$

$$x_6 = \frac{1}{2}(0{\cdot}73438 + 0{\cdot}742190) = 0{\cdot}73829$$

$$f(0{\cdot}73829) = -0{\cdot}0013305$$

The root lies between 0·73829 and 0·74219

$$x_7 = \frac{1}{2}(0{\cdot}73829 + 0{\cdot}74219) = 0{\cdot}7402$$

$$f(0{\cdot}7402) = 0{\cdot}7402 - \cos(0{\cdot}7402) = 0{\cdot}0018663$$

The root lies between 0·73829 and 0·7402

$$x_8 = 0{\cdot}73925$$

$$f(0{\cdot}73925) = 0{\cdot}00027593$$

$$x_9 = 0{\cdot}7388 \qquad \text{(correct to 4 places)}$$

The root is 0·7388.

**Example 4.** *Find the positive of $x^4 - x^3 - 2x^2 - 6x - 4 = 0$ by bisection method.*

**Solution.** Let $f(x) = x^4 - x^3 - 2x^2 - 6x - 4$

$f(2)$ and $f(3)$ are opposite in sign since $f(2) = -ve$ and $f(3) = +ve$

Therefore the root lies between 2 and 3

$$x_0 = \frac{2+3}{2} = 2{\cdot}5$$

$f(2{\cdot}5) = -ve$; hence root lies between 2·5 and 3

$$\therefore \qquad x_1 = \frac{2{\cdot}5 + 3}{2} = 2{\cdot}75$$

Proceeding in the same manner, the sequence of mid-points is 2·5, 2·75, 2·63, 2·69, 2·72, 2·735, 2·728, 2·7315, 2·7298, 2·7307, 2·7311, 2·7313, 2·7314, 2·7315,...

$$f(2{\cdot}7315) = -0{\cdot}0232$$

The root of the equation is 2·7315 approximately.

**Example 5.** *Using bisection method, find the negative root of $x^3 - 4x + 9 = 0$ by bisection method.*

**Solution.** Let

$$f(x) = x^3 - 4x + 9 \qquad ...(1)$$

$$f(-x) = -x^3 + 4x + 9 \qquad ...(2)$$

The negative root of $f(x) = 0$ is the positive root of $f(-x) = 0$.

$\therefore$ We will find the positive root of $f(-x)=0$, firstly,

*i.e.,* $\phi(x)=x^3-4x-9=0$

$$\phi(2)=-ve \quad \text{and} \quad \phi(3)=+ve$$

$\therefore$ The root lies between 2 and 3.

Hence $x_0=\dfrac{2+3}{2}=2{\cdot}5$

$$\phi(2{\cdot}5)=(2{\cdot}5)^3-4\,(2{\cdot}5)-9=-ve$$

Therefore, the root lies between 2·5 and 3.

Hence, $x_1=\frac{1}{2}(2{\cdot}5+3)=2{\cdot}75$

$$\phi(2{\cdot}75)=+ve$$

$\therefore$ The root lies between 2·5 and 2·75

$$x_2=\tfrac{1}{2}(2{\cdot}5+2{\cdot}75)=2{\cdot}625$$

$$\phi(2{\cdot}625)=(2{\cdot}625)^3-4(2{\cdot}625)-9=-1{\cdot}4121=-ve$$

The root lies between 2·625 and 2·75.

$$x_3=\tfrac{1}{2}(2{\cdot}625+2{\cdot}75)=2{\cdot}6875$$

$$\phi(2{\cdot}6875)=-ve$$

$\therefore$ The root lies between 2·6875 and 2·75.

$$x_4=\tfrac{1}{2}(2{\cdot}6875+2{\cdot}75)=2{\cdot}71875$$

$$\phi(2{\cdot}71875)=+ve$$

$\therefore$ The root lies between 2·6875 and 2·71875.

$\therefore$ $x_5=\frac{1}{2}(2{\cdot}6875+2{\cdot}71875)=2{\cdot}703125$

$$\phi(2{\cdot}703125)=(2{\cdot}703125)^3-4(2{\cdot}703125)-9=-ve$$

$\therefore$ The root lies between 2·703125 and 2·71875.

$$x_6=\tfrac{1}{2}(2{\cdot}703125+2{\cdot}71875)=2{\cdot}710938$$

Proceeding in the same way,

$$x_7=2{\cdot}707031,\ x_8=2{\cdot}705078,\ x_9=2{\cdot}706054,$$

$$x_{10}=2{\cdot}70654,\ x_{11}=2{\cdot}706297,\ x_{12}=2{\cdot}706418,$$

$$x_{13}=2{\cdot}70648,\ x_{14}=2{\cdot}70651 \text{ etc.}$$

We can conclude the root to be 2·7065 for $\phi(x)=0$

Hence the negative root of the given equation is $-2{\cdot}7065$.

## 3·2. Iteration method (or Method of successive approximations)

Suppose we want the approximate roots of the equation

$$f(x)=0 \qquad \text{...(1)}$$

Now, write the equation (1) in the form

$$x=\phi(x) \qquad \text{...(2)}$$

Assume $x_0$ to be the starting approximate value to the actual root $\alpha$ of $x = \phi(x)$. Setting $x = x_0$ in the right hand side of (2), we get the first approximation

$$x_1 = \phi(x_0)$$

Again setting $x = x_1$ on the R.H.S. of (2), we get successive approximations.

$$x_2 = \phi(x_1)$$
$$x_3 = \phi(x_2)$$
$$\dots\dots\dots\dots$$
$$\dots\dots\dots\dots$$
$$x_n = \phi(x_{n-1})$$

The sequence of approximate roots $x_1, x_2, \dots, x_n$, if it converges to $\alpha$ is taken as the root of the equation $f(x) = 0$

**Note.** The convergence of the sequence is not guaranteed always unless the choice of $x_0$ is properly chosen.

### 3·2·1. The condition for the convergence of the method

**Theorem.** Let $f(x) = 0$ ...(1)

be the given equation whose actual root is $\alpha$. The equation $f(x) = 0$ be written as $x = \phi(x)$. Let $I$ be the interval containing the root $x = \alpha$. If $|\phi'(x)| < 1$ for all $x$ in $I$, then the sequence of approximations $x_0, x_1, x_2, \dots, x_n$ will converge to $\alpha$, if the initial starting value $x_0$ is chosen in $I$.

**Proof.** Since $\alpha$ is an actual root of $x = \phi(x)$, we have

$$\alpha = \phi(\alpha) \qquad \text{...(2)}$$

Further

$$x_1 = \phi(x_0)$$
$$x_2 = \phi(x_1)$$
$$\dots\dots\dots\dots$$
$$\dots\dots\dots\dots$$
$$x_n = \phi(x_{n-1}) \qquad \text{...(3)}$$

from which the sequence $x_0, x_1, x_2, \dots, x_n$ of approximations is got. Hence,

$$x_n - \alpha = \phi(x_{n-1}) - \phi(\alpha) \qquad \text{...(4)}$$

By mean value theorem of differential calculus,

$\phi(x_{n-1}) - \phi(\alpha) = (x_{n-1} - \alpha)\,\phi'(\theta)$ where $x_{n-1} < \theta < \alpha$

Using in (4),

$$x_n - \alpha = (x_{n-1} - \alpha)\,\phi'(\theta) \qquad \text{...(5)}$$

Let $|\phi'(x)| \le k$ for all $x$ in the interval $I$ which contains

$$x_0, x_1, x_2, \dots\dots, x_n, \alpha$$

Hence, (5) reduces to,

$$| x_n - \alpha | \le | x_{n-1} - \alpha | k$$

Similarly, $| x_{n-1} - \alpha | \le | x_{n-2} - \alpha | k$

$$| x_{n-2} - \alpha | \le | x_{n-3} - \alpha | k$$

..............................................

..............................................

$$| x_1 - \alpha | \le | x_0 - \alpha | k$$

Multiplying vertically and cancelling the factors,

$$| x_n - \alpha | \le k^n | x_0 - \alpha | \qquad ...(6)$$

If $k < 1, k^n \to 0$ as $n \to \infty$

Hence $| x_n - \alpha | \to 0$ as $n \to \infty$

*i.e.*, $\underset{n \to \infty}{\text{Lt}}\, x_n = \alpha$

Therefore, the sequence of approximations $x_0, x_1, x_2, ..., x_n ...$ converges to the exact root $\alpha$ if

$| \phi'(x) | < k < 1$ for all values of $x$ in $I$. The sequence will converge rapidly if $| \phi'(x) |$ is very small.

If $| \phi'(x) | > 1$, $| x_n - \alpha |$ will become very great and the sequence will not converge.

**Note 1.** Since $| x_n - \alpha | \le k | x_{n-1} - \alpha |$ where $k$ is a constant, the convergence is linear and the convergence is of order *one*.

2. The sufficient condition for the convergence is $| \phi'(x) | < 1$ for all $x$ in $I$.

### 3·2·2. Order of convergence of an iterative process

Let $x_0, x_1, x_2, ..., x_n, ...$ be the successive approximations of the root $\alpha$ of $f(x) = 0$. Let $e_i$ be the error in the root $x_i$, $i = 1, 2, 3, ...$

If $\alpha$ is the exact root,

$$e_i = x_i - \alpha \quad \text{and} \quad e_{i+1} = x_{i+1} - \alpha$$

If $p \ge 1$ can be found out such that $| e_{i+1} | \le | e_i |^p \cdot k$ where $k$ is a positive constant for every $i$, then $p$ is called the *order of convergence*.

If $p = 1$, the convergence is linear and if $p = 2$, it is quadratic.

**Example 1.** *Solve $e^x - 3x = 0$ by the method of iteration.*

**Solution.** Let $f(x) = e^x - 3x = 0$

$$f(0) = 1 = +ve\,; \quad f(1) = e - 3 = -ve$$

$\therefore$ a root lies between 0 and 1.

Let $\quad x = \frac{1}{3} e^x = \phi(x)$

$$\phi'(x) = \frac{1}{3} e^x \text{ and } \phi'(0) = 1/3, \phi'(1) < 1$$

In the interval (0, 1), $|\phi'(x)| < 1$

Select $x_0 = 0{\cdot}6, x_1 = \frac{1}{3} e^{x_0} = \frac{1}{3} e^{0{\cdot}6} = 0{\cdot}60737$

$$x_2 = \frac{1}{3} e^{0{\cdot}60737} = 0{\cdot}61187, \; x_3 = \frac{1}{3} e^{0{\cdot}61187} = 0{\cdot}61452$$

$$x_4 = \frac{1}{3} e^{0{\cdot}61452} = 0{\cdot}61626, \; x_5 = \frac{1}{3} e^{0{\cdot}61626} = 0{\cdot}61733$$

$$x_6 = \frac{1}{3} e^{0{\cdot}61733} = 0{\cdot}61799, \; x_7 = \frac{1}{3} e^{0{\cdot}61799} = 0{\cdot}61840$$

$$x_8 = \frac{1}{3} e^{0{\cdot}61840} = 0{\cdot}61865, \; x_9 = \frac{1}{3} e^{0{\cdot}61865} = 0{\cdot}61881$$

$$x_{10} = \frac{1}{3} e^{0{\cdot}61881} = 0{\cdot}61891, \; x_{11} = \frac{1}{3} e^{0{\cdot}61891} = 0{\cdot}61897$$

$$x_{12} = \frac{1}{3} e^{0{\cdot}61897} = 0{\cdot}61900, \; x_{13} = \frac{1}{3} e^{0{\cdot}61900} = 0{\cdot}61902$$

We can take 0·6190 as the correct value of the root of the equation.

**Example 2.** *Find a real root of the equation* $\cos x = 3x - 1$ *correct to 4 decimal places by iteration method.*

**Solution.** Let $f(x) = \cos x - 3x + 1 = 0$

$$f(0) = 2 = +ve \; ; \; f\left(\frac{\pi}{2}\right) = 1 - 3\left(\frac{\pi}{2}\right) = -ve$$

Therefore, a root lies between 0 and $\pi/2$.

The given equation may be written as

$$x = \frac{1}{3}(1 + \cos x) = \phi(x)$$

$$\phi'(x) = -\frac{1}{3} \sin x$$

$|\phi'(x)| = \left| \frac{1}{3} \sin x \right| < 1$ for all $x$ and in particular in $(0, \pi/2)$,

*i.e.*, (0, 1·5708).

Hence, the iteration method may be applied.

Let us take $x_0 = 0{\cdot}6$

$$x_1 = \frac{1}{3}[1 + \cos(0{\cdot}6)] = 0{\cdot}60845$$

$$x_2 = \frac{1}{3}[1 + \cos(0{\cdot}60845)] = 0{\cdot}60684$$

$$x_3 = \frac{1}{3}[1 + \cos(0{\cdot}60684)] = 0{\cdot}60715$$

$$x_4 = \frac{1}{3}[1 + \cos(0{\cdot}60715)] = 0{\cdot}60709$$

$$x_5 = \frac{1}{3}[1 + \cos(0{\cdot}60709)] = 0{\cdot}60710$$

$$x_6 = \frac{1}{3}[1 + \cos(0{\cdot}60710)] = 0{\cdot}60710$$

Due to repetition of $x_5$ and $x_6$, we stop our work here. Hence the root is 0·6071 correct to 4 decimal places.

**Example 3.** *Solve the equation $x^3 + x^2 - 1 = 0$ for the positive root by iteration method.*

**Solution.** Let $f(x) = x^3 + x^2 - 1 = 0$

$f(0) = -1 = -ve$ ; $f(1) = 1 = +ve$

The root lies between 0 and 1.

We write the given equation as $x^2(x + 1) = 1$

*i.e.,*
$$x = \frac{1}{\sqrt{x+1}} = \phi(x)$$

$$\phi'(x) = -\frac{1}{2}\frac{1}{(x+1)^{3/2}}$$

$$|\phi'(0)| = \frac{1}{2} < 1 \quad \text{and} \quad |\phi'(1)| < 1$$

That is $|\phi'(x)| < 1$ for all $x$ in (0, 1).

Hence, the iterative method can be applied.

Take $x_0 = 0{\cdot}75$ as starting value

$$x_1 = \frac{1}{\sqrt{1 + x_0}} = \frac{1}{\sqrt{1{\cdot}75}} = 0{\cdot}75593, \quad x_2 = \frac{1}{\sqrt{1{\cdot}75593}} = 0{\cdot}75465$$

$$x_3 = \frac{1}{\sqrt{1{\cdot}75465}} = 0{\cdot}75493, \quad x_4 = \frac{1}{\sqrt{1{\cdot}75493}} = 0{\cdot}75487$$

$$x_5 = \frac{1}{\sqrt{1{\cdot}75487}} = 0{\cdot}75488, \quad x_6 = \frac{1}{\sqrt{1{\cdot}75488}} = 0{\cdot}75488$$

Hence the root is 0·75488.

**Example 4.** *Solve for x from $\cos x - xe^x = 0$ by iteration method.*

**Solution.** Let $f(x) = \cos x - xe^x$

$f(0) = 1 = +ve$ ; $f(1) = \cos 1 - e^1 = -2{\cdot}1780 = -ve$

Therefore, the root lies between 0 and 1; *i.e.,* in (0, 1)

From $f(x)=0$, we get $x=\dfrac{\cos x}{e^x}=\phi(x)$

$$\phi'(x)=\frac{e^x(-\sin x)-\cos x.e^x}{e^{2x}}$$

$$=\frac{-(\sin x+\cos x)}{e^x}=\frac{-\sqrt{2}\sin\left(\frac{\pi}{4}+x\right)}{e^x}$$

$$|\phi'(x)|<\frac{\sqrt{2}}{e^x}$$

$$|\phi'(0{\cdot}5)|<\frac{\sqrt{2}}{e^{0\cdot5}}=0{\cdot}85776<1$$

$$|\phi'(1)|<\frac{\sqrt{2}}{e}=0{\cdot}52026<1$$

$|\phi'(x)|<|$ for $x$ in the range (0·5, 1)

$$f(0{\cdot}5)=0{\cdot}0532=+ve\ ;\ f(1)=-ve$$

The root lies between 0·5 and 1.

Take $x_0=0{\cdot}52$ as starting value.

$$x_1=\phi(x_0)=\frac{\cos(0{\cdot}52)}{e^{0\cdot52}}=0{\cdot}51594$$

$$x_2=\phi(x_1)=\frac{\cos(0{\cdot}51594)}{e^{0\cdot51594}}=0{\cdot}51924$$

$$x_3=\frac{\cos(0{\cdot}51924)}{e^{0\cdot51924}}=0{\cdot}51655$$

$$x_4=\frac{\cos(0{\cdot}51655)}{e^{0\cdot51655}}=0{\cdot}51874$$

$x_5=0{\cdot}51696$ $x_6=0{\cdot}51841$

$x_7=0{\cdot}51723$ $x_8=0{\cdot}51819$

$x_9=0{\cdot}51741$ $x_{10}=0{\cdot}51804$

$x_{11}=0{\cdot}51753$ $x_{12}=0{\cdot}51794$

$x_{13}=0{\cdot}51761$ $x_{14}=0{\cdot}51788$

$x_{15}=0{\cdot}51766$ $x_{16}=0{\cdot}51784$

$x_{17}=0{\cdot}51769$ $x_{18}=0{\cdot}51781$

$x_{19}=0{\cdot}51771$

The root is 0·5177 correct to 4 decimals.

**Example 5.** *Solve* $x^3=2x+5$ *for the positive root by iteration method.*

**Solution.** Let $f(x) = x^3 - 2x - 5 = 0$

$$f(2) = -1 = -ve\ ; \ f(3) = 16 = +ve$$

The root lies between 2 and 3 and closer to 2. $f(x) = 0$ can be written as

$$x^3 = 2x + 5\ ; \quad i.e., \quad x = (2x+5)^{\frac{1}{3}} = \phi(x)$$

$$\phi'(x) = \frac{2}{3} \cdot \frac{1}{(2x+5)^{2/3}}$$

$|\phi'(x)| < 1$ for all $x$ in (2, 3).

Take $x_0 = 2{\cdot}0$

$$x_1 = (2x_0 + 5)^{1/3} = 9^{1/3} = 2{\cdot}0801$$

$$x_2 = (9{\cdot}1602)^{1/3} = 2{\cdot}0924\ ; \ x_3 = (9{\cdot}1848)^{1/3} = 2{\cdot}0942$$

$$x_4 = (9{\cdot}1884)^{1/3} = 2{\cdot}0945\ ; \ x_5 = (9{\cdot}1890)^{1/3} = 2{\cdot}0945$$

Therefore the root is 2·0945.

**Example 6.** *Find a positive root of* $3x - \sqrt{1 + \sin x} = 0$ *by iteration method.*

**Solution.** Writing the given equation as

$$x = \frac{1}{3}\sqrt{1 + \sin x} = \phi(x), \ \phi'(x) = \frac{\cos x}{6\sqrt{1 + \sin x}}$$

The root of given equation lies in (0, 1)

since $f(0) = -ve$ and $f(1) = +ve$

In (0, 1), $|\phi'(x)| < 1$ for all $x$

So, we can use iteration method.

Taking $x_0 = 0{\cdot}4$, $x_1 = \frac{1}{3}\sqrt{1 + \sin(0{\cdot}4)} = 0{\cdot}39291$

$$x_2 = \frac{1}{3}\sqrt{1 + \sin(0{\cdot}39291)} = 0{\cdot}39199$$

$$x_3 = \frac{1}{3}\sqrt{1 + \sin(0{\cdot}39199)} = 0{\cdot}39187$$

$$x_4 = 0{\cdot}39185$$

$$x_5 = 0{\cdot}39185$$

The root is 0·39185.

## 3·3. Regula Falsi method (or the method of false position)

Consider the equation $f(x) = 0$ and let $f(a)$ and $f(b)$ be of opposite signs. Also, let $a < b$. The curve $y = f(x)$ will meet the $x$-axis at some point between $A(a, f(a))$ and $B(b, f(b))$. The equation of the chord joining the two points $A(a, f(a))$ and $B(b, f(b))$ is $\frac{y - f(a)}{x - a} = \frac{f(a) - f(b)}{a - b}$. The

$x$-coordinate of the point of intersection of this chord with the $x$-axis gives an approximate value for the root of $f(x)=0$. Setting $y=0$ in the chord equation, we get

$$\frac{-f(a)}{x-a}=\frac{f(a)-f(b)}{a-b}$$

$$x[f(a)-f(b)]-af(a)+af(b)=-af(a)+bf(a)$$

$$x[f(a)-f(b)]=bf(a)-af(b)$$

$$\therefore \quad x_1=\frac{af(b)-bf(a)}{f(b)-f(a)}$$

This value of $x_1$ gives an approximate value of the root of $f(x)=0$. $(a<x_1<b)$

Now $f(x_1)$ and $f(a)$ are of opposite signs or $f(x_1)$ and $f(b)$ are of opposite signs.

If $f(x_1).f(a)<0$, then $x_2$ lies between $x_1$ and $a$.

$$\text{Hence } x_2=\frac{af(x_1)-x_1f(a)}{f(x_1)-f(a)}$$

In the same way, we get $x_3, x_4, \ldots$

This sequence $x_1, x_2, x_3, \ldots.$ will converge to the required root. In practice, we get $x_i$ and $x_{i+1}$ such that $|x_i-x_{i+1}|<\varepsilon$, the required accuracy.

### 3·3·1. Geometrical interpretation

If $A(a, f(a))$ and $B(b, f(b))$ are two points on $y=f(x)$ such that $f(a)$ and $f(b)$ are opposite in sign, then the chord $AB$ meets $x$-axis at $x=x_1$. This $x_1$ is the approximate root of $f(x)=0$. Now $c(x_1, f(x_1))$ is on the curve.

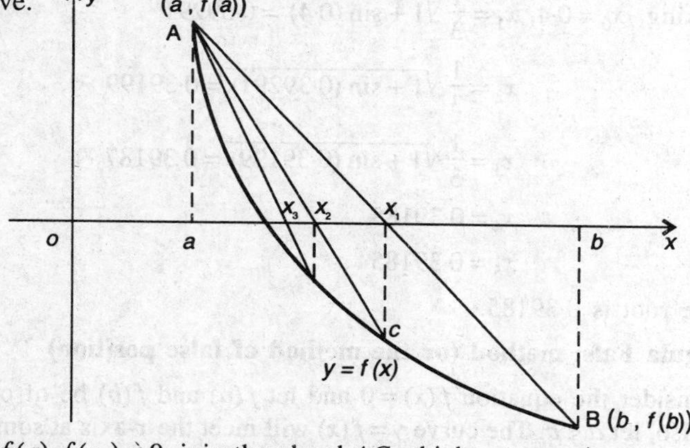


If $f(a).f(x_1)<0$, join the chord $AC$ which cuts $x$-axis at $x=x_2$. Then $x_2$ is the second approximate root of $f(x)=0$. This process is continued until we get the root to the desired accuracy.

*The order of convergence of Regula Falsi method is 1·618.* (This may be assumed.)

**Example 1.** *Solve for a positive root of $x^3 - 4x + 1 = 0$ by Regula Falsi method.*

**Solution.** Let $f(x) = x^3 - 4x + 1 = 0$

$$f(1) = -2 = -ve\ ;\ f(2) = 1 = +ve\ ,\ f(0) = 1 = +ve$$

$\therefore$ a root lies between 0 and 1

Another root lies between 1 and 2

We shall find the root that lies between 0 and 1

Here $a = 0,\ b = 1$

$$x_1 = \frac{af(b) - bf(a)}{f(b) - f(a)} = \frac{0 \times f(1) - 1 \times f(0)}{f(1) - f(0)} = \frac{-1}{-2-1} = 0{\cdot}333333$$

$$f(x_1) = f\left(\frac{1}{3}\right) = \frac{1}{27} - \frac{4}{3} + 1 = -0{\cdot}2963$$

Now $f(0)$ and $f\left(\frac{1}{3}\right)$ are opposite in sign.

Hence the root lies between 0 and 1/3.

Hence $$x_2 = \frac{0.f\left(\frac{1}{3}\right) - \frac{1}{3}f(0)}{f\left(\frac{1}{3}\right) - f(0)}$$

$$x_2 = \frac{-\frac{1}{3}}{-1{\cdot}2963} = 0{\cdot}25714$$

Now $f(x_2) = f(0{\cdot}25714) = -0{\cdot}011558 = -ve$

$\therefore$ The root lies between 0 and 0·25714

$$x_3 = \frac{0 \times f(0{\cdot}25714) - 0{\cdot}25714 f(0)}{f(0{\cdot}25714) - f(0)}$$

$$= \frac{-0{\cdot}25714}{-1{\cdot}011558} = 0{\cdot}25420$$

$$f(x_3) = f(0{\cdot}25420) = -0{\cdot}0003742$$

$\therefore$ The root lies between 0 and 0·25420

$\therefore$ $$x_4 = \frac{0 \times f(0{\cdot}25420) - 0{\cdot}25420 \times f(0)}{f(0{\cdot}25420) - f(0)}$$

$$= \frac{-0{\cdot}25420}{-1{\cdot}0003742} = 0{\cdot}25410$$

$$f(x_4) = f(0{\cdot}25410) = -0{\cdot}000012936$$

The root lies between 0 and 0·25410

$$x_5 = \frac{0 \times f(0{\cdot}25410) - 0{\cdot}25410 \times f(0)}{f(0{\cdot}25410) - f(0)}$$

$$= \frac{-0{\cdot}25410}{-1{\cdot}000012936} = 0{\cdot}25410$$

Hence the root is 0·25410.

**Example 2.** *Find an approximate root of x $log_{10}$ x – 1·2 = 0 by False position method.* [*BR. Ap. '93*]

**Solution.** Let $f(x) = x \log_{10} x - 1{\cdot}2$

$$f(1) = -1{\cdot}2 = -ve;\ f(2) = 2 \times 0{\cdot}30103 - 1{\cdot}2 = -0{\cdot}597940$$

$$f(3) = 3 \times 0{\cdot}47712 - 1{\cdot}2 = 0{\cdot}231364 = +ve$$

Hence a root lies between 2 and 3.

$$\therefore \quad x_1 = \frac{2f(3) - 3f(2)}{f(3) - f(2)} = \frac{2 \times 0{\cdot}23136 - 3 \times (-0{\cdot}59794)}{0{\cdot}23136 + 0{\cdot}59794} = 2{\cdot}721014$$

$$f(x_1) = f(2{\cdot}7210) = -0{\cdot}017104$$

The root lies between $x_1$ and 3.

$$x_2 = \frac{x_1 \times f(3) - 3 \times f(x_1)}{f(3) - f(x_1)}$$

$$= \frac{2{\cdot}721014 \times 0{\cdot}231364 - 3 \times (-0{\cdot}017104)}{0{\cdot}23136 + 0{\cdot}017104}$$

$$= \frac{0{\cdot}68084}{0{\cdot}24846} = 2{\cdot}740211$$

$$f(x_2) = f(2{\cdot}7402) = 2{\cdot}7402 \times \log(2{\cdot}7402) - 1{\cdot}2$$

$$= -0{\cdot}00038905$$

$\therefore$ The root lies between 2·740211 and 3

$$\therefore \quad x_3 = \frac{2{\cdot}7402 \times f(3) - 3 \times f(2{\cdot}7402)}{f(3) - f(2{\cdot}7402)}$$

$$= \frac{2{\cdot}7402 \times 0{\cdot}23136 + 3 \times 0{\cdot}00038905}{0{\cdot}23136 + 0{\cdot}00038905}$$

$$= \frac{0{\cdot}63514}{0{\cdot}23175} = 2{\cdot}740627$$

$$f(2{\cdot}7406) = 0{\cdot}00011998$$

$\therefore$ The root lies between 2·740211 and 2·740627

$$x_4 = \frac{2{\cdot}7402 \times f(2{\cdot}7406) - 2{\cdot}7406 \times f(2{\cdot}7402)}{f(2{\cdot}7406) - f(2{\cdot}7402)}$$

$$= \frac{2{\cdot}7402 \times 0{\cdot}00011998 + 2{\cdot}7406 \times 0{\cdot}00038905}{0{\cdot}00011998 + 0{\cdot}00038905}$$

$$= \frac{0{\cdot}0013950}{0{\cdot}00050903} = 2{\cdot}7405$$

Hence the root is 2·7405.

**Example 3.** *Find the positive root of $x^3 = 2x + 5$ by False Position method.* [*BR Ap. 94*]

**Solution.** Let $f(x) = x^3 - 2x - 5 = 0$

There is only one positive root by Descarte's rule of signs.

$$f(2) = 8 - 9 = -1 = -ve \; ; \; f(3) = 16 = +ve$$

$\therefore$ the positive root lies between 2 and 3. It is closer to 2 also.

$$x_1 = \frac{af(b) - bf(a)}{f(b) - f(a)} = \frac{2 \times f(3) - 3 \times f(2)}{f(3) - f(2)}$$

$$= \frac{32 + 3}{17} = 2{\cdot}058824$$

$$f(x_1) = f(2{\cdot}058824) = -0{\cdot}390795$$

$\therefore$ The root lies between 2·058824 and 3

$$x_2 = \frac{2{\cdot}058824 \times f(3) - 3 \times f(2{\cdot}058824)}{f(3) - f(2{\cdot}058824)}$$

$$= \frac{34{\cdot}113569}{16{\cdot}390795} = 2{\cdot}081264$$

$$f(x_2') = f(2{\cdot}081264) = -0{\cdot}147200$$

$\therefore$ The root lies between 2·081264 and 3

$$x_3 = \frac{2{\cdot}081264 \times 16 - 3 \times (-0{\cdot}147200)}{16 + 0{\cdot}147200} = 2{\cdot}089639$$

$$f(x_3) = f(2{\cdot}089639) = -0{\cdot}054679$$

The root lies between 2·089639 and 3

$$\therefore \qquad x_4 = \frac{2{\cdot}089639 \times f(3) - 3 \times f(2{\cdot}089639)}{f(3) - f(2{\cdot}089639)} = 2{\cdot}092740$$

$$f(x_4) = f(2{\cdot}09274) = -0{\cdot}020198$$

$\therefore$ The root lies between 2·09274 and 3

$$x_5 = \frac{2{\cdot}09274 \times 16 + 3 \times (0{\cdot}020198)}{16{\cdot}020198} = 2{\cdot}093884$$

$$f(x_5) = f(2{\cdot}093884) = -0{\cdot}007447$$

The root lies between 2·093884 and 3

$$x_6 = \frac{2{\cdot}093884 \times 16 + 3 \times 0{\cdot}007447}{16{\cdot}007447} = 2{\cdot}094306$$

$$f(x_6') = f(2{\cdot}094306) = -0{\cdot}002740$$

$\therefore$ The root lies between 2·094306 and 3

$$x_7 = \frac{2{\cdot}094306 \times 16 - 3 \times (-0{\cdot}002740)}{16{\cdot}002740} = 2{\cdot}094461$$

Similarly, $x_8 = 2{\cdot}0945$ correct to 4 decimal places.

**Example 4.** *Solve for a positive root of x – cos x = 0 by Regula Falsi method.*

**Solution.** Let $f(x) = x - \cos x$

$$f(0) = -1 = -ve\ ,\ f(1) = 1 - \cos 1 = 0{\cdot}459698 = +ve$$

$\therefore$ a root lies between 0 and 1

$$\therefore \qquad x_1 = \frac{0 \times f(1) - 1\, f(0)}{f(1) - f(0)}$$

$$= \frac{1}{1{\cdot}459688} = 0{\cdot}685078$$

$$f(0{\cdot}685078) = 0{\cdot}685078 - \cos(0{\cdot}685078) = -\,0{\cdot}089292$$

The root lies between 0·685078 and 1

$$x_2 = \frac{0{\cdot}685078 \times f(1) - 1 \times f(0{\cdot}685078)}{f(1) - f(0{\cdot}685078)}$$

$$= \frac{0{\cdot}404221}{0{\cdot}548990} = 0{\cdot}736299$$

$$f(x_2) = 0{\cdot}736299 - \cos(0{\cdot}736299) = -\,0{\cdot}004660$$

$\therefore$ The root lies between 0·736299 and 1

$$x_3 = \frac{0{\cdot}736299 \times 0{\cdot}459698 + 1 \times 0{\cdot}004660}{0{\cdot}459698 + 0{\cdot}004660} = 0{\cdot}738945$$

$$f(0{\cdot}738945) = -\,0{\cdot}000235$$

The root lies between 0·738945 and 1

$$x_4 = \frac{0{\cdot}738945 \times 0{\cdot}459698 + 1 \times 0{\cdot}000235}{0{\cdot}459698 + 0{\cdot}000235}$$

$$= \frac{0{\cdot}339927}{0{\cdot}459933} = 0{\cdot}739079$$

The root is 0·7391 correct to 4 decimal places.

**Example 5.** *Solve the equation x tan x = – 1 by Regula Falsi method starting with a = 2·5 and b = 3 correct to 3 decimal places.*

[*MS. Nov. 1991*]

**Solution.** Let $f(x) = x \tan x + 1$

$$f(2{\cdot}5) = 2{\cdot}5 \tan(2{\cdot}5) + 1 = -\,0{\cdot}867556$$

$$f(3) = 3 \tan 3 + 1 = 0{\cdot}572360$$

$\therefore$ a root lies between 2·5 and 3

Take $a = 2{\cdot}5$ and $b = 3$

Now, $$x_1 = \frac{2{\cdot}5\, f(3) - 3\, f(2{\cdot}5)}{f(3) - f(2{\cdot}5)}$$

$$= \frac{2{\cdot}5 \times 0{\cdot}572360 + 3 \times 0{\cdot}867556}{0{\cdot}572360 + 0{\cdot}867556}$$

$$= \frac{4.033568}{1.439916} = 2.801252$$

$$f(x_1) = f(2.801252) = 0.008020 = +ve$$

$\therefore$ The root lies between 2·5 and 2·801252

$$x_2 = \frac{2.5 f(2.801252) - 2.801252 f(2.5)}{f(2.801252) - f(2.5)}$$

$$= \frac{2.450293}{0.875576} = 2.806513$$

$$f(2.806513) = 0.022743$$

$\therefore$ The root lies between 2·5 and 2·806513

$$x_3 = \frac{2.5 \times 0.022743 + 2.806513 \times 0.867556}{0.022743 + 0.867556} = 2.798683$$

$$f(x_3) = 0.000831$$

The root lies between $x_4$ = 2·798683 and 2·5

$$x_4 = \frac{2.5 f(2.798683) - (2.798383) f(2.5)}{0.000831 + 0.867556}$$

$$= \frac{2.429831}{0.868387} = 2.7981$$

Hence the root is 2·798 (correct to 3 decimals).

**Example 6.** *Find a positive root of $xe^x = 2$ by the method of False position.* [*BR. Ap.* '93]

**Solution.** Let $f(x) = xe^x - 2$ ; $f(0) = -2 = -ve$ ;

$f(1) = 0.718282 = +ve$

$\therefore$ A root lies between 0 and 1; Take $a = 0,\ b = 1$

$$x_1 = \frac{af(b) - bf(a)}{f(b) - f(a)} = \frac{0 - f(0)}{f(1) - f(0)} = \frac{2}{2.718282} = 0.735759$$

$$f(x_1) = f(0.735759) = -0.464423 = -ve$$

$\therefore$ The root lies between 0·735759 and 1

$$x_2 = \frac{0.735759 \times f(1) - 1 \times f(0.735759)}{f(1) - f(0.735759)} = 0.839521$$

$$f(x_2) = f(0.839521) = -0.056293$$

$\therefore$ The root lies between 0·839521 and 1

$$x_3 = \frac{0.839521 f(1) - 1 \times f(0.839521)}{0.718282 + 0.056293}$$

$$= 0.851184$$

$$f(x_3) = f(0.851184) = -0.006171$$

$\therefore$ The root lies between 0·851184 and 1

Hence, $x_4 = \dfrac{0{\cdot}851184 \times f(1) - 1 \times f(0{\cdot}851184)}{f(1) - f(0{\cdot}851184)} = 0{\cdot}852452$

Now the root lies between 0·852452 and 1

In the same way, $x_5 = 0{\cdot}85261$, $x_6 = 0{\cdot}85261$

Hence the required root is 0·85261.

## EXERCISE 3.1

1. Find a positive root of the following equations by bisection method :

   (i) $x^3 - 4x - 9 = 0$ (ii) $x^3 + 1{\cdot}2x^2 = 4x + 4{\cdot}8$

   (iii) $e^x = 3x$ (iv) $3x = \sqrt{1 + \sin x}$

   (v) $x^3 + 3x - 1 = 0$ (vi) $3x = \cos x + 1$

   (vii) $x^3 + x^2 - 1 = 0$ (viii) $2x = 3 + \cos x$

2. Find a positive root of the above equations by iteration method and Regula Falsi method.

3. Solve the following by iteration method :

   (i) $\sin x = \dfrac{x+1}{x-1}$ (ii) $3x - \cos x - 2 = 0$

   (iii) $3x = 6 + \log_{10} x$ (iv) $x^3 + x + 1 = 0$

   (v) $2x - \log_{10} x = 7$ (vi) $x^3 + 2x^2 + 10x = 20$

   (vii) $2 \sin x = x$ (viii) $3x + \sin x = e^x$

   (ix) $x^3 + x^2 = 100$ (x) $\cos x = 3x - 1$

4. Solve the following for a positive root by False position method :

   (i) $xe^x = 3$ (ii) $4x = e^x$

   (iii) $x \log_{10} x = 1{\cdot}2$ (iv) $\tan x + \tanh x = 0$

   (v) $e^{-x} = \sin x$ (vi) $x^3 - 5x - 7 = 0$

   (vii) $x^3 + 2x^2 + 10x - 20 = 0$ (viii) $2x - \log_{10} x = 7$

   (ix) $xe^x = \cos x$ (x) $x^3 - 5x + 1 = 0$

   (xi) $e^x = 3x$ (xii) $x^2 - \log_e x = 12$

   (xiii) $3x - \cos x = 1$ (xiv) $2x - 3 \sin x = 5$

   (xv) $2x = \cos x + 3$

## 3·4. Newton-Raphson method (or Newton's method)

Given an approximate value of a root of an equation, a better and closer approximation to the root can be found by using an iterative process called Newton's method or Newton-Raphson method.

Let $\alpha_0$ be an *approximate value* of a root of the equation $f(x) = 0$

Let $\alpha$ be the exact root nearer to $\alpha_0$

Then $\alpha = \alpha_0 + h$ where $h$ is very small, positive or negative.

$\therefore \quad f(\alpha) = f(\alpha_0 + h) = 0$ since $\alpha$ is the exact root of $f(x) = 0$

By Taylor expansion,

$$f(\alpha) = f(\alpha_0 + h) = f(\alpha_0) + h f'(\alpha_0) + \frac{h^2}{2!} f''(\alpha_0) + \cdots = 0,$$

*i.e.,* If $h$ is small, neglecting $h^2, h^3, \ldots$ etc, we get

$$f(\alpha_0) + hf'(\alpha_0) \approx 0$$

$$\therefore \qquad h \approx -\frac{f(\alpha_0)}{f'(\alpha_0)} \quad \text{if} \quad f'(\alpha_0) \neq 0$$

$$\therefore \qquad \alpha = \alpha_0 + h = \alpha_0 - \frac{f(\alpha_0)}{f'(\alpha_0)} \text{ approximately}$$

Let this value be $\alpha_1$

$$\therefore \qquad \alpha_1 = \alpha_0 - \frac{f(\alpha_0)}{f'(\alpha_0)}$$

$\alpha_1$ is a better approximate root than $\alpha_0$

Starting with this $\alpha_1$, we get

$$\alpha_2 = \alpha_1 - \frac{f(\alpha_1)}{f'(\alpha_1)} \text{ which is still better.}$$

Continuing like this, we iterate this process until $|\alpha_{r+1} - \alpha_r|$ is less than the quantity desired.

$$\therefore \qquad \alpha_{r+1} = \alpha_r - \frac{f(\alpha_r)}{f'(\alpha_r)}, \quad r = 0, 1, 2, \ldots$$

This is the iterative formula of Newton-Raphson method.

### 3·4·1. Geometrical meaning of Newton's method

Let $x = \alpha$ be an exact root of $f(x) = 0$. The curve cuts the $x$-axis at $P$ whose $x$-coordinate is $\alpha$. The $x$ coordinates of the points where $y = f(x)$ cuts the $x$-axis are the real roots of $f(x) = 0$.

Now, let $\alpha_0$ be an approximate root of $f(x) = 0$. The ordinate at

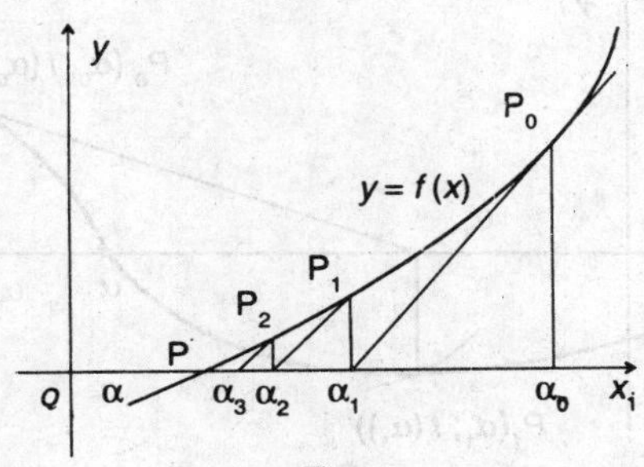


Fig.

$x = \alpha_0$ meets the curve at $P_0(\alpha_0, f(\alpha_0))$. The slope of the tangent at $P_0$ to the curve is $f'(\alpha_0)$. The equation of the tangent at $P_0$ to the curve is

$$y - f(\alpha_0) = f'(\alpha_0)(x - \alpha_0)$$

This cuts the $x$-axis at $x = \alpha_1$. To get the point, solve the equation of the tangent at $P_0$ with $y = 0$.

$$\therefore \quad -f(\alpha_0) = f'(\alpha_0)(x - \alpha_0)$$

$$x - \alpha_0 = \frac{-f(\alpha_0)}{f'(\alpha_0)}$$

$$\therefore \quad x = \alpha_1 = \alpha_0 - \frac{f(\alpha_0)}{f'(\alpha_0)}$$

This is exactly the formula got by Newton's method also.

This $\alpha_1$ is nearer to $\alpha$ than $\alpha_0$

Now $P_1(\alpha_1, f(\alpha_1))$ is on the curve.

The tangent at $P_1$ to the curve meets the $x$-axis at $x = \alpha_2$ where

$$\alpha_2 = \alpha_1 - \frac{f(\alpha_1)}{f'(\alpha_1)}$$

Now $P_2(\alpha_2, f(\alpha_2))$ is on the curve and the tangent at $P_2$ meets the $x$-axis at $x = \alpha_3$ where $\alpha_3 = \alpha_2 - \dfrac{f(\alpha_2)}{f'(\alpha_2)}$. Thus we get a sequence $\alpha_0, \alpha_1, \alpha_2, \ldots$ and every time we get a better approximation. The limit of this sequence is $\alpha$.

**Note 1.** The method is also called *method of tangents.*

**2.** The starting approximate value $\alpha_0$ must be nearer to the exact value $\alpha$. Then only the sequence $\alpha_1, \alpha_2, \alpha_3 \ldots$ will converge (approaches to the value $\alpha$). If the sequence $\alpha_1, \alpha_2, \alpha_3, \ldots$ does not converge, this method of Newton is of no use. For example, the following figure indicates the diverging nature of the sequence $\alpha_1, \alpha_2, \alpha_3, \ldots$

**3·4·2. Criterion for the convergence in Newton-Raphson method**

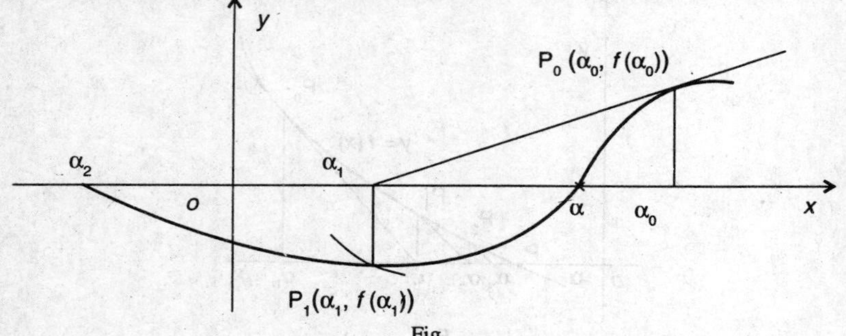


Fig.

Here, in Newton's method,

$$x_{i+1} = x_i - \frac{f(x_i)}{f'(x_i)}$$

This is really an iteration method where

$$x_{i+1} = \phi(x_i) \text{ and } \phi(x_i) = x_i - \frac{f(x_i)}{f'(x_i)}$$

Hence the equation is

$$x = \phi(x) \text{ where } \phi(x) = x - \frac{f(x)}{f'(x)}$$

The sequence $x_1, x_2, x_3,...$ converges to the exact value if $|\phi'(x)| < 1$

*i.e.,* if $\left| 1 - \frac{[f'(x)]^2 - f(x) f''(x)}{[f'(x)]^2} \right| < 1$

*i.e.,* if $\left| \frac{f(x) f''(x)}{[f'(x)]^2} \right| < 1$

*i.e.,* if $|f(x) f''(x)| < [f'(x)]^2$ ...(1)

This is the criterion for the convergence. The interval containing $\alpha$ should be selected in which (1) is satisfied.

**3·4·3. Order of convergence of Newton's method**

Let $\alpha$ be the root of $f(x) = 0$

Let $e_i$ be the error at the $i$th stage of iteration.

*i.e.,* $e_i = x_i - \alpha$ where $x_i$ is the approximate root at the $i$th iteration.

If $f(x) = 0$ is expressed as $x = \phi(x)$, then $x_{i+1} = \phi(x_i)$

$$x_{i+1} = \phi(x_i)$$

$$= \phi(\alpha + e_i)$$

$$= \phi(\alpha) + \frac{e_i}{1!} \phi'(\alpha) + \frac{e_i^2}{2!} \phi''(\alpha) + \cdots$$

$$= \alpha + \frac{e_i}{1!} \phi'(\alpha) + \frac{e_i^2}{2!} \phi''(\alpha) + \cdots$$

$$x_{i+1} - \alpha = \frac{e_i \phi'(\alpha)}{1!} + \frac{e_i^2}{2!} \phi''(\alpha) + \cdots$$

*i.e.,* $$e_{i+1} = \frac{e_i \phi'(\alpha)}{1!} + \frac{e_i^2}{2!} \phi''(\alpha) + \cdots$$ ...(1)

In Newton-Raphson method, $\phi(x) = x - \frac{f(x)}{f'(x)}$

$$\phi'(x) = \frac{f(x) f''(x)}{[f'(x)]^2}$$

$$\phi'(\alpha) = 0 \qquad \text{since } f(\alpha) = 0$$

$$\phi''(x) = \frac{[f'(x)]^2 \{f(x) f'''(x) + f'(x) f''(x)\} - 2f(x)[f''(x)]^2 f'(x)}{[f'(x)]^4}$$

$$\phi''(\alpha) = \frac{f''(\alpha)}{f'(\alpha)} \qquad \text{since } f(\alpha) = 0$$

$\therefore$ (1) becomes,

$$e_{i+1} = \frac{e_i^2}{2} \frac{f''(\alpha)}{f'(\alpha)} \qquad \text{omitting higher power of } e_i$$

$\therefore$ The convergence is quadratic and is of order 2.

**Note 1.** The choice of $\alpha_0$ is very important for the convergence.

**2.** When $f'(x)$ is very large, the correct values of root can be found out with minimum number of iterations.

**3.** If $f(a)$ and $f(b)$ are of opposite signs, a root of $f(x) = 0$ lies between $a$ and $b$. This idea can be used to fix an approximate root.

**4.** The error at any stage is proportional to the square of the error in the previous stage.

**Example 1.** *Find the positive root of $f(x) = 2x^3 - 3x - 6 = 0$ by Newton-Raphson method correct to five decimal places.*

**Solution.** Let $f(x) = 2x^3 - 3x - 6$ ; $f'(x) = 6x^2 - 3$

$f(1) = 2 - 3 - 6 = -7 = -ve$ and $f(2) = 16 - 6 - 6 = 4 = +ve$

$\therefore$ a root lies between 1 and 2

By Descarte's rule of sign, we can prove that there is only one positive root.

Take $\alpha_0 = 2$

$$\therefore \qquad \alpha_1 = \alpha_0 - \frac{f(\alpha_0)}{f'(\alpha_0)} = \alpha_0 - \frac{2\alpha_0^3 - 3\alpha_0 - 6}{6\alpha_0^2 - 3} = \frac{4\alpha_0^3 + 6}{6\alpha_0^2 - 3}$$

$$\alpha_{i+1} = \frac{4\alpha_i^3 + 6}{6\alpha_i^2 - 3}$$

$$\alpha_1 = \frac{4(2)^2 + 6}{6(2)^2 - 3} = \frac{38}{21} = 1{\cdot}809524$$

$$\alpha_2 = \frac{4(1{\cdot}809524)^3 + 6}{6(1{\cdot}809524)^2 - 3} = \frac{29{\cdot}700256}{16{\cdot}646263} = 1{\cdot}784200$$

$$\alpha_3 = \frac{4(1{\cdot}784200)^3 + 6}{6(1{\cdot}784200)^2 - 3} = \frac{28{\cdot}719072}{16{\cdot}100218} = 1{\cdot}783769$$

$$\alpha_4 = \frac{4(1{\cdot}783769)^3 + 6}{6(1{\cdot}783769)^2 - 3} = \frac{28{\cdot}702612}{16{\cdot}090991} = 1{\cdot}783769$$

The better approximate root is 1·783769

**Example 2.** *Using Newton's method, find the root between 0 and 1 of $x^3 = 6x - 4$ correct to 5 decimal places.*

**Solution.** Let $f(x) = x^3 - 6x + 4$; $f(0) = 4 = +ve$ ; $f(1) = -1 = -ve$

$\therefore$ a root lies between 0 and 1

This root is nearer to 1. Take $\alpha_0 = 1$

$$f'(x) = 3x^2 - 6$$

$$x - \frac{f(x)}{f'(x)} = x - \frac{3x^3 - 6x + 4}{3x^2 - 6} = \frac{2x^3 - 4}{3x^2 - 6}$$

$$\therefore \quad \alpha_1 = \frac{2\alpha_0^3 - 4}{3\alpha_0^2 - 6} = \frac{2-4}{3-6} = \frac{2}{3} = 0{\cdot}66666666$$

$$\alpha_2 = \frac{2\left(\frac{2}{3}\right)^3 - 4}{3\left(\frac{2}{3}\right)^2 - 6} = 0{\cdot}73015873$$

$$\alpha_3 = \frac{2(0{\cdot}73015873)^3 - 4}{3(0{\cdot}73015873)^2 - 6} = \frac{3{\cdot}22145837}{4{\cdot}40060469} = 0{\cdot}73204903$$

$$\alpha_4 = \frac{2(0{\cdot}73204903)^3 - 4}{3(0{\cdot}73204903)^2 - 6} = \frac{3{\cdot}21539602}{4{\cdot}39231265} = 0{\cdot}73205081$$

$\therefore$ The root is 0·73205 correct to 5 decimal places.

**Example 3.** *Find the real positive root of $3x - \cos x - 1 = 0$ by Newton's method correct to 6 decimal places.* [*BR. Ap. '93*]

**Solution.** Let $f(x) = 3x - \cos x - 1$; $f(0) = -2 = -ve$

$$f(1) = 3 - \cos 1 - 1 = 2 - \cos 1 = +ve$$

$\therefore$ a root lies between 0 and 1

$$f'(x) = 3 + \sin x$$

$$x - \frac{f(x)}{f'(x)} = x - \frac{3x - \cos x - 1}{3 + \sin x} = \frac{x \sin x + \cos x + 1}{3 + \sin x}$$

$$x_{i+1} = x_i - \frac{f(x_i)}{f'(x_i)}$$

$\therefore$ take $\alpha_0 = 0{\cdot}5$

$$\therefore \quad \alpha_1 = \frac{0{\cdot}5 \sin(0{\cdot}5) + \cos(0{\cdot}5) + 1}{3 + \sin(0{\cdot}5)}$$

$$= \frac{2{\cdot}11729533}{3{\cdot}479425539} = 0{\cdot}608518649$$

$$\alpha_2 = \frac{0{\cdot}608518649 \times \sin(0{\cdot}608518649) + \cos(0{\cdot}608518649) + 1}{3 + \sin(0{\cdot}608518649)}$$

$$= \frac{2{\cdot}16835703}{3{\cdot}57165265} = 0{\cdot}607101878$$

$$\alpha_3 = \frac{0{\cdot}607101878 \times \sin(0{\cdot}607101878) + \cos(0{\cdot}607101878) + 1}{3 + \sin(0{\cdot}607101878)}$$

$$= \frac{2{\cdot}16765013}{3{\cdot}57048962} = 0{\cdot}607101648$$

$\therefore$ The root is 0·607102 correct to six decimals.

**Note.** If we have started with $\alpha_0 = 0{\cdot}6$, the convergence is faster.

**Example 4.** *Find the positive root of $x = \cos x$ using Newton's method.*

**Solution.** Let $f(x) = x - \cos x$

$$f(0) = -1 = -ve\ ;\ f(1) = 1 - \cos 1 = 0{\cdot}459697$$

$\therefore$ a root lies between 0 and 1 and it is closer to 1. Therefore, take $\alpha_0 = 0{\cdot}7$.

$$f'(x) = 1 + \sin x$$

$$x - \frac{f(x)}{f'(x)} = x - \frac{x - \cos x}{1 + \sin x} = \frac{x \sin x + \cos x}{1 + \sin x}$$

$$x_{i+1} = \frac{x_i \sin x_i + \cos x_i}{1 + \sin x_i}$$

$$\alpha_1 = \frac{0{\cdot}7 \sin(0{\cdot}7) + \cos(0{\cdot}7)}{1 + \sin(0{\cdot}7)} = \frac{1{\cdot}21579457}{1{\cdot}64421769} = 0{\cdot}739436499$$

$$\alpha_2 = \frac{0{\cdot}739436499 \times \sin(0{\cdot}739436499) + \cos(0{\cdot}739436499)}{1 + \sin(0{\cdot}739436499)}$$

$$= \frac{1{\cdot}23713372}{1{\cdot}67387168} = 0{\cdot}739085162$$

$$\alpha_3 = \frac{1{\cdot}23694179}{1{\cdot}67361205} = 0{\cdot}739085136$$

$\therefore$ Correct value of the root is 0·7390851.

**Example 5.** *Find an iterative formula to find $\sqrt{N}$ (where N is a positive number) and hence find $\sqrt{5}$.*

**Solution.** $x = \sqrt{N}$ $\therefore$ $x^2 - N = 0$. Let $f(x) = x^2 - N$; $f'(x) = 2x$

$$\alpha_{i+1} = \alpha_i - \frac{\alpha_i^2 - N}{2\alpha_i} = \alpha_i - \frac{\alpha_i}{2} + \frac{N}{2\alpha_i} = \frac{1}{2}\left(\alpha_i + \frac{N}{\alpha_i}\right)$$

$\therefore$ $\alpha_{i+1} = \frac{1}{2}\left(\alpha_i + \frac{N}{\alpha_i}\right)$ is the iterative formula to find $\sqrt{N}$.

To find $\sqrt{5}$, put $N = 5$

Also $x = \sqrt{5}$ lies between 2 and 3. Take $\alpha_0 = 2$

$$\therefore \quad \alpha_1 = \frac{1}{2}\left(\alpha_0 + \frac{5}{\alpha_0}\right) = \frac{1}{2}\left(2 + \frac{5}{2}\right) = 2{\cdot}25$$

$$\alpha_2 = \frac{1}{2}\left(2{\cdot}25 + \frac{5}{2{\cdot}25}\right) = 2{\cdot}23611111$$

$$\alpha_3 = \frac{1}{2}\left(2{\cdot}23611111 + \frac{5}{2{\cdot}23611111}\right) = 2{\cdot}23606798$$

Similarly, $\alpha_4 = \frac{1}{2}\left(\alpha_3 + \frac{5}{\alpha_3}\right) = 2{\cdot}23606798$

Hence the approximate value of $\sqrt{5}$ is 2·23606798.

**Example 6.** *Find an iterative formula to find the reciprocal of a given number N and hence find the value of* $\frac{1}{19}$

**Solution.** Let $x = \frac{1}{N} \quad \therefore \quad N = \frac{1}{x}$

Let $\quad f(x) = \frac{1}{x} - N = 0 \; ; \; f'(x) = -\frac{1}{x^2}$

$$x_{i+1} = x_i - \frac{f(x_i)}{f'(x_i)} = x_i - \frac{\frac{1}{x_i} - N}{\left(-\frac{1}{x_i^2}\right)}$$

$$= x_i + x_i^2\left(\frac{1}{x_i} - N\right) = 2x_i - Nx_i^2 = x_i\,(2 - Nx_i)$$

$\therefore \quad x_{i+1} = x_i\,(2 - Nx_i)$ is the iterative formula.

To find $\frac{1}{19}$, take $N = 19$

Further $\frac{1}{20} = 0{\cdot}05$ ; $\therefore$ take $\alpha_0 = 0{\cdot}05$

$$x_1 = 0{\cdot}05\,(2 - 19 \times 0{\cdot}05) = 0{\cdot}0525$$

$$x_2 = 0{\cdot}0525\,(2 - 19 \times 0{\cdot}0525) = 0{\cdot}05263125$$

$$x_3 = 0{\cdot}05263125\,(2 - 19 \times 0{\cdot}05263125)$$

$$= 0{\cdot}0526315789$$

Similarly $x_4 = 0{\cdot}0526315789$

Hence the value of $\frac{1}{19}$ is 0·0526315789.

**Example 7.** *Find the root of* $4x - e^x = 0$ *that lies between 2 and 3.*

**Solution.** Let $f(x) = 4x - e^x$

$$f(2) = 8 - e^2 = 0{\cdot}6109 = +ve$$

$$f(3) = 12 - e^3 = -8{\cdot}0855 = -ve$$

$\therefore$ a root lies between 2 and 3 and it is closer to 2.

$$x_{i+1} = x_i - \frac{f(x_i)}{f'(x_i)}$$

$$= x_i - \frac{4x_i - e^{x_i}}{4 - e^{x_i}} = \frac{e^{x_i}(1 - x_i)}{4 - e^{x_i}}$$

Take $\alpha_0 = 2$

$$\alpha_1 = \frac{e^2(1-2)}{4 - e^2} = 2{\cdot}18026963$$

$$\alpha_2 = \frac{10{\cdot}4438422}{4{\cdot}87019074} = 2{\cdot}14444213$$

$$\alpha_3 = \frac{9{\cdot}77041972}{4{\cdot}53727722} = 2{\cdot}15336627$$

$$\alpha_4 = \frac{9{\cdot}93487335}{4{\cdot}61380604} = 2{\cdot}15329237$$

$\therefore$ The root is approximately 2·1533 correct to 4 decimal places.

### 3·4·4. Generalised Newton's method

If $\alpha$ is a root of $f(x) = 0$ with multiplicity $p$, then the iteration formula will be

$$x_{n+1} = x_n - p\frac{f(x_n)}{f'(x_n)}$$

This means that $\frac{1}{p}f'(x_n)$ is the slope of the line through $(x_n, y_n)$ and intersecting the axis of $x$ at $(x_{n+1}, 0)$.

Since $\alpha$ is a root of $f(x) = 0$ with multiplicity $p$, it implies that $\alpha$ is also a root of $f'(x) = 0$ with multiplicity $(p-1)$ and it is a root of $f''(x) = 0$ with multiplicity $(p-2)$ and so on. Therefore

$$x_0 - p\frac{f(x_0)}{f'(x_0)}, \quad x_0 - (p-1)\frac{f'(x_0)}{f''(x_0)}, \quad x_0 - (p-2)\frac{f''(x_0)}{f'''(x_0)}$$

will all have the same value if the initial approximation $x_0$ is chosen close to the actual root.

**Example 8.** *Find the double root of* $x^3 - 5{\cdot}4x^2 + 9{\cdot}24x - 5{\cdot}096 = 0$ *given that it is nearer to 1·5.*

**Solution.** Let $f(x) = x^3 - 5{\cdot}4x^2 + 9{\cdot}24x - 5{\cdot}096$

$$f'(x) = 3x^2 - 10{\cdot}8x + 9{\cdot}24$$

$$x - \frac{pf(x)}{f'(x)} = x - \frac{2f(x)}{f'(x)}$$

$$= x - \frac{2(x^3 - 5{\cdot}4x^2 + 9{\cdot}24x - 5{\cdot}096)}{3x^2 - 10{\cdot}8x + 9{\cdot}24}$$

$$= \frac{x^3 - 9{\cdot}24x + 10{\cdot}192}{3x^2 - 10{\cdot}8x + 9{\cdot}24}$$

$$\therefore \qquad \alpha_{i+1} = \frac{\alpha_i^3 - 9{\cdot}24\,\alpha_i + 10{\cdot}192}{3\alpha_i^2 - 10{\cdot}8\,\alpha_i + 9{\cdot}24}$$

Take $\alpha_0 = 1{\cdot}5$

$\alpha_1 = 1{\cdot}3952,$ $\qquad \alpha_2 = 1{\cdot}3966$

$\alpha_3 = 1{\cdot}4024,$ $\qquad \alpha_4 = 1{\cdot}4211$ etc.

The root is approximately 1·4 correct to one decimal place.

## EXERCISE 3.2

Using Newton-Raphson method, solve the following:

**1.** Find the positive root of $x^3 - x - 1 = 0$

**2.** Find a positive root of $f(x) = \cos x - xe^x = 0$

**3.** Find a real root of $x^3 + 2x^2 + 50x + 7 = 0$

**4.** Find the value of $\frac{1}{31}$ using Newton-Raphson method.

**5.** Find a root of $x \log_{10} x = 4{\cdot}772393$

**6.** Find the positive root of $x - 2 \sin x = 0$

**7.** Find a real root of $x^3 + x + 1 = 0$

**8.** Find the cube root of 24 correct to 3 decimal places.

**9.** Find a real root of $x^3 - x - 2 = 0$

**10.** Find a positive root of $x^4 - x - 9 = 0$

**11.** Find a positive root of $2(x - 3) = \log_{10} x$

**12.** Find the value of $\sqrt{35}$

**13.** Find the cube root of 24

**14.** Solve for a positive root of $x^4 - x = 10$

**15.** Solve for a positive root of $x \tan x = 1{\cdot}28$

**16.** Solve for a positive root of $xe^x = 1$

**17.** Find a positive root of $x^3 - 5x + 3 = 0$

**18.** Evaluate $\sqrt{12}$ by Newton's method.

**19.** Find a +ve root of $\sqrt[4]{24}$ and $\sqrt[3]{17}$

**20.** Find a positive root of $\cos x = x^2$

**21.** Solve for a +ve root of $2x - 3 \sin x = 5$

**22.** Find a positive root of $e^{0 \cdot 4x} - 0 \cdot 4x = 9$

**23.** Find the smallest positive root of $x^3 - 2x + 0 \cdot 5 = 0$

**24.** Find a negative root of $\sin x = 1 + x^3$

**25.** Find a positive root of $xe^x = \cos x$

**26.** Find the negative root of $x^2 + 4 \sin x = 0$

**27.** Solve for positive root by Newton's method of $2x - \log_{10} x = 7$

**28.** Using generalised Newton-Raphson method, find the double root of $x^3 - x^2 - x + \quad = 0$ choosing $x_0 = 0 \cdot 8$

**29.** Find a root of $x^3 - 3x - 5 = 0$

**30.** Find a root of the equation $x \sin x + \cos x = 0$

**31.** Using Newton's method, show that the iteration formula for finding
(*i*) the *p*th root of *a* is

$$x_{n+1} = \frac{(p-1)\, x_n^{\,p} + a}{p x_n^{\,p-1}}$$

(*ii*) the reciprocal of the *p*th root of *a* is

$$x_{n+1} = \frac{x_n\, (p + 1 - a x_n^{\,p})}{p}$$

Hence find the values of $(10)^{1/3}$ and $\dfrac{1}{\sqrt{\sin(0 \cdot 5)}}$

## 3·5. Horner's method

This numerical method is employed to determine both the commensurable and the incommensurable real roots of a numerical polynomial equation. Firstly, we find the integral part of the root and then by every iteration, we find each decimal place value in succession.

Suppose a positive root of $f(x) = 0$ lies between $a$ and $a + 1$. (where $a$ is an integer)

Let that root be $a.a_1a_2a_3a_4...$

First, diminish the roots of $f(x) = 0$ by the integral part $a$ and let $\phi_1(x) = 0$ possess the root $0.a_1a_2a_3a_4...$

Secondly, multiply the roots of $\phi_1(x) = 0$ by 10 and let $\phi_2(x) = 0$ possess $a_1.a_2a_3a_4...$ as a root.

Thirdly, find the value of $a_1$ and then diminish the roots by $a_1$ and let $\phi_3(x) = 0$ possess a root $0.a_2a_3a_4...$

Now repeating the process we find $a_2, a_3, a_4, ...$ each time.

**Example 1.** *Find the positive root of $x^3 + 3x - 1 = 0$, correct to two decimal places, by Horner's method.*

**Solution.** Let $f(x) = x^3 + 3x - 1 = 0$

$f(0) = -ve$ ; $f(1) = +ve$. The positive root lies between 0 and 1.

Let it be $0.a_1a_2a_3...$

Since the integral part is zero, diminishing the root by the integral part is not necessary.

Therefore, multiply the roots by 10.

$\therefore \quad \phi_1(x) = x^3 + 300x - 1000 = 0$ has root $a_1.a_2a_3...$

$\phi_1(3) = -ve$ ; $\phi_1(4) = +ve \quad \therefore \quad a_1 = 3$

Now the root is $3.a_2a_3...$

Therefore, diminish root of $\phi_1(x) = 0$ by 3.

By synthetic division,

| | | | | |
|---|---|---|---|---|
| 3 | 1 | 0 | 300 | −1000 |
| | | 3 | 9 | 927 |
| 3 | 1 | 3 | 309 | − 73 |
| | | 3 | 18 | |
| 3 | 1 | 6 | 327 | |
| | | 3 | | |
| | 1 | 9 | | |

$\therefore \quad \phi_2(x) = x^3 + 9x^2 + 327x - 73 = 0$ has the root $0.a_2a_3...$ Multiply the roots of $\phi_2(x) = 0$ by 10.

$\phi_3(x) = x^3 + 90x^2 + 32700x - 73000 = 0$ has root $a_2.a_3a_4...$

Now, $\phi_3(2) = -ve$ and $\phi_3(3) = +ve \quad \therefore \quad a_2 = 2$

Therefore $\phi_3(x) = 0$ has a root $2.a_3a_4...$

Now diminish the roots of $\phi_3(x) = 0$ by 2.

| | | | | |
|---|---|---|---|---|
| 2 | 1 | 90 | 32700 | −73000 |
| | | 2 | 184 | 65768 |
| 2 | 1 | 92 | 32884 | − 7232 |
| | | 2 | 188 | |
| 2 | 1 | 94 | 33072 | |
| | | 2 | | |
| | 1 | 96 | | |

$\therefore \quad \phi_4(x) = x^3 + 96x^2 + 33072x - 7232 = 0$ has a root $0.a_3a_4...$

Multiply the roots of $\phi_4(x) = 0$ by 10

$\therefore$ $\phi_5(x) = x^3 + 960x^2 + 3307200 - 7232000 = 0$ has a root $a_3.a_4...$

$\phi_5(2) = -ve$, $\phi_5(3) = +ve$ $\therefore$ $a_3 = 2$

Hence the root is 0·322.....

$\therefore$ The root, correct to two decimal places, is 0·32.

**Example 2.** *Find the positive root between 1 and 2 which satisfies $x^3 - 3x + 1 = 0$ to 3 decimal places.*

**Solution.** Let $f(x) = x^3 - 3x + 1 = 0$

$f(1) = -ve$ ; $f(2) = +ve$

Therefore a root lies between 1 and 2. Let it be $1.a_1a_2a_3...$

The integral part is 1.

$\therefore$ Diminish the roots of $f(x) = 0$ by 1.

| | | | | |
|---|---|---|---|---|
| 1 | 1 | 0 | – 3 | 1 |
| | | 1 | 1 | – 2 |
| | 1 | 1 | – 2 | – 1 |
| | | 1 | 2 | |
| 1 | 1 | 2 | 0 | |
| | | 1 | | |
| | 1 | 3 | | |

$\phi_2(x) = x^3 + 3x^2 - 1 = 0$ has the root $0.a_1a_2a_3...$

Multiply the roots of $\phi_2(x) = 0$ by 10.

$\therefore$ $\phi_3(x) = x^3 + 30x^2 - 1000 = 0$ has root $a_1.a_2a_3..$

$\phi_3(5) = -ve$, $\phi_3(6) = +ve$ $\therefore$ $\boxed{a_1 = 5}$

$\therefore$ $\phi_3(x) = 0$ has a root $5.a_2a_3...$

Diminish the roots of $\phi_3(x) = 0$ by 5.

| | | | | |
|---|---|---|---|---|
| 5 | 1 | 30 | 0 | – 1000 |
| | | 5 | 175 | 875 |
| 5 | 1 | 35 | 175 | – 125 |
| | | 5 | 200 | |
| 5 | 1 | 40 | 375 | |
| | | 5 | | |
| | 1 | 45 | | |

$\therefore$ $x^3 + 45x^2 + 375x - 125 = 0$ has a root $0.a_2a_3...$

$\therefore$ Multiply the roots by 10

$_4(x) = x^3 + 450x^2 + 37500x - 125000 = 0$ has a root $a_2.a_3a_4..$

Now $\phi_4(3) = -\,ve,\;\; \phi_4(4) = +\,ve \quad \therefore \boxed{a_2 = 3}$

*i.e.*, $\phi_4(x) = 0$ has a root $3.a_3a_4...$

Now diminish the roots of $\phi_4(x) = 0$ by 3.

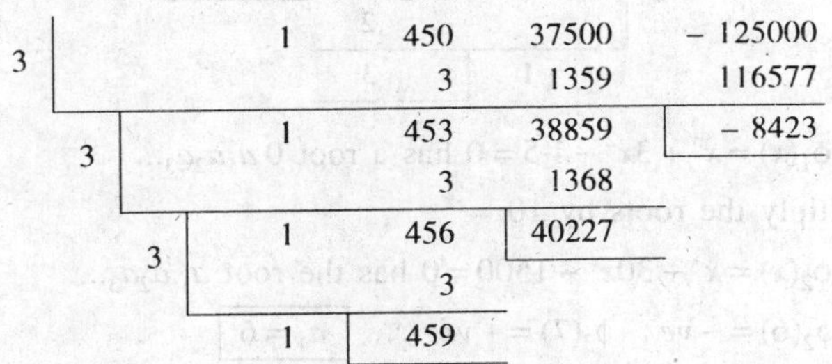

| | | | | |
|---|---|---|---|---|
| 3 | 1 | 450 | 37500 | – 125000 |
| | | 3 | 1359 | 116577 |
| 3 | 1 | 453 | 38859 | – 8423 |
| | | 3 | 1368 | |
| 3 | 1 | 456 | 40227 | |
| | | 3 | | |
| | 1 | 459 | | |

$\phi_5(x) = x^3 + 459x^2 + 40227x - 8423 = 0$ has the root $0.a_3a_4...$

$\therefore$ Multiply the roots of $\phi_5(x) = 0$ by 10.

$\therefore \;\; \phi_6(x) = x^3 + 4590x^2 + 4022700x - 8423000 = 0$ has the root $a_3.a_4a_5...$

$\phi_6(2) = -\,ve\;;\;\; \phi_3(3) = +\,ve \quad \therefore \boxed{a_3 = 2}$

Now diminish the roots of $\phi_6(x) = 0$ by 2.

| | | | | |
|---|---|---|---|---|
| 2 | 1 | 4590 | 4022700 | – 8423000 |
| | | 2 | 9184 | 8063768 |
| 2 | 1 | 4592 | 4031884 | – 359232 |
| | | 2 | 9188 | |
| 2 | 1 | 4594 | 4041072 | |
| | | 2 | | |
| | 1 | 4596 | | |

$\therefore \;\; \phi_7(x) = x^3 + 4596x^2 + 4041072x - 359232 = 0$ has the root $0.a_4a_5...$

The root is 1·532.

**Example 3.** *By Horner's method, find the root of* $x^3 - 3x^2 + 2{\cdot}5 = 0$ *that lies between 2 and 3.*

**Solution.** Let $f(x) = x^3 - 3x^2 + 2{\cdot}5 = 0$

$$f(2) = -\,ve\;;\;\; f(3) = +\,ve$$

$\therefore$ A root lies between 2 and 3. Let it be $2.a_1a_2a_3a_4...$

Diminish the roots of $f(x) = 0$ by 2.

| | | | | |
|---|---|---|---|---|
| 2 | 1 | – 3 | 0 | 2.5 |
| | | 2 | – 2 | – 4 |
| | 1 | – 1 | – 2 | – 1.5 |
| 2 | | 2 | 2 | |
| | 1 | 1 | 0 | |
| 2 | | 2 | | |
| | 1 | 3 | | |

$\therefore \quad \phi_1(x) = x^3 + 3x^2 - 1{\cdot}5 = 0$ has a root $0.a_1a_2a_3...$

Multiply the roots by 10.

$\therefore \quad \phi_2(x) = x^3 + 30x^2 - 1500 = 0$ has the root $a_1.a_2a_3...$

$\phi_2(6) = -ve\,; \quad \phi_3(7) = +ve \quad \therefore \quad \boxed{a_1 = 6}$

Now, diminish the roots of $\phi_2(x) = 0$ by 6.

| | | | | |
|---|---|---|---|---|
| 6 | 1 | 30 | 0 | – 1500 |
| | | 6 | 216 | 1296 |
| | 1 | 36 | 216 | – 204 |
| 6 | | 6 | 252 | |
| | 1 | 42 | 468 | |
| 6 | | 6 | | |
| | 1 | 48 | | |

$\therefore \quad \phi_3(x) = x^3 + 48x^2 + 468x - 204 = 0$ has a root $0.a_2a_3...$

$\therefore$ Multiply the roots by 10.

$\phi_4(x) = x^3 + 480x^2 + 46800x - 204000 = 0$ has root $a_2.a_3...$

$\phi_4(4) = -ve, \quad \phi_4(5) = +ve \quad \therefore \quad \boxed{a_2 = 4}$

Diminish the roots of $\phi_4(x) = 0$ by 4

| | | | | |
|---|---|---|---|---|
| 4 | 1 | 480 | 46800 | – 204000 |
| | | 4 | 1936 | 193944 |
| | 1 | 484 | 48736 | – 10056 |
| 4 | | 4 | 1952 | |
| | 1 | 488 | 50688 | |
| 4 | | 4 | | |
| | 1 | 492 | | |

$\therefore \quad x^3 + 492x^2 + 50688x - 10056 = 0$ has a root $0.a_3a_4...$

Multiply the roots by 10.

$$\phi_5(x) = x^3 + 4920x^2 + 5068800\,x - 10056000 = 0 \text{ has root } a_3.a_4...$$

$$\phi_5(1) = -ve, \quad \phi_5(2) = +ve \quad \therefore \quad \boxed{a_3 = 1}$$

Hence the root is 2·641...

**Note.** Another positive root of this equation is 1·168...

## EXERCISE 3.3

**1.** A sphere of pine wood, 2 metres in diameter, floating in water sinks to the depth of $h$ metre, given by $h^3 - 3h^2 + 2{\cdot}5 = 0$. Find the value of $h$ correct to two decimal places by Horner's method. *[MS.]*

**2.** Solve, for the root specified below, by Horner's method :

(*i*) $x^3 + 6x + 2 = 0$ whose root lies between 0 and $-1$

(*ii*) $x^3 - 2x^2 - 3x - 4 = 0$ whose root lies between 3 and 4

(*iii*) $x^3 - 8x - 40 = 0$ (positive root)

(*iv*) $h^3 + 3h^2 - 12h - 11 = 0$ (positive root)

(*v*) $x^3 - 6x - 18 = 0$ (positive root)

(*vi*) $x^3 - x = 9$ (positive root)

(*vii*) $10x^3 - 15x + 3 = 0$ that lies between 1 and 2

## 3·6. Graeffe's root squaring method

This is a direct method and it is used to find the roots of a polynomial equation with real coefficients, that is, equation of the form

$$a_0x^n + a_1x^{n-1} + a_2x^{n-2} + a_3x^{n-3} + \cdots + a_n = 0 \qquad ...(1)$$

where $a_i$'s are real.

The roots may be real, distinct or equal, or complex. We separate the roots of the equation (1), by forming another polynomial equation, by the method of root squaring process, whose roots are high powers of the roots of the equation (1).

The equation (1) is separated so that even powers of $x$ are on one side and odd powers of $x$ are on the other side; then squaring both sides, we get,

$$\left(a_0x^n + a_2x^{n-2} + a_4x^{n-4} + \cdots\right)^2 = \left(a_1x^{n-1} + a_3x^{x-3} + \cdots\right)^2$$

Simplifying, we get

$$a_0^2x^{2n} - \left(a_1^{\,2} - 2a_0a_2\right)x^{2n-2} + \left(a_2^{\,2} - 2a_1a_3 + 2a_0a_4\right)x^{2n-4} + \cdots + (-1)^n a_n^{\,2} = 0$$

Setting $-x^2 = z$, the equation reduces to

$$b_0z^n + b_1z^{n-1} + b_2z^{n-2} + \cdots + b_{n-1}\,z + b_n = 0 \qquad ...(2)$$

where $\qquad b_0 = a_0^{\,2}$

$$b_1 = a_1^2 - 2a_0a_2$$

$$b_2 = a_2^2 - 2a_1a_3 + 2a_0a_4$$

.................................

.................................

$$b_n = a_n^2$$

Now all $b_i$'s are got in terms of $a_i$'s.

The roots of (2) are $-\alpha_1^2, -\alpha_2^2, \ldots -\alpha_n^2$ if $\alpha_1, \alpha_2, \ldots, \alpha_n$ are the roots of equation (1).

The coefficients $b_i$'s of equation (2), can be easily got from the following table:

| $a_0$ | $a_1$ | $a_2$ | $a_3$ | $a_4$ | $a_5$ | ... | $a_n$ |
|---|---|---|---|---|---|---|---|
| $a_0^2$ | $a_1^2$ | $a_2^2$ | $a_3^2$ | $a_4^2$ | $a_5^2$ | ... | $a_n^2$ |
| | $-2a_0a_2$ | $-2a_1a_3$ | $-2a_2a_4$ | $-2a_3a_5$ | $-2a_4a_6$ | ... | |
| | | $+2a_0a_4$ | $+2a_1a_5$ | $+2a_2a_6$ | $+2a_3a_7$ | ... | |
| | | | $-2a_0a_6$ | | .......... | | |
| $b_0$ | $b_1$ | $b_2$ | $b_3$ | $b_4$ | $b_5$ | ... | $b_n$ |

The $(\gamma + 1)$th column in the above table is got as follows. The terms occuring in the $(r+1)$th column alternate in sign starting with the positive sign for $a_r^2$. The second term is twice the product of the immediate neighbouring coefficients $a_{r-1}$ and $a_{r+1}$. The third term is the twice the product of the next neighbouring coefficients $a_{r-2}$ and $r_{r+2}$ and this procedure is continued until there are no available coefficients to get the product terms. The sum of all such terms will be $b_{r+1}$.

If this procedure is repeated $m$ times, we get the equation

$$B_0x^n + B_1 x^{n-1} + B_2x^{n-2} + \cdots + B_n = 0 \qquad \ldots(3)$$

whose roots are $R_1, R_2, \ldots, R_n$ which are the $2^m$th power of the roots of quation (1) with sign changed.

That is, $R_i = -\alpha_i^{2^m}, i = 1, 2, \ldots, n.$

**Case 1.** Suppose we assume $|\alpha_1| > |\alpha_2| > \cdots > |\alpha_n|$

Then $|R_1| >> |R_2| >> |R_3| \cdots >> |R_n|$

If the roots of (1) differ in magnitude, then the $2^m$th power of the roots are separated widely for higher values of $m$.

Therefore, $\Sigma R_i = \dfrac{-B_1}{B_0}$

$$\Sigma R_i R_j \approx R_1 R_2 = \frac{B_2}{B_0}$$

$$\Sigma R_i R_j R_k \approx R_1 R_2 R_3 = -\frac{B_3}{B_0}$$

$$R_1 R_2 \ldots R_k = (-1)^n \frac{B_n}{B_0}$$

$$| R_i | = \left| \frac{B_i}{B_{i-1}} \right| = | \alpha_i |^{2^m}$$

$$\therefore \quad \log | \alpha_i | = 2^{m-1} (\log | B_i | - \log | B_{i-1} |), i = 1, 2, \ldots, m.$$

From this we can find the values of $| \alpha_i |$. Substituting $+ | \alpha_i |$ or $- | \alpha_i |$ in (1), we can determine the sign of the roots of the equation. The process of squaring is stopped when another process of squaring produces new coefficients which are approximately the squares of the corresponding coefficients $B_i$'s.

**Case 2.** After a few squaring process, if the magnitude of the coefficients $B_i$ is half the square of the magnitude of corresponding coefficient in the previous equation, then this indicates that $\alpha_i$ is a double root.

Since $\quad | R_i | \approx \left| \dfrac{B_i}{B_{i-1}} \right|, \quad | R_{i+1} | \approx \left| \dfrac{B_{i+1}}{B_i} \right|$

and $\quad | R_i R_{i+1} | \approx R_i^2 \approx \left| \dfrac{B_{i+1}}{B_{i-1}} \right|$

$$| R_i^2 | = | \alpha_i |^{2^{m+1}} \approx \left| \frac{B_{i+1}}{B_{i-1}} \right|$$

From this we can get $| \alpha_i |$ double root. The sign of it can be got as before by substitution in (1).

**Case 3.** If $\alpha_k, \alpha_{k+1}$ are two complex conjugate roots, then this would make the coefficients of $x^{n-k}$ in the successive squaring to fluctuate both in magnitude and sign.

If $\alpha_k, \alpha_{k+1} = \beta_k (\cos \phi_k + i \sin \phi_k)$ is the complex pair of roots, then coefficients will fluctuate in magnitude and sign by the quantity $2\beta_k^m \cos m \phi_k$.

A complex pair is located only by such oscillation. If $m$ is large, $\beta_k$ can be got from

$$\beta_k^{2(2^m)} \approx \left| \frac{B_{k+1}}{B_{k-1}} \right| \text{ and } \phi \text{ is got from}$$

$$2\,\beta_k^m \cos m\,\phi_n \approx \frac{B_{k+1}}{B_{k-1}}$$

If the equation possesses only two complex roots $p \pm iq$, we have

$$\alpha_1 + \alpha_2 + \cdots + \alpha_{k-1} + 2p + \alpha_{k+2} + \cdots + \alpha_n = -a_1$$

This gives the value of $p$.

Since $|\beta_k|^2 = p^2 + q^2$ and $|\beta_k|$ is known already $q$ is known from this relation.

**Example 1.** *Find all the roots of the equation $x^3 - 9x^2 + 18x - 6 = 0$ by Graeffe's method. (root squaring method, three times).*

**Solution.** The coefficients of the successive root squaring are tabulated below:

| | $m$ | $2^m$ | *Coefficients* | | | |
|---|---|---|---|---|---|---|
| Given equation | 0 | 1 | 1 | – 9 | 18 | – 6 |
| | | | 1 | 81 | 324 | 36 |
| | | | | – 36 | – 108 | |
| First squaring | 1 | 2 | 1 | 45 | 216 | 36 |
| | | | 1 | 2025 | 46656 | 1296 |
| | | | | – 432 | – 3240 | |
| Second squaring | 1 | 4 | 1 | 1593 | 43416 | 1296 |
| | | | 1 | 2537649 | 1884949056 | 1679616 |
| | | | | – 86832 | – 4129056 | |
| Third squaring | 1 | 8 | 1 | 2450817 | 1880820000 | 1679616 |

$$|R_i| = |\alpha_1|^8 \approx \left|\frac{B_1}{B_0}\right| = 2450817 \quad \therefore \quad |\alpha_1| = 6{\cdot}2901914$$

$$|R_2| = |\alpha_2|^8 \approx \left|\frac{B_2}{B_1}\right| = \frac{1880820000}{2450817} = 767{\cdot}425720$$

$$|\alpha_2| = 2{\cdot}29419085$$

$$|R_3| = |\alpha_3|^8 = \frac{1679616}{1880820000} = 0{\cdot}000893023256$$

$$\therefore \quad |\alpha_3| = 0{\cdot}415774496.$$

Substitute the values of $\alpha$'s to determine the sign.

Substituting $\alpha_1 = +6{\cdot}29$ in $f(x)$, $\quad f(6{\cdot}29) = 0{\cdot}0012$

Similarly $f(+2{\cdot}29) = 0{\cdot}03$

$f(+0{\cdot}415) = -0{\cdot}0085.$

Hence the roots are 6·29019, 2·29419 and 0·41577.

(The roots are not correct to 5 decimals; only for three squarings).

**Example 2.** *Solve by Graeffe's method :* $2x^3 + x^2 - 2x - 1 = 0$ *(4 squarings).*

**Solution.** The coefficients of the successive root squaring are tabulated below :

| | $m$ | $2^m$ | Coefficients | | | |
|---|---|---|---|---|---|---|
| Given equation | 0 | 1 | 2 | 1 | – 2 | – 1 |
| | | | 4 | 1 | 4 | 1 |
| | | | | 8 | 2 | |
| First squaring | 1 | 2 | 4 | 9 | 6 | 1 |
| | | | 16 | 81 | 36 | 1 |
| | | | | – 48 | – 18 | |
| Second squaring | 1 | 4 | 16 | 33 | 18 | 1 |
| | | | 256 | 1089 | 324 | 1 |
| | | | | – 576 | – 66 | |
| 3rd squaring | 1 | 8 | 256 | 513 | 258 | 1 |
| | | | 65536 | 263169 | 66564 | 1 |
| | | | | – 132096 | – 1026 | |
| Fourth squaring | 1 | 16 | 65536 | 131073 | 65538 | 1 |

$$|\alpha_1|^{16} = \frac{131073}{65536}; \qquad \therefore\ |\alpha_1| = 1{\cdot}0442$$

$$|\alpha_2|^{16} = \frac{65538}{131073}; \qquad \therefore\ |\alpha_2| = 0{\cdot}9576$$

$$\therefore\ |\alpha_3|^{16} = \frac{1}{65538}; \qquad |\alpha_3| = 0{\cdot}4999$$

Substituting these values, the sign is fixed.

$\therefore\ \alpha_1 = 1{\cdot}0442,\ \alpha_2 = -0{\cdot}9576,\ \alpha_3 = -0{\cdot}4999$

(The values are not correct to 4 decimals.)

We have seen only four squarings. We will see how the roots converge.

The following table shows the magnitude of the roots at the end of each squaring.

| $m$ | $\|\alpha_1\|$ | $\|\alpha_2\|$ | $\|\alpha_3\|$ |
|---|---|---|---|
| 1 | 1·5 | 0·8165 | 0·4082 |
| 2 | 1·198 | 0·8660 | 0·4855 |
| 3 | 1·1442 | 0·9176 | 0·4995 |
| 4 | 1·0442 | 0·9576 | 0·4999 |

The actual roots are 1, – 1, and – 0·5. That table shows the quick convergence of the third root and slow convergence of the second root.

Strictly speaking, we must do some more squarings to get closer approximate roots.

**Example 3.** *Find all the roots of* $x^3 - 6x^2 + 11x - 6 = 0$ *by the Graeffe's root squaring method.*

**Solution.** The coefficients of the successive root squaring are tabulated below :

| | $m$ | $2^m$ | | | | |
|---|---|---|---|---|---|---|
| Given equation | 0 | 1 | 1 | – 6 | 11 | – 6 |
| | | | 1 | 36 | 121 | 36 |
| | | | | – 22 | – 72 | |
| First squaring | 1 | 2 | 1 | 14 | 49 | 36 |
| | | | 1 | 196 | 2401 | 1296 |
| | | | | – 98 | – 1008 | |
| 2nd squaring | 2 | 4 | 1 | 98 | 1393 | 1296 |
| | | | 1 | 9604 | 1940449 | 1679616 |
| | | | | – 2786 | – 254016 | |
| 3rd squaring | 3 | 8 | 1 | 6818 | 1686433 | 1679616 |
| | | | 1 | 46485124 | $2{\cdot}84405626 \times 10^{12}$ | $2{\cdot}82110991 \times 10^{12}$ |
| | | | | – 3372866 | $-2{\cdot}29032438 \times 10^{10}$ | |
| 4th squaring | 4 | 16 | 1 | 43112258 | $2{\cdot}82115302 \times 10^{12}$ | $2{\cdot}82110991 \times 10^{12}$ |
| | | | 1 | $1{\cdot}85866679 \times 10^{15}$ | $7{\cdot}95890436 \times 10^{24}$ | $7{\cdot}95866112 \times 10^{24}$ |
| | | | | $-5{\cdot}64230604 \times 10^{12}$ | $-2{\cdot}43248837 \times 10^{20}$ | |
| 5th squaring | 5 | 32 | 1 | $1{\cdot}85302448 \times 10^{15}$ | $7{\cdot}95866111 \times 10^{24}$ | $7{\cdot}95866112 \times 10^{24}$ |

Now $\quad |\alpha_1|^{32} = 1{\cdot}85302448 \times 10^{15}\,; \quad \therefore \quad |\alpha_1| = 3{\cdot}00000022$

$$|\alpha_2|^{32} = \frac{7{\cdot}95866111 \times 10^{24}}{1{\cdot}85302448 \times 10^{15}}\,; \quad \therefore \quad |\alpha_2| = 1{\cdot}99999986$$

$$|\alpha_3|^{32} = \frac{7{\cdot}95866112}{7{\cdot}95866111} = 1\,; \quad \therefore \quad |\alpha_3| = 0{\cdot}999999804$$

$$f(3) = 0,\ f(2) = 0,\ f(1) = 0$$

$\therefore$ Exact roots are 3, 2, 1 and the roots as per this method are 3·00000022, 1·99999986, 0·999999804 (all +ve). The roots at the end of 4th squaring are 3·00028526, 1·99981176, and 0·999999550.

**Note.** Even 4 squarings are quite sufficient.

**Example 4.** *Find all the roots of* $x^3 - 4x^2 + 5x - 2 = 0$ *by Graeffe's method.* [*B.Sc. BR. Ap '94*]

| | $m$ | $2^m$ | | | | |
|---|---|---|---|---|---|---|
| Given equation | 0 | 1 | 1 | − 4 | 5 | − 2 |
| | | | 1 | 16 | 25 | 4 |
| | | | | − 10 | − 16 | |
| First squaring | 1 | 2 | 1 | 6 | 9 | 4 |
| | | | 1 | 36 | 81 | 16 |
| | | | | − 18 | − 48 | |
| | 2 | 4 | 1 | 18 | 33 | 16 |
| | | | 1 | 324 | 1089 | 256 |
| | | | | − 66 | − 576 | |
| | 3 | 8 | 1 | 258 | 513 | 256 |
| | | | 1 | 66564 | 263169 | 65536 |
| | | | | − 1026 | − 131073 | |
| | 4 | 16 | 1 | − 65538 | 131073 | 65536 |
| | | | 1 | 4295229444 | 17180131329 | 4294967276 |
| | | | | − 262146 | − 8590196736 | |
| | 5 | 32 | 1 | 4294967298 | 8589934593 | 4294967276 |

Since the magnitude of the coefficient $B_2$ is half of the square of the magnitude of the corresponding coefficient in the previous equation, $\alpha_2$ is double root.

$$|\alpha_1|^{32} = 4294967298\,; \qquad \therefore\ |\alpha_1| = 2{\cdot}00000000$$

$$|\alpha_2| = |\alpha_3| = 1$$

Verifying the signs, we have the roots 2, 1, 1.

**Example 5.** *Solve:* $x^3 - x^2 - x = 2$, *using Graeffe's method.*

**Solution.** The coefficients of the successive root squaring are tabulated below.

| $m$ | $2^m$ | | | | |
|---|---|---|---|---|---|
| 0 | 1 | 1 | − 1 | − 1 | − 2 |
| | | 1 | 1 | 1 | 4 |
| | | | 2 | − 4 | |
| 1 | 2 | 1 | 3 | − 3 | 4 |
| | | 1 | 9 | 9 | 16 |
| | | | 6 | − 24 | |
| 2 | 4 | 1 | 15 | − 15 | 16 |
| | | 1 | 225 | 225 | 256 |
| | | | 30 | − 480 | |
| 3 | 8 | 1 | 255 | − 255 | 256 |

| $m$ | $2^m$ | | | | |
|---|---|---|---|---|---|
| | | 1 | 65025<br>510 | 65025<br>– 130560 | 65536 |
| 4 | 16 | 1 | 65535 | – 65535 | 65536 |
| | | 1 | $4{\cdot}2948362 \times 10^9$<br>+ 131070 | $4{\cdot}2948362 \times 10^9$<br>$-\,8{\cdot}5898035 \times 10^9$ | $4{\cdot}2949673 \times 10^9$ |
| 5 | 32 | 1 | $+\,4{\cdot}2949673 \times 10^9$ | $-\,4{\cdot}2949673 \times 10^9$ | $+\,4{\cdot}2949673 \times 10^9$ |

From above, we see that the magnitude of the coefficient $B_1$ has become constant (upto few decimals), while the magnitude of the coefficient $B_2$ oscillates. Hence $\alpha_1$ is a real root and $\alpha_2, \alpha_3$ are complex. The real root is got from

$$|\alpha_1|^{32} = 4{\cdot}2949673 \times 10^9 \;; \quad \therefore \quad |\alpha_1| = 2{\cdot}00000000$$

Evidently $\alpha_1 = +2$ is the root.

The magnitude of the complex root is got from

$$\beta_2^{64} \approx \left|\frac{B_3}{B_1}\right| = 1{\cdot}000000 \text{ and hence } \beta_2 = 1{\cdot}0000$$

If $\quad \alpha_2 = p + iq, \quad \alpha_3 = p - iq,$

$$\alpha_1 + \alpha_2 + \alpha_3 = -\,a_1 = 1$$

$$2 + 2p = 1 \quad \therefore \quad p = -\,0{\cdot}5$$

$$p^2 + q^2 = \beta_2^2 = 1$$

$$q = \sqrt{1 - p^2} = \sqrt{1 - \tfrac{1}{4}} = \frac{\sqrt{3}}{2} = 0{\cdot}866025$$

Hence, the three roots are,

$$2 \text{ and } -\,0{\cdot}5 \pm (0{\cdot}866025)\, i.$$

**Note.** The exact roots of the given equation are 2·0, $(-\,1{\cdot}0 \pm i\sqrt{3})/2$.

## EXERCISE 3.4

Using Graeffe's method, solve the following equations:

**1.** $x^3 - 2x^2 - 5x + 6 = 0$

**2.** $x^3 - 4{\cdot}5x^2 + 6{\cdot}56x - 3{\cdot}12 = 0$

**3.** $x^3 - x^2 - 17x - 15 = 0$

**4.** $x^3 - 5x^2 - 17x + 20 = 0$

**5.** $x^4 - 10x^3 + 35x^2 - 50x + 24 = 0$

**6.** $x^3 + 3x^2 - 4 = 0$

**7.** $x^3 - 2x + 2 = 0$

**8.** $x^4 - x^3 + 3x^2 + x - 4 = 0$

**9.** $5x^3 + 2x^2 - 15x - 6 = 0$

**10.** $2x^3 - 7x^2 + 7x - 2 = 0$

# ANSWERS

## EXERCISE 3.1 Page 86

**1.** (*i*) 2·7065 (*ii*) – 1·200 (*iii*) 0·6190 (*iv*) 0·391847
(*v*) 0·322 (*vi*) 0·66664 (*vii*) 0·754869 (*viii*) 1·524

**3.** (*i*) – 5·5174 (*ii*) 0·879 (*iii*) 2·108 (*iv*) – 0·682
(*v*) 3·7893 (*vi*) 1·3688 (*vii*) 1·8955 (*viii*) 0·3604
(*ix*) 4·3311 (*x*) 0·607

**4.** (*i*) 1·050 (*ii*) 0·3574, 2·1533 (*iii*) 2·74065 (*iv*) 2·3650
(*v*) 0·5885 (*vi*) 2·7473 (*vii*) 1·3688 (*viii*) 3·7893
(*ix*) 0·51776 (*x*) 0·2031 (*xi*) 6·089 (*xii*) 3·646
(*xiii*) 0·6666441 (*xiv*) 2·8832 (*xv*) 1·5236

## EXERCISE 3.2 Page 97

**1.** 1·3247 **2.** 0·517757 **3.** – 0·1474 **4.** 0·32258
**5.** 6·089114 **6.** 1·89549 **8.** 2·884 **9.** 1·521
**10.** 1·813 **11.** 3·256 **12.** 5·916 **13.** 2·884
**14.** 1·856 **15.** 0·988 **16.** 0·5671 **17.** 0·6566
**18.** 3·4641 **19.** 2·2360, 2·571 **20.** 0·8241 **22.** 6·0921
**23.** 0·2586 **24.** – 1·249 **25.** 0·5177 **26.** – 1·9338
**27.** 3·7893 **28.** 1·0001 **29.** 2·279 **30.** 2·7984
**31.** 2·1544, 1·444

## EXERCISE 3.3 Page 103

**1.** 1·168 **2.** (*i*) – 0·3275 (*ii*) 3·284 (*iii*) 4·189 (*iv*) 2·7689 (*v*) 3·18
(*vi*) 2·24 (*vii*) 1·11

## EXERCISE 3.4 Page 110

**1.** 3·0144, 0·9994, – 1·9914 **2.** 2·012, 1·364, 1·137 **3.** 5, – 3, – 1
**4.** 7·017, – 2·974, 0·958 **5.** 4, 3, 2, 1 **6.** – 2, – 2, 1
**7.** – 1·77, $1 \pm i$ **8.** 1·0912, – 0·9172, $0{\cdot}413 \pm 1{\cdot}956\,i$
**9.** – 0·4, ± 1·732 **10.** 0·5, 1, 2

# 4

# *Solution of Simultaneous Linear Algebraic Equations*

## DIRECT METHODS

### 4·1 Introduction

We come across, very often, simultaneous linear algebraic equations for its solutions, especially, in the fields of science and engineering. In lower classes, we have solved such equations by Cramer's rule (determinant methods) or by matrix methods. These methods become tedious when the number of unknowns in the system is large. After the availability of computers, we go to numerical methods which are suited for computer operations. These numerical methods are of two types namely : (*i*) direct (*ii*) iterative.

We will study a few methods below:

Solution of Simultaneous Linear Algebraic Equations

**4·2 Gauss-Elimination Method** (Direct method). This is a *direct* method based on the elimination of the unknowns by combining equations such that the $n$ equations in $n$ unknowns are reduced to an equivalent upper triangular system which could be solved by back substitution.

Consider the $n$ linear equations in $n$ unknowns, *viz.*

$$\begin{aligned} a_{11}x_1 + a_{12}x_2 + \cdots + a_{1n}x_n &= b_1 \\ a_{21}x_1 + a_{22}x_2 + \cdots + a_{2n}x_n &= b_2 \\ \cdots\cdots\cdots\cdots\cdots\cdots\cdots & \\ a_{n1}x_1 + a_{n2}x_2 + \cdots + a_{nn}x_n &= b_n \end{aligned} \qquad \ldots(1)$$

where $a_{ij}$ and $b_i$ are known constants and $x_i$'s are unknowns.

The system (1) is equivalent to

$$AX = B \qquad \ldots(2)$$

where $A = \begin{pmatrix} a_{11}\, a_{12} \cdots a_{1n} \\ a_{21}\, a_{22} \cdots a_{2n} \\ \cdots\cdots\cdots\cdots \\ a_{n1}\, a_{n2} \cdots a_{nn} \end{pmatrix}$, $X = \begin{pmatrix} x_1 \\ x_2 \\ \vdots \\ x_n \end{pmatrix}$ and $B = \begin{pmatrix} b_1 \\ b_2 \\ \vdots \\ b_n \end{pmatrix}$

Now our aim is to reduce the augmented matrix $(A, B)$ to upper triangular matrix.

$$(A, B) = \left(\begin{array}{cccc|c} a_{11} & a_{12} & \cdots & a_{1n} & b_1 \\ a_{21} & a_{22} & \cdots & a_{2n} & b_2 \\ \cdot & \cdot & \cdots & \cdot & \cdot \\ a_{n1} & a_{n2} & \cdots & a_{nn} & b_n \end{array}\right) \quad \ldots(3)$$

Now, multiply the first row of (3) ( if $a_{11} \neq 0$) by $-\frac{a_{i1}}{a_{11}}$ and add to the $i$th row of $(A, B)$, where $i = 2, 3, \ldots, n$. By this, all elements in the first column of $(A, B)$ except $a_{11}$ are made to zero. Now (3) is of the form

$$\left(\begin{array}{cccc|c} a_{11} & a_{12} & \cdots & a_{1n} & b_1 \\ 0 & b_{22} & \cdots & b_{2n} & c_2 \\ \cdot & \cdot & \cdots & \cdot & \cdot \\ 0 & b_{n2} & \cdots & b_{nn} & c_n \end{array}\right) \quad \ldots(4)$$

Now take the pivot $b_{22}$. Now, considering $b_{22}$ as the pivot, we will make all elements below $b_{22}$ in the second column of (4) as zeros. That is, multiply second row of (4) by $-\frac{b_{i2}}{b_{22}}$ and add to the corresponding elements of the $i$th row ($i = 3, 4, \ldots, n$). Now all elements below $b_{22}$ are reduced to zero. Now (4) reduces to

$$\left(\begin{array}{ccc|c} a_{11} & a_{12} & a_{13} \ldots a_{in} & b_1 \\ 0 & b_{22} & b_{23} \ldots b_{2n} & c_2 \\ 0 & 0 & c_{33} \ldots c_{3n} & d_3 \\ \cdot & \cdot & \cdot \quad \cdot & \cdot \\ 0 & 0 & c_{n3} \ldots c_{nn} & d_n \end{array}\right) \quad \ldots(5)$$

Now taking $c_{33}$ as the pivot, using elementary operations, we make all elements below $c_{33}$ as zeros. Continuing the process, all elements below the leading diagonal elements of $A$ are made to zero.

Hence, we get $(A, B)$ after all these operations as

$$\left(\begin{array}{cccccc|c} a_{11} & a_{12} & a_{13} & \cdots & & a_{1n} & b_1 \\ 0 & b_{22} & b_{23} & \cdots & & b_{2n} & c_2 \\ 0 & 0 & c_{33} & c_{34} & \cdots & c_{3n} & d_3 \\ \cdot & \cdot & \cdot & \cdot & & \cdot & \cdot \\ 0 & 0 & 0 & 0 & & \alpha_{nn} & K_n \end{array}\right) \quad \ldots(6)$$

From, (6), the given system of linear equations is equivalent to

$$a_{11}x_1 + a_{12}x_2 + a_{13}x_3 + \cdots + a_{1n}x_n = b_1$$

$$b_{22}x_2 + b_{23}x_3 + \cdots + b_{2n}x_n = c_2$$

$$c_{33}x_3 + \cdots c_{3n}x_n = d_3$$

$$\cdots\cdots\cdots\cdots\cdots\cdots$$

$$\alpha_{nn}x_n = K_n$$

Going from the bottom of these equation, we solve for $x_n = \frac{K_n}{\alpha_{nn}}$. Using this in the penultimate equation, we get $x_{n-1}$ and so. By this back substitution method, we solve for

$x_n, x_{n-1}, x_{n-2}, \cdots x_2, x_1$.

**Note.** This method of making the matrix $A$ as upper triangular matrix had been taught in lower classes while finding the rank of the matrix $A$.

### 4·2·1 Gauss-Jordan elimination method (Direct method)

This method is a modification of the above Gauss elimination method. In this method, the coefficient matrix $A$ of the system $AX = B$ is brought to a diagonal matrix or unit matrix by making the matrix $A$ not only upper triangular but also lower triangular by making all elements above the leading diagonal of $A$ also as zeros. By this way, the system $AX = B$ will reduce to the form.

$$\left(\begin{array}{ccccc|c} a_{11} & 0 & 0 & 0 & 0 & b_1 \\ 0 & b_{22} & 0 & 0 & 0 & c_2 \\ \cdot & \cdot & \cdot & \cdot & \cdot & d_3 \\ 0 & 0 & 0 & 0 & \alpha_{nn} & K_n \end{array}\right) \qquad \ldots(7)$$

From (7)

$$x_n = \frac{K_n}{\alpha_{nn}}, \ldots, x_2 = \frac{c_2}{b_{22}}, x_1 = \frac{b_1}{a_{11}}$$

**Note.** By this method, the values of $x_1, x_2, \ldots, x_n$ are got immediately without using the process of back substitution.

**Example 1.** *Solve the system of equations by (i) Gauss elimination method (ii) Gauss-Jordan method.*

$x + 2y + z = 3,\quad 2x + 3y + 3z = 10;\quad 3x - y + 2z = 13.$ [MKU 1981]

**Solution. (By Gauss method)**

The given system is equivalent to

$$\underset{A}{\begin{pmatrix} 1 & 2 & 1 \\ 2 & 3 & 3 \\ 3 & -1 & 2 \end{pmatrix}} \underset{X}{\begin{pmatrix} x \\ y \\ z \end{pmatrix}} = \underset{B}{\begin{pmatrix} 3 \\ 10 \\ 13 \end{pmatrix}}$$

$$(A, B) = \left(\begin{array}{ccc|c} 1 & 2 & 1 & 3 \\ 2 & 3 & 3 & 10 \\ 3 & -1 & 2 & 13 \end{array}\right) \qquad \ldots(1)$$

Now, we will make the matrix $A$ upper triangular.

$$(A, B) = \left(\begin{array}{ccc|c} 1 & 2 & 1 & 3 \\ 2 & 3 & 3 & 10 \\ 3 & -1 & 2 & 13 \end{array}\right)$$

$$\sim \left(\begin{array}{ccc|c} 1 & 2 & 1 & 3 \\ 0 & -1 & 1 & 4 \\ 0 & -7 & -1 & 4 \end{array}\right) \quad \begin{array}{l} R_2 + (-2) R_1 \quad i.e., \quad R_{21}(-2) \\ R_3 + (-3) R_1 \quad i.e., \quad R_{31}(-3) \end{array}$$

Now take $b_{22} = -1$ as the pivot and make $b_{32}$ as zero.

$$(A, B) \sim \left(\begin{array}{ccc|c} 1 & 2 & 1 & 3 \\ 0 & -1 & 1 & 4 \\ 0 & 0 & -8 & -24 \end{array}\right) \quad R_{32}(-7) \qquad \text{...(2)}$$

From this, we get

$$x + 2y + z = 3$$

$$-y + z = 4$$

$$-8z = -24$$

$\therefore$ $z = 3, y = -1, x = 2$ by back substitution.

*i.e.,* $x = 2, y = -1, z = 3$

**Solution. (Gauss-Jordan method)**

In stage 2, make the element, in the position (1, 2) , also zero.

$$(A, B) \sim \left(\begin{array}{ccc|c} 1 & 2 & 1 & 3 \\ 0 & -1 & 1 & 4 \\ 0 & 0 & -8 & -24 \end{array}\right)$$

$$\sim \left(\begin{array}{ccc|c} 1 & 0 & 3 & 11 \\ 0 & -1 & 1 & 4 \\ 0 & 0 & -8 & -24 \end{array}\right) \quad R_{12}(2)$$

$$\sim \left(\begin{array}{ccc|c} 1 & 0 & 3 & 11 \\ 0 & -1 & 1 & 4 \\ 0 & 0 & -1 & -3 \end{array}\right) \quad R_3\left(\frac{1}{8}\right)$$

$$\sim \left(\begin{array}{ccc|c} 1 & 0 & 0 & 2 \\ 0 & -1 & 0 & 1 \\ 0 & 0 & -1 & -3 \end{array}\right) \quad R_{13}(3), R_{23}(1)$$

*i.e.,* $x = 2, -y = 1, -z = -3$

*i.e.,* $x = 2, y = -1, z = 3$

**Example 2.** *Solve the system by Gauss-Elimination method*
$2x + 3y - z = 5;$ $4x + 4y - 3z = 3$ *and* $2x - 3y + 2z = 2.$ [*MKU 1980*]

**Solution.** The system is equivalent to

$$\begin{pmatrix} 2 & 3 & -1 \\ 4 & 4 & -3 \\ 2 & -3 & 2 \end{pmatrix} \begin{pmatrix} x \\ y \\ z \end{pmatrix} = \begin{pmatrix} 5 \\ 3 \\ 2 \end{pmatrix}$$

$$A \qquad X = B$$

$$\therefore \quad (A, B) = \left(\begin{array}{ccc|c} 2 & 3 & -1 & 5 \\ 4 & 4 & -3 & 3 \\ 2 & -3 & 2 & 2 \end{array}\right)$$

*Step 1.* Taking $a_{11} = 2$ as the pivot, reduce all elements below that to zero.

$$(A, B) \sim \left(\begin{array}{ccc|c} 2 & 3 & -1 & 5 \\ 0 & -2 & -1 & -7 \\ 0 & -6 & 3 & -3 \end{array}\right) \quad R_{21}(-2), R_{31}(-1)$$

*Step 2.* Taking the element $-2$ in the position (2, 2) as pivot, reduce all elements below that to zero.

$$(A, B) \sim \left(\begin{array}{ccc|c} 2 & 3 & -1 & 5 \\ 0 & -2 & -1 & -7 \\ 0 & 0 & 6 & 18 \end{array}\right) \quad R_{32}(-3)$$

Hence $\quad 2x + 3y - z = 5$

$$-2y - z = -7$$

$$6z = 18$$

$\therefore \quad z = 3, y = 2, x = 1.$ by back substitution.

**Example 3.** *Solve the following system by Gauss-Jordan method:*

$5x_1 + x_2 + x_3 + x_4 = 4; \quad x_1 + 7x_2 + x_3 + x_4 = 12$

$x_1 + x_2 + 6x_3 + x_4 = -5; \quad x_1 + x_2 + x_3 + 4x_4 = -6$

**Solution.** Interchange the first and the last equation, so that the coefficient of $x_1$ in the first equation is 1. Then we have

$$(A, B) = \left(\begin{array}{cccc|c} 1 & 1 & 1 & 4 & -6 \\ 1 & 7 & 1 & 1 & 12 \\ 1 & 1 & 6 & 1 & -5 \\ 5 & 1 & 1 & 1 & 4 \end{array}\right)$$

$$\sim \left(\begin{array}{cccc|c} 1 & 1 & 1 & 4 & -6 \\ 0 & \boxed{6} & 0 & -3 & 18 \\ 0 & 0 & 5 & -3 & 1 \\ 0 & -4 & -4 & -19 & 34 \end{array}\right) \quad R_{21}(-1), R_{31}(-1), R_{41}(-5)$$

$$\sim \left(\begin{array}{cccc|c} 1 & 1 & 1 & 4 & -6 \\ 0 & \boxed{1} & 0 & -0.5 & 3 \\ 0 & 0 & 5 & -3 & 1 \\ 0 & -4 & -4 & -19 & 34 \end{array}\right) \quad R_2\left(\frac{1}{6}\right) \text{ to make the pivot as 1}$$

$$\sim \left(\begin{array}{cccc|c} 1 & 0 & 1 & 4.5 & -9 \\ 0 & 1 & 0 & -0.5 & 3 \\ 0 & 0 & \boxed{5} & -3 & 1 \\ 0 & 0 & -4 & -21 & 46 \end{array}\right) \quad R_{12}(-1),\ R_{42}(4)$$

$$\sim \left(\begin{array}{cccc|c} 1 & 0 & 1 & 4.5 & -9 \\ 0 & 1 & 0 & -0.5 & 3 \\ 0 & 0 & \boxed{1} & -0.6 & 0.2 \\ 0 & 0 & -4 & -21 & 46 \end{array}\right) \quad R_3\left(\frac{1}{5}\right)$$

$$\sim \left(\begin{array}{cccc|c} 1 & 0 & 0 & 5.1 & -9.2 \\ 0 & 1 & 0 & -0.5 & 3 \\ 0 & 0 & 1 & -0.6 & 0.2 \\ 0 & 0 & 0 & -23.4 & 46.8 \end{array}\right) \quad R_{13}(-1),\ R_{43}(4)$$

$$\sim \left(\begin{array}{cccc|c} 1 & 0 & 0 & 5.1 & -9.2 \\ 0 & 1 & 0 & -0.5 & 3 \\ 0 & 0 & 1 & -0.6 & 0.2 \\ 0 & 0 & 0 & -1 & 2 \end{array}\right) \quad R_4\left(\frac{1}{23.4}\right)$$

$$\sim \left(\begin{array}{cccc|c} 1 & 0 & 0 & 0 & 1 \\ 0 & 1 & 0 & 0 & 2 \\ 0 & 0 & 1 & 0 & -1 \\ 0 & 0 & 0 & -1 & 2 \end{array}\right) \quad R_{34}\left(-\frac{3}{5}\right),\ R_{24}\left(-\frac{1}{2}\right),\ R_{14}(5.1)$$

$$x_1 = 1,\ x_2 = 2,\ x_3 = -1,\ x_4 = -2.$$

**Example 4.** *Solve the system of equations by Gauss-Jordan method :*

$$x + y + z + w = 2$$
$$2x - y + 2z - w = -5$$
$$3x + 2y + 3z + 4w = 7$$
$$x - 2y - 3z + 2w = 5$$

**Solution.** $(A, B) = \left(\begin{array}{cccc|c} 1 & 1 & 1 & 1 & 2 \\ 2 & -1 & 2 & -1 & -5 \\ 3 & 2 & 3 & 4 & 7 \\ 1 & -2 & -3 & 2 & 5 \end{array}\right)$

$$\sim \left(\begin{array}{cccc|c} 1 & 1 & 1 & 1 & 2 \\ 0 & -3 & 0 & -3 & -9 \\ 0 & -1 & 0 & 1 & 1 \\ 0 & -3 & -4 & 1 & 3 \end{array}\right) \begin{array}{l} R_2 - 2R_1 \\ R_3 - 3R_1 \\ R_4 - R_1 \end{array}$$

$$\sim \left(\begin{array}{cccc|c} 1 & 1 & 1 & 1 & 2 \\ 0 & \boxed{1} & 0 & 1 & 3 \\ 0 & -1 & 0 & 1 & 1 \\ 0 & -3 & -4 & 1 & 3 \end{array}\right) \quad R_2\left(-\frac{1}{3}\right)$$

$$\sim \left(\begin{array}{cccc|c} 1 & 0 & 1 & 0 & -1 \\ 0 & 1 & 0 & 1 & 3 \\ 0 & 0 & 0 & 2 & 4 \\ 0 & 0 & -4 & 4 & 12 \end{array}\right) \begin{array}{l} R_1 + (-1)\,R_2 \\ R_3 + R_2 \\ R_4 + 3R_2 \end{array}$$

$$\sim \left(\begin{array}{cccc|c} 1 & 0 & 1 & 0 & -1 \\ 0 & 1 & 0 & 1 & 3 \\ 0 & 0 & 0 & 1 & 2 \\ 0 & 0 & 1 & -1 & -3 \end{array}\right) \begin{array}{l} R_3\left(\frac{1}{2}\right) \\ R_4\left(-\frac{1}{4}\right) \end{array}$$

$$\sim \left(\begin{array}{cccc|c} 1 & 0 & 1 & 0 & -1 \\ 0 & 1 & 0 & 1 & 3 \\ 0 & 0 & 1 & -1 & -3 \\ 0 & 0 & 0 & 1 & 2 \end{array}\right) \quad \text{Interchanging } R_3 \text{ and } R_4$$

$$\sim \left(\begin{array}{cccc|c} 1 & 0 & 0 & 1 & 2 \\ 0 & 1 & 0 & 1 & 3 \\ 0 & 0 & 1 & -1 & -3 \\ 0 & 0 & 0 & 1 & 2 \end{array}\right) \quad R_1 + (-1)\,R_3$$

$$\sim \left(\begin{array}{cccc|c} 1 & 0 & 0 & 0 & 0 \\ 0 & 1 & 0 & 0 & 1 \\ 0 & 0 & 1 & 0 & -1 \\ 0 & 0 & 0 & 1 & 2 \end{array}\right) \begin{array}{l} R_1 + (-1)\,R_4 \\ R_2 + (-1)\,R_4 \\ R_3 + R_4 \end{array}$$

$\therefore \quad x = 0,\ y = 1,\ z = -1,\ w = 2.$

**Example 5.** *Apply Gauss-Jordan method to find the solution of the following system :*

*$10x + y + z = 12$; $2x + 10y + z = 13$; $x + y + 5z = 7$.* [*MS 1991*]

**Solution.** Since the coefficient of $x$ in the last equation is unity, we rewrite the equations interchanging the first and the last. Hence the augmented matrix is

$$(A, B) = \left(\begin{array}{ccc|c} 1 & 1 & 5 & 7 \\ 2 & 10 & 1 & 13 \\ 10 & 1 & 1 & 12 \end{array}\right)$$

$$\sim \left(\begin{array}{ccc|c} 1 & 1 & 5 & 7 \\ 0 & 8 & -9 & -1 \\ 0 & -9 & -49 & -58 \end{array}\right) \quad \begin{array}{l} R_2 + (-2)\,R_1 \\ R_3 + (-10)\,R_1 \end{array}$$

$$\sim \left(\begin{array}{ccc|c} 1 & 1 & 5 & 7 \\ 0 & 1 & -\frac{9}{8} & -\frac{1}{8} \\ 0 & -9 & -49 & -58 \end{array}\right) \quad R_2\left(\frac{1}{8}\right)$$

$$\sim \left(\begin{array}{ccc|c} 1 & 1 & 5 & 7 \\ 0 & 1 & -\frac{9}{8} & -\frac{1}{8} \\ 0 & 0 & -\frac{473}{8} & -\frac{473}{8} \end{array}\right)$$

$$\sim \left(\begin{array}{ccc|c} 1 & 1 & 5 & 7 \\ 0 & 1 & -\frac{9}{8} & -\frac{1}{8} \\ 0 & 0 & 1 & 1 \end{array}\right) \quad R_3\left(-\frac{8}{473}\right)$$

$$\sim \left(\begin{array}{ccc|c} 1 & 0 & \frac{49}{8} & \frac{57}{8} \\ 0 & 1 & -\frac{9}{8} & -\frac{1}{8} \\ 0 & 0 & 1 & 1 \end{array}\right) \quad R_1 + (-1)R_2$$

$$\sim \left(\begin{array}{ccc|c} 1 & 0 & 0 & 1 \\ 0 & 1 & 0 & 1 \\ 0 & 0 & 1 & 1 \end{array}\right) \quad \begin{array}{l} R_2 + \left(\frac{9}{8}\right)R_3 \\ R_1 + \left(-\frac{49}{8}\right)R_3 \end{array}$$

$\therefore \quad x = 1, y = 1, z = 1.$

**Example 6.** *Using Gauss-Elimination method, solve the system:*

$$3{\cdot}15x - 1{\cdot}96y + 3{\cdot}85z = 12{\cdot}95$$
$$2{\cdot}13x + 5{\cdot}12y - 2{\cdot}89z = -8{\cdot}61$$
$$5{\cdot}92x + 3{\cdot}05y + 2{\cdot}15z = 6{\cdot}88$$

[*MKU 1981*]

**Solution.** $(A, B) = \left(\begin{array}{ccc|c} 3{\cdot}15 & -1{\cdot}96 & 3{\cdot}85 & 12{\cdot}95 \\ 2{\cdot}13 & 5{\cdot}12 & -2{\cdot}89 & -8{\cdot}61 \\ 5{\cdot}92 & 3{\cdot}05 & 2{\cdot}15 & 6{\cdot}88 \end{array}\right)$

$$\sim \left(\begin{array}{ccc|c} \boxed{3.15} & -1.96 & 3.85 & 12.95 \\ 0 & \boxed{6.4453} & -5.4933 & -17.3666 \\ 0 & 6.7335 & -5.0855 & -17.4578 \end{array}\right) \begin{array}{l} R_2+\left(-\frac{2.13}{3.15}\right)R_1 \\ R_3+\left(\frac{-5.92}{3.15}\right)R_1 \end{array}$$

$$\sim \left(\begin{array}{ccc|c} 3.15 & -1.96 & 3.85 & 12.95 \\ 0 & \boxed{6.4453} & -5.4933 & -17.3666 \\ 0 & 0 & 0.6534 & 0.6853 \end{array}\right)$$

$$\therefore \quad 3.15x - 1.96y + 3.85z = 12.95$$

$$6.4453y - 5.4933z = -17.3666$$

$$0.6534z = 0.6853$$

$$\therefore \quad z = \frac{0.6853}{0.6534} = 1.0488$$

$$y = \frac{5.4933 \times 1.0488 - 17.3666}{6.4453} = -1.8005$$

$$x = \frac{1.96 \times (-1.8005) - 3.85\,(1.0488) + 12.95}{3.15} = 1.7089$$

$\therefore \quad x = 1.7089, y = -1.8005, z = 1.0488.$

**Example 7.** *Solve by Gauss-Elemination method:*
$3x + 4y + 5z = 18, \quad 2x - y + 8z = 13, \quad 5x - 2y + 7z = 20.$

**Solution.** $(A, B) = \left(\begin{array}{ccc|c} 3 & 4 & 5 & 18 \\ 2 & -1 & 8 & 13 \\ 5 & -2 & 7 & 20 \end{array}\right)$

$$\sim \left(\begin{array}{ccc|c} 3 & 4 & 5 & 18 \\ 0 & -\frac{11}{3} & \frac{14}{3} & 1 \\ 0 & -\frac{26}{3} & -\frac{4}{3} & -10 \end{array}\right) \begin{array}{l} R_2 - \frac{2}{3}R_1 \\ R_3 - \frac{5}{3}R_1 \end{array}$$

$$\sim \left(\begin{array}{ccc|c} 3 & 4 & 5 & 18 \\ 0 & -11 & 14 & 3 \\ 0 & 13 & 2 & 15 \end{array}\right) \begin{array}{l} R_2\,(3) \\ R_3\left(-\frac{3}{2}\right) \end{array}$$

$$\sim \left(\begin{array}{ccc|c} 3 & 4 & 5 & 18 \\ 0 & -11 & 14 & 3 \\ 0 & 0 & \frac{204}{11} & \frac{204}{11} \end{array}\right) \quad R_3 + \frac{13}{11}R_2$$

$$\sim \left(\begin{array}{ccc|c} 3 & 4 & 5 & 18 \\ 0 & -11 & 14 & 3 \\ 0 & 0 & 1 & 1 \end{array}\right) \quad R_3\left(\frac{11}{204}\right)$$

$\therefore \qquad z = 1,\ -11y + 14z = 3,\ 3x + 4y + 5z = 18$

Hence, $\qquad z = 1,\ y = \dfrac{3 - 14z}{-11} = 1,\ x = \dfrac{18 - 4y - 5z}{3} = 3$

$\therefore \qquad x = 3,\ y = 1, z = 1.$

## EXERCISE 4.1

Solve the following systems by (*i*) Gauss-Elimination (*ii*) Gauss-Jordan methods:

**1.** $2x + y = 3,\ \ 7x - 3y = 4$

**2.** $11x + 3y = 17,\ \ 2x + 7y = 16$

**3.** $4x - 3y = 11,\ \ 3x + 2y = 4$

**4.** $x - y + z = 1,\ \ -3x + 2y - 3z = -6,\ \ 2x - 5y + 4z = 5$

**5.** $x + 3y + 10z = 24,\ \ 2x + 17y + 4z = 35,\ \ 28x + 4y - z = 32$ [*MS Ap 1992*]

**6.** $x - 3y - z = -30,\ \ 2x - y - 3z = 5,\ \ 5x - y - 2z = 142$

**7.** $5x - 9y - 2z + 4w = 7,\ \ 3x + y + 4z + 11w = 2,$
$10x - 7y + 3z + 5w = 6,\ \ -6x + 8y - z - 4w = 5$

**8.** $10x + y + z = 12,\ \ x + 10y + z = 12,\ \ x + y + 10z = 12$

**9.** $10x + y + z = 18{\cdot}141,\ \ x + 10y + z = 28{\cdot}140,\ \ x + y + 10z = 38{\cdot}139$ [*MS 1991*]

**10.** $3x + y - z = 3,\ 2x - 8y + z = -5,\ x - 2y + 9z = 8$

**11.** $3x - y + 2z = 12,\ x + 2y + 3z = 11,\ 2x - 2y - z = 2$

**12.** $2x - 3y + z = -1,\ x + 4y + 5z = 25,\ 3x - 4y + z = 2$

**13.** $x + 2y + 3z = 6,\ \ 2x + 4y + z = 7,\ \ 3x + 2y + 9z = 14$

**14.** $2x - y + 3z + w = 9,\ \ 3x + y - 4z + 3w = 3,$
$5x - 4y + 3z - 6w = 2,\ \ x - 2y - z + 2w = -2$

**15.** $4x + y + 3z = 11,\ \ 3x + 4y + 2z = 11,\ \ 2x + 3y + z = 7$

**16.** $x + y + 2z = 4,\ \ 3x + y - 3z = -4,\ \ 2x - 3y - 5z = -5$

**17.** $2x + 6y - z = -12,\ \ 5x - y + z = 11,\ \ 4x - y + 3z = 10$ [*MS Ap 87*]

**18.** $x + 2y + z - w = -2,\ \ 2x + 3y - z + 2w = 7$
$x + y + 3z - 2w = -6,\ \ x + y + z + w = 2$ [*MS Nov 86*]

**19.** $4{\cdot}12x - 9{\cdot}68y + 2{\cdot}01z = 4{\cdot}93$
$1{\cdot}88x - 4{\cdot}62y + 5{\cdot}50z = 3{\cdot}11$
$1{\cdot}10x - 0{\cdot}96y + 2{\cdot}72z = 4{\cdot}02$

**20.** $6x - y + z = 13,\ \ x + y + z = 9,\ \ 10x + y - z = 19$

**21.** $x + 2y - 12z + 8w = 27,\ \ 5x + 4y + 7z - 2w = 4,$
$6x - 12y - 8z + 3w = 49,\ \ 3x - 7y - 9z - 5w = -11$

**22.** $x + 0{\cdot}5y + 0{\cdot}33z = 1,\qquad 0{\cdot}33x + 0{\cdot}25y + 0{\cdot}2z = 0,\qquad 0{\cdot}5x + 0{\cdot}33y + 0{\cdot}25z = 0$

**23.** $2x + 4y + z = 3,\ \ 3x + 2y - 2z = -2,\ \ x - y + z = 6$

**24.** $x + y + z - w = 2,\ \ 7x + y + 3z + w = 12,$
$8x - y + z - 3w = 5,\ \ 10x + 5y + 3z + 2w = 20$

**25.** $2x + 4y + 8z = 41,\ \ 4x + 6y + 10z = 56,\ \ 6x + 8y + 10z = 64$

**26.** $2x + 2y - z + w = 4,\ \ 4x + 3y - z + 2w = 6,$
$8x + 5y - 3z + 4w = 12,\ \ 3x + 3y - 2z + 2w = 6$

## 4·3 Inversion of a matrix using Gauss-Elimination method

Let us find the inversion of a non-singular square matrix $A$ of order *three.* If $X$ is the inverse of $A$, then $AX = I$ where $I$ is the unix matrix of order three. Now, we have to find the elements of $X$.

Let $A = \begin{pmatrix} a_{11} & a_{12} & a_{13} \\ a_{21} & a_{22} & a_{23} \\ a_{31} & a_{32} & a_{33} \end{pmatrix}$ and $X = \begin{pmatrix} x_{11} & x_{12} & x_{13} \\ x_{21} & x_{22} & x_{23} \\ x_{31} & x_{32} & x_{33} \end{pmatrix}$

Therefore, $AX = I$ reduces to

$$\begin{pmatrix} a_{11} & a_{12} & a_{13} \\ a_{21} & a_{22} & a_{23} \\ a_{31} & a_{32} & a_{33} \end{pmatrix}\begin{pmatrix} x_{11} & x_{12} & x_{13} \\ x_{21} & x_{22} & x_{23} \\ x_{31} & x_{32} & x_{33} \end{pmatrix} = \begin{pmatrix} 1 & 0 & 0 \\ 0 & 1 & 0 \\ 0 & 0 & 1 \end{pmatrix} \qquad \text{...(1)}$$

This equation is equivalent to the three equations give below:

$$\begin{pmatrix} a_{11} & a_{12} & a_{13} \\ a_{21} & a_{22} & a_{23} \\ a_{31} & a_{32} & a_{33} \end{pmatrix}\begin{pmatrix} x_{11} \\ x_{21} \\ x_{31} \end{pmatrix} = \begin{pmatrix} 1 \\ 0 \\ 0 \end{pmatrix} \qquad \text{...(2)}$$

$$\begin{pmatrix} a_{11} & a_{12} & a_{13} \\ a_{21} & a_{22} & a_{23} \\ a_{31} & a_{32} & a_{33} \end{pmatrix}\begin{pmatrix} x_{12} \\ x_{22} \\ x_{32} \end{pmatrix} = \begin{pmatrix} 0 \\ 1 \\ 0 \end{pmatrix} \qquad \text{...(3)}$$

$$\begin{pmatrix} a_{11} & a_{12} & a_{13} \\ a_{21} & a_{22} & a_{23} \\ a_{31} & a_{32} & a_{33} \end{pmatrix}\begin{pmatrix} x_{13} \\ x_{23} \\ x_{33} \end{pmatrix} = \begin{pmatrix} 0 \\ 0 \\ 1 \end{pmatrix} \qquad \text{...(4)}$$

From equations (2), (3), (4), we can solve for the vectors $\begin{pmatrix} x_{11} \\ x_{21} \\ x_{31} \end{pmatrix}$, $\begin{pmatrix} x_{12} \\ x_{22} \\ x_{32} \end{pmatrix}$ and $\begin{pmatrix} x_{13} \\ x_{23} \\ x_{33} \end{pmatrix}$ by using Gaussian elimination method or even by Gauss-Jordan method. The solution set of each system (2), (3), (4) will be the corresponding column of the inverse matrix $X$.

**Note.** Since the coefficient matrix is same in all equations (2), (3), (4), we can solve all of them simultaneously.

**Example 1.** *Find, by Gaussian elimination method, the inverse of*

$$A = \begin{pmatrix} 3 & -1 & 1 \\ -15 & 6 & -5 \\ 5 & -2 & 2 \end{pmatrix}.$$

**Solution.** *Step 1.* We write down the augmented system $(A, I)$. That is,

$$(A, I) = \left(\begin{array}{ccc|ccc} 3 & -1 & 1 & 1 & 0 & 0 \\ -15 & 6 & -5 & 0 & 1 & 0 \\ 5 & -2 & 2 & 0 & 0 & 1 \end{array}\right) \qquad ...(1)$$

*Step 2.* Our aim is to reduce the matrix $A$ to an upper trianguiar matrix. Now we will reduce all elements below $a_{11}$ to zero. System (1) becomes

$$\left(\begin{array}{ccc|ccc} 3 & -1 & 1 & 1 & 0 & 0 \\ 0 & 1 & 0 & 5 & 1 & 0 \\ 0 & -\frac{1}{3} & \frac{1}{3} & -\frac{5}{3} & 0 & 1 \end{array}\right) \begin{array}{l} R_2 + 5R_1 \\ R_3 + \left(-\frac{5}{3}\right)R_1 \end{array} \qquad ...(2)$$

**Note.** When we reduce the elements below $a_{11}$ in $A$ to zero, only the first column of $I$ is changed while the second and third column remain unchanged.

*Step 3.* Now, we will reduce the elements below the position (2, 2) to zero.

Now the system (1), reduces to

$$\left(\begin{array}{ccc|ccc} 3 & -1 & 1 & 1 & 0 & 0 \\ 0 & 1 & 0 & 5 & 1 & 0 \\ 0 & 0 & \frac{1}{3} & 0 & \frac{1}{3} & 1 \end{array}\right) R_3 + \left(\frac{1}{3}\right)R_2 \qquad ...(3)$$

**Note.** When the elements below the position (2, 2) are reduced to zero, only the second column of $I$ is changed whereas the third column of $I$ is unchanged.

*Step 4.* Now the system is equivalent to the three systems,

$$\left(\begin{array}{ccc|c} 3 & -1 & 1 & 1 \\ 0 & 1 & 0 & 5 \\ 0 & 0 & \frac{1}{3} & 0 \end{array}\right) \qquad ...(4)$$

$$\left(\begin{array}{ccc|c} 3 & -1 & 1 & 0 \\ 0 & 1 & 0 & 1 \\ 0 & 0 & \frac{1}{3} & \frac{1}{3} \end{array}\right) \qquad ...(5)$$

and

$$\left(\begin{array}{ccc|c} 3 & -1 & 1 & 0 \\ 0 & 1 & 0 & 0 \\ 0 & 0 & \frac{1}{3} & 1 \end{array}\right) \qquad ...(6)$$

That is ,

$$\left.\begin{aligned} 3x_{11} - x_{21} + x_{31} &= 1 \\ x_{21} &= 5 \\ \frac{1}{3} x_{31} &= 0 \end{aligned}\right\} \Rightarrow \begin{aligned} x_{31} &= 0 \\ x_{21} &= 5 \\ x_{11} &= 2 \end{aligned}$$

$$\left.\begin{aligned} 3x_{12} - x_{22} + x_{32} &= 0 \\ x_{22} &= 1 \\ \frac{1}{3} x_{32} &= \frac{1}{3} \end{aligned}\right\} \quad \begin{aligned} x_{32} &= 1 \\ x_{22} &= 1 \\ x_{12} &= 0 \end{aligned}$$

and

$$\left.\begin{aligned} 3x_{13} - x_{23} + x_{33} &= 0 \\ x_{23} &= 0 \\ \frac{1}{3} x_{33} &= 1 \end{aligned}\right\} \quad \begin{aligned} x_{33} &= 3 \\ x_{23} &= 0 \\ x_{13} &= -1 \end{aligned}$$

Hence $$A^{-1} = \begin{pmatrix} 2 & 0 & -1 \\ 5 & 1 & 0 \\ 0 & 1 & 3 \end{pmatrix}$$

**Example 2.** *By Gaussian elimination, find the inverse of*

$$A = \begin{pmatrix} 0 & 1 & 1 \\ 1 & 2 & 0 \\ 3 & -1 & -4 \end{pmatrix}.$$

**Solution.** The augmented system $(A, I)$ is

$$(A, I) = \left(\begin{array}{ccc|ccc} 0 & 1 & 1 & 1 & 0 & 0 \\ 1 & 2 & 0 & 0 & 1 & 0 \\ 3 & -1 & -4 & 0 & 0 & 1 \end{array}\right) \qquad \text{...(1)}$$

Since the element $a_{11} = 0$, we will interchange the first and second row. The reduced system is

$$\left(\begin{array}{ccc|ccc} 1 & 2 & 0 & 0 & 1 & 0 \\ 0 & 1 & 1 & 1 & 0 & 0 \\ 3 & -1 & -4 & 0 & 0 & 1 \end{array}\right) \qquad \text{...(2)}$$

By performing $R_3 + (-3) R_1$, we get

$$\left(\begin{array}{ccc|ccc} 1 & 2 & 0 & 0 & 1 & 0 \\ 0 & 1 & 1 & 1 & 0 & 0 \\ 0 & -7 & -4 & 0 & -3 & 1 \end{array}\right) \qquad \text{...(3)}$$

Performing $R_3 + 7R_2$,

$$\left(\begin{array}{ccc|ccc} 1 & 2 & 0 & 0 & 1 & 0 \\ 0 & 1 & 1 & 1 & 0 & 0 \\ 0 & 0 & 3 & 7 & -3 & 1 \end{array}\right)$$

Thus,
$$\left.\begin{array}{r} x_{11} + 2x_{21} = 0 \\ x_{21} + x_{31} = 1 \\ 3x_{31} = 7 \end{array}\right\} \Rightarrow \begin{array}{l} x_{31} = \frac{7}{3} \\ x_{21} = -\frac{4}{3} \\ x_{11} = \frac{8}{3} \end{array}$$

$$\left.\begin{array}{r} x_{12} + 2x_{22} = 1 \\ x_{22} + x_{32} = 0 \\ 3x_{32} = -3 \end{array}\right\} \Rightarrow \begin{array}{l} x_{32} = -1 \\ x_{22} = 1 \\ x_{12} = -1 \end{array}$$

$$\left.\begin{array}{r} x_{13} + 2x_{23} = 0 \\ x_{23} + x_{33} = 0 \\ 3x_{33} = 1 \end{array}\right\} \Rightarrow \begin{array}{l} x_{33} = \frac{1}{3} \\ x_{23} = -\frac{1}{3} \\ x_{13} = \frac{2}{3} \end{array}$$

Hence
$$A^{-1} = \begin{pmatrix} \frac{8}{3} & -1 & \frac{2}{3} \\ -\frac{4}{3} & 1 & -\frac{1}{3} \\ \frac{7}{3} & -1 & \frac{1}{3} \end{pmatrix}$$

**Example 3.** *By Gaussian elimination, find $A^{-1}$ if*

$$A = \begin{pmatrix} 4 & 1 & 2 \\ 2 & 3 & -1 \\ 1 & -2 & 2 \end{pmatrix}.$$

**Solution.**
$$(A, I) \to \left(\begin{array}{ccc|ccc} 4 & 1 & 2 & 1 & 0 & 0 \\ 2 & 3 & -1 & 0 & 1 & 0 \\ 1 & -2 & 2 & 0 & 0 & 1 \end{array}\right) \qquad ...(1)$$

*Stage 1.* Perform $R_2 + \left(-\frac{1}{2}\right)R_1$ and $R_3 + \left(-\frac{1}{4}\right)R_1$. Then (1) reduces to

$$\left(\begin{array}{ccc|ccc} 4 & 1 & 2 & 1 & 0 & 0 \\ 0 & \frac{5}{2} & -2 & -\frac{1}{2} & 1 & 0 \\ 0 & -\frac{9}{4} & \frac{3}{2} & -\frac{1}{4} & 0 & 1 \end{array}\right)$$

*Stage 2.* Again taking $\frac{5}{2}$ as the pivot, reduce the position (3, 2) to zero. Perform $R_3 + \left(\frac{9}{10}\right)R_2$. Then augmented system reduces to

$$\left(\begin{array}{ccc|ccc} 4 & 1 & 2 & 1 & 0 & 0 \\ 0 & \frac{5}{2} & -2 & -\frac{1}{2} & 1 & 0 \\ 0 & 0 & -\frac{3}{10} & -\frac{14}{20} & \frac{9}{10} & 1 \end{array}\right)$$

$$\therefore \quad \left.\begin{aligned} 4x+y+2z &= 1 \\ \tfrac{5}{2}y-2z &= -\tfrac{1}{2} \\ -\tfrac{3}{10}z &= -\tfrac{14}{20} \end{aligned}\right\} \Rightarrow \begin{aligned} z &= \tfrac{7}{3} \\ y &= \tfrac{5}{3} \\ x &= -\tfrac{4}{3} \end{aligned}$$

Again $$\left.\begin{aligned} 4x+y+2z &= 0 \\ \tfrac{5}{2}y-2z &= 1 \\ -\tfrac{3}{10}z &= \tfrac{9}{10} \end{aligned}\right\} \Rightarrow \begin{aligned} z &= -3 \\ y &= -2 \\ x &= 2 \end{aligned}$$

Also $$\left.\begin{aligned} 4x+y+2z &= 0 \\ \tfrac{5}{2}y-2z &= 0 \\ -\tfrac{3}{10}z &= 1 \end{aligned}\right\} \Rightarrow \begin{aligned} z &= -\tfrac{10}{3} \\ y &= -\tfrac{8}{3} \\ x &= \tfrac{7}{3} \end{aligned}$$

$$\therefore \quad A^{-1} = \begin{pmatrix} -\frac{4}{3} & 2 & \frac{7}{3} \\ \frac{5}{3} & -2 & -\frac{8}{3} \\ \frac{7}{3} & -3 & -\frac{10}{3} \end{pmatrix}$$

## EXERCISE 4.2

Find, by Gaussian elimination, the inverses of the following matrices:

**1.** $\begin{pmatrix} 2 & 1 & 1 \\ 3 & 2 & 3 \\ 1 & 4 & 9 \end{pmatrix}$ **2.** $\begin{pmatrix} 3 & -3 & 4 \\ 2 & -3 & 4 \\ 0 & -1 & 1 \end{pmatrix}$ **3.** $\begin{pmatrix} 1 & 1 & 1 \\ 0 & 1 & -2 \\ -1 & 1 & 1 \end{pmatrix}$

**4.** $A = \begin{pmatrix} 3 & 2 & 4 \\ 2 & 1 & 1 \\ 1 & 3 & 5 \end{pmatrix}$ **5.** $A = \begin{pmatrix} 2 & 1 & 1 \\ 3 & 2 & 3 \\ 1 & 4 & 9 \end{pmatrix}$ **6.** $P = \begin{pmatrix} 2 & 1 & -1 \\ 0 & 2 & 1 \\ 5 & 2 & -3 \end{pmatrix}$

**7.** $A = \begin{pmatrix} 1 & 0 & -1 \\ 3 & 4 & 5 \\ 0 & -6 & -7 \end{pmatrix}$ **8.** $A = \begin{pmatrix} 1 & 2 & -1 \\ 3 & 8 & 2 \\ 4 & 9 & -1 \end{pmatrix}$ **9.** $A = \begin{pmatrix} 3 & 1 & 2 \\ 2 & -3 & -1 \\ 1 & 2 & 1 \end{pmatrix}$

### 4.4 Method of Triangularization (Or Method of factorization) (*Direct method*)

This method is also called as *decomposition* method. In this method, the coefficient matrix $A$ of the system $AX = B$, is decomposed or factorized into the product of a lower triangular matrix $L$ and an upper triangular matrix $U$. We will explain this method in the case of three equations in three unknowns.

Consider the system of equations

$$a_{11}x_1 + a_{12}x_2 + a_{13}x_3 = b_1$$
$$a_{21}x_1 + a_{22}x_2 + a_{23}x_3 = b_2 \qquad ...(1)$$
$$a_{31}x_1 + a_{32}x_2 + a_{33}x_3 = b_3$$

This system is equivalent to $AX = B$ ...(2)

where $$A = \begin{pmatrix} a_{11} & a_{12} & a_{13} \\ a_{21} & a_{22} & a_{23} \\ a_{31} & a_{32} & a_{33} \end{pmatrix}, \; X = \begin{pmatrix} x_1 \\ x_2 \\ x_3 \end{pmatrix} \text{ and } B = \begin{pmatrix} b_1 \\ b_2 \\ b_3 \end{pmatrix}$$

Now we will factorize $A$ as the product of lower triangular matrix

$$L = \begin{pmatrix} 1 & 0 & 0 \\ l_{21} & 1 & 0 \\ l_{31} & l_{32} & 1 \end{pmatrix}$$

and an upper triangular matrix

$$U = \begin{pmatrix} u_{11} & u_{12} & u_{13} \\ 0 & u_{22} & u_{23} \\ 0 & 0 & u_{33} \end{pmatrix} \text{ so that}$$

$$LUX = B \qquad ...(3)$$

Let $$UX = Y \qquad ...(4)$$

and hence $$LY = B \qquad ...(5)$$

That is, $$\begin{pmatrix} 1 & 0 & 0 \\ l_{21} & 1 & 0 \\ l_{31} & l_{32} & 1 \end{pmatrix} \begin{pmatrix} y_1 \\ y_2 \\ y_3 \end{pmatrix} = \begin{pmatrix} b_1 \\ b_2 \\ b_3 \end{pmatrix} \qquad ...(6)$$

$\therefore \; y_1 = b, \; l_{21}y_1 + y_2 = b_2, \; l_{31}y_1 + l_{32}y_2 + y_3 = b_3$

By forward substitution, $y_1, y_2, y_3$ can be found out if $L$ is known.

From (4),

$$\begin{pmatrix} u_{11} & u_{12} & u_{13} \\ 0 & u_{22} & u_{23} \\ 0 & 0 & u_{33} \end{pmatrix} \begin{pmatrix} x_1 \\ x_2 \\ x_3 \end{pmatrix} = \begin{pmatrix} y_1 \\ y_2 \\ y_3 \end{pmatrix}$$

*i.e.,* $$u_{11}x_1 + u_{12}x_2 + u_{13}x_3 = y_1$$
$$u_{22}x_2 + u_{23}x_3 = y_2$$
$$u_{33}x_3 = y_3$$

From these, $x_1, x_2, x_3$ can be solved by back substitution, since $y_1, y_2, y_3$ are known if $U$ is known.

Now $L$ and $U$ can be found from

$$LU = A$$

*i.e.*, $\begin{pmatrix} 1 & 0 & 0 \\ l_{21} & 1 & 0 \\ l_{31} & l_{32} & 1 \end{pmatrix}\begin{pmatrix} u_{11} & u_{12} & u_{13} \\ 0 & u_{22} & u_{23} \\ 0 & 0 & u_{33} \end{pmatrix} = \begin{pmatrix} a_{11} & a_{12} & a_{13} \\ a_{21} & a_{22} & a_{23} \\ a_{31} & a_{32} & a_{33} \end{pmatrix}$

*i.e.*, $\begin{pmatrix} u_{11} & u_{12} & u_{13} \\ l_{21} u_{11} & l_{21} u_{12} + u_{22} & l_{21} u_{13} + u_{23} \\ l_{31} u_{11} & l_{31} u_{12} + l_{32} u_{22} & l_{31} u_{13} + l_{32} u_{23} + u_{33} \end{pmatrix} = \begin{pmatrix} a_{11} & a_{12} & a_{13} \\ a_{21} & a_{22} & a_{23} \\ a_{31} & a_{32} & a_{33} \end{pmatrix}$

Equating corresponding coefficients we get nine equations in nine unknowns. From these 9 equations, we can solve for $3l$'s and 6 $u$'s.

That is, $L$ and $U$ are known. Hence $X$ is found out. Going into details, we get $u_{11} = a_{11}$, $u_{12} = a_{12}$, $u_{13} = a_{13}$. That is the elements in the first row of $U$ are same as the elements in the first of $A$.

Also, $\quad l_{21} u_{11} = a_{21}, \; l_{21} u_{12} + u_{22} = a_{22}, \; l_{21} u_{13} + u_{23} = a_{23}$

$$\therefore \quad l_{21} = \frac{a_{21}}{a_{11}}, \; u_{22} = a_{22} - \frac{a_{21}}{a_{11}} \cdot a_{12} \text{ and } u_{23} = a_{23} - \frac{a_{21}}{a_{11}} \cdot a_{13}$$

Again, $l_{31} u_{11} = a_{31}$, $l_{31} u_{12} + l_{32} u_{22} = a_{32}$ and
$l_{31} u_{13} + l_{32} u_{23} + u_{33} = a_{33}$

$$\text{Solving,} \quad l_{31} = \frac{a_{31}}{a_{11}}, \; l_{32} = \frac{a_{32} - \dfrac{a_{31}}{a_{11}} \cdot a_{12}}{a_{22} - \dfrac{a_{21}}{a_{11}} \cdot a_{12}},$$

$$u_{33} = a_{33} - \frac{a_{31}}{a_{11}} \cdot a_{13} - \left( \frac{a_{32} - \dfrac{a_{31}}{a_{11}} \cdot a_{12}}{a_{22} - \dfrac{a_{21}}{a_{11}} \cdot a_{12}} \right) \left( a_{23} - \frac{a_{21}}{a_{11}} \cdot a_{13} \right)$$

Therefore $L$ and $U$ are known.

**Note.** In selecting $L$ and $U$ we can also take as

$$= \begin{pmatrix} l_{11} & 0 & 0 \\ l_{21} & l_{22} & 0 \\ l_{31} & l_{32} & l_{33} \end{pmatrix} \text{ and } U = = \begin{pmatrix} 1 & u_{12} & u_{13} \\ 0 & 1 & u_{23} \\ 0 & 0 & 1 \end{pmatrix}$$

so that $A = LU$.

**Example 1.** *By the method of triangularization, solve the following system:*

$$5x - 2y + z = 4, \; 7x + y - 5z = 8; \; 3x + 7y + 4z = 10.$$

**Solution.** The system is equivalent to

$$\begin{pmatrix} 5 & -2 & 1 \\ 7 & 1 & -5 \\ 3 & 7 & 4 \end{pmatrix}\begin{pmatrix} x \\ y \\ z \end{pmatrix} = \begin{pmatrix} 4 \\ 8 \\ 10 \end{pmatrix} \qquad ...(1)$$

*i.e.,*
$$A \cdot X = B$$

Now, let $LU = A$

That is, $\begin{pmatrix} 1 & 0 & 0 \\ l_{21} & 1 & 0 \\ l_{31} & l_{32} & 1 \end{pmatrix} \begin{pmatrix} u_{11} & u_{12} & u_{13} \\ 0 & u_{22} & u_{23} \\ 0 & 0 & u_{33} \end{pmatrix} = \begin{pmatrix} 5 & -2 & 1 \\ 7 & 1 & -5 \\ 3 & 7 & 4 \end{pmatrix}$

Multiplying and equating coefficients,

$$u_{11} = 5,\ u_{12} = -2,\ u_{13} = 1$$

$$l_{21}\, u_{11} = 7,\ l_{21}\, u_{12} + u_{22} = 1,\ l_{21}\, u_{13} + u_{23} = -5$$

Hence $l_{21} = \frac{7}{5},\ u_{22} = 1 - \frac{7}{5}(-2) = \frac{19}{5}$

$$u_{23} = -5 - \frac{7}{5} \times 1 = -\frac{32}{5}$$

Again equating elements in the third row,

$$l_{31}\, u_{11} = 3,\ l_{31}\, u_{12} + l_{32}\, u_{22} = 7,\ l_{31}\, u_{13} + l_{32}\, u_{23} + u_{33} = 4$$

$$\therefore \quad l_{31} = \frac{3}{5},\ l_{32} = \frac{7 - \frac{3}{5}(-2)}{\frac{19}{5}} = \frac{41}{19}$$

$$u_{33} = 4 - \frac{3}{5}(1) - \frac{41}{19}\left(-\frac{32}{5}\right)$$

$$= 4 - \frac{3}{5} + \frac{1312}{95}$$

$$= \frac{1635}{95} = \frac{327}{19}$$

Now $L$ and $U$ are known.

Since $LUX = B$

*i.e.,* $LY = B$ where $UX = Y$.

From $LY = B$,

$$\begin{pmatrix} 1 & 0 & 0 \\ \frac{7}{5} & 1 & 0 \\ \frac{3}{5} & \frac{41}{19} & 1 \end{pmatrix} \begin{pmatrix} y_1 \\ y_2 \\ y_3 \end{pmatrix} = \begin{pmatrix} 4 \\ 8 \\ 10 \end{pmatrix}$$

$$\therefore \quad y_1 = 4,\ \frac{7}{5} y_1 + y_2 = 8,\ \frac{3}{5} y_1 + \frac{41}{19} y_2 + y_3 = 10$$

$$\therefore \quad y_2 = 8 - \frac{28}{5} = \frac{12}{5}$$

$$y_3 = 10 - \frac{12}{5} - \frac{41}{19} \times \frac{12}{5} = 10 - \frac{12}{5} - \frac{492}{95} = \frac{46}{19}$$

$$UX = Y \text{ gives } \begin{pmatrix} 5 & -2 & 1 \\ 0 & \frac{19}{5} & -\frac{32}{5} \\ 0 & 0 & \frac{327}{19} \end{pmatrix} \begin{pmatrix} x \\ y \\ z \end{pmatrix} = \begin{pmatrix} 4 \\ \frac{12}{5} \\ \frac{46}{19} \end{pmatrix}$$

$$\therefore \quad 5x - 2y + z = 4$$

$$\frac{19}{5}y - \frac{32}{5}z = \frac{12}{5}$$

$$\frac{327}{19}z = \frac{46}{19}; \quad \text{By back substitution,}$$

$$\therefore \quad z = \frac{46}{327}$$

$$\frac{19y}{5} = \frac{12}{5} + \frac{32}{5}\left(\frac{46}{327}\right)$$

$$\therefore \quad y = \frac{284}{327}$$

$$5x = 4 + 2y - z = 4 + \frac{568}{327} - \frac{46}{327}$$

$$\therefore \quad x = \frac{366}{327}$$

$$\therefore \quad x = \frac{366}{327},\ y = \frac{284}{327},\ z = \frac{46}{327}$$

**Example 2.** *Solve, by Triangularization method, the following system:* $x + 5y + z = 14$, $2x + y + 3z = 13$, $3x + y + 4z = 17$.

**Solution.** This is equivalent to

$$\begin{pmatrix} 1 & 5 & 1 \\ 2 & 1 & 3 \\ 3 & 1 & 4 \end{pmatrix} \begin{pmatrix} x \\ y \\ z \end{pmatrix} = \begin{pmatrix} 14 \\ 13 \\ 17 \end{pmatrix}$$

*i.e.* $$A \; X = B$$

Let $$LU = \begin{pmatrix} 1 & 0 & 0 \\ l_{21} & 1 & 0 \\ l_{31} & l_{32} & 1 \end{pmatrix} \begin{pmatrix} u_{11} & u_{12} & u_{13} \\ 0 & u_{22} & u_{23} \\ 0 & 0 & u_{33} \end{pmatrix} = \begin{pmatrix} 1 & 5 & 1 \\ 2 & 1 & 3 \\ 3 & 1 & 4 \end{pmatrix}$$

By seeing, we can write $u_{11} = 1$, $u_{12} = 5$, $u_{13} = 1$.

$$\therefore \quad \begin{pmatrix} 1 & 0 & 0 \\ l_{21} & 1 & 0 \\ l_{31} & l_{32} & 1 \end{pmatrix} \begin{pmatrix} 1 & 5 & 1 \\ 0 & u_{22} & u_{23} \\ 0 & 0 & u_{33} \end{pmatrix} = \begin{pmatrix} 1 & 5 & 1 \\ 2 & 1 & 3 \\ 3 & 1 & 4 \end{pmatrix}$$

Hence, $l_{21} = 2$; $5l_{21} + u_{22} = 1$, $l_{21} + u_{23} = 3$

$$\therefore \quad l_{21} = 2,\ u_{22} = -9,\ u_{23} = 1$$

Again, $l_{31} = 3$; $5l_{31} + l_{32}\,u_{22} = 1$; $l_{31} + l_{32}\,u_{23} + u_{33} = 4$

$\therefore \qquad l_{32} = \frac{1-15}{-9} = \frac{14}{9}\,;\; u_{33} = 4 - 3 - \frac{14}{9} = -\frac{5}{9}$

$LUX = B$ implies $\quad LY = B$ where $UX = Y$

$LY = B$ gives,

$$\begin{pmatrix} 1 & 0 & 0 \\ 2 & 1 & 0 \\ 3 & \frac{14}{9} & 1 \end{pmatrix} \begin{pmatrix} y_1 \\ y_2 \\ y_3 \end{pmatrix} = \begin{pmatrix} 14 \\ 13 \\ 17 \end{pmatrix}$$

*i.e.*, $\qquad y_1 = 14,\; 2y_1 + y_2 = 13,\; 3y_1 + \frac{14}{9} y_2 + y_3 = 17$

$\therefore\; y_1 = 14,\; y_2 = -15,\; y_3 = -\frac{5}{3}$

$UX = Y$ implies,

$$\begin{pmatrix} 1 & 5 & 1 \\ 0 & -9 & 1 \\ 0 & 0 & -\frac{5}{9} \end{pmatrix} \begin{pmatrix} x \\ y \\ z \end{pmatrix} = \begin{pmatrix} 14 \\ -15 \\ -\frac{5}{3} \end{pmatrix}$$

*i.e.*,

$$x + 5y + z = 14$$
$$-9y + z = -15$$
$$-\frac{5}{9} z = -\frac{5}{3}$$

$$\therefore \qquad z = 3,\; y = 2,\; x = 1.$$

**Example 3.** *Solve the following system by triangularization method:*

$$x + y + z = 1,\quad 4x + 3y - z = 6,\quad 3x + 5y + 3z = 4.$$

**Solution.** Here $A = \begin{pmatrix} 1 & 1 & 1 \\ 4 & 3 & -1 \\ 3 & 5 & 3 \end{pmatrix},\; X = \begin{pmatrix} x \\ y \\ z \end{pmatrix},\; B = \begin{pmatrix} 1 \\ 6 \\ 4 \end{pmatrix}$

$$\therefore \qquad LU = \begin{pmatrix} 1 & 0 & 0 \\ l_{21} & 1 & 0 \\ l_{31} & l_{32} & 1 \end{pmatrix} \begin{pmatrix} u_{11} & u_{12} & u_{13} \\ 0 & u_{22} & u_{23} \\ 0 & 0 & u_{33} \end{pmatrix} = \begin{pmatrix} 1 & 1 & 1 \\ 4 & 3 & -1 \\ 3 & 5 & 3 \end{pmatrix}$$

$\therefore \qquad u_{11} = u_{12} = u_{13} = 1.$

$l_{21}\, u_{11} = 4,\; l_{21}\, u_{12} + u_{22} = 3,\; l_{21}\, u_{13} + u_{23} = -1$

$\therefore \qquad l_{21} = 4,\; u_{22} = -1,\; u_{23} = -5$

$l_{31} = 3,\; l_{31} + l_{32}\, u_{22} = 5,\; l_{31} + l_{32}\, u_{23} + u_{33} = 3$

$l_{32} = -2,\; u_{33} = -10$

Now, $LUX = B$ implies $\quad LY = B$ where $UX = Y$

$$\begin{pmatrix} 1 & 0 & 0 \\ 4 & 1 & 0 \\ 3 & -2 & 1 \end{pmatrix}\begin{pmatrix} y_1 \\ y_2 \\ y_3 \end{pmatrix} = \begin{pmatrix} 1 \\ 6 \\ 4 \end{pmatrix}$$

$y_1 = 1;\ 4y_1 + y_2 = 6,\ 3y_1 - 2y_2 + y_3 = 4$

$\therefore\ y_1 = 1,\ y_2 = 2,\ y_3 = 5$

$UX = Y$ gives,

$$\begin{pmatrix} 1 & 1 & 1 \\ 0 & -1 & -5 \\ 0 & 0 & -10 \end{pmatrix}\begin{pmatrix} x \\ y \\ z \end{pmatrix} = \begin{pmatrix} 1 \\ 2 \\ 5 \end{pmatrix}$$

$$x + y + z = 1$$
$$-y - 5z = 2$$
$$-10z = 5$$

Hence, $z = -\frac{1}{2},\ y = \frac{1}{2},\ x = 1.$

## EXERCISE 4.3

Solve the following system of equations by triangularization method:

1. $x + y + 5z = 16,\ 2x + 3y + z = 4$ and $4x + y - z = 4$
2. $x - y + z = 6,\ 2x + 4y + z = 3,\ 3x + 2y - 2z = -2$
3. $2x + y + 4z = 12,\ 8x - 3y + 2z = 20,\ 4x + 11y - z = 33$
4. $x + 3y + 4z = 1,\ x + 4y + 3z = -2,\ x + 3y + 8z = 4$
5. $x + y + z = 1,\ 3x + y - 3z = 5,\ x - 2y - 5z = 10$
6. $2x + y + 4z = 4,\ x - 3y - z = -5,\ 3x - 2y + 2z = -1$
7. $3x + 4y + 5z = 18,\ 2x - y + 8z = 13,\ 5x - 2y + 7z = 20$
8. $x + 2y + 5z = 23,\ 3x + y + 4z = 26,\ 6x + y + 7z = 47$
9. $x - y - 3z = 0,\ x + 2y - z = -1,\ 3x - y - 2z = 5$
10. $x + y + 2z = 4,\ 3x + y - 3z = -4,\ 2x - 3y - 5z = -5$
11. $2x + 3y + 2z = 2,\ 10x + 3y + 4z = 16,\ 3x + 6y + z = -6$
12. $x + y + z = 3,\ 2x + 3y + 4z = 9,\ 3x - 3y + z = 1$
13. $2x - 6y + 8z = 24,\ 3x + y + 2z = 16,\ 5x + 4y - 3z = 2$
14. $x + y - z = 1,\ 3x + y + z = 1,\ 4x + 3y + 2z = -1$
15. $2x + 4y + 6z = 6,\ 2x - 4y - 6z = -4,\ 4x + 8y + 12z = 12$
16. $3x + y + 2z = 3,\ 2x - 3y - z = -3,\ x + 2y + z = 4$

Solution of Simultaneous Linear Algebraic Equations

## 4·5 Crout's method (Direct method)

This is also a direct method. Here also, we decompose the coefficient matrix $A$ as $LU$ and proceed. But we will follow a different technique as suggested by *Crout*

As in the previous article, we want to solve the system

$$AX = B \quad ...(1)$$

where $A = \begin{pmatrix} a_{11} & a_{12} & a_{13} \\ a_{21} & a_{22} & a_{23} \\ a_{31} & a_{32} & a_{33} \end{pmatrix}$, $X = \begin{pmatrix} x_1 \\ x_2 \\ x_3 \end{pmatrix}$ and $B = \begin{pmatrix} b_1 \\ b_2 \\ b_3 \end{pmatrix}$

Suppose we decompose $A = LU$ ...(2)

where $L = \begin{pmatrix} l_{11} & 0 & 0 \\ l_{21} & l_{22} & 0 \\ l_{31} & l_{32} & l_{33} \end{pmatrix}$ and $U = \begin{pmatrix} 1 & u_{12} & u_{13} \\ 0 & 1 & u_{23} \\ 0 & 0 & 1 \end{pmatrix}$

Since $AX = B$, $LUX = B$

$\therefore$ $LY = B$ where $UX = Y$ ...(3)

$LU = A$ reduces to

$$\begin{bmatrix} l_{11} & 0 & 0 \\ l_{21} & l_{22} & 0 \\ l_{31} & l_{32} & l_{33} \end{bmatrix} \begin{bmatrix} 1 & u_{12} & u_{13} \\ 0 & 1 & u_{23} \\ 0 & 0 & 1 \end{bmatrix} = \begin{bmatrix} a_{11} & a_{12} & a_{13} \\ a_{21} & a_{22} & a_{23} \\ a_{31} & a_{32} & a_{33} \end{bmatrix} \quad ...(4)$$

*i.e.*, $$\begin{bmatrix} l_{11} & l_{11} u_{12} & l_{11} u_{13} \\ l_{21} & l_{21} u_{12} + l_{22} & l_{21} u_{13} + l_{22} u_{23} \\ l_{31} & l_{31} u_{12} + l_{32} & l_{31} u_{13} + l_{32} u_{23} + l_{33} \end{bmatrix} = \begin{bmatrix} a_{11} & a_{12} & a_{13} \\ a_{21} & a_{22} & a_{23} \\ a_{31} & a_{32} & a_{33} \end{bmatrix}$$

Equating coefficients and simplifying as in the previous article, we have

$$l_{11} = a_{11},\ l_{21} = a_{21},\ l_{31} = a_{31}$$

$$u_{12} = \frac{a_{12}}{a_{11}},\ u_{13} = \frac{a_{13}}{a_{11}}$$

$$l_{22} = a_{22} - l_{21} u_{12},\ l_{32} = a_{32} - l_{31} u_{12}$$

$$u_{23} = \frac{a_{23} - l_{21} u_{13}}{l_{22}},\ l_{33} = a_{33} - l_{31} u_{13} - l_{32} u_{23}$$

Now $L$ and $U$ are known.

Since $LY = B$, we get

$$\begin{pmatrix} l_{11} & 0 & 0 \\ l_{21} & l_{22} & 0 \\ l_{31} & l_{32} & l_{33} \end{pmatrix} \begin{pmatrix} y_1 \\ y_2 \\ y_3 \end{pmatrix} = \begin{pmatrix} b_1 \\ b_2 \\ b_3 \end{pmatrix}$$

Multiplying and equating coefficients,

| | Therefore |
|---|---|
| $l_{11} y_1 = b_1$ | |
| $l_{21} y_1 + l_{22} y_2 = b_2$ | $y_1 = \dfrac{b_1}{a_{11}}$ |

$$l_{31}\,y_1 + l_{32}\,y_2 + l_{33}\,y_3 = b_3 \qquad y_2 = \frac{b_2 - l_{21}\,y_1}{l_{22}}$$

$$y_3 = \frac{b_3 - l_{31}\,y_1 - l_{32}\,y_2}{l_{33}}$$

Knowing $Y = \begin{pmatrix} y_1 \\ y_2 \\ y_3 \end{pmatrix}$, $L$ and $U$,

$X$ can be found out from $UX = Y$.

**Note.** *Computation scheme by Crout's method :* We write down the 12 unknowns $l_{11}, l_{21}, l_{22}, l_{31}, l_{32}, l_{33}, u_{12}, u_{13}, u_{23}, y_1, y_2, y_3$ as a matrix below, called, auxiliary matrix or derived matrix.

$$\text{derived matrix} = \begin{pmatrix} l_{11} & u_{12} & u_{13} & y_1 \\ l_{21} & l_{22} & u_{23} & y_2 \\ l_{31} & l_{32} & l_{33} & y_3 \end{pmatrix}$$

If we know the derived matrix, we can write $L$, $U$ and $Y$. The derived matrix is got as explained below, using the augmented matrix $(A, B)$.

*Step 1. The first column of D.M.* (derived matrix) is the same as the first column of A.

*Step 2. The remaining elements of first row of D.M.* Each element of the first row of D.M. (except the first element $l_{11}$) is got by dividing the corresponding element in $(A, B)$ by the leading diagonal element of that row.

*Step 3. Remaining elements of second column of D.M.*

Since $l_{22} = a_{22} - l_{21}\,u_{12}$; $l_{32} = a_{32} - l_{31}\,u_{12}$

Each element of second column except the top element $\Big\}$ = Corresponding element in $(A, B)$ minus the product of the first element in that row and in that column.

*Step 4. Remaining elements of second row.*

Each element = Corresponding element in $(A, B)$ minus sum of the inner products of the previously calculated elements in the same row and column divided by diagonal element in that row.

*Step 5. Remaining element of third column.*

$$l_{33} = a_{33} - l_{31}\,u_{13} - l_{32}\,u_{23}$$

The element = Corresponding element of $(A, B)$ – (sum of the inner products of the previously calculated elements in the same row and column).

*Step 6. Remaining element of third row.*

$$y_3 = \frac{b_3 - (l_{31}\, y_1 + l_{32}\, y_2)}{l_{33}}$$

The element = Corresponding element of $(A, B)$ – Sum of the inner products of the previously calculated elements in the same row and column divided by the diagonal element in that row.

**Example 1.** *By Crout's method, solve the system:*

$$2x + 3y + z = -1, \quad 5x + y + z = 9; \quad 3x + 2y + 4z = 11.$$

**Solution.** Augmented matrix $= (A, B) = \left[\begin{array}{ccc|c} 2 & 3 & 1 & -1 \\ 5 & 1 & 1 & 9 \\ 3 & 2 & 4 & 11 \end{array}\right]$

Let the derived matrix be D.M $= \begin{pmatrix} l_{11} & u_{12} & u_{13} & y_1 \\ l_{21} & l_{22} & u_{23} & y_2 \\ l_{31} & l_{32} & l_{33} & y_3 \end{pmatrix}$

*Step 1. Elements of first column of D.M. are* $\begin{bmatrix} 2 & \cdot & \cdot & \cdot \\ 5 & \cdot & \cdot & \cdot \\ 3 & \cdot & \cdot & \cdot \end{bmatrix}$

*Step 2. Elements of first row.*

$$u_{12} = \frac{a_{12}}{l_{11}} = \frac{3}{2}$$

$$u_{13} = \frac{a_{13}}{l_{11}} = \frac{1}{2}$$

$$y_1 = \frac{b_1}{l_{11}} = \frac{-1}{2}$$

$$\text{D.M.} = \begin{bmatrix} 2 & \frac{3}{2} & \frac{1}{2} & -\frac{1}{2} \\ 5 & \cdot & \cdot & \cdot \\ 3 & \cdot & \cdot & \cdot \end{bmatrix}$$

*Step 3. Elements of second column.*

$$l_{22} = a_{22} - u_{12}\, l_{21}$$

$$= 1 - 5 \times \frac{3}{2} = \frac{-13}{2}$$

$$l_{32} = a_{32} - l_{31}\, u_{12}$$

$$= 2 - 3 \times \frac{3}{2} = -\frac{5}{2}$$

$$\text{D.M.} = \begin{bmatrix} 2 & \frac{3}{2} & \frac{1}{2} & -\frac{1}{2} \\ 5 & -\frac{13}{2} & \cdot & \cdot \\ 3 & -\frac{5}{2} & \cdot & \cdot \end{bmatrix}$$

*Step 4. Elements of 2nd row.*

$$u_{23} = \frac{a_{23} - u_{13}\, l_{31}}{l_{22}}$$

$$= \frac{1 - 5 \times \frac{1}{2}}{-13/2} = \frac{3}{13} \qquad \text{D.M.} = \begin{bmatrix} 2 & \frac{3}{2} & \frac{1}{2} & -\frac{1}{2} \\ 5 & \frac{-13}{2} & \frac{3}{13} & \frac{-23}{13} \\ 3 & \frac{-5}{2} & \cdot & \cdot \end{bmatrix}$$

$$y_2 = \frac{9 - 5(-1/2)}{\frac{-13}{2}} = \frac{-23}{13}$$

*Step 5.* $l_{33} = 4 - 3\left(\frac{1}{2}\right) - (-5/2)\left(\frac{3}{13}\right) \qquad \text{D.M.} = \begin{bmatrix} 2 & \frac{3}{2} & \frac{1}{2} & -\frac{1}{2} \\ 5 & \frac{-13}{2} & \frac{3}{13} & \frac{-23}{13} \\ 3 & \frac{-5}{2} & \frac{40}{13} & \cdot \end{bmatrix}$

$$= 4 - \frac{3}{2} + \frac{15}{26} = \frac{40}{13}$$

*Step 6.* $y_3 = \dfrac{11 - 3(-1/2) - (-5/2)\left(\frac{-23}{13}\right)}{\frac{40}{13}} = \dfrac{21}{8}$

$$\therefore \quad \text{D.M.} = \begin{bmatrix} 2 & 3/2 & 1/2 & -1/2 \\ 5 & \frac{-13}{2} & \frac{3}{13} & \frac{-23}{13} \\ 3 & \frac{-5}{2} & \frac{40}{13} & \frac{21}{8} \end{bmatrix}$$

The solution is got from $UX = Y$

*i.e.,*
$$\begin{bmatrix} 1 & u_{12} & u_{13} \\ 0 & 1 & u_{23} \\ 0 & 0 & 1 \end{bmatrix} \begin{bmatrix} x \\ y \\ z \end{bmatrix} = \begin{bmatrix} y_1 \\ y_2 \\ y_3 \end{bmatrix}$$

$$\begin{bmatrix} 1 & \frac{3}{2} & \frac{1}{2} \\ 0 & 1 & \frac{3}{13} \\ 0 & 0 & 1 \end{bmatrix} \begin{bmatrix} x \\ y \\ z \end{bmatrix} = \begin{bmatrix} -\frac{1}{2} \\ -\frac{23}{13} \\ \frac{21}{8} \end{bmatrix}$$

$$\therefore \quad z = \frac{21}{8}; \; y + \frac{3}{13} z = \frac{-23}{13}; \; x + \frac{3y}{2} + \frac{1}{z} = -1/2$$

$$\therefore \quad y = \frac{-23}{13} - \frac{3}{13}\left(\frac{21}{8}\right) = \frac{-19}{8}$$

$$x = -\frac{3}{2}\left(-\frac{19}{8}\right) - \frac{1}{2}\left(\frac{21}{8}\right) - \frac{1}{2} = \frac{7}{4}$$

$$\therefore \quad x = \frac{7}{4}, \; y = -\frac{19}{8}, \; z = \frac{21}{8}$$

**Example 2.** *Solve, by Crout's method, the following:*
$x+y+z=3,\ 2x-y+3z=16,\ 3x+y-z=-3.$ [*MKU 1981*]

**Solution.** Here, $(A, B)=\left[\begin{array}{ccc|c} 1 & 1 & 1 & 3 \\ 2 & -1 & 3 & 16 \\ 3 & 1 & -1 & -3 \end{array}\right]$

Let the derived matrix be: $\text{D.M.}=\left[\begin{array}{ccc|c} l_{11} & u_{12} & u_{13} & y_1 \\ l_{21} & l_{22} & u_{23} & y_2 \\ l_{31} & l_{32} & l_{33} & y_3 \end{array}\right]$

*Step 1.* Elements of first column of D.M. are $=\begin{bmatrix} 1 & \cdot & \cdot & \cdot \\ 2 & \cdot & \cdot & \cdot \\ 3 & \cdot & \cdot & \cdot \end{bmatrix}$

*Step 2.* Elements of first row of D.M.:

$$u_{12}=\frac{1}{1}=1;\quad u_{13}=\frac{1}{1}=1\ ;\quad y_1=\frac{3}{1}=3$$

$$\therefore \qquad \text{D.M.}=\begin{bmatrix} 1 & 1 & 1 & 3 \\ 2 & \cdot & \cdot & \cdot \\ 3 & \cdot & \cdot & \cdot \end{bmatrix}$$

*Step 3.* Elements of second column:

$$l_{22}=a_{22}-u_{12}\,l_{21}=-1-2=-3$$

$$l_{32}=a_{32}-u_{12}\,l_{31}=1-1\times 3=-2$$

$$\therefore\ \text{D.M.}=\begin{bmatrix} 1 & 1 & 1 & 3 \\ 2 & -3 & \cdot & \cdot \\ 3 & -2 & \cdot & \cdot \end{bmatrix}$$

*Step 4.* Elements of second row:

$$u_{23}=\frac{3-1\,(+2)}{-3}=\frac{-1}{3}$$

$$y_2=\frac{16-3\times 2}{-3}=\frac{-10}{3}$$

$$\therefore \qquad \text{D.M.}=\begin{bmatrix} 1 & 1 & 1 & 3 \\ 2 & -3 & -\frac{1}{3} & \frac{-10}{3} \\ 3 & -2 & \cdot & \cdot \end{bmatrix}$$

*Step 5.* Elements of third column:

$$l_{33}=-1-1\,(3)-(-1/3)\,(-2)=-\frac{14}{3}$$

*Step 6.* Elements of third row:

$$y_3 = \frac{-3-(3)(3)-(-2)\left(\frac{-10}{3}\right)}{-\frac{14}{3}} = 4$$

$$\text{D.M.} = \begin{bmatrix} 1 & 1 & 1 & 3 \\ 2 & -3 & -1/3 & \frac{-10}{3} \\ 3 & -2 & \frac{-14}{3} & 4 \end{bmatrix}$$

The solution is got from $UX = Y$, *i.e.*,

$$\begin{bmatrix} 1 & 1 & 1 \\ 0 & 1 & -1/3 \\ 0 & 0 & 1 \end{bmatrix} \begin{bmatrix} x \\ y \\ z \end{bmatrix} = \begin{bmatrix} 3 \\ -10/3 \\ 4 \end{bmatrix}$$

$$x + y + z = 3$$

$$y - \frac{1}{3}z = \frac{-10}{3}$$

$$z = 4$$

By back substitution, $z = 4$, $y = -2$, $x = 1$.

**Example 3.** *By Crout's method, solve the system:*

$$x + 2y + 3z + 4w = 20$$
$$3x - 2y + 8z + 4w = 26$$
$$2x + y - 4z + 7w = 10$$
$$4x + 2y - 8z - 4w = 2$$

**Solution.** The augmented matrix $= (A, B) = \left[\begin{array}{cccc|c} 1 & 2 & 3 & 4 & 20 \\ 3 & -2 & 8 & 4 & 26 \\ 2 & 1 & -4 & 7 & 10 \\ 4 & 2 & -8 & -4 & 2 \end{array}\right]$

The derived matrix = D.M. $= \begin{bmatrix} l_{11} & u_{12} & u_{13} & u_{14} & y_1 \\ l_{21} & l_{22} & u_{23} & u_{24} & y_2 \\ l_{31} & l_{32} & l_{33} & u_{34} & y_3 \\ l_{41} & l_{42} & l_{43} & l_{44} & y_4 \end{bmatrix}$

*Step 1.* The first column of D.M. is $= \begin{bmatrix} 1 & \cdot & \cdot & \cdot & \cdot \\ 3 & \cdot & \cdot & \cdot & \cdot \\ 2 & \cdot & \cdot & \cdot & \cdot \\ 4 & \cdot & \cdot & \cdot & \cdot \end{bmatrix}$

*Step 2.* The elements of first row:

$$u_{12}=\frac{2}{1}=2;\ u_{13}=\frac{3}{1}=3;\ u_{14}=\frac{4}{1}=4;\ y_1=\frac{20}{1}=20$$

$$\text{D.M.}=\left[\begin{array}{cccc|c} 1 & 2 & 3 & 4 & 20 \\ 3 & \cdot & \cdot & \cdot & \cdot \\ 2 & \cdot & \cdot & \cdot & \cdot \\ 4 & \cdot & \cdot & \cdot & \cdot \end{array}\right]$$

*Step 3.* Elements of second column:

$$l_{22}=-2-3\times 2=-8$$

$$l_{32}=1-4=-3$$

$$l_{42}=2-8=-6$$

$$\therefore \quad \text{D.M.}=\left[\begin{array}{cccc|c} 1 & 2 & 3 & 4 & 20 \\ 3 & -8 & \cdot & \cdot & \cdot \\ 2 & -3 & \cdot & \cdot & \cdot \\ 4 & -6 & \cdot & \cdot & \cdot \end{array}\right]$$

*Step 4.* The elements in second row:

$$u_{23}=\frac{a_{23}-l_{21}\,u_{13}}{l_{22}}=\frac{8-9}{-8}=\frac{1}{8}$$

$$u_{24}=\frac{4-4\times 3}{-8}=1$$

$$y_2=\frac{26-20\times 3}{-8}=\frac{17}{4}$$

$$\therefore \quad \text{D.M.}=\left[\begin{array}{cccc|c} 1 & 2 & 3 & 4 & 20 \\ 3 & -8 & \frac{1}{8} & 1 & \frac{17}{4} \\ 2 & -3 & \cdot & \cdot & \cdot \\ 4 & -6 & \cdot & \cdot & \cdot \end{array}\right]$$

*Step 5.* Elements of third column:

$$l_{33}=a_{33}-(l_{31}\,u_{13}+l_{32}\,u_{23})$$

$$=-4-(3\times 2)-(-3)\left(\frac{1}{8}\right)=-\frac{77}{8}$$

$$l_{43}=a_{43}-(l_{41}\,u_{13}+l_{42}\,u_{23})$$

$$=-8-4\times 3-(-6)\left(\frac{1}{8}\right)=-\frac{77}{4}$$

$$\text{Then D.M. is} = \left[\begin{array}{cccc|c} 1 & 2 & 3 & 4 & 20 \\ 3 & -8 & \frac{1}{8} & 1 & \frac{17}{4} \\ 2 & -3 & \frac{-77}{8} & \cdot & \cdot \\ 4 & -6 & \frac{-77}{4} & \cdot & \cdot \end{array}\right]$$

*Step 6.* Elements of third row:

$$u_{34} = \frac{a_{34} - (l_{31}\, u_{14} + l_{32}\, u_{24})}{l_{33}}$$

$$= \frac{7 - 4 \times 2 - (1)\,(-3)}{\frac{-77}{8}} = -\frac{16}{77}$$

$$y_3 = \frac{b_3 - (l_{31}\, y_1 + l_{32}\, y_2)}{l_{33}}$$

$$= \left[\, 10 - 20 \times 2 - (-3)\left(\frac{17}{4}\right)\right] \div \left(\frac{-77}{8}\right) = \frac{138}{77}$$

$$\text{D.M.} = \left[\begin{array}{cccc|c} 1 & 2 & 3 & 4 & 20 \\ 3 & -8 & \frac{1}{8} & 1 & \frac{17}{4} \\ 2 & -3 & \frac{-77}{8} & \frac{-16}{77} & \frac{138}{77} \\ 4 & -6 & \frac{-77}{4} & & \end{array}\right]$$

*Step 7.* Elements of 4th column:

$$l_{44} = -4 - 4 \times 4 - 1\,(-6) - \left(\frac{-16}{77}\right)\left(\frac{-77}{4}\right) = -18$$

*Step 8.* Elements of 4th row:

$$y_4 = \frac{b_4 - (l_{41}\, y_1 + l_{42}\, y_2 + l_{43}\, y_3)}{l_{44}}$$

$$= \frac{2 - (4)\,(20) - (-6)\left(\frac{17}{4}\right) - \left(-\frac{77}{4}\right)\left(\frac{138}{77}\right)}{-18}$$

$$= \frac{2 - 80 + 25{\cdot}5 + \frac{69}{2}}{-18} = 1$$

$$\text{D.M.} = \left[\begin{array}{cccc|c} 1 & 2 & 3 & 4 & 20 \\ 3 & -8 & \frac{1}{8} & 1 & \frac{17}{4} \\ 2 & -3 & \frac{-77}{8} & \frac{-16}{77} & \frac{138}{77} \\ 4 & -6 & \frac{-77}{4} & -18 & 1 \end{array}\right]$$

The solution is got from $UX = Y$. That is,

$$\begin{bmatrix} 1 & 2 & 3 & 4 \\ 0 & 1 & \frac{1}{8} & 1 \\ 0 & 0 & 1 & \frac{-16}{77} \\ 0 & 0 & 0 & 1 \end{bmatrix} \begin{bmatrix} x \\ y \\ z \\ w \end{bmatrix} = \begin{bmatrix} 20 \\ \frac{17}{4} \\ \frac{138}{77} \\ 1 \end{bmatrix}$$

$$\therefore \quad x + 2y + 3z + 4w = 20$$

$$y + \frac{1}{8} z + w = \frac{17}{4}$$

$$z - \frac{16}{77} w = \frac{138}{77}$$

$$w = 1$$

By back substitution, $z = 2$

$$y + \frac{1}{4} + 1 = \frac{17}{4}; \quad \therefore \quad y = 3$$

$$\therefore \quad x = -2y - 3z - 4w + 20 = 4$$

Hence, $x = 4$, $y = 3$, $z = 2$, $w = 1$.

## EXERCISE 4.4

Using Crout's method, solve the following muster of equations:

1. $x + y + 2z = 7$, $3x + 2y + 4z = 13$, $4x + 3y + 2z = 8$
2. $2x + 4y + z = 5$, $4x + 4y + 3z = 8$, $4x + 8y + z = 9$
3. $2x - 6y + 8z = 24$, $5x + 4y - 3z = 2$, $3x + y + 2z = 16$
4. $2x + 3y + 2z = 2$, $3x + 6y + z = -6$, $10x + 3y + 4z = 16$
5. $x + y + z = 2$, $2x + 3y - 2z = -4$, $x - 2y + 4z = 17$
6. $2x - 6y + 8z = 24$, $5x + 4y - 3z = 2$, $3x + y + 2z = 16$
7. $5x + 2y + z = -12$, $-x + 4y + 2z = 20$, $2x - 3y + 10z = 3$
8. $10x + y + z = 12$, $2x + 10y + z = 13$, $2x + 2y + 10z = 14$
9. $x + 2y + 3z = 6$, $2x + 4y + z = 7$, $3x + 2y + 9z = 14$
10. $2x - y + 3z + w = 9$, $-x + 2y + z - 2w = 2$, $3x + y - 4z + 3w = 3$, $5x - 4y + 3z - 6w = 2$
11. $10x - 7y + 3z + 5w = 6$, $5x - 9y - 2z + 4w = 7$, $3x + y + 4z + 11w = 2$, $-6x + 8y - z - 4w = 5$
12. $x + y + z = 1$; $3x + y - 3z = 5$; $x - 2y - 5z = 10$
13. $2x + y + 3z = 13$, $x + 5y + z = 14$, $3x + y + 4z = 17$
14. $x + y + 2z = 4$, $3x + y - 3z = -4$, $2x - 3y - 5z = -5$
15. $x + y + z + w = 4$, $2x + 3y + 4z + 5w = 14$, $3x - y + z + w = 4$, $x - y + 3z + 5w = 8$

### 4·6. Crout's method for finding the inverse of matrix

Our aim is to find the inverse of a square matrix $A$. We have seen already, that $A$ can be decomposed into $A = LU$ where $L$ is lower triangular matrix and $U$ is unit upper triangular matrix.

$$A^{-1} = (LU)^{-1} = U^{-1} L^{-1} \qquad ...(1)$$

If $L$ is lower triangular, then $L^{-1}$ is also lower triangular. Also if $U$ is upper triangular, then $U^{-1}$ is also upper triangular.

Since $LL^{-1} = I$ we can find the lower triangular matrix $L^{-1}$ such that $LL^{-1} = I$ (since $L$ is known).

Similarly, since $UU^{-1} = I$, we can find the upper triangular matrix $U^{-1}$ such that $UU^{-1} = I$.

Having known, $L^{-1}$ and $U^{-1}$, we get $A^{-1} = U^{-1} L^{-1}$.

**Example 1.** *Find the inverse of* $A = \begin{pmatrix} 3 & -1 & 1 \\ -15 & 6 & -5 \\ 5 & -2 & 2 \end{pmatrix}$, *by Crout's method.*

**Solution.** Since $LU = A$, we have $A^{-1} = U^{-1} L^{-1}$ ...(1)

$LU = A$ implies

$$\begin{pmatrix} l_{11} & 0 & 0 \\ l_{21} & l_{22} & 0 \\ l_{31} & l_{32} & l_{33} \end{pmatrix} \begin{pmatrix} 1 & u_{12} & u_{13} \\ 0 & 1 & u_{23} \\ 0 & 0 & 1 \end{pmatrix} = \begin{pmatrix} 3 & -1 & 1 \\ -15 & 6 & -5 \\ 5 & -2 & 2 \end{pmatrix}$$

Using the method used in Crout's method, we have

$$l_{11} = 3,\ l_{21} = -15,\ l_{31} = 5$$

$$u_{12} = \frac{a_{12}}{l_{11}} = \frac{-1}{3},\ u_{13} = \frac{a_{13}}{l_{11}} = \frac{1}{3}$$

$$l_{22} = a_{22} - l_{21}\, u_{12} = 6 - (-15)\left(+\frac{1}{3}\right) = 1$$

$$l_{32} = a_{32} - l_{31}\, u_{12} = -2 - 5\left(-\frac{1}{3}\right) = -\frac{1}{3}$$

$$u_{23} = \frac{a_{23} - l_{21}\, u_{13}}{l_{22}} = \frac{-5 - (-15)\left(\frac{1}{3}\right)}{1} = 0$$

$$l_{33} = a_{33} - l_{31}\, u_{13} - l_{32}\, u_{23}$$

$$= 2 - 5\left(\frac{1}{3}\right) - \left(-\frac{1}{3}\right)(0) = \frac{1}{3}$$

$$\therefore \quad L=\begin{pmatrix} 3 & 0 & 0 \\ -15 & 1 & 0 \\ 5 & -\frac{1}{3} & \frac{1}{3} \end{pmatrix} \text{ and } U=\begin{pmatrix} 1 & -\frac{1}{3} & \frac{1}{3} \\ 0 & 1 & 0 \\ 0 & 0 & 1 \end{pmatrix}$$

*We shall find $L^{-1}$ and $U^{-1}$*: Since $LL^{-1}=I$; and $L^{-1}$ is also lower triangular,

$$\underset{L}{\begin{pmatrix} 3 & 0 & 0 \\ -15 & 1 & 0 \\ 5 & -1/3 & 1/3 \end{pmatrix}} \underset{L^{-1}}{\begin{pmatrix} x_{11} & 0 & 0 \\ x_{21} & x_{22} & 0 \\ x_{31} & x_{32} & x_{33} \end{pmatrix}} = \underset{I}{\begin{pmatrix} 1 & 0 & 0 \\ 0 & 1 & 0 \\ 0 & 0 & 1 \end{pmatrix}}$$

$$3x_{11}=1,\ -15\,x_{11}+x_{21}=0,\ x_{22}=1,\ 5x_{11}-\frac{1}{3}x_{21}+\frac{1}{3}x_{31}=0$$

$$-\frac{1}{3}x_{22}+\frac{1}{3}x_{32}=0,\ \frac{1}{3}x_{33}=1$$

$$\therefore\ x_{11}=\frac{1}{3},\ x_{22}=1,\ x_{33}=3,\ x_{21}=5,\ x_{31}=0,\ x_{32}=1$$

$$\therefore \qquad L^{-1}=\begin{pmatrix} \frac{1}{3} & 0 & 0 \\ 5 & 1 & 0 \\ 0 & 1 & 3 \end{pmatrix}$$

Since, $UU^{-1}=I$, and $U^{-1}$ is upper triangular, we have

$$\begin{pmatrix} 1 & -\frac{1}{3} & \frac{1}{3} \\ 0 & 1 & 0 \\ 0 & 0 & 1 \end{pmatrix} \begin{pmatrix} c_{11} & c_{12} & c_{13} \\ 0 & c_{22} & c_{23} \\ 0 & 0 & c_{33} \end{pmatrix} = \begin{pmatrix} 1 & 0 & 0 \\ 0 & 1 & 0 \\ 0 & 0 & 1 \end{pmatrix}$$

$$c_{11}=1,\ c_{12}-\frac{1}{3}c_{22}=0,\ c_{13}-\frac{1}{3}c_{23}+\frac{1}{3}c_{33}=0$$

$$c_{22}=1,\ c_{23}=0,\ c_{33}=1\ \therefore\ c_{12}=\frac{1}{3},\ c_{13}=-1/3$$

$$\therefore\ U^{-1}=\begin{pmatrix} 1 & \frac{1}{3} & -\frac{1}{3} \\ 0 & 1 & 0 \\ 0 & 0 & 1 \end{pmatrix}$$

**Note.** This shows that if $U$ is unit upper triangular, $U^{-1}$ is also unit upper triangular.

$$\left[\text{Hence, we could have taken } U^{-1}=\begin{pmatrix} 1 & c_{12} & c_{13} \\ 0 & 1 & c_{23} \\ 0 & 0 & 1 \end{pmatrix}\right]$$

$$A^{-1}=(LU)^{-1}=U^{-1}L^{-1}$$

$$= \begin{pmatrix} 1 & \frac{1}{3} & -\frac{1}{3} \\ 0 & 1 & 0 \\ 0 & 0 & 1 \end{pmatrix} \begin{pmatrix} \frac{1}{3} & 0 & 0 \\ 5 & 1 & 0 \\ 0 & 1 & 3 \end{pmatrix}$$

$$A^{-1} = \begin{pmatrix} 2 & 0 & -1 \\ 5 & 1 & 0 \\ 0 & 1 & 3 \end{pmatrix}$$

**Example 2.** *Find the inverse of* $A = \begin{pmatrix} 1 & -2 & 3 \\ 0 & -1 & 4 \\ -2 & 2 & 0 \end{pmatrix}$, *by Crout's method.*

**Solution.** Let us decompose $A$ as $LU$ *i.e.*, $LU = A$ implies,

$$\begin{pmatrix} l_{11} & 0 & 0 \\ l_{21} & l_{22} & 0 \\ l_{31} & l_{32} & l_{33} \end{pmatrix} \begin{pmatrix} 1 & u_{12} & u_{13} \\ 0 & 1 & u_{23} \\ 0 & 0 & 1 \end{pmatrix} = \begin{pmatrix} 1 & -2 & 3 \\ 0 & -1 & 4 \\ -2 & 2 & 0 \end{pmatrix}$$

$$L \qquad U \qquad = \qquad A$$

Equating elements or using the method employed in Crout's method,

$$l_{11} = 1,\ l_{21} = 0,\ l_{31} = -2,\ u_{12} = \frac{a_{12}}{l_{11}} = -2;\ u_{13} = \frac{a_{13}}{l_{11}} = 3$$

$$l_{22} = a_{22} - l_{21}\,u_{12} = -1 - 0 = -1;\ l_{32} = a_{32} - u_{12}\,l_{31} = 2 - 4 = -2$$

$$u_{23} = \frac{a_{23} - u_{13}\,l_{21}}{l_{22}} = \frac{4-0}{1} = -4$$

$$l_{33} = a_{33} - l_{31}\,u_{13} - l_{32}\,u_{23} = 0 + 6 - 8 = -2$$

$$\therefore\ L = \begin{pmatrix} 1 & 0 & 0 \\ 0 & -1 & 0 \\ -2 & -2 & -2 \end{pmatrix},\ U = \begin{pmatrix} 1 & -2 & 3 \\ 0 & 1 & -4 \\ 0 & 0 & 1 \end{pmatrix}$$

*To find* $L^{-1}$: $LL^{-1} = I$. Therefore

$$\begin{pmatrix} 1 & 0 & 0 \\ 0 & -1 & 0 \\ -2 & -2 & -2 \end{pmatrix} \begin{pmatrix} x_{11} & 0 & 0 \\ x_{21} & x_{22} & 0 \\ x_{31} & x_{32} & x_{33} \end{pmatrix} = \begin{pmatrix} 1 & 0 & 0 \\ 0 & 1 & 0 \\ 0 & 0 & 1 \end{pmatrix}$$

$$L \qquad L^{-1} \qquad = \qquad I$$

$$\therefore\ x_{11} = 1,\ x_{22} = -1,\ x_{33} = -1/2$$

$$-x_{21} = 0;\ x_{11} + x_{21} + x_{31} = 0,\ x_{22} + x_{32} = 0$$

$$\therefore\ x_{31} = -1,\ x_{32} = 1$$

$$\therefore \quad L^{-1} = \begin{pmatrix} 1 & 0 & 0 \\ 0 & -1 & 0 \\ -1 & 1 & -1/2 \end{pmatrix}$$

*To find* $U^{-1}$: we have $UU^{-1} = I$. Therefore

$$\begin{pmatrix} 1 & -2 & 3 \\ 0 & 1 & -4 \\ 0 & 0 & 1 \end{pmatrix}\begin{pmatrix} 1 & c_{12} & c_{13} \\ 0 & 1 & c_{23} \\ 0 & 0 & 1 \end{pmatrix} = \begin{pmatrix} 1 & 0 & 0 \\ 0 & 1 & 0 \\ 0 & 0 & 1 \end{pmatrix}$$

Equating elements,

$$c_{12} - 2 = 0, \; c_{13} - 2\,c_{23} + 3 = 0, \; c_{23} - 4 = 0$$

$$\therefore \quad c_{12} = 2, \; c_{23} = 4, \; c_{13} = 5$$

$$\therefore \quad U^{-1} = \begin{pmatrix} 1 & 2 & 5 \\ 0 & 1 & 4 \\ 0 & 0 & 1 \end{pmatrix}$$

Since $A = LU$, $A^{-1} = (LU)^{-1} = U^{-1}\,L^{-1}$

$$\therefore \quad A^{-1} = \begin{pmatrix} 1 & 2 & 5 \\ 0 & 1 & 4 \\ 0 & 0 & 1 \end{pmatrix}\begin{pmatrix} 1 & 0 & 0 \\ 0 & -1 & 0 \\ -1 & 1 & -1/2 \end{pmatrix} = \begin{pmatrix} -4 & 3 & -5/2 \\ -4 & 3 & -2 \\ -1 & 1 & -1/2 \end{pmatrix}$$

## EXERCISE 4.5

Find the inverse of the following matrices using Crout's method:

**1.** $\begin{pmatrix} 2 & 1 & 1 \\ 3 & 2 & 3 \\ 1 & 4 & 9 \end{pmatrix}$ **2.** $\begin{pmatrix} 4 & 1 & 2 \\ 2 & 3 & -1 \\ 1 & -2 & 2 \end{pmatrix}$ **3.** $\begin{pmatrix} 1 & 2 & -1 \\ 3 & 8 & 2 \\ 4 & 9 & -1 \end{pmatrix}$

**4.** $\begin{pmatrix} 3 & -3 & 4 \\ 2 & -3 & 4 \\ 0 & -1 & 1 \end{pmatrix}$ **5.** $\begin{pmatrix} 2 & 1 & -1 \\ 0 & 2 & 1 \\ 5 & 2 & -3 \end{pmatrix}$ **6.** $\begin{pmatrix} 1 & 1 & 1 \\ 1 & 2 & -3 \\ 2 & -1 & 3 \end{pmatrix}$

**7.** Find the inverses of the matrices given under Exercises 4·2 by using Crout's method.

### 4·7 Iterative methods

All the previous methods seen in solving the system of simultaneous algebraic linear equations are direct methods. Now we will see some *indirect methods* or *iterative methods*.

This iterative methods is not always successful to all systems of equations. If this method is to succeed, each equation of the system must possess one large coefficient and the large coefficient must be attached to a different unknown in that equation. This condition will be satisfied if the large coefficients are along the leading diagonal of the coefficient matrix. When this condition is satisfied, the system will be solvable by the iterative method. The system,

$$a_{11}x_1 + a_{12}x_2 + a_{13}x_3 = b_1$$
$$a_{21}x_1 + a_{22}x_2 + a_{23}x_3 = b_2$$
$$a_{31}x_1 + a_{32}x_2 + a_{33}x_3 = b_3$$

will be solvable by this method if

$$|a_{11}| > |a_{12}| + |a_{13}|$$
$$|a_{22}| > |a_{21}| + |a_{23}|$$
$$|a_{33}| > |a_{31}| + |a_{32}|$$

In other words, the solution will exist (iteration will converge) if the absolute values of the leading diagonal elements of the coefficient matrix $A$ of the system $AX = B$ are greater than the sum of absolute values of the other coefficients of that row. The condition is *sufficient* but not *necessary.*

**4·8 Jacobi method of iteration or Gauss-Jacobi method**

Let us explain this method in the case of three equations in three unknowns.

Consider the system of equations,

$$a_1 x + b_1 y + c_1 z = d_1$$
$$a_2 x + b_2 y + c_2 z = d_2 \qquad ...(1)$$
$$a_3 x + b_3 y + c_3 z = d_3$$

Let us assume $|a_1| > |b_1| + |c_1|$

$$|b_2| > |a_2| + |c_2|$$
$$|c_3| > |a_3| + |b_3|$$

Then, iterative method can be used for the system (1). Solve for $x$, $y$, $z$ (whose coefficients are the larger values) in terms of the other variables. That is,

$$x = \frac{1}{a_1}(d_1 - b_1 y - c_1 z)$$

$$y = \frac{1}{b_2}(d_2 - a_2 x - c_2 z) \qquad ...(2)$$

$$z = \frac{1}{c_3}(d_3 - a_3 x - b_3 y)$$

If $x^{(0)}, y^{(0)}, z^{(0)}$ are the initial values of $x, y, z$ respectively, then

$$x^{(1)} = \frac{1}{a_1}(d_1 - b_1 y^{(0)} - c_1 z^{(0)})$$

$$y^{(1)} = \frac{1}{b_2}(d_2 - a_2 x^{(0)} - c_2 z^{(0)}) \qquad ...(3)$$

$$z^{(1)} = \frac{1}{c_3}(d_3 - a_3 x^{(0)} - b_3 y^{(0)})$$

Again using these values $x^{(1)}, y^{(1)}, z^{(1)}$ in (2), we get

$$x^{(2)} = \frac{1}{a_1}(d_1 - b_1 y^{(1)} - c_1 z^{(1)})$$

$$y^{(2)} = \frac{1}{b_2}(d_2 - a_2 x^{(1)} - c_2 z^{(1)}) \qquad \text{...(4)}$$

$$z^{(2)} = \frac{1}{c_3}(d_3 - a_3 x^{(1)} - b_3 y^{(1)})$$

Proceeding in the same way, if the $r$th iterates are $x^{(r)}, y^{(r)}, z^{(r)}$, the interation scheme reduces to

$$x^{(r+1)} = \frac{1}{a_1}(d_1 - b_1 y^{(r)} - c_1 z^{(r)})$$

$$y^{(r+1)} = \frac{1}{b_2}(d_2 - a_2 x^{(r)} - c_2 z^{(r)}) \qquad \text{...(5)}$$

$$z^{(r+1)} = \frac{1}{c_3}(d_3 - a_3 x^{(r)} - b_3 y^{(r)})$$

The procedure is continued till the convergence is assured (correct to required decimals).

**Note 1.** To get the $(r+1)$th iterates, we use the values of the $r$th iterates in the scheme (5).

**2.** In the absence of the initial values of $x$, $y$, $z$, we take, usually, (0, 0, 0) as the initial estimate.

## 4·9 Gauss-Seidel method of iteration

This is only a refinement of Gauss-Jacobi method. As before,

$$x = \frac{1}{a_1}(d_1 - b_1 y - c_1 z)$$

$$y = \frac{1}{b_2}(d_2 - a_2 x - c_2 z) \qquad \text{...(6)}$$

$$z = \frac{1}{c_3}(d_3 - a_3 x - b_3 y)$$

We start with the initial values $y^{(0)}, z^{(0)}$ for $y$ and $z$ and get $x^{(1)}$ from the first equation. That is,

$$x^{(1)} = \frac{1}{a_1}(d_1 - b_1 y^{(0)} - c_1 z^{(0)})$$

While using the second equation, we use $z^{(0)}$ for $z$ and $x^{(1)}$ for $x$ instead of $x^{(0)}$ as in the Jacobi's method, we get

$$y^{(1)} = \frac{1}{b_2}(d_2 - a_2 x^{(1)} - c_2 z^{(0)})$$

Now, having known $x^{(1)}$ and $y^{(1)}$, use $x^{(1)}$ for $x$ and $y^{(1)}$ for $y$ in the third equation, we get

$$z^{(1)} = \frac{1}{c_3}(d_3 - a_3 x^{(1)} - b_3 y^{(1)})$$

In finding the values of the unknowns, we use the latest available values on the right hand side. If $x^{(r)}, y^{(r)}, z^{(r)}$ are the $r$th iterates, then the iteration scheme will be

$$x^{(r+1)} = \frac{1}{a_1}(d_1 - b_1 y^{(r)} - c_1 z^{(r)})$$

$$y^{(r+1)} = \frac{1}{b_2}(d_2 - a_2 x^{(r+1)} - c_2 z^{(r)})$$

$$z^{(r+1)} = \frac{1}{c_3}(d_3 - a_3 x^{(r+1)} - b_3 y^{(r+1)})$$

This process of iteration is continued until the convergence is assured. As the current values of the unknowns at each stage of iteration are used in getting the values of unknowns, the convergence in Gauss-Seidel method is very fast when compared to Gauss-Jacobi method. The rate of convergence in Gauss-Seidel method is roughly two times than that of Gauss-Jacobi method. As we saw the sufficient conditions already, the sufficient condition for the convergence of this method is also the same as we stated earlier. That is, *the method of iteration will converge if in each equation of the given system, the absolute value of the largest coefficient is greater than the sum of the absolute values of all the remaining coefficients.* (The largest coefficients must be the coefficients for different unknowns).

**Note 1.** For all systems of equations, this method will not work (since convergence is not assured). It converges only for special systems of equations.

**2.** Iteration method is self-correcting method. That is, any error made in computation, is corrected in the subsequent iterations.

**3.** The iteration is stopped when the values of $x$, $y$, $z$ start repeating with the required degree of accuracy.

**Example 1.** *Solve the following system by Gauss-Jacobi and Gauss-Seidel methods :*

$$10x - 5y - 2z = 3\ ;\ \ 4x - 10y + 3z = -3\ ;\ \ x + 6y + 10z = -3.$$

[*MS. Ap. 1992*]

**Solution.** Here, we see that the diagonal elements are dominant. Hence, the iteration process can be applied.

That is, the coefficient matrix $\begin{pmatrix} 10 & -5 & -2 \\ 4 & -10 & 3 \\ 1 & 6 & 10 \end{pmatrix}$ is diagonally dominant, since

$$|10| > |-5| + |-2|,\ |-10| > |4| + |3| \text{ and } |10| > |1| + |6|$$

*Gauss-Jacobi method.* Solving for $x, y, z$, we have

$$x = \frac{1}{10}(3 + 5y + 2z) \qquad \text{...(1)}$$

$$y = \frac{1}{10}(3 + 4x + 3z) \qquad \text{...(2)}$$

$$z = \frac{1}{10}(-3 - x - 6y) \qquad \text{...(3)}$$

*First iteration :* Let the initial values be (0, 0, 0).

Using these initial values in (1), (2), (3), we get

$$x^{(1)} = \frac{1}{10}[3 + 5(0) + 2(0)] = 0{\cdot}3$$

$$y^{(1)} = \frac{1}{10}[3 + 4(0) + 3(0)] = 0{\cdot}3$$

$$z^{(1)} = \frac{1}{10}[-3 - (0) - 6(0)] - 0{\cdot}3$$

*Second iteration* : Using these values in (1), (2), (3), we get

$$x^{(2)} = \frac{1}{10}[3 + 5\,(0{\cdot}3) + 2\,(-0{\cdot}3)] = 0{\cdot}39$$

$$y^{(2)} = \frac{1}{10}[3 + 4\,(0{\cdot}3) + 3\,(-0{\cdot}3)] = 0{\cdot}33$$

$$z^{(2)} = \frac{1}{10}[-3 - (0{\cdot}3) - 6\,(0{\cdot}3)] = -0{\cdot}51$$

*Third iteration*: Using the values of $x^{(2)}, y^{(2)}, z^{(2)}$ in (1), (2), (3) we, get

$$x^{(3)} = \frac{1}{10}[3 + 5\,(0{\cdot}33) + 2\,(-0{\cdot}51)] = 0\,363$$

$$y^{(3)} = \frac{1}{10}[3 + 4\,(0{\cdot}39) + 3\,(-0{\cdot}51)] = 0{\cdot}303$$

$$z^{(3)} = \frac{1}{10}[-3 - (0{\cdot}39) - 6\,(0{\cdot}33)] = -0{\cdot}537$$

*Fourth iteration* :

$$x^{(4)} = \frac{1}{10}[3 + 5\,(0{\cdot}303) + 2\,(-0{\cdot}537)] = 0{\cdot}3441$$

$$y^{(4)} = \frac{1}{10}[3 + 4\,(0{\cdot}363) + 3\,(-0{\cdot}537)] = 0{\cdot}2841$$

$$z^{(4)} = \frac{1}{10}[-3 - 0{\cdot}363 - 6\,(0{\cdot}303)] = -\,0{\cdot}5181$$

*Fifth interation* :

$$x^{(5)} = \frac{1}{10}[3 + 5\,(0{\cdot}2841) + 2\,(-\,0{\cdot}5181)] = 0{\cdot}33843$$

$$y^{(5)} = \frac{1}{10}[3 + 4\,(0{\cdot}3441) + 3\,(-\,0{\cdot}5181)] = 0{\cdot}2822$$

$$z^{(5)} = \frac{1}{10}[-3 - (0{\cdot}3441) - 6\,(0{\cdot}2841)] = -\,0{\cdot}50487$$

*Sixth interation* :

$$x^{(6)} = \frac{1}{10}[3 + 5\,(0{\cdot}2822) + 2\,(-\,0{\cdot}50487)] = 0{\cdot}340126$$

$$y^{(6)} = \frac{1}{10}[3 + 4\,(0{\cdot}33843) + 3\,(-\,0{\cdot}50487)] = 0{\cdot}283911$$

$$z^{(6)} = \frac{1}{10}[-3 - (0{\cdot}33843) - 6\,(0{\cdot}2822)] = -\,0{\cdot}503163$$

*Seventh iteration* :

$$x^{(7)} = \frac{1}{10}[3 + 5\,(0{\cdot}283911) + 2\,(-\,0{\cdot}503163)] = 0{\cdot}3413229$$

$$y^{(7)} = \frac{1}{10}[3 + 4\,(0{\cdot}340126) + 3\,(-\,0{\cdot}503163)] = 0{\cdot}2851015$$

$$z^{(7)} = \frac{1}{10}[-3 - (0{\cdot}340126) - 6\,(0{\cdot}283911)] = -\,0{\cdot}5043592$$

*Eighth iteration* :

$$x^{(8)} = \frac{1}{10}[3 + 5\,(0{\cdot}2851015) + 2\,(-\,0{\cdot}5043592)] = 0{\cdot}34167891$$

$$y^{(8)} = \frac{1}{10}[3 + 4\,(0{\cdot}3413229) + 3\,(-\,0{\cdot}5043592)] = 0{\cdot}2852214$$

$$z^{(8)} = \frac{1}{10}[-3 - (0{\cdot}3413229) - 6\,(0{\cdot}2851015)] = -\,0{\cdot}50519319$$

*Nineth iteration* :

$$x^{(9)} = \frac{1}{10}[3 + 5\,(0{\cdot}2852214) + 2\,(-\,0{\cdot}50519319)] = 0{\cdot}341572062$$

$$y^{(9)} = \frac{1}{10}[3 + 4\,(0{\cdot}34167891) + 3\,(-\,0{\cdot}50519319)] = 0{\cdot}285113607$$

$$z^{(9)} = \frac{1}{10}[-3 - (0{\cdot}34167891) - 6\,(0{\cdot}2852214)] = -\,0{\cdot}505300731$$

Hence correct to 3 decimal places, the values are

$$x = 0{\cdot}342,\; y = 0{\cdot}285,\; z = -\,0{\cdot}505$$

*Gauss-Seidel method* : *Initial values* : $y=0,\ z=0.$

*First iteration* :

$$x^{(1)}=\frac{1}{10}[3+5(0)+2(0)]=0{\cdot}3$$

$$y^{(1)}=\frac{1}{10}[3+4\,(0{\cdot}3)+3(0)]=0{\cdot}42$$

$$z^{(1)}=\frac{1}{10}[-3-(0{\cdot}3)-6\,(0{\cdot}42)]=-0{\cdot}582$$

*Second iteration* :

$$x^{(2)}=\frac{1}{10}[3+5\,(0{\cdot}42)+2\,(-0{\cdot}582)]=0{\cdot}3936$$

$$y^{(2)}=\frac{1}{10}[3+4\,(0{\cdot}3936)+3\,(-0{\cdot}582)]=0{\cdot}28284$$

$$z^{(2)}=\frac{1}{10}[-3-(0{\cdot}3936)-6\,(0{\cdot}28284)]=-0{\cdot}509064$$

*Third iteration* :

$$x^{(3)}=\frac{1}{10}[3+5\,(0{\cdot}28284)+2\,(-0{\cdot}509064)]=0{\cdot}3396072$$

$$y^{(3)}=\frac{1}{10}[3+4\,(0{\cdot}3396072)+3\,(-0{\cdot}509064)]=0{\cdot}28312368$$

$$z^{(3)}=\frac{1}{10}[-3-(0{\cdot}3396072)-6\,(0{\cdot}28312368)]=-0{\cdot}503834928$$

*Fourth iteration* :

$$x^{(4)}=\frac{1}{10}[3+5\,(0{\cdot}28312368)+2\,(-0{\cdot}503834928)]=0{\cdot}34079485$$

$$y^{(4)}=\frac{1}{10}[3+4\,(0{\cdot}34079485)+3\,(-0{\cdot}50383492)]=0{\cdot}285167464$$

$$z^{(4)}=\frac{1}{10}[-3-(0{\cdot}34079485)-6\,(0{\cdot}28516746)]=-0{\cdot}50517996$$

*Fifth iteration* :

$$x^{(5)}=\frac{1}{10}[3+5\,(0{\cdot}28516746)+2\,(-0{\cdot}50517996)]=0{\cdot}34155477$$

$$y^{(5)}=\frac{1}{10}[3+4\,(0{\cdot}34155477)+3\,(-0{\cdot}50517996)]=0{\cdot}28506792$$

$$z^{(5)}=\frac{1}{10}[-3-(0{\cdot}34155477)-6\,(0{\cdot}28506792)]=-0{\cdot}505196229$$

*Sixth iteration* :

$$x^{(6)}=\frac{1}{10}[3+5\,(0{\cdot}28506792)+2\,(-0{\cdot}505196229)]=0{\cdot}341494714$$

$$y^{(6)} = \frac{1}{10}[3 + 4\,(0.341494714) + 3\,(-0.505196229)] = 0.285039017$$

$$z^{(6)} = \frac{1}{10}[-3 - (0.341494714) - 6\,(0.285039017)] = -0.5051728$$

*Seventh iteration* :

$$x^{(7)} = \frac{1}{10}[3 + 5\,(0.285039017) + 2\,(-0.5051728)] = 0.3414849$$

$$y^{(7)} = \frac{1}{10}[3 + 4\,(0.3414849) + 3\,(-0.5051728)] = 0.28504212$$

$$z^{(7)} = \frac{1}{10}[-3 - (0.3414849) - 6\,(0.28504212)] = -0.5051737$$

The values at each iteration by both methods are tabulated below:

| Iteration | Gauss-Jacobi method | | | Gauss-Seidel method | | |
|---|---|---|---|---|---|---|
| | $x$ | $y$ | $z$ | $x$ | $y$ | $z$ |
| 1 | 0·3 | 0·3 | – 0·3 | 0·3 | 0·42 | – 0·582 |
| 2 | 0 39 | 0·33 | – 0·51 | 0·3936 | 0·28284 | – 0·509064 |
| 3 | 0·363 | 0·303 | – 0·537 | 0·3396072 | 0·28312364 | – 0·503834928 |
| 4 | 0·3441 | 0·2841 | – 0·5181 | 0·34079485 | 0·28516746 | – 0·50517996 |
| 5 | 0·33843 | 0·2822 | – 0·50487 | 0·3415547 | 0·28506792 | – 0·505196229 |
| 6 | 0·340126 | 0·283911 | – 0·503163 | 0·3414947 | 0·2850390 | – 0·5051728 |
| 7 | 0·3413229 | 0·2851015 | – 0·5043592 | 0·3414849 | 0·28504212 | – 0·5051737 |
| 8 | 0·34167891 | 0·2852214 | – 0·50519319 | | | |
| 9 | 0·341572062 | 0·285113607 | – 0·505300731 | | | |

The values correct to 3 decimal places are

$$x = 0.342,\; y = 0.285,\; z = -0.505$$

**Note.** After getting the values of the unknowns, substitute these values in the given equations, and check the correctness of the results.

**Example 2.** *Solve the following system of equations by using Gauss-Jacobi and Gauss-Seidel methods (correct to 3 decimal places) :*

$$8x - 3y + 2z = 20$$
$$4x + 11y - z = 33$$
$$6x + 3y + 12z = 35. \qquad [BR.\ Ap.\ '94]$$

**Solution.** Since the diagonal elements are dominant in the coefficient matrix, we write $x, y, z$ as follows

$$x = \frac{1}{8}[20 + 3y - 2z] \qquad ...(1)$$

$$y = \frac{1}{11}[33 - 4x + z] \qquad ...(2)$$

$$z = \frac{1}{12}[35 - 6x - 3y] \qquad ...(3)$$

*Gauss-Jacobi method* :

*First iteration:* Let the initial values be $x = 0,\ y = 0,\ z = 0$

Using the values $x = 0,\ y = 0,\ z = 0$ in (1), (2), (3) we get,

$$x^{(1)} = \frac{1}{8}[20 + 3(0) - 2(0)] = 2{\cdot}5$$

$$y^{(1)} = \frac{1}{11}[33 - 4(0) + 0] = 3{\cdot}0$$

$$z^{(1)} = \frac{1}{12}[35 - 6(0) - 3(0)] = 2{\cdot}916666$$

*Second iteration* : Using these values $x^{(1)}, y^{(1)}, z^{(1)}$ again in (1), (2), (3), we get

$$x^{(2)} = \frac{1}{8}[20 + 3\,(3{\cdot}0) - 2\,(2{\cdot}916666)] = 2{\cdot}895833$$

$$y^{(2)} = \frac{1}{11}[33 - 4\,(2{\cdot}5) + (2{\cdot}916666)] = 2{\cdot}356060$$

$$z^{(2)} = \frac{1}{12}[35 - 6\,(2{\cdot}5) - 3\,(3{\cdot}0)] = 0{\cdot}916666$$

*Third interation* :

$$x^{(3)} = \frac{1}{8}[20 + 3\,(2{\cdot}356060) - 2\,(0{\cdot}916666)] = 3{\cdot}154356$$

$$y^{(3)} = \frac{1}{11}[33 - 4\,(2{\cdot}895833) + (0{\cdot}916666)] = 2{\cdot}030303$$

$$z^{(3)} = \frac{1}{12}[35 - 6\,(2{\cdot}895833) - 3\,(2{\cdot}356060)] = 0{\cdot}879735$$

*Fourth iteration* :

$$x^{(4)} = \frac{1}{8}[20 + 3\,(2{\cdot}030303) - 2\,(0{\cdot}879735)] = 3{\cdot}041430$$

$$y^{(4)} = \frac{1}{11}[33 - 4\,(3{\cdot}154356) + (0{\cdot}879735)] = 1{\cdot}932937$$

$$z^{(4)} = \frac{1}{12}[35 - 6\,(3{\cdot}154356) - 3\,(2{\cdot}030303)] = 0{\cdot}831913$$

*Fifth iteration* :

$$x^{(5)} = \frac{1}{8}[20 + 3\,(1{\cdot}932937) - 2\,(0{\cdot}831913)] = 3{\cdot}016873$$

$$y^{(5)} = \frac{1}{11}[33 - 4\,(3{\cdot}041430) + (0{\cdot}831913)] = 1{\cdot}969654$$

$$z^{(5)} = \frac{1}{12}[35 - 6\,(3{\cdot}041430) - 3\,(1{\cdot}932937)] = 0{\cdot}912717$$

*Sixth iteration* :

$$x^{(6)} = \frac{1}{8}[20 + 3\,(1{\cdot}969654) - 2\,(0{\cdot}912717)] = 3{\cdot}010441$$

$$y^{(6)} = \frac{1}{11}[33 - 4(3{\cdot}016873) + (0{\cdot}912717)] = 1{\cdot}985930$$

$$z^{(6)} = \frac{1}{12}[35 - 6(3{\cdot}016873) - 3(1{\cdot}969654)] = 0{\cdot}915817$$

*Seventh iteration* :

$$x^{(7)} = \frac{1}{8}[20 + 3(1{\cdot}985930) - 2(0{\cdot}915817)] = 3{\cdot}015770$$

$$y^{(7)} = \frac{1}{11}[33 - 4(3{\cdot}010441) + (0{\cdot}915817)] = 1{\cdot}988550$$

$$z^{(7)} = \frac{1}{12}[35 - 6(3{\cdot}010441) - 3(1{\cdot}985930)] = 0{\cdot}914964$$

*Eigth iteration* :

$$x^{(8)} = \frac{1}{8}[20 + 3(1{\cdot}988550) - 2(0{\cdot}914964)] = 3{\cdot}016946$$

$$y^{(8)} = \frac{1}{11}[33 - 4(3{\cdot}015770) + (0{\cdot}914964)] = 1{\cdot}986535$$

$$z^{(8)} = \frac{1}{12}[35 - 6(3{\cdot}015770) - 3(1{\cdot}988550)] = 0{\cdot}911644$$

*Ninth iteration* :

$$x^{(9)} = \frac{1}{8}[20 + 3(1{\cdot}986535) - 2(0{\cdot}911644)] = 3{\cdot}017039$$

$$y^{(9)} = \frac{1}{11}[33 - 4(3{\cdot}016946) + (0{\cdot}911644)] = 1{\cdot}985805$$

$$z^{(9)} = \frac{1}{12}[35 - 6(3{\cdot}016946) - 3(1{\cdot}986535)] = 0{\cdot}911560$$

*Tenth iteration* :

$$x^{(10)} = \frac{1}{8}[20 + 3(1{\cdot}985805) - 2(0{\cdot}911560)] = 3{\cdot}016786$$

$$y^{(10)} = \frac{1}{11}[33 - 4(3{\cdot}017039) + (0{\cdot}911560)] = 1{\cdot}985764$$

$$z^{(10)} = \frac{1}{12}[35 - 6(3{\cdot}017039) - 3(1{\cdot}985805)] = 0{\cdot}911696$$

In 8th, 9th and 10th iterations the values of $x$, $y$, $z$ are same correct to 3 decimal places. Hence we stop at this level.

*Gauss-Seidel method* :

We take the initial values as $y = 0, z = 0$ and use equations (1)

*First iteration* :

$$x^{(1)} = \frac{1}{8}[20 + 3(0) - 2(0)] = 2{\cdot}5$$

$$y^{(1)} = \frac{1}{11}[33 - 4(2{\cdot}5) + 0] = 2{\cdot}090909$$

$$z^{(1)} = \frac{1}{12}[35 - 6(2{\cdot}5) - 3(2{\cdot}090909)] = 1{\cdot}143939$$

*Second iteration* :

$$x^{(2)} = \frac{1}{8}[20 + 3(2{\cdot}090909) - 2(1{\cdot}143939)] = 2{\cdot}998106$$

$$y^{(2)} = \frac{1}{11}[33 - 4(2{\cdot}998106) + (1{\cdot}143939)] = 2{\cdot}013774$$

$$z^{(2)} = \frac{1}{12}[35 - 6(2{\cdot}998106) - 3(2{\cdot}013774)] = 0{\cdot}914170$$

*Third iteration* :

$$x^{(3)} = \frac{1}{8}[20 + 3(2{\cdot}013774) - 2(0{\cdot}914170)] = 3{\cdot}026623$$

$$y^{(3)} = \frac{1}{11}[33 - 4(3{\cdot}026623) + (0{\cdot}914170)] = 1{\cdot}982516$$

$$z^{(3)} = \frac{1}{12}[35 - 6(3{\cdot}026623) - 3(1{\cdot}982516)] = 0{\cdot}907726$$

*Fourth iteration* :

$$x^{(4)} = \frac{1}{8}[20 + 3(1{\cdot}982516) - 2(0{\cdot}907726)] = 3{\cdot}016512$$

$$y^{(4)} = \frac{1}{11}[33 - 4(3{\cdot}016512) + (0{\cdot}907726)] = 1{\cdot}985607$$

$$z^{(4)} = \frac{1}{12}[35 - 6(3{\cdot}016512) - 3(1{\cdot}985607)] = 0{\cdot}912009$$

*Fifth iteration* :

$$x^{(5)} = \frac{1}{8}[20 + 3(1{\cdot}985607) - 2(0{\cdot}912009)] = 3{\cdot}016600$$

$$y^{(5)} = \frac{1}{11}[33 - 4(3{\cdot}016600) + (0{\cdot}912009)] = 1{\cdot}985964$$

$$z^{(5)} = \frac{1}{12}[35 - 6(3{\cdot}016600) - 3(1{\cdot}985964)] = 0{\cdot}911876$$

*Sixth iteration* :

$$x^{(6)} = \frac{1}{8}[20 + 3(1{\cdot}985964) - 2(0{\cdot}911876)] = 3{\cdot}016767$$

$$y^{(6)} = \frac{1}{11}[33 - 4(3{\cdot}016767) + (0{\cdot}911876)] = 1{\cdot}985892$$

$$z^{(6)} = \frac{1}{12}[35 - 6(3{\cdot}016767) - 3(1{\cdot}985892)] = 0{\cdot}911810$$

(The values of $x$, $y$, $z$ got by Jacobi method correct to 3 decimal places are got even in the 6th iteration by Gauss-Seidel method.)

*Seventh iteration* :

$$x^{(7)} = \frac{1}{8}[20 + 3(1{\cdot}985892) - 2(0{\cdot}911810)] = 3{\cdot}016757$$

$$y^{(7)} = \frac{1}{11}[33 - 4(3{\cdot}016757) + (0{\cdot}911810)] = 1{\cdot}985889$$

$$z^{(7)} = \frac{1}{12}[35 - 6(3{\cdot}016757) - 3(1{\cdot}985889)] = 0{\cdot}911816$$

Since the seventh and eighth iterations give the same values for $x$, $y$, $z$ correct to 4 decimal places, we stop here.

$\therefore \quad x = 3{\cdot}0168,\ y = 1{\cdot}9859,\ z = 0{\cdot}9118$

The values of $x$, $y$, $z$ by both methods at each iteration are tabulated below:

| Iteration | *Gauss-Jacobi method* | | | *Gauss-Seidel method* | | |
|---|---|---|---|---|---|---|
| | $x$ | $y$ | $z$ | $x$ | $y$ | $z$ |
| 1 | 2·5 | 3·0 | 2·916666 | 2·5 | 2·090909 | 1·143939 |
| 2 | 2·895833 | 2·356060 | 0·916666 | 2·998106 | 2·013774 | 0·914170 |
| 3 | 3·154356 | 2·030303 | 0·879735 | 3·026623 | 1·982516 | 0·907726 |
| 4 | 3·041430 | 1·932937 | 0·831913 | 3·016512 | 1·985607 | 0·912009 |
| 5 | 3·016873 | 1·969654 | 0·912717 | 3·016600 | 1·985964 | 0·911876 |
| 6 | 3·010441 | 1·985930 | 0·915817 | 3·016767 | 1·985892 | 0·911810 |
| 7 | 3·015770 | 1·988550 | 0·914964 | 3·016757 | 1·985889 | 0·911816 |
| 8 | 3·016946 | 1·986535 | 0·911644 | | | |
| 9 | 3·017039 | 1·985805 | 0·911560 | | | |
| 10 | 3·016786 | 1·985764 | 0·911696 | | | |

This shows that the convergence is rapid in Gauss-Seidel method when compared to Gauss-Jacobi method. We see that 10 iterations are necessary in Jacobi method to get the same accuracy as got by 7 iterations in Gauss-Seidel method.

**Example 3.** *Solve the following system of equations by Gauss-Jacobi and Gauss-Seidel method correct to three decimal places :*

$$x + y + 54z = 110$$

$$27x + 6y - z = 85$$

$$6x + 15y + 2z = 72$$

**Solution.** As the coefficient matrix is not diagonally dominant as it is, we rewrite the equation, as noted below, so that the coefficient matrix becomes diagonally dominant

$$27x + 6y - z = 85$$

$$6x + 15y + 2z = 72$$

$$x + y + 54z = 110$$

Solving for *x, y, z,* we get

$$x = \frac{1}{27}[85 - 6y + z] \qquad ...(1)$$

$$y = \frac{1}{15}[72 - 6x - 2z] \qquad ...(2)$$

$$z = \frac{1}{54}[110 - x - y] \qquad ...(3)$$

Starting with the initial value $x = 0, y = 0, z = 0$ and using (1), (2), (3) and repeating the process we get the values of *x, y, z* as the tabulated by both methods. (Gauss-Jacobi and Gauss-Seidel)

| Iteration | *Gauss-Jacobi method* | | | *Gauss-Seidel method* | | |
|---|---|---|---|---|---|---|
| | *x* | *y* | *z* | *x* | *y* | *z* |
| 1 | 3·14815 | 4·8 | 2·03704 | 3·14815 | 3·54074 | 1·91317 |
| 2 | 2·15693 | 3·26913 | 1·88985 | 2·43218 | 3·57204 | 1·92585 |
| 3 | 2·49167 | 3·68525 | 1·93655 | 2·42569 | 3·57294 | 1·92595 |
| 4 | 2·40093 | 3·54513 | 1·92265 | 2·42549 | 3·57301 | 1·92595 |
| 5 | 2·43155 | 3·58327 | 1·92692 | 2·42548 | 3·57301 | 1·92595 |
| 6 | 2·42323 | 3·57046 | 1·92565 | 2·42548 | 3·57301 | 1·92595 |
| 7 | 2·42603 | 3·57395 | 1·92604 | | | |
| 8 | 2·42527 | 3·57278 | 1·92593 | | | |

Hence $x = 2{\cdot}425$, $y = 3{\cdot}573$, and $z = 1{\cdot}926$

(correct to 3 decimal places)

**Example 4.** *Solve, by Gauss-Seidel method, the following system:*

$$28x + 4y - z = 32$$
$$x + 3y + 10z = 24$$
$$2x + 17y + 4z = 35$$

**Solution.** Since the diagonal elements in the coefficient matrix are not dominant, we rearrange the equations, as follows, such that the elements in the coefficient matrix are dominant.

$$28x + 4y - z = 32$$
$$2x + 17y + 4z = 35$$
$$x + 3y + 10z = 24$$

Hence,

$$x = \frac{1}{28}[32 - 4y + z]$$

$$y = \frac{1}{17}[35 - 2x - 4z]$$

$$z = \frac{1}{10}[24 - x - 3y]$$

Setting $y = 0, z = 0$, we get

*First iteration* :

$$x^{(1)} = \frac{1}{28}[32 - 4(0) + 0] = 1{\cdot}1429$$

$$y^{(1)} = \frac{1}{17}[35 - 2(1{\cdot}1429) - 4(0)] = 1{\cdot}9244$$

$$z^{(1)} = \frac{1}{10}[24 - 1{\cdot}1429 - 3(1{\cdot}9244)] = 1{\cdot}8084$$

*Second iteration* :

$$x^{(2)} = \frac{1}{28}[32 - 4(1{\cdot}9244) + 1{\cdot}8084] = 0{\cdot}9325$$

$$y^{(2)} = \frac{1}{17}[35 - 2(0{\cdot}9325) - 4(1{\cdot}8084)] = 1{\cdot}5236$$

$$z^{(3)} = \frac{1}{10}[24 - 0{\cdot}9325 - 3(1{\cdot}5236)] = 1{\cdot}8497$$

*Third iteration* :

$$x^{(3)} = \frac{1}{28}[32 - 4(1{\cdot}5236) + 1{\cdot}8497] = 0{\cdot}9913$$

$$y^{(3)} = \frac{1}{17}[35 - 2(0{\cdot}9913) - 4(1{\cdot}8497)] = 1{\cdot}5070$$

$$z^{(3)} = \frac{1}{10}[24 - 0{\cdot}9913 - 3(1{\cdot}5070)] = 1{\cdot}8488$$

*Fourth iteration* :

$$x^{(4)} = \frac{1}{28}[32 - 4(1{\cdot}5070) + 1{\cdot}8488] = 0{\cdot}9936$$

$$y^{(4)} = \frac{1}{17}[35 - 2(0{\cdot}9936) - 4(1{\cdot}8488)] = 1{\cdot}5069$$

$$z^{(4)} = \frac{1}{10}[24 - 0{\cdot}9936 - 3(1{\cdot}5069)] = 1{\cdot}8486$$

*Fifth iteration* :

$$x^{(5)} = \frac{1}{28}[32 - 4(1{\cdot}5069) + (1{\cdot}8486)] = 0{\cdot}9936$$

$$y^{(6)} = \frac{1}{17}[35 - 2(0{\cdot}9936) - 4(1{\cdot}8486)] = 1{\cdot}5069$$

$$z^{(6)} = \frac{1}{10}[24 - 0{\cdot}9936 - 3(1{\cdot}5069)] = 1{\cdot}8486$$

Since the values of $x$, $y$, $z$ in the 4th and 5th iterations are same, we stop the process here.

Hence, $x = 0{\cdot}9936$, $y = 1{\cdot}5069$, $z = 1{\cdot}8486$

## EXERCISE 4.6

Solve the following system of equations by (*i*) Gauss-Jacobi method and (*ii*) Gauss-Seidel method :

**1.** $5x - 2y + z = -4,\ x + 6y - 2z = -1$, and $3x + y + 5z = 13$

**2.** $8x + y + z = 8,\ 2x + 4y + z = 4,\ x + 3y + 3z = 5$

**3.** $8x - 6y + z = 13{\cdot}67,\ 3x + y - 2z = 17{\cdot}59,\ 2x - 6y + 9z = 29{\cdot}29$

**4.** $30x - 2y + 3z = 75,\ 2x + 2y + 18z = 30,\ x + 17y - 2z = 48$

[**Hint.** Interchange second and third equations.]

**5.** $y - x + 10z = 35{\cdot}61, x + z + 10y = 20{\cdot}08, y - z + 10x = 11{\cdot}19$

**6.** $3{\cdot}122x + 0{\cdot}5756y - 0{\cdot}1565z - 0{\cdot}0067t = 1{\cdot}571$

$0{\cdot}5756x + 2{\cdot}938y + 0{\cdot}1103z - 0{\cdot}0015t = -0{\cdot}9275$

$-0{\cdot}1565x + 0{\cdot}1103y + 4{\cdot}127z + 0{\cdot}2051t = -0{\cdot}0652$

$-0{\cdot}0067x - 0{\cdot}0015y + 0{\cdot}2051z + 4{\cdot}133t = -0{\cdot}0178$

**7.** $10x - 2y + z = 12,\ x + 9y - z = 10,\ 2x - y + 11z = 20$

**8.** $10x - 2y - z - t = 3,\ -2x + 10y - z - t = 15$

$-x - y + 10z - 2t = 27,\ -x - y - 2z + 10t = -9$

**9.** $8x - y + z = 18,\ 2x + 5y - 2z = 3,\ x + y - 3z = -16$

**10.** $2x + y + z = 4,\ x + 2y + z = 4,\ x + y + 2z = 4$ [*MS. Nov.'87*]

**11.** $4x + 2y + z = 14,\ x + 5y - z = 10, x + y + 8z = 20$ [*Ms. Nov. 86*]

**12.** $8x + y + z = 8,\ 2x + 4y + z = 4,\ x + 3y + 5z = 5$ [*Ms. Ap. 92*]

**13.** $14x - 5y = 5{\cdot}5, 2x + 7y = 19{\cdot}3$

**14.** $x - 2y + 10z = 30{\cdot}6,\ 2x + 5y - z = 10{\cdot}5,\ 3x + y + z = 9{\cdot}3$

**15.** $8x - 6y + z = 13{\cdot}67,\ 3x + 11y - 2z = 17{\cdot}59,\ 2x - 6y + 9z = 29{\cdot}29$

**16.** $7{\cdot}6x - 2{\cdot}4y + 1{\cdot}3z = 20{\cdot}396,\ 3{\cdot}7x + 7{\cdot}9y - 2{\cdot}5z = 35{\cdot}866,$

$1{\cdot}9x - 4{\cdot}3y + 8{\cdot}2z = 32{\cdot}514$

**17.** $83x + 11y - 4z = 95,\ 7x + 52y + 13z = 104,\ 3x + 8y + 29z = 71$

## 4·10. Relaxation methods

We will consider a system of three equations in three unknowns as given below for the sake of simplicity. The method is applicable even for more number of equations.

Consider the system of equations,

$$\left.\begin{aligned} a_1x + b_1y + c_1z &= d_1 \\ a_2x + b_2y + c_2z &= d_2 \\ a_3x + b_3y + c_3z &= d_3 \end{aligned}\right\} \quad \text{...(1)}$$

We define the residuals $r_1, r_2, r_3$ by the relations

$$\left.\begin{aligned} r_1 &= a_1x + b_1y + c_1z - d_1 \\ r_2 &= a_2x + b_2y + c_2z - d_2 \\ r_3 &= a_3x + b_3y + c_3z - d_3 \end{aligned}\right\} \quad \text{...(2)}$$

If we can find the values of $x, y, z$ so that $r_1 = 0 = r_2 = r_3$ then those values of $x, y, z$ are the exact values of the system. If it is not possible to make $r_1 = 0 = r_2 = r_3$, then we make simultaneously the values of $r_1, r_2, r_3$ to as close to zero as possible. In other words, we "liquidate" the residuals $r_1, r_2, r_3$ by taking better approximate values of $x, y, z$. If a slight change is made in the values of $x, y, z$, what will be the corresponding changes in the residuals $r_1, r_2, r_3$? We give below an 'operation table' from which we can easily know the corresponding changes in $r_1, r_2, r_3$ for a change of 1 unit in $x$, while there is no change in $y$ and $z$, for a change of 1 unit in $y$ while there in no change in $x$ and $z$; for a change of 1 unit in $z$ while there is no change in $y$ and $x$.

**Operation Table**

| *Operation* | *Changes in (or increment in)* | | | | | |
|---|---|---|---|---|---|---|
| | $x$ | $y$ | $z$ | $r_1$ | $r_2$ | $r_3$ |
| $R_1$ | 1 | 0 | 0 | $a_1$ | $a_2$ | $a_3$ |
| $R_2$ | 0 | 1 | 0 | $b_1$ | $b_2$ | $b_3$ |
| $R_3$ | 0 | 0 | 1 | $c_1$ | $c_2$ | $c_3$ |
| | | $I$ | | | $A'$ | |

What is the meaning of the above table ?

The operator $R_1$ increases the value of $x$ by 1, $y$ by zero, $z$ by zero (no change in $y$ and $z$) and this operation increases the residuals $r_1$ by $a_1$, $r_2$ by $a_2$ and $r_3$ by $a_3$ (the increase in $r_1, r_2, r_3$ are nothing but the coefficients of $x$ in the equations given). Similarly $R_3$ increases the value of $z$ by 1 (while $x, y$ are kept constant) and the effect of this operation increases the values of $r_1, r_2, r_3$ by $c_1, c_2, c_3$ respectively.

One can easily see that the operation table consists of the unit matrix $I$ and the transpose of the matrix $A$ namely $A'$, where $A$ is the coefficient matrix of the system of equations.

## 4·11 Convergence of the relaxation method

If the method should converge, the diagonal elements of the coefficient matrix $A$ should be dominant; that is, $A$ is diagonally dominant. Referring to the system of equations given above; the system can be solved by this method successfully only if

$$|a_1| \geq |b_1| + |c_1|$$
$$|b_2| \geq |a_2| + |c_2|$$
$$|c_3| \geq |a_3| + |b_3|$$

where at least once the strict inequality holds.

**Example 1.** *Solve the following equations using relaxation method*

$$10x - 2y - 2z = 6$$
$$-x + 10y - 2z = 7$$
$$-x - y + 10z = 8$$

**Solution.** Since the diagonal elements are dominant, we will do by relaxation method.

The residuals $r_1, r_2, r_3$ are given by

$$r_1 = 10x - 2y - 2z - 6$$
$$r_2 = -x + 10y - 2z - 7$$
$$r_3 = -x - y + 10z - 8$$

**Operation Table** (Write $I, A'$)

*Changes in*

| | $x$ | $y$ | $z$ | $r_1$ | $r_2$ | $r_3$ |
|---|---|---|---|---|---|---|
| $R_1$ | 1 | 0 | 0 | 10 | − 1 | − 1 |
| $R_2$ | 0 | 1 | 0 | − 2 | 10 | − 1 |
| $R_3$ | 0 | 0 | 1 | − 2 | − 2 | 10 |

We will take the initial values of $x, y, z$ as 0, 0, 0.

Setting $x = 0 = y = z$, we get $r_1 = -6, r_2 = -7, r_3 = -8$

We write these residuals below and *relax* these values making changes in $x, y, z$ as shown below :

| | $x$ | $y$ | $z$ | $r_1$ | $r_2$ | $r_3$ | |
|---|---|---|---|---|---|---|---|
| | 0 | 0 | 0 | − 6 | − 7 | (− 8) (initial) | ...(1) |
| $R_3 \rightarrow$ | 0 | 0 | 1 | − 8 | (− 9) | 2 | ...(2) |
| $R_2 \rightarrow$ | 0 | 1 | 0 | (− 10) | 1 | 1 | ...(3) |
| $R_1 \rightarrow$ | 1 | 0 | 0 | 0 | 0 | 0 | ...(4) |
| | 1 | 1 | 1 | 0 | 0 | 0 | ...(5) |

*Analysis:* In line (1), for $x = 0, y = 0, z = 0$ the residuals are $-6, -7, -8$. The numerically largest residual is − 8 which is encircled.

First, we *liquidate* the numerically largest residual $r_3 = -8$ by a proper multiple of $R_3$. Since $R_3$ operation increases $r_3$ by 10, by operation $1 \cdot R_3$, we get (*i.e.* put $x = 0, y = 0, z = 1$) $r_1 = -6 + (-2) = -8$; $r_2 = -7 + (-2) = -9$, $r_3 = -8 + 10 = 2$ giving line (2) . Now, in line (2), numerically greatest residual is - 9 which is encircled. We will liquidate this $r_2$ by proper multiple of $R_2$. An increase of 1 in $y$ will increase $r_2$ by 10, $r_1$ by − 2 and $r_3$ by −1. Hence doing the operation $1 \cdot R_2$ new $r_1 = -8 - 2 = -10$, $r_2 = -9 + 10 = 1$, $r_3 = 2 + (-1) = 1$ and we get the line (3). Now in line

(3), $r_1 = -10$ is the numerically greatest value. Now, we will liquidate this $r_1 = -10$ by a proper multiple of $R_1$. Doing the operation $R_1 \to (1, 0, 0)$, $r_1 = -10 + 10 = 0$, $r_2 = 1 + (-1) = 0$, $r_3 = 1 + (-1) = 0$. Fortunately all the residuals have become zero after the 3 operations. Adding the values of $x, y, z$ we get $x = 1, y = 1, z = 1$ as the exact solution for the system.

**Example 2.** *By relaxation method, solve* :

$$12x + y + z = 31$$
$$2x + 8y - z = 24$$
$$3x + 4y + 10z = 58$$

**Solution.** The coefficient matrix is diagonally dominant. Hence, we will use relaxation method with confidence. The residuals are

$$r_1 = 12x + y + z - 31$$
$$r_2 = 2x + 8y - z - 24$$
$$r_3 = 3x + 4y + 10z - 58$$

**Operation Table**

| | $x$ | $y$ | $z$ | $r_1$ | $r_2$ | $r_3$ |
|---|---|---|---|---|---|---|
| $R_1$ | 1 | 0 | 0 | 12 | 2 | 3 |
| $R_2$ | 0 | 1 | 0 | 1 | 8 | 4 |
| $R_3$ | 0 | 0 | 1 | 1 | − 1 | 10 |

We will start with the initial values $x = 0, y = 0, z = 0$. Relaxation procedure is given below :

| | $x$ | $y$ | $z$ | $r_1$ | $r_2$ | $r_3$ | |
|---|---|---|---|---|---|---|---|
| (initial) | 0 | 0 | 0 | − 31 | − 24 | (− 58) | ...(1) |
| $6R_3 \to$ | 0 | 0 | 6 | − 25 | (− 30) | 2 | ...(2) |
| $4R_2 \to$ | 0 | 4 | 0 | (− 21) | 2 | 18 | ...(3) |
| $2R_1 \to$ | 2 | 0 | 0 | 3 | 6 | (24) | ...(4) |
| $-2R_3 \to$ | 0 | 0 | − 2 | 1 | (8) | 4 | ...(5) |
| $-1R_2 \to$ | 0 | − 1 | 0 | 0 | 0 | 0 | ...(6) |
| | 2 | 3 | 4 | 0 | 0 | 0 | ...(7) |

Since all the residuals are made to zero, the solution is $x = 2, y = 3, x = 4$.

*Explanation:* In line (1), giving $x = 0, y = 0, z = 0$ we get $r_1 = -31$, $r_2 = -24$, $r_3 = -58$. Here $r_3 = -58$ is numerically the greatest residual. Hence we *liquidate* $r_3 = -58$ by suitable multiple of $R_3$. In $R_3$, a change of 1 in $z$ will cause an addition 10 in $r_3$. To nullify $-58$, we add 6 in $z$

so that a change of 60 is effected in $r_3$. Therefore, using $6R_3$, changes in $r_1, r_2, r_3$ are $6, -6, 60$. Hence new $r_1 = -31 + 6 = -25$, $r_2 = -24 + (-6) = -30$, $r_3 = -58 + 60 = 2$. Which is line number (2). In line (2), the numerically greatest residual is $r_2 = -30$, we *liquidate* this, by a proper multiple of $R_2$. By $R_2$, an increase of 1 in $y$ makes changes 1 in $r_1$, 8 in $r_2$ and 4 in $r_3$. To *liquidate* $-30$, we do operation $4R_2$. So that $4R_2$ causes changes 4, 32, 16 in $r_1, r_2, r_3$ respectively. Hence, by $4R_2$,

Now $r_1 = -25 + (4) = -21$, $r_2 = -30 + 32 = 2$, $r_3 = 2 + 16 = 18$.

Therefore, in line (3), $r_1 = -21$, $r_2 = 2$, $r_3 = 18$. Now, $r_1 = -21$ is the numerically greatest residual. Hence, we now liquidate the value of $r_1 = -21$. An increase of 1 in $x$ (*i.e.*, $R_1$ operation) increases 12 in $r_1$. Hence, we do operation $2 \cdot R_1$ to *liquidate* $r_1 = -21$. This causes for new $r_1 = 3$, $r_2 = 6$, and $r_3 = 24$. Now we *liquidate* 24 by $-2R_3$ since $-2R_3$ increase the value of $r_3$ by $-20$ . After the operation of $-2R_3$, we get $r_1 = 1$, $r_2 = 8$, $r_3 = 4$. Therefore now we liquidate $r_2 = 8$ by $-1R_2$ and we get the resultant $r_1 = 0, r_2 = 0, r_3 = 0$. Adding all the values of $x, y, z$ we get $x = 2, y = 3, z = 4$ as the exact solution.

**Example 3.** *Use relaxation method to solve the system*

$$8x + y + z + w = 14$$
$$2x + 10y + 3z + w = -8$$
$$x - 2y - 20z + 3w = 111$$
$$3x + 2y + 2z + 19w = 53$$

**Solution.** Evidently the coefficient matrix

$$A = \begin{pmatrix} 8 & 1 & 1 & 1 \\ 2 & 10 & 3 & 1 \\ 1 & -2 & -20 & 3 \\ 3 & 2 & 2 & 19 \end{pmatrix}$$ is diagonally dominant, we have the residuals $r_1, r_2, r_3, r_4$.

$$r_1 = 8x + y + z + w - 14$$
$$r_2 = 2x + 10y + 3z + w + 8$$
$$r_3 = x - 2y - 20z + 3w - 111$$
$$r_4 = 3x + 2y + 2z + 19w - 53$$

**Operation Table**

| | $x$ | $y$ | $z$ | $w$ | $r_1$ | $r_2$ | $r_3$ | $r_4$ |
|---|---|---|---|---|---|---|---|---|
| $R_1$ | 1 | 0 | 0 | 0 | 8 | 2 | 1 | 3 |
| $R_2$ | 0 | 1 | 0 | 0 | 1 | 10 | − 2 | 2 |
| $R_3$ | 0 | 0 | 1 | 0 | 1 | 3 | - 20 | 2 |
| $R_4$ | 0 | 0 | 0 | 1 | 1 | 1 | 3 | 19 |

We will start with $x=0, y=0, z=0, w=0$ as initial values.

Relaxation procedure is given below:

| | $x$ | $y$ | $z$ | $w$ | $r_1$ | $r_2$ | $r_3$ | $r_4$ |
|---|---|---|---|---|---|---|---|---|
| | 0 | 0 | 0 | 0 | – 14 | 8 | (– 111) | – 53 |
| $-5R_3 \to$ | 0 | 0 | – 5 | 0 | – 19 | – 7 | – 11 | (– 63) |
| $3R_4 \to$ | 0 | 0 | 0 | 3 | (– 16) | – 4 | – 2 | – 6 |
| $2R_1 \to$ | 2 | 0 | 0 | 0 | 0 | 0 | 0 | 0 |
| Adding | 2 | 0 | – 5 | 3 | 0 | 0 | 0 | 0 |

Since all the residuals are zero, the exact solution is $x=2, y=0, z=-5$ and $w=3$.

**Note.** Since the explanations were given already in examples 1 and 2, the reader is in a position to follow the procedure steps from the table.

**Example 4.** *Solve, by relaxation method, the system*

$$9x - y + 2z = 9$$
$$x + 10y - 2z = 15$$
$$2x - 2y - 13z = -17$$

**Solution.** Evidently, the coefficient matrix is diagonally dominant. The residuals $r_1, r_2, r_3$ are related by

$$\begin{aligned} r_1 &= 9x - y + 2z - 9 \\ r_2 &= x + 10y - 2z - 15 \\ r_3 &= 2x - 2y - 13z + 17 \end{aligned} \qquad \text{...(1)}$$

**The Operation Table**

| | $x$ | $y$ | $z$ | $r_1$ | $r_2$ | $r_3$ |
|---|---|---|---|---|---|---|
| $R_1 \to$ | 1 | 0 | 0 | 9 | 1 | 2 |
| $R_2 \to$ | 0 | 1 | 0 | – 1 | 10 | – 2 |
| $R_3 \to$ | 0 | 0 | 1 | 2 | – 2 | – 13 |

We will start with the initial values $x=0, y=0, z=0$

**Procedure Table**

| Operation | $x$ | $y$ | $z$ | $r_1$ | $r_2$ | $r_3$ | |
|---|---|---|---|---|---|---|---|
| Initial value | 0 | 0 | 0 | – 9 | – 15 | (17) | ...(1) |
| $1R_3 \to$ | 0 | 0 | 1 | – 7 | (– 17) | 4 | ...(2) |
| $2R_2 \to$ | 0 | 2 | 0 | (– 9) | 3 | 0 | ...(3) |
| $1R_1 \to$ | 1 | 0 | 0 | 0 | 4 | 2 | ...(4) |
| | 1 | 2 | 1 | 0 | 4 | 2 | ...(5) |

Multiply the line (5) by 10.

| | | | | | | | |
|---|---|---|---|---|---|---|---|
| | 10 | 20 | 10 | 0 | **40** | 20 | ...(6) |
| $-4R_2 \rightarrow$ | 0 | $-4$ | 0 | 4 | 0 | **28** | ...(7) |
| $2R_3 \rightarrow$ | 0 | 0 | 2 | **8** | $-4$ | 2 | ...(8) |
| $-R_1 \rightarrow$ | $-1$ | 0 | 0 | $-1$ | $-5$ | 0 | ...(9) |
| | 9 | 16 | 12 | $-1$ | $-5$ | 0 | ...(10) |

Multiply the line (10) by 10

| | $x$ | $y$ | $z$ | $r_1$ | $r_2$ | $r_3$ | |
|---|---|---|---|---|---|---|---|
| | 90 | 160 | 120 | $-10$ | **$-50$** | 0 | ...(11) |
| $5R_2 \rightarrow$ | 0 | 5 | 0 | **$-15$** | 0 | $-10$ | ...(12) |
| $2R_1 \rightarrow$ | 2 | 0 | 0 | 3 | 2 | $-6$ | ...(13) |
| | 92 | 165 | 120 | 3 | 2 | $-6$ | ...(14) |

Multiply line (14) by 10

| | | | | | | | |
|---|---|---|---|---|---|---|---|
| | 920 | 1650 | 1200 | 30 | 20 | **$-60$** | ...(15) |
| $-5R_3 \rightarrow$ | 0 | 0 | $-5$ | 20 | **30** | 5 | ...(16) |
| $-3R_2 \rightarrow$ | 0 | $-3$ | 0 | **23** | 0 | 11 | ...(17) |
| $-3R_1 \rightarrow$ | $-3$ | 0 | 0 | $-4$ | $-3$ | 5 | ...(18) |
| | 917 | 1647 | 1195 | $-4$ | $-3$ | 5 | ...(19) |

Since we multiplied by 10 three times,

$10^3 x = 917$, $10^3 y = 1647$, $10^3 z = 1195$ and hence $x = 0{\cdot}917$, $y = 1{\cdot}647$, $z = 1{\cdot}195$ while the residuals are $r_1 = -0{\cdot}004$, $r_2 = -0{\cdot}003$, $r_3 = 0{\cdot}005$.

*Explanation:* Upto step 5, we perform as we did in the previous examples. In line (5), all the residuals are less than their initial values. This indicates that we go for the next decimal point. At line (5), we multiply the line by 10 and get line (6). In line (5), $x = 1, y = 2, z = 1$ make $r_1 = 0, r_2 = 4, r_3 = 2$. In line (6), it means that $10x = 10, 10y = 20, 10z = 10$ and $10r_1 = 0, 10r_2 = 40, 10r_3 = 20$. Again from line (6), we proceed as usual and at line (10), the residuals are again less than the initial residuals and hence we multiply by 10 against line (10) and get line (11). In line (11), it means $10^2 x = 90$, $10^2 y = 160$, $10^2 z = 120$, $10^2 r_1 = -10$, $10^2 r_2 = -50$, $10^2 r_3 = 0$. Again proceeding from (11), at line (14), again the residuals are less than the initial residuals. Hence, we again multiply by 10 at line (14). In line (15), it means, $10^3 x = 920$, $10^3 y = 1650$, $10^3 z = 1200$, $10^3 r_1 = 30$, $10^3 r_2 = 20$ and $10^3 r_3 = -60$. Now again we proceed till line (19) where the residuals are again less than the initial residuals. At line (19), we have,

$10^3x = 917,\ 10^3y = 1647,\ 10^3z = 1195,\ 10^3r_1 = -4,$

$10^3r_2 = -3,\ 10^3r_3 = 5$. From these, we get

$$x = 0{\cdot}917,\ y = 1{\cdot}647,\ z = 1{\cdot}195,\ r_1 = -0{\cdot}004,\ r_2 = -0{\cdot}003,\ r_3 = 0{\cdot}005.$$

*Check:* We will check the result by substitution.

$9\,(0{\cdot}917) - (1{\cdot}647) + 2\,(1{\cdot}195) - 9$ yields $-0{\cdot}004 = r_1$

$0{\cdot}917 + 10\,(1{\cdot}647) - 2\,(1{\cdot}195) - 15$ gives $-0{\cdot}00238 \approx r_2$

$2\,(0{\cdot}917) - 2\,(1{\cdot}647) - 13\,(1{\cdot}195) + 17$ becomes $0{\cdot}005 = r_3$

**Example 5.** *Solve by relaxation method, the system*

$$10x + 2y - w = 11{\cdot}0$$
$$-x + 20y + 2z = 49{\cdot}5$$
$$-x + 10z - w = 27{\cdot}5$$
$$-y + 2z + 20w = 92{\cdot}4$$

**Solution.** Here, there are 4 variables $x$, $y$, $z$ and $w$. Therefore,

$$r_1 = 10x + 2y + 0{\cdot}z - w - 11{\cdot}0$$
$$r_2 = -x + 20y + 2z + 0{\cdot}w - 49{\cdot}5 \qquad \text{...(1)}$$
$$r_3 = -x + 0{\cdot}y + 10z - w - 27{\cdot}5$$
$$r_4 = 0{\cdot}x - y + 2z + 20w - 92{\cdot}5$$

Evidently the coefficient matrix is diagonally dominant.

**Operation Table**

| | $x$ | $y$ | $z$ | $w$ | $r_1$ | $r_2$ | $r_3$ | $r_4$ |
|---|---|---|---|---|---|---|---|---|
| $R_1 \to$ | 1 | 0 | 0 | 0 | 10 | $-1$ | $-1$ | 0 |
| $R_2 \to$ | 0 | 1 | 0 | 0 | 2 | 20 | 0 | $-1$ |
| $R_3 \to$ | 0 | 0 | 1 | 0 | 0 | 2 | 10 | 2 |
| $R_4 \to$ | 0 | 0 | 0 | 1 | $-1$ | 0 | $-1$ | 20 |

We start with initial values $(x, y, z, w) = (0, 0, 0, 0)$. We will give below the procedure table without any explanation as it is already given in the above example :

| Operation | $x$ | $y$ | $z$ | $w$ | $r_1$ | $r_2$ | $r_3$ | $r_4$ |
|---|---|---|---|---|---|---|---|---|
| (initial) | 0 | 0 | 0 | 0 | $-11{\cdot}0$ | $-49{\cdot}5$ | $-27{\cdot}5$ | $-92{\cdot}5$ |
| $4R_4 \to$ | 0 | 0 | 0 | 4 | $-15{\cdot}0$ | $-49{\cdot}5$ | $-31{\cdot}5$ | $-12{\cdot}5$ |
| $2R_2 \to$ | 0 | 2 | 0 | 0 | $-11{\cdot}0$ | $-9{\cdot}5$ | $-31{\cdot}5$ | $-14{\cdot}5$ |
| $3R_3 \to$ | 0 | 0 | 3 | 0 | $-11{\cdot}0$ | $-3{\cdot}5$ | $-1{\cdot}5$ | $-8{\cdot}5$ |
| $1R_1 \to$ | 1 | 0 | 0 | 0 | $-1{\cdot}0$ | $-4{\cdot}5$ | $-2{\cdot}5$ | $-8{\cdot}5$ |
| | 1 | 2 | 3 | 4 | $-1{\cdot}0$ | $-4{\cdot}5$ | $-2{\cdot}5$ | $-8{\cdot}5$ |

Multiply by 10

| | | | | | | | | |
|---|---|---|---|---|---|---|---|---|
| | 10 | 20 | 30 | 40 | − 10 | − 45 | − 25 | (− 85) |
| $4R_4 \rightarrow$ | 0 | 0 | 0 | 4 | − 14 | (− 45) | − 29 | − 5 |
| $2R_2 \rightarrow$ | 0 | 2 | 0 | 0 | − 10 | − 5 | (− 29) | − 7 |
| $3R_3 \rightarrow$ | 0 | 0 | 3 | 0 | (− 10) | 1 | 1 | − 1 |
| $1R_1 \rightarrow$ | 1 | 0 | 0 | 0 | 0 | 0 | 0 | −1 |
| | 11 | 22 | 33 | 44 | 0 | 0 | 0 | − 1 |

Since three residuals are zeros, we can stop here

$10x = 11,\ 10y = 22,\ 10z = 33,\ 10w = 44,\ 10r_1 = 0,\ 10r_2 = 0,\ 10r_3 = 0,$
$10r_4 = -1$

Hence, $x = 1{\cdot}1,\ y = 2{\cdot}2, z = 3{\cdot}3,\ w = 4{\cdot}4$ and $r_1 = r_2 = r_3 = 0, r_4 = -0{\cdot}1$

**Note.** In the above procedure, *we always liquidate the numerically largest residual to zero or nearer to zero.*

*Ill conditioned system:* A system of equations $AX = B$ is *ill-conditioned* or *unstable* if it is *highly sensitive* to small changes in $A$ and $B$. In other words, small changes in $A$ or $B$ results a large change in the solution $X$.

For example, the system $x - y = 1,\ x - 1{\cdot}00001y = 0$ has the solution (100001, 100000). By changing $A = \begin{pmatrix} 1 & -1 \\ 1 & -1{\cdot}00001 \end{pmatrix}$ to $\begin{pmatrix} 1 & -1 \\ 1 & -0{\cdot}99999 \end{pmatrix}$ we get the solution (− 99999,− 100000). The two solutions are very much different. Hence, the system is *ill-conditioned.*

## EXERCISE 4.7

1. Solve the equations given in exercises 4·6 by relaxation method.

Solve the following system of equations by relaxation method.

2. $10x - 2y + z = 12,\ x + 9y - z = 10,\ 2z - y + 11z = 20$
3. $5x - y - z = 3,\ -x + 10y - 2z = 7,\ -x - y + 10z = 8$
4. $2x - y + z = 3,\ 2z + y - z = 1,\ x + y + z = 0$
5. $50x + 2y - 3z = 196,\ 3x + 65y + 2z = 81, -x + y + 33z = 63$
6. $8x + y - z = 8,\ x - 7y + 2z = -4,\ 2x + y + 9z = 12$
7. $27x + 6y - z = 85,\ 6x + 15y + 2z = 72, x + y + 54\,z = 110$
8. $9x - 2y + z = 50,\ x + 5y - 3z = 18,\ -2x + 2y + 7z = 19$
9. $2x - 3y + 10z = 3,\ -x + 4y + 2z = 20,\ 5x + 2y + z = -12$
   (Rearrange the equations)
10. $6x_1 + x_2 - x_3 = 14,\ x_1 + 5x_2 - x_3 = -18,\ 2x_1 + x_2 + 9x_3 = 68$
11. $3x + y - z - w = 0,\ x + 3y - z + 2w + 3 = 0,$
    $-2x + 2y + 3z - 2w - 4 = 0,\ x + 2y + z - 5w + 1 = 0$

**12.** $3x + 9y - 2z = 11,\ 4x + 2y + 13z = 24, 4x - 4y + 3z = -8$

**13.** $10x - 2y - 2z = -6,\ -x + 10y - z = -7,\ -x - y + 10z = -8$

**14.** $9{\cdot}37x + 3{\cdot}04y - 2{\cdot}44z = 9{\cdot}23,\ 3{\cdot}04x + 6{\cdot}18y + 1{\cdot}22z = 8{\cdot}20,$
$-2{\cdot}44x + 1{\cdot}22y + 8{\cdot}44z = 3{\cdot}93.$

**15.** $10x + y + z = 12,\ x + 10y + z = 12,\ x + y + 10z = 12$

**16.** $10x + y + z = 16{\cdot}5,\ x + 10y + z = 26{\cdot}4,\ x + y + 10z = 36{\cdot}3$

**17.** $10x - 2y + z = 12,\ x + 9y - z = 10,\ 2x - y + 11z = 20$

**18.** $10x + y + z + w = 21{\cdot}09,\ x + 10y + z + w = 31{\cdot}08,$
$x + y + 10z + w = 41{\cdot}07,\ x + y + z + 10w = 51{\cdot}06$

**19.** $20x + y + z + w = 23,\ x + 20y + z + w = 23,$
$x + y + 20z + w = 23,\ x + y + z + 20w = 23$

**20.** $15x + 3y - 4z + 2w = 49{\cdot}207,\ 3x + 7y - 5z - 4w = 18{\cdot}024$
$-4x - 5y + 16z + 5w = -23{\cdot}871,\ 2x - y + 5z + 19w = 54{\cdot}907$

# ANSWERS

## EXERCISE 4.1 Page 121

**1.** 1, 1 **2.** 1, 2 **3.** 2, – 1 **4.** – 2, 3, 6

**5.** 0·99, 1·50, 1·84 **6.** 39·2, 16·7, 19 **7.** 1, 4, 5, – 7

**8.** 1, 1, 1 **9.** 1·234, 2·348, 3·455 **10.** 1, 1, 1

**11.** 1, 2, 3 **12.** 8·7, 5·7, – 1·3 **13.** 1, 1, 1

**14.** 1, 2, 2, 2 **15.** 1, 1, 2 **16.** 1, – 1, 2

**17.** 1·64, – 2·49, 0·32 **18.** 1, 0, – 1, 2 **19.** 4·2075, 1·3327, 0·2468

**20.** 2, 3, 4 **21.** 3, – 2, 1, 5 **22.** 55·56, – 277·78, 255·56

**23.** 2, – 1, 3 **24.** 1, 1, 1, 1 **25.** 1·5, 2·5, 3·5

**26.** 1, 1, – 1, – 1

## EXERCISE 4.2 Page 126

**1.** $\frac{1}{2}\begin{pmatrix} -6 & 5 & -1 \\ 24 & -17 & 3 \\ -10 & 7 & -1 \end{pmatrix}$ **2.** $\begin{pmatrix} 1 & -1 & 0 \\ -2 & 3 & -4 \\ -2 & 3 & -3 \end{pmatrix}$ **3.** $\frac{1}{6}\begin{pmatrix} 3 & 0 & -3 \\ 2 & 2 & 2 \\ 1 & -2 & 1 \end{pmatrix}$

**4.** $\frac{1}{8}\begin{pmatrix} 2 & 2 & -2 \\ -9 & 11 & 5 \\ 5 & -7 & -1 \end{pmatrix}$ **5.** $\frac{1}{2}\begin{pmatrix} -6 & 5 & -1 \\ 24 & -17 & 3 \\ -10 & 7 & -1 \end{pmatrix}$ **6.** $\begin{pmatrix} 8 & -1 & -3 \\ -5 & 1 & 2 \\ 10 & -1 & -4 \end{pmatrix}$

**7.** $\frac{1}{10}\begin{pmatrix} 1 & 3 & 2 \\ 21 & \frac{-7}{2} & -4 \\ -9 & 3 & 2 \end{pmatrix}$ **8.** $\begin{pmatrix} -26 & -7 & 12 \\ 11 & 3 & -5 \\ -5 & -1 & 2 \end{pmatrix}$ **9.** $\begin{pmatrix} -1 & 3 & 5 \\ -3 & 1 & 7 \\ 7 & -5 & -11 \end{pmatrix}$

## EXERCISE 4.3 Page 132

**1.** 2, – 1, 3 **2.** 2, – 1, 3 **3.** 1, 2, 3 **4.** $\frac{19}{4}, \frac{-9}{4}, \frac{3}{4}$

**5.** 2, 6, − 7 **6.** 1, 2, 0 **7.** 1, 1, 3 **8.** 2, 3, 4

**9.** 1, 2, − 1 **10.** 1, 2, − 1 **11.** 1, − 2, 3 **12.** 1, 1, 1

**13.** 1, 3, 5 **14.** 1, − 1, − 1 **15.** 0·5, 0·5, 0·5 **16.** 1, 2, − 1

## EXERCISE 4.4 Page 141

**1.** − 1, 2, 3 **2.** $1, \frac{1}{2}, \frac{3}{4}$ **3.** 1, 3, 5 **4.** 1, − 2, 3

**5.** 1, 5, − 4 **6.** 1, 3, 5 **7.** 2, 3, − 4 **8.** 1, 1, 1

**9.** 1, 1, 1 **10.** 1, 2, 2, 2 **11.** 1, 4, 5, − 7 **12.** 2, 6, − 7

**13.** 1, 2, 3 **14.** 1, − 1, 2 **15.** 1, 1, 1, 1.

## EXERCISE 4.5 Page 145

**1.** $\begin{pmatrix} -3 & 2·5 & -0·5 \\ 12 & -8·5 & 1·5 \\ -5 & 3·5 & -0·5 \end{pmatrix}$ **2.** $\frac{1}{3}\begin{pmatrix} -4 & 6 & 7 \\ 5 & -6 & -8 \\ 7 & -9 & -10 \end{pmatrix}$ **3.** $\begin{pmatrix} -26 & -7 & 12 \\ 11 & 3 & -5 \\ -5 & -1 & 2 \end{pmatrix}$

**4.** $\begin{pmatrix} 1 & -1 & 0 \\ -2 & 3 & -4 \\ -2 & 3 & -3 \end{pmatrix}$ **5.** $\begin{pmatrix} 8 & -1 & -3 \\ -5 & 1 & 2 \\ 10 & -1 & -4 \end{pmatrix}$ **6.** $\frac{1}{11}\begin{pmatrix} -3 & 4 & 5 \\ 9 & -1 & -4 \\ 5 & -3 & -1 \end{pmatrix}$

## EXERCISE 4.6 Page 159

**1.** − 1·001, 0·999, 3 **2.** 0·83, 0·32, 1·07 **3.** 2·45, 1·62, 3·79

**4.** 2.5796, 2.7976, 1.0693 **5.** 1·321, 1·522, 3·541

**6.** 0·5835, − 0·4307, 0·0181, − 0·0044 **7.** 1·2624, 1·1591, 1·6940

**8.** 0, 1, 2, 3 **9.** 2,0·9998, 2·9999 **10.** 1, 1, 1

**11.** 2, 2, 2 **12.** 0·876, 0·419, 0·574 **13.** 1·25, 2·40

**14.** 1·2315, 2·2618, 3·3823, Actual 1·2, 2·3, 3·4 **15.** 2·45, 1·62, 3·79

**16.** 3·23, 4·85, 5·76 **17.** 1·06, 1·37, 1·96

## EXERCISE 4.7 Page 167

**2.** 1·3, 1·2, 1·7 **3.** 1, 1, 1 **4.** 1, − 1, 0

**5.** 4, 1, 2 **6.** 1, 1, 1 **7.** 2·473, 3·256, 1·931

**8.** 6·15, 4·31, 3·24 **9.** − 4. 3. 2 **10.** 4. − 3. 7

**1.** 2, −1, 4, 1 **12.** −1.348, 2.103, 1.938 **13.** − 0·971, − 0·892, 0·984

**14.** 0·879, 0·764, 0·615 **15.** 1, 1, 1 **16.** 1·1, 2·2, 3·3

**17.** 1·26, 1·16, 1·69 **18.** 1·11, 2·22, 3·33, 4·44

**19.** 1, 1, 1, 1 **20.** 2·031, 2·683, − 1·118, 3·111

5

# Finite Differences

## 5·1. First difference

Let $y = f(x)$ be a given function of $x$ and let $y_0, y_1, y_2, ..., y_n$ be the values of $y$ corresponding to $x_0, x_1, x_2, ..., x_n$, the values of $x$. The independent variable $x$ is called the *argument* and the corresponding dependent value $y$ is called, the *entry*. In general, the difference between any two consecutive values of $x$ need not be same or equal.

We can write the arguments and entries as below.

| $x$ | $x_0$ | $x_1$ | $x_2$ | .... | $x_{n-1}$ | $x_n$ |
|---|---|---|---|---|---|---|
| $y$ | $y_0$ | $y_1$ | $y_2$ | .... | $y_{n-1}$ | $y_n$ |

If we subtract from each value of $y$ (except $y_0$) the preceding value of $y$, we get

$$y_1 - y_0, y_2 - y_1, y_3 - y_2, ..., y_n - y_{n-1}$$

These results are called the *first differences* of $y$. The first differences of $y$ are denoted by $\Delta y$.

That is,
$$\Delta y_0 = y_1 - y_0$$
$$\Delta y_1 = y_2 - y_1$$
$$\Delta y_2 = y_3 - y_2$$
$$\Delta y_{n-1} = y_n - y_{n-1}$$

Here, the symbol $\Delta$ denotes an operation, called forward difference operator.

*Higher differences*: The second and higher differences are defined as below :

$$\Delta^2 y_0 = \Delta(\Delta y_0) = \Delta(y_1 - y_0) = \Delta y_1 - \Delta y_0$$
$$\Delta^2 y_1 = \Delta(\Delta y_1) = \Delta(y_2 - y_1) = \Delta y_2 - \Delta y_1$$

..........................................................

$$\Delta^2 y_{n-1} = \Delta(\Delta y_{n-1}) = \Delta(y_n - y_{n-1}) = \Delta y_n - \Delta y_{n-1}$$

Here, $\Delta^2$ is an operator called, second order forward difference operator. In the same way, the third order forward difference operator $\Delta^3$ is as follows :

$$\Delta^3 y_0 = \Delta^2 y_1 - \Delta^2 y_0$$

$$\Delta^3 y_1 = \Delta^2 y_2 - \Delta^2 y_1$$

.................................. etc.

In general $\qquad \Delta^n y_i = \Delta^{n-1} y_{i+1} - \Delta^{n-1} y_i$

Though the arguments $x_0, x_1, x_2, \ldots$ need not, in general, be equally spaced, for purposes of practical work, we take them equally spaced.

Usually, the arguments are taken as

$$x_0, x_0 + h, \quad x_0 + 2h, \quad x_0 + 3h, \ldots.$$

so that $\qquad x_1 - x_0 = x_2 - x_1 = x_3 - x_2 = \cdots\cdots = h$

Here, $h$ is called the *interval of differencing.*

Therefore, $\qquad \Delta f(x) = f(x+h) - f(x)$

$$\begin{aligned}
\Delta^2 f(x) &= \Delta\,(\Delta f(x)) \\
&= \Delta f(x+h) - \Delta f(x) \\
&= [f(x+2h) - f(x+h)] - [f(x+h) - f(x)] \\
&= f(x+2h) - 2f(x+h) + f(x)
\end{aligned}$$

$$\begin{aligned}
\Delta^3 f(x) &= \Delta^2[\Delta f(x)] = \Delta[\Delta^2 f(x)] \\
&= \Delta f(x+2h) - 2\Delta f(x+h) + \Delta f(x) \\
&= f(x+3h) - f(x+2h) - 2\,[f(x+2h) - f(x+h)] \\
&\qquad + f(x+h) - f(x) \\
&= f(x+3h) - 3f(x+2h) + 3f(x+h) - f(x)
\end{aligned}$$

and so on.

**Operators.** We have already defined the forward difference operator $\Delta$. We will now see some more operators and the relations connecting them.

*Backward difference operator* $(\nabla)$ :

Backward difference operator $(\nabla)$ is defined as

$$\nabla f(x) = f(x) - f(x-h)$$

By definition $\qquad \nabla y_1 = y_1 - y_0$

$$\nabla y_2 = y_2 - y_1 \text{ etc.}$$

Hence

$$\begin{aligned}
\nabla^2 f(x) &= \nabla[f(x) - f(x-h)] \\
&= \nabla f(x) - \nabla f(x-h) \\
&= f(x) - f(x-h) - [f(x-h) - f(x-2h)] \\
&= f(x) - 2f(x-h) + f(x-2h)
\end{aligned}$$

*Central difference operator* $(\delta)$ :

The central difference operator $\delta$ is defined by

$$\delta f(x) = f\left(x + \frac{h}{2}\right) - f\left(x - \frac{h}{2}\right)$$

or
$$\delta y_x = y_{x+\frac{h}{2}} - y_{x-\frac{h}{2}}$$

*Shifting or displacement or translation operator E:* We define the shifting operator $E$ such that

$$Ef(x) = f(x+h)$$

or
$$E\,y_x = y_{x+h}$$

Hence $E\,y_1 = y_2,\quad E\,(y_2) = y_3$ etc.

$$E^2 y_x = E\,(y_{x+h}) = y_{x+2h}$$

$$E^n y_x = y_{x+nh} \text{ and } E^n f(x) = f(x+nh)$$

Inverse operator $E^{-1}$ is such that

$$E^{-1}\,Ef(x) = f(x)$$

Suppose $E^{-1} f(x) = \phi(x)$

Then $E\phi(x) = f(x)$

Hence $\phi(x+h) = f(x)$

$\therefore$ $\phi(x) = f(x-h)$

$\therefore$ $E^{-1} f(x) = f(x-h)$

Similarly $E^{-r} f(x) = f(x-rh)$

*Averaging operator* $\mu$ : The averaging operator $\mu$ is defined by

$$\mu y_x = \frac{1}{2}\left(y_{x+\frac{h}{2}} + y_{x-\frac{h}{2}}\right)$$

*i.e.,*
$$\mu f(x) = \frac{1}{2}\left[f\left(x + \frac{h}{2}\right) + f\left(x - \frac{h}{2}\right)\right]$$

*Differential operator D :* The differential operator $D$ is defined by

$$D\,f(x) = \frac{d}{dx} f(x)$$

$$D^2 f(x) = \frac{d^2}{dx^2} f(x) \text{ etc.}$$

*Unit operator 1 :* The unit operator 1 is such that

$$1 \cdot f(x) = f(x).$$

*Properties of operators 1.* The operators $\Delta$, $\nabla$, $E$, $\delta$, $\mu$ and $D$ are all linear operators.

**Proof.**
$$\begin{aligned}\Delta(af(x) + b\phi(x)) &= [af(x+h) + b\phi(x+h)] - [af(x) + b\phi(x)] \\ &= a\,[f(x+h) - f(x)] + b\,[\phi(x+h) - \phi(x)] \\ &= a\Delta f(x) + b\Delta\phi(x)\end{aligned}$$

Hence $\Delta$ is a linear operator.

Putting $a = b = 1$, $\Delta[f(x) + g(x)] = \Delta f(x) + \Delta g(x)$

and by putting $b=0$, $\Delta(af(x)) = a\Delta f(x)$

2. The operator is distributive over addition.

$$\Delta^m \Delta^n f(x) = \Delta^{m+n} f(x) = \Delta^n . \Delta^m f(x).$$

$$\Delta^m \Delta^n f(x) = (\Delta.\Delta.\dots\ m \text{ factors})(\Delta.\Delta.\dots n \text{ factors}) f(x)$$
$$= \Delta^{m+n} f(x)$$

All the above operators obey index laws.

3. Also $\Delta[f(x) + g(x)] = \Delta[g(x) + f(x)]$

*Relation between the operators:*

*Relation between $\Delta$ and $E$:*

We know $\Delta f(x) = f(x+h) - f(x)$

$$= Ef(x) - 1 \cdot f(x)$$
$$= (E-1) f(x)$$

$\therefore$ $\Delta = E - 1.$

This is called separation of symbols.

**Note.** Two operators $O_1$ and $O_2$ are equal if $O_1 f(x) = O_2 . f(x)$ for all $f(x)$.

$$\therefore \quad \boxed{\Delta = E - 1} \qquad \dots(1)$$

or

$$\boxed{E = 1 + \Delta} \qquad \dots(2)$$

Here, 1 is not the numeral 1 but it is the unit operator 1 which means $1.f(x) = f(x)$.

*Relation between $E$ and $\nabla$ :*

$$\nabla f(x) = f(x) - f(x-h)$$
$$= 1.f(x) - E^{-1} f(x)$$
$$= (1 - E^{-1}) f(x)$$

$$\therefore \quad \boxed{\nabla = 1 - E^{-1}} \qquad \dots(3)$$

Hence $E^{-1} = 1 - \nabla$

$$\boxed{E = (1 - \nabla)^{-1}} \quad \text{since } (E^{-1})^{-1} = E \qquad \dots(4)$$

*Relation between $E$ and $\delta$ :*

$$\delta f(x) = f\left(x + \frac{h}{2}\right) - f\left(x - \frac{h}{2}\right)$$
$$= E^{1/2} f(x) - E^{-1/2} f(x)$$
$$= (E^{1/2} - E^{-1/2}) f(x)$$

$$\therefore \quad \boxed{\delta = E^{1/2} - E^{-1/2}} = E^{-1/2}[E - 1] = E^{-1/2} \Delta \qquad \dots(5)$$

Also $\delta = E^{1/2}[1 - E^{-1}] = E^{1/2} \nabla$

$$\therefore \quad \delta = E^{-1/2} \Delta = E^{1/2} \nabla \qquad \dots(6)$$

*Relation between E and μ :*

$$\mu f(x) = \frac{1}{2}\left[f\left(x+\frac{h}{2}\right)+f\left(x-\frac{h}{2}\right)\right]$$

$$= \frac{1}{2}\left[E^{1/2} f(x) + E^{-1/2} f(x)\right]$$

$$= \frac{1}{2}\left[E^{1/2} + E^{-1/2}\right] f(x)$$

$$\therefore \quad \boxed{\mu = \frac{1}{2}\left[E^{1/2} + E^{-1/2}\right]} \quad ...(7)$$

*Relation between D and Δ :*

$$Df(x) = \frac{d}{dx} f(x)$$

By Taylor's theorem,

$$f(x+h) = f(x) + \frac{h}{1!} f^1(x) + \frac{h^2}{2!} f^{11}(x) + \cdots\cdots \text{ to } \infty$$

$$\therefore \quad Ef(x) = f(x) + \frac{h}{1!} Df(x) + \frac{h^2}{2!} D^2 f(x) + \cdots\cdots \text{ to } \infty$$

$$= \left[1 + \frac{hD}{1!} + \frac{(hD)^2}{2!} + \frac{(hD)^3}{3!} + \cdots\cdots \text{ to } \infty\right] f(x)$$

$$= e^{hD} f(x)$$

$$\therefore \quad \boxed{E = e^{hD}} \quad ...(8)$$

$$\therefore \quad E = 1 + \Delta = e^{hD}$$

$$hD = \log E = \log(1+\Delta)$$

$$hD = \Delta - \frac{\Delta^2}{2} + \frac{\Delta^3}{3} - ...$$

$$\therefore \quad D = \frac{1}{h}\left[\Delta - \frac{\Delta^2}{2} + \frac{\Delta^3}{3} - ...\right] \quad ...(9)$$

*Forward Difference Table:*

The finite forward differences of a function are represented below in a tabular form :

| $x$ | $y$ | $\Delta y$ | $\Delta^2 y$ | $\Delta^3 y$ | $\Delta^4 y$ | $\Delta^5 y$ | $\Delta^6$ |
|---|---|---|---|---|---|---|---|
| $x_0$ | $y_0$ | | | | | | |
| | | $\Delta y_0$ | $\Delta^2 y_0$ | | | | |
| $x_1$ | $y_1$ | | | $\Delta^3 y_0$ | | | |
| | | $\Delta y_1$ | $\Delta^2 y_1$ | | $\Delta^4 y_0$ | | |
| $x_2$ | $y_2$ | | | $\Delta^3 y_1$ | | $\Delta^5 y_0$ | |
| | | $\Delta y_2$ | $\Delta^2 y_2$ | | $\Delta^4 y_1$ | | $\Delta^6 y_0$ |
| $x_3$ | $y_3$ | | | $\Delta^3 y_2$ | | $\Delta^5 y_1$ | |
| | | $\Delta y_3$ | $\Delta^2 y_3$ | | $\Delta^4 y_2$ | | |
| $x_4$ | $y_4$ | | | $\Delta^3 y_3$ | | | |
| | | $\Delta y_4$ | $\Delta^2 y_4$ | | | | |
| $x_5$ | $y_5$ | | | | | | |
| | | $\Delta y_5$ | | | | | |
| $x_6$ | $y_6$ | | | | | | |

The above table is also called *diagonal difference table.*

**Note 1.** The value $y_0$ (first value of $y$) is called the *leading term* and the differences $\Delta y_0, \Delta^2 y_0, \Delta^3 y_0, \Delta^4 y_0$, .... are called the *leading differences.*

**2.** $\begin{matrix} y_1 \\ \uparrow \rightarrow \Delta y_1 \\ y_2 \end{matrix}$

The difference value $y_2 - y_1$ is written in the next column in between $y_2$ and $y_1$.

*Backward Difference Table :*

The backward differences are given in the following *backward difference table :*

| $x$ | $y$ | $\nabla y$ | $\nabla^2 y$ | $\nabla^3 y$ | $\nabla^4 y$ | $\nabla^5 y$ | $\nabla^6 y$ |
|---|---|---|---|---|---|---|---|
| $x_0$ | $y_0$ | | | | | | |
| | | $\nabla y_1$ | | | | | |
| $x_1$ | $y_1$ | | $\Delta^2 y_2$ | | | | |
| | | $\nabla y_2$ | | $\nabla^3 y_3$ | | | |
| $x_2$ | $y_2$ | | $\nabla^2 y_3$ | | $\nabla^4 y_4$ | | |
| | | $\nabla y_3$ | | $\nabla^3 y_4$ | | $\nabla^5 y_5$ | |
| $x_3$ | $y_3$ | | $\nabla^2 y_4$ | | $\nabla^4 y_5$ | | $\nabla^6 y_6$ |
| | | $\nabla y_4$ | | $\nabla^3 y_5$ | | $\nabla^5 y_6$ | |
| $x_4$ | $y_4$ | | $\nabla^2 y_5$ | | $\nabla^4 y_6$ | | |
| | | $\nabla y_5$ | | $\nabla^3 y_6$ | | | |
| $x_5$ | $y_5$ | | $\nabla^2 y_6$ | | | | |
| | | $\nabla y_6$ | | | | | |
| $x_6$ | $y_6$ | | | | | | |

**Note 1.** In this table $y_6$, the value of $y$ is the leading term and $\nabla y_6, \nabla^2 y_6, \nabla^3 y_6$, ... are leading differences. These leading differences lie along the diagonal sloping upwards at the end.

*Illustration:*

| $x$ | $y$ | $\Delta y$ | $\Delta^2 y$ | $\Delta^3 y$ | $\Delta^4 y$ |
|---|---|---|---|---|---|
| 1 | 4 | | | | |
| | | 11 | | | |
| 2 | 15 | | 14 | | |
| | | 25 | | 6 | |
| 3 | 40 | | 20 | | 0 |
| | | 45 | | 6 | |
| 4 | 85 | | 26 | | 0 |
| | | 71 | | 6 | |
| 5 | 156 | | 32 | | |
| | | 103 | | | |
| 6 | 259 | | | | |

In the table, each difference is written midway between the values subtracted from the previous column. In this example, the third differences are constants and the fourth differences are zeros.

*To find $y_k$ in terms of $y_0, \Delta y_0, \Delta^2 y_0$, ......*

$$y_k = E^k y_0$$

$$= (1 + \Delta)^k y_0$$

$$= (1 + {}^kC_1 \Delta + {}^kC_2 \Delta^2 + \cdots + \Delta^k)\, y_0$$

$$\mathbf{y_k = y_0 + {}^kC_1 \Delta y_0 + {}^kC_2 \Delta^2 y_0 + \cdots + \Delta^k y_0} \quad (k, \text{ positive integer})$$

This formula enables us to know $y_k$ knowing the leading value $y_0$ and its differences.

In the previous illustration

$$y_6 = y\,(x = 7) = y_0 + {}^6C_1 \Delta y_0 + {}^6C_2 \Delta^2 y_0 + {}^6C_3 \Delta^3 y_0 + {}^6C_4 \Delta^4 y_0 + {}^6C_5 \Delta^5 y_0 + \Delta^6 y_0$$

$$= 4 + 6\,(11) + \frac{6 \times 5}{2}\,(14) + \frac{6 \times 5 \times 4}{6}\,(6) + {}^6C_4 \times 0 + 0 + 0$$

$$= 4 + 66 + 210 + 120 = 400.$$

**Example 1.** *Find the 7th term of the sequence 2, 9, 28, 65, 126, 217 and also find the general term.*

**Solution.**

| $x$ | $y$ | $\Delta y$ | $\Delta^2 y$ | $\Delta^3 y$ | $\Delta^4 y$ |
|---|---|---|---|---|---|
| 0 | 2 | | | | |
| | | 7 | | | |
| 1 | 9 | | 12 | | |
| | | 19 | | 6 | |
| 2 | 28 | | 18 | | 0 |
| | | 37 | | 6 | |
| 3 | 65 | | 24 | | 0 |
| | | 61 | | 6 | |
| 4 | 126 | | 30 | | |
| | | 91 | | | |
| 5 | 217 | | | | |

$$\text{7th term} = y_6 = y_0 + {}^6C_1 \Delta y_0 + {}^6C_2 \Delta^2 y_0 + {}^6C_3 \Delta^3 y_0 + {}^6C_4 \Delta^4 y_0 + {}^6C_5 \Delta^5 y_0 + \Delta^6 y_0$$

$$= 2 + 6(7) + 15\,(12) + 20(6) + 15(0)$$

$$= 2 + 42 + 180 + 120 = 344$$

$$y_n = y_0 + {}^nC_1 \Delta y_0 + {}^nC_2 \Delta^2 y_0 + {}^nC_3 \Delta^3 y_0 + {}^nC_4 \Delta^4 y_0 + \cdots\cdots$$

$$= 2 + n(7) + \frac{n\,(n-1)}{2}\,(12) + \frac{n\,(n-1)(n-2)}{6}\,(6) + 0$$

$$= 2 + 7n + 6n^2 - 6n + n^3 - 3n^2 + 2n$$

$$= n^3 + 3n^2 + 3n + 2$$

$$= (n+1)^3 + 1$$

$$\therefore \quad y_6 = (6+1)^3 + 1 = 344$$

**Example 2.** *Find $f(x)$ from the table below. Also find $f(7)$.*

| $x$ : | 0 | 1 | 2 | 3 | 4 | 5 | 6 |
|---|---|---|---|---|---|---|---|
| $f(x)$ : | – 1 | 3 | 19 | 53 | 111 | 199 | 323 |

**Solution.** We will form the difference table

| $x$ | $f(x)$ | $\Delta f(x)$ | $\Delta^2 f(x)$ | $\Delta^3 f(x)$ | $\Delta^4 f(x)$ |
|---|---|---|---|---|---|
| 0 | – 1 | | | | |
| | | 4 | | | |
| 1 | 3 | | 12 | | |
| | | 16 | | 6 | |
| 2 | 19 | | 18 | | 0 |
| | | 34 | | 6 | |
| 3 | 53 | | 24 | | 0 |
| | | 58 | | 6 | |
| 4 | 111 | | 30 | | 0 |
| | | 88 | | 6 | |
| 5 | 199 | | 36 | | |
| | | 124 | | | |
| 6 | 323 | | | | |

$\Delta^4 f(x), \Delta^5 f(x)$, ...... are all zeros.

$$y_x = E^x y_0 = (1+\Delta)^x y_0$$

$$= y_0 + {}^xC_1\, \Delta y_0 + {}^xC_2\, \Delta^2 y_0 + {}^xC_3\, \Delta^3 y_0 + {}^xC_4\, \Delta^4 y_0 + \cdots\cdots$$

$$= (-1) + x\,(4) + \frac{x\,(x-1)}{2}\,(12) + \frac{x\,(x-1)(x-2)}{6}\,(6) + 0$$

$$= -1 + 4x + 6x^2 - 6x + x^3 - 3x^2 + 2x$$

$$f(x) = x^3 + 3x^2 - 1$$

$$f(7) = 7^3 + 3(49) - 1 = 489$$

**Example 3.** *Find the first term of the series whose second and subsequent terms are 8, 3, 0, – 1, 0, ...*

**Solution.** Let $y_0$ be the first term.

$\therefore\;\; y_1 = 8,\; y_2 = 3,\; y_3 = 0,$ etc.

The difference table is

| $x$ | $y$ | $\Delta y$ | $\Delta^2 y$ | $\Delta^3 y$ | $\Delta^4 y$ |
|---|---|---|---|---|---|
| 0 | $y_0$ | | | | |
| | | ... | | | |
| 1 | $y_1 = 8$ | | | | |
| | | – 5 | 2 | | |
| 2 | 3 | | | 0 | |
| | | – 3 | 2 | | |
| 3 | 0 | | | 0 | |
| | | 1 | 2 | | |
| 4 | –1 | | | | |
| | | 1 | | | |
| 5 | 0 | | | | |

The differences of $y_1$ are $y_1 = 8, \Delta y_1 = -5, \;\Delta^2 y_1 = 2, \;\; \Delta^3 y_1 = 0,$ $\Delta^4 y_1 = 0$ etc.

$$y_0 = E^{-1}\, y_1$$

$$= (1+\Delta)^{-1}\, y_1$$

$$= (1 - \Delta + \Delta^2 - \Delta^3 + \Delta^4 - \cdots\cdots)\, y_1$$

$$= y_1 - \Delta y_1 + \Delta^2 y_1 - \Delta^3 y_1 + \cdots\cdots$$

$= 8 - (-5) + (2) - 0 + \cdots\cdots$

$= 15$

**Example 4.** *Find the sixth term of the sequence 8, 12, 19, 29, 42,.....*

**Solution.** The difference table is

| $x$ | $y$ | $\Delta y$ | $\Delta^2 y$ | $\Delta^3 y$ |
|---|---|---|---|---|
| 0 | 8 | | | |
| | | 4 | | |
| 1 | 12 | | 3 | |
| | | 7 | | 0 |
| 2 | 19 | | 3 | |
| | | 10 | | 0 |
| 3 | 29 | | 3 | |
| | | 13 | | |
| 4 | 42 | | | |

$$6\text{th term} = y_5 = E^5 y_0 = (1+\Delta)^5 y_0$$

$$= y_0 + 5\Delta y_0 + 10\Delta^2 y_0 + 10\Delta^3 y_0 + \cdots\cdots$$

$$= 8 + 5(4) + 10(3) + 10(0) + \cdots$$

$$= 58$$

**5·2. Express any value of $y$ in term of $y_n$ and the backward differences of $y_n$.**

We know $\nabla y_n = y_n - y_{n-1}$

$\therefore \quad y_{n-1} = y_n - \nabla y_n = (1-\nabla)\, y_n$

Similarly $\quad y_{n-2} = y_{n-1} - \nabla y_{n-1}$

$$= (1-\nabla)\, y_{n-1}$$

$$= (1-\nabla)(1-\nabla)\, y_n$$

$$= (1-\nabla)^2 y_n \quad \text{and} \quad y_{n-3} = (1-\nabla)^3 y_n$$

Generalising this concept,

$$y_{n-k} = (1-\nabla)^k y_n$$

$$= (1 - {}^kC_1\nabla + {}^kC_2.\nabla^2 - \cdots\cdots + (-1)^k \nabla^k)\, y_n$$

$$\mathbf{y_{n-k} = y_n - {}^kC_1.\nabla y_n + {}^kC_2\nabla^2 y_n - \cdots\cdots + (-1)^k\nabla^k y_n.}$$

**Example 5.** *Find $y(-1)$ if $y(0) = 2$, $y(1) = 9$, $y(2) = 28$, $y(3) = 65$, $y(4) = 126$, $y(5) = 217$.*

**Solution.** Forming the difference table,

| $x$ | $y$ | $\nabla y$ | $\nabla^2 y$ | $\nabla^3 y$ | $\nabla^4 y$ |
|---|---|---|---|---|---|
| 0 | 2 | | | | |
| | | 7 | | | |
| 1 | 9 | | 12 | | |
| | | 19 | | 6 | |
| 2 | 28 | | 18 | | 0 |
| | | 37 | | 6 | |
| 3 | 65 | | 24 | | 0 |
| | | 61 | | 6 | |
| 4 | 126 | | 30 | | |
| | | 91 | | | |
| 5 | 217 | | | | |

$$\nabla y_5 = 91, \nabla^2 y_5 = 30, \ \nabla^3 y_5 = 6, \ \nabla^4 y_5 = 0$$

$$\begin{aligned} y(-1) = y_{-1} &= y_{5-6} \\ &= y_5 - {}^6C_1 \nabla y_5 + {}^6C_2\, \nabla^2 y_5 - {}^6C_3\, \nabla^3 y_5 + {}^6C_4\, \nabla^4 y_5 \cdots\cdots \\ &= 217 - 6(91) + 15\,(30) - 20(6) + 0 \\ &= 217 - 546 + 450 - 120 \\ &= 667 - 666 = 1 \end{aligned}$$

We can verify the value of $y(0)$

$$\begin{aligned} y(0) = y_0 &= y_{5-5} \\ &= y_5 - {}^5C_1\, \nabla y_5 + {}^5C_2 \nabla^2 y_5 - {}^5C_3\, \nabla^3 y_5 + \cdots \\ &= 217 - 5(91) + 10(30) - 10(6) \\ &= 217 - 455 + 300 - 60 = 2 \end{aligned}$$

This is exactly the same given value $y_0 = 2$.

## 5·3. Differences of a polynomial

*Theorem.* The $n$th differences (forward) of a polynomial of the $n$th degree are constants.

That is, if $f(x) = a_0 x^n + a_1 x^{n-1} + a_2 x^{x-2} + \cdots\cdots + a_n$

Then $\Delta^n f(x) = a_0 n\,!\, h^n$

where $h$ is the interval of differencing.

$$\begin{aligned} \Delta f(x) &= f(x+h) - f(x) \\ &= a_0\, [(x+h)^n - x^n] + a_1\, [(x+h)^{n-1} - x^{n-1}] + \cdots\cdots + a_n \\ &= a_0\, [nhx^{n-1} + \cdots\cdots] + \cdots\cdots \\ &= a_0 nhx^{n-1} + \text{terms involving powers of } x \text{ less than } (n-1) \end{aligned}$$

That is, $\Delta f(x) =$ a polynomial of degree $(n - 1)$

$$\begin{aligned} \Delta^2 f(x) &= a_0\, nh\, [(x+h)^{n-1} - x^{n-1}] + \text{terms involving lesser degree} \\ &= a_0 n\,(n-1)\, h^2\, x^{n-2} + \text{terms involving degree less than } (n-2) \end{aligned}$$

*i.e.,* second difference of a polynomial of degree $n$ is a polynomial of degree $x^{n-2}$.

Proceeding like this

$$\begin{aligned} \Delta^n f(x) &= a_0\, n\,!\, h^n x^0 \\ &= a_0\, n\,!\, h^n \end{aligned}$$

**Note 1.** The converse of the theorem is also true. That is, if the $n$th differences of a tabulated function are constants, then the function is a polynomial of degree $n$.

**2.** The $(n+1)$th and higher differences of a polynomial of degree $n$ are zeros.

**3.** The above proof is not rigorous. For a rigorous proof, apply mathematical induction.

## 5·4. Factorial polynomial

A factorial polynomial $x^{(n)}$ is defined as

$$x^{(n)} = x(x-h)(x-2h)....(x-\overline{n-1}\,h)$$

where $n$ is a positive integer.

(Read $x^{(n)}$ as $x$ raised to the power $n$ factorial)

Thus, $x^{(1)} = x$, $x^{(2)} = x(x-h)$, $x^{(3)} = x(x-h)(x-2h)$, ...... etc.

*Differences of* $x^{(n)}$

(*i*) $\Delta x^{(n)} = (x+h)^{(n)} - x^{(n)}$

$$= (x+h)(x)(x-h).....[x-(n-2)h]$$
$$- x(x-h)(x-2h)......[x-(n-1)h]$$
$$= x(x-h)(x-2h)....[x-(n-2)h]\{(x+h)-(x-\overline{n-1}\,h)\}$$
$$= x^{(n-1)}\cdot nh$$
$$= nh\,x^{(n-1)}$$

Similarly $\Delta^2 x^{(n)} = \Delta\,[nh\,x^{(n-1)}]$

$$= (nh)(n-1)\,h\,x^{(n-2)}$$
$$= n(n-1)\,h^2\,x^{(n-2)}$$

Proceeding like this, $\Delta^r x^{(n)} = n(n-1)(n-2)\,.....\,(n-r+1)\,h^r\,x^{(n-r)}$, where $r$ is a positive integer and $r < n$.

**Note 1.** In particular $\Delta^n x^{(n)} = n\,!\,h^n$.

**2.** If $h = 1$, *i.e.*, the interval of differencing is unity, then $\Delta^r x^{(n)} = n(n-1)(n-2).....(n-r+1)\,x^{(n-r)}$ which is analogous to the differentiation of $x^n$.

**3.** If $h = 1$, $\Delta^n x^{(n)} = n\,!$, and $\Delta^r x^{(n)} = 0$ if $r > n$.

**4.** Wherever we require $\Delta^r x^n$, it is difficult to find $\Delta^r x^n$ and hence we express $x^n$ in terms of factorial polynomial and hence we calculate $\Delta^r x^n$.

*Reciprocal factorial*

The reciprocal factorial function $x^{(-n)}$ is defined as $x^{(-n)} = \dfrac{1}{(x+h)(x+2h)....(x+nh)}$ where $n$ is a positive integer.

*Differences of a reciprocal factorial function*

(*i*) $\Delta x^{(-n)} = (x+h)^{(-n)} - x^{(-n)}$

$$= \frac{1}{(x+2h)(x+3h)......[x+(n+1)h]} - \frac{1}{(x+h)(x+2h)......(x+nh)}$$

$$= \frac{1}{(x+h)(x+2h)......[x+(n+1)h]} [(x+h) - (x+\overline{n+1}\,h)]$$

$$= \frac{-nh}{(x+h)(x+2h)......[x+(n+1)h]}$$

$$= (-n)\,h\,x^{(-(n+1))}$$

(*ii*) $\Delta^2 x^{(-n)} = \Delta\,(\Delta x^{-n})$

$$= \Delta\,(-nh\,x^{(-(n+1))})$$

$$= (-nh)\,[-(n+1)\,h]\,x^{(-(n+2))}$$

$$= (-1)^2 h^2 n\,(n+1)\,x^{(-(n+2))}$$

Similarly

$$\Delta^r x^{(-n)} = (-1)^r n\,(n+1)\,(n+2)\,.......(n+r-1)\,x^{(n+r)}\,.\,h^r$$

*Polynomial in factorial notation*

*Any polynomial* $f(x) = a_0 x^n + a_1 x^{n-1} + a_2 x^{n-2} + \cdots + a_n$ *can be expressed in the factorial polynomial form as*

$$A_0 x^{(n)} + A_1 x^{(n-1)} + A_2 x^{(n-2)} + ......\,A_n$$

Since, $f(x) = A_0 x^{(n)} + A_1 x^{(n-1)} + ...... + A_n$

$$= A_0 x\,(x-h)......(x - \overline{n-1}\,h) + A_1 x(x-h)......(x - \overline{n-2}h)$$

$$+ A_2 x\,(x-h)......(x - \overline{n-3}\,h) + ...... + A_{n-1} x + A_n \quad ...(1)$$

Dividing the R.H.S. of (1), by $x$, the remainder is $A_n$ and dividing the quotient again by $x-h$, the remainder is $A_{n-1}$ and then dividing the quotient again by $x-2h$, the remainder is $A_{n-2}$ etc.

Thus, dividing $f(x)$ successively by $x$, $x-h$, $x-2h$, ..... The coefficients $A_n, A_{n-1}, A_{n-2}$, ...... are got which are nothing but the remainders of $f(x)$ in that order.

**Note.** If $h = 1$, divide $f(x)$ successively by $x, x-1, x-2,...$ to get $A_n, A_{n-1}, ...$

**Example 6.** *Express* (*i*) $x^4 + 3x^3 - 5x^2 + 6x - 7$

(*ii*) $3x^3 - 2x^2 + 7x - 6$

(*iii*) $x^3 + x^2 + x + 1$

*in factorial polynomials and get their successive forward differences, taking* $h = 1$.

**Solution.** (*i*) First, divide $x^4 + 3x^3 - 5x^2 + 6x - 7$ successively by $x, x-1, x-2.....$ by synthetic division method.

| | | | | | |
|---|---|---|---|---|---|
| 0 | 1 | 3 | – 5 | 6 | – 7 |
| | | 0 | 0 | 0 | 0 |
| 1 | 1 | 3 | – 5 | 6 | – 7 |
| | | 1 | 4 | –1 | |

| | | | | |
|---|---|---|---|---|
| 2 | 1 | 4 | – 1 | 5 |
| | | 2 | 12 | |
| 3 | 1 | 6 | 11 | |
| | | 3 | | |
| | 1 | 9 | | |

Therefore, factorial polynomial is

$$f(x) = 1\,x^{(4)} + 9x^{(3)} + 11\,x^{(2)} + 5x^{(1)} - 7$$

$$\Delta f(x) = 4x^{(3)} + 27x^{(2)} + 22x^{(1)} + 5$$

$$\Delta^2 f(x) = 12x^{(2)} + 54x^{(1)} + 22$$

$$\Delta^3 f(x) = 24x^{(1)} + 54$$

$$\Delta^4 f(x) = 24$$

$$\Delta^r f(x) = 0 \text{ if } r > 4$$

(*ii*) Now, express $\phi(x) = 3x^3 - 2x^2 + 7x - 6$ is factorial polynomial.

Using synthetic division process,

| | | | | |
|---|---|---|---|---|
| 0 | 3 | – 2 | 7 | – 6 |
| | | 0 | 0 | 0 |
| 1 | 3 | – 2 | 7 | – 6 |
| | | 3 | 1 | |
| 2 | 3 | 1 | 8 | |
| | | 6 | | |
| | 3 | 7 | | |

Hence, $\phi(x) = 3x^{(3)} + 7x^{(2)} + 8x^{(1)} - 6$ (here $h = 1$)

$$\Delta\phi(x) = 9x^{(2)} + 14x^{(1)} + 8$$

$$\Delta^2\phi(x) = 18x^{(1)} + 14$$

$$\Delta^3\phi(x) = 18$$

$$\Delta^r\phi(x) = 0 \text{ for } r > 3$$

(*iii*)

| | | | | |
|---|---|---|---|---|
| 0 | 1 | 1 | 1 | 1 |
| | | 0 | 0 | 0 |
| 1 | 1 | 1 | 1 | 1 |
| | | 1 | 2 | |
| 2 | 1 | 2 | 3 | |
| | | 2 | | |
| | 1 | 4 | | |

$$\phi(x) = x^{(3)} + 4x^{(2)} + 3x^{(1)} + 1$$

$$\Delta\phi(x) = 3x^{(2)} + 8x^{(1)} + 3$$
$$\Delta^2\phi(x) = 6x^{(1)} + 8$$
$$\Delta^3\phi(x) = 6$$
$$\Delta^r\phi(x) = 0 \text{ for } r > 3$$

**Aliter.** (*i*) $y = x^4 + 3x^3 - 5x^2 + 6x - 7$ can be written as

$$y = x^4 + 3x^3 - 5x^2 + 6x - 7 = Ax(x-1)(x-2)(x-3) + Bx(x-1)(x-2) + Cx(x-1) + Dx + E$$
$$= Ax^{(4)} + Bx^{(3)} + Cx^{(2)} + Dx^{(1)} + E$$

*Put* $x = 0$ ; $E = -7$

Put $x = 1$ ; $D + E = -2 \quad \therefore \quad D = 5$

Put $x = 2$ ; $2C + 2D + E = 16 + 24 - 20 + 12 - 7; C = 11$

Put $x = 3$ ; $6B + 6C + 3D + E = 81 + 81 - 45 + 18 - 7$

$6B = 54$ ; $B = 9$

Equate coefficient of $x^3$ on both sides; $A = 1$

$\therefore \quad y = x^{(4)} + 9x^{(3)} + 11x^{(2)} + 5x^{(1)} - 7$

(*ii*) $\phi(x) = 3x^3 - 2x^2 + 7x - 6 = Ax^{(3)} + Bx^{(2)} + Cx^{(1)} + D$

$= Ax(x-1)(x-2) + Bx(x-1) + Cx + D$

Put $x = 0$; $D = -6$

Put $x = 1$; $C + D = 2$ ; $C = 8$

Put $x = 2$ ; $2B + 2C + D = 24 - 8 + 14 - 6 \quad \therefore \quad B = 7$

Equate $x^3$ coefficients on both sides; $A = 3$

$\therefore \quad \phi(x) = 3x^{(3)} + 7x^{(2)} + 8x^{(1)} - 6$

(*iii*) Similarly,

$\phi(x) = x^3 + x^2 + x + 1 = Ax^{(3)} + Bx^{(2)} + Cx^{(1)} + D$

$= x^{(3)} + 4x^{(2)} + 3x^{(1)} + 1$

**Example 7.** *Find the forward differences of*

(*i*) $\dfrac{1}{x(x+4)(x+8)}$ (*ii*) $\dfrac{1}{(3x+1)(3x+4)(3x+7)}$

**Solution**. (*i*) $y = \dfrac{1}{x(x+4)(x+8)} = (x-4)^{(-3)}$ where $h = 4$

$$\Delta y = (-3)(4)(x-4)^{(-4)}$$
$$\Delta^2 y = (-3)(-4)(4)^2(x-4)^{(-5)}$$
$$= \frac{192}{x(x+4)(x+8)(x+12)(x+16)}$$

(*ii*) $f(x) = \dfrac{1}{(3x+1)(3x+4)(3x+8)}$, if $h = 1$

$$= \frac{1}{3^3\left(x+\frac{1}{3}\right)\left(x+\frac{4}{3}\right)\left(x+\frac{7}{3}\right)}$$

$$= \frac{1}{27}\left(x-\frac{2}{3}\right)^{(-3)}$$

$$\Delta f(x) = \frac{1}{27}(-3)\left(x-\frac{2}{3}\right)^{-4} \quad \text{since } h = 1$$

$$\Delta^2 f(x) = \frac{(-3)(-4)}{27}\left(x-\frac{2}{3}\right)^{-5}$$

$$= \frac{4}{9}\cdot\frac{1}{\left(x+\frac{1}{3}\right)\left(x+\frac{4}{3}\right)\left(x+\frac{7}{3}\right)\left(x+\frac{10}{3}\right)\left(x+\frac{13}{3}\right)}$$

$$= \frac{108}{(3x+1)(3x+4)(3x+7)(3x+10)(3x+13)}$$

**Example 8.** *Find* $\Delta^3 f(x)$ *if*

(*i*) $f(x) = (3x+1)(3x+4)(3x+7)......(3x+19)$

(*ii*) $f(x) = x(3x+1)(3x+4)......(3x+19)$

(*i*) **Solution.** $f(x) = (3x+1)(3x+4)(3x+7)......(3x+19)$

(contains 7 factors)

$$= 3^7\left(x+\frac{1}{3}\right)\left(x+\frac{4}{3}\right)......\left(x+\frac{19}{3}\right)$$

$$= 3^7\left(x+\frac{19}{3}\right)^{(7)}$$

$$\Delta f(x) = 3^7(7)\left(x+\frac{19}{3}\right)^{(6)}$$

$$\Delta^2 f(x) = 3^7\times 7\times 6\left(x+\frac{19}{3}\right)^{(5)}$$

$$\Delta^3 f(x) = 3^7\times 7\times 6\times 5\times\left(x+\frac{19}{3}\right)^{(4)}$$

$$= 3^3\times 7\times 6\times 5\,(3x+19)(3x+16)(3x+13)(3x+10)$$

(*ii*) $f(x) = x(3x+1)(3x+4)......(3x+19)$

$$= \frac{1}{3}(3x-2+2)(3x+1)(3x+4).......(3x+19)$$

$$= \frac{1}{3}(3x-2)(3x+1)(3x+4)......(3x+19)$$

$$+\frac{2}{3}(3x+1)(3x+4)...(3x+19)$$

$$=\frac{1}{3}\cdot 3^8\cdot\left(x-\frac{2}{3}\right)\left(x+\frac{1}{3}\right)\left(x+\frac{4}{3}\right)\ldots\ldots\left(x+\frac{19}{3}\right)$$

$$+\frac{2}{3}\cdot 3^7\left(x+\frac{1}{3}\right)\left(x+\frac{4}{3}\right)\ldots\ldots\left(x+\frac{19}{3}\right)$$

$$=3^7\left(x+\frac{19}{3}\right)^{(8)}+2\cdot 3^6\left(x+\frac{19}{3}\right)^{(7)}$$

$$\Delta f(x)=3^7\times 8\times\left(x+\frac{19}{3}\right)^{(7)}+2\cdot 3^6\cdot 7\left(x+\frac{19}{3}\right)^{(6)}$$

$$\Delta^2 f(x)=3^7\cdot 8\cdot 7\left(x+\frac{19}{3}\right)^{(6)}+2\cdot 3^6\cdot 7\cdot 6\left(x+\frac{19}{3}\right)^{(5)}\quad\text{etc.}$$

**Example 9.** *Express* $f(x)=x^3-3x^2+5x+7$ *in terms of factorial polynomial taking* $h=2$ *and find its differences.*

**Solution.**

Let $f(x)=x^3-3x^2+5x+7=Ax(x-h)(x-2h)+Bx(x-h)+Cx+D$

$$=Ax(x-2)(x-4)+Bx(x-2)+Cx+D$$

Set $x=0$ ; $D=7$

Put $x=2$ ; $2C+D=8-12+10+7$ ; $\therefore$ $2C=6$. Hence, $C=3$

Put $x=4$ ; $8B+4C+D=64-48+20+7$ $\therefore$ $8B=24$. Hence $B=3$

Comparing coefficients of $x^3$ on both sides, $A=1$.

$$\therefore\quad f(x)=x^3-3x^2+5x+7=x^{(3)}+3x^{(2)}+3x^{(1)}+7,\quad\text{where } h=2$$

$$\Delta f(x)=3hx^{(2)}+6hx^{(1)}+3h=6x^{(2)}+12x^{(1)}+6$$

$$=6(x)(x-2)+12x+6=6x^2+6$$

$$\Delta^2 f(x)=6h^2x^{(1)}+6h^2=24x^{(1)}+24=24(x+1)$$

$$\Delta^3 f(x)=24h=48\ ;\quad \Delta^n f(x)=0\ \text{ if }\ n>3$$

**Aliter :** *Synthetic division method.*

Divide by $x, x-h, x-2h,$ ...... etc. *i.e.,* $x, x-2, x-4,$ ...... etc.

| | | | | |
|---|---|---|---|---|
| 0 | 1 | −3 | 5 | 7 |
| | | 0 | 0 | 0 |
| 2 | 1 | −3 | 5 | 7 |
| | | 2 | −2 | |
| 4 | 1 | −1 | 3 | |
| | | 4 | | |
| | 1 | 3 | | |

Hence, $x^3-3x^2+5x+7=x^{(3)}+3x^{(2)}+3x^{(1)}+7$ where $h=2$

*Standard Results*

Prove: (*i*) $\Delta[f(x)\,g(x)]=f(x+h)\,\Delta g(x)+g(x)\,\Delta f(x)$

(ii) $\Delta\left[\dfrac{f(x)}{g(x)}\right]=\dfrac{g(x)\,\Delta f(x)-f(x)\,\Delta g(x)}{g(x+h)\,g(x)}$

**Proof.** $\Delta[f(x)\,g(x)]=f(x+h)\,g(x+h)-f(x)\,g(x)$

$$=[f(x+h)\,g(x+h)-f(x+h)\,g(x)]+[f(x+h)\,g(x)-f(x)\,g(x)]$$
$$=f(x+h)\,[g(x+h)-g(x)]+g(x)\,[f(x+h)-f(x)]$$
$$=f(x+h)\,\Delta g(x)+g(x)\,\Delta f(x).$$

(ii) $\Delta\left[\dfrac{f(x)}{g(x)}\right]=\dfrac{f(x+h)}{g(x+h)}-\dfrac{f(x)}{g(x)}$

$$=\frac{f(x+h)\,g(x)-g(x+h)\,f(x)}{g(x+h)\,g(x)}$$
$$=\frac{f(x+h)\,g(x)-f(x)\,g(x)+f(x)\,g(x)-g(x+h)\,f(x)}{g(x+h)\,g(x)}$$
$$=\frac{g(x)\,[f(x+h)-f(x)]-f(x)\,[g(x+h)-g(x)]}{g(x+h)\,g(x)}$$
$$=\frac{g(x)\,\Delta f(x)-f(x)\,\Delta g(x)}{g(x+h)\,g(x)}$$

**Example 10.** *Evaluate* (i) $\Delta^n\,(e^{ax+b})$, (ii) $\Delta^n\,[\sin(ax+b)]$, (iii) $\Delta^n\,[\cos(ax+b)]$ (v) $\Delta\,[\log(ax+b)]$ $\Delta^n\,(a^{bx+c})$, (vi) $\Delta\log f(x)$, (vii) $\Delta\,(\tan^{-1}x)$

**Solution.** (i) $\Delta\,(e^{ax+b})=e^{a(x+h)+b}-e^{ax+b}=e^{ax+b}\,(e^{ah}-1)$

$$\Delta^2\,(e^{ax+b})=(e^{ah}-1)\,\Delta\,(e^{ax+b})=(e^{ah}-1)^2\,e^{ax+b}$$

Similarly $\Delta^n\,(e^{ax+b})=e^{ax+b}\,.\,(e^{ah}-1)^n$.

**Note**. Prove by mathematical induction. The above proof is not rigorous.

(ii) $\Delta\,[\sin(ax+b)]=\sin[a(x+h)+b]-\sin(ax+b)$

$$=2\cos\left(ax+b+\frac{ah}{2}\right)\sin\frac{ah}{2}$$
$$=2\sin\frac{ah}{2}\sin\left(\frac{\pi}{2}+ax+b+\frac{ah}{2}\right)$$
$$=2\sin\frac{ah}{2}\cdot\sin\left(ax+b+\frac{\pi+ah}{2}\right)$$

$$\Delta^2\sin(ax+b)=2\sin\frac{ah}{2}\,\Delta\left[\sin\left(ax+b+\frac{\pi+ah}{2}\right)\right]$$
$$=\left(2\sin\frac{ah}{2}\right)^2.\,\sin\left[ax+b+2\left(\frac{\pi+ah}{2}\right)\right]$$

Similarly proceeding,

$$\Delta^n \sin(ax+b) = \left(2\sin\frac{ah}{2}\right)^n \sin\left(ax+b+\frac{n(\pi+ah)}{2}\right)$$

(*iii*) $\Delta[\cos(ax+b)] = \cos(ax+ah+b) - \cos(ax+b)$

$$= -2\sin\left(ax+b+\frac{ah}{2}\right)\sin\frac{ah}{2}$$

$$= 2\sin\frac{ah}{2}\cos\left(\frac{\pi}{2}+ax+b+\frac{ah}{2}\right)$$

$$= 2\sin\frac{ah}{2}\cos\left(ax+b+\frac{\pi+ah}{2}\right)$$

$$\Delta^2[\cos(ax+b)] = \left(2\sin\frac{ah}{2}\right)^2 . \cos\left(ax+b+\frac{2(\pi+ah)}{2}\right)$$

Proceeding like this,

$$\Delta^n \cos(ax+b) = \left(2\sin\frac{ah}{2}\right)^n \cos\left[ax+b+\frac{n(\pi+ah)}{2}\right]$$

(*iv*) $\Delta[\log(ax+b)] = \log(ax+ah+b) - \log(ax+b)$

$$= \log\left[\frac{ax+ah+b}{ax+b}\right]$$

$$= \log\left[1+\frac{ah}{ax+b}\right]$$

$$= \log\left[1+\frac{\Delta(ax+b)}{ax+b}\right]$$

(*v*) $\Delta(a^{bx+c}) = a^{b(x+h)+c} - a^{bx+c}$

$$= a^{bx+c}(a^{bh}-1)$$

$$\Delta^2(a^{bx+c}) = a^{bx+c}(a^{bh}-1)^2$$

$$\Delta^n(a^{bx+c}) = a^{bx+c}(a^{bh}-1)^n$$

(*vi*) $\Delta \log f(x) = \log f(x+h) - \log f(x)$

$$= \log\left[\frac{f(x+h)}{f(x)}\right] = \log\left[\frac{Ef(x)}{f(x)}\right]$$

$$= \log\left[\frac{f(x)+\Delta f(x)}{f(x)}\right]$$

$$= \log\left[1+\frac{\Delta f(x)}{f(x)}\right]$$

(*vii*) $\Delta(\tan^{-1}x) = \tan^{-1}(x+h) - \tan^{-1}x$

$$= \tan^{-1}\frac{(x+h)-x}{1+x(x+h)}$$

$$= \tan^{-1}\left[\frac{h}{1+x(x+h)}\right]$$

**Example 11.** *Evaluate* (*i*) $\Delta\,(e^{3x}\log 2x)$, (*ii*) $\Delta\,(x \sin x)$ (*iii*) $\Delta\,(xe^x)$ (*iv*) $\Delta\left(\frac{2^x}{x\,!}\right)$ (*v*) $\Delta\left(\frac{x}{\sin 2x}\right)$

**Solution.** (*i*) $\Delta\,(e^{3x}\,.\log 2x) = e^{3(x+h)}\Delta \log 2x + \log 2x\, \Delta\,(e^{3x})$

$$= e^{3(x+h)}.\log\left(1+\frac{\Delta(2x)}{2x}\right) + \log 2x.\, e^{3x}\,(e^{3h}-1)$$

$$= e^{3x}\left[e^{3h}\log\left(1+\frac{h}{x}\right) + (e^{3h}-1)\log(2x)\right]$$

(*ii*) $\Delta\,(x \sin x) = (x+h)\,\Delta\,(\sin x) + \sin x.\,\Delta\,(x)$

$$= (x+h).\,2\sin\frac{h}{2}\cdot\sin\left(x+\frac{\pi+h}{2}\right) + h\sin x$$

(*iii*) $\Delta\,(x\,e^x) = (x+h)\,\Delta\,e^x + e^x\,\Delta\,(x)$

$$= (x+h)\,e^x\,(e^h-1) + e^x.h$$

(*iv*) $\Delta\left(\frac{2^x}{x\,!}\right) = \frac{x\,!\,\Delta\,(2^x) - 2^x\,\Delta\,(x\,!)}{(x+h)\,!\,x\,!}$

$$= \frac{x\,!\,2^x\,(2^h-1) - 2^x.\,[(x+h)\,! - x\,!]}{(x+h)\,!\,x\,!}$$

If $h = 1$, then

$$\Delta\left(\frac{2^x}{x\,!}\right) = \frac{x\,!\,2^x - 2^x.\,x.\,x\,!}{(x+1)\,!\,x\,!} = \frac{2^x\,(1-x)}{(x+1)\,!}$$

(*v*) $\Delta\left(\frac{x}{\sin 2x}\right) = \frac{\sin 2x\,\Delta\,(x) - x\,\Delta\sin 2x}{\sin(2x+2h)\sin 2x}$

$$= \frac{h\sin 2x - x\,(2\sin h)\sin\left(2x+\frac{\pi+2h}{2}\right)}{\sin(2x+2h)\,.\sin 2x}$$

**Example 12.** *Evaluate:* (*i*) $\Delta^3\,(1-x)(1-2x)(1-3x)$ if $h = 1$

(*ii*) $\Delta^{10}\,(1-x)(1-2x)(1-3x)......(1-10x)$ taking $h = 1$

(*iii*) $\Delta^{10}\,[(1-x)(1-2x^2)(1-3x^3)(1-4x^4)$ if $h = 2$

**Solution.** (*i*) $\Delta^3\,(1-x)(1-2x)(1-3x) = \Delta^3\,[-6x^3 + \text{terms of lesser powers}]$

$$= (-6)\,3\,! + 0 = -36$$

(*ii*) $\Delta^{10}\,(1-x)(1-2x)......(1-10x) = \Delta^{10}\,[10\,!\,x^{10} + \text{terms involving lesser degree}]$

$$= 10\,!\,10\,! + 0 = (10\,!)^2$$

(*iii*) $\Delta^{10}\,[(1-x)(1-2x^2)(1-3x^3)(1-4x^4)]$

$= \Delta^{10}\,[24x^{10} + \text{terms of lesser degree}]$

$$= 24\,(10\,!)\,2^{10} + 0, \text{ since } \Delta^n\,(a_0x^n) = a_0\,n\,!\,h^n$$

$$= 24\,(10\,!)\,2^{10}$$

**Example 13.** *Prove* $\left(\dfrac{\Delta^2}{E}\right)e^x \cdot \dfrac{Ee^x}{\Delta^2 e^x} = e^x$, taking h as the interval of differencing.

**Solution.** $\left(\dfrac{\Delta^2}{E}\right)e^x \cdot \dfrac{E\,(e^x)}{\Delta^2(e^x)} = (E^{-1}\Delta^2)\,e^x \cdot \dfrac{E\,(e^x)}{\Delta^2(e^x)}$

$$= (E^{-1})(\Delta^2 e^x) \cdot \frac{e^{x+h}}{e^x\,(e^h - 1)^2}$$

$$= E^{-1}\,[e^x\,(e^h - 1)^2] \cdot \frac{e^h}{(e^h - 1)^2}$$

$$= e^{x-h} \cdot (e^h - 1)^2 \frac{e^h}{(e^h - 1)^2} = e^x$$

**Example 14.** *Prove* $\left(\dfrac{\Delta^2}{E}\right)u_x \neq \dfrac{\Delta^2 u_x}{Eu_x}$ [*MS. Nov., 1991*]

**Solution.** Now, $\left(\dfrac{\Delta^2}{E}\right)u_x = (\Delta^2 E^{-1})\,u_x$

$$= [(E - 1)^2\,E^{-1}]\,u_x$$

$$= [E - 2 + E^{-1}]\,u_x$$

$$= u_{x+h} - 2u_x + u_{x-h} \quad \text{...(1)}$$

$$\frac{\Delta^2 u_x}{Eu_x} = \frac{(E-1)^2 u_x}{u_{x+h}} = \frac{(E^2 - 2E + 1)\,u_x}{u_{x+h}} = \frac{u_{x+2h} - 2u_{x+h} + u_x}{u_{x+h}} \quad \text{...(2)}$$

From (1) and (2), the right hand sides of (1) and (2) are not equal.

Therefore, $\left(\dfrac{\Delta^2}{E}\right)u_x \neq \dfrac{\Delta^2 u_x}{Eu_x}$

**Example 15.** *Prove the results :*

(*i*) $E\nabla = \Delta = \nabla E$ (*ii*) $\delta E^{1/2} = \Delta$

(*iii*) $hD = \log(1 + \Delta) = -\log(1 - \nabla) = \sinh^{-1}(\mu\delta)$

(*iv*) $1 + \mu^2\delta^2 = \left(1 + \frac{1}{2}\delta^2\right)^2$ (*v*) $E^{1/2} = \mu + \frac{1}{2}\delta$

(*vi*) $E^{-1/2} = \mu - \frac{1}{2}\delta$ (*vii*) $\mu\delta = \frac{1}{2}\Delta E^{-1} + \frac{1}{2}\Delta$

(*viii*) $\Delta = \frac{1}{2}\delta^2 + \delta\sqrt{1 + \dfrac{\delta^2}{4}}$ (*ix*) $\nabla\Delta = \Delta - \nabla = \delta^2$

(*x*) $(1 + \Delta)(1 - \nabla) = 1$ (*xi*) $\mu\delta = \frac{1}{2}(\Delta + \nabla)$

(*xii*) $\mu = \dfrac{2+\Delta}{2\sqrt{1+\Delta}} = \sqrt{1+\dfrac{1}{4}\delta^2}$

**Note.** To prove above results, express each in terms of $E$

**Solution.** (*i*) $(E\nabla)\, u_x = E\,(\nabla u_x) = E\,(u_x - u_{x-h})$

$$= Eu_x - E\,u_{x-h}$$

$$= u_{x+h} - u_x \qquad = \Delta u_x$$

$\therefore \quad E\nabla = \Delta$

Also $(\nabla E)\, u_x = \nabla\,(Eu_x) = \nabla u_{x+h}$

$$= u_{x+h} - u_x \quad = \Delta u_x$$

$\therefore \qquad \nabla E = \Delta$

Hence $\qquad E\nabla = \Delta = \nabla E$

(*ii*) $\delta E^{1/2}\, u_x = \delta u_{x+\frac{h}{2}}$

$$= (E^{1/2} - E^{-1/2})\, u_{x+\frac{h}{2}}$$

$$= u_{x+h} - u_x \qquad = \Delta u_x$$

$\therefore \delta E^{1/2} = \Delta$

**Note.** Hereafter, the operand $u_x$ may be dropped and algebra of operators may be used.

(*iii*) We have proved already, $E = e^{hD}$

$\therefore \quad e^{hD} = E = 1 + \Delta$

Taking logarithm,

$hD \log e = \log(1+\Delta)$

$\therefore \qquad hD = \log(1+\Delta) \qquad$ ...(*i*)

Also, $\nabla = 1 - E^{-1} \quad \therefore \quad E^{-1} = 1 - \nabla$

*i.e.*, $e^{-hD} = 1 - \nabla$

Taking logarithm, $\quad -hD = \log(1-\nabla)$

$\therefore \quad hD = -\log(1-\nabla)$

$$\sinh(hD) = \frac{e^{hD} - e^{-hD}}{2} = \frac{E - E^{-1}}{2} = \left(\frac{E^{1/2} + E^{-1/2}}{2}\right)(E^{1/2} - E^{-1/2})$$

$$= \mu\delta$$

$\therefore \quad hD = \sinh^{-1}(\mu\delta)$

(*iv*) $1 + \mu^2\delta^2 = 1 + \left(\dfrac{E^{1/2} + E^{-1/2}}{2}\right)^2 (E^{1/2} - E^{-1/2})^2$

$$= 1 + \left(\frac{E - E^{-1}}{2}\right)^2 = \frac{4 + (E - E^{-1})^2}{4} = \left(\frac{E + E^{-1}}{2}\right)^2 \quad ...(1)$$

$$\left(1 + \frac{1}{2}\delta^2\right)^2 = \left[1 + \frac{1}{2}(E^{1/2} - E^{-1/2})^2\right]^2$$

$$= \left[1 + \frac{1}{2}(E + E^{-1} - 2)\right]^2$$

$$= \left[\frac{E + E^{-1}}{2}\right]^2 \quad ...(2)$$

From (1) and (2), $1 + \mu^2\delta^2 = \left(1 + \frac{1}{2}\delta^2\right)^2$

(*v*) $\mu + \frac{1}{2}\delta = \frac{E^{1/2} + E^{-1/2}}{2} + \frac{E^{1/2} - E^{-1/2}}{2} = E^{1/2}$

(*vi*) $\mu - \frac{1}{2}\delta = \frac{E^{1/2} + E^{-1/2}}{2} - \frac{1}{2}(E^{1/2} - E^{-1/2}) = E^{-1/2}$

(*vii*) $\frac{1}{2}\Delta E^{-1} + \frac{1}{2}\Delta = \frac{1}{2}\Delta(E^{-1} + 1) = \frac{1}{2}(E - 1)(E^{-1} + 1) = \frac{1}{2}(E - E^{-1}) = \mu\delta$

(*viii*) $\frac{1}{2}\delta^2 + \delta\sqrt{1 + \frac{\delta^2}{4}}$

$$= \frac{1}{2}\delta\left[\delta + 2\sqrt{1 + \frac{\delta^2}{4}}\right]$$

$$= \frac{1}{2}\delta\,[\delta + \sqrt{4 + \delta^2}\,]$$

$$= \frac{1}{2}\delta\left[(E^{1/2} - E^{-1/2}) + \sqrt{4 + (E^{1/2} - E^{-1/2})^2}\right]$$

$$= \frac{1}{2}\delta\left[(E^{1/2} - E^{-1/2}) + \sqrt{(E^{1/2} + E^{-1/2})^2}\right]$$

$$= \frac{1}{2}(E^{1/2} - E^{-1/2})\,[E^{1/2} - E^{-1/2} + E^{1/2} + E^{-1/2}]$$

$$= \frac{1}{2} \times 2\,[E^{1/2} - E^{-1/2}]\,E^{1/2}$$

$$= E - 1 = \Delta$$

(*ix*) $\nabla\Delta = (1 - E^{-1})(E - 1) = E + E^{-1} - 2 = (E^{1/2} - E^{-1/2})^2 = \delta^2$

$\Delta - \nabla = (E - 1) - (1 - E^{-1}) = E + E^{-1} - 2 = \delta^2$

(*x*) $(1 + \Delta)(1 - \nabla) = E.E^{-1} = 1$

(*xi*) $\frac{1}{2}(\Delta + \nabla) = \frac{1}{2}[E - 1 + 1 - E^{-1}] = \frac{1}{2}(E - E^{-1}) = \mu\delta$

(xii) $$\frac{2+\Delta}{2\sqrt{1+\Delta}}=\frac{1+E}{2\sqrt{E}}=\frac{1}{2}[E^{-1/2}+E^{1/2}]=\mu$$

$$\sqrt{1+\frac{1}{4}\delta^2}=\frac{1}{2}\sqrt{4+(E^{1/2}-E^{-1/2})^2}$$
$$=\frac{1}{2}\sqrt{(E^{1/2}+E^{-1/2})^2}$$
$$=\frac{1}{2}(E^{1/2}+E^{-1/2})=\mu$$

**Example 16.** *Given* $y_3=2, y_4=-6, y_5=8, y_6=9$ *and* $y_7=17$, *calculate* $\Delta^4 y_3$.

**Solution.** $\Delta^4 y_3=(E-1)^4 y_3=(E^4-4E^3+6E^2-4E+1)\,y_3$

$$=E^4 y_3-4E^3 y_3+6E^2 y_3-4Ey_3+y_3$$
$$=y_7-4y_6+6y_5-4y_4+y_3$$
$$=17-4(9)+6(8)-4(-6)+2=55$$

**Example 17.** *Find* $y_6$ *if* $y_0=9, y_1=18, y_2=20, y_3=24$ *given that the third differences are constants.*

**Solution.** Since third differences are constants, $\Delta^4 y_0=\Delta^5 y_0=\Delta^6 y_0=0$

$$y_6=E^6 y_0=(1+\Delta)^6 y_0$$
$$=\left(1+{}^6C_1\Delta+{}^6C_2\Delta^2+{}^6C_3\Delta^3+{}^6C_4\Delta^4+{}^6C_5\Delta^5+\Delta^6\right)y_0$$
$$=(1+6\Delta+15\Delta^2+20\Delta^3)\,y_0 \text{ since other terms vanish.}$$
$$=[1+6(E-1)+15(E-1)^2+20\,(E-1)^3]\,y_0$$
$$=(1+6E-6+15E^2-30E+15+20E^3-60E^2+60E-20)\,y_0$$
$$=[-10+36E-45E^2+20E^3]\,y_0$$
$$=-10y_0+36y_1-45y_2+20y_3$$
$$=-10(9)+36(18)-45(20)+20(24)$$
$$=-90+648-900+480$$
$$=1128-990=138$$

**Hint.** You can form forward difference table and use the values of $\Delta y_0, \Delta^2 y_0, \Delta^3 y_0,$ ...... to get the result.

**Example 18.** *From the following table, find the missing value.*

| $x$ | : | 2 | 3 | 4 | 5 | 6 |
|---|---|---|---|---|---|---|
| $f(x)$ | : | 45·0 | 49·2 | 54·1 | — | 67·4 |

**Solution.** Since only four values of $f(x)$ are given, we assume that the polynomial which fits the data, that is, collaction polynomial, is of degree three.

Hence fourth differences are zeros.

*i.e.,* $\Delta^4 y_0 = 0 \quad \therefore \quad (E-1)^4 y_0 = 0$

*i.e.,* $(E^4 - 4E^3 + 6E^2 - 4E + 1)\, y_0 = 0$

$y_4 - 4y_3 + 6y_2 - 4y_1 + y_0 = 0$ where $y_0 = 45{\cdot}0$

$67{\cdot}4 - 4y_3 + 6(54{\cdot}1) - 4(49{\cdot}2) + 45{\cdot}0 = 0$

$4y_3 = 240{\cdot}2 \quad \therefore \quad y_3 = 60{\cdot}05$

Missing term is 60·05.

**Example 19.** *Estimate the production for 1964 and 1966 from the following data :*

| *Year* | : | *1961* | *1962* | *1963* | *1964* | *1965* | *1966* | *1967* |
|---|---|---|---|---|---|---|---|---|
| *Production* | : | *200* | *220* | *260* | – | *350* | – | *430* |

**Solution.** Since five values are given, collacation polynomial is of degree four. Hence $\Delta^5 y_K = 0$

*i.e.,* $(E-1)^5 y_K = 0$

$(E^5 - 5E^4 + 10E^3 - 10E^2 + 5E - 1)\, y_K = 0$

$y_5 - 5y_4 + 10y_3 - 10y_2 + 5y_1 - y_0 = 0$, taking $K = 0$

$y_5 - 5(350) + 10y_3 - 10(260) + 5(220) - 200 = 0$

*i.e.,* $y_5 + 10y_3 = 3450$ ...(1)

Taking $K = 1$,

$y_6 - 5y_5 + 10y_4 - 10y_3 + 5y_2 - y_1 = 0$

$430 - 5y_5 + 10(350) - 10y_3 + 5(260) - 220 = 0$

$5y_5 + 10y_3 = 5010$ ...(2)

Solving for $y_3, y_5$ from (1) and (2), $y_3 = 306, y_5 = 390$

Hence missing values are 306 and 390.

**Example 20.** *Find the missing term in the following :*

| *x* : | *1* | *2* | *3* | *4* | *5* | *6* | *7* |
|---|---|---|---|---|---|---|---|
| *y* : | *2* | *4* | *8* | – | *32* | *64* | *128* |

**Solution.** There are 6 given values. We can have a unique fifth degree polynomial to satisfy the data.

Hence, $\Delta^6 y_0 = 0$

$(E-1)^6 y_0 = 0$

$(E^6 - 6E^5 + 15E^4 - 20E^3 + 15E^2 - 6E + 1)\, y_0 = 0$

$y_6 - 6y_5 + 15y_4 - 20y_3 + 15y_2 - 6y_1 + y_0 = 0$

$128 - 6(64) + 15(32) - 20y_3 + 15(8) - 6(4) + 2 = 0$

$\therefore \quad 20y_3 = 322.$ Hence, $y_3 = 16{\cdot}1$

Missing value is 16·1

## 5·5. Error propagation in a difference table

Let $y_0, y_1, y_2, y_3, ..., y_n$ be the exact values of a function corresponding to $x_0, x_1, x_2, ..., x_n$. Suppose an error $e$ is made in entering the value $y_5$ in the table. Now, we will see how this error $e$ in $y_5$ affects the entries in the difference columns.

| $x$ | $y$ | $\Delta y$ | $\Delta^2 y$ | $\Delta^3 y$ | $\Delta^4 y$ |
|---|---|---|---|---|---|
| $x_0$ | $y_0$ | | | | |
| | | $\Delta y_0$ | $\Delta^2 y_0$ | | |
| $x_1$ | $y_1$ | | | $\Delta^3 y_0$ | |
| | | $\Delta y_1$ | $\Delta^2 y_1$ | | $\Delta^4 y_0$ |
| $x_2$ | $y_2$ | | | $\Delta^3 y_1$ | |
| | | $\Delta y_2$ | $\Delta^2 y_2$ | | $\Delta^4 y_1 + e$ |
| $x_3$ | $y_3$ | | | $\Delta^3 y_2 + e$ | |
| | | $\Delta y_3$ | $\Delta^2 y_3 + e$ | | $\Delta^4 y_2 - 4e$ |
| $x_4$ | $y_4$ | | | $\Delta^3 y_3 - 3e$ | |
| | | $\Delta y_4 + e$ | $\Delta^2 y_4 - 2e$ | | $\Delta^4 y_3 + 6e$ |
| $x_5$ | $y_5 + e$ | | | $\Delta^3 y_4 + 3e$ | |
| | | $\Delta y_5 - e$ | $\Delta^2 y_5 + e$ | | $\Delta^4 y_4 - 4e$ |
| $x_6$ | $y_6$ | | | $\Delta^3 y_5 - e$ | |
| | | $\Delta y_6$ | $\Delta^2 y_6$ | | $\Delta^4 y_5 + e$ |
| $x_7$ | $y_7$ | | | $\Delta^3 y_6$ | |
| | | $\Delta y_7$ | $\Delta^2 y_7$ | | $\Delta^4 y_6$ |
| $x_8$ | $y_8$ | | | $\Delta^3 y_7$ | |
| | | $\Delta y_8$ | $\Delta^2 y_8$ | | |
| $x_9$ | $y_9$ | | | | |
| | | $\Delta y_9$ | | | |
| $x_{10}$ | $y_{10}$ | | | | |

The above table shows that an error in an entry in column $y$ affects two entries in column $\Delta y$, three entries in column $\Delta^2 y$, four entries in column $\Delta^3 y$ and so on. We note the following:

1. The error increases with the order of differences.
2. The error spreads out fanwise and the error propagation is confined to a triangular region with vertex at the point of wrong entry.
3. The errors in the column $\Delta^i y$ are given by the coefficients of the binomial expansion $(1 - e)^i$.
4. The important point to be noted is that the errors in any difference column is zero.
5. The maximum error in any difference column appears opposite to the wrong entry made.

The error made in the entry can be identified using the above notes.

*We can also note that the sum of the entries in any column of differences is the difference between the last entry and the first entry in the previous column.*

For example, adding all the entries of the column headed by $\Delta^2 y$, we have

$$\Delta^2 y_0 + \Delta^2 y_1 + \Delta^2 y_2 + \cdots\cdots + \Delta^2 y_8$$

$$= (\Delta y_1 - \Delta y_0) + (\Delta y_2 - \Delta y_1) + (\Delta y_3 - \Delta y_2) + \cdots\cdots + (\Delta y_9 - \Delta y_8)$$

$= \Delta y_9 - \Delta y_0$

This idea can be used to check the entries in the table while calculating the differences.

**Note.** If there are more number of errors in the entries of $y$, the disturbance in the difference columns will be iregular and it will be very difficult to locate the error.

**Example 21.** *Assuming that the following values of $y_x$ belong to a polynomial of degree 4, compute the next three values.*

| $x$ : | 0 | 1 | 2 | 3 | 4 | 5 | 6 | 7 |
|---|---|---|---|---|---|---|---|---|
| $y$ : | 1 | $-1$ | 1 | – | 1 | – | – | – |

[*M.S., 1978*]

**Solution.** Firstly, we form the difference table

| $x$ | $y$ | $\Delta y$ | $\Delta^2 y$ | $\Delta^3 y$ | $\Delta^4 y$ |
|---|---|---|---|---|---|
| 0 | 1 | | | | |
| | | $-2$ | | | |
| 1 | $-1$ | | 4 | | |
| | | 2 | | $-8$ | |
| 2 | 1 | | $-4$ | | 16 |
| | | $-2$ | | 8 | |
| 3 | $-1$ | | 4 | | 16 |
| | | 2 | | $d=24$ | |
| 4 | 1 | | $c=28$ | | 16 |
| | | $b=30$ | | $s=40$ | |
| 5 | $a=31$ | | $r=68$ | | 16 |
| | | $q=98$ | | | |
| 6 | $p=129$ | | | | |
| 7 | | | | | |

All the entries above the diagonal line are got from the given data. Since the polynomial is of degree 4, the fourth differences are constants. Hence, all entries under the column headed by $\Delta^4 y$ must be 16. The unknown values $a, b, c, d$ in the diagonal containing $y_5$ can be calculated as follows :

$$d - 8 = 16 \qquad \therefore \; d = 24$$
$$c - 4 = d \qquad \therefore \; c = 28$$
$$b - 2 = c \qquad \therefore \; b = 30$$
$$a - 1 = b \qquad \therefore \; a = 31$$
$$s - 24 = 16 \qquad \therefore \; s = 40$$
$$r - c = s \qquad \therefore \; r = 68$$
$$q - b = r \qquad \therefore \; q = 30 + 68 = 98$$
$$p - a = q \qquad \therefore \; p = 31 + 98 = 129$$

In the same manner, the values of the entries in the next diagonal can be got.

**Example 22.** *The following table gives the values of y which is a polynomial of degree 5. It is known that $y = f(3)$ is in error. Correct the error.*

[*MS. 1979*]

| $x$ : | 0 | 1 | 2 | 3 | 4 | 5 | 6 |
|---|---|---|---|---|---|---|---|
| $y$ : | 1 | 2 | 33 | 254 | 1025 | 3126 | 7777 |

It is given in the problem that $f(3)$ is in error. Let $e$ be the error. We will form the difference table. All entries in the column headed by $\Delta^5 y$ must be same (constant).

| $x$ | $y$ | $\Delta y$ | $\Delta^2 y$ | $\Delta^3 y$ | $\Delta^4 y$ | $\Delta^5 y$ |
|---|---|---|---|---|---|---|
| 0 | 1 | | | | | |
| | | 1 | | | | |
| 1 | 2 | | 30 | | | |
| | | 31 | | $160 + e$ | | |
| 2 | 33 | | $190 + e$ | | $220 - 4e$ | |
| | | $221 + e$ | | $360 - 3e$ | | $220 + 10e$ |
| 3 | $254 + e$ | | $550 - 2e$ | | $420 + 6e$ | |
| | | $771 - e$ | | $780 + 3e$ | | $20 - 10e$ |
| 4 | 1025 | | $1330 + e$ | | $440 - 4e$ | |
| | | 2101 | | $1220 - e$ | | |
| 5 | 3126 | | 2250 | | | |
| | | 4651 | | | | |
| 6 | 7777 | | | | | |

By hypothesis of the problem, $220 + 10e = 20 - 10e$, *i.e.*, $e = -10$

Hence, $y(3) = 244$.

**Example 23.** *$y = f(x)$ is a polynomial of degree 3 and the following table gives the values of x and y. Locate and correct the wrong values of y.*

| $x$ : | 0 | 1 | 2 | 3 | 4 | 5 | 6 |
|---|---|---|---|---|---|---|---|
| $y$ : | 4 | 10 | 30 | 75 | 160 | 294 | 490 |

**Solution.** We form the difference table.

| $x$ | $y$ | $\Delta y$ | $\Delta^2 y$ | $\Delta^3 y$ | $\Delta^4 y$ |
|---|---|---|---|---|---|
| 0 | 4 | | | | |
| | | 6 | | | |
| 1 | 10 | | 14 | | |
| | | 20 | | 11 | |
| 2 | 30 | | 25 | | |
| | | 45 | | 15 | |
| 3 | 75 | | 40 | | |
| | | 85 | | 9 | |
| 4 | 160 | | 49 | | |
| | | 134 | | 13 | |
| 5 | 294 | | 62 | | |
| | | 196 | | | |
| 6 | 490 | | | | |

Since $y$ is a polynomial of degree 3, the third differences of $y$ are equal (constant).

The sum of the entries of the third differences is 48. Hence each entry in this column may be $\frac{48}{4} = 12$.

$$\text{Hence } \quad 11 = 12 + (-1)$$
$$15 = 12 - 3(-1)$$
$$9 = 12 + 3(-1)$$
$$13 = 12 - 1(-1)$$

Hence $\quad e = -1$

$\therefore$ Correct value of $y(3) = 75 - (-1) = 76.$

**Example 24.** *Find and correct a single error in y in the following table.*

| $x$ : | 0 | 1 | 2 | 3 | 4 | 5 | 6 | 7 |
|---|---|---|---|---|---|---|---|---|
| $y$ : | 0 | 0 | 1 | 6 | 24 | 60 | 120 | 210 |

**Solution.**

| $y$ | $\Delta y$ | $\Delta^2 y$ | $\Delta^3 y$ | $\Delta^4 y$ | $\Delta^5 y$ |
|---|---|---|---|---|---|
| 0 | | | | | |
| | 0 | | | | |
| 0 | | 1 | | | |
| | 1 | | 3 | | |
| 1 | | 4 | | 6 | |
| | 5 | | 9 | | |
| 6 | | 13 | | – 4 | |
| | 18 | | 5 | | |
| 24 | | 18 | | 1 | |
| | 36 | | 6 | | |
| 60 | | 24 | | 0 | |
| | 60 | | 6 | | |
| 120 | | 30 | | | |
| | 90 | | | | |
| 210 | | | | | |

From the difference table, under column $\Delta^3 y$, two entries are 6, 6. It is likely that the third differences are constants and errors are not there in the entries 6's. Referring to the entries under column $\Delta^3 y$,

$$3 = 6 - 3(1)$$
$$9 = 6 + 3(1) \quad \therefore \quad e = 1$$
$$5 = 6 - (1)$$

Hence correct $y(2) = 1 - 1 = 0$ (error in $y(2)$)

**Note.** Since the error is in $y(2)$, the sum of the errors in columns $\Delta^3 y, \Delta^4 y....$ is not zero as explained in the theory.

## 5·6. Finite integration (or Inverse operator $\Delta^{-1}$)

If $\Delta y_x = u_x$ then $y_x = \Delta^{-1} u_x$. Here $\Delta^{-1}$ is called finite integration operator or inverse of operator $\Delta$.

If $C(x)$ is a periodic function of period $h$ which is equal to the interval of differencing,

$$\Delta C(x) = C(x+h) - C(x) \quad \text{by definition of } \Delta$$
$$= C(x) - C(x) \quad \because C(x) \text{ is periodic}$$
$$= 0$$

This shows that, if $C(x)$ is periodic function whose period and interval of differencing is same $h$, then $\Delta C(x) = 0$.

Hence if $\Delta y(x) = u(x)$

then $\Delta(y(x) + C(x)) = \Delta y(x) + \Delta C(x)$

$$= \Delta y(x) + 0 = u(x)$$

$$\therefore \quad \Delta^{-1} u(x) = y(x) + C(x)$$

where $C(x)$ is the periodic function of period $h$. (Similar to constant of integration in integration).

The following inverse operator results can be remembered from the corresponding forward operator results.

1. $\Delta^{-1}(e^{ax+b}) = \dfrac{e^{ax+b}}{e^{ah}-1}$

   Hence, $\Delta^{-1} e^x = \dfrac{e^x}{e^h - 1}$

2. $\Delta^{-1}(a^x) = \dfrac{a^x}{a^h - 1}, \; a \neq 1$

3. $\Delta^{-1}(u_x + v_x) = \Delta^{-1} u_x + \Delta^{-1} v_x$

4. $\Delta^{-1}(Cu_x) = C\,\Delta^{-1} u_x$

5. $\Delta^{-1}(a+bx)^{(n)} = \dfrac{(a+bx)^{(n+1)}}{(n+1)\,hb}, \; n \neq -1$

6. $\Delta^{-1} x^{(n)} = \dfrac{x^{(n+1)}}{n+1}, \; n \neq -1$ and $h = 1$

## 5·7. Summation of Series

An important application of finite calculus is finding the sum of seires. Let us find the sum of the series

$$u_1 + u_2 + u_3 + \cdots\cdots + u_n$$

Let the $x$th term $u_x$ be such that $u_x = \Delta y_x$

$\therefore \quad u_x = \Delta y_x = y_{x+1} - y_x \quad$ (here $h = 1$)

Hence,
$$u_1 = y_2 - y_1$$
$$u_2 = y_3 - y_2$$
$$u_3 = y_4 - y_3$$
$$\cdots\cdots\cdots\cdots$$
$$\cdots\cdots\cdots\cdots$$
$$u_n = y_{n+1} - y_n$$

Adding vertically,

$$S_n = u_1 + u_2 + \cdots\cdots + u_n = y_{n+1} - y_1 = (y_x)_1^{n+1} = [\Delta^{-1}(u_x)]_1^{n+1}$$

Hence, $\displaystyle\sum_{x=1}^{n} u_x = [\Delta^{-1} u_x]_1^{n+1}$

**Example 25.** *Find* $\Delta^{-1} x(x+1)(x+2)$.

**Solution.** Here $\quad (x+2)(x+1)\,x = (x+2)^{(3)}$, if $h = 1$

Hence, $\Delta^{-1}(x+2)(x+1)\,x = \Delta^{-1}(x+2)^{(3)}$

$$= \frac{(x+2)^{(4)}}{4} + C(x)$$

$$= \frac{(x+2)(x+1)(x)(x-1)}{4} + C(x)$$

where $C(x)$ is a periodic function of period 1.

**Example 26.** *Find* $\Delta^{-1} \dfrac{1}{x(x+1)(x+2)}$

**Solution.** $$\frac{1}{x(x+1)(x+2)} = (x-1)^{(-3)}$$

$$\Delta^{-1}\frac{1}{x(x+1)(x+2)} = \Delta^{-1}[(x-1)^{(-3)}]$$

$$= \frac{(x-1)^{(-2)}}{(-2)} + C(x)$$

$$= -\frac{1}{2}\frac{1}{x(x+1)}$$

**Example 27.** *If* $\Delta f(x) = 2x^3 - 6x^2 + 7x + 10$, *find* $f(x)$.
*Express* $2x^3 - 6x^2 + 7x + 10$ *in factorial polynomial.*

**Solution.**

| | | | | |
|---|---|---|---|---|
| 0 | 2 | – 6 | 7 | 10 |
| | | 0 | 0 | 0 |
| 1 | 2 | – 6 | 7 | 10 |
| | | 2 | – 4 | |
| 2 | 2 | – 4 | 3 | |
| | | 4 | | |
| | 2 | 0 | | |

Hence, $2x^3 - 6x^2 + 7x + 10 = \phi(x) = 2x^{(3)} + 3x^{(1)} + 10$

$$\therefore \quad \Delta f(x) = 2x^{(3)} + 3x^{(1)} + 10$$

$$\therefore \quad f(x) = \Delta^{-1}(2x^{(3)} + 3x^{(1)} + 10)$$

$$= 2\frac{x^{(4)}}{4} + 3\frac{x^{(2)}}{2} + 10x^{(1)} + C(x)$$

$$= \frac{1}{2}x(x-1)(x-2)(x-3) + \frac{3}{2}x(x-1) + 10x + C(x)$$

where $C(x)$ is a periodic function of period 1.

**Example 28.** *Sum the series to n terms of*

*1 · 2 · 3 + 2 · 3 · 4 + 3 · 4 · 5 + ···*

**Solution.** nth term $= u_n = n(n+1)(n+2)$

Sum of series to $n$ terms $= \sum_{x=1}^{n} u_x$

$$= [\Delta^{-1} u_x]_1^{n+1}$$

$$= [\Delta^{-1} (x+2)^{(3)}]_1^{n+1}$$

$$= \left[\frac{(x+2)^{(4)}}{4}\right]_1^{n+1}$$

$$= \frac{1}{4}[(n+3)^{(4)} - 3^{(4)}]$$

$$= \frac{1}{4}[(n+3)(n+2)(n+1)\,n - 3\cdot2\cdot1\cdot0]$$

$$= \frac{1}{4}(n+3)(n+2)(n+1)\,n$$

**Example 29.** *Sum to n terms of the series*

$$\frac{1}{1\cdot2\cdot3} + \frac{1}{2\cdot3\cdot4} + \frac{1}{3\cdot4\cdot5} + \ldots\ldots$$

**Solution.** $u_x = \dfrac{1}{x(x+1)(x+2)} = (x-1)^{(-3)}$

Sum to $n$ terms $= \sum_{x=1}^{n} u_x$

$$= (\Delta^{-1} u_x)_1^{n+1}$$

$$= \left[\Delta^{-1}.(x-1)^{(-3)}\right]_1^{n+1}$$

$$= \left[\frac{(x-1)^{(-2)}}{-2}\right]_1^{n+1}$$

$$= -\frac{1}{2}\left[n^{(-2)} - 0^{(-2)}\right]$$

$$= -\frac{1}{2}\left[\frac{1}{(n+1)(n+2)} - \frac{1}{1\cdot2}\right]$$

$$= \frac{1}{2}\left[\frac{1}{2} - \frac{1}{(n+1)(n+2)}\right]$$

**Example 30.** *Find the nth term of the sequence 1, 4. 10, 20, 35, 56,..... Also find 7th term.*

**Solution.** We form the difference table below.

| $x$ | $y$ | $\Delta y$ | $\Delta^2 y$ | $\Delta^3 y$ | $\Delta^4 y$ | $\Delta^5 y$ |
|---|---|---|---|---|---|---|
| 0 | 1 | | | | | |
| | | 3 | | | | |
| 1 | 4 | | 3 | | | |
| | | 6 | | 1 | | |
| 2 | 10 | | 4 | | 0 | |
| | | 10 | | 1 | | 0 |
| 3 | 20 | | 5 | | 0 | |
| | | 15 | | 1 | | |
| 4 | 35 | | 6 | | | |
| | | 21 | | | | |
| 5 | 56 | | | | | |

$$y_n = E^n y_0$$
$$= (1+\Delta)^n y_0$$
$$= \left(1 + {}^nC_1 \Delta + {}^nC_2 \Delta^2 + {}^nC_3 \Delta^3 + {}^nC_4 \Delta^4 + \cdots\cdots\right) y_0$$
$$= y_0 + n\,\Delta y_0 + \frac{n(n-1)}{2}\Delta^2 y_0 + \frac{n(n-1)(n-2)}{6}\Delta^3 y_0 + \cdots\cdots$$
$$= 1 + n(3) + \frac{n(n-1)}{2}(3) + \frac{n(n-1)(n-2)}{6}(1)$$
$$= \frac{1}{6}[6 + 18n + 9n^2 - 9n + n^3 - 3n^2 + 2n]$$
$$= \frac{1}{6}[n^3 + 6n^2 + 11n + 6]$$

$$\text{7th term} = y_6 = \frac{1}{6}[216 + 216 + 66 + 6] = 84$$

## 5·8. Montmort's theorem

$$u_0 + u_1 x + u_2 x^2 + \cdots\cdots \text{ to } \infty = \frac{u_0}{1-x} + \frac{x\,\Delta u_0}{(1-x)^2} + \frac{x^2 \Delta^2 u_0}{(1-x)^3} + \cdots\cdots \text{ to } \infty$$

$$u_0 + u_1 x + u_2 x^2 + \cdots\cdots \text{ to } \infty$$
$$= u_0 + xEu_0 + x^2E^2u_0 + \cdots\cdots \text{ to } \infty$$
$$= (1 + xE + x^2E^2 + \cdots\cdots \text{ to } \infty)\, u_0$$
$$= \frac{1}{1-xE}u_0 \qquad (\because \text{ the series in the bracket is in G.P.})$$
$$= \frac{1}{1-x(1+\Delta)}u_0$$
$$= \frac{1}{1-x-x\Delta}u_0$$
$$= \frac{1}{(1-x)\left[1 - \dfrac{x\Delta}{1-x}\right]}u_0$$

$$= \frac{1}{1-x}\left[1 - \frac{x\Delta}{1-x}\right]^{-1} u_0$$

$$= \frac{1}{1-x}\left[1 + \frac{x\Delta}{1-x} + \frac{x^2\Delta^2}{(1-x)^2} + \cdots\cdots \text{ to } \infty\right] u_0$$

$$= \frac{u_0}{1-x} + \frac{x}{(1-x)^2}\Delta u_0 + \frac{x^2}{(1-x)^3}\Delta^2 u_0 + \cdots\cdots \text{ to } \infty$$

**Example 31.** *Using Montmort's theorem, sum the series $1{\cdot}3 + 3{\cdot}5x + 5{\cdot}7x^2 + 7{\cdot}9x^3 + \cdots$ to $\infty$* [*MI 1980*]

**Solution.** $u_0 = 1 \cdot 3 = 3$ ; $u_1 = 3 \cdot 5 = 15$ ; $u_2 = 5 \cdot 7 = 35$ ; $u_3 = 63$

We form the difference table for the coefficients.

| | | $\Delta u$ | $\Delta^2 u$ | $\Delta^3 u$ |
|---|---|---|---|---|
| $u_0$ | 3 | | | |
| | | 12 | | |
| $u_1$ | 15 | | 8 | |
| | | 20 | | 0 |
| $u_2$ | 35 | | 8 | |
| | | 28 | | |
| $u_3$ | 63 | | | |

$\therefore \quad u_0 = 3, \Delta u_0 = 12, \quad \Delta^2 u_0 = 8, \quad \Delta^3 u_0 = 0$

Therefore, $1 \cdot 3 + 3 \cdot 5x + 5 \cdot 7x^2 + 7 \cdot 9x^3 + \cdots\cdots$ to $\infty$

$$= u_0 + u_1 x + u_2 x^2 + u_3 x^3 + \cdots\cdots \text{ to } \infty$$

$$= \frac{u_0}{1-x} + \frac{x\Delta u_0}{(1-x)^2} + \frac{x^2\Delta^2 u_0}{(1-x)^3} + \cdots\cdots$$

$$= \frac{3}{1-x} + \frac{12x}{(1-x)^2} + \frac{8x^2}{(1-x)^3}, \ x \neq 1$$

**Example 32.** *Using the method of separation of symbols, show that*

$$(u_1 - u_0) - x(u_2 - u_1) + x^2(u_3 - u_2) - \cdots\cdots \text{ to } \infty$$

$$= \frac{\Delta u_0}{1+x} - x\frac{\Delta^2 u_0}{(1+x)^2} + \frac{x^2\Delta^3 u_0}{(1+x)^3} + \cdots\cdots \text{ to } \infty$$

**Solution.** $\text{L.H.S.} = \Delta u_0 - x\Delta u_1 + x^2\Delta u_2 - \cdots\cdots$

$$= \Delta u_0 - x\Delta E u_0 + x^2 \Delta E^2 u_0 \cdots\cdots$$

$$= \Delta(1 - xE + x^2E^2 - \cdots\cdots)\, u_0$$

$$= [\Delta(1 + xE)^{-1}]\, u_0$$

$$= \left(\frac{\Delta}{1 + xE}\right) u_0$$

$$= \left[\frac{\Delta}{1 + x(1+\Delta)}\right] u_0$$

$$= \frac{\Delta}{(1+x)\left[1+\frac{x\Delta}{1+x}\right]} u_0$$

$$= \frac{1}{1+x}\left[1 - \frac{x\Delta}{1+x} + \frac{x^2\Delta^2}{(1+x)^2} - \ldots\ldots\right]\Delta u_0$$

$$= \frac{\Delta u_0}{1+x} - \frac{x\Delta^2 u_0}{(1+x)^2} + \frac{x^2\Delta^3 u_0}{(1+x)^3} - \ldots\ldots = \text{R.H.S.}$$

**Example 33.** *Using the method of separation of symbols, prove*

$$y_x = y_{x-1} + \Delta y_{x-2} + \ldots\ldots + \Delta^{n-1} y_{x-n} + \Delta^n y_{x-n}.$$

**Solution.** R.H.S. $= E^{-1} y_x + \Delta E^{-2} y_x + \ldots\ldots + \Delta^{n-1} E^{-n} y_x + \Delta^n E^{-n} y_x$

$$= E^{-1}\left(1 + \frac{\Delta}{E} + \frac{\Delta^2}{E^2} + \ldots\ldots + \frac{\Delta^{n-1}}{E^{n-1}}\right) y_x + \frac{\Delta^n}{E^n} y_x$$

$$= E^{-1}\left[\frac{\left(\frac{\Delta}{E}\right)^n - 1}{\frac{\Delta}{E} - 1}\right] y_x + \frac{\Delta^n}{E^n} y_x$$

$$= E^{-1}\left[\frac{\Delta^n - E^n}{\Delta - E} \cdot \frac{1}{E^{n-1}}\right] y_x + \frac{\Delta^n}{E^n} y_x$$

$$= \left[-\frac{\Delta^n - E^n}{E^n}\right] y_x + \frac{\Delta^n}{E^n} y_x$$

$$= \left[1 - \frac{\Delta^n}{E^n} + \frac{\Delta^n}{E^n}\right] y_x$$

$$= y_x = \text{L.H.S.}$$

**Example 34.** *Show that*

$$\sum_{x=1}^{n} u_x = u_1 + u_2 + \ldots\ldots + u_n = {}^nC_1\, u_1 + {}^nC_2\, \Delta u_1 + {}^nC_3\, \Delta^2 u_1 + \ldots\ldots + \Delta^{n-1} u_1$$

*and hence sum the series* $1^2 + 2^2 + 3^2 + \ldots\ldots + n^2$.

**Solution.** $\sum_{1}^{n} u_x = u_1 + u_2 + \ldots\ldots + u_n$

$$= u_1 + E u_1 + E^2 u_1 + \ldots\ldots + E^{n-1} u_1$$

$$= (1 + E + E^2 + \cdots + E^{n-1})\, u_1$$

$$= \frac{E^n - 1}{E - 1} \cdot u_1$$

$$= \frac{E^n - 1}{\Delta} u_1 \quad = \frac{(1+\Delta)^n - 1}{\Delta} u_1$$

$$= \left( \frac{{}^nC_1 \Delta + {}^nC_2 \Delta^2 + {}^nC_3 \Delta^3 + \cdots\cdots + {}^nC_n \Delta^n}{\Delta} \right) u_1$$

$$= {}^nC_1 u_1 + {}^nC_2 \Delta u_1 + {}^nC_3 \Delta^2 u_1 + \cdots\cdots + \Delta^{n-1} u_1$$

*Deduction:*

$$u_1 = 1^2 = 1$$
$$u_2 = 2^2 = 4$$
$$u_3 = 3^2 = 9$$
..................
..................
$$u_n = n^2$$

We form the difference table.

| | $u$ | $\Delta u$ | $\Delta^2 u$ | $\Delta^3 u$ |
|---|---|---|---|---|
| $u_1$ | 1 | | | |
| | | 3 | | |
| $u_2$ | 4 | | 2 | |
| | | 5 | | 0 |
| $u_3$ | 9 | | 2 | |
| | | 7 | | 0 |
| $u_4$ | 16 | | 2 | |
| | | 9 | | 0 |
| $u_5$ | 25 | | 2 | |
| | | 11 | | |
| $u_6$ | 36 | | | |

$\therefore \quad u_1 = 1, \ \Delta u_1 = 3, \ \Delta^2 u_1 = 2, \ \Delta^3 u_1 = 0$, etc.

$$1^2 + 2^2 + \cdots\cdots + n^2 = {}^nC_1 u_1 + {}^nC_2 \Delta u_1 + {}^nC_3 \Delta^2 u_1 + \cdots\cdots$$

$$= n(1) + \frac{n(n-1)}{2}(3) + \frac{n(n-1)(n-2)}{6}(2)$$

$$= \frac{1}{6}[6n + 9n^2 - 9n + 2n^3 - 6n^2 + 4n]$$

$$= \frac{1}{6}[2n^3 + 3n^2 + n]$$

$$= \frac{1}{6} n [2n^2 + 3n + 1]$$

$$= \frac{n(n+1)(2n+1)}{6}$$

## EXERCISE 5.1

1. For the function $y = \sinh x$, write down the table by taking $x$ = 1·5, 1·6, 1·7, 1·8, ......, 2·1 [*BR. '94*]
2. Show that $\Delta^3 y_0 = y_3 - 3y_2 + 3y_1 - y_0$. [*MS. 1979*]

3. Prove $y_3 = y_2 + \Delta y_1 + \Delta^2 y_0 + \Delta^3 y_0$. [*MKU 1984*]
4. If $y = x^3 - x^2 + x - 1$, calculate the values of $y$ for $x = 0, 1, 2, 3, 4, 5$ and form the difference table. Find also the value of $y$ at $x = 6$.
5. Find the 5th term of the sequence 3, 6, 11, 18.
6. Obtain the 6th and 7th terms of the sequence 0, 4, 16, 42, 88.
7. Obtain backward difference table for $y = f(x) = x^3 - 3x^2 - 5x - 7$ for $x = -1, 0, 1, 2, 3, 4, 5$. [*MKU '78*]
8. Construct a backward difference table, given $\sin 30° = 0{\cdot}5000$, $\sin 35°$, $= 0{\cdot}5736$, $\sin 40° = 0{\cdot}6428$ and $\sin 45° = 0{\cdot}7071$. Assuming that the third differences are constants, find $\sin 25°$.
9. If the third differences are constants, find $u_6$ if

$$u_0 = 9, u_1 = 18, u_2 = 20, u_3 = 24.$$

10. Calculate $\Delta^4 u_6$ if $u_6 = 2, u_7 = -6, u_8 = 8, u_9 = 9$ and $u_{10} = 17$.
11. Find the first two terms of the series if the subsequent terms are 36, 131, 358, 807, 1592, 2851.
12. Prove $\Delta\left(\dfrac{1}{f(x)}\right) = -\dfrac{\Delta f(x)}{f(x).f(x+1)}$
13. Evaluate $\Delta^{10}(1-ax)(1-bx^2)(1-cx^3)(1-dx^4)$.
14. Express $y = x^4 - 5x^3 + 3x + 4$ in terms of factorial polynomial and obtain $\Delta y, \Delta^2 y, \Delta^3 y, ......$ .
15. Express the following functions in terms of factorial polynomials and hence find their differences :

(*a*) $3x^4 + 8x^3 + 3x^2 - 27x + 9$ (*b*) $7x^4 + 12x^3 - 6x^2 + 5x - 3$ if $h = 2$

(*c*) $x^4 - 12x^3 + 24x^2 - 30x + 9$ (*d*) $2x^3 - 3x^2 + 3x + 10$

(*e*) $2x^3 - 3x^2 + 4x - 8$

16. If $y = \dfrac{1}{(3x+1)(3x+4)(3x+7)}$, show that $y = \dfrac{1}{27}\left(x - \dfrac{2}{3}\right)^{(-3)}$ and

$$\Delta^2 y = \frac{108}{(3x+1)\,(3x+4)\,(3x+7)\,(3x+10)\,(3x+13)}$$

17. If $y = \dfrac{1}{x\,(x+3)(x+6)}$ prove $\Delta^2 y = \dfrac{108}{x\,(x+3)(x+6)(x+9)(x+12)}$
18. Prove $\Delta \tan^{-1}\left(\dfrac{x-1}{x}\right) = \tan^{-1}\left(\dfrac{1}{2x^2}\right)$.
19. Obtain the function whose first difference is

(*a*) $x^3 + 3x^2 + 5x + 12$ (*b*) $x^3 + 4x^2 + 9x + 12$

(c) $4x^{(3)} - 18x^{(2)} - 10x - 17$

20. Evaluate $\Delta^{10}(1-x)(1-2x^2)(1-3x^3)(1-4x^4)$ if $h = 2$ [*MKU 1979*]
21. (*a*) Prove $(E^{-1}\Delta)\, x^3 = 3x^2 - 3x + 1$. [*MKU 1980*]

(*b*) Show that $\dfrac{\Delta^2 x^2}{E\,(x + \log x)} = \dfrac{2}{x + 1 + \log(x+1)}$

**22.** Find the missing terms in the following tables :

(*a*)

| $x$ | : | 0 | 1 | 2 | 3 | 4 |
|---|---|---|---|---|---|---|
| $y$ | : | 1 | 3 | 9 | – | 81 |

(*b*)

| $x$ | : | 7 | 9 | 11 | 13 | 15 | 17 |
|---|---|---|---|---|---|---|---|
| $y$ | : | 32 | 78 | – | 144 | 257 | 381 |

(*c*)

| $x$ | : | 100 | 101 | 102 | 103 | 104 |
|---|---|---|---|---|---|---|
| $y$ | : | 2 | 2·0043 | – | 2·0128 | 2·0170 |

(*d*)

| $x$ | : | 10 | 15 | 20 | 25 | 30 | 35 | 40 |
|---|---|---|---|---|---|---|---|---|
| $y$ | : | 270 | – | 222 | 200 | – | 164 | 148 |

(*e*)

| $x$ | : | 2·0 | 2·1 | 2·2 | 2·3 | 2·4 | 2·5 | 2·6 |
|---|---|---|---|---|---|---|---|---|
| $y$ | : | 0·135 | – | 0·111 | 0·100 | – | 0·082 | 0·074 |

**23.** If $u_0 = 3, u_1 = 12, u_2 = 81, u_3 = 200, u_5 = 8$ find $u_4$ (Assume $u_x$ is a polynomial of degree 4).

**24.** Find the second difference of $f(x) = 7x^4 + 12x^3 - 6x^2 + 5x - 3$ if $h = 2$.

**25.** Prove the results :

(*i*) $\Delta^3 y_2 = \nabla^3 y_3$ (*ii*) $\Delta = \mu\delta + \frac{1}{2}\delta^2$

(*iii*) $\nabla = -\frac{1}{2}\delta^2 + \delta\sqrt{1 + \frac{1}{4}\delta^2}$ (*iv*) $\delta = \Delta(1 + \Delta)^{-1/2} = \nabla(1 - \nabla)^{-1/2}$

(*v*) $\Delta + \nabla = \frac{\Delta}{\nabla} - \frac{\nabla}{\Delta}$ (*vi*) $\Delta^2 = (1 + \Delta)\,\delta^2$

(*vii*) $\nabla = \delta E^{-1/2}$ (*viii*) $\nabla = 1 - e^{-hD}$

**26.** If $y = (3x + 1)(3x + 4)....(3x + 22)$, prove

$$\Delta^4 y = 136080\,(3x + 13)(3x + 16)(3x + 19)(3x + 22).$$

**27.** If $y = \frac{1}{(2x + 1)(2x - 1)(2x - 3)(2x - 5)}$, prove

$$\Delta^3 y = -\frac{960}{(2x + 7)(2x + 5)(2x + 3)(2x + 1)(2x - 1)(2x - 3)(2x - 5)}$$

**28.** Sum the series: $2 \cdot 3 + 3 \cdot 4 + 4 \cdot 5 + \cdots\cdots + (n + 1)(n + 2)$

**29.** Sum to $n$ terms of (*i*) $2 \cdot 5 + 5 \cdot 8 + 8 \cdot 11 + 11 \cdot 14 + \cdots\cdots$

(*ii*) $1^3 + 2^3 + 3^3 + \cdots\cdots + n^3$ (*iii*) $1^2 + 2^2 + 3^2 + \cdots\cdots + n^2$

(*iv*) $1{\cdot}3{\cdot}5 + 2{\cdot}4{\cdot}6 + 3{\cdot}5{\cdot}7 + \cdots\cdots$ (*v*) $\frac{1}{2{\cdot}3} + \frac{1}{3{\cdot}4} + \frac{1}{4{\cdot}5} + \cdots\cdots$

**30.** Find the sum to $n$ terms of the series whose $n$th terms is

(*i*) $n(n - 1)(n - 2)$ (*ii*) $n(n + 2)(n + 4)$

(*iii*) $2n - 1$ (*iv*) $(n + 1)(n + 2)(n + 3)(n + 4)$ (*v*) $n^4$

**31.** Find (*i*) $\Delta^{-1}[x(x + 1)(x + 2)]$ (*ii*) $\Delta^{-1}\frac{1}{x(x + 1)(x + 2)}$

**32.** Find the cubic polynomial from the data below :

| | | | | | | |
|---|---|---|---|---|---|---|
| (*i*) | $x$ : | 0 | 1 | 2 | 3 | 4 |
| | $y$ : | – 5 | – 10 | – 9 | 4 | 35 |
| (*ii*) | $x$ : | 4 | 6 | 8 | 10 | 12 |
| | $y$ : | – 43 | 15 | 185 | 515 | 1053 |

**33.** Prove : (*i*) $\Delta^n e^x = e^{x+n} - {}^nC_1 e^{x+n-1} + {}^nC_2 e^{x+n-2} + \cdots\cdots + (-1)^n e^x$.

(*ii*) $y_{x+n} = y_x + n\,\Delta y_x + {}^nC_2\,\Delta^2 y_x + \cdots\cdots + \Delta^n y_x$

(*iii*) $u_0 + \dfrac{u_1 x}{1\,!} + \dfrac{u_2 x^2}{2\,!} + \cdots = e^x\left(u_0 + x\Delta u_0 + \dfrac{x^2}{2\,!}\Delta^2 u_0 + \cdots\right)$

(*iv*) $u_x = u_{x-1} + \Delta u_{x-2} + \Delta^2 u_{x-3} + \cdots\cdots + \Delta^n u_{x-n-1}$

**34.** Sum the series:

(*i*) $5 + \dfrac{4x}{1\,!} + \dfrac{5x^2}{2\,!} + \dfrac{14x^3}{3\,!} + \dfrac{37x^4}{4\,!} + \dfrac{80x^5}{5\,!} + \cdots\cdots$ to $\infty$

(*ii*) $1 \cdot 3 + 3 \cdot 5n + 5 \cdot 7x^2 + 7 \cdot 9x^3 + \cdots\cdots$ to $\infty$

(*iii*) $1^2 + 2^2 x + 3^2 x^2 + \cdots\cdots$ to $\infty$

(*iv*) $1{\cdot}2 + 2{\cdot}3x + 3{\cdot}4x^2 + \cdots$ to $\infty$

**35.** Prove that

(*i*) $u_0 + u_1 + u_2 + \cdots\cdots + u_n = {}^{n+1}C_1\, u_0 + {}^{n+1}C_2\,\Delta u_0 + \cdots\cdots + {}^{n+1}C_{n+1}\,\Delta^n u_0$.

(*ii*) $u_0 - u_1 + u_2 - u_3 + \cdots\cdots = \dfrac{1}{2}u_0 - \dfrac{1}{4}\Delta u_0 + \dfrac{1}{8}\Delta^2 u_0 - \dfrac{1}{16}\Delta^3 u_0 + \cdots\cdots$

**36.** If $y_x$ is a polynomial of fifth degree in $x$ and $y_1 + y_7 = -786$, $y_2 + y_6 = 686$, $y_3 + y_5 = 1088$, find $y_4$.

**37.** If $y_x$ is a polynomial of degree 7 in $x$ and $y_0 + y_8 = 1{\cdot}9243$, $y_1 + y_7 = 1{\cdot}9590$, $y_2 + y_6 = 1{\cdot}9823$, $y_3 + y_5 = 1{\cdot}9956$, find $y_4$.

**40.** Prove $y_4 = y_3 + \Delta y_2 + \Delta^2 y_1 + \Delta^3 y_1$. [*BR 1995 B.Sc.*]

**41.** Prove $\sum\limits_{k=0}^{n-1} \Delta^2 f_k = \Delta f_n - \Delta f_0$ [*BR 1995 B.Sc.*]

**42.** Find the cubic polynomial $y(x)$ such that $y(0) = 1$, $y(1) = 0$, $y(2) = 1$ and $y(3) = 10$. Hence or otherwise find $y(4)$. [*BR. B.Sc. 1990*]

**43.** Find the cubic polynomial $y(x)$ such that

$y(0) = -5$, $y(1) = 1$, $y(2) = 9$, $y(3) = 25$, $y(4) = 55$, $y(5) = 105$

[*BR. B.Sc., 1992A*]

**44.** Find and correct a misprint in the sequence

$y(x)$ : 1, 3, 11, 31, 69, 113, 223, 351, 521, 739

**45.** Assuming $u_x$ is a polynomial in $x$ of degree 3 correct the $u$ value if one value of $u$ is incorrect in the following table :

| $x$ : | 0 | 1 | 2 | 3 | 4 | 5 | 6 | 7 |
|---|---|---|---|---|---|---|---|---|
| $y$ : | 25 | 21 | 18 | 18 | 27 | 45 | 76 | 123 |

# ANSWERS

## EXERCISE 5.1 Page 204

**5.** 27 **6.** 160, 264 **8.** 0·4225 **9.** 138

**10.** 55 **11.** 2, 7 **13.** $10\,!\ abcd\ h^{10}$

**14.** $x^{(4)} + x^{(3)} - 8x^{(2)} - x^{(1)} + 4$ **15.** (*a*) $3x^{(4)} + 38x^{(3)} + 62x^{(2)} - 11x + 9$

(*b*) $\Delta^2 y = 336x(x-2) + 2304x + 2096$

(*c*) $y = x^{(4)} - 6x^{(3)} - 5x^{(2)} - 17x^{(1)} + 9$ (*d*) $y = 2x^{(3)} + 3x^{(2)} + 2x^{(1)} + 10$

(*e*) $2x^{(3)} + 3x^{(2)} + 3x^{(1)} - 8$

**19.** (*a*) $\frac{1}{4}x(x-1)(x-2)(x-3) + 2x(x-1)(x-2) + \frac{9}{2}x(x-1) + 12x + c(x)$

(*b*) $\frac{1}{4}x(x-1)(x-2)(x-3) + \frac{7}{3}x(x-1)(x-2) + 7x(x-1) + 12x + c(x)$

(*c*) $x^4 - 12x^3 + 24x^2 - 30x + c(x)$

**20.** $24 \times 2^{10} \times 10\,!$ $(h = 2)$ **22.** (*a*) 31 (*b*) 89·4

(*c*) 2·0086 (*d*) 246 and 180·8 (*e*) 0·123, 0·090

**23.** 124·5 **24.** $f(x) = 7x^{(4)} + 96x^{(3)} + 262x^{(2)} + 97x^{(1)} - 3$

$\Delta^2 f(x) = 336x(x-2) + 2304x + 2096$

**28.** $n(n^2 + 6n + 11)/3$ **29.** (*i*) $n(3n^2 + 6n + 1)$ (*ii*) $\frac{n^2(n+1)^2}{4}$,

(*iii*) $\frac{1}{6}n(n+1)(2n+1)$ (*iv*) $n(n+1)(n+4)(n+5)/4$ (*v*) $\frac{1}{2} - \frac{1}{n+2}$

**30.** (*i*) $\frac{n^{(4)}}{4}$ (*ii*) $n(n+1)(n+4)(n+5)/4$ (*iii*) $n^2$

(*iv*) $n(n+1)(n+2)(n+3)(n+4)/5$ (*v*) $\frac{1}{30}n(n+1)(6n^3 + 9n^2 + n - 1)$

**31.** (*i*) $\frac{1}{4}(x+2)(x+1)x(x-1)$ (*ii*) $-\frac{1}{2}\cdot\frac{1}{x(x+1)}$

**32.** (*i*) $x^3 - 6x - 5$ (*ii*) $y = x^3 - 4x^2 - 7x - 15$

**34.** (*i*) $e^x(x^3 + x^2 - x + 5)$ (*ii*) $\frac{3 + 6x - x^2}{(1-x)^3}$ (*iii*) $\frac{1+x}{(1-x)^3}$ (*iv*) $\frac{2}{(1-x)^3}$

**36.** $y_4 = 571$ **37.** $y_4 = 0{\cdot}99996$

**42.** $y = x^3 - 2x^2 + 1$ ; $y(4) = 33$

**44.** 131 instead of 113. **45.** $u(3)$ is wrong and correct $u(3)$ is 19.

# 6

# *Interpolation*

## (For Equal Intervals)

### 6·1. Introduction

Interpolation has been described as the art of reading between the line of a table and in elementary mathematics, it means the *process* of computing intermediate values of a function from a given set of tabular values of the function. Suppose the following table represents a set of corresponding values of $x$ and $y$.

| $x$ : | $x_0$ | $x_1$ | $x_2$ | $x_3$ | ..., $x_n$ |
|---|---|---|---|---|---|
| $y$ : | $y_0$ | $y_1$ | $y_2$ | $y_3$ | ..., $y_n$ |

Now, we require the value of $y = y_i$ corresponding to a value $x = x_i$, where $x_0 < x_i < x_n$.

***Extrapolation*** is used to denote the *process* of finding the values outside the interval $(x_0, x_n)$. But, in general, the word *interpolation* is used in both processes.

Let $y = f(x)$ be the function taking the values $y_0, y_1, \ldots, y_n$ corresponding to $x = x_0, x_1, \ldots, x_n$. In other words, $y_i = f(x_i)$, $i = 0, 1, 2, \ldots, n$. If $f(x)$ is known, the value of $y$ can be calculated for any $x$. But in many cases we have to find $y = f(x)$ such that $y_i = f(x_i)$, from the given table. This is not easy because there are infinity of functions $y = \phi(x)$ such that $y_i = \phi(x_i)$. Hence, from the table, we cannot find a unique $\phi(x)$ such that $y = \phi(x)$ satisfies the set of values given in the table above. Of the sequence of functions $\{\phi(x)\}$, there is a unique $n$th degree polynomial $P_n(x)$ such that $y_i = P_n(x_i)$, $i = 0, 1, 2, \ldots, n$. (Refer Fig. 1).

The function $\phi(x)$ is called *interpolating function* or *smoothing function* or *interpolating formula.*

This polynomial function $P_n(x)$ may be taken as an *interpolating polynomial* or *collocation polynomial* where

$$y_i = f(x_i) = P_n(x_i),\ i = 0, 1, 2, \ldots, n.$$

Other types of approximating function may be taken suitable for

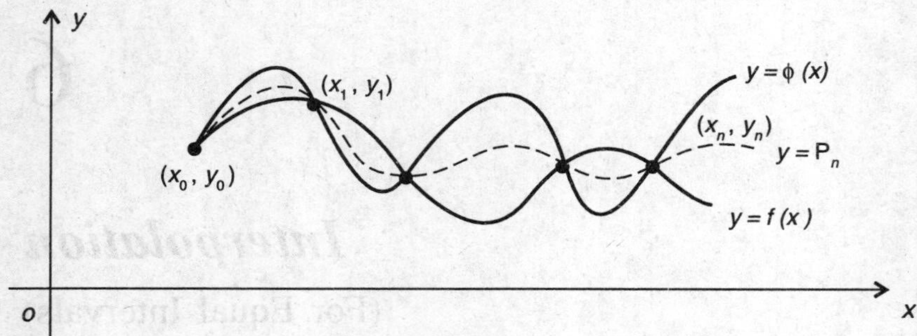


Fig. 1

different purposes. In this chapter, we will be mostly concerned with the polynomial interpolations only.

Polynomial interpolation is mostly preferred because of the following reasons:

1. They are simple forms of functions which can be easily manipulated.
2. Computations for definite values of the argument, integration and differentiation of such functions, are easy.
3. Polynomials are free from singularities whereas rational functions or other types, do have singularities.

The basis of finding such collocation polynomial is the fact that there is exactly only one collocation polynomial $P_n(x)$ of degree $n$ such that the values of $P_n(x)$ at $x_0, x_1, x_2, \ldots, x_n$ coincide with the given functional values $y_0, y_1, y_2, \ldots, y_n$. Here, $P_n(x)$ is called polynomial approximation to $f(x)$. We shall see below a few of the methods of finding such interpolating polynomials.

**6·1a. Linear interpolation or method of proportional parts**

The simplest of all interpolations is the case in which the interpolating polynomial is linear. Let us assume that the set of values of $x$ and $y$ are as given below:

| $x$ : | $x_0$ | $x_1$ | $x_2$ | $x_3$ | ..., $x_n$ |
|---|---|---|---|---|---|
| $y$ : | $y_0$ | $y_1$ | $y_2$ | $y_3$ | ..., $y_n$ |

Now we require the value of $y$ corresponding to $x_k$ which lies between $x_r$ and $x_{r+1}$.

We will assume the polynomial to be linear. (*i.e.* st. line)

The line equation is $\dfrac{y - y_r}{x - x_r} = \dfrac{y_{r+1} - y_r}{x_{r+1} - x_r}$

$\therefore \quad y_k = y_r + \left( \dfrac{y_{r+1} - y_r}{x_{r+1} - x_r} \right)(x_k - x_r)$ gives the value of $y$ at $x = x_k$, $x_r < x_k < x_{r+1}$.

This method may be successful if the difference between succeeding pairs of values of the variables are small and regular. But, if the intervals between the two pairs of values are large, and irregular, this method of simple proportion cannot be used without large error.

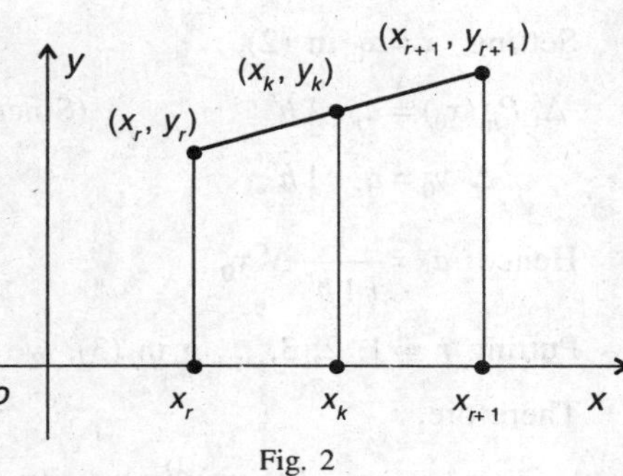


Fig. 2

**Example 1.** *Using the method of proportional parts, find y at $x = 0{\cdot}5$, $x = 0{\cdot}75$, given the following table.*

| $x$ : | *0* | *1* | *2* | *5* |
|---|---|---|---|---|
| $y$ : | *2* | *3* | *12* | *147* |

**Solution.** $y_k = y_r + \left(\dfrac{y_{r+1} - y_r}{x_{r+1} - x_r}\right)(x_k - x_r)$

$$y\,(0{\cdot}5) = 2 + \frac{(3-2)}{(1-0)}(0{\cdot}5 - 0) = 2{\cdot}5$$

$$y\,(0{\cdot}75) = 2 + \frac{(3-2)}{(1-0)}(0{\cdot}75 - 0) = 2{\cdot}75$$

## 6·2. Gregory-Newton forward interpolation formula or Newton's forward interpolation formula (*for equal intervals*)

Let $y = f(x)$ denote a function which takes the values $y_0, y_1, ..., y_n$ corresponding to the values $x_0, x_1, ..., x_n$ respectively of $x$.

Let us suppose that the values of $x$ viz. $x_0, x_1, ..., x_n$ are equidistant. That is, $x_i - x_{i-1} = h$, for $i = 1, 2, ..., n$.

Therefore, $x_i = x_0 + h, \qquad x_2 = x_0 + 2h$, etc.

$\therefore \qquad x_i = x_0 + ih, \qquad i = 1, 2, ..., n.$

Let $P_n(x)$ be a polynomial of the $n$th degree in $x$ such that $y_i = f(x_i) = P_n(x_i)$, $i = 0, 1, 2, ..., n$.

Let us assume $P_n(x)$ in the form givn below

$$P_n(x) = a_0 + a_1\,(x - x_0)^{(1)} + a_2\,(x - x_0)^{(2)} + \cdots + a_r\,(x - x_0)^{(r)} + \cdots$$
$$+ \cdots + a_n\,(x - x_0)^{(n)}. \qquad ...(1)$$

The $(n+1)$ unknowns $a_0, a_1, a_2, ..., a_n$ can be found as follows.

$$P_n\,(x_0) = y_0 = a_0 \qquad \text{(setting } x = x_0 \text{ in (1))}$$

$$\Delta^r P_n\,(x) = a_r\, r\,!\, h^r + \text{terms involving } (x - x_0) \text{ as a factor.} \qquad ...(2)$$

(Since the first $r$ terms vanish)

Setting $x = x_0$ in (2),

$\Delta^r P_n(x_0) = a_r\, r!\, h^r$ (Since the other terms in (2) vanish)

*i.e.,* $\Delta^r y_0 = a_r\, r!\, h^r$

Hence $a_r = \dfrac{1}{r!\,h^r}\Delta^r y_0$ ...(3)

Putting $r = 1, 2, 3, ..., n$ in (3), we get the values of $a_1, a_2, ..., a_n$.

Therefore,

$$P_n(x) = y_0 + \frac{(x-x_0)^{(1)}}{h}\Delta y_0 + \frac{(x-x_0)^{(2)}}{2!\,h^2}\Delta^2 y_0 + \cdots$$

$$+ \cdots + \frac{(x-x_0)^{(r)}}{r!\,h^r}\Delta^r y_0 + \cdots + \frac{(x-x_0)^{(n)}}{n!\,h^n}\Delta^n y_0. \quad ...(4)$$

$$\frac{(x-x_0)^{(r)}}{h^r} = \frac{(x-x_0)(x-x_0-h)(x-x_0-2h)\cdots(x-x_0-\overline{r-1}\,h)}{h^r}$$

$$= \frac{x-x_0}{h}\cdot\left(\frac{x-x_0}{h}-1\right)\left(\frac{x-x_0}{h}-2\right)\cdots\left(\frac{x-x_0}{h}-\overline{r-1}\right)$$

$$= u(u-1)(u-2)\cdots(u-\overline{-1}) \text{ where } u = \frac{x-x_0}{h}$$

$$= u^{(r)}, \text{ (here } h = 1) \text{ and } x = x_0 + uh$$

using in (4),

$$\mathbf{P_n(x) = P_n(x_0 + uh) = y_0 + \frac{u^{(1)}}{1!}\Delta y_0 + \frac{u^{(2)}}{2!}\Delta^2 y_0 + \cdots + \frac{u^{(r)}}{r!}\Delta^r y_0 +}$$

$$\mathbf{+ \cdots + \frac{u^{(n)}}{n!}\Delta^n y_0.} \quad ...(5)$$

where $u^{(r)} = u(u-1)(u-2)\cdots(u-\overline{r-1})$

(If $x$ is given, $u$ is found out).

Equation (5) is known as Gregory-Newton forward interpolation formula.

**Aliter.** We can also prove the above formula using symbolic operator methods.

$$P_n(x) = P_n(x_0 + uh) = E^u P_n(x_0) = E^u y_0$$

$$= (1+\Delta)^u y_0$$

$$= \left[1 + \binom{u}{1}\Delta + \binom{u}{2}\Delta^2 + \binom{u}{3}\Delta^3 + \cdots + \binom{u}{r}\Delta^r + \cdots + \binom{u}{n}\Delta^n + \cdots\right] y_0$$

$$= y_0 + \frac{u^{(1)}}{1!}\Delta y_0 + \frac{u^{(2)}}{2!}\Delta^2 y_0 + \frac{u^{(3)}}{3!}\Delta^3 y_0 + \cdots + \frac{u^{(r)}}{r!}\Delta^r y_0 + \cdots$$

$$+ \frac{u^{(n)}}{n!}\Delta^n y_0 + \cdots$$

where $u = \dfrac{x - x_0}{h}$.

If $y(x)$ is a polynomial of $n$th degree $\Delta^{n+1} y_0$, ... are zero. Hence

$$\mathbf{P_n(x) = P_n(x_0 + uh) = y_0 + \frac{u^{(1)}}{1!}\Delta y_0 + \frac{u^{(2)}}{2!}\Delta^2 y_0 + \cdots + \frac{u^{(n)}}{n!}\Delta^n y_0.}$$

**Note 1.** The first two terms will give the linear interpolation and the first three terms will give a parabolic interpolation and so on.

**2.** Since this formula involves forward differences of $y_0$, we call it Newton's forward interpolation formula. Since this involves the forward differences of $y_0$, this is used to interpolate the values of $y$ nearer to the beginning value of the table.

**3.** This is applicable only if the interval of differencing $h$ is constant.

## 6·3. Gregory-Newton Backward Interpolation Formula.

(*for equal intervals*)

Newton's forward interpolation formula cannot be used for interpolating a value of $y$ nearer to the end of the table of values. For this purpose, we get another backward interpolation formula.

Suppose $y = f(x)$ takes the values $y_0, y_1, ..., y_n$ corresponding to the values $x_0, x_1, ..., x_n$ of $x$.

Let $x_i - x_{i-1} = h$ for $i = 1, 2, ..., n$. (equal intervals)

$\therefore \quad x_i = x_0 + ih, \quad i = 0, 1, 2, ..., n.$

Now, we want to find a collocation polynomial $P_n(x)$ of degree $n$ in $x$ such that

$$P_n(x_i) = y_i, \quad i = 0, 1, 2, ..., n.$$

Let

$$P_n(x) = a_0 + a_1(x - x_n) + a_2(x - x_n)(x - x_{n-1}) + \cdots$$
$$+ a_r(x - x_n)(x - x_{n-1}) \cdots (x - x_{n-r+1}) + \cdots$$
$$+ a_n(x - x_n)(x - x_{n-1}) \cdots (x - x_1) \qquad ...(1)$$

Since $x_{n-1} = x_n - h, \quad x_{n-2} = x_n - 2h, ..., x_{n-r+1} = x_n - (r-1)h$

$x_1 = x_n - (n-1)h$, we have

$$P_n(x) = a_0 + a_1(x - x_n) + a_2(x - x_n)(x - x_n + h)$$
$$+ a_3(x - x_n)(x - x_n + h)(x - x_n + 2h) + \cdots$$
$$+ a_n(x - x_n)(x - x_n + h) \cdots (x - x_n + \overline{n-1}\,h).$$

$$P_n(x) = a_0 + a_1(x - x_n)^{(1)} + a_2(x - x_n + h)^{(2)} + a_3(x - x_n + 2h)^{(3)}$$
$$+ a_r(x - x_n + \overline{r-1}\,h)^{(r)} + \cdots + a_n(x - x_n + \overline{n-1}\,h)^{(n)}. \quad ...(2)$$

We shall find $a_0, a_1, ..., a_n$ such that $P_n(x_i) = y_i$.

Since $\nabla = E^{-1}\Delta$,

$$\nabla^r (x-a)^{(m)} = E^{-r}\Delta^r (x-a)^{(m)}$$
$$= E^{-r}\left[m(m-1)(m-2)\cdots(m-r+1)\,h^r (x-a)^{(m-r)}\right]$$
$$= m(m-1)(m-2)\cdots(m-r+1)\,h^r (x - rh - a)^{(m-r)} \text{ if } r \le m. \quad ...(3)$$

$x - x_n$ is a factor in all terms of RHS of (2) except in $a_0$.

Putting $x = x_n$ in (2),

$$P_n(x_n) = y_n = a_0$$

operating (2) by $\nabla^r$, using (3),

$$\nabla^r P_n(x) = 0 + 0 + \cdots + 0 + a_r\, r!\, h^r + (r+1).r.(r-1)\cdots 2.h^r a_{r+1}(x - x_n)^{(1)}$$
$$+ \text{ terms involving } (x - x_n) \text{ as a factor.}$$

Setting $x = x_n$ in this,

$\nabla^r P_n(x_n) = \nabla^r y_n = a_r\, r!\, h^r$. since other terms vanish.

$$\therefore \quad a_r = \frac{1}{r!\,h^r}\nabla^r y_n \quad ...(4)$$

where $r = 1, 2, ..., n$.

Putting the values of $a_0, a_1, \ldots a_n$ in (2), we get

$$P_n(x) = y_n + \frac{(x - x_n)^{(1)}}{1!\,h}\nabla y_n + \frac{(x - x_n + h)^{(2)}}{2!\,h^2}\nabla^2 y_n + \cdots$$
$$+ \frac{(x - x_n + \overline{r-1}\,h)^{(r)}}{r!\,h^r}\nabla^r y_n + \cdots + \frac{(x - x_n + \overline{n-1}\,h)^{(n)}}{n!\,h^n}\nabla^n y_n \quad ...(5)$$

Let $\dfrac{x - x_n}{h} = v$ ; hence $x = x_n + vh$

Then $\dfrac{(x - x_n + \overline{r-1}\,h)^{(r)}}{h^r} = \dfrac{(vh + \overline{r-1}\,h)^{(r)}}{h^r} = (v + \overline{r-1})^{(r)}$

Therefore, (5) becomes,

$$P_n(x) = P_n(x_n + vh) = y_n + \frac{v^{(1)}}{1!}\nabla y_n + \frac{(v+1)^{(2)}}{2!}\nabla^2 y_n + \cdots$$
$$+ \frac{(v + r - 1)^{(r)}}{r!}\nabla^r y_n + \cdots + \frac{(v + n - 1)^{(n)}}{n!}\nabla^n y_n.$$

$$\therefore \quad \mathbf{P_n(x) = P_n(x_n + vh) = y_n + \frac{v}{1!} \nabla y_n + \frac{v(v+1)}{2!} \nabla^2 y_n}$$

$$\mathbf{+ \frac{v(v+1)(v+2)}{3!} \nabla^3 y_n + \cdots + \frac{v(v+1)(v+2)\cdots(v+n-1)}{n!} \nabla^n y_n} \quad ...(6)$$

Equation (6) is known as *Gregory-Newton backward difference interpolation formula.*

**Aliter.** We can also derive the above formula by symbolic operator methods.

$$P_n(x) = P_n(x_n + vh) = E^v P_n(x_n)$$

$$= (1-\nabla)^{-v} y_n \qquad \text{since } E = (1-\nabla)^{-1}$$

$$= \left[1 + v\nabla + \frac{v(v+1)}{2!}\nabla^2 + \frac{v(v+1)(v+2)}{3!}\nabla^3 + \cdots\right] y_n$$

$$\mathbf{P_n(x) = P_n(x_n + vh) = y_n + v \nabla y_n + \frac{v(v+1)}{2!} \nabla^2 y_n}$$

$$\mathbf{+ \frac{v(v+1)(v+2)}{3!} \nabla^3 y_n + \cdots} \quad ...(7)$$

**where** $\mathbf{v = \dfrac{x - x_n}{h}}$.

**Note 1.** Since the formula involves the backward difference operator, it is named as *backward interpolation formula.*

**2.** This is used to interpolate the values of $y$ nearer to the end of a set tabular values. This may also be used to extrapolate closer to the right of $y_n$.

## 6·4. Error in polynomial interpolation

If $y = f(x)$ is the exact curve and $y = P_n(x)$ is the interpolating polynomial curve, the error in polynomial interpolation is

$$\text{Error} = f(x) - P_n(x) = \frac{(x-x_0)(x-x_1)\cdots(x-x_n)\, f^{(n+1)}(c)}{(n+1)!}$$

for any $x$ where $x_0 < x < x_n$ and $x_0 < c < x_n$.

## 6·5. Error in Newton's forward interpolation formula

$$\text{Error} = f(x) - P_n(x) = \frac{u(u-1)(u-2)\dots(u-n)}{(n+1)!} h^{n+1} f^{n+1}(c)$$

where $u = \dfrac{x - x_0}{h}$

## 6·6. Error in Newton's backward interpolation formula

$$\text{Error} = y(x) - P_n(x)$$

$$= f(x) - P_n(x) = \frac{v(v+1)(v+2)\cdots(v+n)}{(n+1)!} h^{n+1} y^{n+1}(c)$$

where $v = \frac{x - x_n}{h}$. (The result of the error may be assumed).

**Example 1.** *Find the values of y at x = 21 and x = 28 from the following data.*

| $x$ : | 20 | 23 | 26 | 29 |
|---|---|---|---|---|
| $y$ : | 0·3420 | 0·3907 | 0·4384 | 0·4848 |

**Solution.** Since $x = 21$ is nearer to the beginning of the table, we use Newton's forward formula.

We form the difference table. Also $h$ = constant = 3.

| $x$ | $y$ | $\Delta y$ | $\Delta^2 y$ | $\Delta^3 y$ |
|---|---|---|---|---|
| 20 | 0·3420 | | | |
| | | 0·0487 | | |
| 23 | 0·3907 | | – 0·0010 | |
| | | 0·0477 | | – 0·0003 |
| 26 | 0·4384 | | – 0·0013 | |
| | | 0·0464 | | |
| 29 | 0·4848 | | | |

The topmost diagonal gives the forward differences of $y_0$ while the lowermost diagonal gives the backward differences of $y_n$.

There are only 4 data given. Hence the collocation polynomial will be of degree 3.

By Newton's forward interpolation formula,

$$y(x) \approx P_3(x) = y_0 + u\,\Delta y_0 + \frac{u(u-1)}{2!}\Delta^2 y_0 + \frac{u(u-1)(u-2)}{3!}\Delta^3 y_0$$

where $u = \frac{x - x_0}{h} = \frac{21 - 20}{3} = 0{\cdot}3333.$

$$y(21) \approx P_3(21) = 0{\cdot}3420 + (0{\cdot}3333)(0{\cdot}0487) + \frac{(0{\cdot}3333)(-0{\cdot}6666)}{2}(-0{\cdot}001)$$

$$+ \frac{(0{\cdot}3333)(-0{\cdot}6666)(-1{\cdot}6666)}{6}(-0{\cdot}0003)$$

$\therefore \; y(21) \approx 0{\cdot}3583$

Since $x = 28$ is nearer to end value, we use Newton's backward interpolation formula.

$$y(x) \approx P_3(x) = P_3(x_n + vh)$$

$$= y_n + v\,\nabla y_n + \frac{v(v+1)}{2}\nabla^2 y_n + \frac{v(v+1)(v+2)}{6}\nabla^3 y_n + \cdots$$

$$y(28) \approx P_3(28) = P_3\left[29 + \left(-\frac{1}{3}\right)3\right]$$

where $v = \frac{x - x_n}{h} = \frac{28 - 29}{3} = -1/3$

$$= 0{\cdot}4848 + \left(-\frac{1}{3}\right)(0{\cdot}0464) + \frac{\left(-\frac{1}{3}\right)\left(\frac{2}{3}\right)}{2}(-0{\cdot}0013)$$

$$+ \frac{\left(-\frac{1}{3}\right)\left(\frac{2}{3}\right)\left(\frac{5}{3}\right)}{6}(-0{\cdot}0003) + \cdots$$

$$= 0{\cdot}4848 - 0{\cdot}015465 + 0{\cdot}0001444 + 0{\cdot}0000185$$

$$y(28) \approx 0{\cdot}4695$$

**Example 2.** *The hourly declination of the moon on a day is given below. Find the declination at $3^h 35^m 15^s$ and $5^h$.*

| *Hour* | : | *0* | *1* | *2* | *3* | *4* |
|---|---|---|---|---|---|---|
| *Dec* | : | *8° 29′ 53·7″* | *8° 18′ 19·4″* | *8° 6′ 43·5″* | *7° 55′ 6·1″* | *7° 43′ 27·2″* |

**Solution.** We form below the difference table.

| *Hour (x)* | *Dec (y)* | $\nabla y$ | $\nabla^2 y$ | $\nabla^3 y$ | $\nabla^4 y$ |
|---|---|---|---|---|---|
| 0 | 8° 29′ 53·7″ | | | | |
| | | – 11′ 34·3″ | | | |
| 1 | 8° 18′ 19·4″ | | – 1·6″ | | |
| | | – 11′ 35·9″ | | 0·1″ | |
| 2 | 8° 6′ 43·5″ | | – 1·5″ | | – 0·1″ |
| | | – 11′ 37·4″ | | 0·0″ | |
| 3 | 7° 55′ 6·1″ | | – 1·5″ | | |
| | | – 11′ 38·9″ | | | |
| 4 | 7° 43′ 27·2″ | | | | |

Since $3^h\,35^m\,15^s$ and $5^h$ are near the end of the values, we will use Newton's backward interpolation formula. Since $n = 5$, the polynomial is of degree 4.

$$y(x) \approx P_4(x) = P_4(x_n + vh)$$

$$= y_n + v\,\nabla y_n + \frac{v(v+1)}{2}\nabla^2 y_n + \frac{v(v+1)(v+2)}{6}\nabla^3 y_n + \cdots$$

Here $$v = \frac{x - x_n}{h} = \frac{3^h 35^m 15^s - 4^h}{1^h} = \frac{-0^h 24^m 45^s}{1^h} = \frac{-1485^s}{3600^s} = -0{\cdot}4125$$

Hence $$y(3^h 35^m 15^s) = 7°\,43'\,27{\cdot}2'' + (-0{\cdot}4125)(-11'\,38{\cdot}9'')$$

$$+ \frac{(-0{\cdot}4125)(0{\cdot}5875)}{2}(-1{\cdot}5'') + \cdots$$

$$= 7°\,43'\,27{\cdot}2'' + 4'\,48''{\cdot}29 + 0{\cdot}18'' = \mathbf{7°\,48'\,16''}$$

when $x = 5$ (hours), $v = \frac{x - x_n}{h} = \frac{5-4}{1} = 1.$

Hence $y(x=5) \approx P_4(x=5)$

$$= 7°\,43'\,27{\cdot}2'' + (1)(-11'\,38{\cdot}9'') + \frac{(1)(2)}{2}(-1{\cdot}5'') + \cdots$$

$= 7° 31' 46{\cdot}8''$

**Note.** By calculating declination at time = 5 hours, we are doing *extrapolation.*

**Example 3.** *From the following table of half-yearly premium for policies maturing at different ages, estimate the premium for policies maturing at age 46 and 63.*

| *Age* | $x$ : | *45* | *50* | *55* | *60* | *65* |
|---|---|---|---|---|---|---|
| *Fremium* | $y$ : | *114·84* | *96·16* | *83·32* | *74·48* | *68·48* |

(*MS. Uni.*)

**Solution.** Since five datas are given, the interpolating polynomial will be of degree *four.* To find $y(46)$, we use forward interpolation formula while to get $y(63)$, we use Newton's backward difference interpolation formula.

The values of $x$ are equally spaced. $h = 5$.

| $x$ | $y$ | $\Delta y$ | $\Delta^2 y$ | $\Delta^3 y$ | $\Delta^4 y$ |
|---|---|---|---|---|---|
| 45 | 114·84 | | | | |
| | | −18·68 | | | |
| 50 | 96·16 | | 5·84 | | |
| | | − 12·84 | | − 1·84 | |
| 55 | 83·32 | | 4·00 | | 0·68 |
| | | − 8·84 | | − 1·16 | |
| 60 | 74·48 | | 2·84 | | |
| | | − 6·00 | | | |
| 65 | 68·48 | | | | |

$$u = \frac{x - x_0}{h} = \frac{46 - 45}{5} = \frac{1}{5}$$

$$y\,(46) = y\left[\,45 + \left(\frac{1}{5}\right)5\,\right]$$

$$= y_0 + u\,\Delta\,y_0 + \frac{u\,(u-1)}{2}\,\Delta^2\,y_0 + \frac{u\,(u-1)(u-2)}{6}\,\Delta^3\,y_0 + \cdots$$

$$= 114{\cdot}84 + \frac{1}{5}\,(-\,18{\cdot}68) + \frac{\left(\frac{1}{5}\right)\left(-\frac{4}{5}\right)}{2}\,(5{\cdot}84) + \frac{\left(\frac{1}{5}\right)\left(-\frac{4}{5}\right)\left(-\frac{9}{5}\right)}{6}\,(-\,1{\cdot}84)$$

$$+\frac{\left(\frac{1}{5}\right)\left(-\frac{4}{5}\right)\left(-\frac{9}{5}\right)\left(-\frac{14}{5}\right)}{24}\,(0{\cdot}68)$$

$$= 114{\cdot}84 - 3{\cdot}7360 - 0{\cdot}4672 - 0{\cdot}08832 - 0{\cdot}0228$$

$$= \mathbf{110{\cdot}52568}$$

$$y\,(63) = y\,(x_n + vh)$$

$$y\,(63) = y\left[\,65 + \left(-\frac{2}{5}\right)5\,\right], \quad \text{where } v = \frac{x - x_n}{h} = \frac{63 - 65}{5} = -\frac{2}{5}$$

$$= P_4\left[\,65 + \left(-\frac{2}{5}\right)5\,\right]$$

$$= y_n + v\,\nabla y_n + \frac{v(v+1)}{2}\nabla^2 y_n + \cdots$$

$$= 68{\cdot}48 + \left(-\frac{2}{5}\right)(-6{\cdot}0) + \frac{\left(-\frac{2}{5}\right)\left(\frac{3}{5}\right)}{2}(2{\cdot}84)$$

$$+ \frac{\left(-\frac{2}{5}\right)\left(\frac{3}{5}\right)\left(\frac{8}{5}\right)}{6}(-1{\cdot}16) + \frac{\left(-\frac{2}{5}\right)\left(\frac{3}{5}\right)\left(\frac{8}{5}\right)\left(\frac{13}{5}\right)}{24}(0{\cdot}68)$$

$$= 68{\cdot}48 + 2{\cdot}40 - 0{\cdot}3408 + 0{\cdot}07424 - 0{\cdot}028288$$

$$= 70{\cdot}585152$$

**Example 4.** *From the following table, find the value of tan 45° 15′.*

| $x°$ : | 45 | 46 | 47 | 48 | 49 | 50 |
|---|---|---|---|---|---|---|
| tan $x°$ : | 1·00000 | 1·03553 | 1·07237 | 1·11061 | 1·15037 | 1·19175 |

**Solution.** We use forward interportation formula; also $h = 1$

$$u = \frac{x - x_0}{h} = \frac{45°\,15' - 45°}{1°} = (0{\cdot}25) \text{ (}u\text{ is dimensionless)}$$

| $x$ | $y = \tan x°$ | $\Delta y$ | $\Delta^2 y$ | $\Delta^3 y$ | $\Delta^4 y$ | $\Delta^5 y$ |
|---|---|---|---|---|---|---|
| 45° | 1·00000 | | | | | |
| | | 0·03553 | | | | |
| 46° | 1·03553 | | 0·00131 | | | |
| | | 0·03684 | | 0·00009 | | |
| 47° | 1·07237 | | 0·00140 | | 0·00003 | |
| | | 0·03824 | | 0·00012 | | – 0·00005 |
| 48° | 1·11061 | | 0·00152 | | –0·00002 | |
| | | 0·03976 | | 0·00010 | | |
| 49° | 1·15037 | | 0·00162 | | | |
| | | 0·04138 | | | | |
| 50° | 1·19175 | | | | | |

$$y\,(x = 45°\,15') = P_5\,(45°\,15')$$

$$= P_5\left[45° + \left(\frac{1}{4}\right)1°\right]$$

$$= y_0 + u\,\Delta y_0 + \frac{u(u-1)}{2}\Delta^2 y_0 + \cdots$$

$$= 1{\cdot}0000 + \frac{1}{4}(0{\cdot}03553) + \frac{\left(\frac{1}{4}\right)\left(-\frac{3}{4}\right)}{2}(0{\cdot}00131)$$

$$+ \frac{\frac{1}{4}\left(-\frac{3}{4}\right)\left(-\frac{7}{4}\right)}{6}(0{\cdot}00009) + \frac{\frac{1}{4}\left(-\frac{3}{4}\right)\left(\frac{-7}{4}\right)\left(-\frac{11}{4}\right)}{24}(0{\cdot}00003)$$

$$+\frac{\frac{1}{4}\left(-\frac{3}{4}\right)\left(-\frac{7}{4}\right)\left(-\frac{11}{4}\right)\left(-\frac{15}{4}\right)}{120}(-0.00005)$$

$$= 1.0000 + 0.0088825 - 0.0001228 + 0.0000049 \cdots$$

$$= 1.00876.$$

**Example 5.** *The population of a town is as follows.*

| *Year* | $x$ : | *1941* | *1951* | *1961* | *1971* | *1981* | *1991* |
|---|---|---|---|---|---|---|---|
| *Population in lakhs* | $y$ : | *20* | *24* | *29* | *36* | *46* | *51* |

*Estimate the population increase during the period 1946 to 1976.*

**Solution.** Let us find the popultion at $x$ = 1946 and $x$ = 1976.

Since, six data are given, $P(x)$ is of degree 5.

| $x$ | $y$ | $\Delta y$ | $\Delta^2 y$ | $\Delta^3 y$ | $\Delta^4 y$ | $\Delta^5 y$ |
|---|---|---|---|---|---|---|
| 1941 | 20 | | | | | |
| | | 4 | | | | |
| 1951 | 24 | | 1 | | | |
| | | 5 | | 1 | | |
| 1961 | 29 | | 2 | | 0 | |
| | | 7 | | 1 | | – 9 |
| 1971 | 36 | | 3 | | – 9 | |
| | | 10 | | – 8 | | |
| 1981 | 46 | | – 5 | | | |
| | | 5 | | | | |
| 1991 | 51 | | | | | |

$$u = \frac{x - x_0}{h} = \frac{1946 - 1941}{10} = \frac{1}{2}$$

$y\,(1946) \approx P_5\,(1946) = P_5\,[1941 + \frac{1}{2}(10)]$, (use forward formula)

$$= y_0 + u\Delta y_0 + \frac{u\,(u-1)}{2}\Delta^2 y_0 + \frac{u\,(u-1)(u-2)}{6}\Delta^3 y_0 + \cdots$$

$$= 20 + \frac{1}{2}(4) + \frac{\left(\frac{1}{2}\right)\left(-\frac{1}{2}\right)}{2}(1) + \frac{\left(\frac{1}{2}\right)\left(-\frac{1}{2}\right)\left(\frac{-3}{2}\right)}{6}(1)$$

$$+\frac{\left(\frac{1}{2}\right)\left(-\frac{1}{2}\right)\left(-\frac{3}{2}\right)\left(-\frac{5}{2}\right)}{24}(0) + \frac{\frac{1}{2}\left(-\frac{1}{2}\right)\left(-\frac{3}{2}\right)\left(-\frac{5}{2}\right)\left(-\frac{7}{2}\right)}{120}(-9)$$

$$= 20 + 2 - 0.125 + 0.0625 - 0.24609$$

$$= 21.69$$

$$y\,(1976) \approx P_5\left[\;1991 + \left(-\frac{3}{2}\right)10\;\right] \quad \text{(use backward formula)}$$

$$\because \quad v = \frac{1976 - 1991}{10} = -3/2$$

$$= y_n + v\,\nabla y_n + \frac{v(v+1)}{2}\nabla^2 y_n + \frac{v(v+1)(v+2)}{6}\nabla^3 y_n + \cdots$$

$$= 51 - \frac{3}{2}(5) + \frac{\left(-\frac{3}{2}\right)\left(-\frac{1}{2}\right)}{2}(-5) + \frac{\left(-\frac{3}{2}\right)\left(-\frac{1}{2}\right)\left(\frac{1}{2}\right)}{6}(-8)$$

$$+ \frac{\left(-\frac{3}{2}\right)\left(-\frac{1}{2}\right)\left(\frac{1}{2}\right)\left(\frac{3}{2}\right)}{24}(-9) + \frac{\left(-\frac{3}{2}\right)\left(-\frac{1}{2}\right)\left(\frac{1}{2}\right)\left(\frac{3}{2}\right)\left(\frac{5}{2}\right)}{120}(-9)$$

$$= 51 - 7{\cdot}5 - 1{\cdot}875 - 0{\cdot}5 - 0.2109375 - 0.10546875$$

$$= 40{\cdot}8085938$$

Therefore, increase in population during the period

$$= 40.809 - 21.69 = 19.119 \text{ lakhs}$$

**Example 6.** *From the following data, find θ at x = 43 amd x = 84.*

| $x$ : | 40 | 50 | 60 | 70 | 80 | 90 |
|---|---|---|---|---|---|---|
| $\theta$ : | 184 | 204 | 226 | 250 | 276 | 304 |

*Also express θ in terms of x.*

**Solution.** Since six data are given, $P(x)$ is of degree 5. To find $\theta$ at $x = 43$ use forward interpolation and to find $\theta$ at $x = 84$, use backward interpolation formula.

$$u = \frac{x - x_0}{h} = \frac{43 - 40}{10} = 0{\cdot}3$$

**Table**

| $x$ | $\theta$ | $\Delta\theta$ | $\Delta^2\theta$ | $\Delta^3\theta$ | $\Delta^4\theta$ |
|---|---|---|---|---|---|
| 40 | 184 | | | | |
| | | 20 | | | |
| 50 | 204 | | 2 | | |
| | | 22 | | 0 | |
| 60 | 226 | | 2 | | 0 |
| | | 24 | | 0 | |
| 70 | 250 | | 2 | | 0 |
| | | 26 | | 0 | |
| 80 | 276 | | 2 | | |
| | | 28 | | | |
| 90 | 304 | | | | |

$$\theta(x = 43) = \theta\,[40 + (0{\cdot}3)\,10]$$

$$= \theta_0 + u\,\Delta\theta_0 + \frac{u(u-1)}{2}\Delta^2\theta_0 + \cdots$$

$$= 184 + (0{\cdot}3)\,20 + \frac{(0{\cdot}3)(-0{\cdot}7)}{2}(2)$$

$$= 184 + 6{\cdot}0 - 0{\cdot}21$$

$$= \mathbf{189{\cdot}79}$$

$$\theta\,(x=84)=\theta\,[90+(-0{\cdot}6)\,10] \qquad \because\ v=\frac{84-90}{10}=-0{\cdot}6$$

$$=\theta_n+v\,\nabla\,\theta_n+\frac{v\,(v+1)}{2}\nabla^2\,\theta_n+\cdots$$

$$=304+(-0{\cdot}6)\,28+\frac{(-0{\cdot}6)(0{\cdot}4)}{2}\,(2)=\mathbf{286{\cdot}96}$$

$$\theta=\theta_0+u\,\Delta\,\theta_0+\frac{u\,(u-1)}{2!}\Delta^2\,\theta_0+\cdots$$

$$=184+u\,(20)+\frac{u\,(u-1)}{2}\,(2), \qquad \text{where} \quad u=\frac{x-40}{10}$$

$$=184+\frac{20\,(x-40)}{10}+\frac{(x-40)\,(x-50)}{100}$$

$$=184+2x-80+\frac{1}{100}\,[x^2-90x+2000]$$

$$\theta=0{\cdot}01x^2+1{\cdot}1x+124$$

**Example 7.** *Find a polynomial of degree four which takes the values*

| $x$ : | 2 | 4 | 6 | 8 | 10 |
|---|---|---|---|---|---|
| $y$ : | 0 | 0 | 1 | 0 | 0 |

**Solution.** Let us form the difference table.

| $x$ | $y$ | $\Delta y$ | $\Delta^2 y$ | $\Delta^3 y$ | $\Delta^4 y$ |
|---|---|---|---|---|---|
| 2 | 0 | | | | |
| | | 0 | | | |
| 4 | 0 | | 1 | | |
| | | 1 | | – 3 | |
| 6 | 1 | | – 2 | | 6 |
| | | – 1 | | 3 | |
| 8 | 0 | | 1 | | |
| | | 0 | | | |
| 10 | 0 | | | | |

Let us find the polynomial using Newton's forward interpolation formula

$$u=\frac{x-x_0}{h}=\frac{x-2}{2}$$

$$y\,(x)=y_0+u\,\Delta y_0+\frac{u\,(u-1)}{2}\,\Delta^2 y_0+\frac{u\,(u-1)(u-2)}{3!}\,\Delta^3 y_0+\cdots$$

$$=0+u\times 0+\frac{\left(\frac{x-2}{2}\right)\left(\frac{x-4}{2}\right)}{2}\,(1)+\frac{\left(\frac{x-2}{2}\right)\left(\frac{x-4}{2}\right)\left(\frac{x-6}{2}\right)}{6}\,(-3)$$

$$+\frac{\left(\frac{x-2}{2}\right)\left(\frac{x-4}{2}\right)\left(\frac{x-6}{2}\right)\left(\frac{x-8}{2}\right)}{24}\,(6).$$

$$= \frac{(x-2)(x-4)}{8}\left[1 - \frac{1}{2}(x-6) + \frac{1}{8}(x-6)(x-8)\right]$$

$$= \frac{1}{64}(x-2)(x-4)\,[8 - 4x + 24 + x^2 - 14x + 48]$$

$$= \frac{1}{64}(x-2)(x-4)(x-8)(x-10)$$

$$= \frac{1}{64}[x^4 - 24x^3 + 196x^2 - 624x + 640]$$

**Example 8.** *From the data given below, find the number of students whose weight is between 60 and 70.*

| *Weight in lbs.* | : | *0–40* | *40–60* | *60–80* | *80–100* | *100–120* |
|---|---|---|---|---|---|---|
| *No. of students* | : | *250* | *120* | *100* | *70* | *50* |

**Solution. Difference table.**

| $x$ *Weight* | $y$ *(No. of students)* | $\Delta y$ | $\Delta^2 y$ | $\Delta^3 y$ | $\Delta^4 y$ |
|---|---|---|---|---|---|
| Below 40 | 250 | | | | |
| | | 120 | | | |
| Below 60 | 370 | | – 20 | | |
| | | 100 | | – 10 | |
| Below 80 | 470 | | – 30 | | 20 |
| | | 70 | | 10 | |
| Below 100 | 540 | | – 20 | | |
| | | 50 | | | |
| Below 120 | 590 | | | | |

Let us calculate the number of students whose weight is less than 70.

We will use forward difference formula

$$u = \frac{x - x_0}{h} = \frac{70 - 40}{20} = 1{\cdot}5$$

$$y(70) = y_0 + u\Delta y_0 + \frac{u(u-1)}{2}\Delta^2 y_0 + \cdots$$

$$= 250 + (1{\cdot}5)(120) + \frac{(1{\cdot}5)(0{\cdot}5)}{2}(-20)$$

$$+ \frac{(1{\cdot}5)(0{\cdot}5)(-0{\cdot}5)}{6}(-10) + \frac{(1{\cdot}5)(0{\cdot}5)(-0{\cdot}5)(-1{\cdot}5)}{24}(20)$$

$$= 250 + 180 - 7{\cdot}5 + 0{\cdot}625 + 0{\cdot}46875$$

$$= 423{\cdot}59$$

$$\approx 424$$

Number of students whose weight is between 60 and 70

$$= y(70) - y(60) = 424 - 370 = 54$$

**Example 9.** *Find a polynomial of degree two which takes the values*

| $x$ : | 0 | 1 | 2 | 3 | 4 | 5 | 6 | 7 |
|---|---|---|---|---|---|---|---|---|
| $y$ : | 1 | 2 | 4 | 7 | 11 | 16 | 22 | 29 |

**Solution.** We will use Newton's backward interpolation formula to find the polynomial. The table is

| $x$ | $y$ | $\nabla y$ | $\nabla^2 y$ | $\nabla^3 y$ |
|---|---|---|---|---|
| 0 | 1 | | | |
| | | 1 | | |
| 1 | 2 | | 1 | |
| | | 2 | | 0 |
| 2 | 4 | | 1 | |
| | | 3 | | 0 |
| 3 | 7 | | 1 | |
| | | 4 | | 0 |
| 4 | 11 | | 1 | |
| | | 5 | | 0 |
| 5 | 16 | | 1 | |
| | | 6 | | 0 |
| 6 | 22 | | 1 | |
| | | 7 | | |
| 7 | 29 | | | |

Here $v = \dfrac{x - x_n}{h} = \dfrac{x-7}{1} = x - 7.$

Here $y(x) = y_n + v\,\nabla y_n + \dfrac{v(v+1)}{2}\nabla^2 y_n + \cdots$, where $v = \dfrac{x - x_n}{h} = x - 7$

$$= 29 + (x-7)(7) + \frac{(x-7)(x-6)}{2}(1)$$

$$= 29 + 7x - 49 + \frac{1}{2}(x^2 - 13x + 42)$$

$$= \frac{1}{2}(x^2 + x + 2)$$

**Example 10.** *The following data are taken from the steam table.*

| *Temp. °C* | : | *140* | *150* | *160* | *170* | *180* |
|---|---|---|---|---|---|---|
| *Pressure kgf/cm²* | : | *3·685* | *4·854* | *6·302* | *8·076* | *10·225* |

*Find the pressure at temperature $t = 142°$ and $t = 175°$.*

**Solution.** We form the difference table.

| $t$ | $p$ | $\Delta p$ | $\Delta^2 p$ | $\Delta^3 p$ | $\Delta^4 p$ |
|---|---|---|---|---|---|
| 140 | 3·685 | | | | |
| | | 1·169 | | | |
| 150 | 4·854 | | 0·279 | | |
| | | 1·448 | | 0·047 | |
| 160 | 6·302 | | 0·326 | | 0·002 |
| | | 1·774 | | 0·049 | |
| 170 | 8·076 | | 0·375 | | |
| | | 2·149 | | | |
| 180 | 10·225 | | | | |

$$u = \frac{t - t_0}{h} = \frac{142 - 140}{10} = \frac{1}{5} = 0{\cdot}2$$

$$P_4(142) = P_4\left(140 + \frac{1}{5}(10)\right)$$

$$= p_0 + u\,\Delta p_0 + \frac{u(u-1)}{2}\Delta^2 p_0 + \cdots$$

$$= 3{\cdot}685 + (0{\cdot}2)(1{\cdot}169) + \frac{(0{\cdot}2)(-0{\cdot}8)}{2}(0{\cdot}279)$$

$$+ \frac{(0{\cdot}2)(-0{\cdot}8)(-1{\cdot}8)}{6}(0{\cdot}047) + \frac{(0{\cdot}2)(-0{\cdot}8)(-1{\cdot}8)(-2{\cdot}8)}{24} \times (0{\cdot}002)$$

$$= 3{\cdot}685 + 0{\cdot}2338 - 0{\cdot}02332 + 0{\cdot}002256 - 0{\cdot}0000672$$

$$= 3{\cdot}897668$$

$$\approx \mathbf{3{\cdot}898}$$

$$P_4(t = 175°) = P_4\left[180 + \left(-\frac{1}{2}\right) \times 10\right], \quad \text{where } v = \frac{175 - 180}{10} = -0{\cdot}5$$

$$= p_n + v\,\nabla p_n + \frac{v(v+1)}{2}\nabla^2 p_n + \cdots$$

$$= 10{\cdot}225 + (-0{\cdot}5)(2{\cdot}149) + \frac{(-0{\cdot}5)(0{\cdot}5)}{2}(0{\cdot}375)$$

$$+ \frac{(-0{\cdot}5)(0{\cdot}5)(1{\cdot}5)}{6}(0{\cdot}049) + \frac{(-0{\cdot}5)(0{\cdot}5)(1{\cdot}5)(2{\cdot}5)}{24}(0{\cdot}002)$$

$$= 10{\cdot}225 - 1{\cdot}0745 - 0{\cdot}046875 - 0{\cdot}0030625 - 0{\cdot}000078125$$

$$= 9{\cdot}10048438 \approx \mathbf{9{\cdot}100}$$

## 6·7. Equidistant terms with one or more missing values

When one or more of the values of the function $y = f(x)$ corresponding to the equidistant values of $x$ are missing, we can find the missing values by the use of operators $\Delta$ and $E$.

**Example 11.** *Find the missing value of the table given below. What assumption have you made to find it?*

| *Year* | : | *1917* | *1918* | *1919* | *1920* | *1921* | |
|---|---|---|---|---|---|---|---|
| *Export (in tons)* | : | *443* | *384* | — | *397* | *467* | *(MS. Uni.)* |

**Solution.** Since 4 values are given we make an assumption that we get a *third degree polynomial*. Hence 4th differences of $P_3(x)$ are zeros.

We can, without any loss, assume

$$u_0 = 443, u_1 = 384, u_2 = ?, \quad u_3 = 397, u_4 = 467.$$

$$\Delta^4 u_0 = 0$$

$$(E - 1)^4 u_0 = 0$$

*i.e.,*
$$(E^4 - 4E^3 + 6E^2 - 4E + 1)\,u_0 = 0$$

$$u_4 - 4u_3 + 6u_2 - 4u_1 + u_0 = 0$$

$$467 - 4(397) + 6u_2 - 4(384) + 443 = 0$$

$$\therefore \quad 6u_2 = 2214 \; ; \quad \therefore \quad u_2 = \mathbf{369}.$$

**Example 12.** *Find the missing value of the following table.*

| $x$ : | 0 | 1 | 2 | 3 | 4 |
|---|---|---|---|---|---|
| $y$ : | 1 | 2 | 4 | – | 16 |

*Explain why $y\,(x = 3)$ is not $2^3 = 8$ in your answer.* (MKU)

**Solution.** Since only 4 values are given, we assume the collocation polynomial to be of *third degree.* Hence, fourth differences of $P_3(x)$ are zero.

Taking $y_x = P_3(x)$, $y_0 = 1, y_1 = 2, y_2 = 4, y_4 = 16$

Since $\Delta^4 y_0 = 0$, we have,

$$(E-1)^4\, y_0 = 0$$

*i.e.,* $$(E^4 - 4E^3 + 6E^2 - 4E + 1)\, y_0 = 0$$

*i.e.,* $$y_4 - 4y_3 + 6y_2 - 4y_1 + y_0 = 0$$

$$16 - 4y_3 + 6(4) - 4(2) + 1 = 0$$

$$4y_3 = 33 \qquad \therefore \quad \mathbf{y_3 = 8{\cdot}25}$$

By looking at the table, we guess, $y = 2^x$ is the function from which the given table is created. So, we should have got $y\,(3) = 2^3 = 8$. But our answer is 8·25, because in getting this answer, we have *assumed a third degree polynomial* which is only an approximating polynomial and not the actual curve $y = 2^x$. Hence, the difference in the answer is got.

**Example 13.** *From the table given below, find Sin 52° by using Newton's forward interpolation formula. Also estimate the error.*

| $x$ : | 45° | 50° | 55° | 60° |
|---|---|---|---|---|
| $y = \sin x$ : | 0·7071 | 0·7660 | 0·8192 | 0·8660 |

**Solution. Difference table.**

| $x$ | $y = \sin x$ | $\Delta y$ | $\Delta^2 y$ | $\Delta^3 y$ |
|---|---|---|---|---|
| 45° | 0·7071 | | | |
| | | 0·0589 | | |
| 50° | 0·7660 | | – 0·0057 | |
| | | 0·0532 | | – 0·0007 |
| 55° | 0·8192 | | – 0·0064 | |
| | | 0·0468 | | |
| 60° | 0·8660 | | | |

$$y\,(x) = y_0 + u\Delta\, y_0 + \frac{u\,(u-1)}{2}\,\Delta^2\, y_0 + \frac{u\,(u-1)(u-2)}{6}\,\Delta^3\, y_0 + \cdots,$$

where $$u = \frac{52-45}{5} = 1{\cdot}4.$$

$$y\,(x = 52) = 0{\cdot}7071 + (1{\cdot}4)(0{\cdot}0589) + \frac{(1{\cdot}4)(0{\cdot}4)}{2}\,(-\,0{\cdot}0057)$$

$$+ \frac{(1{\cdot}4)(0{\cdot}4)(-\,0{\cdot}6)}{6}\,(-\,0{\cdot}0007)$$

$$= 0{\cdot}7071 + 0{\cdot}08246 - 0{\cdot}001596 + 0{\cdot}0000392$$

$$\text{Sin } 52° = \mathbf{0{\cdot}7880032}$$

$$\text{Error} = \frac{u(u-1)(u-2)\cdots(u-n)}{(n+1)!}\Delta^{n+1}y(c) \quad \text{(from Article 6·5)}$$

$$= \frac{(1{\cdot}4)(0{\cdot}4)(1{\cdot}4-2)}{3!}\Delta^3 y(c), \text{ if } n = 2 \text{ is taken}$$

$$= \frac{(1{\cdot}4)(0{\cdot}4)(-0{\cdot}6)}{6}(-0{\cdot}0007)$$

$$= 0{\cdot}00003920$$

## EXERCISE 6.1

**1.** Find the value of $e^{1{\cdot}85}$ given $e^{1{\cdot}7} = 5{\cdot}4739, e^{1{\cdot}8} = 6{\cdot}0496, e^{1{\cdot}9} = 6{\cdot}6859,$ $e^{2{\cdot}0} = 7{\cdot}3891, e^{2{\cdot}1} = 8{\cdot}1662, e^{2{\cdot}2} = 9{\cdot}0250, e^{2{\cdot}3} = 9{\cdot}9742.$

**2.** Find $\log_{10}\pi$ given

$\log 3{\cdot}141 = 0{\cdot}4970679364$, $\log 3{\cdot}142 = 0{\cdot}4972061807$,
$\log 3{\cdot}143 = 0{\cdot}4973443810$, $\log 3{\cdot}144 = 0{\cdot}4974825374$,
$\log 3{\cdot}145 = 0{\cdot}4976206498$, where $\pi = 3{\cdot}14159$ (*BR. 1993*)

**3.** For the above problem find $\log_{10} 3{\cdot}140$.

**4.** Find the value of $y$ at $x = 1{\cdot}05$ from the table given below:

| $x$ | 1·0 | 1·1 | 1·2 | 1·3 | 1·4 | 1·5 |
|---|---|---|---|---|---|---|
| $y$ | 0·841 | 0·891 | 0·932 | 0·964 | 0·985 | 1·015 |

**5.** Find the value of $f(1{\cdot}02)$ given the following data :

| $x$ | 1·0 | 1·1 | 1·2 | 1·3 | 1·4 |
|---|---|---|---|---|---|
| $f(x)$ | 1·841 | 1·891 | 0·932 | 0·964 | 0·985 |

**6.** Find $y$ at $x = 105$ from the following data :

| $x$ | 80 | 85 | 90 | 95 | 100 |
|---|---|---|---|---|---|
| $y$ | 5026 | 5674 | 6362 | 7088 | 7854 |

**7.** Find the annual premium at the age of 30 given

| Age | 21 | 25 | 29 | 33 |
|---|---|---|---|---|
| Premium | 14·27 | 15·81 | 17·72 | 19·96 |

**8.** Find $y$ (42) from the data given below:

| $x$ | 20 | 25 | 30 | 35 | 40 | 45 |
|---|---|---|---|---|---|---|
| $y$ | 354 | 332 | 291 | 260 | 231 | 204 |

(*MKU*)

**9.** Find the polynomial of least degree passing through the points $(0, -1), (1, 1),$ $(2, 1)$ and $(3, -2)$.

**10.** Construct a polynomial for the data given below. Find also $y\,(x = 5)$.

| $x$ | 4 | 6 | 8 | 10 |
|---|---|---|---|---|
| $y$ | 1 | 3 | 8 | 16 |

**11.** Given the following data, express $y$ as a function of $x$.

| $x$ | 0 | 1 | 2 | 3 | 4 |
|---|---|---|---|---|---|
| $y$ | 3 | 6 | 11 | 18 | 27 |

**12.** Find $y(0{\cdot}47)$ from the data given below :

| $x$ | : | 0 | 0·1 | 0·2 | 0·3 | 0·4 | 0·5 |
|---|---|---|---|---|---|---|---|
| $y$ | : | 1·0000 | 1·1103 | 1·2428 | 1·3997 | 1·5836 | 1·7974 |

**13.** From the table given below find $f(3\ 4)$.

| $x$ | : | 3 | 4 | 5 | 6 |
|---|---|---|---|---|---|
| $f(x)$ | : | 31 | 69 | 131 | 223 |

**14.** Find $f(2{\cdot}5)$ given.

| $x$ | : | 1 | 2 | 3 | 4 | 5 | 6 |
|---|---|---|---|---|---|---|---|
| $y$ | : | 0 | 1 | 8 | 27 | 64 | 125 |

**15.** The following table gives the marks got by 100 students in Numerical methods in a examination.

| *Marks got* | *No. of students* |
|---|---|
| 30–40 | 25 |
| 40–50 | 35 |
| 50–60 | 22 |
| 60–70 | 11 |
| 70–80 | 7 |

How many students got more than 55 marks ?

(**Hint.** Form a table with $x$ and $y$ where $x$ denotes the marks and $y$ denotes the number of students who got less than $x$).

**16.** Find the number of students from the following who scored marks not more than 45.

| Marks range | : | 30–40 | 40–50 | 50–60 | 60–70 | 70–80 |
|---|---|---|---|---|---|---|
| No. of students | : | 35 | 48 | 70 | 40 | 22 |

**17.** Find $f(0{\cdot}2)$ if $f(0) = 176$, $f(1) = 185$, $f(2) = 194$, $f(3) = 203$, $f(4) = 212$, $f(5) = 220$, $f(6) = 229$.

**18.** From the table below, find the number of students who secured marks between 40 and 45

| Marks | : | 30–40 | 40–50 | 50–60 | 60–70 | 70–80 |
|---|---|---|---|---|---|---|
| No. of students | : | 31 | 42 | 51 | 35 | 31 |

**19.** Find $f(0{\cdot}5)$ if $f(-1) = 202$, $f(0) = 175$, $f(1) = 82$ and $f(2) = 55$.

**20.** For the following data, find the forward and backward difference polynomials. Interpolate at $x = 0{\cdot}25$ and $x = 0{\cdot}35$.

| $x$ | : | 0·1 | 0·2 | 0·3 | 0·4 | 0·5 |
|---|---|---|---|---|---|---|
| $f(x)$ | : | 1·40 | 1·56 | 1·76 | 2·00 | 2·28 |

**21.** The following temperature readings were taken on a day.

| Time | : | 2 a.m. | 6 a.m. | 10 a.m. | 2 p.m. |
|---|---|---|---|---|---|
| Temp. | : | 40·2° | 42·4° | 51·0° | 72·4° |

Find the temperature at 3 a.m. and 4 a.m.

**22.** From the following table find tan 17°.

| θ° | : | 0 | 4 | 8 | 12 | 16 | 20 | 24 |
|---|---|---|---|---|---|---|---|---|
| tan θ° | : | 0 | 0·0699 | 0·1405 | 0·2126 | 0·2167 | 0·3640 | 0·4402 |

**23.** Using Newton's backward formula, find the polynomial of degree 3 passing through (3, 6), (4, 24), (5, 60) and (6, 120).

**24.** Find $y(32)$ if $y(10) = 35{\cdot}3$, $y(15) = 32{\cdot}4$, $y(20) = 29{\cdot}2$, $y(25) = 26{\cdot}1$, $y(30) = 23{\cdot}2$ and $y(35) = 20{\cdot}5$.

**25.** The population of a town in the census is given below. Estimate the population in the year 1895 and 1925.

| Year $x$ | 1891 | 1901 | 1911 | 1921 | 1931 |
|---|---|---|---|---|---|
| Population (in 1000's) | 46 | 66 | 81 | 93 | 101 |

**26.** From the following table find tan 0·12 and tan 0·26.

| $x$ : | 0·10 | 0·15 | 0·20 | 0·25 | 0·30 |
|---|---|---|---|---|---|
| *tan x* : | 0·1003 | 0·1511 | 0·2027 | 0·2553 | 0·3093 |

**27.** The following table gives the values of the probability integral $f(x) = \frac{1}{\sqrt{2\pi}} \int_0^x e^{-x^2} dx$ for certain equidistant values of $x$. Find $\frac{1}{\sqrt{2\pi}} \int_0^{0.543} e^{-x^2} dx$ using the data given below:

| $x$ : | 0·51 | 0·52 | 0·53 | 0·54 | 0·55 |
|---|---|---|---|---|---|
| $f(x)$ : | 0·5292 | 0·5379 | 0·5465 | 0·5549 | 0·5633 |

**28.** From the following table estimate sin 28° 24′. Also find the error.

| θ : | 25° | 26° | 27° | 28° | 29° | 30° |
|---|---|---|---|---|---|---|
| sin θ : | 0·42262 | 0·43837 | 0·45399 | 0·46947 | 0·48481 | 0·50000 |

**29.** Find the value of $f(x)$ at $x = 9$ given the table :

| $x$ : | 2 | 5 | 8 | 11 |
|---|---|---|---|---|
| $f(x)$ : | 94·8 | 87·9 | 81·3 | 75·1 |

**30.** Estimate $e^{-1.9}$ from the given data.

| $x$ : | 1·00 | 1·25 | 1·50 | 1·75 | 2·00 |
|---|---|---|---|---|---|
| $e^{-x}$ : | 0·3679 | 0·2865 | 0·2231 | 0·1738 | 0·1353 |

**31.** Estimate sin 38° from the data given below :

| $x$ : | 0 | 10 | 20 | 30 | 40 |
|---|---|---|---|---|---|
| sin $x$ : | 0 | 0·17365 | 0·34202 | 0·50000 | 0·64279 |

**32.** Calculate $\sqrt{5.5}$ given $\sqrt{5} = 2{\cdot}236$, $\sqrt{6} = 2{\cdot}449$, $\sqrt{7} = 2{\cdot}646$ and $\sqrt{8} = 2{\cdot}828$.

**33.** Find $y(8)$ given.

| $x$ : | 0 | 5 | 10 | 15 | 20 | 25 |
|---|---|---|---|---|---|---|
| $y$ : | 7 | 11 | 14 | 18 | 24 | 32 |

(*MS. 1991. Ap.*)

**34.** $u_x$ is a function of $x$ for which fifth differences are constant and $u_1 + u_7 = -784$, $u_2 + u_6 = 686$, $u_3 + u_5 = 1088$. Find $u_4$.

**35.** Find $y(1{\cdot}02)$ given.

| $x$ : | 1·00 | 1·05 | 1·10 | 1·15 | 1·20 |
|---|---|---|---|---|---|
| $y$ : | 0·3413 | 0·3531 | 0·3643 | 0·3749 | 0·3849 |

## ANSWERS

## EXERCISE 6.1 Page 227

**1.** 6·3598 **2.** 0·4971498727 **3.** 0·496929648 **4.** 0·8678

**6.** 8666 **7.** 18.25 8.218.66304 **9.** $-\frac{1}{6}(x^3+3x^2-16x+6)$

**10.** $y=\frac{3}{8}x^2-\frac{11}{4}x+6$ ; $y(5)=13/8$ **11.** $x^2+2x+3$ **12.** 1·7299

**13.** 43·704 **14.** 3·4 **15.** 27 **16.** 51 **17.** 177·8

**18.** 17 **19.** 128·5 **20.** both $2x^2+x+1{\cdot}28$, 1·655, 1·875

**21.** 40·5°, 40·9° **22.** 0·3057 **23.** $y=x^3-3x^2+2x$

**24.** 22·0948 **25.** 54850, 96840 **26.** 0·1205, 0·2662 **27.** 0·55743

**28.** 0·47562; error – 0·01714 **29.** 79·2 **30.** 0·1496

**31.** 0·61566 **32.** 2·344 **33.** 12·7696 **34.** 571 **35.** 0·34614

# 7

# Central Difference Interpolation Formulae

(For Equal Intervals)

## 7·1. Central differences and central difference table

In the chapter on finite differences, we have seen the central difference operator $\delta = E^{1/2} - E^{-1/2}$.

Also, $\delta = \Delta E^{-1/2}$.

Suppose that $y = f(x)$ be the functional relation connecting $x$ and $y$. Let us take the interval of differencing as $h$ (= constant).

Let $x = a$ be the central point and let us consider the values of $x$ on either side of '$a$'.

Let $f(a) = y_0$, $f(a-h) = y_{-1}$, $f(a+h) = y_1$

$$f(a-2h) = y_{-2}, \quad f(a+2h) = y_2$$

$$f(a-3h) = y_{-3}, \quad f(a+3h) = y_3 \text{ etc.}$$

We form the difference table :

**Table 1**

| $x$ | $y$ | $\Delta y$ | $\Delta^2 y$ | $\Delta^3 y$ | $\Delta^4 y$ | $\Delta^5 y$ |
|---|---|---|---|---|---|---|
| $a-3h$ | $y_{-3}$ | | | | | |
| | | $\Delta y_{-3}$ | | | | |
| $a-2h$ | $y_{-2}$ | | $\Delta^2 y_{-3}$ | | | |
| | | $\Delta y_{-2}$ | | $\Delta^3 y_{-3}$ | | |
| $a-h$ | $y_{-1}$ | | $\Delta^2 y_{-2}$ | | $\Delta^4 y_{-3}$ | |
| | | $\Delta y_{-1}$ | | $\Delta^3 y_{-2}$ | | $\Delta^5 y_{-3}$ |
| $a$ | $y_0$ | | $\Delta^2 y_{-1}$ | | $\Delta^4 y_{-2}$ | |
| | | $\Delta y_0$ | | $\Delta^3 y_{-1}$ | | $\Delta^5 y_{-2}$ |
| $a+h$ | $y_1$ | | $\Delta^2 y_0$ | | $\Delta^4 y_{-1}$ | |
| | | $\Delta y_1$ | | $\Delta^3 y_0$ | | |
| $a+2h$ | $y_2$ | | $\Delta^2 y_1$ | | | |
| | | $\Delta y_2$ | | | | |
| $a+3h$ | $y_3$ | | | | | |

The above forward difference table can also be written in terms of backward difference operator and also in terms of central difference operator. We will use $\delta$ operator.

**Table 2**

| $x$ | $y$ | $\delta y$ | $\delta^2 y$ | $\delta^3 y$ | $\delta^4 y$ | $\delta^5 y$ |
|---|---|---|---|---|---|---|
| $a-3h$ | $y_{-3}$ | | | | | |
| | | $\delta y_{-5/2}$ | | | | |
| $a-2h$ | $y_{-2}$ | | $\delta^2 y_{-2}$ | | | |
| | | $\delta y_{-3/2}$ | | $\delta^3 y_{-3/2}$ | | |
| $a-h$ | $y_{-1}$ | | $\delta^2 y_{-1}$ | | $\delta^4 y_{-1}$ | |
| | | $\delta y_{-1/2}$ | | $\delta^3 y_{-1/2}$ | | $\delta^5 y_{-1/2}$ |
| $a$ ........ | $y_0$ ........ | ........ | $\delta^2 y_0$ | ........ | $\delta^4 y_0$ | ........ |
| | | $\delta y_{1/2}$ | | $\delta^3 y_{1/2}$ | | $\delta^5 y_{1/2}$ |
| $a+h$ | $y_1$ | | $\delta^2 y_1$ | | $\delta^4 y_1$ | |
| | | $\delta y_{3/2}$ | | $\delta^3 y_{3/2}$ | | |
| $a+2h$ | $y_2$ | | $\delta^2 y_2$ | | | |
| | | $\delta y_{5/2}$ | | | | |
| $a+3h$ | $y_3$ | | | | | |

The values of the entries of $y$ are same in both tables. Hence, the various differences given in both tables are same in values (in the corresponding positions) and only the notations are different. For example,

$$\delta^3 y_{-3/2} = (\Delta E^{-1/2})^3 y_{-3/2} = \Delta^3 E^{-3/2} y_{-3/2} = \Delta^3 y_{-3}$$

Similarly, $\delta^2 y_0 = \Delta^2 y_{-1}$, $\delta^4 y_0 = \Delta^4 y_{-2}$ etc.

The above two tables are called *central difference tables*, because we consider the functional values of $y$ on either side of the mid-value $x = a$. The table is also symmetrical about the mid-line.

We can combine Table 1 and Table 2 and write a single table for comparison.

| $x$ | $y$ | *First difference* | *Second difference* | *Third difference* | *Fourth difference* | *Fifth difference* |
|---|---|---|---|---|---|---|
| $a-3h$ | $y_{-3}$ | | | | | |
| | | $\Delta y_{-3} = \delta y_{-5/2}$ | | | | |
| $a-2h$ | $y_{-2}$ | | $\Delta^2 y_{-3} = \delta^2 y_{-2}$ | | | |
| | | $\Delta y_{-2} = \delta y_{-3/2}$ | | $\Delta^3 y_{-3} = \delta^3 y_{-3/2}$ | | |
| $a-h$ | $y_{-1}$ | | $\Delta^2 y_{-2} = \delta^2 y_{-1}$ | | $\Delta^4 y_{-3} = \delta^4 y_{-1}$ | |
| | | $\Delta y_{-1} = \delta y_{-1/2}$ | | $\Delta^3 y_{-2} = \delta^3 y_{-1/2}$ | | $\Delta^5 y_{-3} = \delta^5 y_{-1/2}$ |
| $a$ | $y_0$ | ........ | $\Delta^2 y_{-1} = \delta^2 y_0$ | ........ | $\Delta^4 y_{-2} = \delta^4 y_0$ | |
| | | $\Delta y_0 = \delta y_{1/2}$ | | $\Delta^3 y_{-1} = \delta^3 y_{1/2}$ | | $\Delta^5 y_{-2} = \delta^5 y_{1/2}$ |
| $a+h$ | $y_1$ | | $\Delta^2 y_0 = \delta^2 y_1$ | | $\Delta^4 y_{-1} = \delta^4 y_1$ | |
| | | $\Delta y_1 = \delta y_{3/2}$ | | $\Delta^3 y_0 = \delta^3 y_{3/2}$ | | |
| $a+2h$ | $y_2$ | | $\Delta^2 y_1 = \delta^2 y_2$ | | | |
| | | $\Delta y_2 = \delta y_{5/2}$ | | | | |
| $a+3h$ | $y_3$ | | | | | |

## 7·2. Central difference Interpolation formula

In the previous chapter, we had two Newton's interpolation formula which are used only for interpolation near the beginning and the end of the table. They are not applicable to interpolate near the central value (middle value of the table). To get more accurate results near the middle value of the table, we will obtain a more suitable formula which utilises differences close to the middle value of the table. Such formulae are named as *central difference interpolation formulae.*

## 7·3. Gauss's forward interpolation formula

By the Newtons' Gregory forward interpolation formula, we have

$$y(x) = y(x_0 + uh) = y_0 + u\,\Delta y_0 + \frac{u(u-1)}{2!}\Delta^2 y_0 + \frac{u(u-1)(u-2)}{3!}\Delta^3 y_0 + \cdots \qquad \text{...(1)}$$

where $u = \dfrac{x - x_0}{h}$.

Now,

$$\Delta^2 y_0 = \Delta^2 E y_{-1} = \Delta^2 (1+\Delta)\, y_{-1} = \Delta^2 y_{-1} + \Delta^3 y_{-1} \qquad \text{...}(i)$$

$$\Delta^3 y_0 = \Delta^3 E y_{-1} = \Delta^3 (1+\Delta)\, y_{-1} = \Delta^3 y_{-1} + \Delta^4 y_{-1} \qquad \text{...}(ii)$$

$$\Delta^4 y_0 = \Delta^4 y_{-1} + \Delta^5 y_{-1} \qquad \text{...}(iii)$$

Similarly, $\Delta^4 y_{-1} = \Delta^4 y_{-2} + \Delta^5 y_{-2}$ and so on. ...(*iv*)

Substituting the values of $\Delta^2 y_0, \Delta^3 y_0, \ldots$ in (1), we have

$$y(x) = y(x_0 + uh) = y_0 + u\,\Delta y_0 + \frac{u(u-1)}{2!}\left(\Delta^2 y_{-1} + \Delta^3 y_{-1}\right)$$

$$+ \frac{u(u-1)(u-2)}{3!}\left(\Delta^3 y_{-1} + \Delta^4 y_{-1}\right) + \frac{u(u-1)(u-2)(u-3)}{4!}\left(\Delta^4 y_{-1} + \Delta^5 y_{-1}\right) + \cdots$$

$$= y_0 + u\Delta y_0 + \frac{u(u-1)}{2!}\Delta^2 y_{-1} + \left[\binom{u}{2} + \binom{u}{3}\right]\Delta^3 y_{-1} + \left[\binom{u}{3} + \binom{u}{4}\right]\Delta^4 y_{-1} + \cdots$$

$$= y_0 + \binom{u}{1}\Delta y_0 + \binom{u}{2}\Delta^2 y_{-1} + \binom{u+1}{3}\Delta^3 y_{-1} + \binom{u+1}{4}\Delta^4 y_{-1} + \binom{u+1}{5}\Delta^5 y_{-1} + \cdots$$

$$= y_0 + \binom{u}{1}\Delta y_0 + \binom{u}{2}\Delta^2 y_{-1} + \binom{u+1}{3}\Delta^3 y_{-1} + \binom{u+1}{4}\left[\Delta^4 y_{-2} + \Delta^5 y_{-2}\right] + \binom{u+1}{5}\left[\Delta^5 y_{-2} + \Delta^6 y_{-2}\right] + \cdots$$

$$= y_0 + \binom{u}{1}\Delta y_0 + \binom{u}{2}\Delta^2 y_{-1} + \binom{u+1}{3}\Delta^3 y_{-1} + \binom{u+1}{4}\Delta^4 y_{-2} + \left[\binom{u+1}{4} + \binom{u+1}{5}\right]\Delta^5 y_{-2} + \cdots$$

$$\mathbf{y(x_0 + uh) = y_0 + \binom{u}{1}\Delta y_0 + \binom{u}{2}\Delta^2 y_{-1} + \binom{u+1}{3}\Delta^3 y_{-1} + \binom{u+1}{4}\Delta^4 y_{-2} + \binom{u+2}{5}\Delta^5 y_{-2} + \cdots} \qquad \text{...(2)}$$

where $\binom{u}{r} = \dfrac{u(u-1)(u-2)(u-3)\cdots(u-r+1)}{r!}$

**Note 1.** This formula is known as *Gauss's forward interpolation formula.*

**2.** This formula involves *odd* differences below the central line $(x = a)$ and *even* differences on the line.

**3.** Taking the central line and the next line from the Table 1, we have the differences occurring in the formula.

Central line $y_0$ ............... $\Delta^2 y_{-1}$ ............... $\Delta^4 y_{-2}$ ............ $\Delta^6 y_{-3}$

Next line ............... $\Delta y_0$ ............... $\Delta^3 y_{-1}$ ............. $\Delta^5 y_{-2}$

**4.** The formula can be written easily with the help of the following table :

| *Coefficients* | 1 | $\binom{u}{1}$ | $\binom{u}{2}$ | $\binom{u+1}{3}$ | $\binom{u+1}{4}$ | $\binom{u+2}{5}$ ... |
|---|---|---|---|---|---|---|
| *Differences* | $y_0$ | $\Delta y_0$ | $\Delta^2 y_{-1}$ | $\Delta^3 y_{-1}$ | $\Delta^4 y_{-2}$ | $\Delta^5 y_{-2}$.... |

**5.** The formula is useful when $u$ lies between 0 and 1.

## 7·4. Gauss's backward interpolation formula

Starting with Newton-Gregory forward interpolation formula at $x = x_0$, we have

$$y(x) = y(x_0 + uh) = y_0 + u\,\Delta y_0 + \frac{u(u-1)}{2!}\Delta^2 y_0 + \frac{u(u-1)(u-2)}{3!}\Delta^3 y_0 + \cdots \quad ...(1)$$

where $u = \dfrac{x - x_0}{h}$.

Since $\Delta y_0 = \Delta E\, y_{-1} = \Delta(1 + \Delta)\, y_{-1} = \Delta y_{-1} + \Delta^2 y_{-1}$

Similarly $\Delta^2 y_0 = \Delta^2 y_{-1} + \Delta^3 y_{-1}$

$$\Delta^3 y_0 = \Delta^3 y_{-1} + \Delta^4 y_{-1}$$

$$\Delta^3 y_{-1} = \Delta^3 y_{-2} + \Delta^4 y_{-2} \text{ etc.}$$

Substituting the values of $\Delta y_0, \Delta^2 y_0, \Delta^3 y_0 \ldots$ in (1), we get

$$y(x) = y(x_0 + uh) = y_0 + u\left(\Delta y_{-1} + \Delta^2 y_{-1}\right) + \frac{u(u-1)}{2!}\left[\Delta^2 y_{-1} + \Delta^3 y_{-1}\right] + \frac{u(u-1)(u-2)}{3!}\left[\Delta^3 y_{-1} + \Delta^4 y_{-1}\right] + \frac{u(u-1)(u-2)(u-3)}{4!}\left(\Delta^4 y_{-1} + \Delta^5 y_{-1}\right) + \cdots$$

$$= y_0 + u\Delta y_{-1} + \left[\binom{u}{1} + \binom{u}{2}\right]\Delta^2 y_{-1} + \left[\binom{u}{2} + \binom{u}{3}\right]\Delta^3 y_{-1}$$

$$+ \left[\binom{u}{3} + \binom{u}{4}\right]\Delta^4 y_{-1} + \cdots$$

$$= y_0 + \binom{u}{1}\Delta y_{-1} + \binom{u+1}{2}\Delta^2 y_{-1} + \binom{u+1}{3}\Delta^3 y_{-1} + \binom{u+1}{4}\Delta^4 y_{-1} + \cdots$$

$$= y_0 + \binom{u}{1}\Delta y_{-1} + \binom{u+1}{2}\Delta^2 y_{-1} + \binom{u+1}{3}\left[\Delta^3 y_{-2} + \Delta^4 y_{-2}\right]$$

$$+ \binom{u+1}{4}\left[\Delta^4 y_{-2} + \Delta^5 y_{-2}\right] + \cdots$$

$$= y_0 + \binom{u}{1}\Delta y_{-1} + \binom{u+1}{2}\Delta^2 y_{-1} + \binom{u+1}{3}\Delta^3 y_{-2} + \binom{u+2}{4}\Delta^4 y_{-2} + \cdots$$

$$\mathbf{y\,(x) = y\,(x_0 + uh) = y_0 + \binom{u}{1}\Delta y_{-1} + \binom{u+1}{2}\Delta^2 y_{-1} + \binom{u+1}{3}\Delta^3 y_{-2}}$$

$$\mathbf{+ \binom{u+2}{4}\Delta^4 y_{-2} + \cdots} \qquad \ldots(2)$$

**Note 1.** The above formula (2) is known as Gauss's backward formula of interpolation.

**2.** This formula involves *odd* differences above the central line and *even* differences on the central line.

**3.** Taking the central line and the previous line of the Table 1, we have the differences occurring in the formula.

Previous line: ............... $\Delta y_{-1}$ ............... $\Delta^3 y_{-2}$ ........ $\Delta^5 y_{-3}$

Central line: ......... $y_0$ .............. $\Delta^2 y_{-1}$ ........... $\Delta^4 y_{-2}$ .......... $\Delta^6 y_{-3}$

**4.** The formula can be easily written with the help of the following table :

| *Coefficient* | : | 1 | $\binom{u}{1}$ | $\binom{u+1}{2}$ | $\binom{u+1}{3}$ | $\binom{u+2}{4}$ ... |
|---|---|---|---|---|---|---|
| *Differences* | : | $y_0$ | $\Delta y_{-1}$ | $\Delta^2 y_{-1}$ | $\Delta^3 y_{-2}$ | $\Delta^4 y_{-2}$ ... |

**5.** This backward formula is useful when $u$ lies between $-1$ and 0.

**Example 1.** *Apply Gauss's forward central difference formula and estimate f (32) from the following table* :

| $x$ | : | 25 | 30 | 35 | 40 |
|---|---|---|---|---|---|
| $y = f(x)$ | : | 0·2707 | 0·3027 | 0·3386 | 0·3794 |

**Solution.** Let us take 30 as the origin; here $h = 5$

$$\therefore \quad u = \frac{x - x_0}{h} = \frac{32 - 30}{5} = 0{\cdot}4$$

We form below the central difference table.

| $x$ | $u$ | $y$ | $\Delta y$ | $\Delta^2 y$ | $\Delta^3 y$ |
|---|---|---|---|---|---|
| 25 | – 1 | 0·2707 | | | |
| | | | 0·0320 | | |
| 30 | 0 | 0·3027 | | 0·0039 | |
| | | | 0·0359 | | 0·0010 |
| 35 | 1 | 0·3386 | | 0·0049 | |
| | | | 0·0408 | | |
| 40 | 2 | 0·3794 | | | |

Since we apply forward formula of Gauss, we enclose differences occurring in the terms by rectangle.

By Gauss's forward formula, we have,

$$y(x) = y(x_0 + uh) = y_0 + \binom{u}{1}\Delta y_0 + \binom{u}{2}\Delta^2 y_{-1} + \binom{u+1}{3}\Delta^3 y_{-1} + \cdots$$

$$y(x = 32) = y(u = 0{\cdot}4) = 0{\cdot}3027 + \binom{0{\cdot}4}{1}(0{\cdot}0359) + \binom{0{\cdot}4}{2}(0{\cdot}0039) + \binom{1{\cdot}4}{3}(0{\cdot}0010)$$

$$= 0{\cdot}3027 + (0{\cdot}4)(0{\cdot}0359) + \frac{(0{\cdot}4)(-0{\cdot}6)}{2}(0{\cdot}0039) + \frac{(1{\cdot}4)(0{\cdot}4)(-0{\cdot}6)}{6}(0{\cdot}0010)$$

$$= 0{\cdot}3027 + 0{\cdot}01436 - 0{\cdot}000468 - 0{\cdot}00006$$

$$\approx \mathbf{0{\cdot}31653}$$

**Example 2.** *Using the following table, apply Gauss's forward formula to get f (3·75).*

| $x$ | : | 2·5 | 3·0 | 3·5 | 4·0 | 4·5 | 5·0 |
|---|---|---|---|---|---|---|---|
| $f(x)$ | : | 24·145 | 22·043 | 20·225 | 18·644 | 17·262 | 16·047 |

**Solution.** Let us take $x = 3{\cdot}5$ as the origin.

Here $h = 0{\cdot}5$; $u = \dfrac{x - x_0}{h} = \dfrac{3{\cdot}75 - 3{\cdot}5}{0{\cdot}5} = 0{\cdot}5$

We form the central difference table below.

| $x$ | $u$ | $y$ | $\Delta y$ | $\Delta^2 y$ | $\Delta^3 y$ | $\Delta^4 y$ | $\Delta^5 y$ |
|---|---|---|---|---|---|---|---|
| 2·5 | – 2 | 24·145 | | | | | |
| | | | – 2·102 | | | | |
| 3·0 | – 1 | 22·043 | | 0·284 | | | |
| | | | – 1·818 | | – 0·047 | | |
| 3·5 | 0 | 20·225 | | 0·237 | | – 0·009 | |
| | | | – 1·581 | | – 0·038 | | – 0·003 |
| 4·0 | 1 | 18·644 | | 0·199 | | 0·006 | |
| | | | – 1·382 | | – 0·032 | | |
| 4·5 | 2 | 17·262 | | 0·167 | | | |
| | | | – 1·215 | | | | |
| 5·0 | 3 | 16·047 | | | | | |

Gauss's forward interpolation formula is

$$y(x) = y(x_0 + uh) = y_0 + \binom{u}{1}\Delta y_0 + \binom{u}{2}\Delta^2 y_{-1} + \binom{u+1}{3}\Delta^3 y_{-1} + \binom{u+1}{4}\Delta^4 y_{-2} + \cdots$$

$$= 20{\cdot}225 + \binom{\cdot 5}{1}(-1{\cdot}581) + \binom{\cdot 5}{2}(0{\cdot}237) + \binom{1{\cdot}5}{3}(-0{\cdot}038) + \binom{1{\cdot}5}{4}(0{\cdot}009)$$

$$= 20{\cdot}225 + (\cdot 5)(-1{\cdot}581) + \frac{(\cdot 5)(-0{\cdot}5)}{2}(0{\cdot}237) + \frac{(1{\cdot}5)(0{\cdot}5)(-0{\cdot}5)}{6}(-0{\cdot}038) + \frac{(1{\cdot}5)(0{\cdot}5)(-0{\cdot}5)(-1{\cdot}5)}{24}(0{\cdot}009) + \cdots$$

$$= 20{\cdot}225 - 0{\cdot}7905 - 0{\cdot}029625 + 0{\cdot}002375 + 0{\cdot}000210937 - 0{\cdot}0000351562$$

$y(x = 3{\cdot}75) \approx$ **19·4074258**

**Example 3.** *Apply Gauss's forward formula to obtain f (x) at x = 3·5 from the table below.*

| $x$ | : | 2 | 3 | 4 | 5 |
|---|---|---|---|---|---|
| $f(x)$ | : | 2·626 | 3·454 | 4·784 | 6·986 |

**Solution.** Take $x = 3$ as the origin; here $h = 1$

$$u = \frac{x - x_0}{h} = \frac{3{\cdot}5 - 3}{1} = 0{\cdot}5$$

Let us form the central difference table.

| $x$ | $u$ | $y = f(x)$ | $\Delta y$ | $\Delta^2 y$ | $\Delta^3 y$ |
|---|---|---|---|---|---|
| 2 | − 1 | 2·626 | | | |
| | | | 0·828 | | |
| 3 | 0 | [3·454] | | [0·502] | |
| | | | [1·330] | | [0·37] |
| 4 | + 1 | 4·784 | | 0·872 | |
| | | | 2·202 | | |
| 5 | 2 | 6·986 | | | |

The values required are enclosed by rectangles.

$$y(u = 0{\cdot}5) = y_0 + \binom{u}{1}\Delta y_0 + \binom{u}{2}\Delta^2 y_{-1} + \binom{u+1}{3}\Delta^3 y_{-1} + \cdots$$

$$= 3{\cdot}454 + (\cdot 5)(1{\cdot}330) + \frac{(\cdot 5)(-0{\cdot}5)}{2}(0{\cdot}502) + \frac{(1{\cdot}5)(\cdot 5)(-0{\cdot}5)}{6}(0{\cdot}37)$$

$$= 3{\cdot}454 + 0{\cdot}665 - 0{\cdot}06275 - 0{\cdot}023125$$

$\approx$ **4·033125**.

**Example 4.** *Using Gauss's backward interpolation formula find the population for the year 1936 given that*

| | | | | | | | |
|---|---|---|---|---|---|---|---|
| *Year* | $x$ | : | *1901* | *1911* | *1921* | *1931* | *1941* | *1951* |
| *Population in thousand* | $y$ | : | *12* | *15* | *20* | *27* | *39* | *52* |

**Solution.** Since we require at $x = 1936$, take 1941 as the origin :

$$h = 10\,;\; u = \frac{x - 1941}{10} = \frac{1936 - 1941}{10} = -0{\cdot}5$$

We will frame the central difference table.

| $x$ | $u$ | $y$ | $\Delta y$ | $\Delta^2 y$ | $\Delta^3 y$ | $\Delta^4 y$ | $\Delta^5 y$ |
|---|---|---|---|---|---|---|---|
| 1901 | – 4 | 12 | | | | | |
| | | | 3 | | | | |
| 1911 | – 3 | 15 | | 2 | | | |
| | | | 5 | | 0 | | |
| 1921 | – 2 | 20 | | 2 | | 3 | |
| | | | 7 | | 3 | | – 10 |
| 1931 | – 1 | 27 | | 5 | | – 7 | |
| | | | 12 | | – 4 | | |
| 1941 | 0 | 39 | | 1 | | | |
| | | | 13 | | | | |
| 1951 | 1 | 52 | | | | | |

We enclose those values required in the formula by rectangles.

By Gauss's backward formula, we have

$$y\,(x) = y\,(x_0 + uh) = y\,(u = -0{\cdot}5) = y_0 + \binom{u}{1}\Delta y_{-1} + \binom{u+1}{2}\Delta^2 y_{-1} + \binom{u+1}{3}\Delta^3 y_{-2} + \cdots$$

$$= 39 + (-0{\cdot}5)(12) + \binom{0{\cdot}5}{2}(1) + \binom{0{\cdot}5}{3}(-4)$$

$$= 39 - 6 + \frac{(0{\cdot}5)(-0{\cdot}5)}{2} + \frac{(0{\cdot}5)(-0{\cdot}5)(-1{\cdot}5)}{6}(-4)$$

$$= 33 - \frac{1}{8} - \frac{1}{4} = \mathbf{32{\cdot}625} \text{ (thousands).}$$

**Example 5.** *Find the value of cos 51°42′ by using Gauss's backward interpolation formula from the table given below.*

| | | | | | |
|---|---|---|---|---|---|
| $x$ : | *50°* | *51°* | *52°* | *53°* | *54°* |
| $y = \cos x$ : | *0·6428* | *0·6293* | *0·6157* | *0·6018* | *0·5878* |

**Solution.** Since we require interpolation at $x = 51°42'$, we take the origin at 52° (backward); here $h = 1$

$$u = \frac{x - 52°}{1°} = \frac{51°\,42' - 52°}{1°} = \frac{-18'}{60'} = -0{\cdot}3$$

We require $y\,(u = -0{\cdot}3)$.

We will frame the central difference table.

| $x$ | $u$ | $y = \cos x$ | $\Delta y$ | $\Delta^2 y$ | $\Delta^3 y$ | $\Delta^4 y$ |
|---|---|---|---|---|---|---|
| 50° | – 2 | 0·6428 | | | | |
| | | | – 0·0135 | | | |
| 51° | – 1 | 0·6293 | | – 0·0001 | | |
| | | | – 0·0136 | | – 0·0002 | |
| 52° | 0 | 0·6157 | | – 0·0003 | | 0·0004 |
| | | | – 0·0139 | | 0·0002 | |
| 53° | 1 | 0·6018 | | – 0·0001 | | |
| | | | – 0·0140 | | | |
| 54° | 2 | 0·5878 | | | | |

By Gauss's backward formula,

$$y(x) = y(u = -0{\cdot}3)$$

$$= y_0 + \binom{u}{1}\Delta y_{-1} + \binom{u+1}{2}\Delta^2 y_{-1} + \binom{u+1}{3}\Delta^3 y_{-2} + \cdots$$

$$= 0{\cdot}6157 + (-0{\cdot}3)(-0{\cdot}0136) + \frac{(0{\cdot}7)(-0{\cdot}3)}{2}(-0{\cdot}0003)$$

$$+ \frac{(0{\cdot}7)(-0{\cdot}3)(-1{\cdot}3)}{6}(-0{\cdot}0002)$$

$$= 0{\cdot}6157 + 0{\cdot}00408 + 0{\cdot}0000315 - 0{\cdot}000009$$

$\therefore \quad \cos 51°\,42' = 0{\cdot}6198.$

**Example 6.** *If* $\sqrt{12500} = 111{\cdot}803399, \sqrt{12510} = 111{\cdot}848111, \sqrt{12520} = 111{\cdot}892805, \sqrt{12530} = 111{\cdot}937483$, *find* $\sqrt{12516}$ *by Gauss's backward formula.*

**Solution.** Since $\sqrt{12516}$ is wanted by backward formula, take $x = 12520$ as the origin.

Here $h = 10, u = \dfrac{x - x_0}{h} = \dfrac{12516 - 12520}{10} = -0{\cdot}4$

Here $y = \sqrt{x}$.

Let us form the central difference table.

| $x$ | $u$ | $y = \sqrt{x}$ | $\Delta y$ | $\Delta^2 y$ | $\Delta^3 y$ |
|---|---|---|---|---|---|
| 12500 | – 2 | 111·803399 | | | |
| | | | 0·044712 | | |
| 12510 | – 1 | 111·848111 | | – 0·000018 | |
| | | | 0·044694 | | – 0·000002 |
| 12520 | 0 | 111·892805 | | – 0·000016 | |
| | | | 0·044678 | | |
| 12530 | 1 | 111·937483 | | | |

By Gauss's backward formula, we have

$$y(x) = y(x_0 + uh) = y(u = -0{\cdot}4) = y_0 + \binom{u}{1}\Delta y_{-1} + \binom{u+1}{2}\Delta^2 y_{-1}$$

$$+ \binom{u+1}{3}\Delta^3 y_{-2} + \cdots$$

$$= 111{\cdot}892805 + (-0{\cdot}4)(0{\cdot}044694) + \frac{(0{\cdot}6)(-0{\cdot}4)}{2}(-0{\cdot}000016) + \frac{(0{\cdot}6)(-0{\cdot}4)(-1{\cdot}4)}{6}(-0{\cdot}000002)$$

$$= 111{\cdot}8749294$$

$$\sqrt{12516} \approx 111{\cdot}8749294$$

## EXERCISE 7.1

**1.** Using Gauss's forward formula, find $y$ at $x = 0{\cdot}68$ using the following table which gives the probability integral value $y = f(x) = \frac{2}{\sqrt{\pi}} \int_0^x e^{-\frac{1}{2}x^2} dx$ for certain equidistant values of $x$.

| $x$ | : | 0·50 | 0·55 | 0·60 | 0·65 | 0·70 | 0·75 | 0·80 |
|---|---|---|---|---|---|---|---|---|
| $y = f(x)$ | : | 0·1915 | 0·2088 | 0·2258 | 0·2422 | 0·2580 | 0·2734 | 0·2881 |

**2.** In the above question, use Gauss's backward formula to get $y(0{\cdot}68)$.

**3.** Use Gauss's forward formula to get $y_{30}$ given that

$y_{21} = 18{\cdot}4708, y_{25} = 17{\cdot}8144, y_{29} = 17{\cdot}1070, y_{33} = 16{\cdot}3432, y_{37} = 15{\cdot}5154.$

**4.** Use Gauss's interpolation formula to get $y_{16}$ given

| $x$ | : | 5 | 10 | 15 | 20 | 25 |
|---|---|---|---|---|---|---|
| $y$ | : | 26·782 | 19·951 | 14·001 | 8·762 | 4·163 |

**5.** Apply Gauss's backward formula to obtain sin 45° given the table below :

| $x°$ | : | 20 | 30 | 40 | 50 | 60 | 70 |
|---|---|---|---|---|---|---|---|
| $\sin x°$ | : | 0·34202 | 0·50200 | 0·64279 | 0·76604 | 0·86603 | 0·93969 |

**6.** The population of a town is given below. Apply Gauss's backward formula to get the population in 1926.

| Year | $x$ : | 1911 | 1921 | 1931 | 1941 | 1951 |
|---|---|---|---|---|---|---|
| Population in thousands | $y$ : | 15 | 20 | 27 | 39 | 52 |

**7.** Use Gauss's backward formula to find tan 50°42′ given

| $x°$ | : | 50 | 51 | 52 | 53 | 54 |
|---|---|---|---|---|---|---|
| $\tan x$ | : | 1·1918 | 1·2349 | 1·2799 | 1·3270 | 1·3764 |

**8.** The values of $e^{-x}$ for various values of $x$ are given below. Find $e^{-1{\cdot}7425}$ by Gauss's forward formula.

| $x$ | : | 1·72 | 1·73 | 1·74 | 1·75 | 1·76 |
|---|---|---|---|---|---|---|
| $e^{-x}$ | : | 0·17907 | 0·17728 | 0·17552 | 0·17377 | 0·17204 |

**9.** Use Gauss's backward formula, find $f(5{\cdot}8)$ given that $f(x)$ is a polynomial of degree four and $f(4) = 270$, $f(5) = 648$, $\Delta f(5) = 682$ and $\Delta^2 f(4) = 132$.

[**Hint.** $f(6) = f(5) + \Delta f(5)$; $\Delta^3 f(4) = (E-1)^3 f(4)$]

**10.** Given $f(2) = 10, f(1) = 8, f(0) = 5, f(-1) = 10$, find $f(\frac{1}{2})$ by Gauss's forward formula.

**11.** Find $f(25)$ given $f(20) = 14, f(24) = 32, f(28) = 35$ and $f(32) = 40$, using Gauss's formula.

## 7·5. Stirling's formula

By Gauss's forward formula, we have

$$y(x) = y(x_0 + uh) = y_0 + \binom{u}{1}\Delta y_0 + \binom{u}{2}\Delta^2 y_{-1} + \binom{u+1}{3}\Delta^3 y_{-1} + \binom{u+1}{4}\Delta^4 y_{-2} + \binom{u+2}{5}\Delta^5 y_{-2} + \cdots \quad ...(1)$$

By Gauss's backward formula, we have

$$y(u) = y_0 + \binom{u}{1}\Delta y_{-1} + \binom{u+1}{2}\Delta^2 y_{-1} + \binom{u+1}{3}\Delta^3 y_{-2} + \binom{u+2}{4}\Delta^4 y_{-2} + \cdots \quad ...(2)$$

Adding (1) and (2),

$$2y(u) = 2y_0 + \binom{u}{1}[\Delta y_0 + \Delta y_{-1}] + \left[\binom{u}{2} + \binom{u+1}{2}\right]\Delta^2 y_{-1} + \binom{u+1}{3}\left[\Delta^3 y_{-1} + \Delta^3 y_{-2}\right] + \left[\binom{u+2}{4} + \binom{u+1}{4}\right]\Delta^4 y_{-2} + \cdots$$

$$= 2y_0 + \binom{u}{1}[\Delta y_0 + \Delta y_{-1}] + \frac{2u^2}{2!}\Delta^2 y_{-1} + \frac{u(u^2 - 1^2)}{3!}\left(\Delta^3 y_{-1} + \Delta^3 y_{-2}\right) + \frac{2u^2(u^2 - 1^2)}{4!}\Delta^4 y_{-2} + \cdots$$

$$\therefore \quad \mathbf{y(x) = y(x_0 + uh) = y_0 + u\left[\frac{\Delta y_0 + \Delta y_{-1}}{2}\right] + \frac{u^2}{2!}\Delta^2 y_{-1} + \frac{u(u^2 - 1^2)}{3!}\frac{\left(\Delta^3 y_{-1} + \Delta^3 y_{-2}\right)}{2} + \frac{u^2(u^2 - 1^2)}{4!}\Delta^4 y_{-2} + \cdots} \quad ...(3)$$

where $u = \dfrac{x - x_0}{h}$.

Equation (3) is known as *Stirling's formula* and it is the average of the two Gauss's formulae.

**Note 1.** The formula involves the means of the *odd* differences just above and just below the central line and even differences on the central line.

**2.** The formula can be remembered with the help of the following table.

| *Coefficient :* | $1$ | $u$ | $\dfrac{u^2}{2}$ | $\dfrac{u(u^2 - 1^2)}{3!}$ | $\dfrac{u^2(u^2 - 1^2)}{4!}$ |
|---|---|---|---|---|---|
| *Differences :* | $y_0$ | $\frac{1}{2}(\Delta y_0 + \Delta y_{-1})$ | $\Delta^2 y_{-1}$ | $\frac{1}{2}\left(\Delta^3 y_{-1} + \Delta^3 y_{-2}\right)$ | $\Delta^4 y_{-2}$ |

That is, (diagrammatically) the differences in the terms are

$$\begin{matrix} y_0 & \text{———} & \begin{pmatrix} \Delta y_{-1} \\ \\ \Delta y_0 \end{pmatrix} & \text{—} \Delta^2 y_{-1} \text{—} & \begin{pmatrix} \Delta^3 y_{-2} \\ \\ \Delta^2 y_{-1} \end{pmatrix} & \text{—} \Delta^4 y_{-2} \\ y_1 & & | & & | & \\ & & \text{Average} & & \text{Average} & \end{matrix}$$

**3.** To use this formula, we must have $-\frac{1}{2} < u < \frac{1}{2}$.

## 7·6. Bessel's formula

By Gauss's forward formula, we get

$$y(x) = y(x_0 + uh) = y_0 + \binom{u}{1}\Delta y_0 + \binom{u}{2}\Delta^2 y_{-1} + \binom{u+1}{3}\Delta^3 y_{-1} + \binom{u+1}{4}\Delta^4 y_{-2} + \binom{u+2}{5}\Delta^5 y_{-2} + \cdots \quad ...(1)$$

We know, $\Delta y_0 = y_1 - y_0$

$$\therefore \quad y_0 = y_1 - \Delta y_0 \quad ...(i)$$

$$y_{-1} = y_0 - \Delta y_{-1}$$

$$\therefore \quad \Delta^2 y_{-1} = \Delta^2 y_0 - \Delta^3 y_{-1} \quad ...(ii)$$

Also, $\Delta^4 y_{-2} = \Delta^4 y_{-1} - \Delta^5 y_{-2}$ etc.

Hence, (1) is rewritten as,

$$y(x) = y(x_0 + uh) = \left(\frac{y_0}{2} + \frac{y_0}{2}\right) + u\Delta y_0 + \frac{1}{2}\frac{u(u-1)}{2!} \cdot \Delta^2 y_{-1} + \frac{1}{2}\frac{u(u-1)}{2!}\Delta^2 y_{-1} + \frac{(u+1)(u)(u-1)}{3!}\Delta^3 y_{-1} + \cdots \quad ...(2)$$

using (*i*) and (*ii*) in (2)

$$y(x_0 + uh) = \frac{y_0}{2} + \frac{1}{2}(y_1 - \Delta y_0) + u\,\Delta y_0 + \frac{1}{2}\frac{u(u-1)}{2!}\Delta^2 y_{-1} + \frac{1}{2} \cdot \frac{u(u-1)}{2!}\left(\Delta^2 y_0 - \Delta^3 y_{-1}\right) + \frac{(u+1)\,u\,(u-1)}{3!}\Delta^3 y_{-1} + \cdots$$

$$= \frac{y_0 + y_1}{2} + \left(u - \frac{1}{2}\right)\Delta y_0 + \frac{1}{2}\frac{u(u-1)}{2!}\left(\Delta^2 y_{-1} + \Delta^2 y_0\right) + \frac{u(u-1)}{2!}\left(-\frac{1}{2} + \frac{u+1}{3}\right)\Delta^3 y_{-1} + \cdots$$

$$\mathbf{y\,(x) = y\,(x_0 + uh) = \frac{y_0 + y_1}{2} + \left(u - \frac{1}{2}\right)\Delta y_0 + \frac{u\,(u-1)}{2!}\left(\frac{\Delta^2 y_{-1} + \Delta^2 y_0}{2}\right)}$$

$$\mathbf{+ \frac{\left(u - \frac{1}{2}\right) u\,(u-1)}{3!}\Delta^3 y_{-1} + \frac{(u+1)\,u\,(u-1)(u-2)}{4!}\left(\frac{\Delta^4 y_{-2} + \Delta^4 y_{-1}}{2}\right) + \cdots} \quad ...(3)$$

Equation (3) is known as Bessel's formula.

**Note 1.** The formula involves *odd* differences below the central line and means of the even differences on and below the central line.

| | | | | | |
|---|---|---|---|---|---|
| Central line | $y_0$ | $\Delta y_0$ | $\Delta^2 y_{-1}$ | $\Delta^3 y_{-1}$ | $\Delta^4 y_{-2}$ |
| Next line | $y_1$ | | $\Delta^2 y_0$ | | $\Delta^4 y_{-1}$ |
| | average | | average | | average |

If $u = \frac{1}{2}$, the coefficients of all odd order differences are zero.

Hence, setting $u = \frac{1}{2}$, we have

$$y\left(u = \frac{1}{2}\right) = \frac{y_0 + y_1}{2} - \frac{1}{8}\left(\frac{\Delta^2 y_{-1} + \Delta^2 y_0}{2}\right) + \frac{3}{128}\left(\frac{\Delta^4 y_{-2} + \Delta^4 y_{-1}}{2}\right) - \frac{5}{1024}\left(\frac{\Delta^6 y_{-3} + \Delta^6 y_{-2}}{2}\right) + \cdots$$

**Note 1.** This form is suited to compute the values of the function midway between two given values.

**2.** Only even order differences exist in the formula.

This is also known as *formula for interpolating to halves.*

## 7·7. Laplace-Everett formula

Gauss's forward formula is

$$y\,(x) = y\,(x_0 + uh) = y_0 + \binom{u}{1}\Delta y_0 + \binom{u}{2}\Delta^2 y_{-1} + \binom{u+1}{3}\Delta^3 y_{-1} + \binom{u+1}{4}\Delta^4 y_{-2} + \binom{u+2}{5}\Delta^5 y_{-2} + \cdots \quad ...(1)$$

**We have** $\Delta y_0 = y_1 - y_0$

$$\Delta^3 y_{-1} = \Delta^2 y_0 - \Delta^2 y_{-1}$$

$$\Delta^5 y_{-2} = \Delta^4 y_{-1} - \Delta^4 y_{-2} \text{ etc.}$$

**Substituting these in (1), we have**

$$y\,(x_0 + uh) = y_0 + \binom{u}{1}(y_1 - y_0) + \binom{u}{2}\Delta^2 y_{-1} + \binom{u+1}{3}\left(\Delta^2 y_0 - \Delta^2 y_{-1}\right) + \binom{u+1}{4}\Delta^4 y_{-2} + \binom{u+2}{5}\left(\Delta^4 y_{-1} - \Delta^4 y_{-2}\right) + \cdots$$

$$= (1-u)\,y_0 + uy_1 + \left[\binom{u}{2} - \binom{u+1}{3}\right]\Delta^2 y_{-1} + \binom{u+1}{3}\Delta^2 y_0$$

$$+ \left[\binom{u+1}{4} - \binom{u+2}{5}\right]\Delta^4 y_{-2} + \binom{u+2}{5}\Delta^4 y_{-1} + \cdots$$

$$= (1-u)\,y_0 + uy_1 - \binom{u}{3}\Delta^2 y_{-1} + \binom{u+1}{3}\Delta^2 y_0 - \binom{u+1}{5}\Delta^4 y_{-2}$$

$$+ \binom{u+2}{5}\Delta^4 y_{-1} + \cdots \qquad \text{...(2)}$$

Using the result $\binom{u}{r} + \binom{u}{r+1} = \binom{u+1}{r+1}$

Changing $1-u = v$ or $u = 1-v$ in equation (2), we can get an elegant form.

$$\binom{u}{3} = \frac{u\,(u-1)(u-2)}{3!} = \frac{(1-v)(-v)(-v-1)}{3!} = -\frac{(v+1)\,v\,(v-1)}{3!} = -\binom{v+1}{3}$$

Similarly, $\binom{u+1}{5} = -\binom{v+2}{5}$ etc.

Hence, equation (2) reduces to,

$$y\,(x) = y\,(x_0 + uh) = \left[\,vy_0 + \binom{v+1}{3}\Delta^2 y_{-1} + \binom{v+2}{5}\Delta^4 y_{-2} + \cdots\right]$$

$$+ \left[\,uy_1 + \binom{u+1}{3}\Delta^2 y_0 + \binom{u+2}{5}\Delta^4 y_{-1} + \cdots\right] \qquad \text{...(3)}$$

$$= \left[\,vy_0 + \frac{v\,(v^2-1^2)}{3!}\Delta^2 y_{-1} + \frac{v\,(v^2-1^2)(v^2-2^2)}{5!}\Delta^4 y_{-2} + \cdots\right]$$

$$+ \left[\,uy_1 + \frac{u\,(u^2-1^2)}{3!}\Delta^2 y_0 + \frac{u\,(u^2-1^2)(u^2-2^2)}{5!}\Delta^4 y_{-1} + \cdots\right] \qquad \text{...(4)}$$

The form (3) or (4) is known as *Laplace-Everett formula.*

**Note 1.** This formula involves *even differences on and below the central line*.

**2.** It involves only even order differences.

**3.** This can be used if $0 < u < 1$.

## 7·8. Relation between Bessel's and Everett's formulae

The two formulae are very closely related. It is possible to deduce one formula from the other by a convenient rearrangement.

Starting with Bessel's formula,

$$y\,(x_0 + uh) = \frac{y_0 + y_1}{2} + \left(u - \frac{1}{2}\right)\Delta y_0 + \frac{u\,(u-1)}{2!}\left(\frac{\Delta^2 y_{-1} + \Delta^2 y_0}{2}\right)$$

$$+ \frac{\left(u - \frac{1}{2}\right)u\,(u-1)}{3!}\Delta^3 y_{-1} + \frac{(u+1)\,u\,(u-1)(u-2)}{4!}\left(\frac{\Delta^4 y_{-2} + \Delta^4 y_{-1}}{2}\right) + \cdots$$

...(1)

$$= \frac{y_0 + y_1}{2} + \left(u - \frac{1}{2}\right)\Delta y_0 + \frac{u(u-1)}{2}\left(\frac{\Delta^2 y_{-1} + \Delta^2 y_0}{2}\right)$$

$$+ \frac{\left(u - \frac{1}{2}\right)u(u-1)}{3!}\Delta^3 y_{-1} + \cdots \text{ keeping only upto 3rd differences} \quad \ldots.(2)$$

Now we express the odd order differences in terms of the corresponding lower even order differences. That is,

$$\Delta^3 y_{-1} = \Delta^2 y_0 - \Delta^2 y_{-1} \text{ etc.}$$

Then equation (2) reduces to,

$$y(x_0 + uh) = \frac{y_0 + y_1}{2} + \left(u - \frac{1}{2}\right)(y_1 - y_0) + \frac{u(u-1)}{2}\left(\frac{\Delta^2 y_{-1} + \Delta^2 y_0}{2}\right)$$

$$+ \frac{\left(u - \frac{1}{2}\right)u(u-1)}{3!}\left(\Delta^2 y_0 - \Delta^2 y_{-1}\right) + \cdots$$

$$= (1-u)\,y_0 + uy_1 + \binom{u+1}{3}\Delta^2 y_0 - \binom{u}{3}\Delta^2 y_{-1} + \cdots$$

$$= \left[vy_0 + \binom{v+1}{3}\Delta^2 y_{-1} + \cdots\right]$$

$$+ \left[uy_1 + \binom{u+1}{3}\Delta^2 y_0 + \cdots\right] \quad \ldots(3)$$

Equation (3) is nothing but Everett's formula upto second differences.

This shows that *Bessel's formula truncated after the third differences is the same as Everett's formula truncated after the second differences.*

We can also start from Everett's formula and obtain Bessel's formula.

*Advantages of central difference interpolation formula*

In general, the coefficients in the central difference interpolation formulae are smaller and rapidly convergent than those in Newton-Gregory formulae. The coefficients in Stirling's formula decrease more rapidly than those of Bessel's formula. The coefficients in Bessel's formula decrease more rapidly than those in Newton-Gregory formulae. Therefore, it is advisable to use Stirling's or Bessel's central difference formula instead of Newton-Gregory formulae. One can have the following rules in selecting the interpolation formulae.

1. If interpolation is required near the beginning of the tabular values, then use Newton-Gregory forward interpolation formula.
2. If interpolation is required near the end of the tabular values, use Newton-Gregory's backward interpolation formula.

3. If interpolation is required near the middle values of the table, use either Stirling's or Bessel's formula.

4. If $-\frac{1}{4} < u \leq \frac{1}{4}$, then use Stirling's formula.

5. If $\frac{1}{4} < u < \frac{3}{4}$, then use Bessel's formula for better results.

**Example 1.** *Using Stirlings formula, find y (1·22) from the following table.*

| *x* | *1·0* | *1·1* | *1·2* | *1·3* | *1·4* | *1·5* | *1·6* | *1·7* | *1·8* |
|---|---|---|---|---|---|---|---|---|---|
| *y* | *0·84147* | *0·89121* | *0·93204* | *0·96356* | *0·98545* | *0·99749* | *0·99957* | *0·99385* | *0·97385* |

*(Delhi Uni.)*

**Solution.** Since we require $y$ at $x = 1·22$, take the origin at $x = 1·2$ and $h = 0·1$

$$u = \frac{x - x_0}{h} = \frac{1·22 - 1·2}{0·1} = \frac{0·02}{0·1} = 0·2$$

We form the central difference table below. Since $x = 1·2$ is the origin, we take values on both sides of 1·2 to the required stage.

**Difference Table**

| $x$ | $u$ | $y$ | $\Delta y$ | $\Delta^2 y$ | $\Delta^3 y$ | $\Delta^4 y$ |
|---|---|---|---|---|---|---|
| 1·0 | – 2 | 0·84147 | | | | |
| | | | 0·04974 | | | |
| 1·1 | – 1 | 0·89121 | | – 0·00891 | – 0·00040 | |
| | | | 0·04083 $\Delta y_{-1}$ | | $\Delta^3 y_{-2}$ | |
| 1·2 | 0 | 0·93204 $y_0$ | | – 0·00931 $\Delta^2 y_{-1}$ | | 0·00008 $\Delta^4 y_{-2}$ |
| | | | 0·03152 $\Delta y_0$ | | – 0·00032 $\Delta^3 y_{-1}$ | |
| 1·3 | 1 | 0·96356 | | – 0·00963 | | |
| | | | 0·02189 | | | |
| 1·4 | 2 | 0·98545 | | | | |

By Stirling's formula, we have

$$y(x_0 + uh) = y_0 + u\left[\frac{\Delta y_0 + \Delta y_{-1}}{2}\right] + \frac{u^2}{2}\Delta^2 y_{-1}$$

$$+ \frac{u(u^2 - 1^2)}{3!}\left(\frac{\Delta^3 y_{-1} + \Delta^3 y_{-2}}{2}\right) + \frac{u^2(u^2 - 1^2)}{4!}\Delta^4 y_{-2} + \cdots$$

$$y(1·2) = 0·93204 + (0·2)\left[\frac{0·04083 + 0·03152}{2}\right] + \frac{(0·2)^2}{2}(-0·00931)$$

$$+ \frac{(0·2)(0·04 - 1)}{6}\left[\frac{-0·00040 - 0·00032}{2}\right] + \frac{(0·04)(0·04 - 1)}{24}(0·00008) + \cdots$$

$$= 0·93204 + 0·007235 - 0·0001862 + ·00001152 - 0·000000128$$

$$= \mathbf{0·939100192}$$

**Example 2.** *From the following table, estimate $e^{0.644}$ correct to five decimals using (i) Stirling's formula (ii) Bessel's formula (iii) Everett's formula.*

*Also find $e^x$ at $x = 0.638$.*

| $x$ | 0·61 | 0·62 | 0·63 | 0·64 | 0·65 | 0·66 | 0·67 |
|---|---|---|---|---|---|---|---|
| $e^x$ | 1·840431 | 1·858928 | 1·877610 | 1·896481 | 1·915541 | 1·934792 | 1·954237 |

Take $x = 0.64$ as the origin, *(Anna Nov. 2004)*

$$u = \frac{x - x_0}{h} = \frac{0.644 - 0.64}{0.01} = 0.4.$$

**Difference Table**

| $x$ | $u$ | $y = e^x$ | $\Delta y$ | $\Delta^2 y$ | $\Delta^3 y$ | $\Delta^4 y$ |
|---|---|---|---|---|---|---|
| 0·61 | – 3 | 1·840431 | | | | |
| | | | 0·018497 | | | |
| 0·62 | – 2 | 1·858928 | | 0·000185 | | |
| | | | 0·018682 | | 0·000004 | |
| 0·63 | – 1 | 1·877610 | | 0·000189 | | – 0·000004 |
| | | | 0·018871 | | 0·0 | |
| 0·64 | 0 | 1·896481 | | 0·000189 | | 0·000002 |
| | | | 0·019060 | | 0·000002 | |
| 0·65 | 1 | 1·915541 | | 0·000191 | | 0·000001 |
| | | | 0·019251 | | 0·000003 | |
| 0·66 | 2 | 1·934792 | | 0·000194 | | |
| | | | 0·019445 | | | |
| 0·67 | 3 | 1·954237 | | | | |

(*i*) By Stirling's formula,

$$y\,(x = 0.644) = y\,(u = 0.4) = 1.896481 + (0.4)\left(\frac{0.018871 + 0.019060}{2}\right)$$

$$+ \frac{0.16}{2}\,(0.000189) + \frac{(0.4)(0.16 - 1)}{6}\left(\frac{0 + 0.000002}{2}\right) + \cdots$$

$$= 1.896481 + 0.0075862 + 0.00001512 - 0.000000056$$

$$= \mathbf{1.90408226}$$

(*ii*) Using Bessel's formula, we get

$$y\,(0.644) = \frac{1.896481 + 1.915541}{2} + \left(0.4 - \frac{1}{2}\right)(0.019060)$$

$$+ \frac{(0.4)(-0.6)}{2}\left(\frac{0.000189 + 0.000191}{2}\right)$$

$$+ \frac{(0.4)(-0.6)(0.4 - 0.5)}{6}\,(0.000002) + \cdots$$

$$= 1.906011 - 0.001906 - 0.0000228$$

$$= 1.904082$$

(*iii*) Using Everett's formula, we get

$$y(0{\cdot}644) = vy_0 + \frac{v(v^2-1^2)}{3!}\Delta^2 y_{-1} + \frac{v(v^2-1^2)(v^2-2^2)}{5!}\Delta^4 y_{-2} + \cdots$$

$$+ uy_1 + \frac{u(u^2-1^2)}{3!}\Delta^2 y_0 + \frac{u(u^2-1^2)(u^2-2^2)}{5!}\Delta^4 y_{-1} + \cdots$$

$$= (0{\cdot}6)(1{\cdot}896481) + \frac{(\cdot 6)(\cdot 36-1)}{6}(0{\cdot}000189) + \cdots$$

$$+ (0{\cdot}4)(1{\cdot}915541) + \frac{(0{\cdot}4)(0{\cdot}16-1)}{6}(0{\cdot}000191) + \cdots$$

$$= 1{\cdot}1378886 - 0{\cdot}000012096 + 0{\cdot}7662164 - 0{\cdot}00001069$$

$$= 1{\cdot}904082$$

In all the three method, the result is correct upto six decimal places.

II. *To find $e^x$ at $x = 0{\cdot}638$ :*

(*i*) Taking the origin at 0·64; $u = \frac{x - x_0}{h} = \frac{0{\cdot}638 - 0{\cdot}64}{0{\cdot}01} = -0{\cdot}2$

To employ **Stirling's formula**, we require $-\frac{1}{4} \le u \le \frac{1}{4}$ which is true in our case. Hence, using Stirling's formula

$$y(0{\cdot}638) = 1{\cdot}896481 - 0{\cdot}2 \times \frac{1}{2}(0{\cdot}018871 + 0{\cdot}019060) + \frac{0{\cdot}04}{2}(0{\cdot}000189)$$

$$= 1{\cdot}896481 - 0{\cdot}0037931 + 0{\cdot}0000038 = \mathbf{1{\cdot}892692}.$$

(*ii*) To use Bessel's formula, we require $\frac{1}{4} \le u \le \frac{3}{4}$, $u = -0{\cdot}2$ does not satisfy this inequality.

Therefore, now we take the origin as 0·63

Hence $u = \frac{0{\cdot}638 - 0{\cdot}63}{0{\cdot}01} = 0{\cdot}8$

$u = 0{\cdot}8$ is close to the upper limit 3/4.

Hence, we can use Bessel's formula

$$y(0{\cdot}638) = \frac{1}{2}(1{\cdot}877610 + 1{\cdot}896481) + (0{\cdot}8 - 0{\cdot}5)(0{\cdot}018871)$$

$$+ \frac{(0{\cdot}8)(-0{\cdot}2)}{2}\left(\frac{0{\cdot}000189 + 0{\cdot}000189}{2}\right)$$

$$+ \frac{(0{\cdot}8)(-0{\cdot}2)(0{\cdot}3)}{6}(0) + \cdots$$

$$= 1{\cdot}8870455 + 0{\cdot}0056613 - 0{\cdot}00001512$$

$$= 1{\cdot}89269168$$

Both methods give the same result, correct to six decimal places.

**Example 3.** *The following table gives the values of the probability* *integral* $f(x) = \frac{2}{\sqrt{\pi}} \int_0^x e^{-x^2}\, dx$ *for certain values of x. Find the value of this integral when x = 0·5437 using (i) Stirling's formula, (ii) Bessel's formula and (iii) Everett's formula.*

| $x$ | 0·51 | 0·52 | 0·53 | 0·54 | 0·55 | 0·56 | 0·57 |
|---|---|---|---|---|---|---|---|
| $y = f(x)$ | 0·5292437 | 0·5378987 | 0·5464641 | 0·5549392 | 0·5633233 | 0·5716157 | 0·5798158 |

**Solution.** We take the origin $x_0 = 0{\cdot}54$ and $x = 0{\cdot}5437$, $h = {\cdot}01$

Hence, $u = \frac{x - x_0}{h} = \frac{0{\cdot}5437 - 0{\cdot}54}{0{\cdot}01} = 0{\cdot}37$

$v = 1 - u = +0{\cdot}63$

We form below the difference table :

| $x$ | $u$ | $y = f(x)$ | $\Delta y$ | $\Delta^2 y$ | $\Delta^3 y$ | $\Delta^4 y$ |
|---|---|---|---|---|---|---|
| 0·51 | – 3 | 0·5292437 | | | | |
| | | | 0·0086550 | | | |
| 0·52 | – 2 | 0·5378987 | | –0·0000896 | | |
| | | | 0·0085654 | | –0·0000007 | |
| 0·53 | – 1 | 0·5464641 | | –0·0000903 | | 0·0 |
| | | | 0·0084751 | | –0·0000007 | |
| 0·54 | 0 | 0·5549392 | | –0·0000910 | | 0·0 |
| | | | 0·0083841 | | –0·0000007 | |
| 0·55 | 1 | 0·5633232 | | –0·0000917 | | 0·0000001 |
| | | | 0·0082924 | | –0·0000006 | |
| 0·56 | 2 | 0·5716157 | | –0·0000923 | | |
| | | | 0·0082001 | | | |
| 0·57 | 3 | 0·5798158 | | | | |

(*i*) By Stirling's formula,

$$y\,(x = 0{\cdot}5437) = y\,(u = 0{\cdot}37)$$

$$= 0{\cdot}5549392 + 0{\cdot}37\left(\frac{0{\cdot}0083841 + 0{\cdot}0084751}{2}\right)$$

$$+ \frac{(0{\cdot}37)^2}{2}(-0{\cdot}0000910) + \frac{(0{\cdot}37)\,[(0{\cdot}37)^2 - 1)]}{6}(-0{\cdot}0000007)$$

$$= 0{\cdot}5549392 + 0{\cdot}003118952 - 0{\cdot}00000623 + 0{\cdot}00000004$$

$$= \mathbf{0{\cdot}55805196}$$

(*ii*) By Bessel's formula,

$$y\,(x = 0{\cdot}5437) = \frac{1}{2}(y_0 + y_1) + \left(u - \frac{1}{2}\right)\Delta y_0 + \frac{u\,(u-1)}{2}\left(\frac{\Delta^2 y_{-1} + \Delta^2 y_0}{2}\right) + \cdots$$

$$= \frac{1}{2}[0{\cdot}5549392 + 0{\cdot}5633233] + (0{\cdot}37 - 0{\cdot}5)(0{\cdot}0083841)$$

$$+ \frac{(0{\cdot}37)(-0{\cdot}63)}{2}\left(\frac{-0{\cdot}0000910 - 0{\cdot}0000917}{2}\right)$$

$$+ \frac{(0{\cdot}37)(-0{\cdot}63)(0{\cdot}37 - 0{\cdot}5)}{6}(-0{\cdot}0000007) + \cdots$$

$$= 0{\cdot}55913125 - 0{\cdot}001089933 + 0{\cdot}0000106468$$

$$= \mathbf{0{\cdot}55805196}$$

(*iii*) By Everett's formula,

$$y\,(x=0{\cdot}5437)=\left[\,uy_1+\frac{u(u^2-1)}{6}\,\Delta^2 y_0+\frac{u(u^2-1)(u^2-4)}{120}\,\Delta^4 y_{-1}+\cdots\right]$$

$$+\left[\,vy_0+\frac{v(v^2-1)}{6}\,\Delta^2 y_{-1}+\frac{v(v^2-1)(v^2-4)}{120}\,\Delta^4 y_{-2}+\cdots\right]$$

$$=(0{\cdot}37)(0{\cdot}5633233)+\frac{(0{\cdot}37)[(\cdot 37)^2-1]}{6}\,[-\,0{\cdot}0000917]+\cdots$$

$$+\,(0{\cdot}63)(0{\cdot}5549392)+(0{\cdot}63)\,\frac{[(0{\cdot}63)^2-1]}{6}\,[-\,0{\cdot}0000910]+\cdots$$

$$=[0{\cdot}208429621+0{\cdot}00000488+\cdots]$$

$$+\,[0{\cdot}349611696+0{\cdot}00000576262+\cdots]$$

$$=\mathbf{0{\cdot}55805195}.$$

**Note.** By all the three methods, the results are same correct to 7 decimal places.

**Example 4.** *From the following table,*

| $x$ | : | *20* | *25* | *30* | *35* | *40* |
|---|---|---|---|---|---|---|
| $y=f(x)$ | : | *11·4699* | *12·7834* | *13·7648* | *14·4982* | *15·0463* |

*find f (34) using Everett's formula.*

**Solution.** Take the origin $x_0$ as 30; $h$ = 5

$$\therefore\quad u=\frac{x-x_0}{h}=\frac{34-30}{5}=0{\cdot}8\ ;\quad \text{here } v=1-u=0{\cdot}2$$

We will use Everett's formula.

**Difference Table**

| $x$ | $u$ | $y$ | $\Delta y$ | $\Delta^2 y$ | $\Delta^3 y$ | $\Delta^4 y$ |
|---|---|---|---|---|---|---|
| 20 | – 2 | 11·4699 | | | | |
| | | | 1·3135 | | | |
| 25 | – 1 | 12·7834 | | – 0·3321 | | |
| | | | 0·9814 | | 0·0841 | |
| 30 | 0 | 13·7648 | | – 0·2480 | | – 0·0214 |
| | | | 0·7334 | | 0·0627 | |
| 35 | 1 | 14·4982 | | – 0·1853 | | |
| | | | 0·5481 | | | |
| 40 | 2 | 15·0463 | | | | |

By Laplace-Everett's formula,

$$y\,(x)=\left[\,uy_1+\frac{u\,(u^2-1^2)}{3!}\,\Delta^2 y_0+\frac{u\,(u^2-1^2)(u^2-2^2)}{5!}\,\Delta^4 y_{-1}+\cdots\right]$$

$$+\left[\,vy_0+\frac{v\,(v^2-1^2)}{3!}\,\Delta^2 y_{-1}+\frac{v(v^2-1^2)(v^2-2^2)}{5!}\,\Delta^4 y_{-2}+\cdots\right]$$

$$y\,(x=34)=y\,(u=0{\cdot}8)$$

$$= (0.8)(14.4982) + \frac{(0.8)(0.64-1)}{6}(-0.1853) + \cdots$$

$$+ (0.2)(13.7648) + \frac{(0.2)(0.04-1)}{6}(-0.2480)$$

$$+ \frac{(0.2)(.04-1)(.04-4)}{120}(-0.0214) + \cdots$$

$$= \mathbf{14.368214}$$

**Example 5.** *The following table gives the values of the elliptic integral* $f(\theta) = \int_0^\theta \frac{d\theta}{\sqrt{1 - \frac{1}{2}\sin^2\theta}}$ *for certain values of θ. Find the value of* $f(23.5°)$

| θ | 21° | 22° | 23° | 24° | 25° | 26° |
|---|---|---|---|---|---|---|
| $y = f(\theta)$ | 0·370634373 | 0·388705151 | 0·406834931 | 0·425026420 | 0·443282329 | 0·461605362 |

**Solution.** Since we require the value of the function at the mid-point of two given values, we can use formula for interpolating to halves. (See note under Bessel's formula), take 23° as origin.

$$u = \frac{x - x_0}{h} = \frac{23.5° - 23°}{1°} = 0.5.$$

**Difference Table**

| θ | $u$ | $y = f(\theta)$ | $\Delta y$ | $\Delta^2 y$ | $\Delta^3 y$ | $\Delta^4 y$ |
|---|---|---|---|---|---|---|
| 21° | – 2 | 0·370634373 | | | | |
| | | | 0·018070778 | | | |
| 22° | – 1 | 0·388705151 | | 0·000059002 | | |
| | | | 0·018129780 | | 0·000002707 | |
| 23° | 0 | 0·406834931 | | 0·000061709 | | $-4 \times 10^{-9}$ |
| | | | 0·018191489 | | 0·000002711 | |
| 24° | 1 | 0·425026420 | | 0·000064420 | | $-7 \times 10^{-9}$ |
| | | | 0·018255909 | | 0·000002704 | |
| 25° | 2 | 0·443282329 | | 0·000067124 | | |
| | | | 0·018323033 | | | |
| 26° | 3 | 0·461605362 | | | | |

By formula, for interpolating to halves,

$$y\,(u = 0.5) = \frac{y_0 + y_1}{2} - \frac{1}{8}\left(\frac{\Delta^2 y_{-1} + \Delta^2 y_0}{2}\right) + \frac{3}{128}\left(\frac{\Delta^4 y_{-2} + \Delta^4 y_{-1}}{2}\right) - \cdots$$

$$= \frac{0.406834931 + 0.425026420}{2} - \frac{1}{8}\left(\frac{0.000061709 + 0.000064420}{2}\right) + \frac{3}{128}\,\frac{(4-7)\times 10^{-9}}{2}$$

$$= \mathbf{0.415922792.}$$

**Example 6.** *Given the following table, find y (35), by using Stirling's formula and Bessel's formula.*

| $x$ | : | 20 | 30 | 40 | 50 |
|---|---|---|---|---|---|
| $y$ | : | 512 | 439 | 346 | 243 |

**Solution.** We will take $x_0 = 30$ as the origin

$$u = \frac{x - x_0}{h} = \frac{35 - 30}{10} = 0{\cdot}5$$

The difference table is :

| $x$ | $u$ | $y$ | $\Delta y$ | $\Delta^2 y$ | $\Delta^3 y$ |
|---|---|---|---|---|---|
| 20 | − 1 | 512 $(y_{-1})$ | | | |
| | | | − 73 $(\Delta y_{-1})$ | | |
| 30 | 0 | 439 $(y_0)$ | | − 20 $(\Delta^2 y_{-1})$ | |
| | | | − 93 $(\Delta y_0)$ | | 10 $(\Delta^3 y_{-1})$ |
| 40 | 1 | 346 $(y_1)$ | | − 10 $(\Delta^2(y_0))$ | |
| | | | − 103 | | |
| 50 | 2 | 243 | | | |

(*i*) By Stirling's formula,

$$y\,(35) = y\,(u = 0{\cdot}5) = y_0 + \frac{u}{2}(\Delta y_0 + \Delta y_{-1}) + \frac{u^2}{2}\Delta^2 y_{-1} + \frac{u\,(u^2 - 1)}{6}\left(\frac{\Delta^3 y_{-1} + \Delta^3 y_{-2}}{2}\right) + \cdots$$

$$= 439 + \frac{0{\cdot}5}{2}(-93 - 73) + \frac{0{\cdot}25}{2}(-20) + \frac{(0{\cdot}5)(0{\cdot}25 - 1)}{6}(\cdots) + \cdots$$

$$= 439 - 41{\cdot}50 - 2{\cdot}50$$

$$= 395$$

$\therefore\quad y\,(35) = \mathbf{395}$.

(*ii*) Now, $y$ value at the mid-point of two given values of $y$ is required. Hence, *formula for interpolating to halves* can be used.

By above formula,

$$y\,(u = 0{\cdot}5) = \frac{y_0 + y_1}{2} - \frac{1}{8}\left(\frac{\Delta^2 y_{-1} + \Delta^2 y_0}{2}\right) + \frac{3}{128}\left(\frac{\Delta^4 y_{-1} + \Delta^4 y_{-2}}{2}\right) + \cdots$$

$$= \frac{439 + 346}{2} - \frac{1}{8}\left(\frac{-20 - 10}{2}\right) + \cdots$$

$$= 392{\cdot}5 + 1{\cdot}875 = \mathbf{394{\cdot}375}.$$

**Example 7.** *From the following table, using Stirling's formula, estimate the value of tan 16°.*

| $x$ | : | 0° | 5° | 10° | 15° | 20° | 25° | 30° |
|---|---|---|---|---|---|---|---|---|
| $y = \tan x$ | : | 0·0 | 0·0875 | 0·1763 | 0·2679 | 0·3640 | 0·4663 | 0·5774 |

**Solution.** Take $x_0 = 15°$ as the origin and $h = 5°$

$$u = \frac{x - x_0}{h} = \frac{16° - 15°}{5°} = 0{\cdot}2$$

| $x$ | $u$ | $y = tan\,x$ | $\Delta y$ | $\Delta^2 y$ | $\Delta^3 y$ | $\Delta^4 y$ | $\Delta^5 y$ |
|---|---|---|---|---|---|---|---|
| 0° | − 3 | 0 | | | | | |
| | | | 0·0875 | | | | |
| 5° | − 2 | 0·0875 | | 0·0013 | | | |
| | | | 0·0888 | | 0·0015 | | |
| 10° | − 1 | 0·1763 | | 0·0028 | | + 0·0002 | |
| | | | 0·0916 | | 0·0017 | | − 0·0002 |
| 15° | 0 | **[0·2679]** | | **[0·0045]** | | **[0·0000]** | |
| | | | 0·0961 | | 0·0017 | | 0·0009 |
| 20° | 1 | 0·3640 | | 0·0062 | | 0·0009 | |
| | | | 0·1023 | | 0·0026 | | |
| 25° | 2 | 0·4663 | | 0·0088 | | | |
| | | | 0·1411 | | | | |
| 30° | 3 | 0·5774 | | | | | |

By Stirling's formula,

$$y\,(u = 0{\cdot}2) = y_0 + \frac{u}{2}(\Delta y_0 + \Delta y_{-1}) + \frac{u^2}{2}\Delta^2 y_{-1} + \frac{u\,(u^2-1)}{6}\left(\frac{\Delta^3 y_{-1} + \Delta^3 y_{-2}}{2}\right)$$

$$+ \frac{u^2(u^2-1)}{4!}\Delta^4 y_{-2} + \frac{u\,(u^2-1)(u^2-4)}{5!}\left(\frac{\Delta^5 y_{-2} + \Delta^5 y_{-3}}{2}\right) + \cdots$$

$$= 0{\cdot}2679 + \frac{0{\cdot}2}{2}(0{\cdot}0961 + 0{\cdot}0916) + \frac{(0{\cdot}2)^2}{2}(0{\cdot}0045)$$

$$+ \frac{(0{\cdot}2)(0{\cdot}04 - 1)}{6}\left(\frac{0{\cdot}0017 + 0{\cdot}0017}{2}\right) + \frac{0{\cdot}04\,(0{\cdot}04 - 1)}{24}(0)$$

$$+ \frac{(0{\cdot}2)(0{\cdot}04 - 1)(0{\cdot}04 - 4)}{120}\left(\frac{0{\cdot}0009 - 0{\cdot}0002}{2}\right) + \cdots$$

$$= 0{\cdot}2679 + 0{\cdot}01877 + 0{\cdot}00009 - 0{\cdot}0000544 + 0{\cdot}0000022176$$

$$= 0{\cdot}286707817$$

$$\approx \mathbf{0{\cdot}2867}$$

**Example 8.** *From the following table, estimate f (337·5) by proper interpolation formula.*

| $x$ | 310 | 320 | 330 | 340 | 350 | 360 |
|---|---|---|---|---|---|---|
| $f(x) = y = log\,x$ | 2·4913617 | 2·5051500 | 2·5185139 | 2·5314789 | 2·5440680 | 2·5563025 |

**Solution.** Take $x_0 = 330$ as the origin

$$h = 10;\ u = \frac{x - x_0}{h} = \frac{337{\cdot}5 - 330}{10} = 0{\cdot}75$$

Since $u = 0{\cdot}75 > \frac{1}{2}$, we can use Everett's formula for better results; $v = 1 - u = 0{\cdot}25$

**Difference Table**

| $x$ | $u$ | $y=f(x)$ | $\Delta y$ | $\Delta^2 y$ | $\Delta^3 y$ | $\Delta^4 y$ |
|---|---|---|---|---|---|---|
| 310 | – 2 | 2·4913617 | | | | |
| | | | 0·0137883 | | | |
| 320 | – 1 | 2·5051500 | | – 0·0004244 | | |
| | | | 0·0133639 | | 0·0000255 | |
| 330 | 0 | 2·5185139 | | – 0·0003989 | | – 0·0000025 |
| | | | 0·0129650 | | 0·0000230 | |
| 340 | 1 | 2·5314789 | | – 0·0003759 | | – 0·0000017 |
| | | | 0·0125891 | | 0·0000213 | |
| 350 | 2 | 2·5440680 | | – 0·0003546 | | |
| | | | 0·0122345 | | | |
| 360 | 3 | 2·5563025 | | | | |

By Everett's formula,

$$y\,(u=0{\cdot}75)=\left[uy_1+\frac{u\,(u^2-1)}{3!}\Delta^2 y_0+\frac{u\,(u^2-1)(u^2-4)}{5!}\Delta^4 y_{-1}+\cdots\right]$$

$$+\left[vy_0+\frac{v\,(v^2-1)}{3!}\Delta^2 y_{-1}+\frac{v\,(v^2-1)(v^2-4)}{5!}\Delta^4 y_{-2}+\cdots\right]$$

$$=\left[(0{\cdot}75)(2{\cdot}5314789)+\frac{(0{\cdot}75)(0{\cdot}5625-1)}{6}(-0{\cdot}0003759)\right.$$

$$\left.+\frac{(0{\cdot}75)(0{\cdot}5625-1)(0{\cdot}5625-4)}{120}(-0{\cdot}0000017)\right]$$

$$+\left[(0{\cdot}25)(2{\cdot}5185139)+\frac{(0{\cdot}25)(0{\cdot}0625-1)}{6}(-0{\cdot}0003989)\right.$$

$$\left.+\frac{(0{\cdot}25)(0{\cdot}0625-1)(0{\cdot}0625-4)}{120}(-0{\cdot}0000025)\right]$$

$$\approx \mathbf{2{\cdot}5282736}.$$

## EXERCISE 7.2

**1.** Using Stirling's formula, estimate $f\,(1{\cdot}22)$ from the following table.

| $x$ | : | 20 | 25 | 30 | 35 | 40 |
|---|---|---|---|---|---|---|
| $y=f(x)$ | : | 49225 | 48316 | 47236 | 45926 | 44306 |

**2.** Estimate $\sqrt{1{\cdot}12}$ using Stirling's formula from the following table.

| $x$ | : | 1·0 | 1·05 | 1·10 | 1·15 | 1·20 | 1·25 | 1·30 |
|---|---|---|---|---|---|---|---|---|
| $f(x)$ | : | 1·00000 | 1·02470 | 1·04881 | 1·07238 | 1·09544 | 1·11803 | 1·14017 |

**3.** Apply central difference formula to find $f\,(12)$ given.

| $x$ | : | 5 | 10 | 15 | 20 |
|---|---|---|---|---|---|
| $f(x)$ | : | 54·14 | 60·54 | 67·72 | 75·88 |

**4.** From the table below find $y\,(5)$ given, using Bessel's formula.

| $x$ | : | 0 | 4 | 8 | 12 |
|---|---|---|---|---|---|
| $y\,(x)$ | : | 143 | 158 | 177 | 199 |

**5.** Apply Bessel's formula to get the value of $y_{25}$ given $y_{20}=2854$, $y_{24}=3162$, $y_{28}=3544$, $y_{32}=3992$.

**6.** From the following table, evaluate $e^{-1{\cdot}7475}$ using Bessel's formula and Everett's formula.

| $x$ | : | 1·72 | 1·73 | 1·74 | 1·75 | 1·76 | 1·77 | 1·78 |
|---|---|---|---|---|---|---|---|---|
| $e^{-x}$ | : | 0·1790661 | 0·1772844 | 0·1755204 | 0·1737739 | 0·1720448 | 0.1703329 | 0·1686381 |

**7.** Find $f(1{\cdot}2)$ given,

| $x$ | : | 0·2 | 0·6 | 1·0 | 1·4 | 1·8 |
|---|---|---|---|---|---|---|
| $f(x)$ | : | 0·39104 | 0·33322 | 0·24197 | 0·14973 | 0·07895 |

using Bessel's formula.

**8.** Using Bessel's formula estimate $(46{\cdot}24)^{1/3}$ given.

| $x$ | : | 41 | 45 | 49 | 53 |
|---|---|---|---|---|---|
| $x^{1/3}$ | : | 3·4482 | 3·5569 | 3·6593 | 3·7563 |

**9.** Using Bessel's formula find $y(62{\cdot}5)$ given.

| $x$ | : | 60 | 61 | 62 | 63 | 64 | 65 |
|---|---|---|---|---|---|---|---|
| $y(x)$ | : | 7782 | 7853 | 7924 | 7993 | 8062 | 8129 |

**10.** Obtain the value of $y(27{\cdot}4)$ using Bessel's formula, given.

| $x$ | : | 25 | 26 | 27 | 28 | 29 | 30 |
|---|---|---|---|---|---|---|---|
| $y(x)$ | : | 4·000 | 3·846 | 3·704 | 3·571 | 3·448 | 3·333 |

**11.** From the table below find $f(2{\cdot}73)$ using Bessel's formula.

| $x$ | : | 2·5 | 2·6 | 2·7 | 2·8 | 2·9 | 3·0 |
|---|---|---|---|---|---|---|---|
| $f(x)$ | : | 0·4938 | 0·4953 | 0·4965 | 0·4974 | 0·4981 | 0·4987 |

**12.** Using Everett's formula, find log 2375 given.

| $x$ | : | 21 | 22 | 23 | 24 | 25 | 26 |
|---|---|---|---|---|---|---|---|
| $\log x$ | : | 1·3222 | 1·3424 | 1·3617 | 1·3802 | 1·3979 | 1·4150 |

**13.** Find $y(12)$ if $y(0) = 0$, $y(10) = 43214$, $y(20) = 86002$, $y(30) = 128372$ using Everett's formula.

**14.** Using Everett's formula, estimate $y(30)$ given.

| $x$ | : | 20 | 28 | 36 | 44 |
|---|---|---|---|---|---|
| $y(x)$ | : | 2854 | 3162 | 7088 | 7984 |

**15.** Employ Everett's formula to evaluate $y(26)$ and $y(27)$ given.

| $x$ | : | 15 | 20 | 25 | 30 | 35 | 40 |
|---|---|---|---|---|---|---|---|
| $y(x)$ | : | 12·849 | 16·351 | 19·524 | 22·396 | 24·999 | 27·356 |

**16.** Apply Bessel's formula to get the value of $y(45)$ given.

| $x$ | : | 40 | 44 | 48 | 52 |
|---|---|---|---|---|---|
| $y$ | : | 51·08 | 63·24 | 70·88 | 79·84 |

**17.** Using Bessel's formula obtain the value of $y(5)$ given.

| $x$ | : | 0 | 4 | 8 | 12 |
|---|---|---|---|---|---|
| $y$ | : | 14·27 | 15·81 | 17·72 | 19·96 |

**18.** Use Stirling's formula in problems 16 and 17.

**19.** Use Stirling's formula to get tan 89°26′ from the table.

| $x$ | : | 89°21′ | 89°23′ | 89°25′ | 89°27′ | 89°29′ |
|---|---|---|---|---|---|---|
| $\tan x$ | : | 88·14 | 92·91 | 98·22 | 104·17 | 110·90 |

**20.** Use the formula of interpolating to halves in question 19 and estimate.

**21.** Given $\sin(0{\cdot}1) = 0{\cdot}0998$, $\sin(0{\cdot}2) = 0{\cdot}1986$, $\sin(0{\cdot}3) = 0{\cdot}2955$, $\sin(0{\cdot}4) = 0{\cdot}3894$, $\sin(0{\cdot}5) = 0{\cdot}4794$, find $\sin(0{\cdot}31)$, $\sin(0{\cdot}35)$. Use a suitable formula.

## ANSWERS (Chapter 7)

### EXERCISE 7.1 Page 240

**1.** 0·25176 **2.** 0·25177 **3.** 16·9216 **4.** 12·901 **5.** 0·7059913
**6.** 22·898 **7.** 1·2662 **8.** 0·17508 **9.** 1163 **10.** 0·06
**11.** 33·41.

### EXERCISE 7.1 Page 254

**1.** 47692 **2.** 1·05830 **3.** 63·30 **4.** 162·41 **5.** 3250·875
**6.** 0·1742089, 0·1742089 **7.** 0·19445 **8.** 3·5893 **9.** 7957
**10.** 3·6497 **11.** 0·4968 **12.** 3·3756 **13.** 56266 **14.** 4063
**15.** 20·121, 20·707 **16.** 65·0175 **17.** 16·25 **19.** 101·107
**20.** 0·3051, 0·3429.

# 8

# Interpolation With Unequal Intervals

## 8·1. Introduction

In the previous chapters on Interpolation we had the intervals of differencing to be a constant $h$. In other words, we had $x_i - x_{i-1} = h$ constant, for $i = 1, 2, \dots n$. If the values of $x$'s are given at unequal intervals, our Newton's forward, backward formulae and central difference interpolation formulae will not hold good. Hence, we introduce a new idea of divided differences. These divided differences take into consideration the changes of the values of the function $f(x)$ and also the changes in the values of the arguments $x$.

## 8·2. Divided differences

Let the function $y = f(x)$ assume the values $f(x_0), f(x_1), \dots f(x_n)$ corresponding to the arguments $x_0, x_1, \dots x_n$ respectively where the intervals $x_1 - x_0, x_2 - x_1, \dots, x_n - x_{n-1}$ need not be equal.

**Definitions**

The *first divided difference* of $f(x)$ for the arguments $x_0, x_1$ is defined as $\dfrac{f(x_1) - f(x_0)}{x_1 - x_0}\cdot$ It is denoted by $f(x_0, x_1)$ or $[x_0, x_1]$ or $\underset{x_1}{\Delta} f(x_0)$. In other words,

$$f(x_0, x_1) = [x_0, x_1] = \underset{x_1}{\Delta} (f(x_0) = \frac{f(x_1) - f(x_0)}{x_1 - x_0} \qquad \dots(1)$$

In the same notation, we have

$$f(x_1, x_2) = \underset{x_2}{\Delta} f(x_1) = \frac{f(x_2) - f(x_1)}{x_2 - x_1}$$

and $$f(x_{n-1}, x_n) = \underset{x_n}{\Delta} f(x_{n-1}) = \frac{f(x_n) - f(x_{n-1})}{x_n - x_{n-1}}, \; n = 1, 2, \dots n.$$

The *second divided difference* of $f(x)$ for three arguments $x_0, x_1, x_2$ is defined as

$$f(x_0, x_1, x_2) = \underset{x_1, x_2}{\Delta^2} f(x_0) = \frac{f(x_1, x_2) - f(x_0, x_1)}{x_2 - x_0} \qquad \text{...(2)}$$

This shows that to find a second divided difference, we require three continuous arguments.

In the same way, we define the *third divided differences* of $f(x)$ for the four arguments $x_0, x_1, x_2, x_3$ as

$$\underset{x_1, x_2, x_3}{\Delta^3} f(x_0) = f(x_0, x_1, x_2, x_3) = \frac{f(x_1, x_2, x_3) - f(x_0, x_1, x_2)}{x_3 - x_0} \qquad \text{...(3)}$$

Equations (1), (2), (3) refer to divided differences of order *one, two,* and *three* respectively.

We will see below the *divided difference table.*

| *Argument* $x$ | *Entry* $f(x)$ | *First divided difference* $\Delta f(x)$ | *Second divided difference* $\Delta^2 f(x)$ | *Third divided difference* $\Delta^3 f(x)$ |
|---|---|---|---|---|
| $x_0$ | $f(x_0)$ | | | |
| | | $f(x_0, x_1)$ | | |
| $x_1$ | $f(x_1)$ | | $f(x_0, x_1, x_2)$ | |
| | | $f(x_1, x_2)$ | | $f(x_0, x_1, x_2, x_3)$ |
| $x_2$ | $f(x_2)$ | | $f(x_1, x_2, x_3)$ | |
| | | $f(x_2, x_3)$ | | $f(x_1, x_2, x_3, x_4)$ |
| $x_3$ | $f(x_3)$ | | $f(x_2, x_3, x_4)$ | |
| | | $f(x_3, x_4)$ | | |
| $x_4$ | $f(x_4)$ | | | |

*Explanation*: Unlike the formation of forward, backward or central difference table, as seen in the previous chapters, here, in any difference column, the value of the divided difference between the two adjacent values is written by dividing the difference between the two adjacent values immediately in the previous column by the difference between the arguments against the two entries on the two diagonals passing through the divided difference.

**Example 1.** *Form the divided difference table for the following data:*

| $x$ | : | – 2 | 0 | 3 | 5 | 7 | 8 |
|---|---|---|---|---|---|---|---|
| $y = f(x)$ | : | – 792 | 108 | – 72 | 48 | – 144 | – 252 |

**Solution.** We form the table below

| $x$ | $y$ | $\Delta y$ | $\Delta^2 y$ | $\Delta^3 y$ | $\Delta^4 y$ |
|---|---|---|---|---|---|
| $-2$ | $-792$ | | | | |
| | | $\frac{108-(-792)}{0-(-2)}=450$ | | | |
| | | | $\frac{-60-450}{3-(-2)}=-102$ | | |
| $0$ | $108$ | | | | |
| | | $\frac{-72-108}{3-0}=-60$ | | $\frac{24+102}{5+2}=18$ | |
| | | | $\frac{60-(-60)}{5-0}=24$ | | |
| $3$ | $-72$ | | | | $\frac{-9-18}{7+2}=-3$ |
| | | $\frac{48-(-72)}{5-3}=60$ | | $\frac{-39-24}{7-0}=-9$ | |
| $5$ | $48$ | | $\frac{-96-60}{7-3}=-39$ | | $\frac{7+9}{8-0}=2$ |
| | | $\frac{-144-48}{7-5}=-96$ | | $\frac{-4+39}{8-3}=7$ | |
| $7$ | $-144$ | | $\frac{-108+96}{8-5}=-4$ | | |
| | | $\frac{-252-(-144)}{8-7}=-108$ | | | |
| $8$ | $-252$ | | | | |

**Example 2.** *Find the divided differences of* $f(x)=x^3+x+2$ *for the arguments 1, 3, 6, 11.*

**Solution.** We form below the divided difference table.

| $x$ | $f(x)$ | $\Delta f(x)$ | $\Delta^2 f(x)$ | $\Delta^3 f(x)$ |
|---|---|---|---|---|
| 1 | 4 | | | |
| | | $\frac{32-4}{3-1}=14$ | | |
| 3 | 32 | | $\frac{64-14}{6-1}=10$ | |
| | | $\frac{224-32}{6-3}=64$ | | $\frac{20-10}{11-1}=1$ |
| 6 | 224 | | $\frac{224-64}{11-3}=20$ | |
| | | $\frac{1344-224}{11-6}=224$ | | |
| 11 | 1344 | | | |

**Example 3.** *If* $f(x)=\frac{1}{x}$, *show that*

$$f(x_0, x_1, \ldots x_r)=\frac{(-1)^r}{x_0 x_1 x_2 \ldots x_r}$$ *where r is any positive integer.*

**Solution.** *Step 1 :*

$$f(x_0, x_1)=\frac{f(x_1)-f(x_0)}{x_1-x_0}=\frac{\frac{1}{x_1}-\frac{1}{x_0}}{x_1-x_0}=-\frac{1}{x_0x_1}=\frac{(-1)^1}{x_0x_1} \qquad \ldots(1)$$

*Step 2* : Let us prove the result by induction.

Let the result be true for $r=n$.

$$\text{Then } f(x_0, x_1, \ldots x_n)=\frac{(-1)^n}{x_0x_1x_2 \ldots x_n} \qquad \ldots(2)$$

Further $f(x_0, x_1, x_2, \dots x_{n+1}) = \dfrac{f(x_1, x_2, \dots x_{n+1}) - (x_0, x_1, \dots x_n)}{x_{n+1} - x_0}$

$$= \frac{\dfrac{(-1)^n}{x_1 x_2 \dots x_{n+1}} - \dfrac{(-1)^n}{x_0 x_1 x_2 \dots x_n}}{x_{n+1} - x_0}$$

$$= \frac{(-1)^n}{x_0 x_1 x_2 \dots x_{n+1}} \frac{(x_0 - x_{n+1})}{(x_{n+1} - x_0)}$$

$$= \frac{(-1)^{n+1}}{x_0 x_1 x_2 \dots x_{n+1}} \quad \dots(3)$$

Hence, the result is true for $r = n + 1$ by equation (3).

In other words, if the result is true for $r = n$, then it is true for $r = n + 1$. But, by (1), the result is true for $r = 1$. Hence by induction, the result is true for any positive integer $n$.

**Cor. 1.** Setting $r = 3$,

$$f(x_0, x_1, x_2, x_3) = \frac{-1}{x_0 x_1 x_2 x_3}$$

*i.e.,* $$\underset{x_1, x_2, x_3}{\Delta^3} \left( \frac{1}{x_0} \right) = -\frac{1}{x_0 x_1 x_2 x_3}$$

**Note :** This can be proved independently starting with the definition (not using induction method).

**Example 4.** *Show that* $\underset{bcd}{\Delta^3} \left( \frac{1}{a} \right) = -\frac{1}{abcd}$. (*BR. Ap. 1995*)

**Solution.** If $f(x) = \frac{1}{x}$, $f(a) = \frac{1}{a}$

$$f(a, b) = \underset{b}{\Delta} \left( \frac{1}{a} \right) = \frac{\frac{1}{b} - \frac{1}{a}}{b - a} = -\frac{1}{ab}$$

$$f(a, b, c) = \frac{f(b, c) - f(a, b)}{c - a} = \frac{-\frac{1}{bc} + \frac{1}{ab}}{c - a} = \frac{1}{abc} \left( \frac{c - a}{c - a} \right) = \frac{1}{abc}$$

$$f(a, b, c, d) = \frac{f(b, c, d) - f(a, b, c)}{d - a}$$

$$= \frac{\frac{1}{bcd} - \frac{1}{abc}}{d - a} = \frac{1}{abcd} \left( \frac{a - d}{d - a} \right) = -\frac{1}{abcd}.$$

Therefore, $\underset{bcd}{\Delta^3} \left( \frac{1}{a} \right) = -\frac{1}{abcd}$.

## 8·3. Properties of divided differences

**Property 1.** The value of any divided difference is independent of the order of the arguments. That is, the divided differences are symmetrical in all their arguments.

$$f(x_0, x_1) = \frac{f(x_1) - f(x_0)}{x_1 - x_0} = \frac{f(x_0) - f(x_1)}{x_0 - x_1} = f(x_1, x_0) \qquad \text{...(1)}$$

Again, $$f(x_0, x_1) = \frac{f(x_0)}{x_0 - x_1} - \frac{f(x_1)}{x_0 - x_1} = \frac{f(x_0)}{x_0 - x_1} + \frac{f(x_1)}{x_1 - x_0} \qquad \text{...(2)}$$

In the same way, $$f(x_1, x_0) = \frac{f(x_1)}{x_1 - x_0} + \frac{f(x_0)}{x_0 - x_1} \qquad \text{...(3)}$$

From (2) and (3), we have $f(x_0, x_1) = f(x_1, x_0)$

Similarly,

$$f(x_0, x_1, x_2) = \frac{f(x_1, x_2) - f(x_0, x_1)}{x_2 - x_0}$$

$$= \frac{1}{x_2 - x_0}\left[\left(\frac{f(x_1)}{x_1 - x_2} + \frac{f(x_2)}{x_2 - x_1}\right) - \left(\frac{f(x_0)}{x_0 - x_1} + \frac{f(x_1)}{x_1 - x_0}\right)\right]$$

$$= \frac{1}{x_2 - x_0}\left[\left(\frac{1}{x_1 - x_2} - \frac{1}{x_1 - x_0}\right) f(x_1) + \frac{f(x_2)}{x_2 - x_1} - \frac{f(x_0)}{x_0 - x_1}\right]$$

$$= \frac{1}{x_2 - x_0}\left[\frac{x_2 - x_0}{(x_1 - x_2)(x_1 - x_0)} f(x_1) + \frac{f(x_2)}{x_2 - x_1} - \frac{f(x_0)}{x_0 - x_1}\right]$$

$$= \frac{f(x_0)}{(x_0 - x_1)(x_0 - x_2)} + \frac{f(x_1)}{(x_1 - x_0)(x_1 - x_2)} + \frac{f(x_2)}{(x_2 - x_0)(x_2 - x_1)} \qquad \text{...(4)}$$

From (4), we find

$$f(x_0, x_1, x_2) = f(x_1, x_0, x_2) = f(x_1, x_2, x_0) = \cdots$$

This shows that $f(x_0, x_1, x_2)$ is independent of the order of the arguments.

By mathematical induction, we can prove that

$$f(x_0, x_1, x_2, \ldots x_n) = \frac{f(x_0)}{(x_0 - x_1)(x_0 - x_2) \cdots (x_0 - x_n)}$$

$$+ \frac{f(x_1)}{(x_1 - x_0)(x_1 - x_2) \cdots (x_1 - x_n)}$$

$$+ \frac{f(x_2)}{(x_2 - x_0)(x_2 - x_1)(x_2 - x_3) \cdots (x_2 - x_n)} + \cdots$$

$$+ \frac{f(x_n)}{(x_n - x_0)(x_n - x_1) \cdots (x_n - x_{n-1})}.$$

This is symmetrical w.r.t. any two arguments. Therefore, the divided differences are symmetrical w.r.t. any two arguments.

**Property 2.** The operator $\Delta$ is linear.

**Proof.** If $f(x)$ and $g(x)$ are two functions and $\alpha, \beta$ are constants, then,

$$\Delta\,[\alpha f(x)+\beta g(x)]=\frac{[\alpha f(x_1)+\beta g(x_1)]-[\alpha f(x_0)+\beta g(x_0)]}{x_1-x_0}$$

$$=\alpha\frac{f(x_1)-f(x_0)}{x_1-x_0}+\beta.\frac{g(x_1)-g(x_0)}{x_1-x_0}$$

$$=\alpha\,\Delta\, f(x)+\beta\,\Delta\, g(x).$$

**Corollary 1.** Setting $\alpha=\beta=1$,

$$\Delta\,[f(x)+g(x)]=\Delta\, f(x)+\Delta\, g(x).$$

**Corollary 2.** Setting $\beta=0$,

$$\Delta\,[\alpha f(x)]=\alpha\,\Delta\, f(x).$$

**Property 3.** The $n$th divided differences of a polynomial of degree $n$ are constants.

**Proof.** Taking $f(x)=x^n$ where $n$ is a positive integer,

$$f(x_0, x_1)=\frac{f(x_1)-f(x_0)}{x_1-x_0}=\frac{x_1^n-x_0^n}{x_1-x_0}$$

$$=x_1^{n-1}+x_0x_1^{n-2}+x_0^2x_1^{n-3}+\cdots+x_0^{n-1}$$

= a polynomial function of degree $(n-1)$ and symmetrical in $x_0, x_1$ with leading coefficient 1.

Again,

$$f(x_0, x_1, x_2)=\frac{f(x_1, x_2)-f(x_0, x_1)}{x_2-x_0}$$

$$=\frac{(x_2^{n-1}+x_1x_2^{n-2}+\cdots+x_1^{n-1})-(x_0^{n-1}+x_1x_0^{n-2}+\cdots+x_1^{n-1})}{x_2-x_0}$$

$$=\frac{x_2^{n-1}-x_0^{n-1}}{x_2-x_0}+\frac{x_1\,(x_2^{n-2}-x_0^{n-2})}{x_2-x_0}+\cdots+\frac{x_1^{n-2}\,(x_2-x_0)}{x_2-x_0}$$

$$=(x_2^{n-2}+x_0x_2^{n-3}+\cdots+x_0^{n-2})+x_1\,[x_2^{n-3}+x_0x_2^{n-4}+\cdots+x_0^{n-3}]+\cdots+x_1^{n-2}$$

= a polynomial of degree $(n-2)$ and symmetrical i $x_0, x_1, x_2$ with leading coefficient 1.

Proceeding in this way, the $r$th divided differences of $x^n$ will be a polynomial of degree $(n-r)$ and symmetrical in $x_0, x_1, x_2, \ldots x_r$ with leading coefficient 1.

Hence $n$th order divided differences of $x^n$ will be a polynomial of degree $n-n=0$, with leading coefficient 1. That is, its value is 1.

That is $\underset{}{\Delta}^n x^n = 1$.

$$\Delta^{n+i} x^n = 0, \quad \text{for} \quad i = 1, 2, \ldots$$

Hence, $\Delta^n [a_0x^n + a_1x^{n-1} + \cdots + a_n]$

$$= a_0 \Delta^n x^n + a_1 \Delta^n x^{n-1} + \cdots + \Delta^n a_n$$

$$= a_0 \cdot 1 + 0 + 0 + \cdots + 0 = a_0.$$

**Note:** Conversely, if the $n$th divided difference of a polynomial is constant, then the polynomial is of degree $n$.

## 8·4. Relation between divided differences and forward differences

If the arguments $x_0, x_1, x_2, \ldots$ are equally spaced, then we have, $x_1 - x_0 = x_2 - x_1 = x_3 - x_2 = \cdots = x_n - x_{n-1} = h$.

$$\underset{x_1}{\Delta} f(x_0) = f(x_1, x_0) = \frac{f(x_1) - f(x_0)}{x_1 - x_0} = \frac{\Delta f(x_0)}{h}$$

$$\Delta^2 f(x_0) = \frac{\Delta f(x_1) - \Delta f(x_0)}{x_2 - x_0} = \frac{\frac{1}{h}\Delta f(x_1) - \frac{1}{h}\Delta f(x_0)}{2h}$$

$$= \frac{1}{2h^2} \Delta^2 f(x_0)$$

Similarly,

$$\Delta^3 f(x_0) = \frac{\Delta^3 f(x_0)}{3!\, h^3}$$

$$\Delta^n f(x_0) = \frac{\Delta^n f(x_0)}{n!\, h^n}.$$

## 8·5. Theorem: Newton's interpolation formula for unequal intervals (or Newton's divided difference formula)

Let $y = f(x)$ take values $f(x_0), f(x_1) \cdots f(x_n)$ corresponding to the arguments $x_0, x_1, \ldots x_n$.

By definition,

$$f(x, x_0) = \frac{f(x) - f(x_0)}{x - x_0}$$

$$\therefore \quad f(x) = f(x_0) + (x - x_0) f(x, x_0) \qquad \ldots(1)$$

Similarly, $f(x, x_0, x_1) = \dfrac{f(x, x_0) - f(x_0, x_1)}{x - x_1}$

$$\therefore \quad f(x, x_0) = f(x_0, x_1) + (x - x_1) f(x, x_0, x_1)$$

Using this value of $f(x, x_0)$ in (1), we have

$$f(x) = f(x_0) + (x - x_0) f(x_0, x_1) + (x - x_0)(x - x_1) f(x, x_0, x_1) \quad ...(2)$$

Again $f(x, x_0, x_1, x_2) = \dfrac{f(x, x_0, x_1) - f(x_0, x_1, x_2)}{x - x_2}$

$$\therefore \quad f(x, x_0, x_1) = f(x_0, x_1, x_2) + (x - x_2) f(x, x_0, x_1, x_2)$$

Using this value in (2), we get

$$f(x) = f(x_0) + (x - x_0) f(x_0, x_1) + (x - x_0)(x - x_1) f(x_0, x_1, x_2) + (x - x_0)(x - x_1)(x - x_2) f(x, x_0, x_1, x_2) \quad ...(3)$$

Continuing in this manner, we get,

$$f(x) = f(x_0) + (x - x_0) f(x_0, x_1) + (x - x_0)(x - x_1) f(x_0, x_1, x_2) + (x - x_0)(x - x_1)(x - x_2) f(x_0, x_1, x_2, x_3) + \cdots + (x - x_0)(x - x_1)(x - x_2) \cdots (x - x_{n-1}) f(x_0, x_1, x_2, \ldots x_n) + (x - x_0)(x - x_1)(x - x_2) \cdots (x - x_n) f(x, x_0, x_1, \ldots x_n) \quad ...(4)$$

If $f(x)$ is a polynomial of degree $n$, then

$$f(x, x_0, x_1, \ldots x_n) = 0 \quad (\because (n+1)^{\text{th}} \text{ difference})$$

Hence the last equation (4) becomes,

$$\mathbf{f(x) = f(x_0) + (x - x_0) f(x_0, x_1) + (x - x_0)(x - x_1) f(x_0, x_1, x_2) + \cdots + (x - x_0)(x - x_1) \cdots (x - x_{n-1}) f(x_0, x_1, \ldots x_n)} \quad ...(5)$$

**Equation (5) is called Newton's divided difference interpolation formula for unequal intervals.**

**8·6. Deduction: Deduce Gregory Newton interpolation forward formula for equal intervals**

We have seen already, (if intervals are equal) that

$$f(x_1, x_0) = \frac{\Delta f(x_0)}{h}$$

$$f(x_0, x_1, x_2) = \frac{1}{2!\, h^2} \Delta^2 f(x_0)$$

$$f(x_0, x_1, x_2, x_3) = \frac{1}{3!\, h^3} \Delta^3 f(x_0)$$

$$f(x_0, x_1, x_2, \ldots x_n) = \frac{1}{n!\, h^n} \Delta^n f(x_0)$$

If $x - x_0 = uh$, then $x - x_1 = (x - x_0) - (x_1 - x_0) = uh - h = (u - 1) h$

$x - x_2 = (u - 2) h$ etc.

Substituting in equation (5), we get

$$f(x) = f(x_0 + uh) = f(x_0) + uh \frac{\Delta f(x_0)}{h} + \frac{uh(u-1)h}{2!\, h^2} \Delta^2 f(x_0) + \cdots$$

Let $y_0 = \Delta f(x_0)$

$$f(x) = f(x_0 + uh) = y_0 + u\,\Delta y_0 + \frac{u(u-1)}{2!}\Delta^2 y_0 + \frac{u(u-1)(u-2)}{3!}\Delta^3 y_0 + \cdots \qquad \ldots(6)$$

The equation (6) is exactly *Newton's forward interpolation formula for equal intervals.*

**Example 5.** *Show that the divided difference of second order can be expressed as the quotient of two determinants of third order.*

(*B.Sc. BR. Ap. 1995*)

**Solution.** We have seen already,

$$f(x_0, x_1, x_2) = \frac{f(x_0)}{(x_0 - x_1)(x_0 - x_2)} + \frac{f(x_1)}{(x_1 - x_0)(x_1 - x_2)} + \frac{f(x_2)}{(x_2 - x_0)(x_2 - x_1)}$$

$$= \frac{(x_2 - x_1) f(x_0) + (x_0 - x_2) f(x_1) + (x_1 - x_0) f(x_2)}{(x_0 - x_1)(x_1 - x_2)(x_2 - x_0)}$$

$$= \frac{(x_1 - x_2) f(x_0) + (x_2 - x_0) f(x_1) + (x_0 - x_1) f(x_2)}{-(x_0 - x_1)(x_1 - x_2)(x_2 - x_0)}$$

$$= \frac{\begin{vmatrix} f(x_0) & f(x_1) & f(x_2) \\ x_0 & x_1 & x_2 \\ 1 & 1 & 1 \end{vmatrix}}{\begin{vmatrix} x_0^2 & x_1^2 & x_2^2 \\ x_0 & x_1 & x_2 \\ 1 & 1 & 1 \end{vmatrix}}$$

**Note:** This result can be extended to the *n*th order divided differences also.

**Example 6.** *Find the values of* $\underset{y,z}{\Delta^2} x^2$ *and* $\underset{y,z}{\Delta^2} x^3$ *and hence evaluate* $\underset{y,z}{\Delta^2}(ax+b)(cx+d)$ *and* $\underset{y,z}{\Delta^2}(ax+b)(cx+d)(ex+f)$.

**Solution.** $\underset{y}{\Delta} x^2 = \dfrac{y^2 - x^2}{y - x} = y + x = x + y$

$$\underset{y,z}{\Delta^2} x^2 = \frac{1}{z - x}\left[\underset{z}{\Delta} y^2 - \underset{y}{\Delta} x^2\right]$$

$$= \frac{1}{z - x}[(y + z) - (x + y)] = 1 \qquad \ldots(1)$$

$$\underset{y,z}{\Delta^2}(ax+b)(cx+d) = \underset{y,z}{\Delta^2}[ac\,x^2 + (ad + bc)\,x + bd]$$

$$= \underset{y,z}{\Delta^2}(acx^2) + 0 + 0$$

$$= ac\,(1) = ac.$$

$$(ii)\ \underset{y}{\Delta}\, x^3 = \frac{y^3 - x^3}{y - x} = y^2 + x^2 + xy$$

$$\underset{y,\,z}{\Delta^2}\, x^3 = \frac{\underset{z}{\Delta}\, y^3 - \underset{y}{\Delta}\, x^3}{z - x}$$

$$= \frac{(y^2 + z^2 + yz) - (x^2 + y^2 + xy)}{z - x}$$

$$= \frac{(z - x)\,(x + y + z)}{z - x} = x + y + z. \qquad ...(2)$$

Hence, $\underset{y,\,z}{\Delta^2}\,(ax + b)\,(cx + d)\,(ex + f)$

$$= \underset{y,\,z}{\Delta^2}\,[ace\,x^3 + (acf + ceb + aed)\,x^2 + \cdots]$$

$$= ace\,(x + y + z) + (acf + ceb + aed)$$

using (1) and (2).

**Example 7.** *Using Newton's divided difference formula, find the values of $f(2), f(8)$ and $f(15)$ given the following table:*

| $x$ | : | 4 | 5 | 7 | 10 | 11 | 13 |
|---|---|---|---|---|---|---|---|
| $f(x)$ | : | 48 | 100 | 294 | 900 | 1210 | 2028 |

**Solution.** We form the divided difference table since the intervals are unequal.

| $x$ | $f(x)$ | $\Delta f(x)$ | $\Delta^2 f(x)$ | $\Delta^3 f(x)$ | $\Delta^4 f(x)$ |
|---|---|---|---|---|---|
| 4 | 48 | | | | |
| | | $\frac{100-48}{5-4} = 52$ | | | |
| 5 | 100 | | $\frac{97-52}{7-4} = 15$ | | |
| | | $\frac{294-100}{7-5} = 97$ | | $\frac{21-15}{10-4} = 1$ | |
| 7 | 294 | | $\frac{202-97}{10-5} = 21$ | | 0 |
| | | $\frac{900-294}{10-7} = 202$ | | $\frac{27-21}{11-5} = 1$ | |
| 10 | 900 | | $\frac{310-202}{11-7} = 27$ | | 0 |
| | | $\frac{1210-900}{11-10} = 310$ | | $\frac{33-27}{13-7} = 1$ | |
| 11 | 1210 | | $\frac{409-310}{13-10} = 33$ | | |
| | | $\frac{2028-1210}{13-11} = 409$ | | | |
| 13 | 2028 | | | | |

By Newton's divided difference interpolation formula,

$$f(x) = f(x_0) + (x - x_0)\,f(x_0, x_1) + (x - x_0)\,(x - x_1)\,f(x_0, x_1, x_2)$$
$$+ (x - x_0)\,(x - x_1)\,(x - x_2)\,f(x_0, x_1, x_2, x_3) + \cdots \qquad ...(i)$$

In our problem, $x_0 = 4, x_1 = 5, x_2 = 7, x_3 = 10, x_4 = 11, x_5 = 13$ and

$$f(x_0) = 48, f(x_0, x_1) = 52, f(x_0, x_1, x_2) = 15, f(x_0, x_1, x_2, x_3) = 1.$$

Hence using these values in $(i)$, we have

$$f(x) = 48 + (x-4)\,52 + (x-4)(x-5)\,15 + (x-4)(x-5)(x-7)\,1$$
$$f(2) = 48 - 104 + 90 - 30 = 4$$
$$f(8) = 48 + (4)\,52 + (4)(3)\,15 + (4)(3)(1)\,1 = 448$$
$$f(15) = 48 + 11 \times 52 + 11 \times 10 \times 15 + 11 \times 10 \times 8 = 3150.$$

**Example 8.** *From the following table find $f(x)$ and hence $f(6)$ using Newton's interpolation formula.*

| $x$ | : | 1 | 2 | 7 | 8 |
|---|---|---|---|---|---|
| $f(x)$ | : | 1 | 5 | 5 | 4 |

**Solution.** Evidently, intervals are not equal. We form the divided difference table below:

| $x$ | $f(x)$ | $\Delta f(x)$ | $\Delta^2 f(x)$ | $\Delta^3 f(x)$ |
|---|---|---|---|---|
| 1 | 1 | | | |
| | | $\frac{5-1}{2-1} = 4$ | | |
| 2 | 5 | | $\frac{0-4}{7-1} = -\frac{2}{3}$ | |
| | | $\frac{5-5}{7-2} = 0$ | | $\frac{-\frac{1}{6}+\frac{2}{3}}{8-1} = \frac{1}{14}$ |
| 7 | 5 | | $\frac{-1-0}{8-2} = -\frac{1}{6}$ | |
| | | $\frac{4-5}{8-7} = -1$ | | |
| 8 | 4 | | | |

By Newton's divided difference formula,

$$f(x) = f(x_0) + (x - x_0) f(x_0, x_1) + (x - x_0)(x - x_1) f(x_0, x_1, x_2) + \cdots$$
$$= 1 + (x-1)\,4 + (x-1)(x-2)\left(-\frac{2}{3}\right) + (x-1)(x-2)(x-7)\left(\frac{1}{14}\right)$$
$$= \frac{1}{42}(3x^3 - 58x^2 + 321x - 224)$$
$$f(6) = \frac{1}{42}[3 \times 216 - 36 \times 58 + 1926 - 224]$$
$$= 6{\cdot}2380\,9524.$$

**Example 9.** *Find the function $f(x)$ from the following table hence evaluate $f(z)$*

| $x$ | : | 0 | 1 | 2 | 4 | 5 | 7 |
|---|---|---|---|---|---|---|---|
| $f(x)$ | : | 0 | 0 | – 12 | 0 | 600 | 7308 |

**Solution.** Since 6 data are given, we assume the polynomial to be of degree 5.

Since $f(0) = 0, f(1) = 0$, and $f(4) = 0$, it is a clear $x(x-1)(x-4)$ is a factor of $f(x)$.

So, let $f(x) = x(x-1)(x-4)\,\phi(x)$ where $\phi(x)$ is a quadratic polynomial.

Now, $\phi(x) = \dfrac{f(x)}{x(x-1)(x-4)}$

$$\therefore \quad \phi(2) = \frac{f(2)}{2\,(1)\,(-2)} = \frac{-12}{-4} = 3$$

$$\varphi(5) = \frac{f(5)}{5\,(4)\,(1)} = \frac{600}{20} = 30$$

$$\varphi(7) = \frac{f(7)}{7\,(6)\,(3)} = \frac{7308}{126} = 58$$

Now we will find $\phi(x)$ using divided difference formula of Newton,

| $x$ | $\phi(x)$ | $\Delta\,\phi(x)$ | $\Delta^2\,\varphi(x)$ |
|---|---|---|---|
| 2 | 3 | | |
| | | $\frac{30-3}{5-2} = 9$ | |
| 5 | 30 | | $\frac{14-9}{7-2} = 1$ |
| | | $\frac{58-30}{7-5} = 14$ | |
| 7 | 58 | | |

By Newton's formula,

$$\begin{aligned}\phi(x) &= \phi(x_0) + (x - x_0)\,\phi(x_0, x_1) + (x - x_0)(x - x_1)\,\phi(x_0, x_1, x_2)\\ &= 3 + (x-2)\,9 + (x-2)(x-5)\,1\\ &= x^2 + 2x - 5\end{aligned}$$

Hence, $f(x) = x\,(x-1)\,(x-4)\,(x^2 + 2x - 5)$.

**Note:** This procedure is adopted to minimise the work.

**Example 10.** *From the following table, obtain $f(x)$ as a polynomial in powers of $(x-5)$.*

| $x$ | : | 0 | 2 | 3 | 4 | 5 | 6 |
|---|---|---|---|---|---|---|---|
| $f(x)$ | : | 4 | 26 | 58 | 112 | 466 | 922 |

*using Newton's method.*

**Solution.** We will form the divided difference table below:

| $x$ | $f(x)$ | $\Delta f(x)$ | $\Delta^2 f(x)$ | $\Delta^3 f(x)$ |
|---|---|---|---|---|
| 0 | 4 | | | |
| | | 11 | | |
| 2 | 26 | | 7 | 1 |
| | | 32 | | |
| 3 | 58 | | 11 | 1 |
| | | 54 | | |
| 4 | 112 | | 16 | 1 |
| | | 118 | | |
| 5 | 466 | | 22 | $\frac{b-22}{1} = 1$ |
| | | 228 | $\frac{p-228}{-2} = b$ | |
| 6 | 922 | | | |

---

| $x$ | $f(x)$ | $\Delta f(x)$ | $\Delta^2 f(x)$ | $\Delta^3 f(x)$ |
|---|---|---|---|---|
| | | $\frac{a-922}{-4} = p$ | | $\frac{d-b}{5-7} = 1$ |
| 5 | $a$ | | $\frac{q-p}{5-9} = d$ | |
| | | $q$ | | $\frac{k-d}{5-9} = 1$ |
| 5 | | | $k$ | |
| 5 | | | | |

Since the third differences are constants (= 1), we extend the table by introducing $x = 5$ three times and introducing unknowns from the last column.

$$\frac{b-22}{1} = 1 \Rightarrow b = 23, \frac{p-228}{-2} = 23 \Rightarrow p = 182$$

$$\frac{a-922}{-4} = 182 \Rightarrow a = 194$$

$$\frac{d-b}{-2} = 1 \Rightarrow d = 21; \frac{q-p}{-4} = 21 \Rightarrow q = 98.$$

$$\frac{k-d}{-4} = 1 \Rightarrow k = 17.$$

Now take 5 as the origin and proceed.

$$f(x) = f(5) + (x-5) f(x_0, x_1) + (x-5)(x-5) f(x_0, x_1, x_2) + (x-5)^3 f(x_0, x_1, x_2, x_3)$$

$$= a + (x-5) q + (x-5)^2 k + (x-5)^3 \times 1$$

$$= 194 + 98(x-5) + 17(x-5)^2 + (x-5)^3.$$

**Example 11.** *Find the equation $y = f(x)$ of least degree and passing through the points (– 1, – 21), (1, 15) (2, 12), (3, 3). Find also y at x = 0.*

**Solution.** Since the intervals are not equal, we will form divided difference table and use Newton's formula

| $x$ | $f(x)$ | $\Delta f(x)$ | $\Delta^2 f(x)$ | $\Delta^3 f(x)$ |
|---|---|---|---|---|
| – 1 | – 21 | | | |
| | | 18 | | |
| 1 | 15 | | – 7 | |
| | | – 3 | | 1 |
| 2 | 12 | | – 3 | |
| | | – 9 | | |
| 3 | 3 | | | |

We will use Newton's divided difference formula

$$y = f(x) = -21 + (x+1)\,18 + (x+1)(x-1)(-7) + (x+1)(x-1)(x-2)\,1$$

$$= x^3 - 9x^2 + 17x + 6$$

Setting $x = 0$,

$$f(0) = 6.$$

**Example 12.** *The following table gives same relation between steam pressure and temperature. Find the pressure at temperature 372·1°.*

(*B.Sc. BR. Nov. '90*)

| *T* | *361°* | *367°* | *378°* | *387°* | *399°* |
|---|---|---|---|---|---|
| *P* | *154·9* | *167·9* | *191·0* | *212·5* | *244·2* |

**Solution.** **Table (divided difference)**

| $T$ | $P$ | $\Delta P$ | $\Delta^2 P$ | $\Delta^3 P$ | $\Delta^4 P$ |
|---|---|---|---|---|---|
| 361° | 154·9 | | | | |
| | | 2·01666666 | | | |
| 367° | 167·0 | | 0·009714795 | | |
| | | 2·18181818 | | 0·000024566 | |
| 378° | 191·0 | | 0·010353535 | | 0·00000073 |
| | | 2·3888888 | | 0·000052609 | |
| 387° | 212·5 | | 0·012037037 | | |
| | | 2·64166666 | | | |
| 399° | 244·2 | | | | |

By Newton's formula,

$$P\,(T = 372{\cdot}1°) = 154{\cdot}9 + (11{\cdot}1)\,(2{\cdot}01666666) + (11{\cdot}1)\,(5{\cdot}1)\,(0{\cdot}009714795)$$
$$+ (11{\cdot}1)\,(5{\cdot}1)\,(-5{\cdot}9)\,(0{\cdot}000024566)$$
$$+ (11{\cdot}1)\,(5{\cdot}1)\,(-5{\cdot}9)\,(-14{\cdot}9)\,(0{\cdot}00000739)$$
$$= 177{\cdot}8394819.$$

## EXERCISE 8.1

**1.** If $f(x) = \dfrac{1}{x^2}$, find the divided differences

$$f(a, b), f(a, b, c) \text{ and } f(a, b, c, d).$$

**2.** Using the following table, find $f(x)$ as a polynomial by using Newton's formula

| $x$ : | – 1 | 0 | 3 | 6 | 7 |
|---|---|---|---|---|---|
| $f(x)$ : | 3 | – 6 | 39 | 822 | 1611 |

**3.** Find $y\,(x = 20)$ given

| $x$ : | 12 | 18 | 22 | 24 | 32 |
|---|---|---|---|---|---|
| $y\,(x)$ : | 146 | 836 | 19481 | 2796 | 9236 |

**4.** Find a cubic polynomial of $x$ given *(Anna Ap. 2005)*

| $x$ : | 0 | 1 | 2 | 5 |
|---|---|---|---|---|
| $f(x)$ : | 2 | 3 | 12 | 147 |

**5.** Find the third divided difference of $f(x)$ with arguments 2, 4, 9, 10 where $f(x) = x^3 - 2x$.

**6.** Find the polynomial equation $y = f(x)$ passing through (5, 1335), (2, 9), (0, 5), (– 1, 33) and (– 4, 1245).

**7.** If $y(0) = -18, y(1) = 0, y(3) = 0, y(5) = -248, y(6) = 0$ and $y(9) = 13104$, find $y = f(x)$.

**8.** Using the following table, find $f(x)$ as a polynomial in powers of $(x - 6)$. Also find $f'(6), f''(6)$ and $f'''(6)$

| $x$ : | – 1 | 0 | 2 | 3 | 7 | 10 |
|---|---|---|---|---|---|---|
| $f(x)$ : | – 11 | 1 | 1 | 1 | 141 | 561 |

**9.** Find the polynomial equation of degree four passing through the points (8, 1515), (7, 778), (5, 138), (4, 43) and (2, 3).

**10.** Find the pressure of steam at 142°C using Newton's general formula

| Temp °C : | 140 | 150 | 160 | 170 | 180 |
|---|---|---|---|---|---|
| Pressure kgf/cm$^2$ : | 3·685 | 4·854 | 6·302 | 8·076 | 10·225 |

*(B.Sc. BR. Nov. 94)*

**11.** Obtain the value of $\log_{10} 656$ given $\log_{10} 654 = 2{\cdot}8156$, $\log_{10} 658 = 2{\cdot}8182$, $\log_{10} 659 = 2{\cdot}8189$ and $\log_{10} 666 = 2{\cdot}8202$.

**12.** Find $y\ (x = 5{\cdot}60275)$ from the table.

| $x$ : | 5·600 | 5·602 | 5·605 | 5·607 | 5·608 |
|---|---|---|---|---|---|
| $y$ : | 0·77556588 | 0·77682686 | 0·77871250 | 0·77996571 | 0·78059114 |

**13.** Given the data, find $f(x)$ as a polynomial of degree 2.

| $x$ : | 1 | 2 | – 4 |
|---|---|---|---|
| $f(x)$ : | 3 | – 5 | 4 |

**14.** Find a polynomial $f(x)$ of lowest degree which takes the values 3, 7, 9 and 19 when $x$ = 2, 4, 5, 10.

**15.** Find $\log_{10} 323{\cdot}5$ given

| $x$ : | 321·0 | 322·8 | 324·2 | 325·0 |
|---|---|---|---|---|
| $\log_{10} x$ : | 2·50651 | 2·50893 | 2·51081 | 2·51188 |

**16.** From the following table find $f$ (5).

| $x$ : | 0 | 1 | 3 | 6 |
|---|---|---|---|---|
| $f(x)$ : | 1 | 4 | 88 | 1309 |

**17.** Using divided difference table, find $f(x)$ which takes the values 1, 4, 40, 85 as $x$ = 0, 1, 3, 4.

**18.** Find

$\Delta^4 f(x)$ if $f(x) = x(x+1)(x+2)(x+3)$.

**19.** Find the function $y(x)$ in powers of $(x-1)$ given

$y(0) = 8,\ y(1) = 11,\ y(4) = 68,\ y(5) = 123.$

**20.** If $f(x) = u(x)\ v(x)$, show that

$f(x_0, x_1) = u(x_0)\ v(x_0, x_1) + u(x_0, x_1)\ v(x_1).$

## 8·7. Lagrange's interpolation formula (*for unequal intervals*)

The forward and backward interpolation formulae of Newton can be used only when the values of independent variable $x$ are equally spaced. Further, the differences must become ultimately small. In cases, where the values of independent variable are not equally spaced and in cases when the differences of dependent variable are not small, ultimately, we will use *Lagrange's interpolation formula.*

Let $y = f(x)$ be a function such that

$f(x)$ takes the values $y_0, y_1, y_2, \ldots y_n$, corresponding to $x = x_0, x_1, x_2, \ldots x_n$. That is, $y_i = f(x_i)$, $i = 0, 1, 2, \ldots n$.

Now, there are $(n+1)$ paired values $(x_i, y_i)$, $i = 0, 1, 2, \ldots n$ and hence $f(x)$ can be represented by a polynomial function of degree $n$ in $x$.

We will select that $f(x)$ as follows.

$$f(x) = a_0 (x - x_1)(x - x_2) \cdots (x - x_n)$$
$$+ a_1 (x - x_0)(x - x_2)(x - x_3) \cdots (x - x_n)$$
$$+ a_2 (x - x_0)(x - x_1)(x - x_3)(x - x_4) \cdots (x - x_n) + \cdots$$
$$+ a_i (x - x_0)(x - x_1) \cdots (x - x_{i-1})(x - x_{i+1}) \cdots (x - x_n) + \cdots$$
$$+ a_n (x - x_0)(x - x_1) \cdots (x - x_{n-1}) \quad \ldots(1)$$

**Note:** The term in which $a_i$ occurs has the factor $(x - x_i)$ lacking.

This is true for all values of $x$.

Substituting in (1), $x = x_0, y = y_0$, we get

$$y_0 = a_0 (x_0 - x_1)(x_0 - x_2) \cdots (x_0 - x_n)$$

$$\therefore \quad a_0 = \frac{y_0}{(x_0 - x_1)(x_0 - x_2) \cdots (x_0 - x_n)}$$

Similarly, setting $x = x_1, y = y_1$ we have

$$a_1 = \frac{y_1}{(x_1 - x_0)(x_1 - x_2)(x_1 - x_3) \cdots (x_1 - x_n)}$$

In the same way, we get

$$a_2 = \frac{y_2}{(x_2 - x_0)(x_2 - x_1)(x_2 - x_3) \cdots (x_2 - x_n)}$$

..........................................................

$$a_n = \frac{y_n}{(x_n - x_0)(x_n - x_1) \cdots (x_n - x_{n-1})}$$

Substituting these values of $a$'s in (1), we have

$$y = f(x) = \frac{(x - x_1)(x - x_2) \cdots (x - x_n)}{(x_0 - x_1)(x_0 - x_2) \cdots (x_0 - x_n)} \cdot y_0$$
$$+ \frac{(x - x_0)(x - x_2) \cdots (x - x_n)}{(x_1 - x_0)(x_1 - x_2) \cdots (x_1 - x_n)} \cdot y_1$$
$$+ \cdots\cdots\cdots$$
$$+ \frac{(x - x_0)(x - x_1) \cdots (x - x_{i-1})(x - x_{i+1}) \cdots (x - x_n)}{(x_i - x_0)(x_i - x_1) \cdots (x_i - x_{i-1})(x_i - x_{i+1}) \cdots (x_i - x_n)} \cdot y_i$$
$$+ \cdots\cdots\cdots$$
$$+ \frac{(x - x_0)(x - x_1) \cdots (x - x_{n-1})}{(x_n - x_0)(x_n - x_1) \cdots (x_n - x_{n-1})} y_n \quad \ldots(2)$$

Equation (2) is called *Lagrange's interpolation formula for unequal intervals.*

**Cor.** Dividing both sides of equation (2) by

$(x-x_0)(x-x_1)\cdots(x-x_n)$, we get

$$\frac{f(x)}{(x-x_0)(x-x_1)\cdots(x-x_n)}=\frac{y_0}{(x_0-x_1)(x_0-x_2)\cdots(x_0-x_n)}\cdot\frac{1}{x-x_0}$$
$$+\frac{y_1}{(x_1-x_0)(x_1-x_2)\cdots(x_1-x_n)}\cdot\frac{1}{x-x_1}$$
$$+\cdots\cdots\cdots\cdots$$
$$+\frac{y_n}{(x_n-x_0)(x_n-x_1)\cdots(x_n-x_{n-1})}\cdot\frac{1}{x-x_n}.$$

**8·8. Different form of Lagrange's interpolation formula**

The Lagrangian interpolation formula can also be written as

$$f(x)=\sum_{i=0}^{n}\frac{\Pi_n(x)}{(x-x_i)\,\Pi'_n(x_i)}\,y_i \text{ where}$$

$$\Pi_n(x)=(x-x_0)(x-x_1)\cdots(x-x_n) \quad\text{and } \Pi'_n(x)=\frac{d}{dx}[\Pi_n(x)]$$

**Solution.** $\Pi_n(x)=(x-x_0)(x-x_1)\cdots(x-x_n)$

Differentiating this and substituting $x=x_i$, we get

$$\Pi'_n(x_i)=(x_i-x_0)(x_i-x_1)\cdots(x_i-x_{i-1})(x_i-x_{i+1})\cdots(x-x_n)$$

Substituting this in equation (2),

$$f(x)=\frac{\Pi_n(x)}{x-x_0}\cdot\frac{y_0}{\Pi'_n(x_0)}$$
$$+\frac{\Pi_n(x)}{x-x_1}\cdot\frac{y_1}{\Pi'_n(x_1)}+\cdots+\frac{\Pi_n(x)}{x-x_n}\cdot\frac{y_n}{\Pi'_n(x_n)}$$
$$=\sum_{i=0}^{n}\frac{\Pi_n(x)}{\Pi'_n(x_i)}\cdot\frac{y_i}{x-x_i}.$$

**Example 13.** *Using Lagrange's interpolation formula, find* $y(10)$ *from the following table*

| $x$ : | 5 | 6 | 9 | 11 |
|---|---|---|---|---|
| $y$ : | 12 | 13 | 14 | 16 |

**Solution.** By Lagrange's interpolation formula, we have

$$y=f(x)=\frac{(x-x_1)(x-x_2)(x-x_3)\cdot y_0}{(x_0-x_1)(x_0-x_2)(x_0-x_3)}+\frac{(x-x_0)(x-x_2)(x-x_3)}{(x_1-x_0)(x_1-x_2)(x_1-x_3)}y_1$$
$$+\frac{(x-x_0)(x-x_1)(x-x_3)}{(x_2-x_0)(x_2-x_1)(x_2-x_3)}y_2+\frac{(x-x_0)(x-x_1)(x-x_2)}{(x_3-x_0)(x_3-x_1)(x_3-x_2)}\cdot y_3.$$
$$=\frac{(x-6)(x-9)(x-11)}{(5-6)(5-9)(5-11)}\cdot 12+\frac{(x-5)(x-9)(x-11)}{(6-5)(6-9)(6-11)}\cdot 13$$

$$+\frac{(x-5)(x-6)(x-11)}{(9-5)(9-6)(9-11)}\cdot 14+\frac{(x-5)(x-6)(x-9)}{(11-5)(11-6)(11-9)}\cdot 16$$

Putting $x=10$,

$$y(10)=f(10)=\frac{(4)(1)(-1)}{(-1)(-4)(-6)}\cdot 12+\frac{(5)(1)(-1)}{(1)(-3)(-5)}\cdot 13$$

$$+\frac{(5)(4)(-1)}{(4)(3)(-2)}\cdot 14+\frac{(5)(4)(1)}{(6)(5)(2)}\cdot 16$$

$$=14{\cdot}666666.$$

**Example 14.** *Find the parabola of the form $y=ax^2+bx+c$ passing through the points (0, 0), (1, 1) and (2, 20).*

**Solution.** We use Lagrange's interpolation formula

$$y=f(x)=\frac{(x-1)(x-2)}{(0-1)(0-2)}\cdot 0+\frac{(x-0)(x-2)}{(1-0)(1-2)}\cdot 1+\frac{(x-0)(x-1)}{(2-0)(2-1)}\cdot 20$$

$$=0-x(x-2)+10x(x-1)$$

$$y=9x^2-8x.$$

**Example 15.** *Using Lagrange's formula, prove*

$$y_1=y_3-0{\cdot}3\,(y_5-y_{-3})+0{\cdot}2\,(y_{-3}-y_{-5}) \text{ nearly.}$$

**Solution.** $y_{-5}, y_{-3}, y_3, y_5$ occur in the answers. So, we can have the table

| $x$ | : | $-5$ | $-3$ | $3$ | $5$ |
|---|---|---|---|---|---|
| $y$ | : | $y_{-5}$ | $y_{-3}$ | $y_3$ | $y_5$ |

∴ By Lagrange's formula

$$y(x)=\frac{(x+3)(x-3)(x-5)}{(-5+3)(-5-3)(-5-5)}\cdot y_{-5}$$

$$+\frac{(x+5)(x-3)(x-5)}{(-3+5)(-3-3)(-3-5)}\cdot y_{-3}$$

$$+\frac{(x+5)(x+3)(x-5)}{(3+5)(3+3)(3-5)}\cdot y_3+\frac{(x+5)(x+3)(x-3)}{(5+5)(5+3)(5-3)}\,y_5$$

$$y_1=\frac{(4)(-2)(-4)}{(-2)(-8)(-10)}\,y_{-5}+\frac{(6)(-2)(-4)}{(2)(-6)(-8)}\,y_{-3}+\frac{(6)(4)(-4)}{(8)(6)(-2)}\,y_3$$

$$+\frac{(6)(4)(-2)}{(10)(8)(2)}\,y_5$$

$$=-0{\cdot}2\,y_{-5}+0{\cdot}5\,y_{-3}+y_3-0{\cdot}3\,y_5$$

$$y_1=y_3-0{\cdot}3\,(y_5-y_{-3})+0{\cdot}2\,(y_{-3}-y_{-5}).$$

**Example 16.** *The mode of a certain frequency curve $y=f(x)$ is very nearer to $x=9$ and the values of the frequency density $f(x)$ for $x=8{\cdot}9, 9, 9{\cdot}3$ are respectively $0{\cdot}30, 0{\cdot}35$ and $0{\cdot}25$. Calculate the approximate value of the mode.*

**Solution.** We are given that

| $x$ | 8·9 | 9·0 | 9·3 |
|---|---|---|---|
| $f(x)$ | 0·30 | 0·35 | 0·25 |

By Lagrange's interpolation formula,

$$f(x) = \frac{(x-9)(x-9\cdot3)}{(8\cdot9-9)(8\cdot9-9\cdot3)} \times 0\cdot30 + \frac{(x-8\cdot9)(x-9\cdot3)}{(9-8\cdot9)(9-9\cdot3)} \times 0\cdot35 + \frac{(x-8\cdot9)(x-9)}{(9\cdot3-8\cdot9)(9\cdot3-9)} \times 0\cdot25$$

$$= \frac{1}{12}(-25x^2 + 453\cdot5\,x - 2052\cdot3)$$

To get the mode, $f'(x) = 0$ and $f''(x) = -\text{ve}$

$$\therefore \quad f'(x) = 0 \;\Rightarrow\; \frac{1}{12}(-50x + 453\cdot5) = 0$$

*i.e.*, $\quad x = 9\cdot07$

$$f''(9\cdot07) = \frac{1}{12}(-50) = -\text{ve}$$

Hence $f(x)$ is maximum at $x = 9\cdot07$

Therefore, mode is 9·07.

**Example 17.** *Using Lagrange's formula of interpolation find $y(9\cdot5)$ given*

| $x$ | : | 7 | 8 | 9 | 10 |
|---|---|---|---|---|---|
| $y$ | : | 3 | 1 | 1 | 9 |

**Solution.** By Lagrange's formula,

$$y = f(x) = \frac{(x-8)(x-9)(x-10)}{(7-8)(7-9)(7-10)} \times 3 + \frac{(x-7)(x-9)(x-10)}{(8-7)(8-9)(8-10)} \times 1 + \frac{(x-7)(x-8)(x-10)}{(9-7)(9-8)(9-10)} \times 1 + \frac{(x-7)(x-8)(x-9)}{(10-7)(10-8)(10-9)} \times 9$$

$$f(9\cdot5) = \frac{(1\cdot5)(0\cdot5)(-0\cdot5)}{(-1)(-2)(-3)} \times 3 + \frac{(2\cdot5)(0\cdot5)(-0\cdot5)}{(1)(-1)(-2)} + \frac{(2\cdot5)(1\cdot5)(-0\cdot5)}{(2)(1)(-1)} + \frac{(2\cdot5)(1\cdot5)(0\cdot5)}{(3)(2)(1)} \times 9$$

$$= 0\cdot1875 - 0\cdot3125 + 0\cdot9375 + 2\cdot8125$$

$$= 3\cdot625.$$

**Example 18.** *Use Lagrange's formula to fit a polynomial to the data*

| $x$ | : | −1 | 0 | 2 | 3 |
|---|---|---|---|---|---|
| $y$ | : | −8 | 3 | 1 | 12 |

*and hence find $y(x = 1)$.*

**Solution.** By Lagrange's formula,

$$y = f(x) = \frac{(x-0)(x-2)(x-3)}{(-1-0)(-1-2)(-1-3)} \times (-8) + \frac{(x+1)(x-2)(x-3)}{(0+1)(0-2)(0-3)} \times 3$$

$$+\frac{(x+1)(x-0)(x-3)}{(2+1)(2-0)(2-3)}\times 1+\frac{(x+1)(x-0)(x-2)}{(3+1)(3-0)(3-2)}\times 12$$

$$=2x^3-6x^2+3x+3, \text{ on simplification.}$$

$$y(x=1)=2-6+3+3=2.$$

## INVERSE INTERPOLATION

So far, given a set of values of $x$ and $y$ we were finding the values of $y$ corresponding to some $x=x_k$. (which is not given in the table). Here, we treat $y$ as a function of $x$. Now the problem is, given some $y=y_r$, we should find the corresponding $x$. This process of finding $x$ given $y$ is called the *inverse interpolation.*

In such a case, we will take $y$ as independent variable and $x$ as dependent variable and use Lagrange's interpolation formula.

Taking $y$ as independent variable,

$$x=\frac{(y-y_1)(y-y_2)\cdots(y-y_n)}{(y_0-y_1)(y_0-y_2)\cdots(y_0-y_n)}\cdot x_0+\frac{(y-y_0)(y-y_2)\cdots(y-y_n)}{(y_1-y_0)(y_1-y_2)\cdots(y_1-y_n)}x_1$$

$$+\cdots+\frac{(y-y_0)(y-y_1)\cdots(y-y_{n-1})}{(y_n-y_0)(y_n-y_1)\cdots(y_n-y_{n-1})}x_n \quad ...(1)$$

This formula (1) is called *formula of inverse interpolation.*

**Example 19.** *From the data given below, find the value of x when y = 13·5* (*B.Sc. BR. Nov. 94*)

| | | | | | |
|---|---|---|---|---|---|
| $x$ : | *93·0* | *96·2* | *100·0* | *104·2* | *108·7* |
| $y$ : | *11·38* | *12·80* | *14·70* | *17·07* | *19·91* |

**Solution.** By Lagrange's formula for inverse interpolation

$$x=\frac{(y-12{\cdot}80)(y-14{\cdot}70)(y-17{\cdot}07)(y-19{\cdot}91)}{(11{\cdot}38-12{\cdot}80)(11{\cdot}38-14{\cdot}70)(11{\cdot}38-17{\cdot}07)(11{\cdot}38-19{\cdot}91)}\times(93{\cdot}0)$$

$$+\frac{(y-11{\cdot}38)(y-14{\cdot}70)(y-17{\cdot}07)(y-19{\cdot}91)}{(12{\cdot}80-11{\cdot}38)(12{\cdot}80-14{\cdot}70)(12{\cdot}80-17{\cdot}07)(12{\cdot}80-19{\cdot}91)}\times(96{\cdot}2)$$

$$+\frac{(y-11{\cdot}38)(y-12{\cdot}80)(y-17{\cdot}07)(y-19{\cdot}91)}{(14{\cdot}70-11{\cdot}38)(14{\cdot}70-12{\cdot}80)(14{\cdot}70-17{\cdot}07)(14{\cdot}70-19{\cdot}91)}\times(100{\cdot}0)$$

$$+\frac{(y-11{\cdot}38)(y-12{\cdot}80)(y-14{\cdot}70)(y-19{\cdot}91)}{(17{\cdot}07-11{\cdot}38)(17{\cdot}07-12{\cdot}80)(17{\cdot}07-14{\cdot}70)(17{\cdot}07-19{\cdot}91)}\times(104{\cdot}2)$$

$$+\frac{(y-11{\cdot}38)(y-12{\cdot}80)(y-14{\cdot}70)(y-17{\cdot}07)}{(19{\cdot}91-11{\cdot}38)(19{\cdot}91-12{\cdot}80)(19{\cdot}91-14{\cdot}70)(19{\cdot}91-17{\cdot}07)}\times(108{\cdot}7)$$

Putting $y = 13{\cdot}5$ on the right hand side, and simplifying

$$x = -7{\cdot}8126929 + 68{\cdot}3721132 + 43{\cdot}595887 - 7{\cdot}2733429 + 0{\cdot}770084198$$
$$= 97{\cdot}6557503$$

**Example 20.** *Find the value of* $\theta$ *given* $f(\theta) = 0{\cdot}3887$ *where* $f(\theta) = \int_0^\theta \frac{d\theta}{\sqrt{1 - \frac{1}{2}\sin^2\theta}}$ *using the table*

| $\theta$ : | 21° | 23° | 25° |
|---|---|---|---|
| $f(\theta)$ : | 0·3706 | 0·4068 | 0·4433 |

**Solution.** Now take $f(\theta)$ as independent and $\theta$ as dependent

| $y = f(\theta)$ : | 0·3706 | 0·4068 | 0·4433 |
|---|---|---|---|
| $\theta$ : | 21 | 23 | 25 |

$$\theta = \frac{(y - 0{\cdot}4068)(y - 0{\cdot}4433)}{(0{\cdot}3706 - 0{\cdot}4068)(0{\cdot}3706 - 0{\cdot}4433)} \times (21) + \frac{(y - 0{\cdot}3706)(y - 0{\cdot}4433)}{(0{\cdot}4068 - 0{\cdot}3706)(0{\cdot}4068 - 0{\cdot}4433)} \times (23) + \frac{(y - 0{\cdot}3706)(y - 0{\cdot}4068)}{(0{\cdot}4433 - 0{\cdot}3706)(0{\cdot}4433 - 0{\cdot}4068)} \times 25$$

$$\theta\,(y = 0{\cdot}3887) = \frac{(0{\cdot}3887 - 0{\cdot}4068)(0{\cdot}3887 - 0{\cdot}4433)}{(0{\cdot}3706 - 0{\cdot}4068)(0{\cdot}3706 - 0{\cdot}4433)} \times (21) + \frac{(0{\cdot}3887 - 0{\cdot}3706)(0{\cdot}3887 - 0{\cdot}4433)}{(0{\cdot}4068 - 0{\cdot}3706)(0{\cdot}4068 - 0{\cdot}4433)} \times (23) + \frac{(0{\cdot}3887 - 0{\cdot}3706)(0{\cdot}3887 - 0{\cdot}4068)}{(0{\cdot}4433 - 0{\cdot}3706)(0{\cdot}4433 - 0{\cdot}4068)} \times 25$$

$$= 7{\cdot}885832 + 17{\cdot}202739 - 3{\cdot}086525 = \mathbf{22{\cdot}0020°}$$

**Example 21.** *Find the age corresponding to the annuity value 13·6 given the table*

| *Age (x)* : | *30* | *35* | *40* | *45* | *50* |
|---|---|---|---|---|---|
| *Annuity value (y)* : | *15·9* | *14·9* | *14·1* | *13·3* | *12·5* |

(*B.Sc. BR. Nov. 94*)

**Solution.**

$$x = \frac{(13{\cdot}6 - 14{\cdot}9)(13{\cdot}6 - 14{\cdot}1)(13{\cdot}6 - 13{\cdot}3)(13{\cdot}6 - 12{\cdot}5)}{(15{\cdot}9 - 14{\cdot}9)(15{\cdot}9 - 14{\cdot}1)(15{\cdot}9 - 13{\cdot}3)(15{\cdot}9 - 12{\cdot}5)} \times 30 + \frac{(13{\cdot}6 - 15{\cdot}9)(13{\cdot}6 - 14{\cdot}1)(13{\cdot}6 - 13{\cdot}3)(13{\cdot}6 - 12{\cdot}5)}{(14{\cdot}9 - 15{\cdot}9)(14{\cdot}9 - 14{\cdot}1)(14{\cdot}9 - 13{\cdot}3)(14{\cdot}9 - 12{\cdot}5)} \times 35 + \frac{(13{\cdot}6 - 15{\cdot}9)(13{\cdot}6 - 14{\cdot}9)(13{\cdot}6 - 13{\cdot}3)(13{\cdot}6 - 12{\cdot}5)}{(14{\cdot}1 - 15{\cdot}9)(14{\cdot}1 - 14{\cdot}9)(14{\cdot}1 - 13{\cdot}3)(14{\cdot}1 - 12{\cdot}5)} \times 40$$

$$+\frac{(13\cdot6-15\cdot9)(13\cdot6-14\cdot9)(13\cdot6-14\cdot1)(13\cdot6-12\cdot5)}{(13\cdot3-15\cdot9)(13\cdot3-14\cdot9)(13\cdot3-14\cdot1)(13\cdot3-12\cdot5)}\times 45$$

$$+\frac{(13\cdot6-15\cdot9)(13\cdot6-14\cdot9)(13\cdot6-14\cdot1)(13\cdot6-13\cdot3)}{(12\cdot5-15\cdot9)(12\cdot5-14\cdot9)(12\cdot5-14\cdot1)(12\cdot5-13\cdot3)}\times 50$$

$\therefore\ x\,(y=13\cdot6)=43.$

## EXERCISE 8.2

Using Lagrange's interpolation formula, do the problems below:

**1.** From the table given below, find $y\,(x=2)$.

| $x$ | : | 0 | 1 | 3 | 4 |
|---|---|---|---|---|---|
| $y$ | : | 5 | 6 | 50 | 105 |

**2.** Given $u_1=22, u_2=30, u_4=82, u_7=106, u_8=206$, find $u_6$.

**3.** Find $f\,(27)$ given.

| $x$ | : | 14 | 17 | 31 | 35 |
|---|---|---|---|---|---|
| $f(x)$ | : | 68·7 | 64·0 | 44·0 | 39·1 |

**4.** Using Lagrange's formula, find $f\,(6)$ given

| $x$ | : | 2 | 5 | 7 | 10 | 12 |
|---|---|---|---|---|---|---|
| $f(x)$ | : | 18 | 180 | 448 | 1210 | 2028 |

**5.** If $y_1=4, y_3=120, y_4=340, y_6=2544$, find $y_5$.

**6.** Find $y\,(6)$ given $y\,(1)=4, y\,(2)=5, y\,(7)=5, y\,(8)=4$. Also find $x$ for which $y\,(x)$ is maximum or minimum.

**7.** Find $y\,(10)$ given $y\,(5)=12, y\,(6)=13, y\,(9)=14$ and $y\,(11)=16$.

**8.** Interpolate $y$ at $x=5$ given

| $x$ | : | 1 | 2 | 3 | 4 | 7 |
|---|---|---|---|---|---|---|
| $y$ | : | 2 | 4 | 8 | 16 | 128 |

**9.** If $y_0=1, y_3=19, y_4=49$ and $y_6=181$ find $y_5$.

**10.** The following table gives the values of the probability integral $f\,(x)=\frac{2}{\sqrt{\pi}}\int_0^x e^{-x^2}\,dx$ corresponding to certain values of $x$. For what value of $x$ is this integral equal to 0·5

| $x$ | : | 0·46 | 0·47 | 0·48 | 0·49 |
|---|---|---|---|---|---|
| $f(x)$ | : | 0·4846555 | 0·4937452 | 0·5027498 | 0·5116683 |

**11.** Find $f\,(0)$ given

| $x$ | : | – 1 | – 2 | 2 | 4 |
|---|---|---|---|---|---|
| $f(x)$ | : | – 1 | – 9 | 11 | 69 |

**12.** The following are the measurements $t$ made on a curve recorded by the oscillograph representing a change of current $i$ due to a change in the conditions of an electric current.

| $t$ | : | 1·2 | 2·0 | 2·5 | 3·0 |
|---|---|---|---|---|---|
| $i$ | : | 1·36 | 0·58 | 0·34 | 0·20 |

Using Lagrange's formula, find $i$ at $t=1\cdot6$. *(MS. 1967)*

**13.** Find $x$ given $y = 0{\cdot}3$ from the data

| $x$ | : | 0·4 | 0·6 | 0·8 |
|---|---|---|---|---|
| $y$ | : | 0·3683 | 0·3332 | 0·2897 |

**14.** If $\log(300) = 2{\cdot}4771$, $\log(304) = 2{\cdot}4829$, $\log(305) = 2{\cdot}4843$, $\log(307) = 2{\cdot}4871$, find $\log(301)$.

**15.** Find the value of $x$ when $y(x) = 19$ given

| $x$ | : | 0 | 1 | 2 |
|---|---|---|---|---|
| $y$ | : | 0 | 1 | 20 |

*(BSc. BR. Nov. 94)*

**16.** If $\cosh x = 1{\cdot}285$, find $x$ given

| $x$ | : | 0·735 | 0·736 | 0·737 | 0·738 |
|---|---|---|---|---|---|
| $\cosh x$ | : | 1·2824937 | 1·2832974 | 1·2841023 | 1·2849085 |
| $x$ | : | 0·739 | 0·740 | 0·741 | 0·742 |
| $\cosh x$ | : | 1·2857159 | 1·2865247 | 1·2873348 | 1·2881461 |

**17.** Find $y(15)$ given the following table

| $x$ | : | 10 | 12 | 14 | 16 | 18 | 20 |
|---|---|---|---|---|---|---|---|
| $y(x)$ | : | 2420 | 1942 | 1497 | 1109 | 790 | 540 |

**18.** Given $u_0 = -12$, $u_1 = 0$, $u_3 = 6$, $u_4 = 12$ find $u_2$.

**19.** If $f(0) = 6, f(1) = 9, f(3) = 33$ and $f(7) = -15$ find $f(2)$.

**20.** Find $x$ corresponding to $y = 100$ given

| $x$ | : | 3 | 5 | 7 | 9 | 11 |
|---|---|---|---|---|---|---|
| $y$ | : | 6 | 24 | 58 | 108 | 174 |

**21.** Given $f(30) = -30, f(34) = -13, f(38) = 3$ and $f(42) = 18$ find $x$ so that $f(x) = 0$.

**22.** Find $f(x)$ given the table:

| $x$ | : | 0 | 1 | 4 | 5 |
|---|---|---|---|---|---|
| $f(x)$ | : | 4 | 3 | 24 | 39 |

**23.** If $y_0, y_1, y_2, \ldots y_6$ are given, prove

$$y_3 = 0{\cdot}05\,(y_0 + y_6) - 0{\cdot}3\,(y_1 + y_5) + 0{\cdot}75\,(y_2 + y_4).$$

**24.** Find the value of $\tan 33°$ by using Lagrange's formula of interpolation given

| $x$ | : | 30° | 32° | 35° | 38° |
|---|---|---|---|---|---|
| $\tan x$ | : | 0·5774 | 0·6249 | 0·7002 | 0·7813 |

**25.** If $y_3 = 16, y_5 = 36, y_7 = 64, y_8 = 81$ and $y_9 = 100$, find $y_4$.

**26.** Find $x$ corresponding to $y = 85$ given

| $x$ | : | 2 | 5 | 8 | 14 |
|---|---|---|---|---|---|
| $y$ | : | 94·8 | 87·9 | 81·3 | 68·7 |

**27.** Using Lagrange's formula, fit a polynomial to the data

| $x$ | : | 0 | 1 | 3 | 4 |
|---|---|---|---|---|---|
| $y$ | : | − 12 | 0 | 6 | 12 |

Also find $y$ at $x = 2$. *(MKU 1972)*

**28.** Find the parabola passing through the points (0, 1), (1, 3) and (3, 55) using Lagrange's interpolation formula.

**29.** Find $y(1{\cdot}50)$ given

| $x$ | : | 1·0 | 1·2 | 1·4 | 1·6 | 1·8 | 2·0 |
|---|---|---|---|---|---|---|---|
| $y$ | : | 0·2420 | 0·1942 | 0·1497 | 0·1109 | 0·0790 | 0·0540 |

**30.** Given $\begin{array}{c|cccc} x: & 0 & 1 & 3 & 4 \\ \hline y: & -6 & 0 & 0 & 6 \end{array}$ find $y(2)$.

# ANSWERS

## EXERCISE 8.1 Page 270

**1.** $-\dfrac{(a+b)}{a^2b^2}, \dfrac{ab+bc+ca}{a^2b^2c^2}, -\dfrac{(abc+bcd+acd+abd)}{a^2b^2c^2d^2}$ **2.** $x^4-3x^3+5x^2-6$

**3.** 1305·36 **4.** $x^3+x^2-x-2$ **5.** 1 **6.** $3x^4-5x^3+6x^2+14x+5$

**7.** $(x-1)(x-3)(x-6)(x^2+x+1)$

**8.** $f(x)=73+54(x-6)+13(x-6)^2+(x-6)^3$

**9.** $y=x^4-10x^3+36x^2-36x-5$ **10.** 3·8986688 **11.** 2·8169

**12.** 0·777298926 **13.** $-\dfrac{1}{10}(13x^2+41x-84)$ **14.** $2x-1$

**15.** 2·5099063 **16.** 636 **17.** $x^3+x^2+x+1$ **18.** 1

**19.** $y=11+4(x-1)+2(x-1)^2+(x-1)^3$.

## EXERCISES 8.2 Page 278

**1.** 19 **2.** 83·515 **3.** 49·3 **4.** 294 **5.** 1052

**6.** 5·6, $x=4{\cdot}5$ **7.** 14·7 **8.** 32·9 **9.** 101

**10.** 0·476937 **11.** 1 **12.** 0·8932 **13.** 0·07575 **14.** 2·4786

**16.** 0·73811340 **17.** 1295 **18.** 4 **19.** 9

**20.** 8·656 **21.** 37·23 **22.** $2x^2-3x+4$ **24.** 0·6494 **25.** 25

**26.** 6·5928 **27.** $y=x^3-7x^2+18x-12$; 4 **28.** $y=8x^2-6x+1$ **29.** 0, 1295

**30.** 0.

# 9

# *Numerical Differentiation and Integration*

## 9·1. Introduction

So far, we were finding the polynomial curve $y = f(x)$, passing through the $(n+1)$ ordered pairs $(x_i, y_i)$, $i = 0, 1, 2, \dots n$. Now we are trying to find the derivative value of such curves at a given $x = x_k$ (say), whose $x_0 < x_k < x_n$ (or even outside the range but closer to starting or end values). To get the derivative, we first find the curve $y = f(x)$ through the points and then differentiate and get its value at the required point.

If the values of $x$ are equally spaced, we get the interpolating polynomial due to Newton-Gregory. If the derivative is required at a point nearer to the starting value in the table, we use Newton's forward interpolation formula. If we require the derivative at the end of the table, we use Newton's backward interpolation formula. If the value of derivative is required near the middle of the table value we use one of the central difference interpolation formulae. In the case of unequal intervals, we can use Newton's divided difference formula or Lagrange's interpolation formula to get the derivative value.

## 9·2. Newton's forward difference formula to get the derivative

We are given $(n+1)$ ordered pairs $(x_i, y_i)$ $i = 0, 1, \dots n$. We want to find the derivative of $y = f(x)$ passing through the $(n+1)$ points, at a point nearer to the starting value $x = x_0$.

Newton's forward difference interpolation formula is

$$y(x_0 + uh) = y_u = y_0 + u\,\Delta y_0 + \frac{u(u-1)}{2!}\Delta^2 y_0 + \frac{u(u-1)(u-2)}{3!}\Delta^3 y_0 + \cdots \quad \dots(1)$$

where $y(x)$ is a polynomial of degree $n$ in $x$ and $u = \dfrac{x - x_0}{h}$.

Differentiating $y(x)$ w.r.t. $x$,

$$\frac{dy}{dx}=\frac{dy}{du}\cdot\frac{du}{dx}=\frac{1}{h}\cdot\frac{dy}{du}$$

$$\frac{dy}{dx}=\frac{1}{h}\left[\Delta y_0+\frac{2u-1}{2}\Delta^2 y_0+\frac{3u^2-6u+2}{6}\Delta^3 y_0 + \frac{(4u^3-18u^2+22u-6)}{24}\Delta^4 y_0+\cdots\right] \quad ...(2)$$

Equation (2) gives the value of $\frac{dy}{dx}$ at general $x$ which may be anywhere in the interval.

In special case like $x = x_0$, *i.e.*, $u = 0$, (2) reduces to

$$\left(\frac{dy}{dx}\right)_{x=x_0}=\left(\frac{dy}{dx}\right)_{u=0}=\frac{1}{h}\left[\Delta y_0-\frac{1}{2}\Delta^2 y_0+\frac{1}{3}\Delta^3 y_0-\frac{1}{4}\Delta^4 y_0+\cdots\right] \quad ...(3)$$

Differentiating (2) again w.r.t. $x$,

$$\frac{d^2y}{dx^2}=\frac{d}{du}\left(\frac{dy}{dx}\right)\cdot\frac{du}{dx}=\frac{d}{du}\left(\frac{dy}{dx}\right)\cdot\frac{1}{h}$$

$$\frac{d^2y}{dx^2}=\frac{1}{h^2}\left[\Delta^2 y_0+(u-1)\,\Delta^3 y_0+\frac{(6u^2-18u+11)}{12}\Delta^4 y_0+\cdots\right] \quad ...(4)$$

Hence, $$\frac{d^3y}{dx^3}=\frac{1}{h^3}\left[\Delta^3 y_0+\frac{12u-18}{12}\Delta^4 y_0+\cdots\right] \quad ...(5)$$

Equations (4) and (5) give the second and third derivative value at $x = x$.

Setting $x = x_0$ *i.e.*, $u = 0$ in (4) and (5)

$$\left(\frac{d^2y}{dx^2}\right)_{x=x_0}=\frac{1}{h^2}\left[\Delta^2 y_0-\Delta^3 y_0+\frac{11}{12}\Delta^4 y_0+\cdots\right] \quad ...(6)$$

$$\left(\frac{d^3y}{dx^3}\right)_{x=x_0}=\frac{1}{h^3}\left[\Delta^3 y_0-\frac{3}{2}\Delta^4 y_0+\cdots\right] \quad ...(7)$$

Equations (6) and (7) give the values of second and third derivative at the starting value $x = x_0$.

**Note:** We know $E = 1 + \Delta = e^{hD}$.

$$\therefore\quad D=\frac{1}{h}\log(1+\Delta)=\frac{1}{h}\left[\Delta-\frac{1}{2}\Delta^2+\frac{1}{3}\Delta^3-\cdots\right]$$

$$D^2=\frac{1}{h^2}\left[\Delta^2-\Delta^3+\frac{11}{12}\Delta^4-\cdots\right]$$

$$D^3=\frac{1}{h^3}\left[\Delta^3-\frac{3}{2}\Delta^4+\cdots\right]$$

$$\left(\frac{dy}{dx}\right)_{x=x_0} = D\,y_0 = \frac{1}{h}\left[\Delta y_0 - \frac{1}{2}\Delta^2 y_0 + \frac{1}{3}\Delta^3 y_0 - \cdots\right]$$

$$\left(\frac{d^2y}{dx^2}\right)_{x=x_0} = D^2 y_0 = \frac{1}{h^2}\left[\Delta^2 y_0 - \Delta^3 y_0 + \frac{11}{12}\Delta^4 y_0 - \cdots\right] \text{ etc.}$$

## 9·3. Newton's backward difference formula to compute the derivative

Now, consider Newton's backward difference interpolation formula,

$$y(x) = y(x_n + vh) = y_n + v\nabla y_n + \frac{v(v+1)}{2!}\nabla^2 y_n + \frac{v(v+1)(v+2)}{3!}\nabla^3 y_n + \cdots \quad ...(8)$$

where $v = \dfrac{x - x_n}{h}$.

Differentiate (8) w.r.t. $x$,

$$\frac{dy}{dx} = \frac{dy}{dv}\cdot\frac{dv}{dx} = \frac{dy}{dv}\cdot\frac{1}{h}$$

$$\left(\frac{dy}{dx}\right) = \frac{1}{h}\left[\nabla y_n + \frac{2v+1}{2}\nabla^2 y_n + \frac{3v^2+6v+2}{6}\nabla^3 y_n + \frac{4v^3+18v^2+22v+6}{24}\nabla^4 y_n + \cdots\right] \quad ...(9)$$

$$\therefore \quad \frac{d^2y}{dx^2} = \frac{1}{h^2}\left[\nabla^2 y_n + (v+1)\nabla^3 y_n + \frac{6v^2+18v+11}{12}\nabla^4 y_n + \cdots\right] \quad ...(10)$$

$$\therefore \quad \frac{d^3y}{dx^3} = \frac{1}{h^3}\left[\nabla^3 y_n + \frac{12v+18}{12}\nabla^4 y_n + \cdots\right] \quad ...(11)$$

Equations (9), (10), (11) give the first, second, and third derivative at any general $x$.

Setting $x = x_n$ or $v = 0$ in (9), (10), (11), we get

$$\left(\frac{dy}{dx}\right)_{x=x_n} = \frac{1}{h}\left[\nabla y_n + \frac{1}{2}\nabla^2 y_n + \frac{1}{3}\nabla^3 y_n + \frac{1}{4}\nabla^4 y_n + \cdots\right] \quad ...(12)$$

$$\left(\frac{d^2y}{dx^2}\right)_{x=x_n} = \frac{1}{h^2}\left[\nabla^2 y_n + \nabla^3 y_n + \frac{11}{12}\nabla^4 y_n + \cdots\right] \quad ...(13)$$

$$\left(\frac{d^3y}{dx^3}\right)_{x=x_n} = \frac{1}{h^3}\left[\nabla^3 y_n + \frac{3}{2}\nabla^4 y_n + \cdots\right] \quad ...(14)$$

**Note:** Using $E = e^{hD} = \dfrac{1}{1-\nabla}$, we get $D = \dfrac{-1}{h}\log(1-\nabla)$

$$\therefore \qquad D=\frac{1}{h}\left[\nabla+\frac{1}{2}\nabla^2+\frac{1}{3}\nabla^3+\frac{1}{4}\nabla^4+\cdots\right] \qquad ...(15)$$

$$D^2=\frac{1}{h^2}\left[\nabla^2+\nabla^3+\frac{11}{12}\nabla^4+\cdots\right]$$

$$D^3=\frac{1}{h^3}\left[\nabla^3+\frac{3}{2}\nabla^4+\cdots\right]$$

We can get the above results (12), (13) and (14).

## 9·4. Derivative using Stirling's formula

Consider Stirling's formula

$$y(x)=y(x_0+uh)=y_0+\frac{u}{2}[\Delta y_0+\Delta y_{-1}]+\frac{u^2}{2}\Delta^2 y_{-1}$$

$$+\frac{u^3-u}{12}\left(\Delta^3 y_{-1}+\Delta^3 y_{-2}\right)+\frac{u^4-u^2}{24}\Delta^4 y_{-2}+\cdots \qquad ...(16)$$

where $$u=\frac{x-x_0}{h}$$

Differentiating (16) w.r.t. $x$

$$\frac{dy}{dx}=\frac{dy}{du}\cdot\frac{du}{dx}=\frac{1}{h}\frac{dy}{du}$$

$$=\frac{1}{h}\left[\frac{1}{2}(\Delta y_0+\Delta y_{-1})+u\,\Delta^2 y_{-1}+\frac{3u^2-1}{12}\left(\Delta^3 y_{-1}+\Delta^3 y_{-2}\right)\right.$$

$$\left.+\frac{1}{12}(2u^3-u)\,\Delta^4 y_{-2}+\frac{5u^4-15u^2+4}{240}\left(\Delta^5 y_{-2}+\Delta^5 y_{-3}\right)+\cdots\right] \qquad ...(17)$$

Similarly

$$\frac{d^2y}{dx^2}=\frac{1}{h^2}\left[\Delta^2 y_{-1}+\frac{u}{2}\left(\Delta^3 y_{-1}+\Delta^3 y_{-2}\right)+\frac{(6u^2-1)}{12}\Delta^4 y_{-2}+\cdots\right] \qquad ...(18)$$

$$\frac{d^3y}{dx^3}=\frac{1}{h^3}\left[\frac{1}{2}\left(\Delta^3 y_{-1}+\Delta^3 y_{-2}\right)+u.\Delta^4 y_{-2}+\cdots\right] \qquad ...(19)$$

Setting $x=x_0$ *i.e.*, $u=0$ in (17), (18), (19) we get

$$\left(\frac{dy}{dx}\right)_{x=x_0}=\frac{1}{h}\left[\frac{1}{2}(\Delta y_0+\Delta y_{-1})-\frac{1}{12}\left(\Delta^3 y_{-1}+\Delta^3 y_{-2}\right)\right.$$

$$\left.+\frac{1}{60}\left(\Delta^5 y_{-2}+\Delta^5 y_{-3}\right)+\cdots\right] \qquad ...(20)$$

$$\left(\frac{d^2y}{dx^2}\right)_{x=x_0}=\frac{1}{h^2}\left[\Delta^2 y_{-1}-\frac{1}{12}\Delta^4 y_{-2}+\cdots\right] \qquad ...(21)$$

$$\left(\frac{d^3y}{dx^3}\right)_{x=x_0} = \frac{1}{h^3}\left[\frac{1}{2}\left(\Delta^3 y_{-1} + \Delta^3 y_{-2}\right) + \cdots\right] \qquad ...(22)$$

We can also use other *central difference* formula such as Bessel's formula or Everett's formula.

## 9·5. Caution

In interpolation, the polynomial function we find, is only an approximate function to the original function. In other words, $f(x) - P_n(x)$ is small. But $f'(x) - P_n'(x)$ may not be small even if $f(x) - P_n(x)$ is small. That is, the error involved in obtaining $f'(x)$ through $P_n'(x)$ may be great. So, it can be used with confidence only if the differences of some order are constants.

## 9·6. To find maxima and minima of the function given the tabular values

Given the ordered pairs $(x_i, y_i), i = 0, 1, 2, ...n,$ we can get the interpolating polynomial of degree $n$. Now, we want to find the value of $x$ at which the curve is maximum or minimum.

Now, using Newton's forward interpolation formula and getting its derivative, and equating it to zero, we get an equation from which the extremum values of $y$ can be got.

From equation (2), we get

$$\frac{dy}{dx} = \frac{1}{h}\left[\Delta y_0 + \frac{2u-1}{2}\Delta^2 y_0 + \frac{3u^2 - 6u + 2}{6}\Delta^3 y_0 + \cdots\right]$$

$\frac{dy}{dx} = 0$ implies,

$$\Delta y_0 + \frac{2u-1}{2}\Delta^2 y_0 + \frac{3u^2 - 6u + 2}{6}\Delta^3 y_0 + \cdots = 0 \qquad ...(23)$$

If higher differences are small, we can take only the first three terms of (23) and solving it for $u$ (since it is a quadratic in $u$), we get $u$.

Using $x = x_0 + uh$, we can get the values $x$ at which $y$ is an extremum.

**Note:** If the interval of differencing is not constant (*i.e.*, $x$'s are not equally spaced), we get Newton's divided difference formula or Lagrange's interpolation formula for general $x$, and then differenting it w.r.t. $x$ we can get the derivatives at any $x$ in the range.

Setting the particular value for $x$, say $x_k$, we get the derivative value at $x_k$.

**Example 1.** *Find the first two derivatives of* $(x)^{1/3}$ *at* $x = 50$ *and* $x = 56$ *given the table below*:

| $x$ | : | 50 | 51 | 52 | 53 | 54 | 55 | 56 |
|---|---|---|---|---|---|---|---|---|
| $y = x^{1/3}$ | : | 3·6840 | 3·7084 | 3·7325 | 3·7563 | 3·7798 | 3·8030 | 3·8259 |

**Solution.** Since we require $f'(x)$ at $x = 50$ we use Newton's forward formula and to get $f'(x)$ at $x = 56$ we use Newton's backward formula.

**Difference Table**

| $x$ | $y$ | $\Delta y$ | $\Delta^2 y$ | $\Delta^3 y$ |
|---|---|---|---|---|
| 50 | 3.6840 | | | |
| | | 0·0244 | | |
| 51 | 3·7084 | | – 0·0003 | |
| | | 0·0241 | | 0 |
| 52 | 3·7325 | | – 0·0003 | |
| | | 0·0238 | | 0 |
| 53 | 3·7563 | | – 0·0003 | |
| | | 0·0235 | | 0 |
| 54 | 3·7798 | | – 0·0003 | |
| | | 0·0232 | | 0 |
| 55 | 3·8030 | | – 0·0003 | |
| | | 0·0229 | | |
| 56 | 3·8259 | | | |

By Newton's forward formula,

$$\left(\frac{dy}{dx}\right)_{x=x_0} = \left(\frac{dy}{dx}\right)_{u=0}$$

$$= \frac{1}{h}\left[\Delta y_0 - \frac{1}{2}\Delta^2 y_0 + \frac{1}{3}\Delta^3 y_0 \cdots\right]$$

$$= \frac{1}{1}\left[0{\cdot}0244 - \frac{1}{2}(-0{\cdot}0003) + \frac{1}{3}(0)\right]$$

$$= \mathbf{0{\cdot}02455}$$

$$\left(\frac{d^2y}{dx^2}\right)_{x=50} = \frac{1}{h^2}\left[\Delta^2 y_0 - \Delta^3 y_0 + \cdots\right]$$

$$= 1\,[-0{\cdot}0003] = \mathbf{-\,0{\cdot}0003}.$$

By Newton's backward difference formula,

$$\left(\frac{dy}{dx}\right)_{x=x_n} = \left(\frac{dy}{dx}\right)_{v=0} = \frac{1}{h}\left[\nabla y_n + \frac{1}{2}\nabla^2 y_n + \frac{1}{3}\nabla^3 y_n + \cdots\right]$$

from equation (12)

$$\left(\frac{dy}{dx}\right)_{x=56} = \frac{1}{1}\left[0{\cdot}0229 + \frac{1}{2}(-0{\cdot}0003) + 0\right]$$

$$= \mathbf{0{\cdot}02275}$$

$$\left(\frac{d^2y}{dx^2}\right)_{x=56} = \frac{1}{h^2}\left[\nabla^2 y_n + \nabla^3 y_n + \cdots\right] \qquad \text{from equation (13)}$$

$$= \frac{1}{1}[-0.0003] = -\mathbf{0.0003}.$$

**Example 2.** *The population of a certain town is given below. Find the rate of growth of the population in 1931, 1941, 1961 and 1971.*

| | | | | | | | |
|---|---|---|---|---|---|---|---|
| *Year* | $x$ | : | *1931* | *1941* | *1951* | *1961* | *1971* |
| *Population in thousands* | $y$ | : | *40·62* | *60·80* | *79·95* | *103·56* | *132·65* |

**Solution.** We form the difference table.

| $x$ | $y$ | $\Delta y$ | $\Delta^2 y$ | $\Delta^3 y$ | $\Delta^4 y$ |
|---|---|---|---|---|---|
| 1931 | 40·62 | | | | |
| | | 20·18 | | | |
| 1941 | 60·80 | | − 1·03 | | |
| | | 19·15 | | 5·49 | |
| 1951 | 79·95 | | 4·46 | | − 4·47 |
| | | 23·61 | | 1·02 | |
| 1961 | 103·56 | | 5·48 | | |
| | | 29·09 | | | |
| 1971 | 132·65 | | | | |

We use the same table for backward and forward differences.

(*i*) To get $f'(1931)$ and $f'(1941)$ we use forward formula,

$$x_0 = 1931, \quad x_1 = 1941, \ldots$$

$$u = \frac{x - x_0}{h}; \qquad \therefore \quad x_0 = 1931 \text{ corresponds } u = 0.$$

$$\left(\frac{dy}{dx}\right)_{x=1931} = \left(\frac{dy}{dx}\right)_{u=0} = \frac{1}{h}\left[\Delta y_0 - \frac{1}{2}\Delta^2 y_0 + \frac{1}{3}\Delta^3 y_0 - \frac{1}{4}\Delta^4 y_0 + \cdots\right]$$

$$= \frac{1}{10}\left[20.18 - \frac{1}{2}(-1.03) + \frac{1}{3}(5.49) - \frac{1}{4}(-4.47)\right]$$

$$= \frac{1}{10}[20.18 + 0.515 + 1.83 + 1.1175]$$

$$= \mathbf{2.36425}. \qquad \ldots(1)$$

(*ii*) If $x = 1941$, $u = \frac{x - x_0}{h} = \frac{1941 - 1931}{10} = 1$

Putting $u = 1$, in

$$\frac{dy}{dx} = \frac{1}{h}\left[\Delta y_0 + \frac{2u-1}{2}\Delta^2 y_0 + \frac{3u^2 - 6u + 2}{6}\Delta^3 y_0 + \frac{4u^3 - 18u^2 + 22u - 6}{24}\Delta^4 y_0 - \cdots\right]$$

We get

$$\left(\frac{dy}{dx}\right)_{u=1} = \frac{1}{10}\left[20.18 + \frac{1}{2}(-1.03) - \frac{1}{6}(5.49) + \frac{1}{12}(-4.47)\right]$$

$$= \frac{1}{10}[20{\cdot}18 - 0{\cdot}515 - 0{\cdot}915 - 0{\cdot}3725]$$

$$= \mathbf{1{\cdot}83775} \qquad ...(2)$$

**Note:** If we neglect the data against 1931 and take 1941 as $x_0$, we have

$$\Delta y_0 = 19{\cdot}15, \Delta^2 y_0 = 4{\cdot}46, \Delta^3 y_0 = 1{\cdot}02.$$

Now using,

$$\left(\frac{dy}{dx}\right)_{x=1941} = \frac{1}{h}\left[\Delta y_0 - \frac{1}{2}\Delta^2 y_0 + \frac{1}{3}\Delta^3 y_0 - \cdots\right]$$

$$= \frac{1}{10}\left[19{\cdot}15 - \frac{1}{2}(4{\cdot}46) + \frac{1}{3}(1{\cdot}02)\right]$$

$$= \mathbf{1{\cdot}7260}. \qquad ...(3)$$

Evidently the values given by (2) and (3) are not same. In getting the answer given by (2), we have assumed a polynomial of degree 4 whereas in getting the answer given by (3), we have assumed the interpolating polynomial of degree 3 only. In fact, both polynomials assumed are different. Hence we see the difference in answers.

(*iii*) To get $f'(1971)$, we use the formula,

$$\left(\frac{dy}{dx}\right)_{x=x_n} = \frac{1}{h}\left[\nabla y_n + \frac{1}{2}\nabla^2 y_n + \frac{1}{3}\nabla^3 y_n + \frac{1}{4}\nabla^4 y_n + \cdots\right]$$

$$= \frac{1}{10}\left[29{\cdot}09 + \frac{1}{2}(5{\cdot}48) + \frac{1}{3}(1{\cdot}02) + \frac{1}{4}(-4{\cdot}47)\right]$$

$$\left(\frac{dy}{dx}\right)_{1971} = \frac{1}{10}[31{\cdot}0525] = \mathbf{3{\cdot}10525}.$$

(*iv*) To get $f'(1961)$, we use $v = \frac{x - x_n}{h} = \frac{1961 - 1971}{10} = -1$

$$\left(\frac{dy}{dx}\right)_{x=1961} = \left(\frac{dy}{dx}\right)_{v=-1} = \frac{1}{h}\left[\nabla y_n + \frac{2v+1}{2}\nabla^2 y_n + \frac{3v^2+6v+2}{6}\nabla^3 y_n + \cdots\right]_{v=-1}$$

$$= \frac{1}{10}\left[29{\cdot}09 - \frac{1}{2}(5{\cdot}48) - \frac{1}{6}(1{\cdot}02) - \frac{1}{12}(-4{\cdot}47)\right]$$

$$= \frac{1}{10}[29{\cdot}09 - 2{\cdot}74 - 0{\cdot}17 + 0{\cdot}3725]$$

$$= \mathbf{2{\cdot}65525}.$$

**Example 3.** *Find the gradient of the road at the middle point of the elevation above a datum line of seven points of road which are given below*:

| $x$ : | 0 | 300 | 600 | 900 | 1200 | 1500 | 1800 |
|---|---|---|---|---|---|---|---|
| $y$ : | 135 | 149 | 157 | 183 | 201 | 205 | 193 |

**Solution.** We require $\left(\dfrac{dy}{dx}\right)_{x=900}$

**Table**

| $x$ | $y$ | $\Delta y$ | $\Delta^2 y$ | $\Delta^3 y$ | $\Delta^4 y$ | $\Delta^5 y$ | $\Delta^6 y$ |
|---|---|---|---|---|---|---|---|
| 0 | 135 | | | | | | |
| | | 14 | | | | | |
| 300 | 149 | | – 6 | | | | |
| | | 8 | | 24 | | | |
| 600 | 157 | | 18 | | – 50 | | |
| | | 26 | | – 26 | | 70 | |
| 900 | 183 ($y_0$) | | – 8 | | 20 | | – 86 |
| | | 18 | | – 6 | | – 16 | |
| 1200 | 201 | | – 14 | | 4 | | |
| | | 4 | | – 2 | | | |
| 1500 | 205 | | – 16 | | | | |
| | | – 12 | | | | | |
| 1800 | 193 | | | | | | |

Since $x = 900$ is in the middle of the table we use one of the central difference formula, in particular *Stirling's* formula.

$$\left(\frac{dy}{dx}\right)_{x=x_0} = \frac{1}{h}\left[\frac{1}{2}\left(\Delta y_0 + \Delta y_{-1}\right) - \frac{1}{12}\left(\Delta^3 y_{-1} + \Delta^3 y_{-2}\right) + \frac{1}{60}\left(\Delta^5 y_{-2} + \Delta^5 y_{-3}\right) + \cdots\right]$$

$$= \frac{1}{300}\left[\frac{1}{2}(18+26) - \frac{1}{12}(-6-26) + \frac{1}{60}(70-16)\right]$$

$$= \frac{1}{300}[22 + 2{\cdot}6666 + 0{\cdot}9]$$

$$= \mathbf{0{\cdot}085222}$$

Hence, the gradient of the road at the middle point is **0·084776**.

**Example 4.** *The table below gives the results of an observation; θ is the observed temperature in degrees centigrade of a vessel of cooling water; t is the time in minutes from the beginning of observation.*

| $t$ : | 1 | 3 | 5 | 7 | 9 |
|---|---|---|---|---|---|
| θ : | 85·3 | 74·5 | 67·0 | 60·5 | 54·3 |

*Find the approximate rate of cooling at t = 3 and 3·5.*

**Solution.** We form below the difference table.

| $t$ | $\theta$ | $\Delta\theta$ | $\Delta^2\theta$ | $\Delta^3\theta$ | $\Delta^4\theta$ |
|---|---|---|---|---|---|
| 1 | 85·3 | | | | |
| | | – 10·8 | | | |
| 3 | 74·5 | | 3·3 | | |
| | | – 7·5 | | – 2·3 | |
| 5 | 67·0 | | 1·0 | | 1·6 |
| | | – 6·5 | | – 0·7 | |
| 7 | 60·5 | | 0·3 | | |
| | | – 6·2 | | | |
| 9 | 54·3 | | | | |

$\dfrac{d\theta}{dt}$ represents the rate of cooling.

$$u = \frac{t - t_0}{h} = \frac{t-1}{2} \qquad \text{At } \ t = 3, \ u = 1 \qquad \text{At } \ t = 3{\cdot}5, \ u = 1{\cdot}25$$

(*i*) Putting $u = 1$ in equation (2),

$$\left(\frac{d\theta}{dt}\right)_{u=1} = \frac{1}{2}\left[ -10{\cdot}8 + \frac{1}{2}(3{\cdot}3) - \frac{1}{6}(-2{\cdot}3) + \frac{1}{12}(1{\cdot}6)\right]$$

$$= \frac{1}{2}[-10{\cdot}8 + 1{\cdot}65 + 0{\cdot}38333 + 0{\cdot}13333]$$

$$\left(\frac{d\theta}{dt}\right)_{t=3} = \mathbf{-4{\cdot}31667}$$

(*ii*) Putting $u = 1{\cdot}25$ in (2), $\left(\dfrac{d\theta}{dt}\right)_{u=1\cdot25} = \dfrac{1}{2}[-10{\cdot}8 + 0{\cdot}75\,(3{\cdot}3)$

$$-(0{\cdot}1354)(-2{\cdot}3) + (0.04948)\,(1.6)] = -4{\cdot}0067$$

$$\left(\frac{d\theta}{dt}\right)_{t=3\cdot5} = \mathbf{-3{\cdot}96718}$$

**Example 5.** *Find the value of $f'(0{\cdot}5)$ using Stirling's formula from the following data*:

| $x$ : | *0·35* | *0·40* | *0·45* | *0·50* | *0·55* | *0·60* | *0·65* |
|---|---|---|---|---|---|---|---|
| $y = f(x)$ : | *1·521* | *1·506* | *1·488* | *1·467* | *1·444* | *1·418* | *1·389* |

**Solution.**

| $x$ | $y$ | $\Delta y$ | $\Delta^2 y$ | $\Delta^3 y$ | $\Delta^4 y$ | $\Delta^5 y$ |
|---|---|---|---|---|---|---|
| 0·35 | 1·521 | | | | | |
| | | – 0·015 | – 0·003 | | | |
| 0·40 | 1·506 | | | 0 | | |
| | | – 0·018 | – 0·003 | | 0·001 | |
| 0·45 | 1·488 | | ($\Delta^2 y_{-2}$) | 0·001 | | – 0·003 |
| | | – 0·021 | | ($\Delta^3 y_{-2}$) | – 0·002 | ($\Delta^5 y_{-3}$) |
| 0·50 | 1·467 ($y_0$) | ($\Delta y_{-1}$) | – 0·002 | | | |
| | | – 0·023 | ($\Delta^2 y_{-1}$) | – 0·001 | | 0·003 |
| 0·55 | 1·444 | ($\Delta y_0$) | | ($\Delta^3 y_{-1}$) | – 0·001 | ($\Delta^5 y_{-2}$) |
| | | | | | ($\Delta^4 y_{-1}$) | |
| 0·60 | 1·418 | – 0·026 | – 0·003 | 0 | | |
| 0·65 | 1·389 | – 0·029 | – 0·003 | | | |

Since $x = 0{\cdot}5$ is in the middle of the table, we use Stirling's formula taking 0·50 as the origin

$\therefore \quad x_0 = 0{\cdot}50,\ y_0 = 1{\cdot}467$

By Stirling's formula, from equation (20), we have

$$\left(\frac{dy}{dx}\right)_{x=x_0} = \frac{1}{h}\left[\frac{1}{2}\left(\Delta y_0 + \Delta y_{-1}\right) - \frac{1}{12}\left(\Delta^3 y_{-1} + \Delta^3 y_{-2}\right) + \frac{1}{60}\left(\Delta^5 y_{-2} + \Delta^5 y_{-3}\right) + \cdots\right]$$

$$= \frac{1}{0{\cdot}05}\left[\frac{1}{2}(-0{\cdot}023 - 0{\cdot}021) - \frac{1}{12}(-0{\cdot}001 + 0{\cdot}001) + \frac{1}{60}(0{\cdot}003 - 0{\cdot}003)\right]$$

$$= \frac{1}{0{\cdot}05}\left[-\frac{1}{2} \times 0{\cdot}044\right]$$

$$= -0{\cdot}44.$$

**Example 6.** *Find the first and second derivative of the function tabulated below at x = 0·6*

| *x* | : | *0·4* | *0·5* | *0·6* | *0·7* | *0·8* |
|---|---|---|---|---|---|---|
| *y* | : | *1·5836* | *1·7974* | *2·0442* | *2·3275* | *2·6511* |

**Solution.** Since $x = 0{\cdot}6$ is in the middle of the table, we will use Stirling's formula.

**Difference Table**

| $x$ | $y$ | $\Delta y$ | $\Delta^2 y$ | $\Delta^3 y$ | $\Delta^4 y$ |
|---|---|---|---|---|---|
| 0·4 | 1·5836 | | | | |
| | | 0·2138 | | | |
| | | | 0·0330 | | |
| 0·5 | 1·7974 | | | 0·0035 | |
| | | 0·2468 | | | |
| | | | 0·0365 | 0·0035 ($\Delta^3 y_{-2}$) | 0·0003 |
| 0·6 | 2·0442 ($y_0$) | ($\Delta y_{-1}$) | ($\Delta^2 y_{-1}$) | | ($\Delta^4 y_{-2}$) |
| | | 0·2833 ($\Delta y_0$) | | 0·0038 ($\Delta^3 y_{-1}$) | |
| | | | 0·0403 ($\Delta^2 y_0$) | | |
| 0·7 | 2·3275 | | | | |
| | | 0·3236 | | | |
| 0·8 | 2·6511 | | | | |

By Stirling's formula,

$$\left(\frac{dy}{dx}\right)_{x=x_0} = \frac{1}{h}\left[\frac{1}{2}(\Delta y_0 + \Delta y_{-1}) - \frac{1}{12}\left(\Delta^3 y_{-1} + \Delta^3 y_{-2}\right) + \cdots\right]$$

$$= \frac{1}{0{\cdot}1}\left[\frac{1}{2}(0{\cdot}2833 + 0{\cdot}2468) - \frac{1}{12}(0{\cdot}0038 + 0{\cdot}0035)\right]$$

$$\left(\frac{dy}{dx}\right)_{x=0{\cdot}6} = 10\,[0{\cdot}26505 - 0{\cdot}0006083]$$

$$= \mathbf{2{\cdot}64442}$$

$$\left(\frac{d^2y}{dx^2}\right)_{x=x_0} = \frac{1}{h^2}\left[\Delta^2 y_{-1} - \frac{1}{12}\Delta^4 y_{-2} + \cdots\right] \text{ from (21).}$$

$$\left(\frac{d^2y}{dx^2}\right)_{x=0\cdot 6} = \frac{1}{(\cdot 01)}\left[0\cdot 0365 - \frac{1}{12}(0\cdot 0003)\right]$$

$$= \mathbf{3{\cdot}6475}.$$

**Example 7.** *Obtain the value of $f'(0{\cdot}04)$ using Bessel's formula given the table below:*

| $x$ | : | 0·01 | 0·02 | 0·03 | 0·04 | 0·05 | 0·06 |
|---|---|---|---|---|---|---|---|
| $f(x)$ | : | 0·1023 | 0·1047 | 0·1071 | 0·1096 | 0·1122 | 0·1148 |

**Solution.** Since $x = 0{\cdot}04$ is in the middle of the table we use central difference formula and in particular Bessel's formula

We form the central difference table.

| $x$ | $u$ | $y$ | $\Delta y$ | $\Delta^2 y$ | $\Delta^3 y$ | $\Delta^4 y$ | $\Delta^5 y$ |
|---|---|---|---|---|---|---|---|
| 0·01 | – 3 | 0·1023 | | | | | |
| | | | 0·0024 | | | | |
| 0·02 | – 2 | 0·1047 | | 0·0 | | | |
| | | | 0·0024 | | 0·0001 | | |
| 0·03 | – 1 | 0·1071 | | 0·0001 | | – 0·0001 | |
| | | | 0·0025 | | 0·0 | | 0·0 |
| 0·04 | 0 | 0·1096 ($y_0$) | | 0·0001 | | – 0·0001 | |
| | | | 0·0026 | | – 0·0001 | | |
| 0·05 | 1 | 0·1122 | | 0·0 ($\Delta^2 y_0$) | | | |
| | | | 0·0026 | | | | |
| 0·06 | 2 | 0·1148 | | | | | |

Since $u = \dfrac{x - x_0}{h} = \dfrac{x - 0{\cdot}04}{\cdot 01}$

Taking $x_0 = 0{\cdot}04$ as the origin

$$y_0 = 0{\cdot}1096, \quad \Delta y_0 = 0{\cdot}0026, \quad \Delta y_{-1} = 0{\cdot}0025, \quad \Delta y_{-2} = 0{\cdot}0024$$

By Bessel's formula,

$$y(x_0 + uh) = \frac{1}{2}(y_0 + y_1) + \left(u - \frac{1}{2}\right)\Delta y_0 + \frac{u(u-1)}{4}\left(\Delta^2 y_{-1} + \Delta^2 y_0\right)$$

$$+ \frac{u\left(u - \frac{1}{2}\right)(u-1)}{6}\Delta^3 y_{-1} + \frac{(u+1)\,u\,(u-1)(u-2)}{48}\left(\Delta^4 y_{-2} + \Delta^4 y_{-1}\right)$$

$$y'(x) = \frac{1}{h}\left[\Delta y_0 + \frac{2u-1}{4}\left(\Delta^2 y_{-1} + \Delta^2 y_0\right) + \frac{\left(3u^2 - 3u + \frac{1}{2}\right)}{6}\Delta^3 y_{-1} + \cdots\right]$$

$$y'(x_0) = \frac{1}{0{\cdot}01}\left[0{\cdot}0026 - \frac{1}{4}(0 + 0{\cdot}0001) + \frac{1}{12}(-0{\cdot}0001) + \frac{1}{24}(-0{\cdot}0001)\right]$$

$$= \frac{1}{0 \cdot 24}[24 \times 0 \cdot 0026 - 0 \cdot 0006 - 0 \cdot 0003]$$

$$f'(0 \cdot 04) = \mathbf{0 \cdot 25625}.$$

**Example 8.** *Given the following data, find y ′ (6) and the maximum value of y.*

| $x$ | : | 0 | 2 | 3 | 4 | 7 | 9 |
|---|---|---|---|---|---|---|---|
| $y$ | : | 4 | 26 | 58 | 112 | 466 | 922 |

**Solution.** Since the arguments are not equally spaced, we will use Newton's divided difference formula (or even Lagrange's formula).

**Divided Difference Table**

| $x$ | $y = f(x)$ | $\Delta f(x)$ | $\Delta^2 f(x)$ | $\Delta^3 f(x)$ | $\Delta^4 f(x)$ |
|---|---|---|---|---|---|
| 0 | 4 | | | | |
| | | 11 | | | |
| 2 | 26 | | 7 | | |
| | | 32 | | 1 | |
| 3 | 58 | | 11 | | 0 |
| | | 54 | | 1 | |
| 4 | 112 | | 16 | | 0 |
| | | 118 | | 1 | |
| 7 | 466 | | 22 | | |
| | | 228 | | | |
| 9 | 922 | | | | |

By Newton's divided difference formula,

$$y = f(x) = f(x_0) + (x - x_0) f(x_0, x_1) + (x - x_0)(x - x_1) f(x_0, x_1, x_2) + \cdots$$

$$= 4 + (x - 0)\ 11 + (x - 0)(x - 2)\ 7 + (x - 0)(x - 2)(x - 3) \cdot 1$$

$$= x^3 + 2x^2 + 3x + 4$$

Therefore, $y'(x) = 3x^2 + 4x + 3$

$$y'(6) = 3(6)^2 + 4(6) + 3 = \mathbf{135}.$$

$y(x)$ is maximum if $y'(x) = 0 \quad \therefore \quad 3x^2 + 4x + 3 = 0$. But the roots are imaginary. Therefore, there is no extremum value in the range. In fact, it is an increasing curve.

**Example 9.** *From the following table, find the value of x for which f (x) is a maximum. Also find the maximum value of f (x) from the table of values given below.*

| $x$ | : | 60 | 75 | 90 | 105 | 120 |
|---|---|---|---|---|---|---|
| $f(x)$ | : | 28·2 | 38·2 | 43·2 | 40·9 | 37·7 |

**Solution.** The maximum value appears to be in the neighbourhood of $x = 90$. Hence, we will use Stirling's formula. Please note that $h = 15$. ($x$'s are equally spaced).

| $x$ | $y = f(x)$ | $\Delta y$ | $\Delta^2 y$ | $\Delta^3 y$ | $\Delta^4 y$ |
|---|---|---|---|---|---|
| 60 | 28·2 | | | | |
| | | 10 | | | |
| 75 | 38·2 | | – 5 $(\Delta^2 y_{-2})$ | | |
| | | 5 $(\Delta y_{-1})$ | | – 2·3 $(\Delta^3 y_{-1})$ | |
| 90 | 43·2 $(y_0)$ | | – 7·3 $(\Delta^2 y_{-1})$ | | 8·7 |
| | | – 2·3 $(\Delta y_0)$ | | 6·4 $(\Delta^3 y_{-2})$ | |
| 105 | 40·9 | | – 0·9 $(\Delta^2 y_0)$ | | |
| | | – 3·2 | | | |
| 120 | 37·7 | | | | |

By Stirling's formula,

$$y(x) = y(x_0 + uh) = y_0 + \frac{u}{2}(\Delta y_0 + \Delta y_{-1}) + \frac{u^2}{2}\Delta^2 y_{-1}$$

$$+ \frac{u(u^2 - 1^2)}{12}\left(\Delta^3 y_{-1} + \Delta^3 y_{-2}\right) + \frac{u^2(u^2 - 1^2)}{24}\Delta^2 y_{-2} + \cdots \quad \ldots(1)$$

Here, $x_0 = 90$, $y_0 = 43{\cdot}2$, $\Delta y_0 = -2{\cdot}3$, $\Delta^2 y_0 = -0{\cdot}9$

$= \Delta y_{-1} = 5$, $\Delta^2 y_{-1} = -7{\cdot}3$, $\Delta^2 y_{-2} = -5$ etc.

$$\therefore \quad y = 43{\cdot}2 + \frac{u}{2}(-2{\cdot}3 + 5) + \frac{u^2}{2}(-7{\cdot}3) + \frac{(u^3 - u)}{12}(-2{\cdot}3 + 6{\cdot}4)$$

$$= 43{\cdot}2 + 1{\cdot}35u - 3{\cdot}65u^2 + 0{\cdot}3417(u^3 - u)$$

$$= 0{\cdot}3417u^3 - 3{\cdot}65u^2 + 1{\cdot}0083u + 43{\cdot}2$$

If $y$ is maximum, $\dfrac{dy}{du} = 0$. Hence,

$$3 \times 0{\cdot}3417u^2 - 2 \times 3{\cdot}65u + 1{\cdot}0083 = 0$$

$$1{\cdot}0251u^2 - 7{\cdot}30u + 1{\cdot}0083 = 0$$

$$u = \frac{7{\cdot}30 \pm \sqrt{(7{\cdot}30)^2 - 4(1{\cdot}0251)(1{\cdot}0083)}}{2 \times 1{\cdot}0251}$$

$$= \frac{7{\cdot}3 \pm 7{\cdot}0111}{2{\cdot}0502} = 6{\cdot}9803 \text{ or } 0{\cdot}1409$$

$u = 6{\cdot}9803$ goes beyond the range.

Therefore take $u = 0{\cdot}1409$

$$x = x_0 + uh = 90 + 15\,(0{\cdot}1409) = 92{\cdot}1135$$

$$\text{Maximum } y = 0{\cdot}3417\,(0{\cdot}1409)^3 - 3{\cdot}65\,(0{\cdot}1409)^2 + 1{\cdot}0083\,(0{\cdot}1409) + 43{\cdot}2$$

$$= 43{\cdot}27$$

$f(x)$ is maximum at $x = 92{\cdot}1135$ and the maximum value is $43{\cdot}27$.

**Example 10.** *Find the value of x for which y is minimum and find the minimum value from the table.*

| $x$ | : | 0·60 | 0·65 | 0·70 | 0·75 |
|---|---|---|---|---|---|
| $y$ | : | 0·6221 | 0·6155 | 0·6138 | 0·6170 |

**Solution.** We form the difference table first.

| $x$ | $y$ | $\Delta y$ | $\Delta^2 y$ | $\Delta^3 y$ |
|---|---|---|---|---|
| 0·60 | 0·6221 | | | |
| | | − 0·0066 | | |
| 0·65 | 0·6155 | | 0·0049 | |
| | | − 0·0017 | | 0 |
| 0·70 | 0·6138 | | 0·0049 | |
| | | 0·0032 | | |
| 0·75 | 0·6170 | | | |

Taking 0·60 as the origin,

$$y(x) = y(x_0 + uh) = y_0 + u\Delta y_0 + \frac{u(u-1)}{2}\Delta^2 y_0 + \cdots$$

$$= 0{\cdot}6221 + u(-0{\cdot}0066) + \frac{u^2 - u}{2} \times (0{\cdot}0049)$$

where $u = \dfrac{x - 0{\cdot}60}{0{\cdot}05}$

$$\frac{dy}{dx} = 0 \Rightarrow \frac{1}{h}\left[-0{\cdot}0066 + \frac{2u-1}{2}(0{\cdot}0049)\right] = 0$$

*i.e.,* $(2u - 1)(0{\cdot}0049) = 0{\cdot}0132$

$$u = 1{\cdot}8469$$

Corresponding $x = x_0 + uh = 0{\cdot}60 + (0{\cdot}05)(1{\cdot}8469) = 0{\cdot}6923$

$y$ is minimum when $x = \mathbf{0{\cdot}6923}$.

(This is evidently a minimum as we look at the table.)

Minimum $y = 0{\cdot}6221 - 0{\cdot}0066 \times 1{\cdot}8469 + 0{\cdot}00245\,[1{\cdot}8469][0{\cdot}8469]$

$= \mathbf{0{\cdot}6137426}$.

**Example 11.** *The table given below reveals the velocity v of a body during the time 't' specified. Find its acceleration at t = 1·1.*

| $t$ | : | 1·0 | 1·1 | 1·2 | 1·3 | 1·4 |
|---|---|---|---|---|---|---|
| $v$ | : | 43·1 | 47·7 | 52·1 | 56·4 | 60·8 |

**Solution.** $v$ is dependent on time $t$ *i.e.,* $v = v(t)$. We require acceleration $= \dfrac{dv}{dt}$.

Therefore, we have to find $v'(1{\cdot}1)$.

That is, it is a problem on numerical differentiation.

| $t$ | $v$ | $\Delta v$ | $\Delta^2 v$ | $\Delta^3 v$ | $\Delta^4 v$ |
|---|---|---|---|---|---|
| 1·0 | 43·1 | | | | |
| | | 4·6 | | | |
| 1·1 | 47·7 | | − 0·2 | | |
| | | 4·4 | | 0·1 | |
| 1·2 | 52·1 | | − 0·1 | | 0·1 |
| | | 4·3 | | 0·2 | |
| 1·3 | 56·4 | | 0·1 | | |
| | | 4·4 | | | |
| 1·4 | 60·8 | | | | |

As $\frac{dv}{dt}$ at $t = 1{\cdot}1$ is required, (nearer to beginning value), we use forward formula of Newton.

$$v(t) = v(t_0 + uh) = v_0 + u\Delta v_0 + \frac{u(u-1)}{2}\Delta^2 v_0 + \frac{u(u-1)(u-2)}{3!}\Delta^3 v_0 + \cdots$$

$$\frac{dv}{dt} = \frac{1}{h}\cdot\frac{dv}{du} = \frac{1}{h}\left[\Delta v_0 + \frac{2u-1}{2}\Delta^2 v_0 + \frac{3u^2 - 6u + 2}{6}\Delta^3 y_0 + \cdots\right]$$

where $u = \frac{t - t_0}{h} = \frac{1{\cdot}1 - 1{\cdot}0}{0{\cdot}1} = 1$

$$\left(\frac{dv}{dt}\right)_{t=1\cdot1} = \left(\frac{dv}{dt}\right)_{u=1} = \frac{1}{0{\cdot}1}\left[4{\cdot}6 + \frac{1}{2}(-0{\cdot}2) - \frac{1}{6}(0{\cdot}1) + \frac{1}{12}(0{\cdot}1)\right]$$

$$= 10\,[4{\cdot}6 - 0{\cdot}1 - 0{\cdot}0166 + 0{\cdot}0083]$$

$$= \mathbf{44{\cdot}917}.$$

**Example 12.** *A rod is rotating in a plane. The following table gives the angle θ (in radians) through which the rod has turned for various values of time t (seconds). Calculate the angular velocity and angular acceleration of the rod at t = 0·6 seconds.*

| $t$ | : | 0 | 0·2 | 0·4 | 0·6 | 0·8 | 1·0 |
|---|---|---|---|---|---|---|---|
| $\theta$ | : | 0 | 0·12 | 0·49 | 1·12 | 2·02 | 3·20 |

**Solution.** We form the difference table below:

| $t$ | $\theta$ | $\nabla\theta$ | $\nabla^2\theta$ | $\nabla^3\theta$ | $\nabla^4\theta$ |
|---|---|---|---|---|---|
| 0 | 0 | | | | |
| | | 0·12 | | | |
| 0·2 | 0·12 | | 0·25 | | |
| | | 0·37 | | 0·01 | |
| 0·4 | 0·49 | | 0·26 | | 0 |
| | | 0·63 | | 0·01 | |
| 0·6 | 1·12 | | 0·27 | | 0 |
| | | 0·90 | | 0·01 ($\nabla^3\theta_n$) | |
| 0·8 | 2·02 | | 0·28 ($\nabla^2\theta_n$) | | |
| | | 1·18 ($\nabla\theta_n$) | | | |
| 1·0 | 3·20 | | | | |

Since $x = 0{\cdot}6$ is towards the end, we will use backward difference formula. (We can also use central difference formula).

By Newton's backward difference formula,

$$\left(\frac{dy}{dx}\right)_{x=x} = \frac{1}{h}\left[\nabla y_n + \frac{2v+1}{2}\nabla^2 y_n + \frac{3v^2+6v+2}{6}\nabla^3 y_n + \frac{4v^3+18v^2+22v+6}{24}\nabla^4 y_n + \cdots\right] \quad \ldots(1)$$

Here $v = \frac{x - x_n}{h} = \frac{0.6 - 1.0}{0.2} = -2$

Using in (1),

$$\left(\frac{d\theta}{dt}\right)_{t=0.6} = \frac{1}{0.2}\left[1.18 - \frac{3}{2}(0.28) + \frac{1}{3}(0.01)\right]$$

$$= 5\,[1.18 - 0.42 + 0.00333]$$

$$= \mathbf{3.81665} \text{ radians/sec.}$$

Also, $\frac{d^2y}{dx^2} = \frac{1}{h^2}\left[\nabla^2 y_n + (v+1)\,\nabla^3 y_n + \cdots\right]$

$$\left(\frac{d^2\theta}{dt^2}\right)_{t=0.6} = \frac{1}{0.04}\,[0.28 - 0.01]$$

$$= \mathbf{6.75} \text{ radians/sec.}^2$$

## EXERCISE 9.1

**1.** Find the first and second derivative of the function tabulated below at $x = 3$.

| $x$ | : | 3·0 | 3·2 | 3·4 | 3·6 | 3·8 | 4·0 |
|---|---|---|---|---|---|---|---|
| $f(x)$ | : | – 14 | – 10·032 | – 5·296 | – 0·256 | 6·672 | 14 |

**2.** Find the first three derivatives of the function at $x = 1.5$ from the table below.

| $x$ | : | 1·5 | 2·0 | 2·5 | 3·0 | 3·5 | 4·0 |
|---|---|---|---|---|---|---|---|
| $y$ | : | 3·375 | 7·0 | 13·625 | 24·0 | 38·875 | 59·0 |

**3.** From the table below find $y'$ and $y''$ at $x = 1.05$.

| $x$ | : | 1·00 | 1·05 | 1·10 | 1·15 | 1·20 | 1·25 | 1·30 |
|---|---|---|---|---|---|---|---|---|
| $y$ | : | 1·00000 | 1·02470 | 1·04881 | 1·07238 | 1·09544 | 1·11803 | 1·14017 |

**4.** Find the first and second derivative of $\sqrt{x}$ at $x = 15$ from the table below.

| $x$ | : | 15 | 17 | 19 | 21 | 23 | 25 |
|---|---|---|---|---|---|---|---|
| $\sqrt{x}$ | : | 3·873 | 4·123 | 4·359 | 4·583 | 4·796 | 5·000 |

(*B.Sc. BR. 1989*)

**5.** The following data give the corresponding values for pressure and specific volume of a superheated steam.

| Volume $v$ | : | 2 | 4 | 6 | 8 | 10 |
|---|---|---|---|---|---|---|
| Pressure $p$ | : | 105 | 42·7 | 25·3 | 16·7 | 13·0 |

Find the rate of change of pressure w.r.t. volume when $v = 2$.

**6.** Obtain the second derivative of $y$ at $x = 0.96$ from the data.

| $x$ | : | 0·96 | 0·98 | 1·00 | 1·02 | 1·04 |
|---|---|---|---|---|---|---|
| $y$ | : | 0·7825 | 0·7739 | 0·7651 | 0·7563 | 0·7473 |

**7.** Find the value of cos (1·74) from the following table.

| $x$ | : | 1·7 | 1·74 | 1·78 | 1·82 | 1·86 |
|---|---|---|---|---|---|---|
| sin $x$ | : | 0·9916 | 0·9857 | 0·9781 | 0·9691 | 0·9584 |

$\left[\textbf{Hint. } \frac{d}{dx} \sin x = \cos x\right]$

**8.** In Problem 3, find $y'$ and $y''$ at $x = 1{\cdot}25$.

**9.** In Problem 4, find the first two derivatives at $x = 23$.

**10.** The population of a town is given below.

| *Year* | : | 1921 | 1931 | 1941 | 1951 | 1961 |
|---|---|---|---|---|---|---|
| *Population in thousands* | : | 19·96 | 38·65 | 58·81 | 77·21 | 94·61 |

**11.** In a machine, a slider moves along a fixed straight rod. Its distance $x$ cms along the rod is given below for various values of time $t$ secs. Find the velocity and acceleration of the slider when $t = 0{\cdot}3$.

| *t (sec)* | : | 0·0 | 0·1 | 0·2 | 0·3 | 0·4 | 0·5 | 0·6 |
|---|---|---|---|---|---|---|---|---|
| *x (cm)* | : | 30·13 | 31·62 | 32·87 | 33·64 | 33·95 | 33·81 | 33·24 |

**12.** Find the extremum values of $y$ given the table below.

| $x$ | : | 2 | 3 | 4 | 5 | 6 |
|---|---|---|---|---|---|---|
| $y$ | : | 31·1875 | 12·0275 | 2·8655 | 3·7052 | 14·5440 |

**13.** Find the maximum and minimum values of $y$ from the table.

| $x$ | : | 0 | 1 | 2 | 3 | 4 | 5 |
|---|---|---|---|---|---|---|---|
| $y$ | : | 0 | 0·25 | 0 | 2·25 | 16·00 | 56·25 |

*(B.Sc. BR. Nov. '89)*

**14.** Determine $f'$ (4) from the following table.

| $x$ | : | 1 | 2 | 4 | 8 | 10 |
|---|---|---|---|---|---|---|
| $f(x)$ | : | 0 | 1 | 5 | 21 | 27 |

(**Note**: Intervals are unequal.)

**15.** Evaluate $y'$ and $y''$ at $x = 2$ given

| $x$ | : | 0 | 1 | 3 | 6 |
|---|---|---|---|---|---|
| $y$ | : | 18 | 10 | – 18 | 40 |

**16.** Find $f'$ (8) given $f$ (6) = 1·556, $f$ (7) = 1·690, $f$ (9) = 1·908, $f$ (12) = 2·158.

**17.** From the following data find $f'$ (5).

| $x$ | : | 0 | 2 | 3 | 4 | 7 | 9 |
|---|---|---|---|---|---|---|---|
| $f(x)$ | : | 4 | 26 | 58 | 112 | 486 | 922 |

**18.** Find the minimum value of $f(x)$ which has values.

| $x$ | : | 0 | 2 | 4 | 6 |
|---|---|---|---|---|---|
| $f(x)$ | : | 3 | 3 | 11 | 27 |

**19.** A curve passes through the points (0, 18), (1, 10) (3, – 18) and (6, 90). Find the slope of the curve at $x = 2$.

**20.** Find the value of sec 31° using the following table.

| θ *(in degrees)* | : | 31° | 32° | 33° | 34° |
|---|---|---|---|---|---|
| tan θ | : | 0·6008 | 0·6249 | 0·6494 | 0·6745 |

$\left[\textbf{Hint. } \frac{d}{dt}(\tan \theta) = \sec^2 \theta\right]$ *(Anna Nov. 2004)*

**21.** From the table given below, find $f'(30)$, $f'(31)$ and $f'(35)$.

| $x$ | : | 30 | 31 | 32 | 33 | 34 | 35 | 36 |
|---|---|---|---|---|---|---|---|---|
| $f(x)$ | : | 85·90 | 86·85 | 87·73 | 88·64 | 89·52 | 90·37 | 91·1′ |

**22.** Find $y'$ and $y''$ at $x = 1{\cdot}2$ given.

| $x$ | : | 1·0 | 1·2 | 1·4 | 1·6 | 1·8 | 2·0 | 2·2 |
|---|---|---|---|---|---|---|---|---|
| $y$ | : | 2·7183 | 3·3201 | 4·0552 | 4·9530 | 6·0496 | 7·3891 | 9·0250 |

**23.** Find the maximum value of $f(x)$ given the table.

| $x$ | : | 1·2 | 1·3 | 1·4 | 1·5 | 1·6 |
|---|---|---|---|---|---|---|
| $f(x)$ | : | 0·9320 | 0·9636 | 0·9855 | 0·9975 | 0·9996 |

## NUMERICAL INTEGRATION

### 9·7. Introduction

We know that $\int_a^b f(x)\,dx$ represents the area between $y = f(x)$, $x$-axis and the ordinates $x = a$ and $x = b$. This integration is possible only if the $f(x)$ is explicitly given and if it is integrable. The problem of numerical integration can be stated as follows: Given a set of $(n+1)$ paired values $(x_i, y_i)$, $i = 0, 1, 2, \ldots n$ of the function $y = f(x)$, where $f(x)$ is not known explicitly, it is required to compute $\int_{x_0}^{x_n} y\,dx$.

As we did in the case of interpolation or numerical differentiation, we replace $f(x)$ by an interpolating polynomial $P_n(x)$ and obtain $\int_{x_0}^{x_n} P_n(x)\,dx$ which is approximately taken as the value for $\int_{x_0}^{x_n} f(x)\,dx$.

### 9·8. A general quadrature formula for equidistant ordinates (*or Newton-cote's formula*)

For equally spaced intervals, we have Newton's forward difference formula as

$$y(x) = y(x_0 + uh) = y_0 + u\,\Delta y_0 + \frac{u(u-1)}{2!}\Delta^2 y_0 + \frac{u(u-1)(u-2)}{3!}\Delta^3 y_0 + \cdots \quad \ldots(1)$$

Now, instead of $f(x)$, we will replace it by this interpolating formula of Newton.

Here, $u = \dfrac{x - x_0}{h}$ where $h$ is interval of differencing.

Since $x_n = x_0 + nh$, and $u = \dfrac{x - x_0}{h}$ we have $\dfrac{x - x_0}{h} = n = u$.

$$\int_{x_0}^{x_n} f(x)\,dx = \int_{x_0}^{x_0 + nh} f(x)\,dx$$

$$\approx \int_{x_0}^{x_0+nh} P_n(x)\,dx \text{ where } P_n(x) \text{ is interpolating polynomial of degree } n.$$

$$\approx \int_0^n \left( y_0 + u\,\Delta y_0 + \frac{u(u-1)}{2!}\Delta^2 y_0 + \frac{u(u-1)(u-2)}{3!}\Delta^3 y_0 + \cdots \right) \cdot h\,du$$

since $dx = h\,du$, and when $x = x_0$, $u = 0$ and when $x = x_0 + nh$, $u = n$

$$= h \int_0^n \left( y_0 + u\,\Delta y_0 + \frac{u^2 - u}{2!}\Delta^2 y_0 + \frac{u^3 - 3u^2 + 2u}{3!}\Delta^3 y_0 + \cdots \right) du$$

$$= h \left[ y_0(u) + \frac{u^2}{2}\Delta y_0 + \frac{\left(\frac{u^3}{3} - \frac{u^2}{2}\right)}{2}\Delta^2 y_0 + \frac{1}{6}\left(\frac{u^4}{4} - u^3 + u^2\right)\Delta^3 y_0 + \cdots \right]_0^n$$

$$\int_{x_0}^{x_n} f(x)\,dx \approx h\left[ n y_0 + \frac{n^2}{2}\Delta y_0 + \frac{1}{2}\left(\frac{n^3}{3} - \frac{n^2}{2}\right)\Delta^2 y_0 + \frac{1}{6}\left(\frac{n^4}{4} - n^3 + n^2\right)\Delta^3 y_0 + \cdots \right] \quad \ldots(2)$$

The equation (2), called Newton-Cote's quadrature formula is a general quadrature formula. Giving various values for $n$, we get a number of special formula.

### 9·9. Trapezoidal rule

By putting $n = 1$, in the quadrature formula (*i.e.*, there are only two paired values and interpolating polynomial is linear.)

$$\int_{x_0}^{x_0+h} f(x)\,dx \approx h\left[ 1 \cdot y_0 + \frac{1}{2}\Delta y_0 \right] \text{ since other differences do not exist if } n = 1.$$

$$\approx h\left[ y_0 + \frac{1}{2}(y_1 - y_0) \right]$$

$$= \frac{h}{2}(y_0 + y_1) \quad \ldots(3)$$

$$\int_{x_0}^{x_n} f(x)\,dx \approx \int_{x_0}^{x_0+nh} f(x)\,dx$$

$$= \int_{x_0}^{x_0+h} f(x)\,dx + \int_{x_0+h}^{x_0+2h} f(x)\,dx + \cdots + \int_{x_0+(n-1)h}^{x_0+nh} f(x)\,dx$$

$$= \frac{h}{2}(y_0 + y_1) + \frac{h}{2}(y_1 + y_2) + \cdots + \frac{h}{2}(y_{n-1} + y_n)$$

$$= \frac{h}{2} [(y_0 + y_n) + 2 (y_1 + y_2 + y_3 + \cdots + y_{n-1})]$$

$$= \frac{h}{2} [(\text{Sum of the first and the last ordinates})$$

$$+ 2 (\text{Sum of the remaining ordinates}) ]$$

This is known as Trapezoidal Rule.

## 9·10. Geometrical interpretation

Geometrically, if the ordered pairs $(x_i, y_i), i = 0, 1, 2, \ldots n$ are plotted, and if any two consecutive points are joined by straight lines, we get the figure as shown.

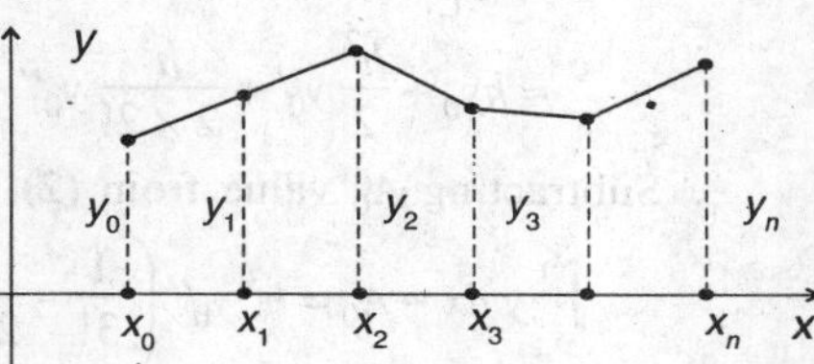


The area between $f(x)$, $x$-axis and ordinates $x = x_0$ and $x = x_n$ is approximated to the sum of the trapeziums as shown in the figure.

**Note:** Though this method is very simple for calculation purposes of numerical integration, the error in this case is significant. The accuracy of the result can be improved by increasing the number of intervals and decreasing the value of *h*.

## 9·11. Truncation error in Trapezoidal rule

In the neighbourhood of $x = x_0$, we can expand $y = f(x)$ by Taylor series in powers of $x - x_0$. That is,

$$y(x) = y_0 + \frac{(x - x_0)}{1!} y_0' + \frac{(x - x_0)^2}{2!} y_0'' + \cdots + \cdots \qquad \ldots(1)$$

where $y'_0 = [y'(x)]_{x = x_0}$.

$$\int_{x_0}^{x_1} y\, dx = \int_{x_0}^{x_1} \left[ y_0 + \frac{(x - x_0)}{1!} y_0' + \frac{(x - x_0)^2}{2!} y_0'' + \cdots \right] dx$$

$$= \left[ y_0 x + \frac{(x - x_0)^2}{2!} y_0' + \frac{(x - x_0)^3}{3!} y_0'' + \cdots \right]_{x_0}^{x_1}$$

$$= y_0 (x_1 - x_0) + \frac{(x_1 - x_0)^2}{2!} y_0' + \frac{(x_1 - x_0)^3}{3!} y_0'' + \cdots$$

$$= h y_0 + \frac{h^2}{2!} y_0' + \frac{h^3}{3!} y_0'' + \cdots \qquad \ldots(2)$$

if $h$ is the equal interval length.

$$\text{Also } \int_{x_0}^{x_1} y\, dx \approx \frac{h}{2} (y_0 + y_1) = \text{area of the first trapezium.} = A_0 \qquad \ldots(3)$$

Putting $x = x_1$ in (1),

$$y(x_1) = y_1 = y_0 + \frac{(x_1 - x_0)}{1!} y_0' + \frac{(x_1 - x_0)^2}{2!} y_0'' + \cdots$$

*i.e.,*
$$y_1 = y_0 + \frac{h}{1!} y_0' + \frac{h^2}{2!} y_0'' + \cdots \qquad \text{...(4)}$$

$$A_0 \approx \frac{h}{2}\left[ y_0 + y_0 + \frac{h}{1!} y_0' + \frac{h^2}{2!} y_0'' + \cdots \right] \text{ using (4) in (3).}$$

$$\approx h y_0 + \frac{h^2}{2} y_0' + \frac{h^3}{2 \times 2!} y_0'' + \cdots$$

Subtracting $A_0$ value from (2),

$$\int_{x_0}^{x_1} y\,dx - A_0 = h^3 y_0'' \left( \frac{1}{3!} - \frac{1}{2 \times 2!} \right) + \cdots\cdots$$

$$= -\frac{1}{12} h^3 y_0'' + \cdots$$

Therefore the error in the first interval $(x_0, x_1)$ is $-\frac{1}{12} h^3 y_0''$ (neglecting other terms).

Similarly the error in the $i$th interval $= -\frac{1}{12} h^3 y''_{i-1}$

Therefore, the total cumulative error (approx.),

$$E = -\frac{1}{12} h^3 (y_0'' + y_1'' + y_2'' + \cdots + y''_{n-1})$$

$$|E| < \frac{nh^3}{12} \cdot M \text{ where } M \text{ is the maximum value of}$$

$$|y_0''|, |y_1''|, |y_2''|, \ldots$$

$$< \frac{(b-a)h^2}{12} \cdot M \text{ if the interval is } (a, b) \text{ and } h = \frac{b-a}{n}.$$

Hence, the error in the trapezoidal rule is of the order $h^2$.

## 9·12. Romberg's method

As trapezoidal rule is a rough rule, a modification to it is done using the idea of truncation error.

For an interval of size $h$, let the error in the trapezoidal rule be $kh^2$ where $k$ is a constant. Suppose we evaluate $I = \int_{x_0}^{x_n} y\,dx$, taking two different values of $h$, say $h_1$ and $h_2$, then

$$I = I_1 + E_1 = I_1 + kh_1^2 \qquad \text{...(1)}$$

$$I = I_2 + E_2 = I_2 + kh_2^2 \qquad \text{...(2)}$$

where $I_1, I_2$ are the values of $I$ got by two different values of $h$, by trapezoidal rule and $E_1, E_2$ are the corresponding errors.

$$\therefore \quad I_1 + kh_1^2 = I_2 + kh_2^2$$

$$\therefore \quad k = \frac{I_1 - I_2}{h_2^2 - h_1^2}$$

Substituting in (1),

$$I = I_1 + \left(\frac{I_1 - I_2}{h_2^2 - h_1^2}\right) h_1^2$$

$$I = \frac{I_1 h_2^2 - I_2 h_1^2}{h_2^2 - h_1^2}$$

This $I$ is a better result than either $I_1$ or $I_2$.

If $h_1 = h$ and $h_2 = \frac{1}{2} h$, then we get

$$I = \frac{I_1\left(\frac{1}{4} h^2\right) - I_2 h^2}{\frac{1}{4} h^2 - h^2}$$

$$= \frac{4I_2 - I_1}{3} = I_2 + \frac{1}{3}(I_2 - I_1)$$

$$I = I_2 + \frac{1}{3}(I_2 - I_1) \qquad \text{...(3)}$$

We got this result by applying Trapezoidal rule twice. By applying the trapezoidal rule many times, every time halving $h$, we get a sequence of results $A_1, A_2, A_3, \ldots$ we apply the formula given by (3), to each of adjacent pairs and get the resultants $B_1, B_2, B_3 \ldots$ (which are improved values). Again applying the formula given by (3), to each of pairs $B_1, B_2, B_3 \ldots$ we get another sequence of better results $C_1, C_2, \ldots$ continuing in this way, we proceed until we get two successive values which are very close to each other. This systematic improvement of *Richardson's method* is called *Romberg method* or *Romberg integration.*

## 9·13. Simpson's one-third rule

Setting $n = 2$ in Newton-cote's quadrature formula, we have

$$\int_{x_0}^{x_2} f(x)\, dx \approx h\left[2y_0 + \frac{4}{2}\Delta y_0 + \frac{1}{2}\left(\frac{8}{3} - \frac{4}{2}\right)\Delta^2 y_0\right]$$

(since other terms vanish)

$$\approx h\left[2y_0 + 2(y_1 - y_0) + \frac{1}{3}(E - 1)^2 y_0\right]$$

$$= h\left[2y_0 + 2y_1 - 2y_0 + \frac{1}{3}(y_2 - 2y_1 + y_0)\right]$$

$$= h\left[\frac{1}{3}y_2 + \frac{4}{3}y_1 + \frac{1}{3}y_0\right]$$

$$= \frac{h}{3}(y_2 + 4y_1 + y_0)$$

Similarly, $\int_{x_2}^{x_4} f(x)\,dx = \frac{h}{3}(y_2 + 4y_3 + y_4)$

$$\int_{x_i}^{x_{i+2}} f(x)\,dx = \frac{h}{3}(y_i + 4y_{i+1} + y_{i+2})$$

If $n$ is an even integer, last integral will be

$$\int_{x_{n-2}}^{x_n} f(x)\,dx = \frac{h}{3}(y_{n-2} + 4y_{n-1} + y_n)$$

Adding all these integrals, if $n$ is an even positive integer, that is, the number of ordinates $y_0, y_1, \ldots y_n$ is odd, we have

$$\int_{x_0}^{x_n} f(x)\,dx = \int_{x_0}^{x_2} f(x)\,dx + \int_{x_2}^{x_4} f(x)\,dx + \cdots + \int_{x_{n-2}}^{x_n} f(x)\,dx$$

$$= \frac{h}{3}[(y_0 + 4y_1 + y_2) + (y_2 + 4y_3 + y_4) + \cdots + (y_{n-2} + 4y_{n-1} + y_n)]$$

$$= \frac{h}{3}[(y_0 + y_n) + 2(y_2 + y_4 + \cdots) + 4(y_1 + y_3 + \cdots)]$$

$= \frac{h}{3}$ [sum of the first and last ordinates
+ 2 (sum of remaining odd ordinates)
+ 4 (sum of even ordinates)]

**Note:** Though $y_2$ has suffix even, it is the third ordinate (odd).

## 9·14. Simpson's three-eighths rule

Putting $n = 3$ in Newton-cotes formula (equation 2, §9·8)

$$\int_{x_0}^{x_3} f(x)\,dx = h\left[3y_0 + \frac{9}{2}\Delta y_0 + \frac{1}{2}\left(\frac{9}{2}\right)\Delta^2 y_0 + \frac{1}{6}\left(\frac{81}{4} - 27 + 9\right)\Delta^3 y_0\right]$$

$$= h\left[3y_0 + \frac{9}{2}(y_1 - y_0) + \frac{9}{4}(E-1)^2 y_0 + \frac{3}{8}(E-1)^3 y_0\right]$$

$$= h\left[3y_0 + \frac{9}{2}y_1 - \frac{9}{2}y_0 + \frac{9}{4}(y_2 - 2y_1 + y_0)\right.$$

$$\left. + \frac{3}{8}(y_3 - 3y_2 + 3y_1 - y_0)\right]$$

$$= \frac{3h}{8}[y_3 + 3y_2 + 3y_1 + y_0]$$

If $n$ is a multiple of 3,

$$\int_{x_0}^{x_0+nh} f(x)\,dx = \int_{x_0}^{x_0+3h} f(x)\,dx + \int_{x_0+3h}^{x_0+6h} f(x)\,dx + \cdots + \int_{x_0+(n-3)h}^{x_0+nh} f(x)\,dx$$

$$= \frac{3h}{8}\Big[(y_0 + 3y_1 + 3y_2 + y_3) + (y_3 + 3y_4 + 3y_5 + y_6) + \cdots + (y_{n-3} + 3y_{n-2} + 3y_{n-1} + y_n)\Big]$$

$$= \frac{3h}{8}\Big[(y_0 + y_n) + 3(y_1 + y_2 + y_4 + y_5 + \cdots + y_{n-1}) + 2(y_3 + y_6 + y_9 + \cdots + y_n)\Big] \quad \ldots(2)$$

Equation (2) is called *Simpson's three-eighths rule* which is applicable only when $n$ is a multiple of 3.

## 9·15. Weddle's rule

Putting $n = 6$ in Newton-cotes formula

$$\int_{x_0}^{x_0+6h} f(x)\,dx = h\Big[6y_0 + 18\,\Delta y_0 + \frac{1}{2}(72 - 18)\,\Delta^2 y_0 + \frac{1}{6}(324 - 216 + 36)\,\Delta^3 y_0 + \cdots\Big]$$

$$= h\Big[6y_0 + 18\,\Delta y_0 + 27\,\Delta^2 y_0 + 24\,\Delta^3 y_0 + \frac{123}{10}\Delta^4 y_0 + \frac{33}{10}\Delta^5 y_0 + \frac{41}{140}\Delta^6 y_0\Big]$$

Replace the term $\frac{41}{140}\Delta^6 y_0$ by $\frac{42}{140}\Delta^6 y_0$. By this change, the error introduced is only $\frac{h}{140}\Delta^6 y_0$ which is negligible when $h$ and $\Delta^6 y_0$ are small. Using $\Delta = E - 1$ and replacing all differences in terms of $y$'s, we get

$$\int_{x_0}^{x_0+6h} f(x)\,dx = \frac{3h}{10}[y_0 + 5y_1 + y_2 + 6y_3 + y_4 + 5y_5 + y_6]$$

Similarly,

$$\int_{x_0+6h}^{x_0+12h} f(x)\,dx = \frac{3h}{10}[y_6 + 5y_7 + y_8 + 6y_9 + y_{10} + 5y_{11} + y_{12}]$$

.................................................................................................

$$\int_{x_0+(n-6)h}^{x_0+nh} f(x)\,dx = \frac{3h}{10}[y_{n-6} + 5y_{n-5} + y_{n-4} + 6y_{n-3} + y_{n-2} + 5y_{n-1} + y_n]$$

Adding all these integrals, we get

$$\int_{x_0}^{x_0+nh} f(x)\,dx = \frac{3h}{10}\,[(y_0+5y_1+y_2+6y_3+y_4+5y_5)$$

$$+(2y_6+5y_7+y_8+6y_9+y_{10}+5y_{11})$$

$$+(\cdots\cdots\cdots\cdots\cdots\cdots)$$

$$+(2y_{n-6}+5y_{n-5}+y_{n-4}+6y_{n-3}+y_{n-2}+5y_{n-1}+y_n)] \qquad \ldots(1)$$

Equation (1) is called *Weddle's rule.*

In the above formula, the coefficients may be remembered in groups of six.

| | | | | |
|---|---|---|---|---|
| First group : Coefficients | : 1, 5, | 1, 6, | 1, 5 | |
| All interior groups : Coefficients | : 2, 5, | 1, 6, | 1, 5 | |
| Last group : Coefficients | : 2, 5, | 1, 6, | 1, 5, | 1. |

**Note:** If there are only 7 ordinates, the coefficients are 1, 5, 1, 6, 1, 5, 1.

**Notes:** **1.** In trapezoidal rule, $y(x)$ is a linear function of $x$. The rule is the simplest one but it is least accurate.

**2.** In Simpson's one-third rule, $y(x)$ is a polynomial of degree *two.* To apply this rule, $n$, the number of intervals must be *even*. That is, the number of ordinates must be *odd.*

**3.** In Simpson's three-eighths rule, $y(x)$ is a polynomial of degree *three.* This rule is applicable if $n$, the number of intervals is a multiple of 3.

**4.** In Weddle's rule, $y(x)$ is a polynomial of degree *six* and this rule is applicable only if $n$, the number of intervals, is a multiple of *six.* A minimum number of 7 ordinates is necessary.

## 9·16. Truncation error in Simpson's formula

By Taylor expansion of $y=f(x)$ in the neighourhood of $x=x_0$, we get,

$$y = y_0 + \frac{(x-x_0)}{1!}\,y_0' + \frac{(x-x_0)^2}{2!}\,y_0'' + \cdots \qquad \ldots(1)$$

$$\int_{x_0}^{x_2} y\,dx = \int_{x_0}^{x_2}\left[\,y_0 + \frac{(x-x_0)}{1!}\,y_0' + \frac{(x-x_0)^2}{2!}\,y_0'' + \cdots\right]dx$$

$$= \left[\,y_0 x + \frac{(x-x_0)^2}{2!}\,y_0' + \frac{(x-x_0)^3}{3!}\,y_0'' + \cdots\right]_{x_0}^{x_2}$$

$$= y_0\,(x_2-x_0) + \frac{(x_2-x_0)^2}{2!}\,y_0' + \frac{(x_2-x_0)^3}{3!}\,y_0'' + \cdots$$

$$= 2hy_0 + \frac{4h^2}{2!}\,y_0' + \frac{8h^3}{3!}\,y_0'' + \frac{16h^4}{4!}\,y_0''' + \cdots$$

$$= 2hy_0 + 2h^2 y_0' + \frac{4}{3} h^3 y_0'' + \frac{2h^4}{3} y_0''' + \frac{4h^5}{15} y_0'''' + \cdots \qquad ...(2)$$

$$A_1 = \text{area} = \int_{x_0}^{x_2} y\,dx = \frac{h}{3}(y_0 + 4y_1 + y_2), \text{ by Simpson's rule} \qquad ...(3)$$

Putting $x = x_1$ in (1),

$$y_1 = y_0 + \frac{(x_1 - x_0)}{1!} y_0' + \frac{(x_1 - x_0)^2}{2!} y_0'' + \cdots$$

$$= y_0 + \frac{h}{1!} y_0' + \frac{h^2}{2!} y_0'' + \cdots \qquad ...(4)$$

Putting $x = x_2$, in equation (1),

$$y_2 = y_0 + \frac{2h}{1!} y_0' + \frac{4h^2}{2!} y_0'' + \cdots \qquad ...(5)$$

Substituting (4) in (5), in (3),

$$A_1 = 2\,hy_0 + 2\,h^2 y_0' + \frac{4h^3}{3} y_0'' + \frac{2h^4}{3} y_0''' + \frac{5h^5}{18} y_0'''' + \cdots \qquad ...(6)$$

Equations (2) – (6) give

$$\int_{x_0}^{x_2} y\,dx - A_1 = \left(\frac{4}{15} - \frac{5}{18}\right) h^5 y_0'''' + \cdots$$

$$= \frac{-h^5}{90} y_0'''' + \cdots$$

Leaving the remaining terms involving $h^6$ and higher powers of $h$, Principal part of the error in $(x_0, x_2)$ is

$$= \frac{-h^5}{90} y_0''''$$

Similarly the principal part of the error in $(x_2, x_4)$ is

$$= \frac{-h^5}{90} y_2'''' \text{ and so for each interval.}$$

Hence the total error in all the intervals is given by

$$E = \frac{-h^5}{90}(y_0'''' + y_2'''' + \cdots)$$

$\therefore \quad |E| < \frac{nh^5}{90} M$ where $M$ is the numerically greater value of $y_0'''', y_2'''', \cdots y_{2n-2}$ since $(x_{2n}, y_{2n})$ is the last paired value because we require odd number of ordinates to apply Simpson's one-third rule. (*i.e.*, $2n$ intervals).

If the interval is $(a, b)$ then $b - a = h\,(2n)$. Using this,

$$|E| < \frac{(b-a)\,h^4}{180} \cdot M.$$

Hence, the error in Simpson's one-third rule is of the order $h^4$.

**Example 1.** *Evaluate* $\int_{-3}^{3} x^4 dx$ *by using (1) Trapezoidal rule (2) Simpson's rule. Verify your results by actual integration.*

**Solution.** Here $y(x) = x^4$. Interval length $(b-a) = 6$. So, we divide 6 equal intervals with $h = \frac{6}{6} = 1$. We form below the table

| $x$ | : | $-3$ | $-2$ | $-1$ | $0$ | $1$ | $2$ | $3$ |
|---|---|---|---|---|---|---|---|---|
| $y$ | : | 81 | 16 | 1 | 0 | 1 | 16 | 81 |

(*i*) By Trapezoidal rule,

$$\int_{-3}^{3} y\,dx \approx \frac{h}{2}\,[(\text{sum of the first and last ordinates}$$

$$+\,2\,(\text{sum of the remaining ordinates})]$$

$$\approx \frac{1}{2}\,[(81+81)+2\,(16+1+0+1+16)]$$

$$\approx 115$$

(*ii*) By Simpson's one-third rule (since number of ordinates is odd)

$$\int_{-3}^{3} y\,dx \approx \frac{1}{3}\,[(81+81)+2\,(1+1)+4\,(16+0+16)]$$

$$\approx 98.$$

(*iii*) Since $n = 6$, (multiple of three), we can also use Simpson's three-eighths rule. By this rule,

$$\int_{-3}^{3} y\,dx \approx \frac{3}{8}\,[(81+81)+3\,(16+1+1+16)+2\,(0)] \;\approx 99.$$

(*iv*) By actual integration,

$$\int_{-3}^{3} x^4 dx = 2 \times \left(\frac{x^5}{5}\right)_0^3 = \frac{2 \times 243}{5} = 97{\cdot}2.$$

From the results obtained by various methods, we see that Simpson's rule gives better result than Trapezoidal rule (It is true in general; but not always—refer example 8).

**Example 2.** *Evaluate* $\int_0^1 \frac{dx}{1+x^2}$, *using Trapezoidal rule with* $h = 0{\cdot}2$. *Hence obtain an approximate value of* $\pi$. *Can you use other formulae in this case.* (*MS. Ap. '92*)

**Solution.** Let $y(x) = \frac{1}{1+x^2}$

Interval is $(1-0)=1$ ∵ The value of $y$ are calculated as points taking $h=0{\cdot}2$

| $x$ | : | 0 | 0·2 | 0·4 | 0·6 | 0·8 | 1·0 |
|---|---|---|---|---|---|---|---|
| $y=\dfrac{1}{1+x^2}$ | : | 1 | 0·96154 | 0·86207 | 0·73529 | 0·60976 | 0·50000 |

(*i*) By trapezoidal rule,

$$\int_0^1 \frac{dx}{1+x^2} = \frac{h}{2}\,[(y_0+y_n)+2\,(y_1+y_2+\cdots+y_{n-1})]$$

$$= \frac{0{\cdot}2}{2}\,[(1+0{\cdot}5)+2\,(0{\cdot}96154+0{\cdot}86207+0{\cdot}73529+0{\cdot}60976)]$$

$$= (0{\cdot}1)\,[1{\cdot}5+6{\cdot}33732]$$

$$= 0{\cdot}783732$$

By actual integration,

$$\int_0^1 \frac{dx}{1+x^2} = (\tan^{-1}x)_0^1 = \pi/4$$

$$\therefore \qquad \frac{\pi}{4} \approx 0{\cdot}783732$$

$$\therefore \qquad \pi \approx 3{\cdot}13493 \text{ (approximately)}.$$

In this case, we cannot use Simpson's rule (both) and Weddle's rule. (since number of intervals is 5).

**Example 3.** *From the following table, find the area bounded by the curve and the x-axis from $x=7{\cdot}47$ to $x=7{\cdot}52$.*

| $x$ | : | *7·47* | *7·48* | *7·49* | *7·50* | *7·51* | *7·52* |
|---|---|---|---|---|---|---|---|
| $y=f(x)$ | : | *1·93* | *1·95* | *1·98* | *2·01* | *2·03* | *2·06* |

**Solution.** Since only 6 ordinates ($n=5$) are given, we cannot use Simpson's rule or Weddle's rule. So, we will use Trapezoidal rule.

$$\text{Area} = \int_{7\cdot47}^{7\cdot52} f(x)\,dx = \frac{0{\cdot}01}{2}\,[(1{\cdot}93+2{\cdot}06)+2\,(1{\cdot}95+1{\cdot}98+2{\cdot}01+2{\cdot}03)]$$

$$= \mathbf{0{\cdot}09965.}$$

**Example 4.** *Evaluate the integral* $I=\int_4^{5\cdot2} \log_e x\,dx$ *using Trapezoidal, Simpson's and Weddle's rules.*

**Solution.** Here $b-a=5{\cdot}2-4=1{\cdot}2$. We shall divide the interval into 6 equal parts.

Hence, $h=\dfrac{1{\cdot}2}{6}=0{\cdot}2$. We form the table.

| $x$ | 4 | 4·2 | 4·4 | 4·6 | 4·8 | 5·0 | 5·2 |
|---|---|---|---|---|---|---|---|
| $f(x)=\log_e x$ | 1·3862944 | 1·4350845 | 1·4816045 | 1·5260563 | 1·5686159 | 1·6094379 | 1·6486586 |

(*i*) By Trapezoidal rule,

$$\int_4^{5.2} \log x \, dx = \frac{0.2}{2} [(1.3862944 + 1.6486586) + 2 (1.4350845 + 1.4816045 + 1.5260563 + 1.5686159 + 1.6094379)]$$

$$= \mathbf{1.82765512}$$

(*ii*) Since $n = 6$, we can use Simpson's rule and Weddle's rule also. By Simpson's one-third rule,

$$I = \frac{0.2}{3} [(1.3862944 + 1.6486586) + 2 (1.4816045 + 1.5686159) + 4 (1.4350845 + 1.5260563)]$$

$$= \mathbf{1.82784724}$$

(*iii*) By Simpson, three-eighths rule,

$$I = \frac{3\,(0.2)}{8} [(1.3862944 + 1.6486586) + 3 (1.4350845 + 1.4816045 + 1.5686159 + 1.6094379 + 2 (1.5260563)]$$

$$= \mathbf{1.82784705}$$

(*iv*) By Weddle's rule,

$$I = \frac{3\,(0.2)}{10} [1.3862944 + 5 (1.4350845) + 1.4816045 + 6 (1.5260563) + 1.5686159 + 5 (1.6094379) + 1.6486586]$$

$$= \mathbf{1.82784739}$$

**Note:** If the number of intervals is a multiple of six, we can use all the above formulae.

**Example 5.** *Evaluate* $I = \int_0^6 \frac{1}{1+x} dx$ *using* (*i*) *Trapezoidal rule* (*ii*) *Simpson's rule* (*both*) (*iii*) *Weddle's rule. Also, check up by direct integration.*

**Solution.** Take the number of intervals as 6.

$$\therefore \qquad h = \frac{6-0}{6} = 1.$$

| $x$ : | 0 | 1 | 2 | 3 | 4 | 5 | 6 |
|---|---|---|---|---|---|---|---|
| $y = \frac{1}{1+x}$ : | 1 | 0.5 | $\frac{1}{3}$ | $\frac{1}{4}$ | $\frac{1}{5}$ | $\frac{1}{6}$ | $\frac{1}{7}$ |

(*i*) By Trapezoidal rule,

$$\int_0^6 \frac{dx}{1+x} = \frac{1}{2}\left[\left(1 + \frac{1}{7}\right) + 2\left(0.5 + \frac{1}{3} + \frac{1}{4} + \frac{1}{5} + \frac{1}{6}\right)\right]$$

$$= \mathbf{2.02142857}$$

(*ii*) By Simpson's one-third rule,

$$I=\frac{1}{3}\left[\left(1+\frac{1}{7}\right)+2\left(\frac{1}{3}+\frac{1}{5}\right)+4\left(\frac{1}{2}+\frac{1}{4}+\frac{1}{6}\right)\right]$$

$$=\frac{1}{3}\left(1+\frac{1}{7}+\frac{16}{15}+\frac{22}{6}\right)=\mathbf{1{\cdot}95873016}$$

(*iii*) By Simpson's three-eighth's rule,

$$I=\frac{3\times 1}{8}\left[\left(1+\frac{1}{7}\right)+3\left(0{\cdot}5+\frac{1}{3}+\frac{1}{5}+\frac{1}{6}\right)+2\left(\frac{1}{4}\right)\right]$$

$$=\mathbf{1{\cdot}96607143}$$

(*iv*) By Weddle's rule,

$$I=\frac{3\times 1}{10}\left[1+5\,(0{\cdot}5)+\frac{1}{3}+6\left(\frac{1}{4}\right)+\frac{1}{5}+5\left(\frac{1}{6}\right)+\frac{1}{7}\right]$$

$$=\mathbf{1{\cdot}95285714}$$

(*v*) By actual integration,

$$\int_0^6 \frac{1}{1+x}\,dx=[\log\,(1+x)]_0^6=\log_e 7=1{\cdot}94591015.$$

**Example 6.** *By dividing the range into ten equal parts, evaluate* $\int_0^\pi \sin x\,dx$ *by Trapezoidal and Simpson's rule. Verify your answer with integration.*

**Solution.** Range $=\pi-0=\pi$

Hence $\qquad h=\dfrac{\pi}{10}\cdot$

We tabulate below the values of $y$ at different $x$'s.

| $x$ | : | $0$ | $\frac{\pi}{10}$ | $\frac{2\pi}{10}$ | $\frac{3\pi}{10}$ | $\frac{4\pi}{10}$ | $\frac{5\pi}{10}$ |
|---|---|---|---|---|---|---|---|
| $y=\sin x$ | : | 0·0 | 0·3090 | 0·5878 | 0·8090 | 0·9511 | 1·0 |
| $x$ | : | $\frac{6\pi}{10}$ | $\frac{7\pi}{10}$ | $\frac{8\pi}{10}$ | $\frac{9\pi}{10}$ | $\pi$ | |
| $y=\sin x$ | : | 0·9511 | 0·8090 | 0·5878 | 0·3090 | 0 | |

$\left(\text{Note that the values are symmetrical about } x=\dfrac{\pi}{2}\right)$

(*i*) By Trapezoidal rule,

$$I=\frac{\pi}{20}[(0+0)+2\,(0{\cdot}3090+0{\cdot}5878+0{\cdot}8090+0{\cdot}9511+1{\cdot}0$$
$$+0{\cdot}9511+0{\cdot}8090+0{\cdot}5878+0{\cdot}3090)]$$

$=1{\cdot}9843$ nearly.

(*ii*) By Simpson's one-third rule (since three are 11 ordinates),

$$I = \frac{1}{3}\left(\frac{\pi}{10}\right)[(0+0) + 2\,(0{\cdot}5878 + 0{\cdot}9511 + 0{\cdot}9511 + 0{\cdot}5878) + 4\,(0{\cdot}3090 + 0{\cdot}8090 + 1 + 0{\cdot}8090 + 0{\cdot}3090)]$$

$$= 2{\cdot}00091$$

**Note:** We cannot use Simpson's three-eighth's rule or Weddle's rule here.

(*iii*) By actual integration, $I = (-\cos x)_0^{\pi} = 2$

Hence, Simpson's rule is more accurate than the Trapezoidal rule.

**Example 7.** *Evaluate* $\int_0^1 e^x\,dx$ *by Simpson's one-third rule correct to five decimal places, by proper choice of h.*

**Solution.** Here, interval length $= b - a = 1$

$$y = e^x;\ y^{(iv)} = e^x.$$

Error $= |E| < \frac{(b-a)}{180} h^4 \cdot M$, where $M = \text{Max}\,(e^x)$ in the range.

$$< \frac{1}{180} h^4 \cdot e$$

We require $(E) < 10^{-6}$

$$\frac{h^4 e}{180} < 10^{-6}$$

$$h < \left(\frac{180 \times 10^{-6}}{e}\right)^{1/4} = 0{\cdot}148$$

Hence we take $h = 0{\cdot}1$ to have the accuracy required.

$$\therefore \quad \int_0^1 e^x\,dx = \frac{0{\cdot}1}{3}\,[(1+e) + 2\,(e^{0.2} + e^{0.4} + e^{0.6} + e^{0.8}) + 4\,(e^{0.1} + e^{0.3} + e^{0.5} + e^{0.7} + e^{0.9})]$$

$$= 1{\cdot}718283$$

By actual integration, $\int_0^1 e^x\,dx = (e^x)_0^1 = e - 1 = 1{\cdot}71828183$

Correct to five decimal places, the answer is $1{\cdot}71828$.

**Example 8.** *Evaluate* $\int_0^6 \frac{dx}{1+x^2}$ *by (i) Trapezoidal rule (ii) Simpson's rule (iii) Weddle's rule. Also check up the results by actual integration*

**Solution.** Here, $b - a = 6 - 0 = 6$. Divide into 6 equal parts $h = \frac{6}{6} = 1$. Hence, the table is

| $x$ | : | 0 | 1 | 2 | 3 | 4 | 5 | 6 |
|---|---|---|---|---|---|---|---|---|
| $\frac{1}{1+x^2} = f(x)$ | : | 1·00 | 0·500 | 0·200 | 0·100 | 0·058824 | 0·038462 | 0·027027 |

There are 7 ordinates ($n = 6$). We can use all the formula.

(*i*) By Trapezoidal rule,

$$I = \int_0^6 \frac{dx}{1+x^2} = \frac{1}{2}\,[(1 + 0{\cdot}027027) + 2\,(0{\cdot}5 + 0{\cdot}2 + 0{\cdot}1 + 0{\cdot}058824 + 0{\cdot}038462)]$$

$$= \mathbf{1{\cdot}41079950}$$

(*ii*) By Simpson's one-third rule,

$$I = \frac{1}{3}\,[(1 + 0{\cdot}027027) + 2\,(0{\cdot}2 + 0{\cdot}058824) + 4\,(0{\cdot}5 + 0{\cdot}1 + 0{\cdot}038462)]$$

$$= \frac{1}{3}\,(1{\cdot}027027 + 0{\cdot}517648 + 2{\cdot}553848)$$

$$= \mathbf{1{\cdot}36617433}$$

(*iii*) By Simpson's three-eighths rule,

$$I = \frac{3 \times 1}{8}\,[(1 + 0{\cdot}027027) + 3\,(0{\cdot}5 + 0{\cdot}2 + 0{\cdot}058824 + 0{\cdot}038462) + 2\,(0{\cdot}1)]$$

$$= \mathbf{1{\cdot}35708188}$$

(*iv*) By Weddle's rule,

$$I = \frac{3 \times 1}{10}\,[1 + 5\,(0{\cdot}5) + 0{\cdot}2 + 6\,(0{\cdot}1) + 0{\cdot}058824 + 5\,(0{\cdot}038462) + 0{\cdot}027027]$$

$$= \mathbf{1{\cdot}37344830}$$

(*v*) By actual integration,

$$I = \int_0^6 \frac{dx}{1+x^2} = (\tan^{-1} x)_0^6 = \tan^{-1} 6 = \mathbf{1{\cdot}40564765}$$

**Note:** Here, the value by trapezoidal rule is closer to the actual value than the value by Simpson's rule.

**Example 9.** *Evaluate* $\int_0^1 \frac{dx}{1+x^2}$ *using Romberg's method. Hence, obtain an approximate value for* $\pi$.

**Solution.** To use the method, we shall give various values of $h$ and evaluate the integral.

By taking $h = 0{\cdot}5$, tabulate the values of $y = \frac{1}{1+x^2}$

| $x$ | : | 0 | 0·5 | 1 |
|---|---|---|---|---|
| $y$ | : | 1·0 | 0·80 | 0·50 |

$$\therefore \quad I = \frac{0{\cdot}5}{2}\,[1{\cdot}5 + 2\,(0{\cdot}8)] = \mathbf{0{\cdot}775}$$

By taking $h = 0{\cdot}25$, we have the table

| $x$ | : | 0 | 0·25 | 0·5 | 0·75 | 1 |
|---|---|---|---|---|---|---|
| $y$ | : | 1 | 0·9412 | 0·8 | 0·64 | 0·5 |

$\therefore \quad I = \frac{0{\cdot}25}{2}[1{\cdot}5 + 2(0{\cdot}9412 + 0{\cdot}8 + 0{\cdot}64)] = \mathbf{0{\cdot}78280}$

By taking $h = 0{\cdot}125$, the tabular values are

| $x$ | : | 0 | 0·125 | 0·25 | 0·375 | 0·5 | 0·625 | 0·75 | 0·875 | 1 |
|---|---|---|---|---|---|---|---|---|---|---|
| $y$ | : | 1 | 0·9846 | 0·9412 | 0·8767 | 0·8 | 0·7191 | 0·64 | 0·5664 | 0·5 |

$$I = \frac{0{\cdot}125}{2}[(1 + 0{\cdot}5) + 2(0{\cdot}9846 + 0{\cdot}9412 + 0{\cdot}8767 + 0{\cdot}8 + 0{\cdot}7191 + 0{\cdot}64 + 0{\cdot}5664)]$$

$$= \mathbf{0{\cdot}784750}$$

The different values got by Trapezoidal rule for various $h$'s are

0·77500 0·78280 0·78475

Applying the formula $I = I_2 + \frac{1}{3}(I_2 - I_1)$ we will get two improved values, namely $0{\cdot}7828 + \frac{1}{3}(0{\cdot}7828 - 0{\cdot}7750)$

and $0{\cdot}78475 + \frac{1}{3}(0{\cdot}78475 - 0{\cdot}78280)$ *i.e.*, 0·7854 and 0·7854

As these two values happen to be equal, we finalise the result. Hence $I = \mathbf{0{\cdot}7854}$.

(*ii*) By actual integration,

$$\int_0^1 \frac{dx}{1+x^2} = \tan^{-1} 1 = 0{\cdot}7844875$$

The difference comes only in the third digit.

$$I = \tan^{-1} 1 = \pi/4$$

$\therefore \quad \frac{\pi}{4} \approx 0{\cdot}7854$

$\therefore \quad \pi \approx \mathbf{3{\cdot}1416.}$

**Example 10.** *Using Romberg's method, evaluate* $I = \int_0^1 \frac{dx}{1+x}$ *correct to three decimal places. Hence evaluate* $\log_e 2$.

**Solution.** We will take $h = 0{\cdot}5, 0{\cdot}25$ and $0{\cdot}125$ as in the previous example and calculate the values of $I$.

(*i*)

| $x$ : | 0 | 0·5 | 1 |
|---|---|---|---|
| $y$ : | 1 | 0·6666 | 0·5 |

$\therefore \quad I = \frac{0{\cdot}5}{2}[1{\cdot}5 + 2(0{\cdot}6666)] = \mathbf{0{\cdot}7083}$

(*ii*)

| $x$ | : | 0 | 0·25 | 0·5 | 0·75 | 1 |
|---|---|---|---|---|---|---|
| $y$ | : | 1 | 0·8 | 0·6666 | 0·5714 | 05· |

$\therefore \quad I = \frac{0{\cdot}25}{2}[1{\cdot}5 + 2(0{\cdot}8 + 0{\cdot}6666 + 0{\cdot}5714)]$

$= \mathbf{0{\cdot}6970}$

(iii)

| $x$ : | 0 | 0·125 | 0·25 | 0·375 | 0·5 | 0·625 | 0·75 | 0·875 | 1 |
|---|---|---|---|---|---|---|---|---|---|
| $y$ : | 1 | 0·8889 | 0·8 | 0·7273 | 0·6667 | 0·6154 | 0·5714 | 0·5333 | 0·5 |

$$I = \frac{0{\cdot}125}{2}[1{\cdot}5 + 2\,(0{\cdot}8889 + 0{\cdot}8 + 0{\cdot}7273 + 0{\cdot}6667 + 0{\cdot}6154 + 0{\cdot}5333 + 0{\cdot}5714)]$$

$$= 0{\cdot}6941.$$

The three values are 0·7083, 0·6970, 0·6941.

Using $I = I_2 + \frac{1}{3}(I_2 - I_1)$ we get ...(1)

$$0{\cdot}6970 + \frac{1}{3}(0{\cdot}6970 - 0{\cdot}7083) \text{ and } 0{\cdot}6941 + \frac{1}{3}(0{\cdot}6941 - 0{\cdot}6970)$$

That is, 0·6932 and 0·6931.

Now taking these 2 values and using formula (1),

we get, $$I = 0{\cdot}6931 + \frac{1}{3}(0{\cdot}6931 - 0{\cdot}6932)$$

$$= 0{\cdot}6931$$

Hence, the most approximate value is **0·6931**.

By integration, $I = [\log(1+x)]_0^1 = \log 2$

Hence $\log 2 \approx 0{\cdot}6931$ which is also the exact value correct to 4 decimal places.

**Example 11.** *A curve passes through the points (1, 2), (1·5, 2·4), (2·0, 2·7), (2·5, 2·8), (3, 3), (3·5, 2·6) and (4·0, 2·1). Obtain the area bounded by the curve, the x axis and x = 1 and x = 4.*

*Also find the volume of solid of revolution got by revolving this area about the x axis.* (*MS. 1973*)

**Solution.** Area $= \int_a^b y\,dx = \int_1^4 y\,dx$; here $h = 0{\cdot}5$

$$= \frac{0{\cdot}5}{3}[(2 + 2{\cdot}1) + 2\,(2{\cdot}7 + 3) + 4\,(2{\cdot}4 + 2{\cdot}8 + 2{\cdot}6)]$$

$$= \frac{1}{6}[4{\cdot}1 + 11{\cdot}4 + 31{\cdot}2] = \mathbf{7{\cdot}7833} \text{ sq.units.}$$

Volume $= \pi \int_a^b y^2 dx$

$$\int_1^4 y^2 dx = \frac{0{\cdot}5}{3}\{[2^2 + (2{\cdot}1)^2] + 2\,[(2{\cdot}7)^2 + 3^2] + 4\,[(2{\cdot}4)^2 + (2{\cdot}8)^2 + (2{\cdot}6)^2]\}$$

$$= \frac{1}{6}[(8{\cdot}41) + 32{\cdot}58 + 81{\cdot}44] = 20{\cdot}405$$

Volume $= \pi \times 20{\cdot}405 =$ **64·13 cu. units.**

**Example 12.** *A river is 80 metres wide. The depth 'd' in metres at a distance x metres from one bank is given by the following table. Calculate the area of cross-section of the river using Simpson's rule.*

| x | : | 0 | 10 | 20 | 30 | 40 | 50 | 60 | 70 | 80 |
|---|---|---|---|---|---|---|---|---|---|---|
| d | : | 0 | 4 | 7 | 9 | 12 | 15 | 14 | 8 | 3 |

*(A.M.I.E.)*

**Solution.** Here $h = 10$. Area of cross-section is $\int_0^{80} y\,dx$

$$A = \frac{10}{3}[(0+3)+2(7+12+14)+4(4+9+15+8)]$$

$$= \frac{10}{3}[3+66+144] = \mathbf{710} \text{ sq. metres.}$$

**Example 13.** *The table below gives the velocity v of a moving particle at time t seconds. Find the distance covered by the particle in 12 seconds and also the acceleration at t = 2 seconds.*

| t | : | 0 | 2 | 4 | 6 | 8 | 10 | 12 |
|---|---|---|---|---|---|---|---|---|
| v | : | 4 | 6 | 16 | 34 | 60 | 94 | 136 |

***(MS 1971)***

**Solution.** We know $\frac{ds}{dt} = v$; and $a = \frac{dv}{dt}$.

$\therefore \quad S = \int v\,dt$

To get $S$, we have to integrate $v$.

$$\therefore \quad S = \int_0^{12} v\,dt = \frac{2}{3}[(4+136)+2(16+60)+4(6+34+94)]$$

(using Simpson's one-third rule)

$$= \frac{2}{3}[140+152+536] = \mathbf{552} \text{ metres}$$

Acceleration $= a = \left(\frac{dv}{dt}\right)_{t=2}$

$\therefore$ Hence we require differentiation.

Now we form difference table.

| $t$ | $v$ | $\Delta v$ | $\Delta^2 v$ | $\Delta^3 v$ |
|---|---|---|---|---|
| 0 | 4 | | | |
| | | 2 | | |
| 2 | 6 | | 8 | |
| | | 10 | | 0 |
| 4 | 16 | | 8 | |
| | | 18 | | 0 |
| 6 | 34 | | 8 | |
| | | 26 | | 0 |
| 8 | 60 | | 8 | |
| | | 34 | | 0 |
| 10 | 94 | | 8 | |
| | | 42 | | |
| 12 | 136 | | | |

$$\left(\frac{dv}{dt}\right)_{t=2} = \frac{1}{h}\left[\Delta v_0 - \frac{1}{2}\Delta^2 v_0 + \frac{1}{3}\Delta^3 v_0\right] \text{ taking } v_0 = 6$$

$$= \frac{1}{2}\left[10 - \frac{1}{2}(8)\right] = 3 \text{ m/s}^2.$$

## EXERCISE 9.2

1. Evaluate $\int_1^2 \frac{dx}{1+x^2}$ taking $h = 0{\cdot}2$, using Trapezoidal rule. Can you use Simpson's rule ? Give reasons. *(BR. B.Sc Ap. '91)*

2. Compute the value of $\int_1^2 \frac{dx}{x}$ using Simpson's rule and Trapezoidal rule. Take $h = 0{\cdot}25$. *(MKU 1972)*

3. Evaluate $\int_0^2 \frac{dx}{x^2 + x + 1}$ to three decimals, dividing the range of integration into 8 equal parts using Simpson's rule. *(MS 1992)*

4. Evaluate $\int_0^1 \sqrt{\sin x + \cos x}\, dx$ correct to two decimal places using seven ordinates.

5. Calculate $\int_0^{\pi/2} \sin x\, dx$ by dividing the interval into ten equal parts, using Trapezoidal rule and Simpson's rule. *(B.Sc. BR. Nov. '94)*

6. Find the value of $\log 2^{1/3}$ from $\int_0^1 \frac{x^2}{1+x^3}\, dx$ using Simpson's one-third rule with $h = 0{\cdot}25$. *(MS. Ap. 1991)*

7. Compute the value of $\int_{0{\cdot}2}^{1{\cdot}4} (\sin x - \log x + e^x)\, dx$ taking $h = 0{\cdot}2$ and using Trapezoidal rule, Simpson's rule and Weddle's rule. Compare your results by integration.

8. Work out the problem in question 7 by taking $h = 0{\cdot}1$.

9. The velocity $v$ of a particle at distance $S$ from a point on its path is given by the table below.

| $S$ in metre | 0 | 10 | 20 | 30 | 40 | 50 | 60 |
|---|---|---|---|---|---|---|---|
| v m/sec | 47 | 58 | 64 | 65 | 61 | 52 | 38 |

Estimate the time taken to travel 60 metres by using Simpson's one-third rule. Compare your answer with Simpson's 3/8 rule and Weddle's rule.

$\left[\textbf{Hint: } v = \frac{ds}{dt},\ t = \int_0^{60} \frac{1}{v}\, ds;\ \text{Take } y = \frac{1}{v}.\right]$

10. When a train is moving at 30 m/sec. steam is shut off and brakes are applied. The speed of the train per second after $t$ seconds is given by

| Time ($t$) : | 0 | 5 | 10 | 15 | 20 | 25 | 30 | 35 | 40 |
|---|---|---|---|---|---|---|---|---|---|
| Speed ($v$) : | 30 | 24 | 19·5 | 16 | 13·6 | 11·7 | 10·0 | 8·5 | 7·0 |

Using Simpon's rule, determine the distance moved by the train in 40 seconds.

**11.** Given $e^0 = 1, e^1 = 2{\cdot}72, e^2 = 7{\cdot}39, e^3 = 20{\cdot}09, e^4 = 54{\cdot}60$, use Simpson's rule to evaluate $\int_0^4 e^x\,dx$. Compose your result with exact value. *(A.M.I.E. '88)*

**12.** A solid of revolution is formed by rotating about the $x$ axis, the area between $x$ axis, $x = 0, x = 1$ and the curve through the points (0, 1), (0·25, 0·9896), (0·5, 0·9589), (0·75, 0·9089) and (1, 0·8415). Find the volume of solid.

**13.** Evaluate $\int_3^7 x^2 \log x\,dx$ taking 4 strips.

**14.** Show that the difference between the values of $\int_{x_0}^{x_6} f(x)\,dx$ obtained by Simpson's one-third rule and Weddle's rule with six sub-intervals is $\frac{h}{30}(\Delta^4 + \Delta^5 + \Delta^6) f(x_0)$ where $h = \frac{x_6 - x_0}{6}$.

**15.** Evaluate $\int_0^1 \frac{dx}{1+x}$ by (*i*) Trapezoidal rule

(*ii*) Simpson's one-third and three-eighths rule.

(*iii*) Weddle's rule.

(Take $n = 6$)

**16.** Evaluate $\int_0^1 e^x dx$ taking $h = 0{\cdot}05$, using Trapezoidal rule.

**17.** Evaluate $\int_0^1 e^{-x^2} dx$ dividing the range into 4 equal parts by (*i*) Trapezoidal rule and (*ii*) Simpson's one-third rule. *(MS. Nov. 1991)*

**18.** Evaluate $\int_1^{1{\cdot}4} e^{-x^2} dx$ by taking $h = 0{\cdot}1$ using Simpson's rule.

**19.** Compute $\int_5^{12} \frac{dx}{x}$.

**20.** Evaluate $\int_0^{10} \frac{dx}{1+x}$ by dividing the range into 8 equal parts.

**21.** Evaluate $\int_0^{\pi/2} e^{\sin x} dx$ taking $h = \frac{\pi}{6}$.

**22.** Evaluate $\int_0^2 e^x dx$ taking 6 intervals.

**23.** Evaluate $\int_1^2 \frac{\sin x}{x} dx$ taking 6 intervals.

**24.** Calculate $\int_0^{\pi} \sin^3 x\,dx$ taking $h = \pi/6$.

**25.** From the following table, calculate $\int_0^6 y\,dx$.

| $x$ | : | 0 | 1 | 2 | 3 | 4 | 5 | 6 |
|---|---|---|---|---|---|---|---|---|
| $y$ | : | 0·146 | 0·161 | 0·176 | 0·190 | 0·204 | 0·217 | 0·230 |

by various methods.

**26.** Calculate $\int_{0.5}^{0.7} e^{-x} x^{1/2}\, dx$ taking 5 ordinates by Simpson's rule.

**27.** Evaluate $\int_0^{\frac{1}{2}} \frac{dx}{\sqrt{1-x^2}}$ by Weddle's rule, taking $n = 6$.

**28.** The velocity of a train which starts from rest is given by the following table, time being reckoned in minutes from the start and speed in miles per hour.

| *Minutes* : | 2 | 4 | 6 | 8 | 10 | 12 | 14 | 16 | 18 | 20 |
|---|---|---|---|---|---|---|---|---|---|---|
| *Miles/hour* : | 10 | 18 | 25 | 29 | 32 | 20 | 11 | 5 | 2 | 0 |

Find the total distance covered in 20 minutes.

[**Hint:** It is given that it starts from rest. So, at $t = 0$, $v = 0$. Introduce this idea to get 11 ordinates to use Simpson's rule.]

**29.** The velocity $v$ of a particle moving in a straight line covers a distance $x$ in time $t$. They are related as follows:

| $x$ | : | 0 | 10 | 20 | 30 | 40 |
|---|---|---|---|---|---|---|
| $v$ | : | 45 | 60 | 65 | 54 | 42 |

Find time taken to traverse the distance of 40 units. *(MKU BE '73)*

**30.** Find the distance travelled by the train between 11·50 A.M and 12·30 P.M. from the data given below:

| *Time* : | 11·50 A.M. | 12·00 noon | 12·10 P.M. | 12·20 P.M. | 12·30 P.M. |
|---|---|---|---|---|---|
| *Speed in kmph* : | 48·2 | 70·0 | 82·6 | 85·6 | 78·4 |

**31.** Evaluate $\int_{1.0}^{1.3} \sqrt{x}\, dx$ taking $h = 0.05$ by various methods. What is the error made in using Trapezoidal rule.

**32.** By using Trapezoidal rule, taking sub-interval lengths as $h, \frac{h}{2}, \frac{h}{4}, \frac{h}{8}$, the integral $\int_0^{\pi/2} \sin x\, dx$ was evaluated (for a specific $h$). The values of the integrals are 0·987116, 0·996785, 0·999196 and 0·999799. Using Romberg's method, improve the result.

**33.** Find the approximate value of $\int_0^1 \frac{dx}{1+x}$ by Trapezoidal rule taking $h = 1, \frac{1}{2}, \frac{1}{4}, \frac{1}{8}$ and then use Romberg's method to get more accurate result.

**34.** Evaluate $\int_0^{\pi/2} \sqrt{\sin\theta}\, d\theta$, using Simpson's rule taking six equal intervals.

**35.** A curve passes through the points (1, 0·2), (2, 0·7), (3, 1), (4, 1·3), (5, 1·5), (6, 1·7), (7, 1·9), (8, 2·1), (9, 2·3). Find the volume of the solid generated by revolving the area between the curve, the $x$-axis and $x = 1, x = 0$ about the $x$-axis.

**36.** (*a*) Evaluate $\int_0^{\pi} \frac{\sin x}{x}\,dx$ dividing into six equal parts using Simpson's rule, Weddle's rule and Trapezoidal rule.

(*b*) Evaluate $\int_0^{0\cdot 8} e^{-x^2}\,dx$, by Romberg's method with $h = 0\cdot 1$ and $h = 0\cdot 2$.

(*BR. 1995 N*)

**37.** A reservoir discharging water through sluices as a depth $h$ metre below the water surface, has a surface area $A$ for various values of $h$ as given below:

| *h* (*metre*) | : | 10 | 11 | 12 | 13 | 14 |
|---|---|---|---|---|---|---|
| Δ (*sq. metre*) | : | 950 | 1070 | 1200 | 1350 | 1530 |

If $t$ denotes time in minutes, the rate of fall of surface area is given by $\frac{dh}{dt} = -\frac{48\sqrt{h}}{A}$ · Estimate the time taken for the water level to fall from 14 to 10 metres above the sluices.

**38.** A river is 40 m wide. The depth $d$ in metres at a distance $x$ metres from one bank is given by the table below:

| $x$ | : | 0 | 5 | 10 | 15 | 20 | 25 | 30 | 35 | 40 |
|---|---|---|---|---|---|---|---|---|---|---|
| $y$ | : | 0 | 3 | 6 | 8 | 7 | 6 | 4 | 3 | 0 |

Find the cross-section of the river by Simpson's rule. (*MKU 1980*)

**39.** A curve passes through the points (0, 0), (1, 2), (2, 2·5), (3, 2·3), (4, 2), (5, 1·7), (6, 1·5).

Calculate $\bar{x} = \frac{\int_0^6 xy\,dx}{\int_0^6 y\,dx}$. (*MKU 1976*)

**40.** Evaluate $\int_0^1 e^{-x}\,dx$ with 10 intervals by Trapezoidal and Simpson's methods.

(*MKU 1980*)

**41.** Apply Simpson's rule to find the value of $\int_0^2 \frac{dx}{1+x^3}$ dividing into 4 equal parts. (*MKU '73*)

**42.** The speeds of a train at various times are given by

| *t* (*hour*) | : | 0 | 0·5 | 1 | 1·5 | 2 | 2·5 | 3 | 3·25 | 3·5 |
|---|---|---|---|---|---|---|---|---|---|---|
| *v* (*in kmph*) | : | 0 | 13 | 33 | 39·5 | 40 | 40 | 36 | 15 | 0 |

Find the total distance covered.

# ANSWERS

## EXERCISE 9.1 Page 297

**1.** $f'(3) = f''(3) = 18$ **2.** 4·75, 9·0, 6·0 **3.** 0·4879, – 0·2353
**4.** 0·1289, – 0·004 **5.** – 52·4 **6.** – 1·91666 **7.** –0.17125
**8.** 0·44733, – 0·158332 **9.** 0·1041, – 0·0023 **10.** 1·79

**11.** 5·375 cm/sec, – 46·083 cm/sec$^2$ **12.** $x = 4{\cdot}42$, min $y = 2$
**13.** Min at 0, 2 is 0, Max at 1 is 0·25 **14.** 2·83 **15.** – 16, 4
**16.** 0·109 **17.** 98 **18.** 2·25 **19.** – 16 **20.** 1·17
**21.** $f'(30) = 1{\cdot}403, f'(31) = 0{\cdot}806, f'(35) = 0{\cdot}894$ **22.** 3·3205, 3·32
**23.** $x = 1{\cdot}58$.

## EXERCISE 9.2 Page 317

**1.** 0·32284 **2.** 0·6931, 0·6971 **3.** 0·8145 **4.** 1·13935
**5.** 0·9981, 1·0006 **6.** 0·2310846 **7.** 4·0715, 4·05214, 4·05145
**8.** 4·05106, 4·05098 **9.** 1·0635166 secs, 1·0640655 secs, 1·0624248 secs
**10.** 606·66 m **11.** 53·8733, 53·598 **12.** 2·819 **13.** 177·483
**15.** 0·6949, 0·6931, 0·6932, 0·6932 **16.** 1·713870 **17.** 0·7428, 0·7467
**18.** 0·972 **19.** 0·875468 **20.** 1·299 **21.** 0·91111
**22.** 6·4481, 6·3894 **23.** 0·65901, 0·65933 **24.** 1·305 **25.** 1·136
**26.** 0·08409 **27.** 0·5235989 **28** 5·16 miles **29.** 0·725 units of time
**30.** 50·8 km **31.** 0·32147, 0·32149, error = 0·00002 **32.** 1·000000
**33.** 0·75, 0·708333, 0·697024, 0·694122, 0·693148 **34.** 1·1877
**35.** 59·68 **36.** 1·8521 **37.** 29 minutes nearly **38.** 190 sq. m.
**39.** 3·032 **40.** 0·6686, 0·6321 **41.** 1·096 **42.** 1·6666 km

## AT A GLANCE

| Rule | Degree of $y(x)$ | No. of intervals | Error | Order |
|---|---|---|---|---|
| Trapezoidal rule | One | any | $\lvert E \rvert < \frac{(b-a)h^2}{12}.M.$ | $h^2$ |
| Simson's 1/3 rule | Two | even | $\lvert E \rvert < \frac{(b-a)h^4}{180}.M.$ | $h^4$ |
| Simson's 3/8 rule | three | Multiple of 3 | $\lvert E \rvert < \frac{(b-a)h^4}{80}.M.$ | $h^4$ |
| Weddle's rule | Six | Multiple of 6 | $\lvert E \rvert < \frac{(b-a)h^6}{840}.M.$ | $h^6$ |

# 10

# *Difference Equations*

## 10·1. Definition

An equation which expresses a relation between the independent variable, the dependent variable and the successive differences of the dependent variable is called a *difference equation.*

For example,

$$\Delta^3 y_x - 4\,\Delta y_x + 7y_x = x^2 + \cos x + 7 \qquad ...(1)$$

$$\Delta^2 y_x - 2\,\Delta y_x + y_x = 0 \text{ are difference equations.}$$

Using $\Delta = E - 1$, $\Delta^r = (E-1)^r$, we can write

$$\Delta y_x = (E-1)\,y_x = Ey_x - y_x = y_{x+1} - y_x$$

$$\Delta^2 y_x = (E-1)^2 y_x = y_{x+2} - 2\,y_{x+1} + y_x \text{ etc.}$$

(we assume the interval of differencing as 1)

Hence, $\Delta^2 y_x - 2\,\Delta y_x + 3\,y_x = x^2$ can be written as

$$y_{x+2} - 4\,y_{x+1} + 6y_x = x^2 \qquad ...(2)$$

or as $\quad y(x+2) - 4y(x+1) + 6y(x) = x^2 \qquad ...(3)$

or as $\quad E^2 y_x - 4\,Ey_x + 6y_x = x^2$

*i.e.,* $\quad (E^2 - 4E + 6)\,y_x = x^2. \qquad ...(4)$

This indicates that a difference equation can be written in various forms such as (1), (2), (3) and (4).

## 10·2. Order and degree of a difference equation

The *order* of a difference equation written in the form free from $\Delta$'s, is the difference between the highest and lowest subscripts of $y$ or arguments of $y$. Thus the order of $y_{x+3} - 5y_{x+2} + 7y_{x+1} + y_x = 10x$ is

$$(x+3) - (x) = 3$$

The order of $y_{x+3} - 5y_{x+2} + y_{x+1} = 0$ is $(x+3) - (x+1) = 2$ and not 3.

The order of $y(x+3) - y(x+2) = 5x^2$ is 1 and not 3.

The *degree* of a difference equation written in a form free from $\Delta$'s in the highest power of the $y$'s. For example, $y_{x+1}\,y_{x+2}^5 - y_{x+1}\,y_x$

$+ y_{x+3}^2 = \cos x$ is of degree 5 and of order 3.

You find below some examples of difference equations, their orders and degrees.

| Difference equations | Order | Degree |
|---|---|---|
| $\Delta^2 u_x - 5\Delta u_x + 7u_x = 0$ | 2 | 1 |
| $y_{x+3} - 7y_{x+1} + 8y_x = \cos x$ | 3 | 1 |
| $y(x+3) - y(x+2) + 7y(x+1) + 10y(x) = 0$ | 3 | 1 |
| $(E^2 - 5E + 16)\, y_x = e^x$ | 2 | 1 |
| $y_x\, y_{x+1}^2 - y_{x+2}\, y_x + 5y_x = x^2 + 7$ | 2 | 2 |

**Note:** $y_{x+3} - 5y_{x+2} + 7y_{x+1} = x^2$ is of order 2 only since it can be written as $u_{x+2} - 5u_{x+1} + 7u_x = x^2$ where $y_{x+1} = u_x$.

After getting the value of $u_x$, we can get $y_x$ using $y_x = u_{x-1}$.

**Note:** In most of the physical situations, the interval of differencing $h$ is unity. Hence, we take $h = 1$ and proceed unless otherwise specifically mentioned.

The study of difference equation is similar to the study of differential equation.

A *solution* of a difference equation is a function which satisfies the difference equation.

*A general solution* of a difference equation of order $n$ is a solution which contains $n$ arbitrary constants or $n$ arbitrary functions which are periodic of period equal to the interval of differencing.

A *particular solution* of a difference equation is a solution got from the general solution by giving particular values to the arbitrary constants. For example, $y_x = A \cdot 3^x + B(-3)^x$ is the general solution of

$$y_{x+2} - 9y_x = 0 \qquad \text{...(5)}$$

while $y_x = 3^x$ or $y_x = (-3)^x$ or $y_x = 2 \cdot 3^x + 5 \cdot (-3)^x$ are particular solutions of (5).

## 10·3. Linear difference equations

An equation of the form

$$a_0 y_{x+n} + a_1 y_{x+n-1} + a_2 y_{x+n-2} + \cdots + a_{n-1} y_{x+1} + a_n y_x = \phi(x) \qquad \text{...(1)}$$

*i.e.*, $(a_0 E^n + a_1 E^{n-1} + a_2 E^{n-2} + \cdots + a_n)\, y_x = \phi(x)$ ...(2)

where $a_0, a_1, a_2, \cdots a_n$ and $\phi(x)$ are known functions of $x$ is called a linear difference equation in $y_x$. In a linear difference equation.

The successive values of $y$ *viz.*, $y_x, y_{x+1}, y_{x+2}, \cdots$ occur in the equation only in first degree and are not multiplied together.

The equation (1) or (2) can be written as

$$f(E)\, y_x = \phi(x) \qquad ...(3)$$

where $f(E)$ is a polynomial expression in $E$. If the right hand side of (3),

*i.e.*, $\phi(x)$ is zero,

then $$f(E)\, y_x = 0 \qquad ...(4)$$

is called the *homogeneous equation corresponding to (3).* The solution of the *non-homogeneous linear equation* (3) depends upon the corresponding homogeneous linear equation (4).

We can easily prove (here we assume) the following:

1. If $y_x = f_1(x)$ is a solution of homogeneous equation (4), then $y_x = C_1 f_1(x)$ is also a solution of (4).
2. If $y_x = f_1(x), y_x = f_2(x), \cdots, y_x = f_n(x)$ are $n$ independent solutions of (4), then

   $y_x = \sum_{i=1}^{n} C_i f_i(x)$ is also a solution of (4), where $C_1, C_2, \cdots C_n$ are constants (or periodic functions of period equal to the interval of differencing).
3. If $y_x = u_x$ is a particular solution of the non-homogeneous equation (3), then

   $y_x = \sum_{i=1}^{n} C_i f_i(x) + u_x$ is the general solution of (3).

   $\sum_{i=1}^{n} C_i f_i(x)$ is called the complementary function of (3) or general solution of (4) $y_x = \text{C.F.} + \text{P.I.}$ is the general solution of (3).

**Note :** If $a_0, a_1, a_2, \ldots a_n$ are constants in the equation (2), then (2) is called a linear equation with constant coefficients.

## 10·4. To find complementary function of $\mathbf{f(E)\, y_x = \phi(x)}$ ...(1)

Replacing $E$ by $a$ in $f(E)$, $f(a) = 0$ is called the auxiliary equation of ($i$).

If the roots of $f(a) = 0$ are $a_1, a_2, \ldots a_n$ then

$$f(E) = (E - a_1)(E - a_2) \cdots (E - a_n).$$

The corresponding homogeneous equation is $f(E)\, y_x = 0$. That is,

$$(E - a_1)(E - a_2) \cdots (E - a_n)\, y_x = 0.$$

If $u(x)$ satisfies $(E - a_1)\, y_x = 0$, then it will satisfy

$$(E - a_1)(E - a_2) \cdots (E - a_n)\, y_x = 0 \text{ also.}$$

Hence the complete solution of $f(E)\, y_x = 0$ is composed the component equations of

$$(E - a_1)\, y_x = 0,\ (E - a_2)\, y_x = 0\ \ldots,\ (E - a_n)\, y_x = 0.$$

To solve: $(E - a_1)\, y_x = 0$.

*i.e.,* $y_{x+1} - a_1 y_x = 0$

Multiply by $a_1^{-x-1}$,

then $a_1^{-(x+1)}\, y_{x+1} - a_1^{-x}\, y_x = 0$

*i.e.,*
$$\Delta\left( a_1^{-x} y_x \right) = 0$$

$\therefore$
$$a_1^{-x} y_x = c_1$$

$$y_x = c_1\, a_1^x$$

*i.e.,* $(E - a_i)\, y_x = 0$ has a solution $y_x = c_1\, a_i^x,\ i = 1, 2, \cdots n$.

**Case 1.** Hence if $a_1, a_2, \cdots a_n$ are distinct,

$y_x = c_1 a_1^x + c_2 a_2^x + \cdots + c_n a_n^x$ is the complementary function of (1) or complete solution of

$$f(E)\, y_x = 0.$$

**Case 2.** If $a_1 = a_2$, then $y_x = \sum_{i=1}^{n} c_i\, a_i^x$ cannot be the general solution since $c_1 + c_2 = c$ will mean that there are only $(n - 1)$ arbitrary constants.

To solve, $(E - a_1)^2\, y_x = 0$ we follow as below.

Let $y_x = v_x a_1^x$ be a solution.

Then $(E - a_1)^2\, y_x = 0$ becomes

*i.e.,*
$$y_{x+2} - 2a_1 y_{x+1} + a_1^2 y_x = 0$$

$$v_{x+2}\, a_1^{x+2} - 2a_1\, v_{x+1}\, a_1^{x+1} + a_1^2\, v_x\, a_1^x = 0$$

*i.e.,*
$$(v_{x+2} - 2v_{x+1} + v_x)\, a_1^{x+2} = 0$$

$\therefore\ v_{x+2} - 2v_{x+1} + v_x = 0$ since $a_1^{x+2} \neq 0$

$$(E - 1)^2\, v_x = 0$$

*i.e.,*
$$\Delta^2 v_x = 0$$

$\therefore$
$$v_x = c_1 + c_2 x$$

$\therefore$ $y_x = (c_1 + c_2 x)\, a_1^x$ is the solution of

$$(E - a_1)^2 y_x = 0.$$

$\therefore$ If $a_1 = a_2$, the complementary function of (1) or complete solution of $f(E)\, y_x = 0$ is

$$y_x = (c_1 + c_2 x)\, a_1^x + c_3\, a_3^x + \cdots + c_n\, a_n^x.$$

**Note:**

If $a_1 = a_2 = \cdots = a_r$ then the corresponding complete solution of $f(E)\, y_x = 0$ is

$$y_x = \left( c_1 + c_2 x + c_3 x^2 + \cdots + c_r x^{r-1} \right) a_r^x.$$

**Case 3.** If $a_1 = \alpha + i\beta,\ a_2 = \alpha - i\beta$, (complex roots)

Then
$$y_x = A\,(\alpha + i\beta)^x + B\,(\alpha - i\beta)^x + c_3\, a_3^x + \cdots + c_n\, a_n^x$$
$$= A\,[r\,(\cos\theta + i\sin\,)]^2 + B\,[r\,(\cos\theta - i\sin\theta)]^x + c_3\, a_3^x + \cdots + c_n\, a_n^x$$
$$y_x = r^x\,(c_1 \cos\theta x + c_2 \sin\theta x) + c_3\, a_3^x + \cdots + c_n\, a_n^x$$

where $= r = |\,\alpha + i\beta\,|\,;\ \theta = \text{amp.}\,(\alpha + i\beta) = \tan^{-1}\dfrac{\beta}{\alpha}$.

**Case 4.** If $a_1 = a_2 = \alpha + i\beta$,

$a_3 = a_4 = \alpha - i\beta$ (complex roots repeated twice)

then the complete solution of $f(E)\, y_x = 0$ is

$$y_x = r^x\,[\,(c_1 + c_2 x)\cos\theta\, x + (c_3 + c_4 x)\sin\theta x\,] + c_5\, a_5^x + \cdots + c_n\, a_n^x.$$

**10·5. In working problems, one can easily remember the summary of the above to find the complementary function**

Let $f(E)\, y_x = \phi\,(x)$ be the linear equation. ...(1)

Write down the auxiliary equation $f(a) = 0$ and get the roots $a_1, a_2, \cdots a_n$.

**Case 1.** If the roots $a_1, a_2, \cdots a_n$ are all real and distinct the corresponding complementary function of (1) or complete solution of $f(E)\, y_x = 0$ is

$$y_x = c_1\, a_1^x + c_2\, a_2^x + \cdots + c_n\, a_n^x.$$

**Case 2.** If $a_1 = a_2$, the corresponding C.F. is

$$(c_1 + c_2 x)\, a_1^x + c_3\, a_3^x + \cdots + c_n\, a_n^x.$$

**Case 3.** If $a_1 = \alpha + i\beta,\ a_2 = \alpha - i\beta$, and $r = |\,\alpha + i\beta\,| = \sqrt{\alpha^2 + \beta^2}$

$$\theta = \text{amp.}\,(\alpha + i\beta) = \tan^{-1}\left(\frac{\beta}{\alpha}\right).$$

Complementary function is

$$r^x\,(c_1 \cos\theta x + c_2 \sin\theta x) + c_3\, a_3^x + \cdots + c_n\, a_n^x\,.$$

**Case 4.** *Repeated complex roots*: If four roots are of the type $\alpha \pm i\beta$, each twice then the complementary function is

$$r^x \Big[\,(c_1 + c_2 x)\cos\theta x + (c_3 + c_4 x)\sin\theta x\,\Big]\, c_5\, a_5^x + \cdots + c_n\, a_n^x.$$

**10·6. To find particular integral of $\mathbf{f\,(E) \cdot y_x = \phi\,(x)}$** **...(1)**

**Type 1.** Suppose $\varphi\,(x) = \text{R.H.S.} = a^x$, where $a$ is a constant.

Then $f(E)\,a^x = \left(a_0 E^n + a_1 E^{n-1} + \cdots + a_n\right) a^x$

$$= a_0\, a^{x+n} + a_1\, a^{x+n-1} + \cdots + a_n\, a^x$$

$$= \left(a_0 \cdot a^n + a_1 \cdot a^{n-1} + \cdots + a_n\right) a^x$$

$$= f(a) \cdot a^x.$$

Operating by $\dfrac{1}{f(E)}$,

$$\frac{1}{f(E)} \cdot f(E)\, a^x = f(a) \cdot \frac{1}{f(E)}\, a^x$$

$$\therefore \quad a^x = f(a) \cdot \frac{a^x}{f(E)}.$$

$$\therefore \quad \frac{a^x}{f(E)} = \frac{a^x}{f(a)} \quad \text{if } f(a) \neq 0.$$

If $f(a) = 0$ then $E - a$ is a factor of $f(E)$.

$$\therefore \quad \boxed{\frac{a^x}{f(E)} = \frac{a^x}{(E-a)\,\psi(E)}}$$

$$= \frac{a^x}{(E-a)\,\psi(a)} \quad \text{if } \psi(a) \neq 0$$

$$= \frac{1}{\psi(a)} \cdot \frac{a^x}{E-a} = \frac{1}{\psi(a)} \cdot x a^{x-1}$$

For let $\dfrac{a^x}{E-a} = u_x$

$$u_{x+1} - a u_x = a^x$$

$$a^{-(x+1)}\, u_{x+1} - a^{-x}\, u_x = a^{-1}$$

$$\Delta(a^{-x}\, u_x) = a^{-1}$$

$$a^{-x}\, u_x = a^{-1}\, x$$

$$u_x = x\, a^{x-1}$$

$$\therefore \quad \frac{a^x}{E-a} = x\, e^{x-1}$$

Similarly $\dfrac{a^x}{(E-a)^2} = \dfrac{x(x-1)}{2} \cdot a^{x-2} = \dfrac{x^{(2)}}{2!}\, a^{x-2}.$

In general, $\boxed{\dfrac{a^x}{(E-a)^r} = \dfrac{x^{(r)}}{r!} \cdot a^{x-r}}$

**Type 2.** Let $\varphi(x)$ = a polynomial in $x$ of degree $m$.

Then $$\text{P.I.} = \frac{\varphi(x)}{f(E)}$$
$$= [f(1+\Delta)]^{-1} \phi(x)$$

We expand $[f(1+\Delta)]^{-1}$ in ascending powers of $\Delta$ and then operate on $\varphi(x)$.

**Type 3.** Let $\varphi(x) = a^x F(x)$ where $F(x)$ is some function of $x$.

$$f(E) \cdot [a^x F(x)] = (a_0 E^n + a_1 E^{n-1} + \cdots + a_n)[a^x F(x)]$$
$$= a_0 a^{x+n} F(x+n) + a_1 a^{x+n-1} \cdot F(x+n-1) + \cdots + a_n a^x F(x).$$
$$= \left[ a_0 a^n E^n F(x) + a_1 a^{n-1} E^{n-1} F(x) + \cdots + a_n F(x) \right] a^x$$
$$= a^x f(aE) \cdot F(x) \qquad \text{...(2)}$$
$$f(E)\, y_x = a^x F(x) \quad (3) \text{ (given equation)}$$

Let $y_x = a^x v_x$ be a particular solution of (3).

(3) becomes; $f(E)\left( a^x v_x \right) = a^x F(x)$

*i.e.,* $$a^x f(aE)\, v_x = a^x F(x) \quad \text{using (2)}$$

$\therefore$ $$f(aE)\, v_x = F(x)$$
$$v_x = \frac{F(x)}{f(aE)}$$

$\therefore$ $$\text{P.I.} = y_x = a^x v_x = a^x \cdot \frac{F(x)}{f(aE)}$$

$\therefore$ $$\boxed{\frac{a^x F(x)}{f(E)} = a^x \cdot \frac{F(x)}{f(aE)}}$$

**Type 4.** If R.H.S. $\varphi(x) = \cos kx$ or $\sin kx$,

use $\cos kx$ = Rl part of $e^{ikx}$

$\sin kx$ = Im. part of $e^{ikx}$ and proceed.

**OR** Take $$\cos kx = \frac{e^{ikx} + e^{-ikx}}{2}$$

and $$\sin kx = \frac{e^{ikx} - e^{-ikx}}{2i}$$ and proceed.

**Example 1.** *Form the difference equations of lowest order by eliminating the arbitrary constants a and b given*

(*i*) $y = a \cdot 2^x + b \cdot 3^x$

(*ii*) $y = (a + bx)\, 2^x$

(*iii*) $y = ax^2 + bx + 7$

(*iv*) $y = 2^{\frac{x}{2}}\left( a\cos\frac{\pi}{4}x + b\sin\frac{\pi}{4}x \right)$.

**Solution.** (*i*) $y_x = a \cdot 2^x + b \cdot 3^x$ ...(1)

$$y_{x+1} = a \cdot 2^{x+1} + b \cdot 3^{x+1} \quad ...(2)$$

$$y_{x+2} = a \cdot 2^{x+2} + b \cdot 3^{x+2} \quad ...(3)$$

(1) × 2 – (2) gives, $2y_x - y_{x+1} = -b \cdot 3^x$ ...(4)

Similarly, $2y_{x+1} - y_{x+2} = -b \cdot 3^{x+1}$ ...(5)

Divide (4) by (5), and cross multiply to get the result,

or $2y_{x+1} - y_{x+2} = 3(2y_x - y_{x+1})$

*i.e.*, $y_{x+2} - 5y_{x+1} + 6y_x = 0$ is the required equation.

(*ii*) $y_x = (a + bx)\,2^x$ ...(1)

$$y_{x+1} = (a + bx + b)\,2^{x+1} = 2(a + bx + b)\,2^x \quad ...(2)$$

$$y_{x+2} = (a + bx + 2b)\,2^{x+2} = 4(a + bx + 2b)\,2^x \quad ...(3)$$

$$y_{x+2} - 4y_{x+1} + 4y_x = 0.$$

(*iii*) $y_x = ax^2 + bx + 7$ ...(1)

∴ $y_{x+1} = a(x+1)^2 + b(x+1) + 7$ ...(2)

∴ $y_{x+2} = a(x+2)^2 + b(x+2) + 7$ ...(3)

Eliminate $a$ and $b$ from (1), (2), (3) and get the result.

***OR***, $y_x = ax^2 + bx + 7$

*i.e.*, $y_x = a(x^{(2)} + x^{(1)}) + bx^{(1)} + 7$

$$y_x = ax^{(2)} + (a + b)\,x^{(1)} + 7 \quad ...(4)$$

$$\Delta y_x = 2a\,x^{(1)} + (a + b) \quad ...(5)$$

$$\Delta^2 y_x = 2a \quad ...(6)$$

(4) – (5) × $x$ gives,

$$y_x - x \cdot \Delta y_x = ax^{(2)} + 7 - 2\,ax^2$$

$$= a(-x - x^2) + 7$$

$$= -\frac{(x + x^2)}{2}\Delta^2 y_x + 7 \quad \text{using (6)}$$

$$2y_x - 2x\,\Delta y_x = -(x + x^2)\,\Delta^2 y_x + 14$$

$$(x + x^2)\,\Delta^2 y_x - 2x\,\Delta y_x + 2y_x - 14 = 0.$$

(iv) $$y_x = 2^{\frac{x}{2}}\left(a\cos\frac{\pi x}{4} + b\sin\frac{\pi x}{4}\right) \quad ...(1)$$

$$y_{x+1} = 2^{\frac{x+1}{2}}\left(a\cos\frac{\pi(x+1)}{4} + b\sin\frac{\pi(x+1)}{4}\right)$$

$$= 2^{\frac{x}{2}}\left(a\cos\frac{\pi x}{4} - a\sin\frac{\pi x}{4} + b\sin\frac{\pi x}{4} + b\cos\frac{\pi x}{4}\right)$$

$$y_{x+1} = 2^{\frac{x}{2}}\left[(a+b)\cos\frac{\pi x}{4} + (b-a)\sin\frac{\pi x}{4}\right] \quad ...(2)$$

$$y_{x+2} = 2^{\frac{x}{2}}\left[(a+b)\cos\frac{\pi x}{4} - (a+b)\sin\frac{\pi x}{4} + (b-a)\sin\frac{\pi x}{4} + (b-a)\cos\frac{\pi x}{4}\right]$$

$$= 2^{\frac{x}{2}}\left[2b\cos\frac{\pi x}{4} - 2a\sin\frac{\pi x}{4}\right] \quad ...(3)$$

$\therefore \quad y_{x+2} - 2y_{x+1} + 2y_x = 0.$

**Example 2.** *Form the difference equation given*

$$y_n = (An + B).\ 3^n. \qquad (MKU\ 1976)$$

**Solution.** $$y_n = (An + B)\ 3^n \quad ...(1)$$

$$y_{n+1} = (An + A + B)\ 3^{n+1} \quad ...(2)$$

$$y_{n+2} = (An + 2A + B)\ 3^{n+2} \quad ...(3)$$

$$y_n = (An + B)\ 3^n \quad ...(4)$$

$$\frac{1}{3}y_{n+1} = (An + A + B)\ 3^n \quad ...(5)$$

$$\frac{1}{9}y_{n+2} = (An + 2A + B)\ 3^n \quad ...(6)$$

(4) + (6) – 2 (·5) gives,

$$y_n + \frac{1}{9}y_{n+2} - \frac{2}{3}y_{n+1} = 0$$

$$y_{n+2} - 6\ y_{n+1} + 9y_n = 0.$$

**Example 3.** *Solve:* $y_{x+3} - 2y_{x+2} - y_{x+1} + 2y_x = 0.$

**Solution.** Writing in the shift operator form,

$$(E^3 - 2E^2 - E + 2)\ y_x = 0$$

The auxiliary equation is $a^3 - 2a^2 - a + 2 = 0$

*i.e.,* $(a-1)(a+1)(a-2) = 0$

$\therefore \quad a = 1, -1, 2$

Since the equation is homogeneous equation, the complete solution is

$$y_x = A \cdot 1^x + B(-1)^x + C(2)^x$$
$$= A + B(-1)^x + C \cdot 2^x.$$

**Example 4.** *Solve* $y_{x+2} - y_{x+1} + y_x = 0$ *given* $y_0 = 1, y_1 = \frac{\sqrt{3}+1}{2}$.

*(Ap. 91)*

**Solution.** The given equation becomes,

$$(E^2 - E + 1)\, y_x = 0$$

The auxiliary equation is $a^2 - a + 1 = 0$

*i.e.,* $$a = \frac{1}{2} \pm \frac{\sqrt{3}}{2} i$$

$$\frac{1}{2} + \frac{\sqrt{3}}{2} i = 1\left(\cos\frac{\pi}{3} + i\sin\frac{\pi}{3}\right) \quad \therefore\ r = 1, \theta = \pi/3$$

$$\left[\text{or, } r = \sqrt{\left(\frac{1}{2}\right)^2 + \left(\frac{\sqrt{3}}{2}\right)^2} = 1, \quad \theta = \tan^{-1}\sqrt{3} = \pi/3\right]$$

$\therefore$ $$y_x = 1^x\left(A\cos\frac{\pi}{3}x + B\sin\frac{\pi}{3}x\right)$$

*i.e.,* $$y_x = A\cos\frac{\pi}{3}x + B\sin\frac{\pi}{3}x. \qquad \text{...(1)}$$

Since $y_0 = 1$, $A = 1$

$$y_1 = 1\cos\frac{\pi}{3} + B\sin\frac{\pi}{3} = \frac{\sqrt{3}+1}{2}$$

$$\frac{1}{2} + \frac{\sqrt{3}}{2}B = \frac{\sqrt{3}+1}{2}$$

$\therefore$ $$B = 1$$

Hence, the solution is

$$y_x = \cos\frac{\pi x}{3} + \sin\frac{\pi x}{3}.$$

**Example 5.** *Solve:* $y_{x+1} - 2y_x \cos\alpha + y_{x-1} = 0.$

**Solution.** Rewriting as, $(E^2 - 2E\cos\alpha + 1)\, y_{x-1} = 0$

The auxiliary equation is $a^2 - 2a\cos\alpha + 1 = 0$

$\therefore$ $$a = \frac{2\cos\alpha \pm \sqrt{4\cos^2\alpha - 4}}{2} = \cos\alpha \pm i\sin\alpha$$

$\therefore$ $$r = 1, \ \theta = \alpha$$

$\therefore$ The solution is

$$y_{x-1} = 1^{x-1}\left[A\cos\alpha(x-1) + B\sin\alpha(x-1)\right]$$

*i.e.,* $y_{x-1} = A\cos\alpha\,(x-1) + B\sin\alpha\,(x-1)$

or $y_x = A\cos\alpha\, x + B\sin\alpha x.$

**Example 6.** *Form the Fibanacci difference equation and solve it.* (*MKU '81*)

**Solution.** The integers 0, 1, 1, 2, 3, 5, 8, 13, 21, ... are said to form a Fibanacci sequence.

Let $y_n$ be the $n$th term of this sequence.

Then, $y_n = y_{n-1} + y_{n-2}$ if $n > 2$

or $y_{n+2} - y_{n+1} - y_n = 0$ if $n > 0$

*i.e.,* $(E^2 - E - 1)\, y_n = 0$

The auxiliary equation is $a^2 - a - 1 = 0$

$$\therefore \quad a = \frac{1 \pm \sqrt{1+4}}{2} = \frac{1 \pm \sqrt{5}}{2}$$

Hence, $y_n = A\left(\frac{1+\sqrt{5}}{2}\right)^n + B\left(\frac{1-\sqrt{5}}{2}\right)^n$ if $n > 0$ ...(1)

$$\left(\frac{1+\sqrt{5}}{2}\right) + B\left(\frac{1-\sqrt{5}}{2}\right) = 0 \quad ...(2)$$

$$y_2 = A\left(\frac{1+\sqrt{5}}{2}\right)^2 + B\left(\frac{1-\sqrt{5}}{2}\right)^2 = 1 \quad ...(3)$$

Solving (2) and (3), we get

$$A = \frac{5-\sqrt{5}}{10}, \quad B = \frac{5+\sqrt{5}}{10}.$$

Hence the $n$th term of the sequence is

$$y_n = \left(\frac{5-\sqrt{5}}{10}\right)\left(\frac{1+\sqrt{5}}{2}\right)^n + \left(\frac{5+\sqrt{5}}{10}\right)\left(\frac{1-\sqrt{5}}{2}\right)^n.$$

**Example 7.** *If* $y_k$ *satisfies the difference equation* $y_{k+1} - \lambda y_k + y_{k-1} = 0$, $k = 1, 2, 3$ *and the end conditions* $y_0 = y_4 = 0$, *determine* $\lambda$ *for which a non-trivial solution exists.*

**Solution.** Since the difference equation is true for $k = 1, 2, 3$

$$y_2 - \lambda y_1 + y_0 = 0 \quad ...(1)$$

$$y_3 - \lambda y_2 + y_1 = 0 \quad ...(2)$$

$$y_4 - \lambda y_3 + y_2 = 0 \quad ...(3)$$

Using $y_0 = 0 = y_4$,

we get,

$$y_2 - \lambda y_1 = 0$$

$$y_3 - \lambda y_2 + y_1 = 0$$

$$-\lambda y_3 + y_2 + 0 = 0$$

If a non-trivial solution exists,

$$\begin{vmatrix} 0 & 1 & -\lambda \\ 1 & -\lambda & 1 \\ -\lambda & 1 & 0 \end{vmatrix} = 0$$

*i.e.*, $\lambda(\lambda^2 - 2) = 0$ *i.e.*, $\lambda = 0$ or $\pm\sqrt{2}$.

For non-trivial solution, $\lambda$ should be $0, \sqrt{2}, -\sqrt{2}$.

**Example 8.** *If $y_n$ satisfies*

*$y_{n+1} - 2y_n \cos\alpha + y_{n-1} = 0$ for $n = 1, 2, \ldots$ and if $y_0 = 0, y_1 = 1$, find $y_2, y_3, y_4$.*

**Solution.** Substituting $n = 1, 2, 3$ we have

$$y_2 - 2y_1 \cos\alpha + y_0 = 0 \quad \text{...(1)}$$

$$y_3 - 2y_2 \cos\alpha + y_1 = 0 \quad \text{...(2)}$$

$$y_4 - 2y_3 \cos\alpha + y_2 = 0 \quad \text{...(3)}$$

From (1), using given conditions, $y_0 = 0, y_1 = 1, y_2 = 2\cos\alpha$

From (2), $y_3 = 4\cos^2\alpha - 1$

From (3), $y_4 = 8\cos^3\alpha - 4\cos\alpha$.

**Aliter:** We can solve for $y_{n-1}$ treating the given equation as a difference equation in the usual manner.

**Example 9.** *Solve $y_{n+2} - 4y_{n+1} + 3y_n = 2^n + 3^n + 7$.*

**Solution.** This can be written as,

$$(E^2 - 4E + 3)\, y_n = 2^n + 3^n + 7 \quad \text{...(1)}$$

Auxiliary equation is $a^2 - 4a + 3 = 0$

*i.e.*, $a = 1, 3$

$\therefore$ C.F. is $A\,1^n + B \cdot 3^n$ ...(2)

$$= A + B \cdot 3^n$$

$$(PI)_1 = \frac{2^n}{E^2 - 4E + 3}$$

$$= \frac{2^n}{4 - 8 + 3}, \text{ replacing } E \text{ by } 2$$

$$= -2^n$$

$$(PI)_2 = \frac{3^n}{(E-1)(E-3)}$$

$$= \frac{3^n}{(3-1)(E-3)} = \frac{1}{2} \cdot \frac{3^n}{E-3}$$

$$= \frac{1}{2} \cdot n\, 3^{n-1}$$

$$(PI)_3 = \frac{7 \cdot 1^n}{E^2 - 4E + 3}$$

$$= \frac{7 \cdot 1^n}{(E-1)(1-3)} = -\frac{7}{2} \cdot n \cdot 1^{n-1}$$

$$= -\frac{7}{2} n$$

Hence the complete solution is

$$y_n = CF + PI$$

$$y_n = A + B \cdot 3^n - 2^n + \frac{1}{2} n \cdot 3^{n-1} - \frac{7}{2} n.$$

**Example 10.** *Solve* $y_{n+2} - 4y_{n+1} + 4y_n = 2^n + 3^n + \pi$.

**Solution.** The equation reduces to

$$(E^2 - 4E + 4)\, y_n = 2^n + 3^n + \pi \qquad ...(1)$$

Auxiliary equation is $a^2 - 4a + 4 = 0$

$\therefore \qquad a = 2, 2$

$\therefore$ C.P. is $(A + Bn) \cdot 2^n$ ...(2)

$$(PI)_1 = \frac{2^n}{(E-2)^2} = \frac{n^{(2)}}{2!} 2^{n-2} = n\,(n-1)\, 2^{n-3}$$

$$(PI)_2 = \frac{3^n}{(E-2)^2} = \frac{3^n}{1}, \text{ replacing } E \text{ by } 3$$

$$(PI)_3 = \frac{\pi \cdot 1^n}{(E-2)^2} = \frac{\pi}{(1-2)^2} = \pi$$

Hence, the complete solution is

$$y_n = (A + Bn)\, 2^n + n\,(n-1) \cdot 2^{n-3} + 3^n + \pi.$$

**Example 11.** *Solve* $y_{x+2} - 4y_x = 9x^2$. *(BR '90)*

**Solution.** This equation becomes,

$$(E^2 - 4)\, y_x = 9x^2 \qquad ...(1)$$

Auxiliary equation is $a^2 - 4 = 0$

$\therefore \qquad a = \pm 2$

C.F. is $A2^x + B(-2)^x$ ...(2)

$$\text{P.I.} = \frac{9x^2}{E^2 - 4}$$

$$= \frac{9x^2}{(1+\Delta)^2 - 4} = \frac{9\,(x^2)}{\Delta^2 + 2\Delta - 3}$$

$$= -\frac{1}{3}\,\frac{9x^2}{1-\dfrac{(\Delta^2+2\Delta)}{3}}$$

$$= -3\left[1-\frac{\Delta^2+2\Delta}{3}\right]^{-1} x^2$$

$$= -3\left[1+\frac{\Delta^2+2\Delta}{3}+\left(\frac{\Delta^2+2\Delta}{3}\right)^2+\cdots\right]x^2$$

$$= -3\left[1+\frac{2\Delta}{3}\div\frac{7}{9}\Delta^2+\cdots\right](x^{(2)}+x^{(1)})$$

$$= -3\left[x^{(2)}+x^{(1)}+\frac{2}{3}(2x^{(1)}+1)+\frac{7}{9}(2)\right]$$

$$= -3\left[x(x-1)+x+\frac{2}{3}(2x+1)+\frac{14}{9}\right]$$

$$= -3\left[x^2+\frac{4x}{3}+\frac{20}{9}\right]$$

Hence the complete solution is

$$y_x = A\cdot 2^x + B(-2)^x - 3\left(x^2+\frac{4x}{3}+\frac{20}{9}\right).$$

**Aliter:** To find the P.I., assume the particular integral

$$y_x = ax^2+bx+c$$

Substituting in (1),

$$a(x+2)^2+b(x+2)+c-4(ax^2+bx+c)=9x^2$$

$$-3ax^2+x(4a-3b)+4a+2b-3c=9x^2$$

Equating the coefficients,

$$-3a=9;\ 4a-3b=0,\ 4a+2b-3c=0$$

$$\therefore\ a=-3;\ b=-4,\ c=\frac{20}{-3}$$

$$\therefore\ \text{P.I. is } -3x^2-4x-\frac{20}{3}.$$

**Example 12.** *Solve:* $y_{x+2}-5y_{x+1}+6y_x=x^2+x+1.$

**Solution.** Writing in the operator form, we get

$$(E^2-5E+6)\,y_x = x^2+x+1 \qquad \text{...(1)}$$

Auxiliary equation is $a^2-5a+6=0$

$$\therefore \qquad a=2,3.$$

Hence, C.F. is $A\cdot 2^x + B\cdot 3^x$ ...(2)

$$\text{P.I.} = \frac{x^2+x+1}{E^2-5E+6}$$

$$= \frac{x^2+x+1}{(1+\Delta)^2 - 5(1+\Delta)+6}$$

$$= \frac{x^2+x+1}{\Delta^2-3\Delta+2}$$

$$= \frac{1}{2}\left(1+\frac{\Delta^2-3\Delta}{2}\right)^{-1}(x^2+x+1)$$

$$= \frac{1}{2}\left[1-\left(\frac{\Delta^2-3\Delta}{2}\right)+\left(\frac{\Delta^2-3\Delta}{2}\right)^2 - \cdots\right](x^2+x+1)$$

$$= \frac{1}{2}\left[1+\frac{3\Delta}{2}+\frac{7}{4}\Delta^2+\cdots\right](x^{(2)}+2x^{(1)}+1)$$

$$= \frac{1}{2}\left[x^{(2)}+2x^{(1)}+1+\frac{3}{2}(2x^{(1)}+2)+\frac{7}{4}(2)\right]$$

$$= \frac{1}{2}\left[x^2+x+1+3x+3+\frac{7}{2}\right]$$

$$= \frac{1}{2}\left(x^2+4x+\frac{15}{2}\right)$$

Hence, the complete solution is

$$y_x = A\cdot 2^x + B\cdot 3^x + \frac{1}{2}\left(x^2+4x+\frac{15}{2}\right).$$

**Aliter for P.I.** Assume $y_x = Ax^2+Bx+C$ ($\because$ R.H.S. is a quadratic)

Substituting in given equation,

$$A(x+2)^2 + B(x+2) + C - 5[A(x+1)^2 + B(x+1) + C] + 6(Ax^2+Bx+C) = x^2+x+1$$

Solve for $A$, $B$, $C$ equating the coefficients of like powers.

**Example 13.** *Solve* $\Delta^2 u_x + 2\,\Delta u_x + u_x = 3x+2.$ *(Ap. '87)*

**Solution.** The equation looks as if it is of order 2. But we will see that it is neither of order 2 nor even a difference equation.

The given equation is

$$(\Delta^2+2\Delta+1)\,u_x = 3x+2$$

$$(1+\Delta)^2\,u_x = 3x+2$$

$$E^2\,u_x = 3x+2$$

$$u_{x+2} = 3x+2$$

$\therefore$ Replacing $x$ by $x-2$,

$$u_x \equiv 3(x-2)+2 = 3x-4.$$

**Note:** This is not a difference equation at all.

**Example 14.** *Solve:* $y_{x+2} - 7y_{x+1} - 8y_x = x(x-1)\,2^x$. (*Nov. '86*)

**Solution.** The given equation can be written as

$$(E^2 - 7E - 8)\,y_x = x(x-1)\cdot 2^x$$

Auxiliary equation is $a^2 - 7a - 8 = 0$

$$(a-8)(a+1) = 0$$

$$\therefore \quad a = 8, -1$$

C.F. is $A\cdot 8^x + B(-1)^x$ ...(2)

$$\text{P.I.} = \frac{x(x-1)\cdot 2^x}{E^2 - 7E - 8}$$

$$= 2^x \cdot \frac{x(x-1)}{(2E)^2 - 7(2E) - 8}$$

$$= 2^x \cdot \frac{x(x-1)}{4E^2 - 14E - 8}$$

$$= 2^x \frac{x(x-1)}{4(1+\Delta)^2 - 14(1+\Delta) - 8}$$

$$= 2^x \frac{x(x-1)}{4\Delta^2 - 6\Delta - 18}$$

$$= 2^{x-1} \frac{x(x-1)}{2\Delta^2 - 3\Delta - 9}$$

$$= \frac{2^{x-1}}{-9}\left(1 + \frac{2\Delta^2 - 3\Delta}{-9}\right)^{-1} x(x-1)$$

$$= -\frac{1}{9}\cdot 2^{x-1}\left[1 + \left(\frac{2\Delta^2 - 3\Delta}{9}\right) + \left(\frac{2\Delta^2 - 3\Delta}{9}\right)^2 + \cdots\right] x^{(2)}$$

$$= -\frac{1}{9}\cdot 2^{x-1}\left[1 - \frac{\Delta}{3} + \frac{1}{3}\Delta^2 + \cdots\right] x^{(2)}$$

$$= -\frac{1}{9}\cdot 2^{x-1}\left[x^{(2)} - \frac{2}{3}x^{(1)} + \frac{1}{3}(2)\right]$$

$$= -\frac{1}{9}\cdot 2^{x-1}\left[x(x-1) - \frac{2x}{3} + \frac{2}{3}\right]$$

$$= -\frac{1}{9}\cdot 2^{x-1}\left[x^2 - \frac{5}{3}x + \frac{2}{3}\right]$$

Hence, the solution is,

$$y_x = A \cdot 8^x + B \cdot (-1)^x - \frac{1}{9} \cdot 2^{x-1}\left(x^2 - \frac{5x}{3} + \frac{2}{3}\right).$$

**Example 15.** *Solve* $u(x+1) - a\,u(x) = \cos nx$.

**Solution.** This can be written as,

$$(E-a)\,u_x = \cos nx.$$

Auxiliary equation is $m - a = 0$

$$\therefore \qquad m = a$$

C.F. is $Aa^x$. ...(1)

$$\text{P.I.} = \frac{\cos nx}{E-a}$$

$$= \text{Real part of } \frac{e^{inx}}{E-a}$$

$$= \text{R.p. of } \frac{(e^{in})^x}{E-a}$$

$$= \text{R.p. of } \frac{e^{inx}}{e^{in} - a}$$

$$= \text{R.p. of } \frac{e^{inx}(e^{-in} - a)}{(e^{in} - a)(e^{-in} - a)}$$

$$= \text{R.p. of } \frac{e^{in(x-1)} - ae^{inx}}{1 - a(e^{in} + e^{-in}) + a^2}$$

$$= \frac{\cos n(x-1) - a\cos nx}{1 - 2a\cos n + a^2}$$

Complete solution is

$$u_x = A\,a^x + \frac{\cos n(x-1) - a\cos nx}{1 - 2a\cos n + a^2}.$$

**Example 16.** *Solve:* $\Delta u_x + \Delta^2 u_x = \cos x$.

**Solution.** The equation reduces to

$$[(E-1)^2 + (E-1)]\,u_x = \cos x$$

*i.e.,* $$(E^2 - E)\,u_x = \cos x \qquad ...(1)$$

$$(E-1)\,u_{x+1} = \cos x.$$

(This is of order 1 only and not of order 2.)

Replace $u_{x+1}$ by $v_x$. The equation is

$$(E-1)\,v_x = \cos x$$

Auxiliary equation is $a-1=0$ $\therefore$ $a=1$

C.F. is $A \cdot 1^x = A$.

$$\text{P.I.} = \frac{\cos x}{E-1}$$

$$= \text{Real part of } \frac{e^{ix}}{E-1}$$

$$= \text{R.p.} \frac{e^{ix}}{e^i - 1}$$

$$= \text{R.p.} \frac{e^{ix}(e^{-i}-1)}{(e^i-1)(e^{-i}-1)}$$

$$= \text{R.p.} \frac{e^{i(x-1)} - e^{ix}}{1-(e^i+e^{-i})+1}$$

$$= \frac{\cos(x-1) - \cos x}{2 - 2\cos 1}$$

$$\therefore \quad v_x = u_{x+1} = A + \frac{\cos(x-1) - \cos x}{2(1-\cos 1)}$$

$$\therefore \quad u_x = A + \frac{\cos(x-2) - \cos(x-1)}{2(1-\cos 1)}.$$

**Example 17.** *Solve:* $\Delta u_x + \Delta^2 u_x = \sin x$.

**Solution.** This reduces to $(E-1)\,u_{x+1} = \sin x$, as in the previous problem.

$$(E-1)\,v_x = \sin x, \quad \text{where} \quad u_{x+1} = v_x.$$

C.F. is $A \cdot 1^x = A$.

$$\text{P.I.} = \frac{\sin x}{E-1}$$

$$= \text{Ima. part. of } \frac{e^{ix}}{E-1}$$

$$= \text{I.p. of } \frac{(e^i)^x}{e^i - 1}$$

$$= \text{I.p. of } \frac{e^{ix}}{e^i - 1}$$

$$= \text{I.p.} \frac{e^{i(x-1)} - e^{ix}}{2 - 2\cos 1}$$

$$= \frac{\sin (x-1) - \sin x}{2(1-\cos 1)}$$

Hence, $$u_x = A + \frac{\sin (x-2) - \sin (x-1)}{2(1-\cos 1)}.$$

**Example 18.** *Solve:* $u_{x+2} + u_x = \sin x$.

**Solution.** This can be written as,

$$(E^2 + 1)\, u_x = \sin x.$$

Auxiliary equation is $a^2 + 1 = 0$, $a = \pm i$

$$i = 1\left(\cos\frac{\pi}{2} + i \sin\frac{\pi}{2}\right) \quad \therefore \quad r = 1; \theta = \pi/2.$$

Hence, C.F. is $1^x\left(A\cos\frac{\pi}{2}x + B\sin\frac{\pi}{2}x\right)$ ...(1)

$$\text{P.I.} = \frac{\sin x}{E^2 + 1}$$

$$= \text{Im. part of } \frac{(e^i)^x}{e^{2i} + 1}$$

$$= \text{I.p.}\ \frac{e^{ix}(1 + e^{-2i})}{(1 + e^{2i})(1 + e^{-2i})}$$

$$= \text{I.p.}\ \frac{e^{ix} + e^{(x-2)i}}{1 + 1 + (e^{2i} + e^{-2i})}$$

$$= \frac{\sin x + \sin (x-2)}{2(1 + \cos 2)}$$

$\therefore$ Complete solution is

$$u_x = A\cos\frac{\pi x}{2} + B\sin\frac{\pi x}{2} + \frac{\sin x + \sin (x-2)}{2(1+\cos 2)}.$$

**Example 19.** *Solve* $u_{n+2} - 7u_{n+1} - 8u_n = 2^n \cdot n^2$. (*Nov. '89*)

**Solution.** The equation reduces to

$$(E^2 - 7E - 8)\, y = 2^n \cdot n^2$$

Auxiliary equation is $a^2 - 7a - 8 = 0$

$\therefore$ $$a = 8, -1$$

C.F. is $A\, 8^n + B\,(-1)^n$ ...(2)

$$\text{P.I.} = \frac{2^n n^2}{E^2 - 7E - 8}$$

$$= 2^n \cdot \frac{n^2}{(2E)^2 - 7(2E) - 8}$$

$$= 2^n \cdot \frac{n^2}{4E^2 - 14\,E - 8}$$

$$= 2^n \cdot \frac{n^2}{4\,\Delta^2 - 6\Delta - 18}$$

$$= 2^{n-1} \cdot \frac{n^2}{2\Delta^2 - 3\Delta - 9}$$

$$= \frac{2^{n-1}}{-9}\left[1 + \frac{2\Delta^2 - 3\Delta}{9} + \left(\frac{2\Delta^2 - 3\Delta}{9}\right)^2 + \cdots\right] n^2$$

$$= -\frac{1}{9} \cdot 2^{n-1}\left[1 - \frac{\Delta}{3} + \frac{\Delta^2}{3} - \cdots\right]\left(n^{(2)} + n^{(1)}\right)$$

$$= -\frac{1}{9} \cdot 2^{n-1}\left[n^2 - \frac{1}{3}(2n+1) + \frac{2}{3}\right]$$

$$= -\frac{1}{9} \cdot 2^{n-1}\left[n^2 - \frac{2}{3}n + \frac{1}{3}\right]$$

Hence, $$u_n = A\,8^n + B\,(-1)^n - \frac{2^{n-1}}{9}\left(n^2 - \frac{2n}{3} + \frac{1}{3}\right).$$

**Example 20.** *Solve:* $y_{x+2} - 2y_{x+1} + y_x = 2^x . x^2$. *(Nov. '91)*

**Solution.** The equation is

$$(E^2 - 2E + 1)\,y_x = 2^x \cdot x^2 \qquad ...(1)$$

Auxiliary equation is $a^2 - 2a + 1 = 0$

$\therefore$ $a = 1, 1$

C.F. is $(A + Bx)\,1^x = A + Bx$ ...(2)

$$\text{P.I.} = \frac{2^x\,x^2}{(E-1)^2} = \frac{2^x\,x^2}{\Delta^2}$$

Assume P.I. as $2^x\,(Ax^2 + Bx + C)$. Using in (1),

$$2^{x+2}\,[A\,(x+2)^2 + B\,(x+2) + C] - 2 \cdot 2^{x+1}\,[A\,(x+1)^2 + B\,(x+1) + C] + 2^x\,[Ax^2 + Bx + C] = 2^x \cdot x^2$$

$$4\,[Ax^2 + x\,(4A + B) + 4A + 2B + C) - 4\,[Ax^2 + x\,(2A + B) + A + B + C] + [Ax^2 + Bx + C] = x^2$$

Equating coefficients,

$A = 1;\ 16A + 4B - 8A - 4B + B = 0$

and $16A + 8B + 4C - 4A - 4B - 4C + C = 0$

$\therefore$ $A = 1,\ B = -8,\ C = 20$

Hence $y_x = A + Bx + 2^x\,(x^2 - 8x + 20)$.

**Example 21.** *Solve:* $y_{n+1} = \sqrt{y_n}$ .

**Solution.** Taking logarithm,

$$\log y_{n+1} = \frac{1}{2} \log y_n$$

$$E \log y_n - \frac{1}{2} \log y_n = 0$$

*i.e.,* $$\left(E - \frac{1}{2}\right) \log y_n = 0$$

*i.e.,* $$\left(E - \frac{1}{2}\right) v_n = 0 \text{ where } v_n = \log y_n$$

Auxiliary equation is $a = 1/2$

Further R.H.S. is zero.

Hence $v_n = \log y_n = A \left(\frac{1}{2}\right)^n$

$\therefore \quad y_n = e^{A\left(\frac{1}{2}\right)^n}$.

**Example 22.** *Evaluate the determinant given below (nth order) by forming the difference equation.*

$$A_n = \begin{vmatrix} 2\cos\theta & 1 & 0 & 0 \ldots & 0 \\ 1 & 2\cos\theta & 1 & 0 \ldots & 0 \\ 0 & 1 & 2\cos\theta & 1 \ldots & 0 \\ . & . & . & . \ldots & . \\ 0 & . & 0 & 1 \ldots & 2\cos\theta \end{vmatrix} \quad \text{(AMIE)}$$

**Solution.** Expanding

$$A_n = 2\cos\theta \cdot A_{n-1} - 1 \cdot A_{n-2}$$

$$\therefore \quad A_n - 2\cos\theta \, A_{n-1} + A_{n-2} = 0$$

$$(E^2 - 2\cos\theta \, E + 1) A_{n-2} = 0$$

Auxiliary equation is $a^2 - 2a\cos\theta + 1 = 0$

*i.e.,* $$(a - \cos\theta)^2 = \cos^2\theta - 1$$

$$a - \cos\theta = \pm\sqrt{-\sin^2\theta}$$

$$\therefore \quad a = \cos\theta \pm i\sin\theta$$

$$= e^{\pm i\theta}$$

$$\therefore \quad A_n = A\,e^{in\theta} + B\,e^{-in\theta}$$

*i.e.,* $$A_n = a \cos n\theta + b \sin n\theta \quad ...(2)$$

$$A_1 = a \cos \theta + b \sin \theta = | \, 2 \cos \theta \, | = 2 \cos \theta$$

$$A_2 = a \cos 2\theta + b \sin 2\theta = 4 \cos^2 \theta - 1 = 2 \cos 2\theta + 1$$

*i.e.,* $$a \cos \theta + b \sin \theta = 2 \cos \theta \quad ...(3)$$

$$a \cos 2\theta + b \sin 2\theta = 2 \cos 2\theta + 1 \quad ...(4)$$

Solving, $a = 1, b = \cot \theta$

$$\therefore \quad A_r = \cos n\theta + \cot \theta \cdot \sin n\theta$$

$$= \frac{\sin (n+1) \theta}{\sin \theta}.$$

**Example 23.** *A solid is constructed so that every face is a triangle. Show that the number of faces of such a solid having n vertices is* $(2n - 4)$.

**Solution.** Let $y_n$ be the number of faces of solid with $n$ vertices. Adding one more vertex we gain 3 faces and lose one face. Hence

$$y_{n+1} = y_n + 2$$

$$y_{n+1} - y_n = 2$$

$$\Delta y_n = 2$$

$$y_n = \Delta^{-1} (2) = 2n + C$$

when $$n = 4, y_4 = 4$$

$$\therefore \quad y_4 = 8 + C = 4 \quad \therefore \quad C = -4$$

Hence $$y_n = 2n - 4, n \geq 4.$$

**Example 24.** *Show that n straight lines, no two of which are parallel and no three of which meet in a point, divide a plane into* $\frac{1}{2}(n^2 + n + 2)$ *parts.*

**Solution.** Let $y_n$ denote the number of compartments formed by $n$ straight lines. If $(n+1)$th line is drawn it will meet each of the existing $n$ lines in $n$ points and divide $(n+1)$ previously existing parts and adding $(n+1)$ parts more to the existing parts.

Thus, $$y_{n+1} = y_n + n + 1$$

$$y_{n+1} - y_n = n + 1$$

$$\Delta y_n = n + 1$$

$$y_n = \Delta^{-1} (n+1)$$

$$= \frac{n^{(2)}}{2} + n^{(1)} + C$$

$$y_n = \frac{1}{2} n (n-1) + n + C$$

when $n = 1, \; y_1 = 2$

$\therefore \quad y_1 = 1 + C = 2 \quad \therefore \quad C = 1$

Hence, $\quad y_n = \frac{1}{2} n(n-1) + n + 1$

$$y_n = \frac{1}{2}(n^2 + n + 2)$$

**Note:** We can also find C.F. and P.I. and complete the problem. Finite integration is easier in this case.

## 10·7. Solution of homogeneous linear equation

Consider the homogeneous linear equation of the form

$$u_{x+1} - A(x)\, u_x = 0$$

Now
$$u_1 = A(0)\, u_0$$
$$u_2 = A(1)\, u_1$$
$$u_3 = A(2)\, u_2$$
$$\cdots\cdots\cdots\cdots$$
$$u_x = A(x-1)\, u_{x-1}$$

Multiplying these equations, and cancelling factors on both sides,

$$u_1 u_2 \cdots u_x = A(0)\, A(1)\, A(2) \cdots A(x-1)\, u_0 u_1 \cdots u_{x-1}$$

$$u_x = A(0)\, A(1) \cdots A(x-1)\, u_0$$

$$u_x = u_0 \prod_{x=0}^{x-1} A(x) = C \prod_{x=0}^{x-1} A(x).$$

**Example 25.** *Solve* $u_{x+1} - \frac{1}{x} u_x = 0,\ x > 0.$

**Solution.** Taking $A(x) = \frac{1}{x}$.

$$u_x = C \prod_{x=1}^{x-1} \frac{1}{x}$$

$$u_x = C \frac{1}{(x-1)!}.$$

## EXERCISE 10

Solve the difference equations:

1. $y_{x+1} - 3y_x = 0$
2. $y_{x+2} - 5\, y_{x+1} + 6y_x = 0$
3. $\Delta^3 y_x - 5\,\Delta y_x + 4y_x = 0$
4. $u_{x+2} + 2\, u_{x+1} + 4u_x = 0$
5. $y_{n+2} - 6y_{n+1} + 9y_n = 0$ given $y_0 = 1, y_1 = 0$
6. $y_{n+3} - 3y_{n+1} + 2y_n = 0$ given $y_1 = 0, y_2 = 8, y_3 = -8$
7. $y_{x+2} - 4y_{x+1} + 4y_x = 0$
8. $u_n - 2u_{n-1} + u_{n-2} = 0$
9. $y_{x+2} - 2y_{x+1} + 2y_x = 0$
10. $y_{x+3} + y_{x+2} - 8\, y_{x+1} - 12y_x = 0$

Form the difference equations by eliminating arbitrary constants:

**11.** $y = A4^x + B5^x$ **12.** $y(x) = (A + Bx)\, 2^x$

**13.** $y = ax^2 - bx$ *(MKU '71)*

**14.** $y_n = A \cos n\alpha + B \sin n\alpha$ **15.** $y = A \cdot 2^n + B$

Solve the following difference equations:

**16.** $y_{x+2} - 6y_{x+1} + 8y_x = 4^x$ *(Ap. '92)*

**17.** $y_{x+2} - 8y_{x+1} + 16y_x = 4^x$ *(Nov. '91)*

**18.** $(E^3 - 5E^2 + 3E + 9)\, y_x = 2^x + 3^x$ *(Ap. '89)*

**19.** $u_{x+2} - 5u_{x+1} + 6u_x = 36$ *(Nov. '89)*

**20.** $y_{k+2} - 5y_{k+1} + 6y_k = 6^k + 5$ *(Ap. '87)*

**21.** $y_{k+2} + 10y_{k+1} + 20y_k = 2^k + 10$ *(Ap. '92)*

**22.** $y_{x+2} - 7y_{x+1} + 12y_x = 2^x$

**23.** $y_{x+2} - 6y_{x+1} + 9y_x = 8 \cdot 3^x$

**24.** $y_{n+2} - 3y_{n+1} + 2y_n = 5^n + 2^n$ *(Ap. '92)*

**25.** $u(x+2) - 5u(x+1) + 6u(x) = 5^x$

**26.** $u_{n+2} - 2u_{n+1} + u_n = 3n + 4$

**27.** $y_{x+2} + y_x = xa^x$

**28.** $u(x+2) - 4u(x) = 9x^2$

**29.** $y_{x+2} - 4y_x = x^2 - 1$

**30.** $\Delta^2 y + \Delta y + y = x^2$ **31.** Solve $u_{x+2} + u_x = 5 \cdot 2^x$ given $u_0 = 1, u_1 = 0$

**32.** $u_{x+2} - 4u_x = 2^x$ **33.** $y_{n+2} + y_{n+1} - 56y_n = 2^n (n^2 - 3)$

**34.** $(E^2 - 5E + 6)\, y_n = 4^n (n^2 - n + 5)$ **35.** $y_{n+2} - 16y_n = \cos \frac{n}{2}$

**36.** $(E^2 + 1)\, y_n = \cos \frac{n\pi}{2}$ **37.** $y_{n+2} - y_{n+1} = \cos \frac{n}{2}$

**38.** $u_{x+2} - 7u_{x+1} + 12u_x = \cos x$ **39.** $(E^2 + 1)\, y_x = \sin x$

**40.** $u_{x+2} + a^2 u_x = \cos ax$ **41.** $u_{x+2} + u_x = \sin \frac{x}{2}$

**42.** $y_{n+2} - 4y_n = n^2 + n - 1$ **43.** $(x+1)\, u_{x+1} - x\, u_x = 0, x > 0$

**44.** In a plane, $n$ circles are drawn so that each circle intersects all the other circles and no three of them meet in a point. Prove that the plane is divided into $(n^2 - n + 2)$ compartments.
(**Hint:** Assume $y_n$ to be the number of compartments when $n$ circles are drawn. The $(n+1)$th circle will cut each of the other circles twice getting new $2n$ compartments $y_{n+1} = y_n + 2n$)

**45.** $u_{x+2} - 6u_{x+1} + 9u_x = 5 \cdot 3^x$ **46.** $(E^2 - 6E + 8)\, u_x = 10 \cdot 2^x$

47. $u_{n+3} - 2u_{n+2} - 5u_{n+1} + 6u_n = 0$

48. $u_{x+2} - 7u_{x+1} + 10u_x = 12 \cdot 4^x + 40$

49. $y_{n+1} - 3y_n = n$ given $y_0 = 1$

50. $u_x - u_{x-1} + 2u_{x-2} = x + 2^x$

## ANSWERS

## EXERCISE 10 Page 344

1. $y_x = A \cdot 3^x$

2. $y_x = A \cdot 2^x + B \cdot 3^x$

3. $y_x = A \cdot 2^x + B\left(\dfrac{1+\sqrt{17}}{2}\right)^x + C\left(\dfrac{1-\sqrt{17}}{2}\right)^x$

4. $u_x = 2^x\left[A\cos\left(-\dfrac{\pi}{3}x\right) + B\sin\left(-\dfrac{\pi}{3}x\right)\right]$

5. $y_n = (1-n)\,3^n$

6. $y_n = \dfrac{4}{3}(-2)^n + \dfrac{8}{3}$

7. $y_x = (Ax+B)\,2^x$

8. $u_n = An + B$

9. $y_x = (\sqrt{2}\,)^x\left[A\cos\dfrac{\pi x}{4} + B\sin\dfrac{\pi x}{4}\right]$

10. $y_x = A \cdot 3^x + (Bx + C)(-2)^x$

11. $y_{x+2} - 9y_{x+1} + 20y_x = 0$

12. $y_{x+2} - 4y_{x+1} + 4y_x = 0$

13. $(x^2 + x)\,\Delta^2 y - 2x\,\Delta y + 2y = 0$

14. $y_{n+2} - 2y_{n+1}\cos\alpha + y_n = 0$

15. $y_{n+2} - 3y_{n+1} + 2y_{n=0}$

16. $y_x = A \cdot 2^x + B \cdot 4^x + \dfrac{x}{2}\,4^{x-1}$

17. $y_x = (Ax+B)\,4^x + \dfrac{x(x-1)}{32} \cdot 4^x$

18. $y_x = A(-1)^x + (Bx+C)\,3^x + \dfrac{2^x}{3} + \dfrac{x(x-1)}{8} \cdot 3^{x-2}$

19. $u_x = A \cdot 3^x + B \cdot 2^x + 18$

20. $y_k = A \cdot 3^k + B \cdot 2^k + \dfrac{6^k}{12} + \dfrac{5}{2}$

21. $y_k = A(-5+\sqrt{5}\,)^k + B(-5-\sqrt{5}\,)^k + \dfrac{2^k}{44} + \dfrac{10}{31}$

22. $y_x = A \cdot 3^x + B \cdot 4^x + 2^{x-1}$

23. $y_x = (Ax+B)\,3^x + 4x(x-1) \cdot 3^{x-2}$

24. $y_n = A + B\;\;2^n + \dfrac{5^n}{12} - n \cdot 2^{n-1}$

25. $u(x) = A \cdot 2^x + B \cdot 3^x + \dfrac{5^x}{6}$

26. $u_n = An + B + \dfrac{n(n-1)(n+2)}{2}$

27. $y_x = A\cos\dfrac{\pi x}{2} + B\sin\dfrac{\pi x}{2} + \dfrac{a^x}{1+a^2}\left(x - \dfrac{2a^2}{1+a^2}\right)$

28. $u(x) = A \cdot 2^x + B(-2)^x - 3\left(x^2 + \dfrac{4x}{3} + \dfrac{20}{9}\right)$

29. $y_x = A \cdot 2^x + B(-2)^x - \dfrac{1}{27}(9x^2 + 12x + 11)$

30. $y = A\cos\dfrac{\pi x}{3} + B\sin\dfrac{\pi x}{3} + x^2 - 1 - 2x$

31. $u_x = 2^x - 2\sin\dfrac{\pi x}{2}$

**32.** $u_x = A2^x + B(-2)^x + \frac{x}{8}2^x$

**33.** $y_n = A(-8)^n + B\cdot 7^n - \frac{2^{n-1}}{25}\left(n^2 + \frac{2n}{5} - \frac{64}{25}\right)$

**34.** $y_n = A2^n + B\cdot 3^n + \frac{1}{2}\cdot 4^n(n^2 - 13n + 61)$

**35.** $y_n = A\cdot 4^n + B(-4)^n + \dfrac{\cos\left(\frac{n}{2} - 1\right) - 16\cos\frac{n}{2}}{257 - 32\cos 1}$

**36.** $y_n = A\cos\frac{n\pi}{2} + B\sin\frac{n\pi}{2} + \frac{n}{2}\sin(n-1)\frac{\pi}{2}$

**37.** $y_n = B + \frac{1}{2}\operatorname{cosec}\frac{1}{4}\cdot\sin\left(\frac{2n-3}{4}\right)$

**38.** $u_x = A\cdot 3^x + B\cdot 4^x + \dfrac{\cos(x-2) - 7\cos(x-1) + 12\cos x}{24\cos 2 - 182\cos 1 + 194}$

**39.** $y_x = A\cos\frac{\pi}{2}x + B\sin\frac{\pi}{2}x + \dfrac{\sin x + \sin(x-2)}{2(1+\cos 2)}$

**40.** $u_x = \left(A\cos\frac{\pi}{2}x + B\sin\frac{\pi}{2}x\right)a^x + \dfrac{a^2\cos ax + \cos a(x-2)}{1 + 2a^2\cos 2a + a^4}$

**41.** $u_x = A\cos\frac{\pi}{2}x + B\sin\frac{\pi}{2}x + \dfrac{\cos\frac{1}{2}\cdot\sin\frac{x-1}{2}}{1+\sin 1}$

**42.** $y_n = A\cdot 2^n + B\cdot(-2)^n - \frac{1}{3}\left[n^2 + \frac{7}{3}n + \frac{17}{9}\right]$

**43.** $x\,u_x = C$

**45.** $u_x = (Ax+B)\,3^x + \frac{5}{2}\cdot x(x-1)\,3^{x-2}$

**46.** $u_x = A\cdot 2^x + B\cdot 4^x - 5x\cdot 2^{x-1}$

**47.** $u_n = A + B(-2)^n + C(3)^n$

**48.** $u_x = A\cdot 2^x + B\cdot 5^x - 6\cdot 4^x + 10$

**49.** $y_n = \frac{5}{4}\cdot 3^n - \frac{1}{4}(2n+1)$

**50.** $u_x = A\left(\frac{1+i\sqrt{7}}{2}\right)^x + B\left(\frac{1-i\sqrt{7}}{2}\right)^x + \frac{1}{2}\left(x + \frac{3}{2}\right) + 2^x$

# 11

# *Numerical Solution of Ordinary Differential Equations*

## 11·1. Introduction

In the fields of Engineering and Science, we come across physical and natural phenomena which, when represented by mathematical models happen to be differential equations. For example, simple harmonic motion, equation of motion, deflection of a beam etc., are represented by differen- tial equations. Hence, the solution of differential equations is a necessity in such studies. There are number of differential equations which we studied in Calculus to get closed form solutions. But, all differential equations do not possess closed form or finite form solutions. Even if they possess closed form solutions, we do not know the method of getting it. In such situations, depending upon the need of the hour, we go in for numerical solutions of differential equations. In researches, especially after the advent of computer, the numerical solutions of the differential equations have become easy for manipulation. Hence, we present below some of the methods of numerical solutions of the ordinary differential equations. No doubt, such numerical solutions are approximate solutions. But, in many cases, approximate solutions to the required accuracy are quite sufficient.

**11·2.** In solving a differential equation for approximate solution we find numerical values of $y_1, y_2, y_3 \ldots$ corresponding to given numerical values of independent variable values $x_1, x_2, x_3 \ldots$ so that the ordered pairs $(x_1, y_1), (x_2, y_2), \ldots$ satisfy a particular solution, though approximately. A solution of this type is called a *pointwise solution.* Suppose we require to solve $\dfrac{dy}{dx} = f(x, y)$ with the initial condition $y(x_0) = y_0$. By numerical solution of the differential equation, let $y(x_0) = y_0, y(x_1), y(x_2), \ldots$ be the solutions of $y$ at $x = x_0, x_1, x_2, \ldots$ Let $y = y(x)$ be the exact solution. If we plot and draw the graph of $y = y(x)$, (exact curve) and also draw the approximate curve by plotting $(x_0, y_0), (x_1, y_1), (x_2, y_2), \ldots$ we get two curves.

$PM$ = exact value; $QM$ = approximate value at $x = x_i$. Then

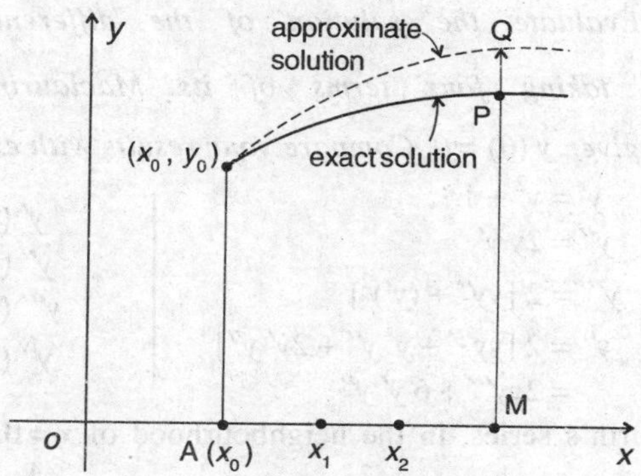


$QP = MQ - MP = y_i - y(x_i) = \varepsilon_i$ is called the *truncation error* at $x = x_i$.

## 11·3. Power series approximations

Let us suppose that we require to find the solution of

$$y' = \frac{dy}{dx} = f(x, y) \qquad \text{...(1)}$$

subject to the initial condition

$$y(x_0) = y_0 \qquad \text{...(2)}$$

we call this an initial value problem.

We can expand $y(x)$ as a power series of $x - x_0$ in the neighourhood of $x_0$ by Taylor series. That is, if $x$ is close to $x_0$, then by Taylor series, we have

$$y(x) = y(x_0) + \frac{(x - x_0)}{1!} y'(x_0) + \frac{(x - x_0)^2}{2!} y''(x_0) + \cdots \qquad \text{...(3)}$$

where $y'(x_0) = \left(\frac{dy}{dx}\right)_{x = x_0}$, $y''(x_0) = \left(\frac{d^2y}{dx^2}\right)_{x = x_0}$ etc.

If $x = x_1$ is close to $x_0$, substitute $x = x_1$ in (3) and get $y_1 = y(x_1)$. Again starting from $x_1$, express $y(x)$ in a power series of $x - x_1$ and then substitute $x = x_2$ to get $y_2 = y(x_2)$. In this way we can get sequence of $y$ values $y_0, y_1, y_2, \ldots$

If $x = x_0 = 0$ (origin) we get the Maclaurin series expansion,

$$y(x) = y(0) + \frac{x}{1!} y'(0) + \frac{x^2}{2!} y''(0) + \cdots \qquad \text{...(4)}$$

**Example 1.** *Evaluate the solution of the differential equation* $\frac{dy}{dx} = y^2 + 1$ *by taking four terms of its Maclaurin series for* $x = 0\,(0{\cdot}2)\,(0{\cdot}6)$ *given* $y(0) = 0$. *Compare your results with exact solutions.*

**Example 1.** *Evaluate the solution of the differential equation* $\frac{dy}{dx} = y^2 + 1$ *by taking four terms of its Maclaurin series for* $x = 0\ (0{\cdot}2)\ (0{\cdot}6)$ *given* $y\ (0) = 0$. *Compare your results with exact solutions.*

**Solution.** we have,

$$\begin{aligned} y' &= y^2 + 1 \\ y'' &= 2y{\cdot}y' \\ y''' &= 2\,[yy'' + (y')^2] \\ y^{iv} &= 2\,[yy''' + y'\,y'' + 2y'{\cdot}y''] \\ &= 2yy''' + 6\,y'\,y'' \end{aligned} \qquad \begin{aligned} y'\,(0) &= 1 \\ y''\,(0) &= 0 \\ y'''\,(0) &= 2 \\ y^{iv}\,(0) &= 0 \end{aligned}$$

By Maclaurin's series, in the neighbourhood of $x = 0$, we have

$$y\,(x) = y\,(0) + \frac{x}{1!}\,y'\,(0) + \frac{x^2}{2!}\,y''\,(0) + \frac{x^3}{3!}\,y'''\,(0) + \frac{x^4}{4!}\,y^{iv}\,(0) + \cdots$$

$$= 0 + x + \frac{x^3}{3} + \cdots \text{ using the values of the derivative at } x = 0$$

$$y\,(0{\cdot}2) = 0{\cdot}2 + \frac{(0{\cdot}2)^3}{3} \approx 0{\cdot}2 + \frac{0{\cdot}008}{3} = 0{\cdot}20266$$

$$y\,(0{\cdot}4) = 0{\cdot}4 + \frac{(0{\cdot}4)^3}{3} \approx 0{\cdot}4213$$

$$y\,(0{\cdot}6) = 0{\cdot}6 + \frac{(0{\cdot}6)^3}{3} = 0{\cdot}6720$$

*Exact solution:* $\frac{dy}{dx} = y^2 + 1.$

$$\therefore \int \frac{dy}{y^2 + 1} = \int dx \text{ i.e., } \tan^{-1} y = x + c$$

Using $x = 0, y = 0,$ we get $c = 0$

Hence $y = \tan x$.

$$\begin{aligned} \tan\,(0) &= 0 \\ \tan\,(0{\cdot}2) &= 0{\cdot}2027 \\ \tan\,(0{\cdot}4) &= 0{\cdot}4228 \\ \tan\,(0{\cdot}6) &= 0{\cdot}6841 \end{aligned}$$

| Values of $x$ | 0 | 0·2 | 0·4 | 0·6 |
|---|---|---|---|---|
| Correct value of $y$ | 0 | 0·2027 | 0·4228 | 0·6841 |
| Approximate values of $y$ | 0 | 0·2027 | 0·4213 | 0·6720 |
| Error | 0 | 0 | 0·0015 | 0·0121 |
| Percentage of error | 0 | 0 | 0·35 | 1·77 |

This shows that when the distance of $x$ from $x_0$ increases the error also increases.

In this working, we expanded $y\,(x)$ in the neighbourhood of $x = 0$ and used the same result for $x = 0{\cdot}2, x = 0{\cdot}4$, and $x = 0{\cdot}6$.

Instead, after getting $y(x_1) = y(0{\cdot}2)$, expand $y(x)$ again in the neighbourhood of $x = 0{\cdot}2$ and use this result to calculate $y(0{\cdot}4)$. Again expand $y(x)$ in the neighbourhood of $x = 0{\cdot}4$ and use this result to get $y(0{\cdot}6)$. By this way, we can minimise the error. Certainly, the work is laborious.

For the gain of accuracy, you should incur the loss of labour. It is justice !

In the neighbourhood of $x = 0{\cdot}2$,

$$y(x) = y(0{\cdot}2) + \frac{(x - 0{\cdot}2)}{1!} y'(0{\cdot}2) + \frac{(x - 0{\cdot}2)^2}{2!} y''(0{\cdot}2) + \frac{(x - 0{\cdot}2)^3}{3!} y'''(0{\cdot}2) + \cdots \quad \ldots(5)$$

$$\begin{aligned} y(0{\cdot}2) &= 0{\cdot}2027, \\ y'(0{\cdot}2) &= [y(0{\cdot}2)]^2 + 1 = 1{\cdot}0411 \\ y''(0{\cdot}2) &= 2y(0{\cdot}2)\, y'(0{\cdot}2) = 0{\cdot}4221 \\ y'''(0{\cdot}2) &= 2\,\{y(0{\cdot}2)\, y''(0{\cdot}2) + [y'(\cdot 2)]^2\} \\ &= 2\,[0{\cdot}08556 + 1{\cdot}0839] \\ &= 2{\cdot}3389. \end{aligned}$$

Putting $x = 0{\cdot}4$ in (5),

$$\begin{aligned} y(0{\cdot}4) &= 0{\cdot}2027 + 0{\cdot}2 \times 1{\cdot}0411 + 0{\cdot}02 \times 0{\cdot}4221 + 0{\cdot}00133 \times 2{\cdot}3389 + \cdots \\ &= 0{\cdot}4225 \text{ (approx.)} \end{aligned}$$

Taking this value with the correct value of $y(0{\cdot}4) = 0{\cdot}4228$, we see the error is only $0{\cdot}0003$. That is the error is $0{\cdot}07\%$.

The error has decreased from $0{\cdot}35\%$ to $0{\cdot}07\%$ by again expanding $y(x)$ in the neighbourhood of $x = 0{\cdot}2$. Therefore to reduce the error, obtain the power series of $y(x)$ at $x = x_i$ and using this obtain $y(x_{i+1})$ and again expand power series of $y(x)$ at $x = x_{i+1}$ and use this to get $y(x_{i+2})$ and so on.

The method explained above is called the *method of starting the solution.*

**Note:** The approximating function (Here, Taylor series) approximates the solution closely only in the neighbourhood of $x_0$ about which the expansion is done.

## 11·4. Pointwise methods

In the previous example, first we got $y(x) = x + \frac{x^3}{3} + \cdots$ in terms of $x$ and then we substituted $x = x_1 = 0{\cdot}2$.

Instead, without getting $y(x)$ as a function of $x$ we can directly get $y(x_1) = y(0{\cdot}2)$ as

$$y(0{\cdot}2) = y(0) + \frac{0{\cdot}2}{1} y'(0) + \frac{(0{\cdot}2)^2}{2!} y''(0) + \cdots$$

*i.e.*, we get $(x_1, y_1), (x_2, y_2)$ directly. So, *a pointwise* solution is a series points $(x_1, y_1)$ $(x_2, y_2)$, ... which satisfy approximately a pre-assigned but not known particular solution.

## 11·5. Solution by Taylor series (Type 1)

**AIM**: To find the numerical solution of the equation

$$\frac{dy}{dx} = f(x, y) \qquad ...(1)$$

given the initial condition $y(x_0) = y_0$. ...(2)

Now, we expand $y(x)$ about the point $x = x_0$ in a Taylor's series in powers of $(x - x_0)$. That is,

$$y(x) = y(x_0) + \frac{(x - x_0)}{1!} y'(x_0) + \frac{(x - x_0)^2}{2!} y''(x_0) + \cdots \qquad ...(3)$$

where $y^{(r)}(x_0) = \left(\frac{d^r y}{dx^r}\right)_{x = x_0}$

*i.e.*, $$y(x) = y_0 + \frac{(x - x_0)}{1!} y_0' + \frac{(x - x_0)^2}{2!} y_0'' + \cdots$$

$$y_1 = y(x_1) = y_0 + \frac{h}{1!} y_0' + \frac{h^2}{2!} y_0'' + \frac{h^3}{3!} y_0''' + \cdots \qquad ...(4)$$

where $h = x_1 - x_0$ or $x_1 = x_0 + h$.

To find $y_0', y_0''$, ... we use (1) and its derivatives at $x = x_0$. Though the series (4) is an infinite series, we can truncate it at any convenient term, if $h$ is small and the accuracy is obtained. Now, having got $y_1$, we can calculate

$$y_1', y_1'', y_1''', \ldots \text{ etc., by using } y' = f(x, y).$$

Now expanding $y(x)$, in a Taylor's series about the point $x = x_1$, we get

$$y_2 = y_1 + \frac{h}{1!} y_1' + \frac{h^2}{2!} y_1'' + \frac{h^3}{3!} y_1''' + \cdots \qquad ...(5)$$

Proceeding in the same way, we get

$$y_{n+1} = y_n + \frac{h}{1!} y_n' + \frac{h^2}{2!} y_n'' + \frac{h^3}{3!} y_n''' + \cdots \qquad ...(6)$$

where $$y_n^r = \left(\frac{d^r y}{dx^r}\right)_{(x_n\, y_n)}$$

(6) is an infinite series and hence we have to truncate at some term to

have the numerical value calculated.

If we retain, for calculation purpose, the terms upto and including $h^n$ and neglect terms involving $h^{n+1}$ and higher powers of $h$, the Taylor algorithm used is said to be of *nth order.* The truncation error is $0\,(h^{n+1})$. By including more number of terms for calculation, the error can be reduced further.

If $h$ is small and the terms after $n$ terms are neglected, the error is $\frac{h^n}{n!} f^n(\theta)$ where $x_0 < \theta < x_1$ if $x_1 - x_0 = h$.

**Example 2.** *Solve* $\frac{dy}{dx} = x + y$, *given* $y(1) = 0$, *and get* $y(1{\cdot}1)$, $y(1{\cdot}2)$ *by Taylor series method. Compare your result with the explicit solution.*

**Solution.** Here, $x_0 = 1, y_0 = 0,\ h = 0{\cdot}1$

$$y' = x + y \qquad y_0 = y(x=1) = 0$$
$$y'' = 1 + y' \qquad y_0' = x_0 + y_0 = 1 + 0 = 1$$
$$y''' = y'' \qquad y_0'' = 1 + y_0' = 2$$
$$y^{iv} = y''' \qquad y_0''' = y_0'' = 2$$
$$y_0^{iv} = 2 \text{ etc.}$$

By Taylor series, we have

$$y_1 = y_0 + \frac{h}{1!} y_0' + \frac{h^2}{2!} y_0'' + \frac{h^3}{3!} y_0''' + \frac{h^4}{4!} y_0''' + \cdots$$

$$\therefore\ y_1 = y(1{\cdot}1) = 0 + \frac{0{\cdot}1}{1}(1) + \frac{(0{\cdot}1)^2}{2}(2) + \frac{(0{\cdot}1)^3}{6}(2) + \frac{(0{\cdot}1)^4}{24}(2) + \frac{(0{\cdot}1)^5}{120}(2) + \cdots \quad ...(2)$$

$$= 0{\cdot}1 + 0{\cdot}01 + 0{\cdot}00033 + 0{\cdot}00000833 + 0{\cdot}000000166 + \cdots$$

$y(1{\cdot}1) = 0{\cdot}11033847$

Now, take $x_0 = 1{\cdot}1, h = 0{\cdot}1$,

$$y_2 = y_1 + \frac{h}{1!} y_1' + \frac{h^2}{2!} y_1'' + \frac{h^3}{3!} y_1''' + \frac{h^4}{4!} y_1^{iv} + \cdots \quad ...(3)$$

We calculate $y_1', y_1'', y_1''', \ldots;\ x_1 = 1.1,\ y_1 = 0.110341833$

$$y_1' = x_1 + y_1 = 1{\cdot}1 + 0{\cdot}11033847 = 1{\cdot}21033847$$
$$y_1'' = 1 + y_1' = 2{\cdot}21033847$$
$$y_1''' = y_1'' = y_1^{iv} = y_1^{v} = \cdots = 2{\cdot}21033847$$

using in (3),

$$y_2 = y(i\cdot2) = 0\cdot11033847 + \frac{0\cdot1}{1}(1\cdot21033847) + \frac{(0\cdot1)^2}{2}(2\cdot21033847)$$

$$+ \frac{(0\cdot1)^3}{6}(2\cdot21033847) + \frac{(0\cdot1)^4}{24}(2\cdot21033847) + \cdots$$

$$= 0\cdot11033847 + 0\cdot121033847 + 2\cdot21033847\,(0\cdot005 + \cdot0016666 + \cdots)$$

$$= 0.24280160$$

The exact solution of $\frac{dy}{dx} = x + y$ is

$$y = -x - 1 + 2e^{x-1}$$

$$y(1\cdot1) = -1\cdot1 - 1 + 2\,e^{0\cdot1}$$

$$= 0\cdot11034$$

$$y(1\cdot2) = -1\cdot2 - 1 + 2\,e^{0\cdot2} = 0\cdot2428$$

$$y(1\cdot1) = 0\cdot11033847$$

$$y(1\cdot2) = 0\cdot2461077$$

*Exact values:* $y(1\cdot1) = 0\cdot110341836$

$$y(1\cdot2) = 0\cdot24280552.$$

**Example 3.** *Using Taylor series method, find, correct to four decimal places, the value of $y(0\cdot1)$, given $\frac{dy}{dx} = x^2 + y^2$ and $y(0) = 1$.*

(*B.Sc. BR. Ap. 1992*)

**Solution.** We have, $y' = x^2 + y^2$

$x_0 = 0,\ y_0 = 1,\ h = 0\cdot1$

$x_1 = 0\cdot1,\ y_1 = y(0\cdot1) = ?$

$$y'' = 2x + 2yy'$$

$$y''' = 2 + 2yy'' + 2(y')^2$$

$$y^{iv} = 2yy''' + 2y'y'' + 4y'y''$$

$$= 2yy''' + 6y'y''$$

$$y_0' = x_0^2 + y_0^2 = 0 + 1 = 1$$

$$y_0'' = 2x_0 + 2y_0\,y_0' = 2$$

$$y_0''' = 2 + 2y_0\,y_0'' + 2(y_0')^2$$

$$= 2 + 2(1)(2) + 2(1)^2 = 8$$

$$y_0^{iv} = 2y_0\,y_0''' + 6\,y_0'\,y_0''$$

$$= 2 \times 1 \times 8 + 6(1)(2) = 28$$

By Taylor series method,

$$y_1 = y_0 + \frac{h}{1!}y_0' + \frac{h^2}{2!}y_0'' + \frac{h^3}{3!}y_0''' + \cdots$$

$$y(0\cdot1) = y_1 = 1 + \frac{0\cdot1}{1}(1) + \frac{(0\cdot1)^2}{2}(2) + \frac{(0\cdot1)^3}{6}(8) + \frac{(0\cdot1)^4}{24}(28) + \cdots$$

$$= 1 + 0\cdot1 + 0\cdot01 + 0\cdot001333333 + 0\cdot000116666$$

$$= 1{\cdot}11144999$$
$$\approx 1{\cdot}11145$$

**Example 4.** *Using Taylor method, compute y (0·2) and y (0·4) correct to 4 decimal places given* $\frac{dy}{dx} = 1 - 2xy$ *and* $y(0) = 0$.

**Solution.** We know,

$$y' = 1 - 2xy$$
$$y'' = -2(xy' + y)$$
$$y''' = -2(xy'' + 2y')$$
$$y^{iv} = -2(xy''' + 3y'')$$
$$y^{v} = -2(xy^{iv} + 4y''')$$
$$\ldots\ldots\ldots\ldots\ldots\ldots$$

Here $x_0 = 0, y_0 = 0, h = 0{\cdot}2$

$$y_0' = 1 - 2x_0y_0 = 1$$
$$y_0'' = 0$$
$$y_0''' = -4$$
$$y_0^{iv} = 0$$
$$y_0^{v} = 32$$
$$\ldots\ldots\ldots$$

By Taylor series,

$$y_1 = y_0 + \frac{h}{1!}y_0' + \frac{h^2}{2!}y_0'' + \frac{h^3}{3!}y_0''' + \cdots \qquad \ldots(1)$$

$$y_1 = y(0{\cdot}2) = 0 + \frac{0{\cdot}2}{1}(1) + \frac{(0{\cdot}2)^2}{2}(0) + \frac{(0{\cdot}2)^3}{6}(-4) + \frac{(0{\cdot}2)^4}{24}(0) + \frac{(0{\cdot}2)^5}{120}(32) + \cdots$$

$$= 0{\cdot}2 - 0{\cdot}00533333 + 0{\cdot}000085333$$
$$= 0{\cdot}194752003$$

Now again starting with $x = 0{\cdot}2$ as the starting value $x_0$, use again equation (1).

Now $x_0 = 0{\cdot}2, y_0 = 0{\cdot}194752003, h = 0{\cdot}2$

$$y_0' = 1 - 2x_0y_0 = 1 - 2(0{\cdot}2)(0{\cdot}194752003) = 0{\cdot}9220992$$
$$y_0'' = -2(x_0y_0' + y_0) = -2[(0{\cdot}2)(0{\cdot}9220992) + 0{\cdot}194752003]$$
$$= -0{\cdot}758343686$$
$$y_0''' = -2[x_0y_0'' + 2y_0']$$
$$= -2[(0{\cdot}2)(-0{\cdot}758343686) + 2(0{\cdot}9220992)]$$
$$= -3{\cdot}38505933$$
$$y_0^{iv} = -2[(0{\cdot}2)(-3{\cdot}38505933) + 3(-0{\cdot}758343686)]$$
$$= 5{\cdot}90408585$$

using equation (1) again,

$$y_2 = y(0{\cdot}4) = 0{\cdot}194752003 + (0{\cdot}2)(0{\cdot}9220992) + \frac{(0{\cdot}2)^2}{2}(-0{\cdot}758343686)$$

$$+\frac{(0\cdot2)^3}{6}(-3\cdot38505933)+\frac{(0\cdot2)^4}{24}(5\cdot90408585)$$

$$= 0.359883723$$

**Note:** To find $y(0\cdot2)$ we can also take $h = 0\cdot1$ and get $y(0\cdot1)$ first and starting from this, we can obtain $y(0\cdot2)$. This will be more accurate since $h$ is small.

**Example 5.** *Using Taylor series method, find $y(1\cdot1)$ and $y(1\cdot2)$ correct to four decimal places given* (*BR M.Sc. '86, MS. Nov. 1991*)

$\frac{dy}{dx} = xy^{1/3}$ *and* $y(1) = 1$.

**Solution.** Take $x_0 = 1, y_0 = 1, h = 0\cdot1$

$$y' = xy^{1/3}$$

$$y'' = \frac{1}{3}xy^{-2/3}y' + y^{1/3}$$

$$= \frac{1}{3}x^2y^{-1/3} + y^{1/3}$$

$$y''' = \left[\frac{x^2}{3}\left(-\frac{1}{3}\right)y^{-\frac{4}{3}}y' + \frac{2x}{3}y^{-\frac{1}{3}} + \frac{1}{3}y^{-\frac{2}{3}}y'\right]$$

$$y_0' = 1(1)^{1/3} = 1$$

$$y_0'' = \frac{1}{3}x_0y_0^{-\frac{2}{3}}y_0' + y_0^{\frac{1}{3}} = 4/3$$

$$y_0''' = \frac{8}{9}$$

By Taylor series,

$$y_1 = y_0 + hy_0' + \frac{h^2}{2!}y_0'' + \cdots$$

$$y_1 = y(1\cdot1) = 1 + (0\cdot1)(1) + \frac{(\cdot1)^2}{2}\left(\frac{4}{3}\right) + \frac{(\cdot1)^3}{6}\left(\frac{8}{9}\right) + \cdots$$

$$= 1 + 0\cdot1 + 0\cdot00666 + 0\cdot000148 + \cdots$$

$$= \mathbf{1\cdot10681}$$

We start with $(x_1, y_1)$ as the starting value.

$$y_1 = 1\cdot10681$$

$$y_1' = x_1y_1^{1/3} = (1\cdot1)(1\cdot10681)^{1/3} = 1\cdot13785$$

$$y_1'' = \frac{1}{3}x_1y_1^{-2/3}y_1' + y_1^{1/3}$$

$$= \frac{1}{3}(1\cdot1)(1\cdot10681)^{-2/3}(1\cdot13785) + (1\cdot10681)^{1/3}$$

$$= 0\cdot38992 + 1\cdot03441 = 1\cdot42433$$

$$y_1''' = 0\cdot929787$$

$$\therefore \quad y_2 = y_1 + hy_1' + \frac{h^2}{2!}y_1'' + \cdots$$

$$y(1\cdot2) = 1\cdot10681 + (0\cdot1)(1\cdot13785) + \frac{0\cdot01}{2}(1\cdot42433) + \frac{\cdot001}{6}(\cdot929787) + \cdots$$

$$= \mathbf{1{\cdot}22772}.$$

**Example 6.** *Using Taylor series method, find y at $x = 0{\cdot}1\ (0{\cdot}1)\ 0{\cdot}4$ given $\frac{dy}{dx} = x^2 - y$, $y\,(0) = 1$ (correct to 4 decimal places).*

**Solution.** $x_0 = 0, y_0 = 1, h = 0{\cdot}1, x_1 = 0{\cdot}1, x_2 = 0{\cdot}2, \ldots$

| | |
|---|---|
| $y' = x^2 - y$ | $y_0' = x_0^2 - y_0 = -1$ |
| $y'' = 2x - y'$ | $y_0'' = 0 - (-1) = 1$ |
| $y''' = 2 - y''$ | $y_0''' = 2 - 1 = 1$ |
| $y^{iv} = - y'''$ | $y_0^{iv} = -1$ etc., |

$$y_1 = y_0 + h\, y_0' + \frac{h^2}{2!}\, y_0'' + \frac{h^3}{6}\, y_0''' + \frac{h^4}{24}\, y_0^{iv} + \cdots$$

$$y_1 = y\,(0{\cdot}1) = 1 + (0{\cdot}1)\,(-1) + \frac{({\cdot}01)}{2}\,(1) + \frac{({\cdot}001)}{6}\,(1) + \frac{({\cdot}0001)}{24}\,(-1) + \cdots$$

$$= 1 - 0{\cdot}1 + {\cdot}005 + {\cdot}0001666 - 0{\cdot}0000416 + \cdots$$

$$= \mathbf{0{\cdot}905125}$$

$$y_1' = x_1^2 - y_1 = 0{\cdot}01 - 0{\cdot}905125 = -0{\cdot}895125$$

$$y_1'' = 2x_1 - y_1' = 0{\cdot}2 + 0{\cdot}895125 = 1{\cdot}095125$$

$$y_1''' = 2 - y_1'' = 2 - 1{\cdot}095125 = 0{\cdot}904875$$

$$\therefore \quad y_2 = y_1 + \frac{h}{1}\, y_1' + \frac{h^2}{2!}\, y_1'' + \cdots$$

$$y\,(0{\cdot}2) = y_2 = 0{\cdot}905125 + (0{\cdot}1)\,(-0{\cdot}895125) + \frac{{\cdot}01}{2}\,(1{\cdot}095125) + \frac{{\cdot}001}{6}\,(0{\cdot}904875) + \cdots$$

$$= 0.128268$$

Similarly $y\,(0{\cdot}3) = 0{\cdot}7492$ (4 decimals)

$y\,(0{\cdot}4) = 0{\cdot}6897$ (4 decimals)

**Example 7.** *By means of Taylor series expansion, find y at $x = 0{\cdot}1$, $0{\cdot}2$ correct to three significant digits given*

$$\frac{dy}{dx} - 2y = 3e^x,\ y\,(0) = 0.$$

**Solution.** Here $x_0 = 0,\ y_0 = 0, x_1 = 0{\cdot}1, x_2 = 0{\cdot}2, x_3 = 0{\cdot}3, h = 0{\cdot}1$

| | |
|---|---|
| $y' = 2y + 3e^x$ | $y_0' = 2y_0 + 3e^{x_0} = 3$ |
| $y'' = 2y' + 3e^x$ | $y_0'' = 2y_0' + 3e^{x_0} = 9$ |
| $y''' = 2y'' + 3e^x$ | $y_0''' = 18 + 3 = 21$ |
| $y^{iv} = 2y''' + 3e^x$ | $y_0^{iv} = 42 + 3 = 45$ |

$$\therefore \qquad y_1 = y_0 + \frac{h}{1} y_0' + \frac{h^2}{2} y_0'' + \frac{h^3}{6} y_0''' + \frac{h^4}{24} y_0^{iv} + \cdots$$

$$y(0{\cdot}1) = y_1 = 0 + (0{\cdot}1)(3) + \frac{(0{\cdot}01)}{2}(9) + \frac{(0{\cdot}001)}{6}(21) + \frac{0{\cdot}0001}{24}(45) + \cdots$$

$$= 0{\cdot}3 + 0{\cdot}045 + 0{\cdot}0035 + 0{\cdot}0001875 + \cdots$$

$$= \mathbf{0{\cdot}3486875 \approx 0{\cdot}349} \qquad \text{(three decimals)}$$

$$y_1' = 2y_1 + 3e^{x_1} = 0{\cdot}3486875 \times 2 + 3e^{0{\cdot}1} = 4{\cdot}012887$$

$$y_1'' = 2y_1' + 3e^{x_1} = 11{\cdot}025774$$

$$y_1''' = 2y_1'' + 3e^{x_1} = 25{\cdot}3670608$$

$$y_2 = y(0{\cdot}2) = y_1 + \frac{h}{1} y_1' + \frac{h^2}{2} y_1'' + \cdots$$

$$= 0{\cdot}3486875 + (0{\cdot}1)(4{\cdot}012887) + \frac{0{\cdot}01}{2}(11{\cdot}341286) + \left(\frac{0{\cdot}001}{6}\right)(25{\cdot}99808) + \cdots$$

$$\approx \mathbf{0{\cdot}8110156 = 0.811} \qquad \text{(three digits)}$$

The exact value of $y(0{\cdot}1) = 0{\cdot}3486955$
and $y(0{\cdot}2) = 0{\cdot}8112658$.

## 11·6. Taylor series method for simultaneous first order differential equations

The equations of the type $\dfrac{dy}{dx} = f_1(x, y, z)$

$\dfrac{dz}{dx} = f_2(x, y, z)$ with initial conditions

$y(x_0) = y_0, z(x_0) = z_0$ can be solved by Taylor series method as given below.

**Example 8.** *Solve* $\dfrac{dy}{dx} = z - x, \dfrac{dz}{dx} = y + x$ *with* $y(0) = 1, z(0) = 1$, *by taking* $h = 0{\cdot}1$, *to get* $y(0{\cdot}1)$ *and* $z(0{\cdot}1)$. *Here y and z are dependent variables and x is independent.*

**Solution.** $y' = z - x$
Take $x_0 = 0, y_0 = 1$
$y_1 = y(0{\cdot}1) = ?$
$y' = z - x$
$y'' = z' - 1$
$y''' = z''$ etc.

and $z' = x + y$
Take $x_0 = 0, z_0 = 1$ and $h = 0{\cdot}1$
$z_1 = z(0{\cdot}1) = ?$
$z' = x + y$
$z'' = 1 + y'$
$z''' = y''$ etc.

By Talyor series, for $y_1$ and $z_1$, we have

$$y_1 = y(0 \cdot 1) = y_0 + hy_0' + \frac{h^2}{2!} y_0'' + \frac{h^3}{3!} y_0''' + \cdots \qquad \text{...(1)}$$

and $$z_1 = z(0 \cdot 1) = z_0 + hz_0' + \frac{h^2}{2} z_0'' + \frac{h^3}{6} z_0''' + \cdots \qquad \text{...(2)}$$

$y_0 = 1$

$y_0' = z_0 - x_0 = 1 - 0 = 1$ $\qquad z_0 = 1$

$y_0'' = z_0' - 1 = 1 - 1 = 0$ $\qquad z_0' = x_0 + y_0 + 0 = 1 = 1$

$y_0''' = z_0'' = 2$ $\qquad z_0'' = 1 + y_0' = 1 + 1 = 2$

$z_0''' = y_0'' = 0$

Substituting in (1) and (2), we get, $\qquad z_0^{iv} = y_0''' = 2$

$$y_1 = y(0 \cdot 1) = 1 + (0 \cdot 1) + \frac{(0 \cdot 01)}{2}(0) + \frac{(0 \cdot 001)}{6} \cdot (2) + \cdots$$

$= 1 + 0 \cdot 1 + 0 \cdot 000333 + \cdots =$ **1·1003** (correct to 4 decimals)

$$z_1 = z(0 \cdot 1) = 1 + (0 \cdot 1)\, 1 + \frac{(0 \cdot 01)}{2}(2) + \frac{(0 \cdot 001)}{6}(0) + \frac{0 \cdot 0001}{24} \times (2) + \cdots$$

$= 1 + 0 \cdot 1 + 0 \cdot 01 + 0 \cdot 0000083 + \cdots$

$= 1 \cdot 1100$ (correct 4 decimal places)

$\therefore \quad y(0 \cdot 1) =$ **1·1003** and $z(0 \cdot 1) =$ **1·1100**.

## 11·7. Taylor series method for second order differential equation

Any differential equation of the second or higher order can be solved by reducing it to a lower order differential equation. A second order differential equation can be reduced to a first order differential equation by transformation $y' = z$ and then the latter one can be solved as usual.

Suppose $\dfrac{d^2y}{dx^2} = f\left(x, y, \dfrac{dy}{dx}\right)$ *i.e.*, $y'' = f(x, y, y')$ ...(1)

is the given differential equation together with the initial conditions

$$y(x_0) = y_0 \qquad \text{...(2)}$$

and $$y'(x_0) = y_0' \qquad \text{...(3)}$$

where $y_0, y_0'$ are known values.

Setting $\quad y' = p$ ...(4)

We get $\quad y'' = p'$ and the equation (1) becomes

$$p' = f(x, y, p) \qquad \text{...(5)}$$

with initial conditions,

$$y(x_0) = y_0 \qquad \text{...(6)}$$

and $\quad p(x_0) = p_0 = y_0'$ ...(7)

Now, we resort to solve (5) together with (6) and (7) using Taylor series method.

$$p_1 = p_0 + hp_0' + \frac{h^2}{2!} p_0'' + \frac{h^3}{3!} p_0''' + \cdots \qquad ...(8)$$

where $p_1 = p\,(x = x_1)$ where $x_1 - x_0 = h$.

From (4),

$$y_1 = y_0 + hy_0' + \frac{h^2}{2!} y_0'' + \cdots \text{ becomes}$$

$$y_1 = y_0 + p_0 + \frac{h^2}{2!} p_0' + \frac{h^3}{3!} p_0'' + \cdots \qquad ...(9)$$

Equation (5) gives $p'$ and differentiating it, we get $p'', p''', \ldots$ Hence $p_0', p_0'', p_0''', \ldots$ can be got using (9) and (8) we can get $y_1$ and $p_1$. Since we know $y_1, p_1$ we can get $p_1', p_1'', p_1''', \ldots$ at $(x_1, y_1)$. Again using

$$p_2 = p_1 + hp_1' + \frac{h^2}{2!} p_1'' + \cdots \text{ we get } p_2 \text{ and using}$$

$$y_2 = y_1 + hy_1' + \frac{h^2}{2!} y_1'' + \cdots \text{ we get } y_2$$

since we can calculate $y_1', y_1'', \ldots$ from (4).

Thus we calculate $y_1, y_2, \ldots$

**Example 9.** *Evaluate the values of* $y\,(0{\cdot}1)$ *and* $y\,(0{\cdot}2)$ *given* $y'' - x\,(y')^2 + y^2 = 0$; $y\,(0) = 1$, $y'\,(0) = 0$ *by using Taylor series method.*

**Solution.** $y'' - x\,(y')^2 + y^2 = 0$

Put $y' = z$ ...(1)

Hence the equation reduces to

$$z' - xz^2 + y^2 = 0$$

$$\therefore \qquad z' = xz^2 - y^2 \qquad ...(2)$$

By initial condition, $y_0 = y\,(0) = 1$, $z_0 = y_0' = 0$ ...(3)

Now we solve (2) given $z_0 = z\,(0) = 0$, and $x_0 = 0$.

Here, $$z_1 = z_0 + hz_0' + \frac{h^2}{2!} z_0'' + \cdots \qquad ...(4)$$

From (2), we get the derivatives of $z$.

$$\left.\begin{aligned} z' &= xz^2 - y^2 \qquad\qquad\qquad \Big|\; y'' = z' \\ z'' &= z^2 + 2xzz' - 2yy' \qquad \Big|\; y''' = z'' \\ z''' &= 2zz' + 2\,[xzz'' + zz' + x\,(z')^2] - 2\,[yy'' + (y')^2] \\ \therefore\; z_0' &= x_0 z_0^2 - y_0^2 = -1 \\ z_0'' &= z_0^2 + 2x_0 z_0\, z_0' - 2y_0\, y_0' = 0 \end{aligned}\right\} \qquad ...(5)$$

$$z_0''' = 0 - 2\,[1 \times (-1) + 0] = 2$$

Substituting in (4)

$$z_1 = 0 + (0{\cdot}1)(-1) + \frac{(0{\cdot}01)}{2}(0) + \frac{0{\cdot}001}{6}(2) + \cdots$$
$$= -0{\cdot}1 + 0{\cdot}000333 + \cdots$$
$$= -0{\cdot}0997$$

By Taylor series for $y_1$,

$$y_1 = y(0{\cdot}1) = y_0 + hy_0' + \frac{h^2}{\underline{|2}}y_0'' + \cdots$$
$$= 1 + (0{\cdot}1)(z_0) + \frac{(0{\cdot}01)}{2}z_0' + \frac{(0{\cdot}001)}{6}(z_0'') + \cdots$$
$$= 1 + (0{\cdot}1)(0) + \frac{0{\cdot}01}{2}(-1) + \frac{0{\cdot}001}{6}(0) + \cdots$$
$$= 1 - 0{\cdot}005$$
$$= 0{\cdot}995$$

Similarly,

$$y_2 = y(x_2) = y_1 + \frac{h}{1!}y_1' + \frac{h^2}{2!}y_1'' + \cdots$$
$$= 0{\cdot}995 + \frac{(0{\cdot}1)}{2}z_1 + \frac{0{\cdot}01}{2}z_1' + \frac{0{\cdot}001}{6}z_1'' + \cdots \qquad \text{...(6)}$$

$$z_1' = x_1 z_1^2 - y_1^2 = (0{\cdot}1)(-0{\cdot}0997)^2 - (0{\cdot}995)^2 = -0{\cdot}9890$$
$$z_1'' = -0{\cdot}1687$$

Using in (6)

$$y_2 = 0{\cdot}995 + \frac{0{\cdot}1}{1}(-0{\cdot}0997) + \frac{0{\cdot}01}{2}(-0{\cdot}9890) + \frac{0{\cdot}001}{6}(-0{\cdot}1687) + \cdots$$
$$= 0{\cdot}9801$$

$\therefore\ y(0{\cdot}1) = 0{\cdot}9950$ and $y(0{\cdot}2) = 0{\cdot}9801$.

**Example 10.** *Solve* $y'' = y + xy'$ *given* $y(0) = 1$, $y'(0) = 0$ *and calculate* $y(0{\cdot}1)$.

**Solution.** Here $x_0 = 0, y_0 = 1, y_0' = 0.$

$$y'' = y + xy'$$

Differentiating w.r.t. $x$;

$$y''' = y' + y' + xy'' = 2y' + xy''$$
$$y^{iv} = 2y'' + y'' + xy''' = 3y'' + xy'''$$
$$y^{v} = 4y''' + xy^{iv}$$
$$y^{vi} = 5y^{iv} + xy^{v}$$

$$y_0'' = y_0 + x_0 y_0' = 1$$
$$y_0''' = 2y_0' + x_0 y_0'' = 0$$
$$y_0^{iv} = 3y_0'' + x_0 y_0''' = 3$$
$$y_0^{v} = 0;\ y_0^{vi} = 15$$

Here, $y(x) = y_0 + xy_0' + \frac{x^2}{2!}y_0'' + \frac{x^3}{3!}y_0''' + \cdots$

$$= 1 + 0 + \frac{x^2}{2}(1) + 0 + \frac{x^4}{4!}(3) + \cdots$$

$$= 1 + \frac{x^2}{2} + \frac{x^4}{8} + \frac{x^6}{6!}(15) + \cdots$$

$$= 1 + \frac{x^2}{2} + \frac{x^4}{8} + \frac{x^6}{48} + \cdots$$

$$\therefore \quad y(0{\cdot}1) = 1 + \frac{(0{\cdot}1)^2}{2} + \frac{(0{\cdot}1)^4}{8} + \frac{(0{\cdot}1)^6}{48} + \cdots$$

$$= 1 + 0{\cdot}005 + 0{\cdot}0000125 + 0{\cdot}00000002 + \cdots$$

$$= 1{\cdot}00501252.$$

## EXERCISE 11.1

Using Taylor series method, find the values required in each problem:

1. Find $y(0{\cdot}1)$ given $\frac{dy}{dx} = x + y,\ y(0) = 1.$ *(Anna Ap. 2005)*
2. Find $y(0{\cdot}1)$ given $y' = x^2y - 1,\ y(0) = 1.$ *(Nov. '92)*
3. Given $y' = 3x + \frac{1}{2}y$ and $y(0) = 1$, find the values of $y(0{\cdot}1)$ and $y(0{\cdot}2)$. *(Nov. '91)*
4. Solve $y' = xy + y^2, y(0) = 1$ at $x = 0{\cdot}1, 0{\cdot}2$, and $0{\cdot}3$.
5. Obtain $y(4{\cdot}2)$ and $y(4{\cdot}4)$ given $\frac{dy}{dx} = \frac{1}{x^2 + y}$, $y(4) = 4$ taking $h = 0{\cdot}2$.
6. Solve $y' = x + \frac{1}{10}y^2, y(1{\cdot}8) = 0$ for $y(2)$.
7. Find $y(0{\cdot}1)$ and $y(0{\cdot}2)$ given $y' = xy^2 + y;\ y(0) = 1$.
8. Solve $\frac{dy}{dx} = y + x^3$ for $x = 1{\cdot}1, 1{\cdot}2, 1{\cdot}3$ given $y(1) = 1$.
9. Find $y(0{\cdot}1)$ if $y' = x - y^2$ and $y(0) = 1$.
10. Find $y(1{\cdot}1)$ given $y' = 2x - y$ and $y(1) = 3$.
11. Find $y(0{\cdot}1), y(0{\cdot}2), y(0{\cdot}3)$ given
    $y' = (x^3 + xy^2)/e^x,\ y(0) = 1.$ *(Nov. '90)*
12. Find $y(0{\cdot}2), y(0{\cdot}4)$ given $\frac{dy}{dx} = xy^2 + 1,\ y(0) = 1.$
13. Find $y(0{\cdot}1), y(0{\cdot}2), z(0{\cdot}1), z(0{\cdot}2)$ given
    $\frac{dy}{dx} = x + z, \frac{dz}{dx} = x - y^2$ and $y(0) = 2, z(0) = 1$.
14. Evaluate $x(0{\cdot}1), y(0{\cdot}1), x(0{\cdot}2), y(0{\cdot}2)$ given
    $\frac{dx}{dt} = ty + 1,\ \frac{dy}{dt} = -tx$ given $x = 0, y = 1$ at $t = 0$.
15. Solve for $x$ and $y$: $\frac{dx}{dt} = x + y + t; \frac{dy}{dt} = 2x - t$ given $x = 0, y = 1$, at $t = 1$.

**16.** Solve $y'' = x^2 - xy$, given $y(0) = 1, y'(0) = 0$.

**17.** Obtain the values of $y$ at $x = 0{\cdot}1\ (0{\cdot}1)\ 0{\cdot}3$ if $y$ satisfies $y'' = -xy$ and $y(0) = 1, y'(0) = 0{\cdot}5$.

**18.** Find $y$ at $x = 1{\cdot}1\ (0{\cdot}1)\ (1{\cdot}3)$ given

$y'' + y^2y' = x^3,\ y(1) = 1,\ y'(1) = 1.$

**19.** Find $y(0{\cdot}2)$ and $y(0{\cdot}4)$ given

$$y'' = xy, \text{ if } y(0) = 1, y'(0) = 1. \qquad (MKU)$$

**20.** Find $y(0{\cdot}1), y(0{\cdot}2)$ given

$$y'' + xy = 0 \text{ and } y(0) = 1, y'(0) = 0{\cdot}5.$$

**21.** Find $y(0{\cdot}3), z(0{\cdot}3)$ given

$\frac{dz}{dx} = -xy,\ \frac{dy}{dx} = 1 + xz$ where $y(0) = 0, z(0) = 1$.

**22.** Find $y(0{\cdot}2), y(0{\cdot}4)$ given $y'' + y = 0$ given $y(0) = 1, y'(0) = 0$.

**23.** Express $y$ as a power series given,

$$y' = (0{\cdot}1)(x^2 + y^2),\ y(0) = 1.$$

**24.** Find $y(0{\cdot}4)$ if $y' = 1 + xy$ given $y(0) = 2$, taking $h = 0{\cdot}2$.

**25.** Find $y(0{\cdot}2), y(0{\cdot}4)$ given $y' = x - y^2$ and $y(0) = 1$.

## 11·8. Picard's method of successive approximations

**AIM.** To solve $\frac{dy}{dx} = f(x, y)$ subject to $y(x_0) = y_0$.

Now $$\frac{dy}{dx} = f(x, y) \qquad \text{...(1)}$$

$\therefore$ $$dy = f(x, y)\, dx$$

Integrating, $$y = \int^x f(x, y)\, dx + c \qquad \text{...(2)}$$

Setting $x = x_0$ on the R.H.S. after integration and $y = y_0$ on the L.H.S., we have

$$y_0 = \int^{x_0} f(x, y)\, dx + c \qquad \text{...(3)}$$

(2) – (3) gives

$$y - y_0 = \int_{x_0}^{x} f(x, y)\, dx \qquad \text{...(3)}$$

$\therefore$ $$y = y_0 + \int_{x_0}^{x} f(x, y)\, dx \qquad \text{...(4)}$$

In equation (4), the R.H.S. integrand $f(x, y)$ involves $y$ also. This type of equation is called *an integral equation.* As the integration is not possible as it is, we will solve it by successive approximation.

Substitute the initial values of $y$ namely $y_0$ in the integrand $f(x, y)$ in place of $y$ and then integrate the R.H.S. to get an approximate value of $y$ on the L.H.S.

*i.e.*, $$y^{(1)} = y_0 + \int_{x_0}^{x} f(x, y_0)\, dx \qquad ...(5)$$

Since $f(x, y_0)$ is a function of $x$ also, it is possible to integrate it w.r.t. $x$.

After getting the first approximation $y^{(1)}$ for $y$, use this value $y^{(1)}$ in the place $y$ in $f(x, y)$ of (4) and then integrate to get the second approximation of $y$ namely $y^{(2)}$

*i.e.*, $$y^{(2)} = y_0 + \int_{x_0}^{x} f(x, y^{(1)})\, dx \qquad ...(6)$$

Proceeding in this way, we get the $n$th approximate value of $y$ as

$$y^{(n)} = y_0 + \int_{x_0}^{x} f(x, y^{(n-1)})\, dx \qquad ...(7)$$

Equation (7) gives the general iterative formula for $y$. It is called *Picard's iteration formula.*

The sequence $y^{(1)}, y^{(2)}, y^{(3)}, \ldots y^{(n)}$ should converge to $y(x)$; otherwise the process is not valid.

The condition for the convergence of the sequence are $f(x, y)$ and $\frac{\partial f}{\partial y}$ are continuous.

That is, $|f(x, y)| \le k_1$ and $\left|\frac{\partial f}{\partial y}\right| \le k_2$ in a region containing the point $(x_0, y_0)$ where $k_1, k_2$ are constants. By extending this to the second order,

$y'' = f(x, y, y')$, given $y(x_0) = y_0$, $y'(x_0) = y_0'$, we get

$$y^{(n+1)} = y_0 + (x - x_0)\, y_0' + \int_{x_0}^{x} (x - t)\, f\left(t, y^{(k)}(t), \frac{dy^{(k)}}{dt}(t)\right) dt.$$

**Example 1.** *Solve $y' = y - x^2$, $y(0) = 1$, by Picard's method upto the third approximation. Hence, find the value of $y(0{\cdot}1)$, $y(0{\cdot}2)$.*

(*BR. Nov. 1995*)

**Solution.** $y' = y - x^2$

$\therefore$ $$y = y_0 + \int_{x_0}^{x} (y - x^2)\, dx; \text{ here } f(x, y) = y - x^2,\ x_0 = 0,\ y_0 = 1.$$

$\therefore$ $$y = 1 + \int_0^x (y - x^2)\, dx \qquad ...(1)$$

use $y = y_0 = 1$ on the R.H.S. and integrate

$$\therefore\ y^{(1)} = 1 + \int_0^x (1 - x^2)\, dx = 1 + x - \frac{x^3}{3} \qquad ...(2)$$

use this again in (1),

$$y^{(2)} = 1 + \int_0^x \left(1 + x - \frac{x^3}{3} - x^2\right) dx$$

$$= 1 + x + \frac{x^2}{2} - \frac{x^4}{12} - \frac{x^3}{3} \qquad \text{...(3)}$$

using this again in (1),

$$y^{(3)} = 1 + \int_0^x \left(1 + x + \frac{x^2}{2} - \frac{x^3}{3} - \frac{x^4}{12} - x^2\right) dx$$

$$\therefore \; y^{(3)} = 1 + x + \frac{x^2}{2} - \frac{x^3}{6} - \frac{x^4}{12} - \frac{x^5}{60} + \cdots \qquad \text{...(4)}$$

Putting $x = 0{\cdot}1$ in (4)

$$y\,(0{\cdot}1) = 1 + (0{\cdot}1) + \frac{(0{\cdot}1)^2}{2} - \frac{(0{\cdot}1)^3}{6} - \frac{(0{\cdot}1)^4}{12} - \frac{(0{\cdot}1)^5}{60} + \cdots$$

$$= 1 + 0{\cdot}1 + 0{\cdot}005 - 0{\cdot}0001666 - 0{\cdot}00000833 - 0{\cdot}000000166$$

$$= \mathbf{1{\cdot}1048249}$$

$$y\,(0{\cdot}2) = 1 + (0{\cdot}2) + \frac{(0{\cdot}2)^2}{2} - \frac{(0{\cdot}2)^3}{6} - \frac{(0{\cdot}2)^4}{12} - \frac{(0{\cdot}2)^5}{60} - \cdots$$

$$= 1{\cdot}2 + \frac{0{\cdot}04}{2} - \frac{0{\cdot}008}{6} - \frac{0{\cdot}0016}{12} - \frac{0{\cdot}00032}{60} - \cdots$$

$$= 1{\cdot}2 + 0{\cdot}02 - 0{\cdot}00133333 - 0{\cdot}00013333 - 0{\cdot}000005333$$

$$= \mathbf{1{\cdot}218528}$$

**Note:** In getting the value $y\,(0{\cdot}2)$ we could have started with $x_0 = 0{\cdot}1$ and $y_0 = 1{\cdot}1048249$ to get a closer value of $y_2 = y\,(0{\cdot}2)$.

We will adopt this procedure.

Now $y = y_0 + \int_{x_0}^x f(x, y)\, dx$

*i.e.,*
$$y = 1{\cdot}1048249 + \int_{0{\cdot}1}^x (y_0 - x^2)\, dx$$

$$y^{(1)} = 1{\cdot}1048249 + \left[ y_0 x - \frac{x^3}{3} \right]_{0{\cdot}1}^x$$

$$= 1{\cdot}1048249 + 1{\cdot}1048249\, x - \frac{x^3}{3} - (0{\cdot}1)\,(1{\cdot}1048249) + \frac{(0{\cdot}1)^3}{3}$$

$$= 0{\cdot}99467574 + 1{\cdot}1048249\, x - \frac{x^3}{3}$$

$$y^{(2)} = 1{\cdot}1048249 + \int_{0{\cdot}1}^x \left(0{\cdot}99467574 + 1{\cdot}1048249\, x - \frac{x^3}{3} - x^2\right) dx$$

$$= 1{\cdot}1048249 + \left( 0{\cdot}99467574\, x + 1{\cdot}1048289 \frac{x^2}{2} - \frac{x^4}{12} - \frac{x^3}{3} \right)_{0\cdot 1}^{x}$$

$$= 1{\cdot}1048249 + 0{\cdot}99467574\,(x - 0{\cdot}1) + \frac{1{\cdot}1048249}{2}\,(x^2 - (0{\cdot}1)^2$$

$$- \frac{1}{12}\,(x^4 - (0{\cdot}1)^4) - \frac{1}{3}\,(x^3 - (0{\cdot}1)^3$$

$y^{(2)}(0{\cdot}2) =$ **1·2184066.**

**Example 2.** *Solve* $\frac{dy}{dx} = x + y$ *given* $y\,(0) = 1$. *Obtain the values of* $y\,(0{\cdot}1)$, $y\,(0{\cdot}2)$ *using Picard's method and check your answer with the exact solution.*

**Solution.** Here $f\,(x, y) = x + y$, $x_0 = 0$, $y_0 = 1$.

$$\therefore \qquad y = y_0 + \int_{x_0}^{x} f\,(x, y)\, dx$$

$$y = 1 + \int_{0}^{x} f\,(x, y)\, dx \qquad ...(1)$$

Putting $y = y_0$ on the R.H.S.,

$$y^{(1)} = 1 + \int_{0}^{x} f\,(x, 1)\, dx$$

$$= 1 + \int_{0}^{x} (x + 1)\, dx = 1 + x + \frac{x^2}{2} \qquad ...(2)$$

Again using $y = y^{(1)}$ on the R.H.S. of (1), we get

$$y^{(2)} = 1 + \int_{0}^{x} \left( x + 1 + x + \frac{x^2}{2} \right) dx$$

$$= 1 + x + x^2 + \frac{1}{6}\, x^3 \qquad ...(3)$$

Again using on the R.H.S.

$$y^{(3)} = 1 + \int_{0}^{x} \left( x + 1 + x + x^2 + \frac{1}{6}\, x^3 \right) dx = 1 + x + x^2 + \frac{x^3}{3} + \frac{1}{24}\, x^4$$

$$\therefore \qquad y\,(x) = 1 + x + x^2 + \frac{x^3}{3} + \frac{x^4}{24} + \cdots$$

Setting $\quad x = 0{\cdot}1$,

$$y\,(0{\cdot}1) = 1 + 0{\cdot}1 + 0{\cdot}01 + \frac{1}{3}\,(0{\cdot}001) + \frac{1}{24}\,(0{\cdot}0001)$$

$$= 1 + 0{\cdot}1 + 0{\cdot}01 + 0{\cdot}0003333 + 0{\cdot}0000041$$

$$= \mathbf{1{\cdot}1103374}$$

$$y(0{\cdot}2) = 1 + 0{\cdot}2 + (0{\cdot}2)^2 + \frac{(0{\cdot}2)^3}{3} + \frac{(0{\cdot}2)^4}{24}$$

$$\approx \mathbf{1{\cdot}242733}$$

Integrating $\frac{dy}{dx} = x + y$, we get $y = 2e^x - x - 1$

$$\therefore \qquad y(0{\cdot}1) = 2e^{0{\cdot}1} - 1 - 0{\cdot}1 = \mathbf{1{\cdot}11034184} \text{ (actual value)}$$

$$y(0{\cdot}2) = 2e^{0{\cdot}2} - 0{\cdot}2 - 1 = \mathbf{1{\cdot}24280555}$$

In both cases, $y(0{\cdot}1)$ are same (correct to 4 decimal places) and the values of $y(0{\cdot}2)$ differ only by 0·0001.

**Example 3.** *Solve* $\frac{dy}{dx} = x^2 + y^2, y(0) = 1$ *by Picard's method.*

**Solution.** Here $x_0 = 0, y_0 = 1$; by Picard's method,

$$y = y_0 + \int_{x_0}^{x} f(x, y)\, dx$$

$$= 1 + \int_0^x (x^2 + y^2)\, dx \qquad \text{...(1)}$$

$$y^{(1)} = 1 + \int_0^x (1 + x^2)\, dx = 1 + x + \frac{x^3}{3} \qquad \text{...(2)}$$

$$y^{(2)} = 1 + \int_0^x \left[ x^2 + \left( 1 + x + \frac{x^3}{3} \right)^2 \right] dx$$

$$= 1 + \left[ x + \frac{2x^3}{3} + \frac{x^7}{63} + x^2 + \frac{2}{15}x^5 + \frac{1}{6}x^4 \right]$$

$$= 1 + x + x^2 + \frac{2}{3}x^3 + \frac{1}{6}x^4 + \frac{1}{63}x^7 + \frac{2}{15}x^5 \qquad \text{...(3)}$$

Calculation of $y^{(3)}$ is tedious and hence approximate value is $y^{(2)}$ given by (3).

**Example 4.** *Solve* $y' + y = e^x, y(0) = 0$, *by Picard's method.*

**Solution.** By Picard's method,

$$y = y_0 + \int_{x_0}^{x} f(x, y)\, dx$$

$$= 0 + \int_0^x (e^x - y)\, dx$$

Here $\qquad x_0 = 0, y_0 = 0,$

$$\therefore \qquad y^{(1)} = \int_0^x (e^x - 0)\, dx = e^x - 1$$

$$y^{(2)} = \int_0^x (e^x - e^x + 1)\, dx$$

$$= x$$

$$y^{(3)} = \int_0^x (e^x - x)\, dx = e^x - \frac{x^2}{2} - 1$$

$$y^{(4)} = \int_0^x \left[ e^x - \left( e^x - \frac{x^2}{2} - 1 \right) \right] dx$$

$$= \frac{x^3}{6} + x$$

$$y^{(5)} = \int_0^x \left( e^x - x - \frac{x^3}{6} \right) dx$$

$$= e^x - \frac{x^2}{2} - \frac{x^4}{24} - 1$$

Approximate $y = e^x - \frac{x^2}{2} - \frac{x^4}{24} - 1.$

## EXERCISE 11.2

Using Picard's iterative formula, solve the following problems. Also calculate the values at the required points.

**1.** Solve $\frac{dy}{dx} = x + y^2 + 1$, given $y(0) = 0$.

**2.** Obtain $y(0{\cdot}1)$ given $y' = \frac{y - x}{y + x}$ and $y(0) = 1$.

**3.** Solve: $y' = 1 + 2yx$, given $y(0) = 0$.

**4.** Solve: $y' = 1 + xy$, given $y(0) = 1$. **5.** Solve: $y' = x - y^2$, given $y(0) = 1$.

**6.** Find the values of $y$ for $x = 0(0{\cdot}1)(0{\cdot}5)$ given $y' = 1 + xy$ and which passes through (0, 1).

**7.** Solve: $y' = x + y^2$ given $y(0) = 1$.

**8.** Given $y' = \frac{x^2}{1 + y^2}$ and $y(0) = 0$ find $y(0{\cdot}25)$, $y(0{\cdot}5)$.

**9.** Solve: $y' = 1 + xy$ given $y(2) = 0$.

**10.** Solve: $y' = x^2 + y^2$ given $y(0) = 0$.

**11.** Solve: $y' = 2x - y$ with $y(1) = 3$. Find also $y(1{\cdot}1)$.

**12.** Solve: $y' = 1 + y^2$ given $y(0) = 0$.
Also find $y(0{\cdot}2)$ and $y(0{\cdot}4)$.

## 11·9. Euler's method

In solving a first order differential equation by numerical methods, we come across two types of solutions:

(*i*) A series solution of $y$ in terms of $x$, which will yield the value of $y$ at a particular value of $x$ by direct substitution in the series solution.

(*ii*) Values of $y$ at specified values of $x$.

The two methods due to Taylor and Picard studied earlier belong to the first category and the following methods due to Euler, Runge-Kutta, Adam-Bashforth and Milne come under the second category.

The methods of second category are called step-by-step methods because the values of $y$ are calculated by short steps ahead of equal interval $h$ of the independent variable $x$.

**Euler's method**

**AIM.** *To solve* $\frac{dy}{dx} = f(x, y)$ *with initial condition* $y(x_0) = y_0$. ...(1)

Let us take the points $x = x_0, x_1, x_2, \ldots$ where $x_i - x_{i-1} = h$,

$$i.e., \quad x_i = x_0 + ih, \quad i = 0, 1, 2, \ldots$$

Let the actual solution of the differential equation be denoted by the graph (continuous line graph) $P_0(x_0, y_0)$ lies on the curve. We require the value of $y$ of the curve at $x = x_1$.

The equation of tangent at $(x_0, y_0)$ to the curve is

$$y - y_0 = y'_{(x_0, y_0)}(x - x_0)$$

$$= f(x_0, y_0) \cdot (x - x_0)$$

$$\therefore \quad y = y_0 + f(x_0, y_0) \cdot (x - x_0) \quad \text{...(2)}$$

This $y$ is the value of $y$ on the tangent corresponding to $x = x$. In the interval $(x_0, x_1)$, the curve is approximated by the tangent. Therefore, the value of $y$ on the curve is approximately equal to the value of $y$ on the tangent at $(x_0, y_0)$ corresponding to $x = x_1$.

$$\therefore \quad y_1 = y_0 + f(x_0, y_0)(x_1 - x_0)$$

$$i.e., \quad y_1 = y_0 + hy_0'. \qquad \text{where } h = x_1 - x_0.$$

$(M_1P_1 \approx M_1Q_1 = y_1)$ *(See figure on Page 370)*

Again, we approximate curve by the line through $(x_1, y_1)$ and whose slope is $f(x_1, y_1)$ we get

$$y_2 = y_1 + hf(x_1, y_1) = y_1 + hy_1'$$

Thus $\mathbf{y_{n+1} = y_n + h\,f(x_n, y_n)}$; **n = 0, 1, 2...**

This formula is called **Euler's algorithm**.

In other words,

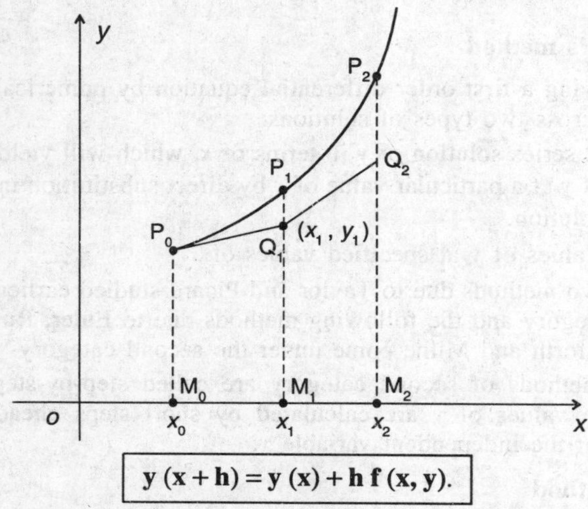


$$\boxed{\mathbf{y\,(x+h) = y\,(x) + h\,f\,(x, y).}}$$

In this method, the actual curve is approximated by a sequence of short straight lines. As the intervals increase the straight line deviates much from the actual curve. Hence the accuracy cannot be obtained as the number of intervals increase.

$$Q_1P_1 = \text{error at } x = x_1$$

$$= \frac{(x_1 - x_0)^2}{2!}\, y''\,(x_1, y_1) = \frac{h^2}{2}\, y''\,(x_1, y_1)$$

$\therefore$ It is of order $h^2$.

## 11·10. Improved Euler method

Let the tangent at $(x_0, y_0)$ to the curve be $P_0A$. In the interval $(x_0, x_1)$, by previous Euler's method, we approximate the curve by the tangent $P_0A$.

$$\therefore\quad y_1^{(1)} = y_0 + h\,f\,(x_0, y_0) \text{ where } y_1^{(1)} = M_1Q_1. \qquad ...(1)$$

$Q_1\left(x_1, y_1^{(1)}\right)$. Let $Q_1\,C$ be the line at $Q_1$ whose slope is $f\,(x_1, y_1^{(1)})$. Now take the average of the slopes at $P_0$ and $Q_1$ *i.e.*,

$$\frac{1}{2}\left[f\,(x_0, y_0) + f\,(x_1, y_1^{(1)})\right]$$

Now draw a line $P_0D$ through $P_0\,(x_0, y_0)$ with this as the slope.

$$\text{That is, } y - y_0 = \frac{1}{2}\left[f\,(x_0, y_0) + f\,(x_1, y_1^{(1)})\right](x - x_0) \qquad ...(2)$$

This line intersects $x = x_1$ at

$$y_1 = y_0 + \frac{1}{2}\,h\left[f\,(x_0, y_0) + f\,(x_1, y_1^{(1)})\right]$$

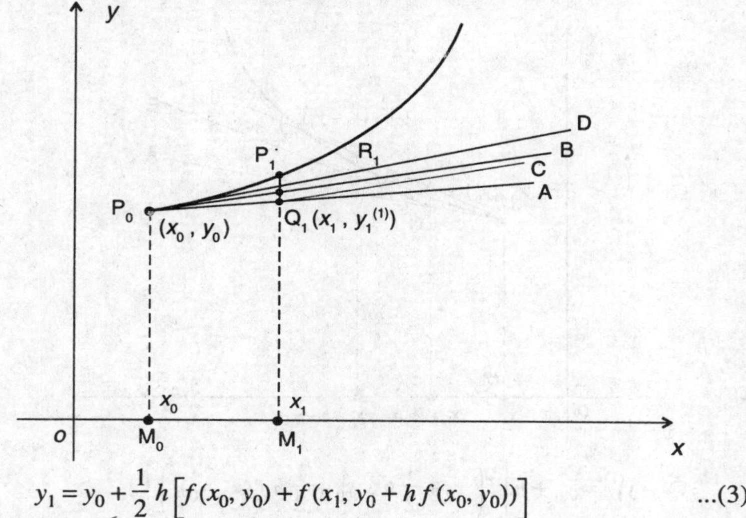


$$y_1 = y_0 + \frac{1}{2} h \left[ f(x_0, y_0) + f(x_1, y_0 + h f(x_0, y_0)) \right] \qquad \text{...(3)}$$

Writing generally,

$$\mathbf{y_{n+1} = y_n + \frac{1}{2} h \left[ f(x_n, y_n) + f(x_n + h, y_n + h f(x_n, y_n)) \right]} \qquad \text{...(4)}$$

Equation (4) gives the formula for $y_{n+1}$. This is improved Euler's method.

**Note 1.** The difference between Euler's method and improved Euler's method is that in the latter we take the average of the slopes at $(x_0, y_0)$ and $(x_1, y_1^{(1)})$ instead of the slope at $(x_0, y_0)$ in the former method.

## 11·11. Modified Euler method

In the previous improved Euler method, *we averaged the slopes*, whereas in modified Euler method, we will average the *points*.

Let $P_0\ (x_0, y_0)$ be the point on the solution curve.

Let $P_0A$ be the tangent at $(x_0, y_0)$ to the curve. Now let this tangent meet the ordinate at $x = x_0 + \frac{1}{2} h$ at $N_1$

$$y\text{-coordinate of } N_1 = y_0 + \frac{1}{2} h f(x_0, y_0) \qquad \text{...(1)}$$

Calculate the slope at $N_1$ *i.e.*, $f\left( x_0 + \frac{1}{2} h, y_0 + \frac{1}{2} h f(x_0, y_0) \right)$

Now draw the line through $P\ (x_0, y_0)$ with this slope as the slope. Let this line meet $x = x_1$ at $K_1\ (x_1, y_1^{(1)})$. This $y_1^{(1)}$ is taken as the approximate value of $y$ at $x = x_1$.

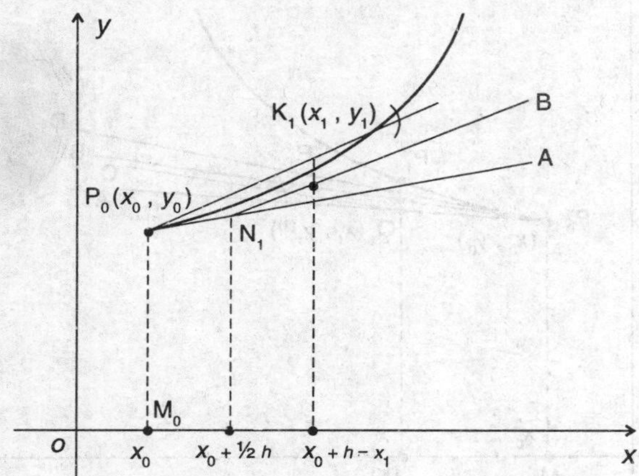


$$\therefore \quad y_1^{(1)} = y_0 + h\left[f\left(x_0 + \frac{1}{2}h,\ y_0 + \frac{1}{2}hf(x_0, y_0)\right)\right]$$

In general,

$$\mathbf{y_{n+1} = y_n + h\left[f\left(x_n + \frac{1}{2}h,\ y_n + \frac{1}{2}h\,f\,(x_n, y_n)\right)\right]} \quad ...(2)$$

or

$$\mathbf{y\,(x+h) = y\,(x) + h\left[f\left(x + \frac{1}{2}h,\ y + \frac{1}{2}h\,f\,(x, y)\right)\right]} \quad ...(3)$$

Equations (2) or (3) is called **modified Euler's formula.**

**Note 2.** Hence the Euler predictor is

$$y_{n+1} = y_n + h\,y_n'$$

and the corrector is

$$y_{n+1} = y_n + \frac{h}{2}\left(y_n' + y'_{n+1}\right)$$

in the *Improved Euler method:*

**Note 3.** There is a lot of confusion among the authors: Some take the improved Euler method as the modified Euler method and the modified Euler method is not mentioned at all. You can see this in some books.

**Example 1.** *Given $y' = -y$ and $y\,(0) = 1$, determine the values of y at $x = (0{\cdot}01)\ (0{\cdot}01)\ (0{\cdot}04)$ by Euler method.*

**Solution.** $y' = -y$ and $y\,(0) = 1$; $f(x, y) = -y$.

Here, $x_0 = 0,\ y_0 = 1,\ x_1 = 0{\cdot}01,\ x_2 = 0{\cdot}02,\ x_3 = 0{\cdot}03,\ x_4 = 0{\cdot}04.$

We have to find $y_1, y_2, y_3, y_4$. Take $h = 0{\cdot}01$.

By Euler algorithm,

$$y_{n+1} = y_n + h\,y_n' = y_n + h\,f(x_n, y_n) \quad ...(1)$$

$$y_1 = y_0 + h\,f(x_0, y_0) = 1 + (0{\cdot}01)(-1) = 1 - 0{\cdot}01 = \mathbf{0{\cdot}99}.$$

$$y_2 = y_1 + h\,y_1' = 0{\cdot}99 + (0{\cdot}01)(-y_1)$$
$$= 0{\cdot}99 + (0{\cdot}01)(-0{\cdot}99)$$
$$= \mathbf{0{\cdot}9801}$$
$$y_3 = y_2 + h f(x_2, y_2) = 0{\cdot}9801 + (0{\cdot}01)(-0{\cdot}9801)$$
$$= \mathbf{0{\cdot}9703}$$
$$y_4 = y_3 + h f(x_3, y_3) = 0{\cdot}9703 + (0{\cdot}01)(-0{\cdot}9703)$$
$$= \mathbf{0{\cdot}9606}$$

Tabular values (step values) are:

| $x$ | 0 | 0·01 | 0·02 | 0·03 | 0·04 |
|---|---|---|---|---|---|
| $y$ | 1 | 0·9900 | 0·9801 | 0·9703 | 0·9606 |
| Exact $y$ | 1 | 0·9900 | 0·9802 | 0·9704 | 0·9608 |

since, $y = e^{-x}$ is the exact solution.

**Example 2.** *Using Euler's method, solve numerically the equation,*

$$y' = x + y,\ y(0) = 1,\ \text{for } x = 0{\cdot}0\ (0{\cdot}2)(1{\cdot}0)$$

*check your answer with the exact solution.*

**Solution.** Here $h = 0{\cdot}2$, $f(x, y) = x + y$, $x_0 = 0, y_0 = 1$

$$x_1 = 0{\cdot}2,\ x_2 = 0{\cdot}4,\ x_3 = 0{\cdot}6,\ x_4 = 0{\cdot}8,\ x_5 = 1{\cdot}0$$

By Euler algorithm,

$$y_1 = y_0 + h f(x_0, y_0) = y_0 + h\,[x_0 + y_0]$$
$$= 1 + (0{\cdot}2)(0 + 1) = 1{\cdot}2$$
$$y_2 = y_1 + h\,[x_1 + y_1] = 1{\cdot}2 + (0{\cdot}2)(0{\cdot}2 + 1{\cdot}2) = 1{\cdot}48$$
$$y_3 = y_2 + h\,[x_2 + y_2]$$
$$= 1{\cdot}48 + (0{\cdot}2)\,(0{\cdot}4 + 1{\cdot}48) = 1{\cdot}856$$
$$y_4 = 1{\cdot}856 + (0{\cdot}2)(0{\cdot}6 + 1{\cdot}856) = 2{\cdot}3472$$
$$y_5 = 2{\cdot}3472 + (0{\cdot}2)(0{\cdot}8 + 2{\cdot}3472) = 2{\cdot}94664$$

Exact solution is $y = 2e^x - x - 1$. Hence the tabular values are:

| $x$ | 0 | 0·2 | 0·4 | 0·6 | 0·8 | 1·0 |
|---|---|---|---|---|---|---|
| Euler $y$ | 1 | 1·2 | 1·48 | 1·856 | 2·3472 | 2·94664 |
| Exact $y$ | 1 | 1·2428 | 1·5836 | 2·0442 | 2·6511 | 3·4366 |

The values of $y$ deviates from the exact values as $x$ increases. Hence we require to use either Modied Euler or Improved Euler method for the above problem.

**Example 3.** *Solve numerically $y' = y + e^x$, $y(0) = 0$ for $x = 0{\cdot}2$, $0{\cdot}4$ by Improved Euler method.*

**Solution.** $y' = y + e^x, y(0) = 0;\ f(x, y) = y + e^x.$

$$x_0 = 0,\ y_0 = 0, x_1 = 0{\cdot}2, x_2 = 0{\cdot}4, h = 0{\cdot}2.$$

By Improved Euler method,

$$y_{n+1} = y_n + \frac{1}{2} h [f(x_n, y_n) + f(x_n + h, y_n + hf(x_n, y_n))]$$

$$\therefore \quad y_1 = y_0 + \frac{1}{2} h [f(x_0, y_0) + f(x_1, y_0 + hf(x_0, y_0))] \qquad ...(1)$$

$$= 0 + \frac{0{\cdot}2}{2} [y_0 + e^{x_0} + y_0 + h(y_0 + e^{x_0}) + e^{x_0 + h}]$$

$$= (0{\cdot}1)[0 + 1 + 0 + 0{\cdot}2(0 + 1) + e^{0{\cdot}2}]$$

$$y(0{\cdot}2) = (0{\cdot}1)[1 + 0{\cdot}2 + 1{\cdot}2214] = \mathbf{0{\cdot}24214}$$

$$y_2 = y_1 + \frac{1}{2} h [f(x_1, y_1) + f(x_1 + h, y_1 + hf(x_1, y_1))] \qquad ...(2)$$

Here $f(x_1, y_1) = y_1 + e^{x_1} = 0{\cdot}24214 + e^{0{\cdot}2} = 1{\cdot}46354$

$$y_1 + hf(x_1, y_1) = 0{\cdot}24214 + (0{\cdot}2)(1{\cdot}46354) = 0{\cdot}53485$$

$$f(x_1 + h, y_1 + hf(x_1, y_1)) = f(0{\cdot}4, 0{\cdot}53485)$$

$$= 0{\cdot}53485 + e^{0{\cdot}4}$$

$$= 2{\cdot}02667$$

using (2),

$$y_2 = y(0{\cdot}4) = 0{\cdot}24214 + (0{\cdot}1)[1{\cdot}46354 + 2{\cdot}02667]$$

$$= 0{\cdot}59116$$

$$y(0{\cdot}4) = \mathbf{0{\cdot}59116}$$

**Example 4.** *Compute y at x = 0·25 by Modified Euler method given $y' = 2xy$, $y(0) = 1$.* *(BR. Nov. 1995)*

**Solution.** Here, $f(x, y) = 2xy$ : $x_0 = 0$, $y_0 = 1$.

Take $h = 0{\cdot}25$, $x_1 = 0{\cdot}25$

By Modified Euler method,

$$y_{n+1} = y_n + h\left[f\left(x_n + \frac{1}{2}h,\ y_n + \frac{1}{2}hf(x_n, y_n)\right)\right] \qquad ...(1)$$

$$\therefore \quad y_1 = y_0 + h\left[f\left(x_0 + \frac{1}{2}h,\ y_0 + \frac{1}{2}hf(x_0, y_0)\right)\right]$$

$$f(x_0, y_0) = f(0, 1) = 2(0)(1) = 0.$$

$$\therefore \quad y_1 = 1 + (0{\cdot}25)[f(0{\cdot}125, 1)]$$

$$= 1 + (0{\cdot}25)[2 \times 0{\cdot}125 \times 1]$$

$$y(0{\cdot}25) = \mathbf{1{\cdot}0625}$$

By solving $\frac{dy}{dx} = 2xy$, we get $y = e^{x^2}$ using $y(0) = 1$,

$y(0{\cdot}25) = e^{(0{\cdot}25)^2} = 1{\cdot}0645$

Exact value of $y(0{\cdot}25) = \mathbf{1{\cdot}0645}$

Error is only 0·002.

**Note:** To improve the result we can take $h = 0{\cdot}125$ and get $y(0{\cdot}125)$ first and then get $y(0{\cdot}25)$. Of course, labour is more.

**Example 5.** *Solve the equation* $\frac{dy}{dx} = 1 - y$, *given* $y(0) = 0$ *using* ***Modified Euler's method*** *and tabulate the solutions at* $x = 0{\cdot}1,\ 0{\cdot}2$, *and* $0{\cdot}3$. *Compare your results with the* ***exact solutions.***

Also, get the solutions by ***Improved Euler method.*** *(Anna Ap. 2005)*

*(B.R. Nov. 1991)*

**Solution.** Here, $x_0 = 0, y_0 = 0, x_1 = 0{\cdot}1, x_2 = 0{\cdot}2, x_3 = 0{\cdot}3, h = 0{\cdot}1$

$$y' = 1 - y \quad \therefore \quad f(x, y) = 1 - y; \ \ f(x_0, y_0) = 1 - y_0 = 1$$

By *Modified Euler method,*

$$y_{n+1} = y_n + hf\left(x_n + \frac{1}{2}h, y_n + \frac{1}{2}hf(x_n, y_n)\right) \qquad \text{...(1)}$$

$$\therefore \quad y_1 = y_0 + hf\left(x_0 + \frac{1}{2}h, y_0 + \frac{1}{2}hf(x_0, y_0)\right) \qquad \text{...(2)}$$

$$x_0 + \frac{1}{2}h = \frac{0{\cdot}1}{2} = 0{\cdot}05$$

$$y_0 + \frac{1}{2}hf(x_0, y_0) = 0 + \frac{0{\cdot}1}{2}[1] = 0{\cdot}05$$

using (2),

$$\therefore \quad y_1 = 0 + 0{\cdot}1\,[f(0{\cdot}05, 0{\cdot}05)] = (0{\cdot}1)(1 - 0{\cdot}05)$$

$$y_1 = y(0{\cdot}1) = \mathbf{0{\cdot}095}$$

$$\therefore \quad f(x_1, y_1) = 1 - y_1 = 0{\cdot}905;$$

$$y_2 = y_1 + hf\left(x_1 + \frac{1}{2}h, y_1 + \frac{1}{2}hf(x_1, y_1)\right)$$

$$= 0{\cdot}095 + (0{\cdot}1)\,[f(0{\cdot}15, 0{\cdot}14025)]$$

$$= 0{\cdot}095 + (0{\cdot}1)\,[1 - 0{\cdot}14025]$$

$$y(0{\cdot}2) = \mathbf{0{\cdot}18098}$$

$$y_3 = y_2 + hf\left(x_2 + \frac{1}{2}h, y_2 + \frac{1}{2}hf(x_2, y_2)\right) \qquad \text{...(3)}$$

$$x_2 + \frac{1}{2}h = 0{\cdot}25$$

$$y_2 + \frac{1}{2}hf(x_2, y_2) = 0{\cdot}18098 + (0{\cdot}05)\,[1 - 0{\cdot}18098]$$

$$= 0{\cdot}22193$$

using (3), we get

$$y(0{\cdot}3) = y_3 = 0{\cdot}18098 + (0{\cdot}1)\,[1 - 0{\cdot}22193] = \mathbf{0{\cdot}258787}.$$

*Exact solution:* $\frac{dy}{dx} = 1 - y$ gives $\frac{dy}{1 - y} = dx$

$$\therefore \quad -\log(1 - y) = x + c$$

$$\log(1 - y) = -x - c$$

$\therefore \quad 1-y=e^{-x}A$

At $x=0, y=0 \quad \therefore \quad A = 1 \quad \therefore \quad y=1-e^{-x}$ ...(4)

using this exact solution,

$$y(0{\cdot}1)=1-e^{-0{\cdot}1}=0{\cdot}09516258$$

$$y(0{\cdot}2)=1-e^{-0{\cdot}2}=0{\cdot}181269247$$

$$y(0{\cdot}3)=1-e^{-0{\cdot}3}=0{\cdot}259181779$$

*By Improved Euler method,*

$$y_{n+1}=y_n+\frac{1}{2}h\,[f(x_n, y_n)+f(x_n+h, y_n+hf(x_n, y_n))] \quad ...(5)$$

$$\therefore \quad y_1=y_0+\frac{1}{2}h\,[f(x_0, y_0)+f(x_1, y_0+hf(x_0, y_0))] \quad ...(6)$$

$$f(x_0, y_0)=1-y=1-0=1$$

$$f(x_1, y_0+hf(x_0, y_0))=f(0{\cdot}1, 0{\cdot}1)=1-0{\cdot}1=0{\cdot}9$$

using in (6),

$$y_1=y(0{\cdot}1)=0+\frac{0{\cdot}1}{2}[1+0{\cdot}9]=\frac{0{\cdot}19}{2}=\mathbf{0{\cdot}095}$$

$$y_2=y_1+\frac{1}{2}h\,[f(x_1, y_1)+f(x_2, y_1+hf(x_1, y_1))] \quad ...(7)$$

$$f(x_1, y_1)=1-y_1=1-0{\cdot}095=0{\cdot}905$$

$$f(x_2, y_1+hf(x_1, y_1))=f(0{\cdot}2, 0{\cdot}095+(0{\cdot}1)(0{\cdot}905))=0{\cdot}8145$$

using in (7), we get

$$y_2=y(0{\cdot}2)=0{\cdot}095+\frac{0{\cdot}1}{2}[0{\cdot}905+0{\cdot}8145]$$

$$y(0{\cdot}2)=\mathbf{0{\cdot}18098}$$

$$y_3=y_2+\frac{1}{2}h\,[f(x_2, y_2)+f(x_3, y_2+hf(x_2, y_2))] \quad ...(8)$$

$$f(x_2, y_2)=1-y_2=1-0{\cdot}18098=0{\cdot}81902$$

$$y_2+hf(x_2, y_2)=0{\cdot}18098+(0{\cdot}1)(0{\cdot}81902)=0{\cdot}26288$$

using in (8),

$$y_3=y(0{\cdot}3)=0{\cdot}18098+\frac{0{\cdot}1}{2}[0{\cdot}81902+1-0{\cdot}26288]$$

$$y(0{\cdot}3)=\mathbf{0{\cdot}258787}$$

The values are tabulated.

| $x$ | *Modified Euler* | *Improved Euler* | *Exact solution* |
|---|---|---|---|
| 0·1 | 0·095 | 0·095 | 0·09516 |
| 0·2 | 0·18098 | 0·18098 | 0·18127 |
| 0·3 | 0·258787 | 0·258787 | 0·25918 |

Modified Euler and Improved Euler methods give the same values correct to six decimal places.

**Example 6.** *Given $y' = x^2 - y$, $y(0) = 1$, find correct to four decimal places the value of $y(0\cdot 1)$, by using Improved Euler method.*

**Solution.** By improved Euler method,

$$y_{n+1} = y_n + \frac{1}{2} h [f(x_n, y_n) + f(x_n + h, y_n + h f(x_n, y_n))]$$

$$\therefore \quad y_1 = y_0 + \frac{1}{2} h [f(x_0, y_0) + f(x_1, y_0 + h f(x_0, y_0))]$$

$$x_0 = 0, y_0 = 1, x_1 = 0\cdot 1$$

$$f(x_0, y_0) = x_0^2 - y_0 = 0 - 1 = -1$$

$$y_0 + h f(x_0, y_0) = 1 + (0\cdot 1)(-1) = 1 - 0\cdot 1 = 0\cdot 9$$

$$f(x_1, y_0 + hf(x_0, y_0)) = x_1^2 - 0\cdot 9 = (0\cdot 1)^2 - (0\cdot 9) = -0\cdot 89$$

$$\therefore \quad y_1 = 1 + \frac{0\cdot 1}{2} [-1 + (-0\cdot 89)]$$

$$y(0\cdot 1) = 1 - \frac{0\cdot 1}{2} \times 1\cdot 89 = \mathbf{0\cdot 9055}.$$

**Examr le 7.** *Using improved Euler method find y at $x = 0\cdot 1$ and y at $x = 0\cdot 2$ given*

$$\frac{dy}{dx} = y - \frac{2x}{y}, \; y(0) = 1. \qquad (MS.\ Ap.\ 1991)$$

**Solution.** By Improved Euler method,

$$y_{n+1} = y_n + \frac{1}{2} h [f(x_n, y_n) + f(x_n + h, y_n + hf(x_n, y_n))] \qquad ...(1)$$

$$\therefore \quad y_1 = y_0 + \frac{1}{2} h [f(x_0, y_0) + f(x_1, y_0 + h f(x_0, y_0))] \qquad ...(2)$$

$$f(x_0, y_0) = y_0 - \frac{2x_0}{y_0} = 1 - 0 = 1$$

$$f(x_1, y_0 + hf(x_0, y_0)) = f(0\cdot 1, 1\cdot 1) = 1\cdot 1 - \frac{2 \times (0\cdot 1)}{1\cdot 1} = 0\cdot 91818$$

$$y(0\cdot 1) = y_1 = 1 + \frac{0\cdot 1}{2} [1 + 0\cdot 91818] = \mathbf{1\cdot 095909}$$

$$y_2 = y(0\cdot 2) = y_1 + \frac{1}{2} h [f(x_1, y_1) + f(x_2, y_1 + h f(x_1, y_1))] \qquad ...(3)$$

$$f(x_1, y_1) = y_1 - \frac{2x_1}{y_1} = 1\cdot 095909 - \frac{2 \times 0\cdot 1}{1\cdot 095909}$$

$$= 0\cdot 913412$$

$$f(x_2, y_1 + h f(x_1, y_1)) = f(0\cdot 2, 1\cdot 095909 + (0\cdot 1)(0\cdot 913412))$$

$$= f(0{\cdot}2, 1{\cdot}18732) = 1{\cdot}18732 - \frac{2 \times 0{\cdot}2}{1{\cdot}18732} = 0{\cdot}8504268$$

using in (3),

$$y_2 = 1{\cdot}095909 + \frac{0{\cdot}1}{2}[0{\cdot}913412 + 0{\cdot}850427]$$

$$= \mathbf{1{\cdot}1841009}$$

| $x$ | 0 | 0·1 | 0·2 |
|---|---|---|---|
| $y$ | 1 | 1·095907 | 1·1841009 |

**Example 8.** *Using Modified Euler method, find y (0·2), y (0·1) given*

$$\frac{dy}{dx} = x^2 + y^2,\ y\ (0) = 1. \qquad \text{(MS. Ap. '92)}$$

**Solution.** Here, $x_0 = 0$, $y_0 = 1$, $h = 0{\cdot}1$, $x_1 = 0{\cdot}1$, $f(x, y) = x^2 + y^2$

By Modified Euler method,

$$y_1 = y_0 + hf\left(x_0 + \frac{1}{2}h,\ y_0 + \frac{1}{2}hf(x_0, y_0)\right) \qquad ...(1)$$

$$y_0 + \frac{1}{2}hf(x_0, y_0) = y_0 + \frac{1}{2}h\left(x_0^2 + y_0^2\right)$$

$$= 1 + \frac{0{\cdot}1}{2}(0 + 1) = 1{\cdot}05$$

using in (1)

$$y_1 = 1 + (0{\cdot}1)\,[f(0{\cdot}05, 1{\cdot}05)]$$

$$y\,(0{\cdot}1) = 1 + (0{\cdot}1)\,[(0{\cdot}05)^2 + (1{\cdot}05)^2] = \mathbf{1{\cdot}1105}$$

$$y_2 = y_1 + hf\left(x_1 + \frac{1}{2}h,\ y_1 + \frac{1}{2}hf(x_1, y_1)\right)$$

$$f(x_1, y_1) = f(0{\cdot}1, 1{\cdot}1105) = (0{\cdot}1)^2 + (1{\cdot}1105)^2 = 1{\cdot}24321$$

$$y_1 + \frac{1}{2}hf(x_1, y_1) = 1{\cdot}1105 + (0{\cdot}05)(1{\cdot}24321) = 1{\cdot}172660$$

$$\therefore\quad y_2 = 1{\cdot}1105 + (0{\cdot}1)\,[f(0{\cdot}15, 1{\cdot}172660)]$$

$$= 1{\cdot}1105 + (0{\cdot}1)\,[(0{\cdot}15)^2 + (1{\cdot}17266)^2]$$

$$y\,(0{\cdot}2) = \mathbf{1{\cdot}25026}.$$

## EXERCISE 11.3

1. Compute $y$ (0·3) taking $h$ = 0·1 given $\frac{dy}{dx} = y - \frac{2x}{y}$, $y$ (0) = 1 using improved Euler method.

**2.** Find $y(0{\cdot}6), y(0{\cdot}8), y(1)$ given $\frac{dy}{dx} = x + y, y(0) = 0$ taking $h = 0{\cdot}2$ by improved Euler method.

**3.** Using Improved Euler method find

$$y(0{\cdot}2), y(0{\cdot}4) \text{ given } \frac{dy}{dx} = y + x^2, y(0) = 1.$$

**4.** Use Euler's method to find $y(0{\cdot}4)$ given $y' = xy, y(0) = 1$.

**5.** Use Improved Euler method to find $y(0{\cdot}1)$ given $y' = \frac{y-x}{y+x}, y(0) = 1$.

**6.** Use Modified Euler method and obtain $y(0{\cdot}2)$ given $\frac{dy}{dx} = \log(x+y), y(0) = 1, h = 0{\cdot}2$.

**7.** Using Modified Euler method, get $y(0{\cdot}2), y(0{\cdot}4), y(0{\cdot}6)$ given $\frac{dy}{dx} = y - x^2, y(0) = 1$.

**8.** Using Euler's Improved method, find $y(0{\cdot}2), y(0{\cdot}4)$ given

$$\frac{dy}{dx} = x + |\sqrt{y}|, \; y(0) = 1.$$

**9.** Find $y(0{\cdot}1)$ given $y' = x^2 + y, y(0) = 1$ using Improved Euler method.

*Using Euler's method do the problems (10-11):*

**10.** Find $y(1{\cdot}5)$ taking $h = 0{\cdot}5$ given

$$y' = y - 1, y(0) = 1{\cdot}1.$$

**11.** If $y' = 1 + y^2, y(0) = 1, h = 0{\cdot}1$, find $y(0{\cdot}4)$.

**12.** Use Euler's improved method to calculate $y(0{\cdot}5)$, taking $h = 0{\cdot}1$, and $y' = y + \sin x, y(0) = 2$.

**13.** Find $y(1{\cdot}6)$ if $y' = x\log y - y\log x, y(1) = 1$ if $h = 0{\cdot}1$.

**14.** Find by Improved Euler to get $y(1{\cdot}2), y(1{\cdot}4)$ given $\frac{dy}{dx} = \frac{2y}{x} + x^3$ if $y(1) = 0{\cdot}5$.

**15.** Use Improved Euler and Modified Euler method, to get $y(1{\cdot}6)$ if

$$\frac{dy}{dx} = y^2 - \frac{y}{x}, \text{ if } y(1) = 1.$$

**16.** Solve $y' = 3x^2 + y$ given $y(0) = 4$, if $h = 0{\cdot}25$ to obtain $y(0{\cdot}25), y(0{\cdot}5)$.

**17.** Given $y' = \frac{y}{x} - \frac{5}{2}x^2y^3; y(1) = \frac{1}{\sqrt{2}}$ find $y(2)$ if $h = 0{\cdot}125$.

**18.** Find $y(0{\cdot}2)$ by Improved Euler method, given $y' = -xy^2, y(0) = 2$ if $h = 0{\cdot}1$.

## 11·12. Runge-Kutta Method

The use of the previous methods to solve the differential equation numerically is restricted due to either slow convergence or due to labour involved, especially in Taylor-series method. But, in Runge-Kutta methods, the derivatives of higher order are not required and we require only the given function values at different points. Since the derivation of fourth order Runge-Kutta method is tedious, we will derive Runge-Kutta method of second order.

**11·13. Second order Runge-Kutta method (for first order O.D.E.)**

**AIM.** To solve $\dfrac{dy}{dx}=f(x, y)$ given $y(x_0)=y_0$. ...(1)

**Proof.** By Taylor series, we have,

$$y(x+h)=y(x)+hy'(x)+\frac{h^2}{2!}y''(x)+O(h^3) \quad ...(2)$$

Differentiating the equation (1) w.r.t. $x$,

$$y''=\frac{\partial f}{\partial x}+\frac{\partial f}{\partial y}\cdot\frac{dy}{dx}=f_x+y' f_y=f_x+ff_y \quad ...(3)$$

Using the values of $y'$ and $y''$ got from (1) and (3), in (2), we get,

$$y(x+h)-y(x)=hf+\frac{1}{2}h^2[f_x+ff_y]+O(h^3)$$

$$\therefore \quad \Delta y=hf+\frac{1}{2}h^2(f_x+ff_y)+O(h^3) \quad ...(4)$$

$$\text{Let } \Delta_1 y=k_1=f(x, y).\ \Delta x=hf(x, y) \quad ...(5)$$

$$\Delta_2 y=k_2=hf(x+mh, y+mk_1) \quad ...(6)$$

$$\text{and le } \Delta y=ak_1+bk_2 \quad ...(7)$$

where $a$, $b$ and $m$ are constants to be determined to get the better accuracy of $\Delta y$.

Expand $k_2$ and $\Delta y$ in powers of $h$.

Expanding $k_2$, by Taylor series for two variables, we have

$$k_2=hf(x+mh, y+mk_1)$$

$$=h\left[f(x, y)+\left(mh\frac{\partial}{\partial x}+mk_1\frac{\partial}{\partial y}\right)f+\frac{\left(mh\frac{\partial}{\partial x}+mk_1\frac{\partial}{\partial y}\right)^2}{2!}f+\cdots\right]$$

$$=h\left[f+mhf_x+mhff_y+\frac{\left(mh\frac{\partial}{\partial x}+mk_1\frac{\partial}{\partial y}\right)^2 f}{2!}+\cdots\right] \quad ...(8)$$

since $k_1=hf$

$$=hf+mh^2(f_x+ff_y)+\cdots \text{ higher powers of } h \quad ...(9)$$

Substituting $k_1$, $k_2$ in (7),

$$\Delta y=ahf+b\left[hf+mh^2(f_x+ff_y)+O(h^3)\right]$$

$$=(a+b)hf+bmh^2(f_x+ff_y)+O(h^3) \quad ...(10)$$

Equating $\Delta y$ from (4) and (10), we get

$$= hf + mh^2 (f_x + ff_y) + \cdots \text{ higher powers of } h \qquad ...(9)$$

Substituting $k_1, k_2$ in (7),

$$\Delta y = ahf + b\left[hf + mh^2 (f_x + ff_y) + O(h^3)\right]$$

$$= (a+b)\, hf + bmh^2 (f_x + ff_y) + O(h^3) \qquad ...(10)$$

Equating $\Delta y$ from (4) and (10), we get

$$a + b = 1 \quad \text{and} \quad bm = \frac{1}{2} \qquad ...(11)$$

Now we have only two equations given by (1) to solve for three unknowns $a, b, m$.

From $a + b = 1, a = 1 - b$ and also $m = \dfrac{1}{2b}$ using (7),

$$\Delta y = (1 - b)\, k_1 + bk_2$$

where $\quad k_1 = hf(x, y)$

$$k_2 = hf\left(x + \frac{h}{2b}, y + \frac{hf}{2b}\right)$$

Now $\quad \Delta y = y(x+h) - y(x)$

$$\therefore y(x+h) = y(x) + (1-b)\, hf + bhf\left(x + \frac{h}{2b}, y + \frac{hf}{2b}\right)$$

*i.e.,*
$$y_{n+1} = y_n + (1-b)\, hf(x_n, y_n)$$
$$+ bhf\left(x_n + \frac{h}{2b}, y_n + \frac{h}{2b} f(x_n, y_n)\right) + O(h^3)$$

From this general second order Runge-Kutta formula, setting $a = 0, b = 1, m = \dfrac{1}{2}$, we get the second order Runge-Kutta algorithm as

$$k_1 = hf(x, y)$$

$$k_2 = hf\left(x + \frac{1}{2}h, y + \frac{1}{2}k_1\right) \qquad \text{Second order R.K. algorithm}$$

and $\quad \Delta y = K_2 \quad$ where $h = \Delta x$.

Since the derivations of third and fourth order Runge-Kutta algorithms are tedious, we state them below for use.

The third order Runge-Kutta method algorithm is given below:

$$k_1 = hf(x, y)$$

$$k_2 = hf\left(x + \frac{1}{2}h, y + \frac{1}{2}k_1\right)$$

$$k_3 = hf(x + h, y + 2k_2 - k_1)$$

and $\quad \Delta y = \dfrac{1}{6}(k_1 + 4k_2 + k_3)$

Third order R.K. algorithm

The fourth order Runge-Kutta method algorithm is mostly used in problems unless otherwise mentioned. It is

$$k_1 = hf(x, y)$$

$$k_2 = hf\left(x + \frac{1}{2}h, y + \frac{1}{2}k_1\right)$$

$$k_3 = hf\left(x + \frac{1}{2}h, y + \frac{1}{2}k_2\right)$$

$$k_4 = hf(x + h, y + k_3)$$

and $$\Delta y = \frac{1}{6}(k_1 + 2k_2 + 2k_3 + k_4)$$

$$y(x + h) = y(x) + \Delta y$$

Fourth order R.K. algorithm

**Working Rule:** To solve $\frac{dy}{dx} = f(x, y), y(x_0) = y_0$.

Calculate $$k_1 = hf(x_0, y_0)$$

$$k_2 = hf\left(x_0 + \frac{1}{2}h, y_0 + \frac{1}{2}k_1\right)$$

$$k_3 = hf\left(x_0 + \frac{1}{2}h, y_0 + \frac{1}{2}k_2\right)$$

$$k_4 = hf(x_0 + h, y_0 + k_3)$$

and $$\Delta y = \frac{1}{6}(k_1 + 2k_2 + 2k_3 + k_4)$$

where $\Delta x = h$.

Now $y_1 = y_0 + \Delta y$.

Now starting from $(x_1, y_1)$ and repeating the process, we get $(x_2, y_2)$ etc.

**Note 1.** In second order Runge-Kutta method,

$$\Delta y_0 = k_2 = hf\left(x_0 + \frac{h}{2}, y_0 + \frac{1}{2}k_1\right)$$

$$\Delta y_0 = hf\left(x_0 + \frac{h}{2}, y_0 + \frac{1}{2}hf(x_0, y_0)\right)$$

$$\therefore \quad y_1 = y_0 + \Delta y_0 = y_0 + hf\left(x_0 + \frac{h}{2}, y_0 + \frac{1}{2}hf(x_0, y_0)\right)$$

This is exactly the *Modified Euler method.*

So, **the Runge-Kutta method of second order is nothing but the Modified Euler method.**

**Note 2.** If $f(x, y) = f(x)$, *i.e.,* only a function $x$ alone, then the fourth order Runge-Kutta method reduces to

$$k_1 = hf(x_0)$$

$$\Delta y = \frac{1}{6}h\left[f(x_0) + 4f\left(x_0 + \frac{h}{2}\right) + f(x_0 + h)\right]$$

$$= \frac{\left(\frac{h}{2}\right)}{3}\left[f(x_0) + 4f\left(x_0 + \frac{h}{2}\right) + f(x_0 + h)\right]$$

= the area of $y = f(x)$ between $x = x_0$ and $x = x_0 + h$ with 2 equal intervals of length $\frac{h}{2}$ by Simpson's one-third rule.

*i.e.,* $\Delta y$ reduces to the area by Simpson's one-third rule.

**Note 3.** In all the three methods, (2nd order, 3rd order and 4th order) the values of $k_1, k_2$ are same. Therefore, one need not repeat the work while doing by all the three methods.

**Example 1.** *Apply the fourth order Runge-Kutta method to find $y(0{\cdot}2)$ given that $y' = x + y$, $y(0) = 1$.* *(Ap. 1992)*

**Solution.** Since $h$ is not mentioned in the question we take $h = 0{\cdot}1$

$$y' = x + y;\ y(0) = 1 \quad \therefore \quad f(x, y) = x + y,\ x_0 = 0,\ y_0 = 1$$

$$x_1 = 0{\cdot}1,\ x_2 = 0{\cdot}2$$

By fourth order Runge-Kutta method, for the first interval,

$$k_1 = hf(x_0, y_0) = (0{\cdot}1)(x_0 + y_0) = (0{\cdot}1)(0 + 1) = 0{\cdot}1$$

$$k_2 = hf\left(x_0 + \frac{1}{2}h,\ y_0 + \frac{1}{2}k_1\right) = (0{\cdot}1)f(0{\cdot}05,\ 1{\cdot}05)$$

$$= (0{\cdot}1)(0{\cdot}05 + 1{\cdot}05) = 0{\cdot}11$$

$$k_3 = hf\left(x_0 + \frac{1}{2}h,\ y_0 + \frac{1}{2}k_2\right)$$

$$= (0{\cdot}1)f(0{\cdot}05,\ 1{\cdot}055) = (0{\cdot}1)(0{\cdot}05 + 1{\cdot}055) = 0{\cdot}1105$$

$$k_4 = hf(x_0 + h,\ y_0 + k_3)$$

$$= (0{\cdot}1)f(0{\cdot}1,\ 1{\cdot}1105) = (0{\cdot}1)(0{\cdot}1 + 1{\cdot}1105) = 0{\cdot}12105$$

$$\therefore \quad \Delta y = \frac{1}{6}(k_1 + 2k_2 + 2k_3 + k_4)$$

$$= \frac{1}{6}(0{\cdot}1 + 0{\cdot}22 + 0{\cdot}2210 + 0{\cdot}12105) = 0{\cdot}110341667.$$

$$y(0{\cdot}1) = y_1 = y_0 + \Delta y = 1{\cdot}110341667 \approx \mathbf{1{\cdot}110342.}$$

Now starting from $(x_1, y_1)$ we get $(x_2, y_2)$. Again apply Runge-Kutta algorithm replacing $(x_0, y_0)$ by $(x_1, y_1)$.

$$k_1 = hf(x_1, y_1) = (0{\cdot}1)(x_1 + y_1) = (0{\cdot}1)(0{\cdot}1 + 1{\cdot}110342) = 0{\cdot}1210342$$

$$k_2 = hf\left(x_1 + \frac{h}{2},\ y_1 + \frac{1}{2}k_1\right) = (0{\cdot}1)f(0{\cdot}15,\ 1{\cdot}170859)$$

$$= (0{\cdot}1)(0{\cdot}15 + 1{\cdot}170859) = 0{\cdot}1320859$$

$$k_3 = hf\left(x_1 + \frac{h}{2}, y_1 + \frac{1}{2}k_2\right) = (0\cdot1)\,f(0\cdot15,\ 1\cdot1763848)$$

$$= (0\cdot1)(0\cdot15 + 1\cdot1763848) = 0\cdot13263848$$

$$k_4 = hf(x_1 + h, y_1 + k_3) = (0\cdot1)\,f(0\cdot2,\ 1\cdot24298048)$$

$$= 0\cdot144298048$$

$$y(0\cdot2) = y(0\cdot1) + \frac{1}{6}(k_1 + 2k_2 + 2k_3 + k_4) = 1\cdot110342 + \frac{1}{6}(0\cdot794781008)$$

$y(0\cdot2) = \mathbf{1\cdot2428055}$

Correct to four decimal places, $y(0\cdot2) = \mathbf{1\cdot2428}$.

**Example 2.** *Obtain the values of y at x = 0·1, 0·2 using R.K. method of (i) second order (ii) third order and (iii) fourth order for the differential equation y′ = – y, given y (0) = 1.* *(MKU 1971)*

**Solution.** Here, $f(x, y) = -y$, $x_0 = 0$, $y_0 = 1$, $x_1 = 0\cdot1$, $x_2 = 0\cdot2$.

**(*i*) Second order:**

$$k_1 = hf(x_0, y_0) = (0\cdot1)(-y_0) = -0\cdot1$$

$$k_2 = hf\left(x_0 + \frac{1}{2}h, y_0 + \frac{1}{2}k_1\right) = (0\cdot1)\,f(0\cdot05, 0\cdot95)$$

$$= -0\cdot1 \times 0\cdot95 = -0\cdot095 = \Delta y$$

$$y_1 = y_0 + \Delta y = 1 - 0\cdot095 = 0\cdot905$$

$$y_1 = y(0\cdot1) = \mathbf{0\cdot905}$$

Again starting from $(0\cdot1, 0\cdot905)$ replacing $(x_0, y_0)$ by $(x_1, y_1)$ we get

$$k_1 = (0\cdot1)\,f(x_1, y_1) = (0\cdot1)(-0\cdot905) = -0\cdot0905$$

$$k_2 = hf\left(x_1 + \frac{1}{2}h, y_1 + \frac{1}{2}k_1\right)$$

$$= (0\cdot1)\,[f(0\cdot15, 0\cdot85975)] = (0\cdot1)(-0\cdot85975) = -0\cdot085975$$

$$\Delta y = k_2$$

$$\therefore\ y_2 = y(0\cdot2) = y_1 + \Delta y = \mathbf{0\cdot819025}$$

**(*ii*) Third order:**

$$k_1 = hf(x_0, y_0) = -0\cdot1$$

$$k_2 = hf\left(x_0 + \frac{1}{2}h, y_0 + \frac{1}{2}k_1\right) = -0\cdot095$$

$$k_3 = hf(x_0 + h, y_0 + 2k_2 - k_1)$$

$$= (0\cdot1)\,f(0\cdot1, 0\cdot9) = (0\cdot1)(-0\cdot9) = -0\cdot09$$

$$\Delta y = \frac{1}{6}(k_1 + 4k_2 + k_3)$$

$$y(0\cdot1) = y_1 = y_0 + \Delta y = 1 - 0\cdot09 = \mathbf{0\cdot91}$$

Again taking $(x_1, y_1)$ as $(x_0, y_0)$ repeat the process.

$$\therefore \quad k_1 = h\,f(x_1, y_1) = (0{\cdot}1)(-0{\cdot}91) = -0{\cdot}091$$

$$k_2 = h\,f\left(x_1 + \frac{1}{2}h,\, y_1 + \frac{1}{2}k_1\right)$$

$$= (0{\cdot}1)\,f(0{\cdot}15, 0{\cdot}865) = (0{\cdot}1)(-0{\cdot}865) = -0{\cdot}0865$$

$$k_3 = hf(x_1 + h, y_1 + 2k_2 - k_1)$$

$$= (0{\cdot}1)\,f(0{\cdot}2, 0{\cdot}828) = -0{\cdot}0828$$

$$y_2 = y_1 + \Delta y = 0{\cdot}91 + \frac{1}{6}(k_1 + 4k_2 + k_3)$$

$$= 0{\cdot}91 + \frac{1}{6}(-0{\cdot}091 - 0{\cdot}3460 - 0{\cdot}0828)$$

$$y(0{\cdot}2) = \mathbf{0{\cdot}823366}$$

***(iii)* Fourth order:**

$$k_1 = h\,f(x_0, y_0) = (0{\cdot}1)\,f(0, 1) = -0{\cdot}1$$

$$k_2 = h\,f\left(x_0 + \frac{1}{2}h,\, y_0 + \frac{1}{2}k_1\right) = (0{\cdot}1)\,f(0{\cdot}05, 0{\cdot}95) = -0{\cdot}095$$

$$k_3 = h\,f\left(x_0 + \frac{1}{2}h,\, y_0 + \frac{1}{2}k_2\right) = (0{\cdot}1)\,f(0{\cdot}05, 0{\cdot}9525)$$

$$= -0{\cdot}09525$$

$$k_4 = h\,f(x_0 + h, y_0 + k_3) = (0{\cdot}1)\,f(0{\cdot}1, 0{\cdot}90475)$$

$$= -\mathbf{0{\cdot}090475}$$

$$\Delta y = \frac{1}{6}(k_1 + 2k_2 + 2k_3 + k_4)$$

$$y_1 = y_0 + \Delta y = 1 + \frac{1}{6}(k_1 + 2k_2 + 2k_3 + k_4)$$

$$y_1 = y(0{\cdot}1) = \mathbf{0{\cdot}9048375}$$

Again start from this $(x_1, y_1)$ and replace $(x_0, y_0)$ and repeat

$$k_1 = hf(x_1, y_1) = (0{\cdot}1)(-y_1) = -0{\cdot}09048375$$

$$k_2 = h\,f\left(x_1 + \frac{1}{2}h,\, y_1 + \frac{1}{2}k_1\right)$$

$= (0{\cdot}1)\,f(0{\cdot}15, 0{\cdot}8595956) = -$ 0 cdot 08595956

$$k_3 = h\,f\left(x_1 + \frac{1}{2}h,\, y_1 + \frac{1}{2}k_2\right)$$

$= (0{\cdot}1)\,f(0{\cdot}15, 0{\cdot}8618577) = -$ 0 cdot 08618577

$$k_4 = h\,f(x_1 + h, y_1 + k_3)$$

$$= (0{\cdot}1)\,f(0{\cdot}2, 0{\cdot}8186517) = -0{\cdot}08186517$$

$$\Delta y = \frac{1}{6}(-0{\cdot}09048375 - 2 \times 0{\cdot}08595956$$

$$- 2 \times 0{\cdot}08618577 - 0{\cdot}08186517)$$

$= -0{\cdot}0861066067$

$y_2 = y(0{\cdot}2) = y_1 + \Delta y = \mathbf{0{\cdot}81873089}$

Tabular values are:

| $x$ | *Second order* | *Third order* | *Fourth order* | *Exact value* $y = e^{-x}$ |
|---|---|---|---|---|
| 0·1 | 0·905 | 0·91 | 0·9048375 | 0·904837418 |
| 0·2 | 0·819025 | 0·823366 | 0·81873089 | 0·818730753 |

Fourth order values are more closer to exact values.

**Example 3.** *Compute* $y(0{\cdot}3)$ *given* $\frac{dy}{dx} + y + xy^2 = 0$, $y(0) = 1$ *by taking* $h = 0{\cdot}1$ *using R.K method of fourth order (correct to 4 decimals).*

**Solution.** $y' = -(xy^2 + y) = f(x, y)$; $x_0 = 0$, $y_0 = 1$, $h = 0{\cdot}1$, $x_1 = 0{\cdot}1$, $x_2 = 0{\cdot}2$, $x_3 = 0{\cdot}3$, $y_3 = ?$

*For 1st interval*:

$$k_1 = hf(x_0, y_0) = (0{\cdot}1)\,[-(x_0y_0^2 + y_0)] = -0{\cdot}1$$

$$k_2 = hf\left(x_0 + \frac{h}{2}, y_0 + \frac{1}{2}k_1\right) = (0{\cdot}1)\,f(0{\cdot}05, 0{\cdot}95)$$

$$= -0{\cdot}1\,[(0{\cdot}05)\,(0{\cdot}95)^2 + 0{\cdot}95] = -0{\cdot}0995$$

$$k_3 = hf\left(x_0 + \frac{h}{2}, y_0 + \frac{1}{2}k_2\right) = (0{\cdot}1)\,f(0{\cdot}05, 0{\cdot}95025)$$

$$= (0{\cdot}1)\,[-(0{\cdot}05 \times 0{\cdot}95025 + 1)\,(0{\cdot}95025)\,]$$

$$= -0{\cdot}09953987 \approx -0{\cdot}0995$$

$$k_4 = hf(x_0 + h, y_0 + k_3)$$

$$= (0{\cdot}1)\,f(0{\cdot}1, 0{\cdot}9005) = -0{\cdot}0982$$

$$y_1 = 1 + \frac{1}{6}\,[-0{\cdot}1 + 2\,(-0{\cdot}0995) + 2\,(-0{\cdot}0995) - 0{\cdot}0982]$$

$y(0{\cdot}1) = \mathbf{0{\cdot}9006}$

Again taking $(x_1, y_1)$ in place of $(x_0, y_0)$ repeat the process.

$$k_1 = hf(x_1, y_1) = (0{\cdot}1)\,f(0{\cdot}1, 0{\cdot}9006)$$
$$= -0{\cdot}0982$$
$$k_2 = hf\left(x_1 + \frac{h}{2}, y_1 + \frac{1}{2}k_1\right) = (0{\cdot}1)\,f(0{\cdot}15, 0{\cdot}8515)$$
$$= -0{\cdot}0960$$
$$k_3 = hf\left(x_1 + \frac{h}{2}, y_1 + \frac{1}{2}k_2\right) = (0{\cdot}1)\,f(0{\cdot}15, 0{\cdot}8526)$$
$$= -0{\cdot}0962$$
$$k_4 = hf(x_1 + h, y_1 + k_3) = (0{\cdot}1)\,f(0{\cdot}2, 0{\cdot}8044)$$
$$= -0{\cdot}0934$$
$$y_2 = y_1 + \frac{1}{6}(k_1 + 2k_2 + 2k_3 + k_4)$$
$$= 0{\cdot}9006 + \frac{1}{6}[-0{\cdot}0982 + 2 \times (-0{\cdot}0960) + 2\,(-0{\cdot}0962) + (-0{\cdot}0934)]$$

$y\,(0{\cdot}2) = \mathbf{0{\cdot}8046}$

Again, starting from $(x_2, y_2)$ in place of $(x_0, y_0)$

$$k_1 = -0{\cdot}0934, \quad k_2 = -0{\cdot}0902, \quad k_3 = -0{\cdot}0904, \quad k_4 = -0{\cdot}0867$$
$$\therefore \quad y_3 = y_2 + \frac{1}{6}\Delta y = y_2 + \frac{1}{6}(k_1 + 2k_2 + 2k_3 + k_4)$$

$y\,(0{\cdot}3) = \mathbf{0{\cdot}7144.}$

**Example 4.** *Using R.K. method of fourth order, find* $y\,(0{\cdot}8)$ *correct to 4 decimal places if* $y' = y - x^2$, $y\,(0{\cdot}6) = 1{\cdot}7379$. *(April 1991)*

**Solution.** Here, $x_0 = 0{\cdot}6$, $y_0 = 1{\cdot}7379$, $h = 0{\cdot}1$, $x_1 = 0{\cdot}7$, $x_2 = 0{\cdot}8$

$$f(x, y) = y - x^2$$

By R.K. method of 4th order

$$y_1 = y_0 + \frac{1}{6}(k_1 + 2k_2 + 2k_3 + k_4) \quad \text{...(1)}$$

where $k_1 = hf(x_0, y_0) = (0{\cdot}1)\,f(0{\cdot}6, 1{\cdot}7379)$

$$= (0{\cdot}1)\,[1{\cdot}7379 - (0{\cdot}6)^2] = 0{\cdot}1378$$
$$k_2 = hf\left(x_0 + \frac{h}{2}, y_0 + \frac{1}{2}k_1\right)$$
$$= (0{\cdot}1)\,f(0{\cdot}65, 1{\cdot}8068) = (0{\cdot}1)\,[1{\cdot}8068 - (0{\cdot}65)^2] = 0{\cdot}1384$$
$$k_3 = hf\left(x_0 + \frac{h}{2}, y_0 + \frac{1}{2}k_2\right)$$
$$= (0{\cdot}1)\,f(0{\cdot}65, 1{\cdot}8071)$$

$$= (0\cdot1)\,[1\cdot8071 - (0\cdot65)^2] = 0\cdot1385$$

$$k_4 = hf(x_0 + h, y_0 + k_3) = (0\cdot1)\,f(0\cdot7, 1\cdot8764)$$

$$= (0\cdot1)\,[(1\cdot8764) - (0\cdot7)^2] = 0\cdot1386$$

Hence, using (1),

$$y\,(0\cdot7) = y_1 = 1\cdot7379 + \frac{1}{6}\,[0\cdot1378 + 2\,(0\cdot1384) + 2\,(0\cdot1385) + 0\cdot1386]$$

**y (0·7) = 1·8763.**

To find $y_2 = y\,(0\cdot8)$, we again start from $(x_1, y_1) = (0\cdot7, 1\cdot8763)$

Now, $$y_2 = y_1 + \frac{1}{6}\,[k_1 + 2k_2 + 2k_3 + k_4] \qquad ...(2)$$

where $$k_1 = hf(x_1, y_1) = (0\cdot1)\,[1\cdot8763 - (0\cdot7)^2\,] = 0\cdot1386$$

$$k_2 = hf\left(x_1 + \frac{h}{2}, y_1 + \frac{1}{2}k_1\right) = (0\cdot1)\,f(0\cdot75, 1\cdot9456)$$

$$= (0\cdot1)\,[1\cdot9456 - (0\cdot75)^2\,] = 0\cdot1383$$

$$k_3 = hf\left(x_1 + \frac{h}{2}, y_1 + \frac{1}{2}k_2\right)$$

$$= (0\cdot1)\,f(0\cdot75, 1\cdot9455)$$

$$= (0\cdot1)\,[1\cdot9455 - (0\cdot75)^2\,] = 0\cdot1383$$

$$k_4 = hf(x_1 + h, y_1 + k_3)$$

$$= (0\cdot1)\,f(0\cdot8, 2\cdot0146)$$

$$= (0\cdot1)\,[2\cdot0146 - (0\cdot8)^2\,] = 0\cdot1375$$

Using (2),

$$y_2 = y\,(0\cdot8) = 1\cdot8763 + \frac{1}{6}\,[0\cdot1386 + 2\,(1\cdot1383) + 2\,(1\cdot1383) + 0\cdot1375]$$

$$= 2\cdot0145$$

$\mathbf{y_2 = y\,(0\cdot8) = 2\cdot0145.}$

**Example 5.** *Using Runge-Kutta method of fourth order, solve* $\frac{dy}{dx} = \frac{y^2 - x^2}{y^2 + x^2}$ *given* $y\,(0) = 1$ *at* $x = 0\cdot2, 0\cdot4.$ *(MS. April '92)*

*(Anna Ap. 2005)*

*(Anna Nov. 2004)*

**Solution.** $y' = f(x, y) = \frac{y^2 - x^2}{y^2 + x^2}$;

Here $x_0 = 0, h = 0\cdot2, x_1 = 0\cdot2, x_2 = 0\cdot4, y_0 = 1$

$$f(x_0, y_0) = f(0, 1) = \frac{1 - 0}{1 + 0} = 1$$

$$k_1 = hf(x_0, y_0) = (0\cdot2) \times 1 = 0\cdot2$$

$$k_2 = hf\left(x_0 + \frac{1}{2}h, y_0 + \frac{1}{2}k_1\right) = (0\cdot2)\,f(0\cdot1, 1\cdot1)$$

$$= (0{\cdot}2)\left[\frac{(1{\cdot}1)^2 - (0{\cdot}1)^2}{(1{\cdot}1)^2 + (0{\cdot}1)^2}\right] = (0{\cdot}2)\left[\frac{1{\cdot}21 - 0{\cdot}01}{1{\cdot}21 + 0{\cdot}01}\right]$$

$$= 0{\cdot}1967213$$

$$k_3 = hf\left(x_0 + \frac{1}{2}h, y_0 + \frac{1}{2}k_2\right)$$

$$= (0{\cdot}2) f\left(0{\cdot}1, 1 + \frac{1}{2}(0{\cdot}1967213)\right)$$

$$= (0{\cdot}2) f(0{\cdot}1, 1{\cdot}0983606)$$

$$= (0{\cdot}2)\left[\frac{(1{\cdot}0983606)^2 - (0{\cdot}01)}{(1{\cdot}0983606)^2 + (0{\cdot}01)}\right] = 0{\cdot}1967$$

$$k_4 = hf(x_0 + h, y_0 + k_3)$$

$$= (0{\cdot}2) f(0{\cdot}2, 1{\cdot}1967)$$

$$= (0{\cdot}2)\left[\frac{(1{\cdot}1967)^2 - (0{\cdot}2)^2}{(1{\cdot}1967)^2 + (0{\cdot}2)^2}\right] = 0{\cdot}1891$$

$$\therefore \quad \Delta y = \frac{1}{6}[k_1 + 2k_2 + 2k_3 + k_4]$$

$$= \frac{1}{6}[0{\cdot}2 + 2(0{\cdot}19672) + 2(1{\cdot}1967) + 0{\cdot}1891]$$

$$= 0{\cdot}19598$$

$$\mathbf{y(0{\cdot}2) = y_1 = y_0 + \Delta y = 1{\cdot}19598.}$$

Again to find $y(0{\cdot}4)$, start from $(x_1, y_1) = (0{\cdot}2, 1{\cdot}19598)$.

Now,

$$\therefore \quad k_1 = hf(x_1, y_1) = (0{\cdot}2)\left[\frac{(1{\cdot}19598)^2 - (0{\cdot}2)^2}{(1{\cdot}19598)^2 + (0{\cdot}2)^2}\right] = 0{\cdot}1891$$

$$k_2 = hf\left(x_1 + \frac{1}{2}h, y_1 + \frac{1}{2}k_1\right) = (0{\cdot}2) f(0{\cdot}3, 1{\cdot}29055)$$

$$= (0{\cdot}2)\left[\frac{(1{\cdot}29055)^2 - (0{\cdot}3)^2}{(1{\cdot}29055)^2 + (0{\cdot}3)^2}\right] = 0{\cdot}17949$$

$$k_3 = (0{\cdot}2) f(0{\cdot}3, 1{\cdot}28572) = 0{\cdot}1793$$

$$k_4 = (0{\cdot}2) f(0{\cdot}4, y_1 + k_3) = (0{\cdot}2) f(0{\cdot}4, 1{\cdot}37528)$$

$$= 0{\cdot}1687$$

$$\Delta y = \frac{1}{6}(k_1 + 2k_2 + 2k_3 + k_4)$$

$$= \frac{1}{6}[0{\cdot}1891 + 2(0{\cdot}1795) + 2(0{\cdot}1793) + 0{\cdot}1687]$$

$$= 0{\cdot}1792$$

$\therefore \; \mathbf{y_2 = y\,(0{\cdot}4) = y_1 + \Delta y = 1{\cdot}3751.}$

## 11·14. Runge-Kutta method for simultaneous first order differential equations

**AIM.** To solve numerically the simultaneous equations $\dfrac{dy}{dx} = f_1\,(x, y, z)$ and $\dfrac{dz}{dx} = f_2\,(x, y, z)$ given the initial conditions $y\,(x_0) = y_0$, $z\,(x_0) = z_0$.

[Here, $x$ is independent variable while $y$ and $z$ are dependent.]

Now, starting from $(x_0, y_0, z_0)$ the increments $\Delta y$ and $\Delta z$ in $y$ and $z$ respectively are given by formulae,

$$k_1 = hf_1\,(x_0, y_0, z_0)$$

$$k_2 = hf_1\left(x_0 + \frac{1}{2}h, y_0 + \frac{1}{2}k_1, z_0 + \frac{1}{2}l_1\right)$$

$$k_3 = hf_1\left(x_0 + \frac{1}{2}h, y_0 + \frac{1}{2}k_2, z_0 + \frac{1}{2}l_2\right)$$

$$k_4 = hf_1\,(x_0 + h, y_0 + k_3, z_0 + l_3)$$

$$\Delta y = \frac{1}{6}(k_1 + 2\,k_2 + 2\,k_3 + k_4) \text{ where } h = \Delta x$$

$$l_1 = hf_2\,(x_0, y_0, z_0)$$

$$l_2 = hf_2\left(x_0 + \frac{1}{2}h, y_0 + \frac{1}{2}k_1, z_0 + \frac{1}{2}l_1\right)$$

$$l_3 = hf_2\left(x_0 + \frac{1}{2}h, y_0 + \frac{1}{2}k_2, z_0 + \frac{1}{2}l_2\right)$$

$$l_4 = hf_2\,(x_0 + h, y_0 + k_3, z_0 + l_3)$$

$$\Delta z = \frac{1}{6}(l_1 + 2l_2 + 2l_3 + l_4)$$

$$y_1 = y_0 + \Delta y \text{ and } z_1 = z_0 + \Delta z.$$

Having got $(x_1, y_1, z_1)$ we get $(x_2, y_2, z_2)$ by repeating the above algorithm once again starting from $(x_1, y_1, z_1)$.

If we consider the *second order Runge-Kutta method*, then

$$k_1 = hf_1\,(x_0, y_0, z_0)$$

$$k_2 = hf_1\left(x_0 + \frac{1}{2}h, y_0 + \frac{1}{2}k_1, z_0 + \frac{1}{2}l_1\right)$$

$$\Delta y = k_2$$

and $$l_1 = hf_2(x_0, y_0, z_0)$$

$$l_2 = hf_2\left(x_0 + \frac{1}{2}h, y_0 + \frac{1}{2}k_1, z_0 + \frac{1}{2}l_1\right)$$

$$\Delta z = l_2$$

Then $x_1 = x_0 + h,\ y_1 = y_0 + \Delta y,\ z_1 = z_0 + \Delta z.$

**Example 6.** *Find* $y(0{\cdot}1), z(0{\cdot}1)$ *from the system of equations,* $\frac{dy}{dx} = x + z, \frac{dz}{dx} = x - y^2$ *given* $y(0) = 2, z(0) = 1$ *using Runge-Kutta method of fourth order.*

**Solution.** Now $\frac{dy}{dx} = x + z, \frac{dz}{dx} = x - y^2$

$\therefore\ f_1(x, y, z) = x + z, f_2(x, y, z) = x - y^2$

$x_0 = 0, y_0 = 2, z_0 = 1, h = 0{\cdot}1$

We use

$$k_1 = hf_1(x_0, y_0, z_0)$$

$$k_2 = hf_1\left(x_0 + \frac{1}{2}h, y_0 + \frac{k_1}{2}, z_0 + \frac{l_1}{2}\right)$$

$$k_3 = hf_1\left(x_0 + \frac{h}{2}, y_0 + \frac{k_2}{2}, z_0 + \frac{l_2}{2}\right)$$

$$k_4 = hf_1(x_0 + h, y_0 + k_3, z_0 + l_3)$$

$$\Delta y = \frac{1}{6}(k_1 + 2k_2 + 2k_3 + k_4)$$

$$l_1 = hf_2(x_0, y_0, z_0)$$

$$l_2 = hf_2\left(x_0 + \frac{1}{2}h, y_0 + \frac{k_1}{2}, z_0 + \frac{1}{2}l_1\right)$$

$$l_3 = hf_3\left(x_0 + \frac{1}{2}h, y_0 + \frac{1}{2}k_2, z_0 + \frac{1}{2}l_2\right)$$

$$l_4 = hf_3(x_0 + h, y_0 + k_3, z_0 + l_3)$$

$$\Delta z = \frac{1}{6}(l_1 + 2l_2 + 2l_3 + l_4)$$

We will calculate $k_i$ and $l_i$ and then to $k_{i+1}$.

$$k_1 = (0{\cdot}1) f_1(0, 2, 1) = (0{\cdot}1)(0 + 1) = 0{\cdot}1$$

$$l_1 = (0{\cdot}1) f_2(0, 2, 1) = (0{\cdot}1)(0 - 2^2) = -0{\cdot}4$$

$$k_2 = (0{\cdot}1) f(0{\cdot}05, 2{\cdot}05, 0{\cdot}8) = (0{\cdot}1)(0{\cdot}05 + 0{\cdot}8) = 0{\cdot}085$$

$$l_2 = (0{\cdot}1) f_2(0{\cdot}05, 2{\cdot}05, 0{\cdot}8) = (0{\cdot}1)[0{\cdot}05 - (2{\cdot}05)^2] = -0{\cdot}41525$$

$$k_3 = (0{\cdot}1) f(0{\cdot}05, 2{\cdot}0425, 0{\cdot}79238) = (0{\cdot}1)(0{\cdot}05 + 0{\cdot}79238) = 0{\cdot}084238$$

$$l_3 = (0{\cdot}1) f(0{\cdot}05, 2{\cdot}0425, 0{\cdot}79238) = (0{\cdot}1)[0{\cdot}05 - (2{\cdot}0425)^2] = -0{\cdot}4122$$

$k_4 = (0{\cdot}1) f(0{\cdot}1, 2{\cdot}084238, 0{\cdot}5878);$ $\quad l_4 = (0{\cdot}1)\,(0{\cdot}1 - (2{\cdot}084238)^2)$

$= (0{\cdot}1)\,(0{\cdot}1 + 0{\cdot}5878)$ $\quad = -\,0{\cdot}4244$

$= 0{\cdot}06878$

$$y_1 = 2 + \frac{1}{6}\,[0{\cdot}1 + 2\,(0{\cdot}085 + 0{\cdot}084238) + 0{\cdot}06878] = 2{\cdot}0845$$

$$z_1 = 1 + \frac{1}{6}\,[-\,0{\cdot}4 - (0{\cdot}41525 + 0{\cdot}4122) \times 2 - 0{\cdot}4244]$$

$$= 0{\cdot}5868$$

**y (0·1) = 2·0845 andz (0·1) = 0·5868.**

## 11·15. Runge-Kutta method for second order differential equation

**AIM.** *To solve* $y'' = f(x, y, y')$, *given* $y(x_0) = y_0,\ y'(x_0) = y_0'$.

Now, set $y' = z$ and $y'' = z'$

Hence, differential equation reduces to

$$\frac{dy}{dx} = y' = z$$

and $$\frac{dz}{dx} = z' = y'' = f(x, y, y') = f(x, y, z)$$

$$\therefore \quad \frac{dy}{dx} = z$$

and $$\frac{dz}{dx} = f(x, y, z)$$

are simultaneous equations where $f_1(x, y, z) = z$, $f_2(x, y, z) = f(x, y, z)$ given. Also $y(0)$ and $z(0)$ are given.

Starting from these equations, we can use the previous article and solve the problem.

**Example 7.** *Given* $y'' + xy' + y = 0,\ y(0) = 1,\ y'(0) = 0$, *find the value of* $y(0{\cdot}1)$ *by using Runge-Kutta method of fourth order.*

**Solution.** $y'' = -\,xy' - y,\ y(0) = 1,\ y'(0) = 0,\ h = 0{\cdot}1,\ y_0 = 1,$

$x_0 = 0,\ y_1 = y(0{\cdot}1)$

Setting $\quad y' = z$

The equation becomes,

$$y'' = z' = -\,xz - y$$

$$\therefore \quad \frac{dy}{dx} = z = f_1(x, y, z) \qquad ...(1)$$

$$\frac{dz}{dx} = -\,xz - y = f_2(x, y, z) \qquad ...(2)$$

given $\quad y_0 = 1,\ z_0 = y_0' = 0.$

By algorithm,

$$k_1 = hf_1(x_0, y_0, z_0) = (0{\cdot}1) f_1(0, 1, 0) = (0{\cdot}1)\,(0) \quad = 0$$

$$l_1 = hf_2(x_0, y_0, z_0) = (0{\cdot}1) f_2(0, 1, 0) = (-\,1)\,(0{\cdot}1) = -\,0{\cdot}1$$

$$k_2 = hf_1\left(x_0 + \frac{1}{2}h, y_0 + \frac{1}{2}k_1, z_0 + \frac{1}{2}l_1\right)$$

$$= (0{\cdot}1)\, f_1\,(0{\cdot}05, 1, -0{\cdot}05) = (0{\cdot}1)\,(-0{\cdot}05) = -0{\cdot}005$$

$$l_2 = (0{\cdot}1)\, f_2\,(0{\cdot}05, 1, -0{\cdot}05) = (0{\cdot}1)\,[+(0{\cdot}05)\,(0{\cdot}05) - 1]$$

$$= -0{\cdot}09975$$

$$k_3 = hf_1\left(x_0 + \frac{h}{2}, y_0 + \frac{1}{2}k_2, z_0 + \frac{1}{2}l_2\right)$$

$$= (0{\cdot}1)\, f_1\,(0{\cdot}05, 0{\cdot}9975, -0{\cdot}0499)$$

$$= (0{\cdot}1)\,(-0{\cdot}0499) = -0{\cdot}00499$$

$$l_3 = hf_2\,(0{\cdot}05, 0{\cdot}9975, -0{\cdot}0499)$$

$$= -(0{\cdot}1)\,[(0{\cdot}05)\,(-0{\cdot}04991) + 0{\cdot}9975]$$

$$= -0{\cdot}09950$$

$$k_4 = hf_1\,(x_0 + h, y_0 + k_3, z_0 + l_3)$$

$$= (0{\cdot}1)\, f_1\,(0{\cdot}1, 0{\cdot}99511, -0{\cdot}0995)$$

$$= (0{\cdot}1)\,(-0{\cdot}0995) = -0{\cdot}00995$$

$$l_4 = hf_2\,(0{\cdot}1, 0{\cdot}99511, -0{\cdot}0995)$$

$$= (0{\cdot}1)\,[-\{(0{\cdot}1)\,(-0{\cdot}0995) + 0{\cdot}99511\}]$$

$$= -0{\cdot}0985$$

$$\therefore \quad y_1 = y_0 + \Delta y = 1 + \frac{1}{6}\,[0 + 2\,(-0{\cdot}005) + 2\,(-0{\cdot}00499) - 0{\cdot}00995]$$

$$= 0{\cdot}9950$$

**y (0·1) = 0·9950.**

## EXERCISE 11.4

*Evaluate using Runge-Kutta methods. Unless otherwise mentioned, use fourth order R.K. method.*

**1.** Find $y\,(0{\cdot}2)$ given $\dfrac{dy}{dx} = y - x$, $y\,(0) = 2$ taking $h = 0{\cdot}1$.

**2.** Evaluate $y\,(1{\cdot}4)$ given $\dfrac{dy}{dx} = x + y$, $y\,(1{\cdot}2) = 2$.

**3.** Obtain the value of $y$ at $x = 0{\cdot}2$ if $y$ satisfies

$\dfrac{dy}{dx} - x^2 y = x$; $y\,(0) = 1$ taking $h = 0{\cdot}1$.

**4.** Solve $\dfrac{dy}{dx} = xy$ for $x = 1{\cdot}4$, taking $y\,(1) = 2$, $h = 0{\cdot}2$.

**5.** Solve: $y' = \dfrac{y - x}{y + x}$ given $y\,(0) = 1$, to obtain $y\,(0{\cdot}2)$.

**6.** Solve the initial value problem

$\frac{du}{dt} = -2tu^2$, $u(0) = 1$ with $h = 0{\cdot}2$ on the interval $(0, 0{\cdot}6)$ by using fourth order R.K. method. *(Nov. 1991)*

**7.** Evaluate for $y(0{\cdot}1), y(0{\cdot}2), y(0{\cdot}3)$ given

$y' = \frac{1}{2}(1+x)y^2, y(0) = 1.$

**8.** Solve: $\frac{dy}{dx} + \frac{y}{x} = \frac{1}{x^2}$, $y(1) = 1$ for $y(1{\cdot}1)$ taking $h = 0{\cdot}05$.

**9.** Find $y(0{\cdot}5), y(1), y(1{\cdot}5), y(2)$ taking $h = 0{\cdot}5$ given $y' = \frac{1}{x+y}$, $y(0) = 1$.

**10.** Evaluate $y(1{\cdot}2)$ and $y(1{\cdot}4)$ given $y' = \frac{2xy + e^x}{x^2 + xe^x}$, $y(1) = 0$. *(MS. Ap. 1989)*

**11.** Find $y$ for $x = 0{\cdot}2\ (0{\cdot}2)\ 0{\cdot}6$ given $\frac{dy}{dx} = 1 + y^2, y(0) = 0.$

**12.** Find $y(0{\cdot}2)$ given $\frac{dy}{dx} = -xy, y(0) = 1$, taking $h = 0{\cdot}2$ by R.K. method of 4th order.

**13.** Find $y(0{\cdot}1), y(0{\cdot}2)$ given $y' = x - 2y, y(0) = 1$ taking $h = 0{\cdot}1$ by (1) second order, third order and fourth order R.K. method.

**14.** Determine $y$ at $x = 0{\cdot}2\ (0{\cdot}2)\ (0{\cdot}6)$ by R.K method given $\frac{dy}{dx} = \frac{1}{1+x}$, given $y(0) = 0$.

**15.** Find $y(0{\cdot}2)$ given

$y' = 3x + \frac{1}{2}y, y(0) = 1$ by using Runge-Kutta method of 4th order.

**16.** Solve $y' = xy + 1$ as $x = 0{\cdot}2, 0{\cdot}4, 0{\cdot}6$ given $y(0) = 2$, taking $h = 0{\cdot}2$.

**17.** Given $y' = x^3 + \frac{1}{2}y, y(1) = 2$, find $y(1{\cdot}1), y(1{\cdot}2)$.

**18.** Solve $10y' = x^2 + y^2$, given $y(0) = 1$ for $x = 0{\cdot}1\ (0{\cdot}1)\ (0{\cdot}3)$.

**19.** Solve $8y' = x + y^2$ given $y(0) = 0{\cdot}5$ for $x = 0{\cdot}1\ (0{\cdot}1)\ (0{\cdot}4)$.

**20.** Solve the system: $\frac{dy}{dx} = xz + 1, \frac{dz}{dx} = -xy$ for $x = 0{\cdot}3\ (0{\cdot}3)\ (0{\cdot}9)$ taking $x = 0$, $y = 0, z = 1$. *(MKU 1979)*

**21.** Solve: $\frac{dy}{dx} = x + z, \frac{dz}{dx} = x - y$, given $y(0) = 0, z(0) = 1$ for $x = 0{\cdot}0$ to $0{\cdot}2$ taking $h = 0{\cdot}1$.

**22.** Solve $\frac{dy}{dx} = -xz, \frac{dz}{dx} = y^2$, given $y(0) = 1, z(0) = 1$ for $x = 0\ (0{\cdot}2)\ (0{\cdot}4)$.

**23.** Evaluate $y(1{\cdot}1), z(1{\cdot}1)$ given $\frac{dy}{dx} = xyz, \frac{dz}{dx} = \frac{xy}{z}$, $y(1) = 1/3, z(1) = 1$.

**24.** Using R.K. method determine $x(0{\cdot}1), y(0{\cdot}1)$ given $\frac{dx}{dt} = xy + t,\ \ x(0) = 1$

$\frac{dy}{dt} = ty + x,\ y(0) = -1.$

**25.** Find $x(0{\cdot}1), y(0{\cdot}1)$ given $\frac{dx}{dt} = 2x + y,\ \frac{dy}{dt} = x - 3y$, given $x(0) = 0, y(0) = 0{\cdot}5$.

**26.** Solve $y'' - x(y')^2 + y^2 = 0$ using R.K. method for $x = 0{\cdot}2$ given $y(0) = 1, y'(0) = 0$, taking $h = 0{\cdot}2$.

**27.** Find $y(0{\cdot}1)$ given $y'' = y^3, y(0) = 10, y'(0) = 5$ by R.K. method.

**28.** Find $y(0{\cdot}1), y(0{\cdot}2)$ given $y'' - x^2y' - 2xy = 1, y(0) = 1, y'(0) = 0$.

**29.** Find $y(0{\cdot}1)$ given $y'' + 2xy' - 4y = 0, y(0) = 0{\cdot}2, y'(0) = 0{\cdot}5$.

**30.** Obtain the value of $x(0{\cdot}1)$ given

$\frac{d^2x}{dt^2} = \frac{tdx}{dt} - 4x,\ x(0) = 3, x'(0) = 0.$

**31.** Compute the value of $y(0{\cdot}2)$ given

$$y'' = -y,\ y(0) = 1,\ y'(0) = 0.$$

## 11·16. Predictor-Corrector methods

The methods which we have discussed so far are called single-step methods because they use only the information from the last step computed. The methods of Milne's predictor-corrector, Adams-Bashforth predictor corrector formulae are multi-step methods.

In solving the equation $\frac{dy}{dx} = f(x, y), y(x_0) = y_0$ we used Euler's formula

$$y_{i+1} = y_i + hf'(x_i, y_i),\ i = 0, 1, 2, \ldots \qquad \ldots(1)$$

We improved this value by Improved Euler method

$$y_{i+1} = y_i + \frac{1}{2} h\,[f(x_i, y_i) + f(x_{i+1}, y_{i+1})\,] \qquad \ldots(2)$$

In the equation (2), to get the value of $y_{i+1}$ we require $y_{i+1}$ on the R.H.S. To overcome this difficulty, we calculate $y_{i+1}$ using Euler's formula (1) and then we use it on the R.H.S. of (2), to get the L.H.S. of (2). This $y_{i+1}$ can be used further to get refined $y_{i+1}$ on the L.H.S. Here, we *predict* a value of $y_{i+1}$ from the rough formula (1) and use in (2) to correct the value. Every time, we improve using (2). Hence equation (1) Euler's formula is a *predictor* and (2) is a corrector. A predictor formula is used to *predict* the value of $y$ at $x_{i+1}$ and a *corrector* formula is used to correct the error and to improve that value of $y_{i+1}$.

## 11·17. Milne's Predictor Corrector Formulae

Suppose our aim is to solve $\frac{dy}{dx} = f(x, y), y(x_0) = y_0 \qquad \ldots(1)$

numerically.

Starting from $y_0 = y(x_0)$, we have to estimate successively

$$y_1 = y(x_0 + h) = y(x_1),\ y_2 = y(x_0 + 2h) = y(x_2),\ y_3 = y(x_0 + 3h) = y(x_3)$$

where $h$ is a suitable accepted spacing, which is very small.

By Newton's forward interpolation formula, we have,

$$y = y_0 + u\,\Delta y_0 + \frac{u(u-1)}{2!}\Delta^2 y_0 + \frac{u(u-1)(u-2)}{3!}\Delta^3 y_0 + \cdots$$

where $u = \dfrac{x - x_0}{h}$, *i.e.*, $x = x_0 = uh$. Changing $y$ to $y'$,

$$y' = y_0' + u\Delta y_0' + \frac{u(u-1)}{2!}\Delta^2 y_0' + \frac{u(u-1)(u-2)}{3!}\Delta^3 y_0' + \cdots \quad ...(2)$$

Integrating both sides from $x_0$ to $x_4$,

$$\int_{x_0}^{x_4} y'\,dx = \int_{x_0}^{x_0+4h}\left(y_0' + u\Delta y_0' + \frac{u(u-1)}{2!}\Delta^2 y_0' + \cdots\right)dx$$

$$(y)_{x_0}^{x_0+4h} = h\int_0^4\left(y_0' + u\,\Delta y_0' + \frac{u(u-1)}{2}\Delta^2 y_0' + \cdots\right)du$$

since $x = x_0 + uh$ and $dx = h\,du$

$$y_4 - y_0 = h\left[y_0' u + \Delta y_0'\frac{u^2}{2} + \frac{1}{2}\Delta^2 y_0'\left(\frac{u^3}{3} - \frac{u^2}{2}\right) + \frac{1}{6}\Delta^3 y_0'\left(\frac{u^4}{4} - u^3 + u^2\right) + \cdots\right]_0^4$$

$$= h\left[4y_0' + 8\,\Delta y_0 + \frac{1}{2}\left(\frac{64}{3} - 8\right)\Delta^2 y_0' + \frac{1}{6}\Delta^3 y_0'(64 - 64 + 16) + \cdots\right]$$

$$= h\left[4y_0' + 8\,\Delta y_0' + \frac{20}{3}\Delta^2 y_0' + \frac{8}{3}\Delta^3 y_0' + \frac{14}{45}\Delta^4 y_0' + \cdots\right]$$

$$= h\left[4y_0' + 8(E-1)\,y_0' + \frac{20}{3}(E-1)^2 y_0' + \frac{8}{3}(E-1)^3 y_0' + \frac{14}{45}\Delta^4 y_0' + \cdots\right]$$

$$= h\left[4y_0' + 8(y_1' - y_0') + \frac{20}{3}(y_2' - 2y_1' + y_0') + \frac{8}{3}(y_3' - 3y_2' + 3y_1' - y_0) + \frac{14}{45}\Delta^4 y_0' + \cdots\right]$$

$$= h\left[\left(4 - 8 + \frac{20}{3} - \frac{8}{3}\right)y_0' + \left(8 - \frac{40}{3} + 8\right)y_1' + \left(\frac{20}{3} - 8\right)y_2' + \frac{8}{3}y_3'\right] + \frac{14h}{45}\Delta^4 y_0' + \cdots$$

$$= h\left[\frac{8}{3}y_1' - \frac{4}{3}y_2' + \frac{8}{3}y_3'\right] + \frac{14\,h}{45}\Delta^4 y_0' + \cdots$$

$$= \frac{4h}{3}(2y_1' - y_2' + 2y_3') + \frac{14\,h}{45}\Delta^4 y_0' + \cdots \qquad \text{...(3)}$$

Taking into account only upto the third order equation, (3) gives (neglecting $\Delta^4 y_0'$ etc...)

$$y_4 = y_0 + \frac{4h}{3}(2y_1' - y_2' + 2y_3') \qquad \text{...(4)}$$

$$= y_0 + \frac{4h}{3}(2f_1 - f_2 + 2f_3)$$

The error committed in (4) is $\frac{14\,h}{45}\Delta^4 y_0' + \cdots$ and this can be proved to be $\frac{14\,h^5}{45}y^{(v)}(\xi)$ where $x_0 < \xi < x_4$ since $\Delta = E - 1 = e^{hD} - 1 = hD$ for small values of $h$.

$\therefore$ The error $= \frac{14\,h^5}{45}y^{(v)}(\xi)$

(3) becomes,

$$y_4 = y_0 + \frac{4h}{3}(2\,y_1' - y_2' + 2\,y_3') + \frac{14\,h^5}{45}y^{(v)}(\xi) \qquad \text{...(5)}$$

In general,

$$\mathbf{y_{n+1} = y_{n-3} + \frac{4h}{3}(2y'_{n-2} - y'_{n-1} + 2\,y_n') + \frac{14\,h^5}{45}y^{(v)}(\xi_1)} \qquad \text{...(6)}$$

where $x_{n-3} < \xi_1 < x_{n+1}$.

**Equation (6) is called *Milne's predictor* formula.**

To get Milne's corrector formula, integrate equation (2) between the limits $x_0$ to $x_0 + 2h$.

Therefore

$$\int_{x_0}^{x_0+2h} y'\,dx = \int_{x_0}^{x_0+2h}\left(y_0' + u\,\Delta y_0' + \frac{u(u-1)}{2}\Delta^2 y_0' + \cdots\right)dx$$

$$y_2 - y_0 = h\int_0^2\left(y_0' + u\,\Delta y_0' + \frac{u^2 - u}{2}\Delta^2 y_0' + \cdots\right)du$$

$$= h\left[y_0'\,u + \frac{u^2}{2}\Delta y_0' + \frac{1}{2}\left(\frac{u^3}{3} - \frac{u^2}{2}\right)\Delta^2 y_0' + \cdots\right]_0^2$$

$$= h\left[2y_0' + 2(E-1)\,y_0' + \frac{1}{2}\left(\frac{8}{3} - 2\right)(E-1)^2 y_0' - \frac{4}{15}\cdot\frac{1}{24}\Delta^4 y_0' + \cdots\right]$$

$$= h\left[ 2y_0' + 2(y_1' - y_0') + \frac{1}{3}(y_2' - 2y_1' + y_0') - \frac{1}{90}\Delta^4 y_0' + \cdots \right]$$

$$= \frac{h}{3}[y_0' + 4y_1' + y_2'] - \frac{h}{90}\Delta^4 y_0' + \cdots \qquad \ldots(7)$$

Taking into account only upto third order,

$$y_2 = y_0 + \frac{h}{3}[y_0' + 4y_1' + y_2'] \qquad \ldots(8)$$

and the error in (8) is $= -\frac{h}{90}\Delta^4 y_0' + \cdots$

and this can be proved to be $= -\frac{h^5}{90} y^{(v)}(\xi)$, where $x_0 < \xi < x_2$.

(7) becomes,

$$y_2 = y_0 + \frac{h}{3}(y_0' + 4y_1' + y_2') - \frac{h^5}{20} y^{(v)}(\xi) \qquad \ldots(9)$$

In general,

$$y_{n+1} = y_{n-1} + \frac{h}{3}(y'_{n-1} + 4y'_n + y'_{n+1}) - \frac{h^5}{90} y^{(v)}(\xi_2) \qquad \ldots(10)$$

where $x_{n-1} < \xi_2 < x_{n+1}$.

Equation (10) is called *Milne's corrector* formula.

Hence we predict from

$$y_{n+1,p} = y_{n-3} + \frac{4h}{3}(2y'_{n-2} - y'_{n-1} + 2y'_n) \qquad \ldots(11)$$

*i.e.,* $$\mathbf{y_{n+1,p} = y_{n-3} + \frac{4h}{3}(2f_{n-2} - f_{n-1} + 2f_n)}$$

and correct using

$$y_{n+1,c} = y_{n-1} + \frac{h}{3}(y'_{n-1} + 4y'_n + y'_{n+1}) \qquad \ldots(12)$$

*i.e.,* $$\mathbf{y_{n+1,c} = y_{n-1} + \frac{h}{3}(f_{n-1} + 4f_n + f_{n+1})}$$

**Note:** Knowing 4 consecutive values of $y$ namely, $y_{n-3}, y_{n-2}, y_{n-1}$ and $y_n$ we calculate $y_{n+1}$ using predictor formula. Use this $y_{n+1}$ on the R.H.S. of corrector formula to get $y_{n+1}$ after correction. To refine the value further, we can use this latest $y_{n+1}$ on the R.H.S. of (12) and get a better $y_{n+1}$.

**Example 1.** *Find y (2) if y (x) is the solution of* $\frac{dy}{dx} = \frac{1}{2}(x + y)$ *given y (0) = 2, y (0·5) = 2·636, y (1) = 3·595 and y (1·5) = 4·968.*

**Solution.** Here, $x_0 = 0, x_1 = 0{\cdot}5, x_2 = 1{\cdot}0, x_3 = 1{\cdot}5, x_4 = 2{\cdot}0, \quad h = 0{\cdot}5,$ $y_0 = 2, y_1 = 2{\cdot}636, y_2 = 3{\cdot}595, y_3 = 4{\cdot}968.$

$$f(x, y) = \frac{1}{2}(x + y) = y' \qquad ...(1)$$

By Milne's predictor formula,

$$y_{n+1, p} = y_{n-3} + \frac{4h}{3}(2y'_{n-2} - y'_{n-1} + 2y'_n)$$

$$\therefore \quad y_{4, p} = y_0 + \frac{4h}{3}(2y_1' - y_2' + 2y_3') \qquad ...(2)$$

From (1),

$$y_1' = \frac{1}{2}(x_1 + y_1) = \frac{1}{2}(0.5 + 2.636) = 1.5680$$

$$y_2' = \frac{1}{2}(x_2 + y_2) = \frac{1}{2}(1 + 3.595) = 2.2975$$

$$y_3' = \frac{1}{2}(x_3 + y_3) = \frac{1}{2}(1.5 + 4.968) = 3.2340$$

By (2),

$$y_{4, p} = 2 + \frac{4(0.5)}{3}[2(1.5680) - (2.2975) + 2(3.2340)]$$

$$= 6.8710$$

Using Milne's corrector formula,

$$y_{n+1, c} = y_{n-1} + \frac{h}{3}(y'_{n-1} + 4y'_n + y'_{n+1})$$

*i.e.,*

$$y_{4, c} = y_2 + \frac{h}{3}(y_2' + 4y_3' + y_4') \qquad ...(3)$$

$$y_4' = \frac{1}{2}(x_4 + y_4) = \frac{1}{2}(2 + 6.8710) = 4.4355$$

Using (3), we get

$$y_{4, c} = 3.595 + \frac{0.5}{3}[2.2975 + 4(3.2340) + 4.4355]$$

$$= 6.8732$$

$\therefore$ Corrected value of $y$ at $x = 2$ is **6.8732.**

**Example 2.** *Using Milne's method find $y(4.4)$ given $5xy' + y^2 - 2 = 0$ given $y(4) = 1$, $y(4.1) = 1.0049$, $y(4.2) = 1.0097$ and $y(4.3) = 1.0143$.*

*(Anna Nov. 2004)*

**Solution.** $y' = \frac{2 - y^2}{5x}$, $x_0 = 4$, $x_1 = 4.1$, $x_2 = 4.2$, $x_3 = 4.3$

$x_4 = 4.4$, $y_0 = 1$, $y_1 = 1.0049$, $y_2 = 1.0097$, $y_3 = 1.0143.$

$$y_1' = \frac{2 - y_1^2}{5x_1} = \frac{2 - (1.0049)^2}{5(4.1)} = 0.0493$$

$$y_2' = \frac{2-y_2^2}{5x_2} = \frac{2-(1{\cdot}0097)^2}{5\ (4{\cdot}2)} = 0{\cdot}0467$$

$$y_3^2 = \frac{2-y_3^2}{5x_3} = \frac{2-(1{\cdot}0143)^2}{5\ (4{\cdot}3)} = 0{\cdot}0452$$

By Milne's predictor formula,

$$y_{4,\,p} = y_0 + \frac{4h}{3}\ (2y_1' - y_2' + 2y_3') \qquad ...(1)$$

$$= 1 + \frac{4\ (0{\cdot}1)}{3}\ [2\ (0{\cdot}0493) - 0{\cdot}0467 + 2\ (0{\cdot}0452)\ ]$$

$$= 1{\cdot}01897$$

$$y_4' = \frac{2-y_4^2}{5\ (x_4)} = \frac{2-(1{\cdot}01897)^2}{5\ (4{\cdot}4)} = 0{\cdot}0437$$

using

$$y_{4,\,c} = y_2 + \frac{h}{3}\left(y_2' + 4y_3' + y_4'\right) \qquad ...(2)$$

$$= 1{\cdot}0097 + \frac{0{\cdot}1}{3}\ [0{\cdot}0467 + 4\ (0{\cdot}0452) + 0{\cdot}0437]$$

$$y_{4,\,c} = \mathbf{1{\cdot}01874}.$$

**Note:** Use this corrected $y_{4,\,c}$ and find $y'_{4,\,c}$ and again use (2)

$$y'_{4,\,c} = \frac{2-y_4^2}{5\ (x_4)} = \frac{2-(1{\cdot}01874)^2}{5\ (4{\cdot}4)} = 0{\cdot}043735$$

Now using (2),

$$y_{4,\,c}^{(2)} = 1{\cdot}0097 + \frac{0{\cdot}1}{3}\ [0{\cdot}0467 + 4\ (0{\cdot}0452) + 0{\cdot}043735]$$

$$= 1{\cdot}01874$$

Since two consecutive values of $y_{4,\,c}$ are equal, we take $y_4 = 1{\cdot}01874$ (correct to 5 decimals).

**Example 3.** *Determine the value of* $y\,(0{\cdot}4)$ *using Milne's method given* $y' = xy + y^2,\ y\,(0) = 1$; *use Taylor series to get the values of* $y\,(0{\cdot}1),\ y\,(0{\cdot}2)$ *and* $y\,(0{\cdot}3)$. *(MS. Ap. 1989)*

**Solution.** Here $x_0 = 0,\ y_0 = 1,\ x_1 = 0{\cdot}1,\ x_2 = 0{\cdot}2,\ x_3 = 0{\cdot}3,\ x_4 = 0{\cdot}4$

$$y' = xy + y^2$$

$$y'' = xy' + y + 2yy'$$

$$y''' = xy'' + y' + y' + 2yy'' + 2\ (y')^2$$

$$= xy'' + 2y' + 2yy'' + 2\ (y')^2$$

$$y_0' = x_0y_0 + y_0^2 = 1$$

$$y_0'' = x_0y_0' + y_0 + 2y_0\ y_0' = 3$$

$$y_0''' = x_0y_0'' + 2y_0' + 2y_0\ y_0'' + 2\ (y_0')^2$$

$$= 10$$

$$y_1 = y_0 + hy_0' + \frac{h^2}{2}\ y_0'' + \frac{h^3}{3!}\ y_0''' + \cdots$$

$$= 1 + (0{\cdot}1)\,(1) + \frac{0{\cdot}01}{2}\,(3) + \frac{0{\cdot}001}{6} \times 10 + \cdots$$

$$= 1 + 0{\cdot}1 + 0{\cdot}015 + 0{\cdot}001666$$

$$= 1{\cdot}1167$$

$y\,(0{\cdot}1) = \mathbf{1{\cdot}1167}$.

$$y_1' = x_1y_1 + y_1^2 = (0{\cdot}1)\,(1{\cdot}1167) + (1{\cdot}1167)^2 = 1{\cdot}3587$$

$$y_1'' = x_1y_1' + y_1 + 2y_1y_1' = (0{\cdot}1)\,(1{\cdot}3587) + 1{\cdot}1167 + 2\,(1{\cdot}1167)\,(1{\cdot}3587)$$

$$= 4{\cdot}2871$$

$$y_1''' = x_1y_1'' + 2y_1' + 2y_1y_1'' + 2\,(y_1')^2$$

$$= 16{\cdot}4131$$

$$\therefore \quad y_2 = y_1 + hy_1' + \frac{h^2}{2}\,y_1'' + \frac{h^3}{6}\,y_1''' + \cdots$$

$$= 1{\cdot}1167 + \frac{0{\cdot}1}{1}\,(1{\cdot}3587) + \frac{{\cdot}01}{2}\,(4{\cdot}2871) + \frac{0{\cdot}001}{6}\,(16{\cdot}4131)$$

$\mathbf{y\,(0{\cdot}2) = 1{\cdot}2767}$

$$y_2' = x_2y_2 + y_2^2 = (0{\cdot}2)\,(1{\cdot}2767) + (1{\cdot}2767)^2 = 1{\cdot}8853$$

$$y_2'' = x_2y_2' + y_2 + 2y_2y_2' = (0{\cdot}2)\,(1{\cdot}8853) + 1{\cdot}2767 + 2\,(1{\cdot}2767)\,(1{\cdot}8853)$$

$$= 6{\cdot}4677$$

$$y_2''' = x_2y_2'' + 2y_2' + 2\,[y_2y_2'' + (y_2')^2] = 28{\cdot}6875$$

$$y_3 = y_2 + hy_2' + \frac{h^2}{2}\,y_2'' + \frac{h^3}{6}\,y_2''' + \cdots$$

$$= 1{\cdot}2767 + (0{\cdot}1)\,(1{\cdot}8853) + \frac{0{\cdot}01}{2}\,(6{\cdot}4677) + \frac{0{\cdot}001}{6}\,(28{\cdot}6875)$$

$$= 1{\cdot}5023$$

$y\,(0{\cdot}3) = \mathbf{1{\cdot}5023}$.

Now, knowing $y_0, y_1, y_2, y_3$ we will find $y_4$.

By Milne's predictor formula,

$$y_{4,\,p} = y_0 + \frac{4h}{3}\,[2y_1' - y_2' + 2y_3'] \qquad \ldots(1)$$

$$y_1' = x_1y_1 + y_1^2 = (0{\cdot}1)\,(1{\cdot}1167) + (1{\cdot}1167)^2 = \mathbf{1{\cdot}3587}$$

$$y_2' = x_2y_2 + y_2^2 = (0{\cdot}2)\,(1{\cdot}2767) + (1{\cdot}2767)^2 = \mathbf{1{\cdot}8853}$$

$$y_3' = x_3y_3 + y_3^2 = (0{\cdot}3)\,(1{\cdot}5023) + (1{\cdot}5023)^2 = \mathbf{2{\cdot}7076}$$

Using (1),

$$y_{4,\,p} = 1 + \frac{4\,(0{\cdot}1)}{3}\,[2\,(1{\cdot}3587) - 1{\cdot}8853 + 2\,(2{\cdot}7076)]$$

$$= \mathbf{1{\cdot}83297}$$

Now $\quad y'_{4,\,p} = x_4y_4 + y_4^2 = (0{\cdot}4)\,(1{\cdot}83297) + (1{\cdot}83297)^2 = \mathbf{4{\cdot}09296}$

Using, Milne's corrector formula,

$$y_{4,c} = y_2 + \frac{h}{3}[y_2' + 4y_3' + y'_{4,p}] \quad ...(2)$$

$$= 1{\cdot}2767 + \frac{0{\cdot}1}{3}[1{\cdot}8853 + 4\,(2{\cdot}7076) + 4{\cdot}09296]$$

$$= 1{\cdot}83698$$

$\therefore$ **y (0·4) = 1·83698**.

**Note:** We can use this $y$ (0·4) on the R.H.S. of (2) and get an improved value of $y_4$.

**Example 4.** *Given* $\frac{dy}{dx} = \frac{1}{2}(1+x^2)y^2$ *and* $y\,(0) = 1, y\,(0{\cdot}1) = 1{\cdot}06, y\,(0{\cdot}2) = 1{\cdot}12, y\,(0{\cdot}3) = 1{\cdot}21$, *evaluate* $y\,(0{\cdot}4)$ *by Milne's predictor corrector method.* *(Nov. 1991)*

**Solution.** $x_0 = 0, x_1 = 0{\cdot}1, x_2 = 0{\cdot}2, x_3 = 0{\cdot}3, x_4 = 0{\cdot}4$

$y_0 = 1, y_1 = 1{\cdot}06, y_2 = 1{\cdot}12, y_3 = 1{\cdot}21, h = 0{\cdot}1$

$$y' = f(x, y) = \frac{1}{2}(1+x^2)\,y^2$$

$$y_0' = \frac{1}{2}\left(1 + x_0^2\right)y_0^2 = \frac{1}{2}(1+0)\,1 = 1/2$$

$$y_1' = \frac{1}{2}\left(1 + x_1^2\right)y_1^2 = \frac{1}{2}[1 + (0{\cdot}1)^2]\,[1{\cdot}06]^2 = 0{\cdot}5674$$

$$y_2' = \frac{1}{2}\left(1 + x_2^2\right)y_2^2 = \frac{1}{2}[1 + (0{\cdot}2)^2]\,[1{\cdot}12]^2 = 0{\cdot}6522$$

$$y_3' = \frac{1}{2}\left(1 + x_3^2\right)\left(y_3^2\right) = \frac{1}{2}[1 + (0{\cdot}3)^2]\,(1{\cdot}21)^2 = 0{\cdot}7979$$

By Milne's method,

$$y_{4,p} = y_0 + \frac{4h}{3}\left[2y_1' - y_2' + 2y_3'\right]$$

$$= 1 + \frac{4\,(0{\cdot}1)}{3}[2\,(0{\cdot}5674) - 0{\cdot}6522 + 2\,(0{\cdot}7979)]$$

$$= \mathbf{1{\cdot}2771}$$

$$y_4' = \frac{1}{2}[1 + (x_4)^2]\,(y_4^2)$$

$$= \frac{1}{2}[1 + 0{\cdot}16]\,[1{\cdot}2771]^2 = \mathbf{0{\cdot}9460}$$

By corrector method,

$$y_{4,c1} = y_2 + \frac{h}{3}\left[y_2' + 4y_3' + y'_{4,p}\right] \quad ...(2)$$

$$= 1{\cdot}12 + \frac{0{\cdot}1}{3}[0{\cdot}6522 + 4\,(0{\cdot}7979) + 0{\cdot}9460]$$

$= \mathbf{1{\cdot}2797}$

Now use this on the R.H.S. of (2) and get $y_{4,c}$.

$$y'_{4,c1} = \frac{1}{2}[1 + 0{\cdot}16](1{\cdot}2797)^2 = 0{\cdot}9498$$

Again using (2),

$$y_{4,c2} = 1{\cdot}12 + \frac{0{\cdot}1}{3}[0{\cdot}6522 + 4(0{\cdot}7979) + 0{\cdot}9498] = 1{\cdot}2798$$

$\therefore \quad y(0{\cdot}4) = 1{\cdot}2798.$

**Example 5.** *Given $y' = 1 - y$, and $y(0) = 0$, find*

(*i*) *$y(0{\cdot}1)$ by Euler method Using that value obtain.*

(*ii*) *$y(0{\cdot}2)$ by modified Euler method.*

(*iii*) *Obtain $y(0{\cdot}3)$ by improved Euler method and find*

(*iv*) *$y(0{\cdot}4)$ by Milne's method.*

**Solution.** By **Euler method,**

$$y_1 = y_0 + hf(x_0, y_0) = 0 + (0{\cdot}1)(1 - y_0) = \mathbf{0{\cdot}1}$$

**By modified Euler method:**

$$y_2 = y_1 + hf\left(x_1 + \frac{1}{2}h, y_1 + \frac{1}{2}hf(x_1, y_1)\right)$$

$$= 0{\cdot}1 + (0{\cdot}1)\left[1 - \left(y_1 + \frac{1}{2}hf(x_1, y_1)\right)\right]$$

$$= (0{\cdot}1) + (0{\cdot}1)\left[1 - \left(0{\cdot}1 + \frac{0{\cdot}1}{2}(1 - 0{\cdot}1)\right)\right]$$

$$= \mathbf{0{\cdot}1855}$$

**By improved Euler method:**

$$y_3 = y_2 + \frac{1}{2}h[f(x_2, y_2) + f(x_3, y_2 + hf(x_2, y_2))]$$

$$= 0{\cdot}1855 + \frac{0{\cdot}1}{2}[1 - y_2 + 1 - y_2 - hf(x_2, y_2)]$$

$$= 0{\cdot}1855 + \frac{0{\cdot}1}{2}[2 - 2y_2 - h(1 - y_2)]$$

$$= 0{\cdot}1855 + \frac{0{\cdot}1}{2}(1 - y_2)(2 - h)$$

$$= \mathbf{0{\cdot}2629}$$

Now knowing $y_0, y_1, y_2, y_3$, we will find $y_4$.

**By Milne's method:**

$$y_{4,p} = y_0 + \frac{4h}{3}\left[2y_1' - y_2' + 2y_3'\right]$$

$$= 0 + \frac{4\,(0{\cdot}1)}{3}\,[2\,(1 - y_1) - (1 - y_2) + 2\,(1 - y_3)]$$

$$= \frac{0{\cdot}4}{3}\,[3 - 2y_1 + y_2 - 2y_3]$$

$$= \frac{0{\cdot}4}{3}\,[3 - 2\,(0{\cdot}1) + (0{\cdot}1855) - 2\,(0{\cdot}2629)\,]$$

$$= \mathbf{0{\cdot}3280}$$

$$y_4{}' = 1 - y_4 = 1 - 0{\cdot}3280 = 0{\cdot}6720$$

$$y_{4,\,c} = y_2 + \frac{h}{3}\left( y_2{}' + 4y_3{}' + y'_{4,\,p} \right)$$

$$= 0{\cdot}1855 + \frac{0{\cdot}1}{3}\,[1 - y_2 + 4\,(1 - y_3) + 1 - y_{4,\,p}]$$

$$= 0{\cdot}1855 + \frac{0{\cdot}1}{3}\,[6 - y_2 - 4y_3 - y_{4,\,p}]$$

$$\mathbf{y\,(0{\cdot}4) = 0{\cdot}3333.}$$

## 11·18. Adam-Bashforth (or Adam's) predictor-corrector method

We state below another *predictor-corrector method,* called *Adam's* method or *Adam-Bashforth* method. We give below predictor and corrector formula without proof. Here also, we require four continuous values of $y$ to find the value of $y$ at the fifth point similar to Milne's method.

$$\textit{Predictor:}\ y_{n+1,\,p} = y_n + \frac{h}{24}\left[\,55y_n{}' - 59y'_{n-1} + 37\,y'_{n-2} - 9y'_{n-3}\right]$$

$$\textit{Corrector:}\ y_{n+1,\,c} = y_n + \frac{h}{24}\left[\,9y'_{n+1} + 19y'_n - 5y'_{n-1} + y'_{n-2}\right]$$

**Example 6.** *Solve and get* $y\,(2)$ *given* $\dfrac{dy}{dx} = \dfrac{1}{2}\,(x + y),\ y\,(0) = 2$ $y\,(0{\cdot}5) = 2{\cdot}636,\ y\,(1) = 3{\cdot}595,\ y\,(1{\cdot}5) = 4{\cdot}968$ *by Adam's method.*

**Solution.** From Example 1 under Milne's method,

we have $y_0{}' = \frac{1}{2}\,(0 + 2) = 1$

$$y_1{}' = 1{\cdot}5680,\ y_2{}' = 2{\cdot}2975,\ y_3{}' = 3{\cdot}2340.$$

By Adam's predictor formula,

$$y_{n+1,\,p} = y_n + \frac{h}{24}\left[\,55y'_n - 59y'_{n-1} + 37y'_{n-2} - 9y'_{n-3}\right]$$

$$\therefore\ \ y_{4,\,p} = y_3 + \frac{h}{24}\left[\,55y'_3 - 59y'_2 + 37y'_1 - 9y'_0\right] \quad ...(1)$$

$$= 4{\cdot}968 + \frac{0{\cdot}5}{24}\,[55\,(3{\cdot}2340) - 59\,(2{\cdot}2975) + 37\,(1{\cdot}5680) - 9\,(1)\,]$$

$$= 6{\cdot}8708$$

$$y_4' = \frac{1}{2}(x_4 + y_4) = \frac{1}{2}(2 + 6\cdot8708) = 4\cdot4354$$

By corrector,

$$y_{4,c} = y_3 + \frac{h}{24}\left[9y_4' + 19y_3' - 5y_2' + y_1'\right] \qquad ...(2)$$

$$= 4\cdot968 + \frac{0\cdot5}{24}[9(4\cdot4354) + 19(3\cdot234) - 5(2\cdot2975) + 1\cdot5680]$$

$$= 6\cdot8731.$$

**Note:** We can further improve using this latest $y_{4,c}$ again in (2).

**Example 7.** *Using Adam's method find y (0·4) given*

$$\frac{dy}{dx} = \frac{1}{2}xy,\ y(0) = 1,\ y(0\cdot1) = 1\cdot01,\ y(0\cdot2) = 1\cdot022,\ y(0\cdot3) = 1\cdot023.$$

(*MS. 1992*)

**Solution.** $x_0 = 0, x_1 = 0\cdot1, x_2 = 0\cdot2, x_3 = 0\cdot3, x_4 = 0\cdot4$

$$y_0 = 1, y_1 = 1\cdot01, y_2 = 1\cdot022, y_3 = 1\cdot023, y_4 = ?$$

By Adam's method,

Predictor: $y_{n+1,p} = y_n + \frac{h}{24}\left[55y_n' - 59y_{n-1}' + 37y_{n-2}' - 9y_{n-3}'\right]$

$$\therefore \quad y_{4,p} = y_3 + \frac{h}{24}\left[55y_3' - 59y_2' + 37y_1' - 9y_0'\right] \qquad ...(1)$$

Here $y_0' = \frac{1}{2}x_0y_0 = 0$

$$y_1' = \frac{1}{2}x_1y_1 = \frac{(0\cdot1)(1\cdot01)}{2} = 0\cdot0505$$

$$y_2' = \frac{1}{2}x_2y_2 = \frac{(0\cdot2)(1\cdot022)}{2} = 0\cdot1022$$

$$y_3' = \frac{1}{2}x_3y_3 = \frac{(0\cdot3)(1\cdot023)}{2} = 0\cdot1535$$

Using in (1),

$$y_{4,p} = 1\cdot023 + \frac{0\cdot1}{24}[55(0\cdot1535) - 59(0\cdot1022) + 37(0\cdot0505) - 9(0)]$$

$$= \mathbf{1\cdot0408}$$

$$y_{4,p}' = \frac{1}{2}x_4y_4 = \frac{1}{2}(0\cdot4)(1\cdot0408) = 0\cdot20816.$$

By Adam's corrector formula

$$y_{n+1,c} = y_n + \frac{h}{24}\left[9y_{n+1}' + 19y_n' - 5y_{n-1}' + y_{n-2}'\right]$$

$$y_{4,c} = y_3 + \frac{h}{24}[9y_4' + 19y_3' - 5y_2' + y_1']$$

$$= 1{\cdot}023 + \frac{0{\cdot}1}{24} [9\,(0{\cdot}2082) + 19\,(0{\cdot}1535) - 5\,(0{\cdot}1022) + 0{\cdot}0505]$$

$$= \mathbf{1{\cdot}0410}$$

$y\,(0{\cdot}4) = y_{4,\,c} = \mathbf{1{\cdot}0410}$.

**Example 8.** *Find y (0·1), y (0·2), y (0·3) from* $\frac{dy}{dx} = xy + y^2$, $y\,(0) = 1$ *by using Runge-Kutta method and hence obtain y (0·4) using Adam's method.*

**Solution.** $f(x, y) = xy + y^2$, $x_0 = 0$, $x_1 = 0{\cdot}1$, $x_2 = 0{\cdot}2$, $x_3 = 0{\cdot}4$, $x_4 = 0{\cdot}4$, $y_0 = 1$,

$$k_1 = hf(x_0, y_0) = (0{\cdot}1)\, f(0, 1) = (0{\cdot}1)\, 1 = 0{\cdot}1$$

$$k_2 = hf\left(0{\cdot}05, y_0 + \frac{k_1}{2}\right) = (0{\cdot}1)\, f(0{\cdot}05, 1{\cdot}05)$$

$$= (0{\cdot}1)\, [(0{\cdot}05)\,(1{\cdot}05) + (1{\cdot}05)^2] = 0{\cdot}1155$$

$$k_3 = hf\left(0{\cdot}05, y_0 + \frac{k_2}{2}\right) = (0{\cdot}1)\, f(0{\cdot}05, 1{\cdot}0578)$$

$$= (0{\cdot}1)\, [(0{\cdot}05)\,(1{\cdot}0578) + (1{\cdot}0578)^2\,]$$

$$= 0{\cdot}1172$$

$$k_4 = hf(x_0 + h, y_0 + k_3)$$

$$= (0{\cdot}1)\, f(0{\cdot}1, 1{\cdot}1172)$$

$$= (0{\cdot}1)\, [(0{\cdot}1)\,(1{\cdot}1172) + (1{\cdot}1172)^2\,] = 0{\cdot}13598$$

$$y_1 = y_0 + \frac{1}{6}\, [k_1 + 2k_2 + 2k_3 + k_4]$$

$$= 1{\cdot}1169$$

**y (0·1) = 1·1169**.

*Again, start from* $y_1$ :

$$k_1 = hf(x_1, y_1) = (0{\cdot}1)\, f(0{\cdot}1, 1{\cdot}1169)$$

$$= 0{\cdot}1359$$

$$k_2 = hf\left(x_1 + \frac{h}{2}, y_1 + \frac{k_1}{2}\right) = (0{\cdot}1)\, f(0{\cdot}15, 1{\cdot}1849)$$

$$= 0{\cdot}1582$$

$$k_3 = hf\left(0{\cdot}15, y_1 + \frac{k_3}{2}\right) = (0{\cdot}1)\, f(0{\cdot}15, 1{\cdot}196)$$

$$= 0{\cdot}16098$$

$$k_4 = (0{\cdot}1)\, f(0{\cdot}2, 1{\cdot}2779) = 0{\cdot}1889$$

$$y_2 = 1{\cdot}1169 + \frac{1}{6}\, [0{\cdot}1359 + 2\,(0{\cdot}1582 + 0{\cdot}16098) + 0{\cdot}1889]$$

**y (0·2) = 1·2774.**

*Start from* $(x_2, y_2)$ *to get* $y_3$ :

$$k_1 = hf(x_2, y_2) = (0{\cdot}1)\, f(0{\cdot}2,\ 1{\cdot}2774) = \mathbf{0{\cdot}1887}$$

$$k_2 = hf\left(x_2 + \frac{h}{2}, y_2 + \frac{k_1}{2}\right) = (0{\cdot}1)\, f(0{\cdot}25,\ 1{\cdot}3718)$$

$$= \mathbf{0{\cdot}2225}$$

$$k_3 = hf\left(x_2 + \frac{h}{2}, y_2 + \frac{k_2}{2}\right) = (0{\cdot}1)\, f(0{\cdot}25,\ 1{\cdot}3887)$$

$$= \mathbf{0{\cdot}2274}$$

$$k_4 = hf\left(x_3, y_2 + \frac{k_3}{2}\right) = (0{\cdot}1)\, f(0{\cdot}3,\ 1{\cdot}5048)$$

$$= \mathbf{0{\cdot}2716}$$

$$y_3 = 1{\cdot}2774 + \frac{1}{6}[0{\cdot}1887 + 2\,(0{\cdot}2225) + 2\,(0{\cdot}2274) + 0{\cdot}2716]$$

$$= \mathbf{1{\cdot}5041}$$

Now we use Adam's predictor formula.

$$y_{4,\,p} = y_3 + \frac{h}{24}\left[\,55y_3' - 59y_2' + 37y_1' - 9y_0'\,\right] \qquad ...(2)$$

$$y_0' = x_0y_0 + y_0^2 = \mathbf{1}$$

$$y_1' = x_1y_1 + y_1^2 = \mathbf{1{\cdot}3592}$$

$$y_2' = x_2y_2 + y_2^2 = \mathbf{1{\cdot}8872}$$

$$y_3' = x_3y_3 + y_3^2 = \mathbf{2{\cdot}7135}$$

Using (2),

$$y_{4,\,p} = 1{\cdot}5041 + \frac{0{\cdot}1}{2}[55\,(2{\cdot}7135) - 59\,(1{\cdot}8872) + 37\,(1{\cdot}3592) - 9\,(1)\,]$$

$$= \mathbf{1{\cdot}8341}$$

$$y'_{4,\,p} = x_4y_4 + y_4^2 = (0{\cdot}4)\,(1{\cdot}8341) + (1{\cdot}8341)^2 = \mathbf{4{\cdot}0976}$$

$$y_{4,\,c} = y_3 + \frac{h}{24}\left[\,9y_4' + 19y_3' - 5y_2' + y_1'\,\right]$$

$$= 1{\cdot}5041 + \frac{0{\cdot}1}{24}[9\,(4{\cdot}0976) + 19\,(2{\cdot}7135) - 5\,(1{\cdot}8872) + 1{\cdot}3592]$$

$$= \mathbf{1{\cdot}8389}$$

$$\mathbf{y\,(0{\cdot}4) = 1{\cdot}8389.}$$

**Example 9.** *Obtain* $y\,(0{\cdot}6)$ *given* $\frac{dy}{dx} = x + y,\ y\,(0) = 1$ *with* $h = 0{\cdot}2$ *by Adam's method.*

**Solution.** $y' = x + y;\ f(x, y) = x + y$

$$x_0 = 0,\ x_1 = 0{\cdot}2,\ x_2 = 0{\cdot}4,\ x_3 = 0{\cdot}6,\ y_1 = 1$$

We require $y\,(0{\cdot}6)$.

We find $y_2, y_1, y_{-1}$ so that $y_3$ can be found out.

$$y' = x + y \qquad y_0' = 1,\ y_0'' = 2,\ y_0''' = 2$$

$$y'' = 1 + y'$$

$$y''' = y''$$

$$y^{iv} = y'''$$

$$y_1 = y_0 + hy_0' + \frac{h^2}{2} y_0'' + \frac{h^3}{6} y_0''' + \cdots$$

$$y_1 \text{ (at } x = 0{\cdot}2) = 1 + (0{\cdot}2)\,1 + \frac{(0{\cdot}2)^2}{2}(2) + \frac{(0{\cdot}2)^3}{6}(2) + \cdots$$

$$= 1{\cdot}2427$$

$$y_1' = 1{\cdot}4427,\ y_1'' = 2{\cdot}4427,\ y_1''' = 2{\cdot}4427$$

$$y_2 = 1{\cdot}2427 + (0{\cdot}2)\,(1{\cdot}4427) + \frac{(0{\cdot}2)^2}{2}(2{\cdot}4427) + \frac{(0{\cdot}2)^3}{6}(2{\cdot}4427) + \cdots$$

$$= 1{\cdot}5834$$

$$y_{-1} = y_0 - (0{\cdot}2)\,y_0' + \frac{(0{\cdot}2)^2}{2} y_0'' - \frac{(0{\cdot}2)^3}{6} y_0''' + \cdots$$

$$= 0{\cdot}8373$$

$$y'_{-1} = x_{-1} + y_{-1} = (-\,0{\cdot}2) + (0{\cdot}8373) = 0{\cdot}6373$$

$$y_0' = x_0 + y_0 = 1$$

$$y_1' = x_1 + y_1 = 1{\cdot}4427$$

$$y_2' = x_2 + y_2 = 1{\cdot}9834$$

$$y_{3,p} = 1{\cdot}5834 + \frac{0{\cdot}2}{24}\,[55\,(1{\cdot}9834) - 59\,(1{\cdot}4427) + 37\,(1) - 9\,(0{\cdot}6373)\,]$$

$$= 2{\cdot}0437$$

$$y'_{3,p} = x_3 + y_{3,p} = 2{\cdot}6437$$

$$y_{3,c} = 1{\cdot}5834 + \frac{0{\cdot}2}{24}\,[9\,(2{\cdot}6437) + 19\,(1{\cdot}9834) - 5\,(1{\cdot}14427) + 1]$$

$$= 2{\cdot}0439$$

$$\mathbf{y\,(0{\cdot}6) = 2{\cdot}0439.}$$

## EXERCISE 11.5

1. Using Milne's method, find $y\,(0{\cdot}2)$ given
   $\frac{dy}{dx} = (0{\cdot}2)\,x + (0{\cdot}1)\,y,\ y\,(0) = 2,\ y\,(0{\cdot}05) = 2{\cdot}0103,\ \ y\,(0{\cdot}1) = 2{\cdot}0211,$
   $y\,(0{\cdot}15) = 2{\cdot}0323.$
2. Find $y\,(0{\cdot}8)$ given $y' = y - x^2,\ y\,(0) = 1,\ y\,(0{\cdot}2) = 1{\cdot}12186,\ y\,(0{\cdot}4) = 1{\cdot}46820,$

$y(0{\cdot}6) = 1{\cdot}73790.$

**3.** Using Runge-Kutta method of fourth order find $y$ at $x = 0{\cdot}1, 0{\cdot}2, 0{\cdot}3$ given $y' = xy + y^2, y(0) = 1$. Continue your work to get $y(0{\cdot}4)$ by Milne's method.

**4.** Solve $y' = \frac{1}{2}(1 + x)\, y^2, y(0) = 1$ by Taylor series method at $x = 0{\cdot}2, 0{\cdot}4, 0{\cdot}6$ and hence find $y(0{\cdot}8)$ and $y(1)$ by Milne's method.

**5.** Given $y' = x^2 - y, y(0) = 1, y(0{\cdot}1) = 0{\cdot}9052, y(0{\cdot}2) = 0{\cdot}8213$, find $y(0{\cdot}3)$ by Taylor series. Also find $y(0{\cdot}4)$ and $y(0{\cdot}5)$ by Milne's method. *(Nov. 1991)*

**6.** If $\frac{dy}{dx} = 2e^x - y, y(0) = 2, y(0{\cdot}1) = 2{\cdot}010, y(0{\cdot}2) = 2{\cdot}040, y(0{\cdot}3) = 2{\cdot}090$, find $y(0{\cdot}4)$ and $y(0{\cdot}5)$ by Milne's method.

**7.** Given $y' = 1 + y^2, y(0) = 0, y(0{\cdot}2) = 0{\cdot}2027, y(0{\cdot}4) = 0{\cdot}4228, y(0{\cdot}6) = 0{\cdot}6841$, estimate $y(0{\cdot}8), y(1)$ using Milne's method upto three decimals.

**8.** Solve $y' = x - y^2, y(0) = 1$ to obtain $y(0{\cdot}4)$ by Milne's method. Obtain the data you require by any method of your liking.

**9.** Do the worked examples 1 to 5 by Adam's method and 6 to 9 by Milne's method.

**10.** Using both predictor-corrector methods, estimate $y(1{\cdot}4)$ if $y$ satisfies $\frac{dy}{dx} + \frac{y}{x} = \frac{1}{x^2}$, and $y(1) = 1, y(1{\cdot}1) = 0{\cdot}996, y(1{\cdot}2) = 0{\cdot}986, y(1{\cdot}3) = 0{\cdot}972.$

*(MKU)*

**11.** Solve $y' = x^2 + y^2 - 2$, using Milne's method and Adam's method at $x = 0{\cdot}3$ given $y(0) = 1$. The values of $y$ at $x = -0{\cdot}1, 0{\cdot}1, 0{\cdot}2$ may be computed by Taylor's series.

**12.** Compute $y(0{\cdot}6)$ by Milne's method given $y' = x + y, y(0) = 1$ with $h = 0{\cdot}2$. Obtain the required data by Taylor series method.

**13.** Find $y(0{\cdot}4)$ given $y' = y - \frac{2x}{y}$, $y(0) = 1, y(0{\cdot}1) = 1{\cdot}0959, y(0{\cdot}2) = 1{\cdot}1841$, $y(0{\cdot}3) = 1{\cdot}2662$ using Milne's method and Adam's method.

**14.** Given $y' = y - x^2, y(0) = 1, y(0{\cdot}2) = 1{\cdot}1218, y(0{\cdot}4) = 1{\cdot}4682, y(0{\cdot}6) = 1{\cdot}7379$, estimate $y(0{\cdot}8)$ by Adam-Bashforth method.

**15.** Obtain the solution of $y' = x^2(1 + y), y(1) = 1$ at $x = 1\,(0{\cdot}1)\,(1{\cdot}3)$ by any numerical method and estimate at $x = 1{\cdot}4$ by Adam's method.

**16.** Given $y' = 3e^x + 2y, y(0) = 0$, find $y(0{\cdot}1)$ by Euler method; $y(0{\cdot}2)$ by Taylor method; $y(0{\cdot}3)$ by Runge-Kutta method and $y(0{\cdot}4)$ by both Adam's and Milne's method. Also estimate $y(0{\cdot}5)$ by both methods.

**17.** Given $y' = 1 + y^2, y(0) = 0$, find $y(0{\cdot}2)$ by Taylor method; $y(0{\cdot}4)$ by modified Euler method; $y(0{\cdot}6)$ by Runge-Kutta method. Hence find $y(0{\cdot}8)$ by both Adam's method and Milne's method.

**18.** Given $y' = \frac{1}{x + y}$, $y(0) = 2, y(0{\cdot}2) = 2{\cdot}0933, y(0{\cdot}4) = 2{\cdot}1755, y(0{\cdot}6) = 2{\cdot}2493$, find $y(0{\cdot}8)$ by Milne's predictor-corrector method. *(MS. Ap. 92)*

19. Given $y' = x(x^2 + y^2)e^{-x}$, $y(0) = 1$, find $y$ at $x = 0{\cdot}1, 0{\cdot}2$ and $0{\cdot}3$ by Taylor method; compute $y(0{\cdot}4)$ by Milne's method. (*MS. Nov. '90*)

20. Given $y' = x^2 + \frac{1}{2}y$, $y(1) = 2$, $y(1{\cdot}1) = 2{\cdot}2156$, $y(1{\cdot}2) = 2{\cdot}4649$, $y(1{\cdot}3) = 2{\cdot}7514$, use Milne's method and Adam's method to estimate $y(1{\cdot}4)$ correct to 4 decimal places.

21. Given $y' = x^2 + y$, $y(0) = 1$, find $y(0{\cdot}1)$ by Picard's method; $y(0{\cdot}2)$ by modified Euler method; $y(0{\cdot}3)$ by Runge-Kutta method; and $y(0{\cdot}4)$ by both Adam's and Milne's method.

22. Given $y' = 1 + xy$, $y(0) = 1$ obtain $y(0{\cdot}1)$ by Picard's method; $y(0{\cdot}2)$ by Taylor method; $y(0{\cdot}3)$ by Runge-Kutta method; $y(0{\cdot}4)$ by Milne's predictor-corrector method.

23. Given $\frac{dy}{dx} = \frac{1}{x^2 + y}$, $y(4) = 4$, obtain $y(4{\cdot}1), y(4{\cdot}2), y(4{\cdot}3)$ by Euler method; Picard's method and R.K. method respectively. Hence estimate $y(4{\cdot}4)$ by both predictor-corrector methods.

24. Given $y' = 2 - xy^2$, $y(0) = 10$, obtain power series by Picard's method; using Milne's method, estimate and show that $y(1) = 1{\cdot}6505$, $h = 0{\cdot}2$.

25. Find $y(0{\cdot}8)$ given $y' = \frac{y - x}{y + x}$, $y(0) = 1$ taking $h = 0{\cdot}2$ using predictor-corrector methods.

26. Find $y(0{\cdot}4)$ given $\frac{dy}{dx} = \frac{xy}{x^2 + y^2}$, $y(0) = 1$ using predictor-corrector method. Obtain $y(0{\cdot}1), y(0{\cdot}2), y(0{\cdot}3)$ by using Picard's method, modified Euler method and Runge-Kutta method.

27. Estimate $y(0{\cdot}5), y(0{\cdot}4)$ given $y' = x + y^2$, $y(0) = 1$ using $h = 0{\cdot}1$.

28. Given $\frac{dy}{dx} = x^2 + y^2$, $y(0) = 1$, find $y(0{\cdot}3)$ by Milne's method and Adam's method after finding $y(-0{\cdot}1), y(0{\cdot}1)$ and $y(0{\cdot}2)$.

# ANSWERS

## EXERCISE 11.1 Page 362

**1.** 1·1103 **2.** 0·9003 **3.** 1·0665, 1·1672 **4.** 1·1167, 1·2767, 1·5023

**5.** 4·0098, 4·0185 **6.** 0·3809 **7.** 1·111, 1·248

**8.** 1·225, 1·512, 1·874 **9.** 0·9138 **11.** 1·0047, 1·01812, 1·03995

**12.** 1·226, 1·5421 **13.** 2·0845, 2·1367, 0·5867, 0·1550

**14.** 0·105, 0·9987, $x(0{\cdot}2) = 0{\cdot}21998$, $y(0{\cdot}2) = 0{\cdot}9972$

**15.** $x = 2t + t^2 + \frac{5}{6}t^3 + \cdots, \; y = 1 - t + \frac{3}{2}t^2 + \frac{2}{3}t^3 + \cdots$

**16.** $y = 1 - \frac{x^2}{2} - \frac{1}{6}x^3 + \frac{1}{12}x^4 + \frac{1}{40}x^5 + \frac{1}{180}x^6$

**17.** 1·049834, 1·0985719, 1·145 **18.** 1·1002, 1·2015, 1·306

**20.** 1·0498, 1·0986 **21.** $y(0{\cdot}3) = 0{\cdot}3448$, $z(0{\cdot}3) = 0{\cdot}991$

**22.** $y(0{\cdot}2) = 1{\cdot}0204$, $y(0{\cdot}4) = 1{\cdot}0$

**23.** $y = 1{\cdot}0 + 0{\cdot}1\, x + 0{\cdot}01\, x^2 + 0{\cdot}001\, x^3 + 0{\cdot}0251\, x^4 + 0{\cdot}00101\, x^5 + \cdots$

**24.** 2·588419 **25.** 0·8511043, 0·7750643.

## EXERCISE 11.2 Page 368

**1.** $y = x + \dfrac{x^2}{2} + \dfrac{x^3}{3} + \dfrac{x^4}{4} + \dfrac{x^5}{20}$ **2.** $y(0{\cdot}1) = 1{\cdot}0906$

**3.** $y = x + \dfrac{2}{3}x^2 + \dfrac{4}{15}x^5$ **4.** $y = x + \dfrac{1}{3}x^3 + \dfrac{1}{15}x^5$

**5.** $y = 1 - x + \dfrac{5}{2}x^2 - 2x^3 + x^4 - \dfrac{1}{4}x^5$ **6.** 1·105, 1·223, 1·355, 1·505, 1·677

**7.** $y = 1 + x + \dfrac{3}{2}x^2 + \dfrac{4}{3}x^3 + \dfrac{17}{12}x^4$ **8.** 0·005, 0·042

**9.** $y = x - \dfrac{2}{3}x^2 + \dfrac{1}{3}x^3 - \dfrac{1}{4}x^4 + \dfrac{1}{15}x^5 - \dfrac{22}{15}$ **10.** $y = \dfrac{1}{5}x^3 + \dfrac{1}{63}x^7 + \dfrac{2}{2079}x^{11} + \cdots$

**11.** $y = \dfrac{73}{12} - \dfrac{35}{6}x + \dfrac{7}{2}x^2 - \dfrac{5}{6}x^3 + \dfrac{x^4}{12}$; 2·914508

**12.** 0·2027, )·4227; $y = x + \dfrac{x^3}{3} + \cdots$

## EXERCISE 11.3 Page 378

**1.** 1·2662 **2.** 0·2158, 0·4153, 0·7027 **3.** 1·224, 1·514

**4.** 1·061106 **5.** 1·0932 **6.** $y(0{\cdot}2) = 1{\cdot}0095$

**7.** 1·218, 1·467, 1·737 **8.** 1·2309, 1·5253 **9.** 1·1055

**11.** 1·2125, 2·1596 **12.** 3·4394 **13.** 0·8032

**14.** 1·0228, 1·8847 **15.** 1·1766 **17.** $y(2) = 0{\cdot}34939$ **18.** 1·9227.

## EXERCISE 11.4 Page 393

**1.** 2·4214 **2.** 2·7299 **3.** 1·0224 **4.** 2·994858

**5.** 1·165 **6.** 0·9615, 0·862, 0·7353 **7.** 1·0552, 1·123, 1·2073

**8.** 0·9958 **9.** 1·3559, 1·5836, 1·7554, 1·6440 **10.** 0·1402, 0·2705

**11.** 0·2027, 0·4228, 0·6841 **12.** 0·9802

**13.** II order: 0·825, 0·6905; III order: 0·8234, 0·6878; 4th order: 0·82342, 0·6879

**15.** 1·16722 **16.** 2·243, 2·589, 3·072 **17.** 2·2213, 2·4914

**20.** $y(0{\cdot}3) = 0{\cdot}3448$, $z(0{\cdot}3) = 0{\cdot}99$ $y(0{\cdot}6) = 0{\cdot}7738$, $z(0{\cdot}6) = 0{\cdot}9121$, $y(0{\cdot}9) = 1{\cdot}255$, $z(0{\cdot}9) = 0{\cdot}6806$

**21.** $y(0{\cdot}1) = 0{\cdot}1050$, $z(0{\cdot}1) = 0{\cdot}9998$, $y(0{\cdot}2) = 0{\cdot}2199$, $z(0{\cdot}2) = 0{\cdot}9986$

**22.** $y(0{\cdot}2) = 0{\cdot}9774$, $z(0{\cdot}2) = 1{\cdot}1971$, $y(0{\cdot}4) = 0{\cdot}9$, $z(0{\cdot}4) = 1{\cdot}375$

**23.** 0·3707, 1·03615

**24.** $x(0\cdot1) = 0\cdot9139$, $y(0\cdot1) = -0\cdot9092$ **26.** 0·9801 **27.** 17·4148
**28.** 1·005334 **29.** 0·2542 **30.** $x(0\cdot1) = 2\cdot9399$ **31.** 1·0204.

## EXERCISE 11.5 Page 408

**1.** 2·0444 **2.** 2·01105 **3.** 1·1169, 1·2773, 1·5039, 1·8385
**4.** 1·123, 1·3135, 1·6312, 2·2376, 3·6028
**5.** $y(0\cdot4) = 0\cdot6897$, $y(0\cdot5) = 0\cdot6435$ **6.** 2·1621, 2·2546
**7.** 1·029, 1·555 **8.** 0·7796 **10.** 0·949 **11.** 0·6148
**12.** 2·0442 **13.** 1·3428, 1·3431 **14.** 2·0138
**15.** 2·5751 **18.** 2·3162, 2·3164
**19.** 1·0047, 1·01813, 1·03975, $y(0\cdot4) = 1\cdot0709$
**20.** 3·0794 **28.** 1·4378.

# 12

# Numerical Solution of Partial Differential Equations

## 12·1. Introduction

Partial differential equations occur very frequently in Science, Engineering and Applied Mathematics. Many partial differential equations cannot be solved by analytical methods in closed form solution. In most of the research work in fields like, applied elasticity, theory of plates and shells, hydrodynamics, quantum mechanics etc., the research problems reduce to partial differential equations. Since analytical solutions are not available, we go in for numerical solutions of the partial differential equations by various methods. Certain types of boundary value problems can be solved by replacing the differential equation by the corresponding difference equation and then solving the latter by a process of iteration. This method was devised and first used by L.F. Richardson and it was later improved by H. Liebmann.

## 12·2. Difference Quotients

A *difference quotient* is the quotient obtained by dividing the difference between two values of a function by the difference between two corresponding values of the independent variable.

We know $\frac{dy}{dx} = \underset{h \to 0}{\text{Lt}} \frac{y(x+h) - y(x)}{h}$

If $h$ is small, we approximate

$$\frac{dy}{dx} \approx \frac{y(x+h) - y(x)}{h} = \frac{y(x+h) - y(x)}{(x+h) - x} \quad ...(1)$$

The right-side is a difference quotient. Therefore, the derivative is replaced by a difference quotient. In the case of partial derivatives, we have two independent variables (at least) and hence we consider the differences in both variables.

If $y_0$ is fixed and $x$ is a variable, by Taylor series,

$$u(x, y_0) = u(x_0, y_0) + (x - x_0)\, u_x(x_0, y_0) + \frac{(x - x_0)^2}{2!}\, u_{xx}(\theta, y_0) \qquad ...(2)$$

where $x_0 < \theta < x$.

Setting $x = x_0 + h$,

$$u(x_0 + h, y_0) = u(x_0, y_0) + h\, u_x(x_0, y_0) + \frac{h^2}{2!}\, u_{xx}(\theta, y_0) \qquad ...(3)$$

*i.e.*, $$\frac{u(x_0 + h, y_0) - u(x_0, y_0)}{h} = u_x(x_0, y_0) + \frac{h}{2}\, u_{xx}(\theta, y_0)$$

$$\therefore \quad u_x(x_0, y_0) = \frac{u(x_0 + h, y_0) - u(x_0, y_0)}{h} - \frac{h}{2}\, u_{xx}(\theta, y_0) \qquad ...(4)$$

(4) indicates, that if $u_x(x_0, y_0)$ is replaced by difference quotient $\frac{u(x_0 + h, y_0) - u(x_0, y_0)}{h}$, the truncation error is $-\frac{1}{2}\, h\, u_{xx}(\theta, y_0)$, where $x_0 < \theta < x_0 + h$.

$\therefore$ Approximately,

$$\boxed{\mathbf{u_x(x_0, y_0) = \frac{u(x_0 + h, y_0) - u(x_0, y_0)}{h}}} \qquad ...(5)$$

This is forward difference approximation to $u_x(x_0, y_0)$.

Similarly, backward difference approximation to $u_x(x_0, y_0)$ is

$$\boxed{\mathbf{u_x(x_0, y_0) = \frac{u(x_0, y_0) - u(x_0 - h, y_0)}{h}}} \qquad ...(6)$$

(got by changing $h$ to $-h$ in (5))

In the same way,

$$u_{xx}(x_0, y_0) = \frac{u_x(x_0 + h, y_0) - u_x(x_0, y_0)}{h} \qquad ...(7)$$

If we use forward differences for $u_x$ on the R.H.S., the result would be biased again in the forward direction. To avoid this effect, we use backward differences for $u_x$ on the R.H.S.,

$$u_x(x_0, y_0) = \frac{u(x_0, y_0) - u(x_0 - h, y_0)}{h} \qquad ...(8)$$

Also $$u_x(x_0 + h, y_0) = \frac{u(x_0 + h, y_0) - u(x_0, y_0)}{h} \qquad ...(9)$$

Using (8), (9), in (7),

$$u_{xx}(x_0, y_0) = \frac{1}{h}\left[\frac{u(x_0 + h, y_0) - u(x_0, y_0)}{h} - \frac{u(x_0, y_0) - u(x_0 - h, y_0)}{h}\right]$$

$$u_{xx}(x_0, y_0) = \frac{1}{h^2}[u(x_0+h) - 2u(x_0, y_0) + u(x_0-h, y_0)] \quad ...(10)$$

By Taylor series,

$$u(x_0+h, y_0) = u(x_0, y_0) + h\,u_x(x_0, y_0) + \frac{h^2}{2}u_{xx}(x_0, y_0)$$
$$+\frac{h^3}{6}u_{xxx}(x_0, y_0) + \frac{h^4}{24}u_{xxxx}(\theta_1, y_0) \quad ...(11)$$

$$u(x_0-h, y_0) = u(x_0, y_0) - h\,u_x(x_0, y_0) + \frac{1}{2}h^2 u_{xx}(x_0, y_0)$$
$$-\frac{h^3}{6}u_{xxx}(x_0, y_0) + \frac{h^4}{24}u_{xxxx}(\theta_2, y_0) \quad ...(12)$$

Adding (11) and (12), we get

$$u(x_0+h, y_0) + u(x_0-h, y_0) = 2u(x_0, y_0) + h^2 u_{xx}(x_0, y_0)$$
$$+\frac{h^4}{24}\left[u_{xxxx}(\theta_1, y_0) + u_{xxxx}(\theta_2, y_0)\right]$$

$$\therefore \quad \frac{u(x_0+h, y_0) + u(x_0-h, y_0) - 2u(x_0, y_0)}{h^2} = u_{xx}(x_0, y_0)$$
$$+\frac{h^2}{24}\left[u_{xxxx}(\theta_1, y_0) + u_{xxxx}(\theta_2, y_0)\right]$$
$$= u_{xx}(x_0, y_0) + \frac{h^2}{12}u_{xxxx}(\theta, y_0)$$

where $x_0 - h < \theta < x_0 + h$.

Therefore, $u_{xx}(x_0, y_0) = \dfrac{u(x_0+h, y_0) - 2u(x_0, y_0) + u(x_0-h, y_0)}{h^2}$

$$-\frac{h^2}{12}u_{xxxx}(\theta, y_0)$$

If we replace $u_{xx}(x_0, y_0)$ by $\dfrac{u(x_0+h, y_0) - 2u(x_0, y_0) + u(x_0-h, y_0)}{h^2}$

the truncation error is $-\dfrac{h^2}{12}u_{xxxx}(\theta, y_0)$ where $x_0 - h < \theta < x_0 + h$.

If we keep $x$ as fixed $x_0$, and $y$ to vary,

$$\boxed{\mathbf{u_y(x_0, y_0) = \frac{u(x_0, y_0+k) - u(x_0, y_0)}{k}}} \quad ...(13)$$

or

$$\boxed{\mathbf{u_y(x_0, y_0) = \frac{u(x_0, y_0) - u(x_0, y_0-k)}{k}}} \quad ...(14)$$

where $k$ is the step-size in $y$-direction

and $$\mathbf{u_{yy}(x_0, y_0) = \frac{u(x_0, y_0 + k) - 2u(x_0, y_0) + u(x_0, y_0 - k)}{k^2}} \quad ...(5)$$

and the truncation error is $-\frac{k^2}{12} u_{yyyy}(x_0, \eta)$ where $y_0 - k < \eta < y_0 + k$.

## 2·3. Graphical Representation of Partial Quotients

The $xy$ plane is divided into a series of rectangles whose sides are parallel to $x$ and $y$-axes such that $\Delta x = h$ and $\Delta y = k$. The grid points or mesh points or lattice points are

$$(x, y), (x + h, y), (x + 2h, y) \cdots ((x - h), y), (x - 2h, y),...$$

If $(x_i, y_i)$ is any grid point,

$x_i = x_0 + ih, \quad y_j = y_0 + jk$. If we take one corner as origin,

$x_i = ih, y_j = jk, i, j = 0, 1, 2,...$

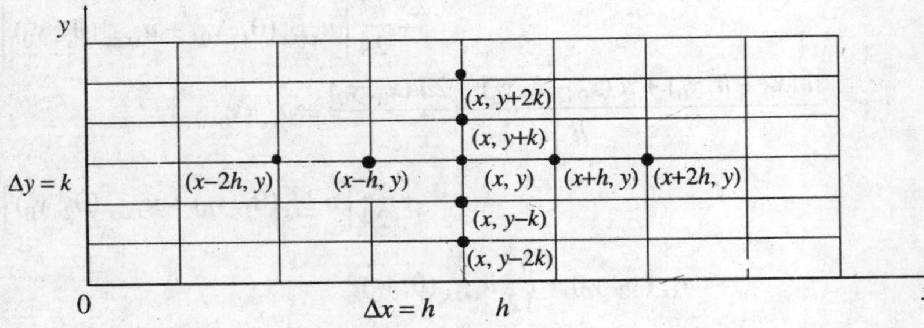


Coordinates of grid points

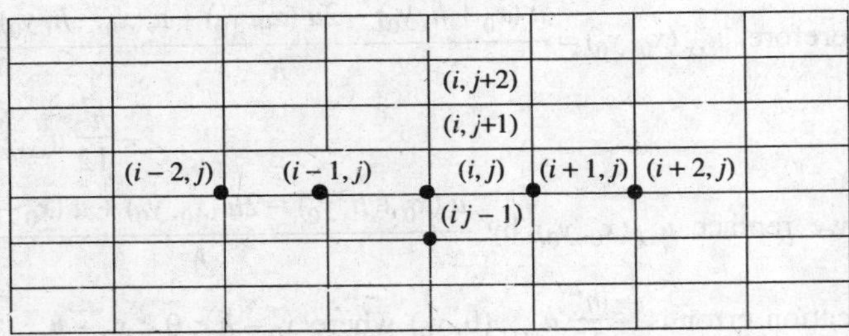


Mesh points denoted by suffices.

Here $(x = ih, y = jk)$ is denoted by $(i, j)$.

From the figures,

$$u_x = \frac{u_{i+1,j} - u_{i,j}}{h} \quad \text{(forward difference)} \quad ...(1)$$

$$u_x = \frac{u_{i,j} - u_{i-1,j}}{h} \quad \text{(backward difference)} \quad ...(2)$$

$$u_y = \frac{u_{i,j+1} - u_{i,j}}{k} \quad \text{(forward difference)} \quad ...(3)$$

$$u_y = \frac{u_{i,j} - u_{i,j-1}}{k} \quad \text{(backward difference)} \quad ...(4)$$

$$u_{xx} = \frac{u_{i+1,j} - 2u_{i,j} + u_{i-1,j}}{h^2}$$

$$u_{yy} = \frac{u_{i,j+1} - 2u_{i,j} + u_{i,j-1}}{k^2}$$

we can also write

$$u_x = \frac{u_{i+1,j} - u_{i-1,j}}{2h}$$

$$u_y = \frac{u_{i,j+1} - u_{i,j-1}}{2k}.$$

## 12·4. Classification of Partial Differential Equations of the Second Order

The most general linear partial differential equation of second order can be written as

$$A\frac{\partial^2 u}{\partial x^2} + B\frac{\partial^2 u}{\partial x \partial y} + C\frac{\partial^2 u}{\partial y^2} + D\frac{\partial u}{\partial x} + E\frac{\partial u}{\partial y} + Fu = 0$$

*i.e.,*

$$A\,u_{xx} + Bu_{xy} + Cu_{yy} + Du_x + Eu_y + Fu = 0 \quad ...(1)$$

where $A, B, C, D, E, F$ are in general functions of $x$ and $y$.

The above equation of second order (linear) (1) is said to

(*i*) *elliptic* at a point $(x, y)$ in the plane if $B^2 - 4AC < 0$

(*ii*) *parabolic* if $B^2 - 4AC = 0$

(*iii*) *hyperbolic if* $B^2 - 4AC > 0$.

**Note:** The same differential equation may be elliptic in one region, parabolic in another and hyperbolic in some other region. For example, $xu_{xx} + u_{yy} = 0$ is elliptic if $x > 0$, hyperbolic if $x < 0$ and parabolic if $x = 0$.

### Examples

| | Elliptic Type | Parabolic Type | Hyperbolic Type |
|---|---|---|---|
| 1. | $\frac{\partial^2 u}{\partial x^2} + \frac{\partial^2 u}{\partial y^2} = 0$ (Laplace Equation in two dimension) | $\frac{\partial^2 u}{\partial x^2} = \frac{1}{\alpha^2}\frac{\partial u}{\partial t}$ (one dimensional heat equation) | $\frac{\partial^2 u}{\partial x^2} = \frac{1}{\alpha^2}\cdot\frac{\partial^2 u}{\partial t^2}$ (one dimensional wave equation) |
| 2. | $\frac{\partial^2 u}{\partial x^2} + \frac{\partial^2 u}{\partial y^2} = f(x, y)$ (Poisson's equation) | | |

Example 1. *Classify the following equations:*

(*i*) $\frac{\partial^2 u}{\partial x^2} + 2\frac{\partial^2 u}{\partial x \partial y} + \frac{\partial^2 u}{\partial y^2} = 0$

(*ii*) $x^2 f_{xx} + (1 - y^2) f_{yy} = 0$ (*B.E. 1974*)

(*i*) Here $A = 1, B = 2, C = 1$

$B^2 - 4AC = 4 - 4 = 0$, for all $x$, $y$.

Hence, the equation is parabolic at all points.

(*ii*) $A = x^2, B = 0, C = 1 - y^2$

$$B^2 - 4AC = -4x^2(1 - y^2)$$
$$= 4x^2(y^2 - 1)$$

For all $x$ except $x = 0$, $x^2$ is +ve.

If $-1 < y < 1$, $y^2 - 1$ is negative.

$\therefore$ $B^2 - 4AC$ is –ve if $-1 < y < 1, x \neq 0$

$\therefore$ For $-\infty < x < \infty$ $(x \neq 0)$, $-1 < y < 1$, the equation is elliptic.

For $-\infty < x < \infty, x \neq 0, y < -1$ or $y > 1$, the equation is hyperbolic.

For $x = 0$ for all $y$ or for all $x$, $y = \pm 1$ the equation is parabolic.

**Example 2.** *Classify the following partial differential equations:*

(*i*) $u_{xx} + 4u_{xy} + (x^2 + 4y^2) u_{yy} = \sin(x + y)$ (*MS. Nov. '91*)

(*ii*) $(x + 1) u_{xx} - 2(x + 2) u_{xy} + (x + 3) u_{yy} = 0$ (*MS. Nov. '92*)

(*iii*) $x f_{xx} + y f_{yy} = 0, x > 0, y > 0$.

**Solution.** (*i*) Here, $A = 1, B = 4, C = (x^2 + 4y^2)$

$$B^2 - 4AC = 16 - 4(x^2 + 4y^2)$$
$$= 4[4 - x^2 - 4y^2]$$

The equation is elliptic if $4 - x^2 - 4y^2 < 0$

*i.e.,* $$x^2 + 4y^2 > 4$$

*i.e.,* $$\frac{x^2}{4} + \frac{y^2}{1} > 1$$

$\therefore$ It is elliptic in the region *outside the ellipse*

$$\frac{x^2}{4} + \frac{y^2}{1} = 1.$$

It is hyperbolic *inside the ellipse* $\frac{x^2}{4} + \frac{y^2}{1} = 1$.

It is parabolic *on the ellipse* $\frac{x^2}{4} + \frac{y^2}{1} = 1$.

(*ii*) Here, $A = x + 1, \quad B = -2(x+2), \quad C = x + 3$

$$B^2 - 4AC = 4(x+2)^2 - 4(x+1)(x+3)$$
$$= 4[1] = 4 > 0$$

$\therefore$ The equation is hyperbolic at all points of the region.

(*iii*) $A = x, B = 0, C = y$

$$B^2 - 4AC = -4xy, \quad (x > 0, y > 0 \text{ given})$$
$$= -\text{ve}$$

$\therefore$ It is elliptic for all $x > 0$, $y > 0$.

## EXERCISE 12.1

Classify the following equations as elliptic, parabolic, or hyperbolic.

**1.** $f_{xx} - 2f_{xy} = 0$ **2.** $f_{xx} + 2f_{xy} + 4f_{yy} = 0$

**3.** $f_{xx} - 2f_{xy} + f_{yy} = 0$ **4.** $f_{xy} - f_x = 0$

**5.** $u_{xx} = u_t$

**6.** Derive $u_x(x_0, y_0) = \dfrac{u(x_0 + h, y_0) - u(x_0 - h, y_0)}{2h}$

where the truncation error is $-\dfrac{1}{6} h^2 u_{xxx}(\theta, y_0)$

where $x_0 - h < \theta < x_0 + h$. (*MS. 1974*)

**2.** Show that

$$u_{xy} = \frac{1}{4hk}[u(x_0 + h, y_0 + k) - u(x_0 - h, y_0 + k)$$
$$- u(x_0 + h, y_0 - k) + u(x_0 - h, y_0 - k)]$$

and discuss the truncation error. (*MS. 1970*)

## 12·5. Elliptic Equations

An important and frequently occurring elliptic equation is Laplace's equation, *i.e.*,

$$\frac{\partial^2 u}{\partial x^2} + \frac{\partial^2 u}{\partial y^2} = 0 \quad i.e., \quad \nabla^2 u = 0 \quad \text{or} \quad u_{xx} + u_{yy} = 0: \qquad ...(1)$$

Replacing the derivatives by difference quotients given under Article 12·3, of this chapter, we get,

$$\frac{u_{i+1,j} - 2u_{i,j} + u_{i-1,j}}{h^2} + \frac{u_{i,j+1} - 2u_{i,j} + u_{i,j-1}}{k^2} = 0$$

Taking $k = h$, (square mesh) in the above equation,

$$4u_{i,j} = u_{i-1,j} + u_{i+1,j} + u_{i,j-1} + u_{i,j+1}$$

$$\therefore \quad \boxed{\mathbf{u_{i,j} = \frac{1}{4}\left[u_{i-1,j} + u_{i+1,j} + u_{i,j-1} + u_{i,j+1}\right]}} \qquad ...(1)$$

*That is, the value of u at any interior point is the arithmetic mean of the values of u at the four lattice points (Two of them are vertically just above and below and the other two in the horizontal line just after and before this point).*

**This is called standard five point formula.**

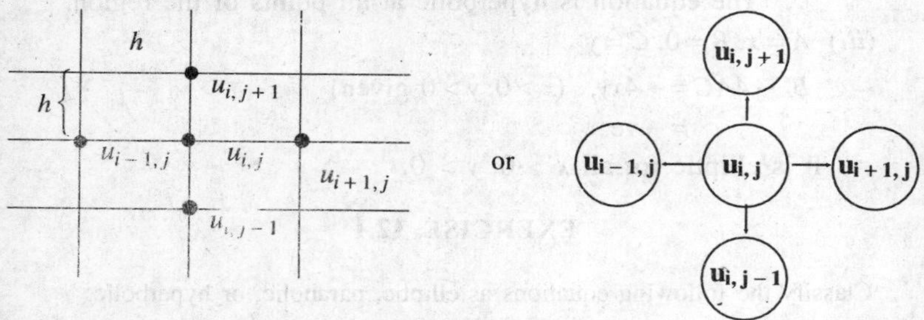


Schematic diagram.

Central value = average of the other four values.

**Diagonal five-point formula**

Instead of the formula (1), we can also use the formula

$$u_{i,j} = \frac{1}{4}\left(u_{i-1,j-1} + u_{i-1,j+1}, u_{i+1,j-1} + u_{i+1,j+1}\right) \quad ...(2)$$

which is called the *diagonal five-point formula* since this formula involves the values on the diagonals through $u_{i,j}$. Since the Laplace equation is invariant in any coordinate system, the formula remains same when the coordinate axes are rotated through 45°. But the error in the diagonal formula is four times the error in the standard formula. Therefore, we always prefer the standard formula to the diagonal formula.

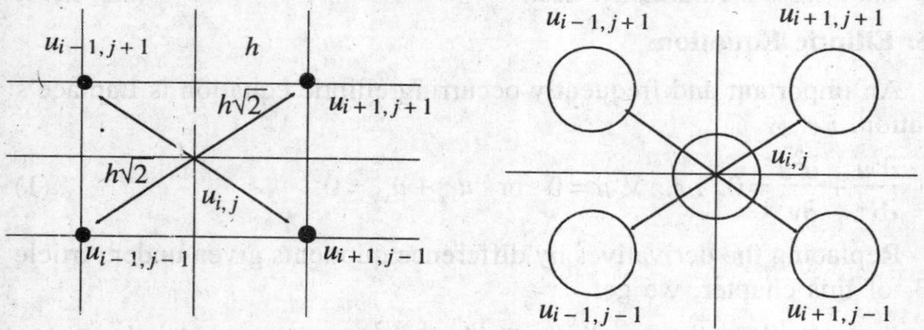


Schematic diagram of diagonal formula.

## 12·6. Solution of Laplace's Eqation: (By Liebmann's iteration process)

**AIM**: To solve the Laplace's equation $u_{xx} + u_{yy} = 0$ (i) in bounded square region $R$ with a boundary $C$ when the boundary values of $u$ are given on the boundary (or at least at the grid points in the boundary).

Let us divide the square region into a network of sub-squares of side $h$ (refer to the figure).

| $b_1$ | $b_2$ | $b_3$ | $b_4$ | $b_5$ |
|---|---|---|---|---|
| $b_{16}$ | $u_1$ | $u_2$ | $u_3$ | $b_6$ |
| $b_{15}$ | $u_4$ | $u_5$ | $u_6$ | $b_7$ |
| $b_{14}$ | $u_7$ | $u_8$ | $u_9$ | $b_8$ |
| $b_{13}$ | $b_{12}$ | $b_{11}$ | $b_{10}$ | $b_9$ |

The boundary values of $u$ at the grid points are given and noted by $b_1, b_2, \ldots b_{16}$. The values of $u$ at the interior lattice or grid points are assumed to be $u_1, u_2, \ldots u_9$.

To start the iteration process, initially we find rough values at interior points and then we improve them by iterative process mostly using standard five point formula.

*Find $u_5$ first*: $u_5 = \frac{1}{4}(b_3 + b_7 + b_{11} + b_{15})$ (by standard five point formula—SFPF)

Knowing $u_5$, we find $u_1, u_3, u_7, u_9$, that is the values at the centres of the four larger inner squares by using diagonal five point formula—DFPF.

That is, $u_1 = \frac{1}{4}(b_3 + b_{15} + b_1 + u_5)$

$$u_3 = \frac{1}{4}(b_5 + u_5 + b_3 + b_7)$$

$$u_7 = \frac{1}{4}(u_5 + b_{13} + b_{11} + b_{15})$$

$$u_9 = \frac{1}{4}(b_7 + b_{11} + b_9 + u_5)$$

The remaining 4 values $u_2, u_4, u_6, u_8$ can be got by using SFPF.

That is, $u_2 = \frac{1}{4}(b_3 + u_5 + u_1 + u_3)$

$$u_4 = \frac{1}{4}(u_1 + u_7 + u_5 + b_{15})$$

$$u_6 = \frac{1}{4}(u_3 + u_9 + u_5 + b_7)$$

$$u_8 = \frac{1}{4}(u_5 + b_{11} + u_7 + u_9)$$

Now we know all the boundary values of $u$ and rough values of $u$ at every grid point in the interior of the region $R$. Now, we iterate the process and improve the values of $u$ with accuracy. Start with $u_5$ and proceed to get the values of $u_1, u_3, \ldots u_9$ always using SFPF, taking into account the latest available values of $u$ to use in the formula. The iterative formula is

$$u_{i,j}^{(n+1)} = \frac{1}{4}\left(u_{i+1,j}^{(n)}\, u_{i-1,j}^{(n+1)} + u_{i,j-1}^{(n)} + u_{i,j+1}^{(n+1)}\right) \quad \ldots \text{I}$$

where the superscript of $u$ denotes the iteration number.

Equation I is called **LIEBMANN'S** iteration process. The process is stoppd once we get the values with desired accuracy.

**Note:** To solve the nine unknowns $u_1, u_2, \ldots u_9$ from the nine equations, we can also use Gauss-Seidel method or other method.

**Example 3.** *Find by the Liebmann's method the values at the interior lattice points of a square region of the harmonic function u whose boundary values are as shown in the following figure.*

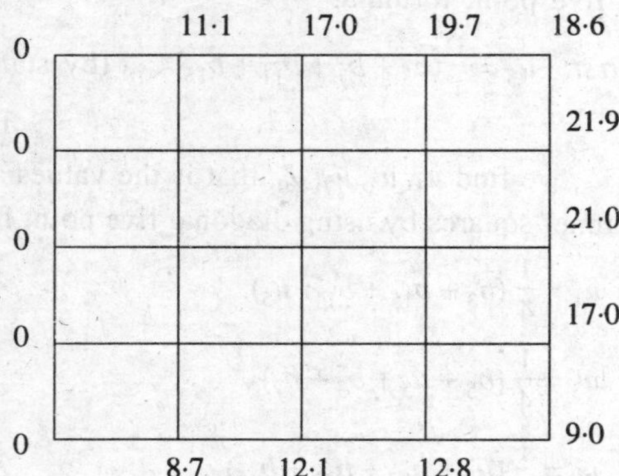


(*MKU. 1970, 75*)

**Solution.** Since $u$ is harmonic, it satisfies Laplace's equation

$$\frac{\partial^2 u}{\partial x^2} + \frac{\partial^2 u}{\partial y^2} = 0 \text{ in the square.} \quad \ldots(1)$$

Let the interior values of $u$ at the 9 grid points be $u_1, u_2, \ldots u_9$. We will find the values of $u$ at the interior mesh points as explained in the previous article. We will first find the rough values of $u$ and then proceed to refine them.

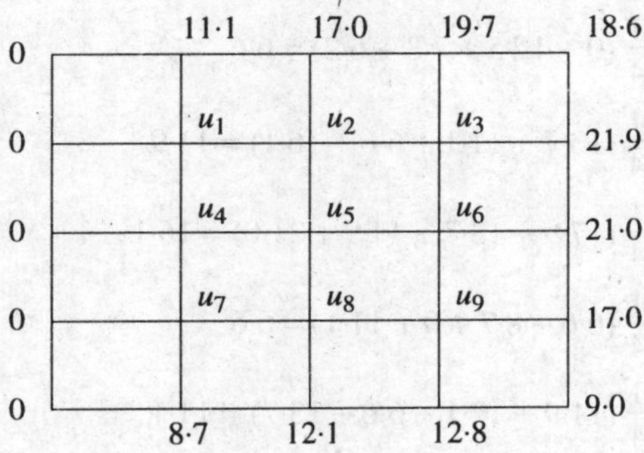


*Finding rough values*:

$$u_5 = \frac{1}{4}(0 + 17{\cdot}0 + 21{\cdot}0 + 12{\cdot}1) = 12{\cdot}5 \qquad \text{(SFPF)}$$

$$u_1 = \frac{1}{4}(0 + 12{\cdot}5 + 17{\cdot}0) = 7{\cdot}4 \qquad \text{(DFPF)}$$

$$u_3 = \frac{1}{4}(12{\cdot}5 + 18{\cdot}6 + 17{\cdot}0 + 1{\cdot}0) = 17{\cdot}3 \qquad \text{(DFPF)}$$

$$u_7 = \frac{1}{4}(12{\cdot}5 + 0 + 0 + 12{\cdot}1) = 6{\cdot}2 \qquad \text{(DFPF)}$$

$$u_9 = \frac{1}{4}(12{\cdot}5 + 9{\cdot}0 + 12{\cdot}1 + 21{\cdot}0) = 13{\cdot}7 \qquad \text{(DFPF)}$$

$$u_2 = \frac{1}{4}(17{\cdot}0 + 12{\cdot}5 + 7{\cdot}4 + 17{\cdot}3) = 13{\cdot}6 \qquad \text{(SFPF)}$$

$$u_4 = \frac{1}{4}(7{\cdot}4 + 6{\cdot}2 + 0 + 12{\cdot}5) = 6{\cdot}5 \qquad \text{(SFPF)}$$

$$u_6 = \frac{1}{4}(12{\cdot}5 + 21{\cdot}0 + 17{\cdot}3 + 13{\cdot}7) = 16{\cdot}1 \qquad \text{(SFPF)}$$

$$u_8 = \frac{1}{4}(12{\cdot}5 + 12{\cdot}1 + 6{\cdot}2 + 13{\cdot}7) = 11{\cdot}1 \qquad \text{(SFPF)}$$

Now, we have got the rough values at all interior grid points and already we possess the boundary values at the lattice points. We will now improve the values by using always SFPF.

*First iteration:* (We obtain all values by SFPF)

$$u_1^{(1)} = \frac{1}{4}(0 + 11{\cdot}1 + u_2 + u_4) = \frac{1}{4}(0 + 11{\cdot}1 + 13{\cdot}6 + 6{\cdot}5) = 7{\cdot}8$$

$$u_2^{(1)} = \frac{1}{4}(17{\cdot}0 + 12{\cdot}5 + 7{\cdot}8 + 17{\cdot}3) = 13{\cdot}7$$

$$u_3^{(1)} = \frac{1}{4}(13{\cdot}7 + 21{\cdot}9 + 19{\cdot}7 + 16{\cdot}1) = 17{\cdot}9$$

$$u_4^{(1)} = \frac{1}{4}(0 + 12{\cdot}5 + 7{\cdot}8 + 6{\cdot}2) = 6{\cdot}6$$

$$u_5^{(1)} = \frac{1}{4}(13{\cdot}7 + 11{\cdot}1 + 6{\cdot}6 + 16{\cdot}1) = 11{\cdot}9$$

$$u_6^{(1)} = \frac{1}{4}(17{\cdot}9 + 13{\cdot}7 + 11{\cdot}9 + 21{\cdot}0) = 16{\cdot}1$$

$$u_7^{(1)} = \frac{1}{4}(6{\cdot}6 + 8{\cdot}7 + 0 + 11{\cdot}1) = 6{\cdot}6$$

$$u_8^{(1)} = \frac{1}{4}(11{\cdot}9 + 12{\cdot}1 + 6{\cdot}6 + 13{\cdot}7) = 11{\cdot}1$$

$$u_9^{(1)} = \frac{1}{4}(16{\cdot}1 + 12{\cdot}8 + 17{\cdot}0 + 11{\cdot}1) = 14{\cdot}3$$

Now we go for the second iteration.

*Second iteration:*

$$u_1^{(2)} = \frac{1}{4}(0 + 11{\cdot}1 + 13{\cdot}7 + 6{\cdot}6) = 7{\cdot}9$$

$$u_2^{(2)} = \frac{1}{4}(17{\cdot}0 + 17{\cdot}9 + 7{\cdot}9 + 11{\cdot}9) = 13{\cdot}7$$

$$u_3^{(2)} = \frac{1}{4}(13{\cdot}7 + 19{\cdot}7 + 21{\cdot}9 + 16{\cdot}1) = 17{\cdot}9$$

$$u_4^{(2)} = \frac{1}{4}(7{\cdot}9 + 0 + 11{\cdot}9 + 6{\cdot}6) = 6{\cdot}6$$

$$u_5^{(2)} = \frac{1}{4}(13{\cdot}7 + 6{\cdot}6 + 16{\cdot}1 + 11{\cdot}1) = 11{\cdot}9$$

$$u_6^{(2)} = \frac{1}{4}(11{\cdot}9 + 17{\cdot}9 + 21{\cdot}0 + 14{\cdot}3) = 16{\cdot}3$$

$$u_7^{(2)} = \frac{1}{4}(0 + 6{\cdot}6 + 11{\cdot}1 + 8{\cdot}7) = 6{\cdot}6$$

$$u_8^{(2)} = \frac{1}{4}(6{\cdot}6 + 11{\cdot}9 + 14{\cdot}3 + 12{\cdot}1) = 11{\cdot}2$$

$$u_9^{(2)} = \frac{1}{4}(11{\cdot}2 + 16{\cdot}3 + 17{\cdot}0 + 12{\cdot}8) = 14{\cdot}3$$

*Third iteration:*

$$u_1^{(3)} = \frac{1}{4}(0 + 11{\cdot}1 + 13{\cdot}7 + 6{\cdot}6) = 7{\cdot}9$$

$$u_2^{(3)} = \frac{1}{4}(7{\cdot}9 + 17{\cdot}9 + 17{\cdot}0 + 11{\cdot}9) = 13{\cdot}7$$

$$u_3^{(3)} = \frac{1}{4}(13{\cdot}7 + 21{\cdot}9 + 19{\cdot}7 + 16{\cdot}3) = 17{\cdot}9$$

$$u_4^{(3)} = \frac{1}{4}(6{\cdot}6 + 0 + 7{\cdot}9 + 11{\cdot}9) = 6{\cdot}6$$

$$u_5^{(3)} = \frac{1}{4}(11{\cdot}2 + 6{\cdot}6 + 13{\cdot}7 + 16{\cdot}3) = 11{\cdot}9$$

$$u_6^{(3)} = \frac{1}{4}(11{\cdot}9 + 21{\cdot}0 + 17{\cdot}9 + 14{\cdot}3) = 16{\cdot}3$$

$$u_7^{(3)} = \frac{1}{4}(0 + 6{\cdot}6 + 11{\cdot}2 + 8{\cdot}7) = 6{\cdot}6$$

$$u_8^{(3)} = \frac{1}{4}(6{\cdot}6 + 14{\cdot}3 + 11{\cdot}9 + 12{\cdot}1) = 11{\cdot}2$$

$$u_9^{(3)} = \frac{1}{4}(11{\cdot}2 + 16{\cdot}3 + 17{\cdot}0 + 12{\cdot}8) = 14{\cdot}3$$

Now, all the 9 values of $u$ of the third iteration are same as the corresponding values of the second iteration. Hence we stop the procedure and accept

$u_1 = 7{\cdot}9$, $u_2 = 13{\cdot}7$, $u_3 = 17{\cdot}9$, $u_4 = 6{\cdot}6$, $u_5 = 11{\cdot}9$
$u_6 = 16{\cdot}3$, $u_7 = 6{\cdot}6$, $u_8 = 11{\cdot}2$ and $u_9 = 14{\cdot}3$.

Instead of working out so elaborately, we can write the values of $u$'s at each grid paint and work out the scheme easily. The values of $u$'s are shown below:

| | | | | |
|---|---|---|---|---|
| 0 | 11·1 | 17·0 | 19·7 | 18·6 |
| 0 | $u_1$<br>7·4<br>7·8<br>7·9<br>7·9 | $u_2$<br>13·6<br>13·7<br>13·7<br>13·7 | $u_3$<br>17·3<br>17·9<br>17·9<br>17·9 | 21·9 |
| 0 | $u_4$<br>6·5<br>6·6<br>6·6<br>6·6 | $u_5$<br>12·5<br>11·9<br>11·9<br>11·9 | $u_6$<br>16·1<br>16·1<br>16·3<br>16·3 | 21·0 |
| 0 | $u_7$<br>6·2<br>6·6<br>6·6<br>6·6 | $u_8$<br>11·1<br>11·1<br>11·2<br>11·2 | $u_9$<br>13·7<br>14·3<br>14·3<br>14·3 | 17·0 |
| 0 | 8·7 | 12·1 | 12·8 | 9·0 |

(Use always the latest available values in the formula.)

**Example 4.** *Solve the equation* $\nabla^2 u = 0$ *for the following mesh, with boundary values as shown, using Leibmann's iteration procedure.*

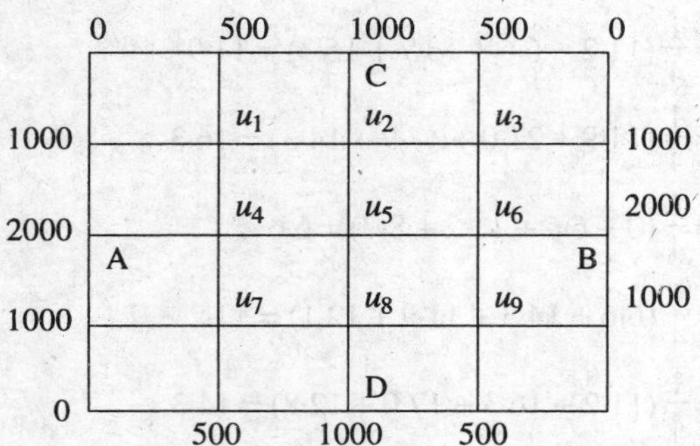


*(MKU, 1971, 73)*

**Solution.** Take the central horizontal and vertical lines as *AB* and *CD*.

Let $u_1$, $u_2$, ...$u_9$ be the values of *u* at the interior grid points of the mesh.

The values of *u* on the boundary are symmetrical w.r.t. the lines *AB* and *CD*.

Hence, the values of *u* inside the mesh will also be symmetrical about *AB* and *CD*.

∴ $u_1 = u_3 = u_7 = u_9$; $u_2 = u_8$; $u_4 = u_6$ and $u_5$ is not equal to any value.

∴ It is enough if we find $u_1$, $u_2$, $u_4$ and $u_5$.

*Rough values of u's*:

$$u_5 = \frac{1}{4}(2000 + 2000 + 1000 + 1000) = 1500 \qquad \text{(SFPF)}$$

$$u_1 = \frac{1}{4}(0 + 1500 + 1000 + 2000) = 1125 \qquad \text{(DFPF)}$$

$$u_2 = \frac{1}{4}(1000 + 1500 + 1125 + 1125) = 1187{\cdot}5 \qquad \text{(SFPF)}$$

$$u_4 = \frac{1}{4}(u_1 + u_5 + u_7 + 2000) = 1437{\cdot}5 \qquad \text{(SFPF)}$$

$$u_5 = \frac{1}{4}(2u_2 + 2u_4) = 1312{\cdot}5$$

Hereafter we use only SFPF.

*First iteration* :

$$u_1^{(1)} = \frac{1}{4}(1000 + 500 + 1187{\cdot}5 + 1437{\cdot}5) = 1031{\cdot}25$$

$$u_2^{(1)} = \frac{1}{4}(1000 + 1031{\cdot}25 + 1031{\cdot}25 + 1312{\cdot}5) = 1093{\cdot}75$$

$$u_4^{(1)} = \frac{1}{4}(2000 + 2\,(1031{\cdot}25) + 1312{\cdot}5) = 1343{\cdot}75$$

$$u_5^{(1)} = \frac{1}{4}(2u_2 + 2u_4)$$

$$= \frac{1}{2}(1093{\cdot}75 + 1343{\cdot}75) = 1218{\cdot}75$$

Now we go to *second iteration.*

$$u_1^{(2)} = 984{\cdot}38$$

$$u_2^{(2)} = 1046{\cdot}88$$

$$u_4^{(2)} = 1296{\cdot}88$$

$$u_5^{(2)} = 1171{\cdot}88$$

Proceeding like this, we enter the values at each node $u_1, u_2, u_4, u_5$ in the following figure.

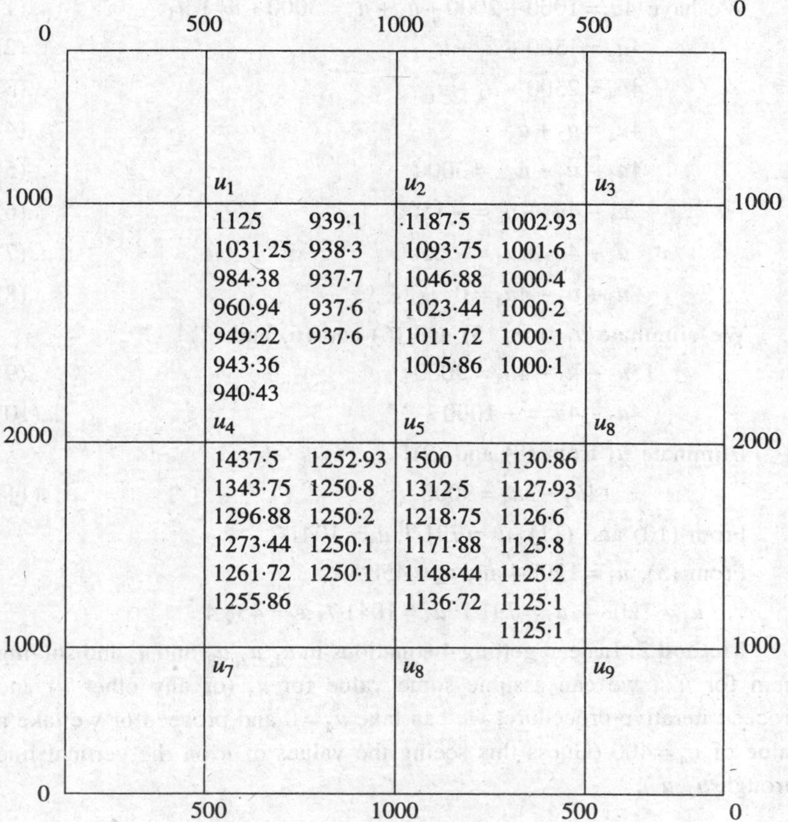

Hence the solution is

$$u_1 = 937{\cdot}6,\ u_2 = 1000{\cdot}1,\ u_4 = 1250{\cdot}1,\ u_5 = 1125{\cdot}1.$$

**Example 5.** *Evaluate the function u (x, y) satisfying $\nabla^2 u = 0$ at the laltice points given the boundary values as follows.* (*MS. 1973*)

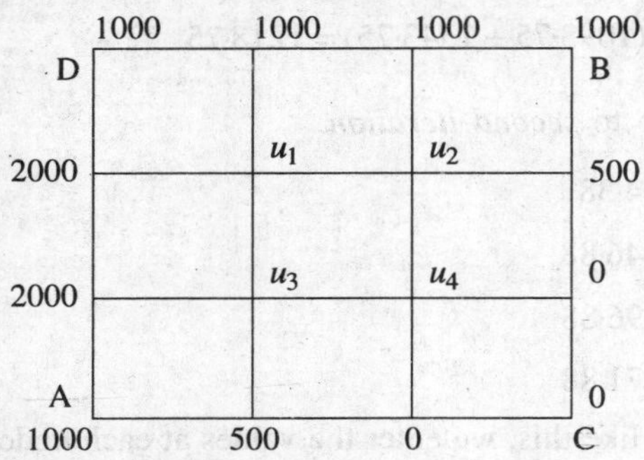


**Solution. Method 1:**

We have $4u_1 = 1000 + 2000 + u_3 + u_2 = 3000 + u_2 + u_3$ ...(1)

$$4u_2 = 1500 + u_1 + u_4 \quad ...(2)$$

$$4u_3 = 2500 + u_4 + u_1 \quad ...(3)$$

$$4u_4 = u_2 + u_3 \quad ...(4)$$

*i.e.*,

$$4u_1 - u_2 - u_3 = 3000 \quad ...(5)$$

$$u_1 - 4u_2 + u_4 = -1500 \quad ...(6)$$

$$u_1 - 4u_3 + u_4 = -2500 \quad ...(7)$$

$$u_2 + u_3 - 4u_4 = 0 \quad ...(8)$$

We eliminate $u_1$ from (5) and (6) and (6) and (7)

$$15u_2 - u_3 - 4u_4 = 9000 \quad ...(9)$$

$$4u_2 - 4u_3 = -1000 \quad ...(10)$$

Eliminate $u_4$ from (8) and (9)

$$14u_2 - 2u_3 = 9000 \quad ...(11)$$

From (10) and (11), $u_2 = 791{\cdot}7$, $u_3 = 1041{\cdot}7$.

From (5), $u_1 = 1208{\cdot}4$ and $u_4 = 458{\cdot}4$.

$\therefore\ u_1 = 1208{\cdot}4,\ u_2 = 791{\cdot}7,\ u_3 = 1041{\cdot}7,\ u_4 = 458{\cdot}4.$

**Method 2:** Instead getting 4 equations in $u_1, u_2, u_3,$ and $u_4$ and solving them for $u$'s, we can assume some value for $u_4$ (or any other $u$) and proceed iterative procedure; we can take $u_4 = 0$ and proceed or we take a value of $u_4 = 400$ (Guess this seeing the values of $u$ on the vertical line through $u_2$, $u_4$).

*Rough values*:

$$u_1 = (1000 + 2000 + 1000 + 400)/4 = 1100 \quad \text{(DFPF)}$$

$$u_2 = \frac{1}{4}(u_1 + u_4 + 1500) = 750 \quad \text{(SFPF)}$$

$$u_3 = \frac{1}{4}(u_1 + u_4 + 2500) = 1000 \quad \text{(SFPF)}$$

$$u_4 = \frac{1}{4}(u_2 + u_3) = 437{\cdot}5 \quad \text{(SFPF)}$$

*First iteration*: Here after we adopt only SFPF.

$$u_1^{(1)} = \frac{1}{4}(750 + 1000 + 3000) = 1187{\cdot}5$$

$$u_2^{(1)} = \frac{1}{4}(1187{\cdot}5 + 437{\cdot}5 + 1500) = 781{\cdot}25$$

$$u_3^{(1)} = \frac{1}{4}(1187{\cdot}5 + 437{\cdot}5 + 2500) = 1031{\cdot}25$$

$$u_4^{(1)} = \frac{1}{4}(781{\cdot}25 + 1031{\cdot}25) = 453{\cdot}125$$

*Second iteration*:

$$u_1^{(2)} = \frac{1}{4}(781{\cdot}25 + 1031{\cdot}25 + 3000) = 1203{\cdot}125$$

$$u_2^{(2)} = \frac{1}{4}(1203{\cdot}125 + 453{\cdot}125 + 1500) = 789{\cdot}1$$

$$u_3^{(2)} = \frac{1}{4}(1203{\cdot}125 + 453{\cdot}125 + 2500) = 1039{\cdot}1$$

$$u_4^{(2)} = \frac{1}{4}(789{\cdot}1 + 1039{\cdot}1) = 457{\cdot}1$$

*Third iteration*:

$$u_1^{(3)} = \frac{1}{4}(789{\cdot}1 + 1039{\cdot}1 + 3000) = 1207{\cdot}1$$

$$u_2^{(3)} = \frac{1}{4}(1207{\cdot}1 + 457{\cdot}1 + 1500) = 791{\cdot}1$$

$$u_3^{(3)} = \frac{1}{4}(1207{\cdot}1 + 457{\cdot}1 + 2500) = 1041{\cdot}1$$

$$u_4^{(3)} = \frac{1}{4}(791{\cdot}1 + 1041{\cdot}1) = 458{\cdot}1$$

*Fourth iteration*:

$$u_1^{(4)} = \frac{1}{4}(791{\cdot}1 + 1041{\cdot}1 + 3000) = 1208{\cdot}1$$

$$u_2^{(4)} = \frac{1}{4}(1208{\cdot}1 + 458{\cdot}1 + 1500) = 791{\cdot}6$$

$$u_3^{(4)} = \frac{1}{4}(1208{\cdot}1 + 458{\cdot}1 + 2500) = 1041{\cdot}6$$

$$u_4^{(4)} = \frac{1}{4}(791{\cdot}6 + 1041{\cdot}6) = 458{\cdot}3$$

*Fifth iteration*:

$$u_1^{(5)} = \frac{1}{4}(791{\cdot}6 + 1041{\cdot}6 + 3000) = 1208{\cdot}3$$

$$u_2^{(5)} = \frac{1}{4}(1208{\cdot}3 + 458{\cdot}3 + 1500) = 791{\cdot}7$$

$$u_3^{(5)} = \frac{1}{4}(1208{\cdot}3 + 458{\cdot}3 + 2500) = 1041{\cdot}7$$

$$u_4^{(5)} = \frac{1}{4}(791{\cdot}7 + 1041{\cdot}7) = 458{\cdot}4$$

We are getting result correct to one decimal place. Further the increase in the value is $< 0{\cdot}1$.

We stop here. One more iteration will give you the decision to make.

$$\therefore \quad \mathbf{u_1 = 1208{\cdot}3,\ u_2 = 791{\cdot}7,\ u_3 = 1041{\cdot}7,\ u_4 = 458{\cdot}4}$$

**Note:** Instead of taking $u_4 = 400$, if we have started with $u_4 = 0$, we require more iterations. So avoid this excess labour, *judiciously* assume the value.

**Example 6.** *Solve $u_{xx} + u_{yy} = 0$ for the following square mesh with boundary conditions as shown below. Iterate until the maximum difference between successive values at any grid point is less than 0.001.*

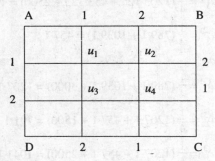

| A | 1 | 2 | B |
|---|---|---|---|
| 1 | $u_1$ | $u_2$ | 2 |
| 2 | $u_3$ | $u_4$ | 1 |
| D | 2 | 1 | C |

**Solution.** From the above figure, we see that it is symmetrical about the diagonals $AC$ and $BD$.

Let $u_1, u_2, u_3, u_4$ be the values at the interior grid points.

By symmentry, $u_1 = u_4$, $u_2 = u_3$.

Therefore, we need to find only two values $u_1$ and $u_2$.

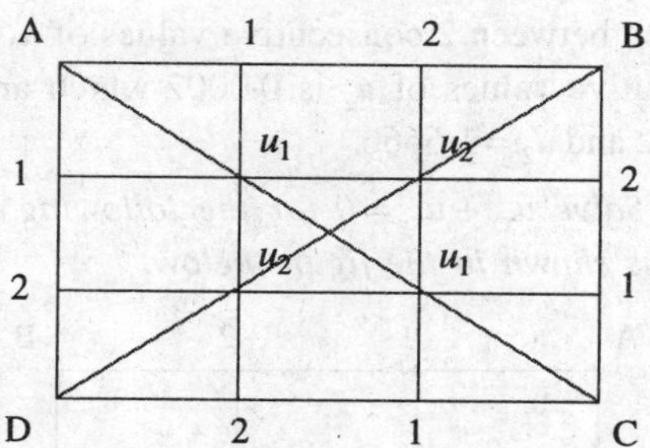


*Since the corner values are not known, assuming $u_2$, we will get $u_1$. But assume $u_2$ judiciously seeing the values of u in the vertical line through $u_2$.* Therefore let $u_2 = 1{\cdot}6$ (Please note $u_2$ is $\frac{1}{3}$ distance of the side length from the volue 2).

*Rough values estimation*:

$$u_2 = 1{\cdot}6$$

$$u_1 = \frac{1}{4}(1 + 1 + 1{\cdot}6 + 1{\cdot}6) = 1{\cdot}3$$

$$u_2 = \frac{1}{4}(2 + 2 + 1{\cdot}3 + 1{\cdot}3) = 1{\cdot}65$$

**Method 1**

*First iteration*:

$$u_1 = \frac{1}{4}(2 + 2u_2) = \frac{1}{2}(1 + u_2) = 1{\cdot}325$$

$$u_2 = \frac{1}{4}(4 + 2u_1) = \frac{1}{2}(2 + u_1) = 1.6625$$

*Second iteration*:

$$u_1 = \frac{1}{2}(1 + u_2) = \frac{1}{2}(1 + 1{\cdot}6625) = 1{\cdot}33125$$

$$u_2 = \frac{1}{2}(2 + u_1) = \frac{1}{2}(3{\cdot}33125) = 1{\cdot}6656$$

*Third iteration*:

$$u_1 = \frac{1}{2}(1 + 1{\cdot}6656) = 1{\cdot}3328$$

$$u_2 = \frac{1}{2}(3{\cdot}3328) = 1{\cdot}6664$$

*Fourth iteration*:

$$u_1 = \frac{1}{2}(1 + 1{\cdot}6664) = 1{\cdot}3332$$

$$u_2 = \frac{1}{2}(3{\cdot}3332) = 1{\cdot}6666$$

**Method 2**

$$u_1 = \frac{1}{2}(1 + u_2)$$

$$u_2 = \frac{1}{2}(2 + u_1)$$

Solving

$$u_1 = 4/3 = 1{\cdot}3333$$

and $u_2 = 5/3 = 1{\cdot}6666$

The difference between 2 consecutive values of $u_1$ is 0·0004 and that between 2 consecutive values of $u_2$ is 0·0002 which are less than 0·001. Hence, $u_1 = 1{\cdot}3332$ and $u_2 = 1{\cdot}6666$.

**Example 7.** *Solve $u_{xx} + u_{yy} = 0$ for the following square mesh with boundary values as shown in the figure below.* (*BR. Nov. 1995*)

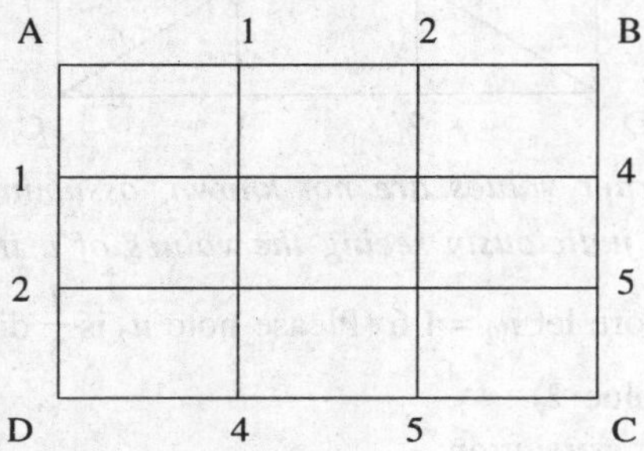


**Solution.** Evidently the boundary values are symmetrical about the diagonal AC *but not* about BD (as in the previous example). Let the values at the interval grid points be $u_1, u_2, u_3, u_4$.

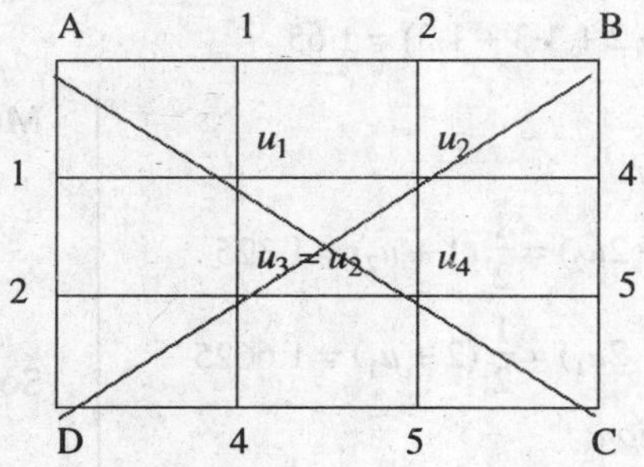


By symmetry, $u_2 = u_3$; $u_1 \neq u_4$

We need to find $u_1, u_2, u_4$ only.

Assume $u_2 = 3$ (since $u_2$ is at 1/3 distance from the

value $u = 2$, we *assume roughly* $u_2 = 2 + \frac{1}{3}(5 - 2) = 3$)

*Rough values :* $u_1 = \frac{1}{4}(1 + 1 + 2u_2) = 2.$ (SFPF)

$$u_2 = 3$$

$$u_4 = \frac{1}{4}(5 + 5 + 2u_2) = \frac{1}{2}(u_2 + 5) = 4$$

$$u_2 = \frac{1}{4}(u_1 + u_4 + 2 + 4) = 3$$

*First iteration*: $u_1 = \frac{1}{2}(1 + u_2) = 2$

$$u_2 = \frac{1}{4}(6 + u_1 + u_4) = \frac{1}{4}(6 + 2 + 4) = 3$$

$$u_4 = \frac{1}{2}(5 + u_2) = 4$$

Since the values in rough estimation and first iteration are equal, we conclude $u_1 = 2,\ u_2 = 3,\ u_4 = 4.$

**Note:** If we had assumed $u_2 = 0$, we should have gone through more iterations to get the best values. Hence selection of $u_2$ can be done more judiciously. there is *no sanctity in assuming $u_2$ as zero only. Our aim must be to get best values of u expending least quantity of labour.*

**Method 2:**

$$u_1 = \frac{1}{2}(1 + u_2);\ u_2 = \frac{1}{4}(6 + u_1 + u_4)$$

$u_4 = \frac{1}{2}(5 + u_2)$; solving these equations we get,

$u_1 = 2;\ u_2 = 3;\ u_4 = 4.$

**Example 8.** *Solve $u_{xx} + u_{yy} = 0$ over the square mesh of side 4 units; satisfying the following boundary conditions*:

(*i*) $u(0, y) = 0$ *for* $0 \le y \le 4$

(*ii*) $u(4, y) = 12 + y$, *for* $0 \le y \le 4$

(*iii*) $u(x, 0) = 3x$ *for* $0 \le x \le 4$

(*iv*) $u(x, 4) = x^2$ *for* $0 \le x \le 4.$ (*B.E. 1979*)

**Solution.** We divide the square mesh into 16 sub-squares of side 1 unit and calculate the numerical values of *u* on the boundary using given analytical expressions.

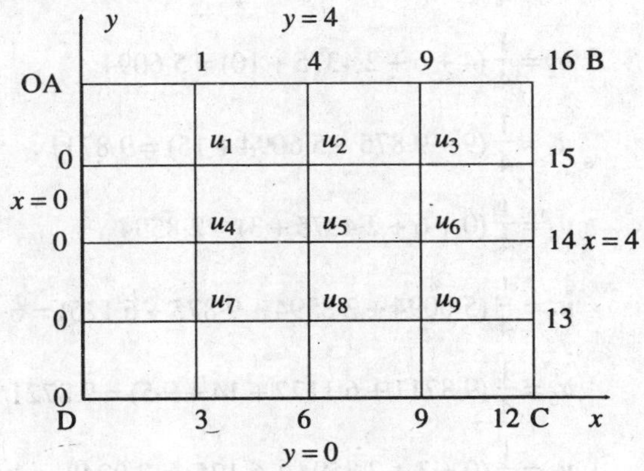

Using the coordinates of each grid point on the boundary in the analytical expressions, we mark the boundary values in numerical form.

Let the internal grid points be $u_1, u_2, \ldots u_9$.

*Rough values*:

$$u_5 = \frac{1}{4}(4 + 6 + 0 + 14) = 6 \qquad \text{(SFPF)}$$

$$u_1 = \frac{1}{4}(0 + 6 + 4 + 0) = 2{\cdot}5 \qquad \text{(DFPF)}$$

$$u_3 = \frac{1}{4}(16 + 6 + 14 + 4) = 10 \qquad \text{(DFPF)}$$

$$u_7 = \frac{1}{4}(0 + 6 + 0 + 6) = 3 \qquad \text{(DFPF)}$$

$$u_9 = \frac{1}{4}(6 + 14 + 6 + 12) = 9{\cdot}5 \qquad \text{(DFPF)}$$

We use SFPF to get the other values of $u$

$$u_2 = \frac{1}{4}(4 + 6 + 2{\cdot}5 + 10) = 5{\cdot}625$$

$$u_4 = \frac{1}{4}(0 + 6 + 2{\cdot}5 + 3) = 3{\cdot}125$$

$$u_6 = \frac{1}{4}(6 + 14 + 10 + 9.5) = 9{\cdot}875$$

$$u_8 = \frac{1}{4}(6 + 6 + 3 + 9{\cdot}5) = 6{\cdot}125$$

Now we proceed for iteration using always SFPF.

*First iteration*:

$$u_1 = \frac{1}{4}(0 + 1 + u_2 + u_4) = \frac{1}{4}(1 + 5{\cdot}625 + 3{\cdot}125) = 2{\cdot}4375$$

$$u_2 = \frac{1}{4}(4 + 6 + 2{\cdot}4375 + 10) = 5{\cdot}6094$$

$$u_3 = \frac{1}{4}(9 + 9{\cdot}875 + 5{\cdot}6094 + 15) = 9{\cdot}8711$$

$$u_4 = \frac{1}{4}(0 + 6 + 2{\cdot}4375 + 3) = 2{\cdot}8594$$

$$u_5 = \frac{1}{4}(5{\cdot}6094 + 2{\cdot}8594 + 9{\cdot}875 + 6{\cdot}125) = 6{\cdot}1172$$

$$u_6 = \frac{1}{4}(9{\cdot}8711 + 6{\cdot}1172 + 14 + 9{\cdot}5) = 9{\cdot}8721$$

$$u_7 = \frac{1}{4}(0 + 3 + 2{\cdot}8594 + 6{\cdot}125) = 2{\cdot}9948$$

$$u_8 = \frac{1}{4}(6{\cdot}1172 + 2{\cdot}9948 + 6 + 9{\cdot}5) = 6{\cdot}153$$

$$u_9 = \frac{1}{4}(9{\cdot}8721 + 6{\cdot}153 + 13 + 9) = 9{\cdot}5063.$$

*Second iteration*:

$$u_1 = \frac{1}{4}(1 + 0 + 5{\cdot}6094 + 2{\cdot}8594) = 2{\cdot}3672$$

$$u_2 = \frac{1}{4}(2{\cdot}3672 + 4 + 9{\cdot}8711 + 6{\cdot}1172) = 5{\cdot}5888$$

$$u_3 = \frac{1}{4}(9 + 15 + 5{\cdot}5888 + 9{\cdot}8721) = 9{\cdot}8652$$

$$u_4 = \frac{1}{4}(0 + 2{\cdot}3672 + 6{\cdot}1172 + 2{\cdot}9948) = 2{\cdot}8698$$

$$u_5 = \frac{1}{4}(5{\cdot}5888 + 2{\cdot}8698 + 9{\cdot}8721 + 6{\cdot}153) = 6{\cdot}1209$$

$$u_6 = \frac{1}{4}(14 + 9{\cdot}8652 + 6{\cdot}1209 + 9{\cdot}5063) = 9{\cdot}8731$$

$$u_7 = \frac{1}{4}(0 + 3 + 2{\cdot}8698 + 6{\cdot}153) = 3{\cdot}0057$$

$$u_8 = \frac{1}{4}(6{\cdot}1209 + 3{\cdot}0057 + 6 + 9{\cdot}5063) = 6{\cdot}1582$$

$$u_9 = \frac{1}{4}(9{\cdot}8731 + 6{\cdot}1587 + 13 + 9) = 9{\cdot}5078$$

Repeating one more iteration, we conclude, correct to two decimals,

$u_1 = 2{\cdot}37,\ u_2 = 5{\cdot}59,\ u_3 = 9{\cdot}87,\ u_4 = 2{\cdot}88,\ u_5 = 6{\cdot}13,\ u_6 = 9{\cdot}88,$

$u_7 = 3{\cdot}01,\ u_8 = 6{\cdot}16,\ u_9 = 9{\cdot}51.$

## 12·7. Poisson's Equation

An equation of the form $\nabla^2 u = f(x, y)$

*i.e.*,
$$\frac{\partial^2 u}{\partial x^2} + \frac{\partial^2 u}{\partial y^2} = f(x, y) \qquad ...(1)$$

is called as POISSON'S equation where $f(x, y)$ is a function of $x$ and $y$ only.

We will solve the above equation numerically at the points of the square mesh, replacing the derivatives by difference quotients. Taking $x = ih,\ y = jk = jh$ (here) the differential equation reduces to

$$\frac{u_{i-1,j} - 2u_{i,j} + u_{i+1,j}}{h^2} + \frac{u_{i,j-1} - 2u_{i,j} + u_{i,j+1}}{h^2} = f(ih, jh)$$

*i.e.*,
$$u_{i-1,j} + u_{i+1,j} + u_{i,j-1} + u_{i,j+1} - 4u_{i,j} = h^2 f(ih, jh) \qquad ...(2)$$

By applying the above formula at each mesh point, we get a system of linear equation in the pivotal values *i, j*.

We can follow this method easily by working out the following example.

**Example 9.** *Solve* $\nabla^2 u = -10(x^2 + y^2 + 10)$ *over the square mesh with sides* $x = 0,\ y = 0,\ x = 3,\ y = 3$ *with* $u = 0$ *on the boundary and mesh length 1 unit.* *(MS. 1976)*

**Solution.**

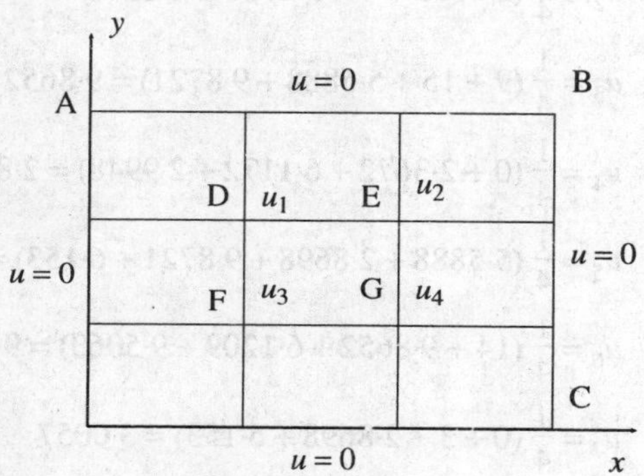


The P.D.E. is $\nabla^2 u = -10(x^2 + y^2 + 10)$ ...(1)

using the theory, (here $h = 1$)

$$u_{i-1,j} + u_{i+1,j} + u_{i,j-1} + u_{i,j+1} - 4u_{i,j} = -10(i^2 + j^2 + 10) \quad ...(2)$$

Applying the formula (2) at $D$ $(i = 1, j = 2)$

$$0 + 0 + u_2 + u_3 - 4u_1 = -10(15) = -150$$

$$u_2 + u_3 - 4u_1 = -150 \quad ...(3)$$

Applying at $E$ $(i = 2, j = 2)$

$$u_1 + u_4 - 4u_2 = -180 \quad ...(4)$$

Applying (2) at $F$, $(i = 1, j = 1)$

$$u_1 + u_4 - 4u_3 = -120 \quad ...(5)$$

Applying (2) at $G$, $(i = 2, j = 1)$

$$u_2 + u_3 - 4u_4 = -10(2^2 + 1^2 + 10) = -150 \quad ...(6)$$

We can solve the equation (3), (4), (5), (6) either by direct elimination or by Gauss-Seidel method.

**Method 1.** (5) – (4) gives, (Eliminate $u_1$)

$$4(u_2 - u_3) = 60$$

$$u_2 - u_3 = 15 \quad ...(7)$$

Eliminate $u_1$ from (3) and (4); (3) + 4(4) gives,

$$-15u_2 + u_3 + 4u_4 = -870 \qquad ...(8)$$

Adding (6) and (8) $-7u_2 + u_3 = -510$ ...(9)

From (7), (9) adding, $u_2 = 82{\cdot}5$

Using (7), $u_3 = u_2 - 15 = 82{\cdot}5 - 15 = 67{\cdot}5$

Put in (3), $4u_1 = 300 \therefore u_1 = 75$

$$4u_4 = 150 + 150; \quad u_4 = 75$$

$$\boxed{\therefore \quad \mathbf{u_1 = u_4 = 75, \; u_2 = 82{\cdot}5, \; u_3 = 67{\cdot}5}}$$

**Note:** Since the differential equation is unchanged when $x$, $y$ are interchanged and boundary conditions are also same after interchange $x$ and $y$, the result will be symmetrical about the line $y = x$ $\therefore u_4 = u_1$.

If we use this idea the 4 equations would have reduced to 3 equations namely,

$$u_2 + u_3 - 4u_1 = -150, \; 2u_1 - 4u_2 = -180,$$

$$2u_1 - 4u_3 = -120 \text{ and } u_2 + u_3 - 4u_1 = -150.$$

Solving will be easier now.

**Method 2.** We can use Gauss-Seidel method to solve.

$$u_1 = \frac{1}{4}(150 + u_2 + u_3)$$

$$u_2 = \frac{1}{4}(2u_1 + 180)$$

$$u_3 = \frac{1}{4}(2u_1 + 120)$$

The tabular values are:

| | 1 | 2 | 3 | 4 | 5 | 6 | 7 | 8 | 9 | 10 |
|---|---|---|---|---|---|---|---|---|---|---|
| $u_4 = u_1$ | – | 37·5 | 65·56 | 72·64 | 74·41 | 74·85 | 74·96 | 74·99 | 75 | 75 |
| $u_2$ | 0 | 63·75 | 77·79 | 81·32 | 82·21 | 82·43 | 82·48 | 82·5 | 82·5 | 82·5 |
| $u_3$ | 0 | 48·75 | 62·78 | 66·32 | 67·21 | 67·43 | 67·48 | 67·5 | 67·5 | 67·5 |

We get the values after 9 iterations as

$$\boxed{\mathbf{u_1 = 75 = u_4, \; u_2 = 82{\cdot}5, \; u_3 = 67{\cdot}5}}$$

**Example 10.** *Solve* $\nabla^2 u = 8x^2y^2$ *for square mesh given* $u = 0$ *on the 4 boundaries dividing the square into 16 sub-squares of lenght 1 unit.*

**Solution.**

$y \quad u = 0$

| | | | |
|---|---|---|---|
| $u_1$ | $u_2$ | $u_3$ | |
| $u_4$ | $u_5$ | $u_6$ | $x$ |
| $u_7$ | $u_8$ | $u_9$ | |

$u = 0$ (left), $0$ (origin), $u = 0$ (right), $u = 0$ (bottom)

Take the coordinate system with origin at the centre of the square. Since the P.D.E. and boundary conditions are symmetrical about $x$, $y$ axes and $y = x$ we have, $u_1 = u_3 = u_7 = u_9$

$$u_2 = u_4 = u_6 = u_8$$

$\therefore$ We need to find $u_1, u_2, u_5$ only. (Here $h = 1$)

As per the five point formula, (here $f(x, y) = 8x^2y^2$)

$$u_{i-1,j} + u_{i+1,j} + u_{i,j-1} + u_{i,j+1} - 4u_{i,j} = h^2 f(ih, jh) = f(i, j) \qquad ...(1)$$

At $(i = -i, j = -1)$, we have, $u_2 + u_4 - 4u_1 = 8(-1)^2(-1)^2 = 8$

*i.e.*,
$$u_2 - 2u_1 = 4 \qquad ...(2)$$

At $(i = 0, j = 1)$,
$$u_1 + u_3 + u_5 - 4u_2 = 0$$
$$2u_1 - 4u_2 + u_5 = 0 \qquad ...(3)$$

At $(i = 0, j = 0)$,
$$u_2 + u_4 + u_6 + u_8 - 4u_5 = 0$$
$$4u_2 - 4u_5 = 0$$

*i.e.*,
$$u_2 - u_5 = 0 \qquad ...(4)$$

From (2), $\quad u_1 = \frac{1}{2}(u_2 - 4)$

From (4), $\quad u_5 = u_2$

Using in (3), $u_2 - 4 - 4u_2 + u_2 = 0 \;\therefore\; u_2 = -2$

$\therefore \; u_5 = -2, u_1 = -3$

$$\boxed{\therefore \; \mathbf{u_1 = -3, \; u_2 = -2 = u_5}}$$

**Note :** We can also use any numerical method such as Gauss-Seidel method to solve numerically.

## EXERCISE 12.2

**1.** Sove the boundary value problem $\nabla^2 u = 0$ for the square of sides three units.

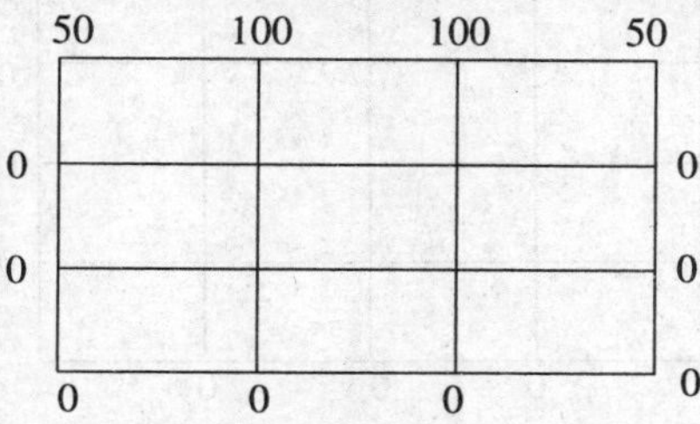


*(B.E. 1978)*

**2.** Sove $\nabla^2 u = 0$ at the nodal points for the following square region given the boundary conditions.

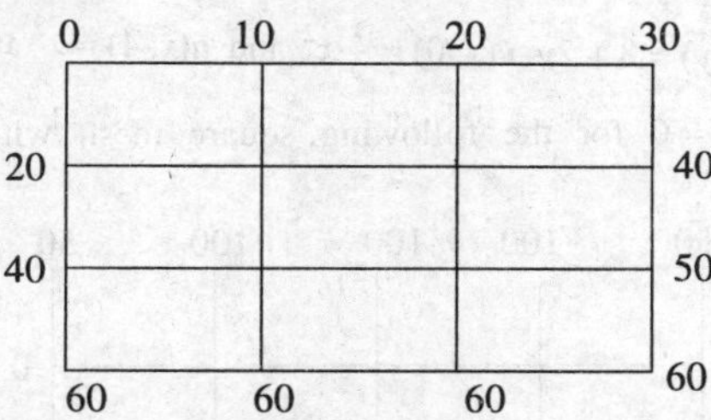


**3.** Solve $\nabla^2 u = 0$ for the square region with the given boundary conditions.

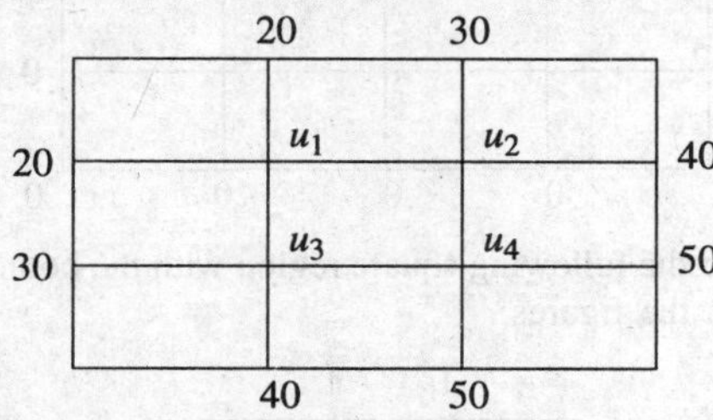


**4.** Solve $\nabla^2 u = 0$ for the following square mesh with the boundary conditions as given below. Get the values correct to three decimal places.

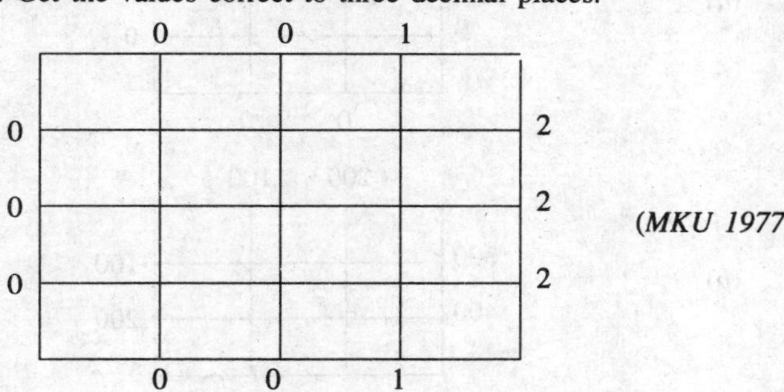


*(MKU 1977)*

**5.** Solve $\nabla^2 u = 0$ for the following square mesh.

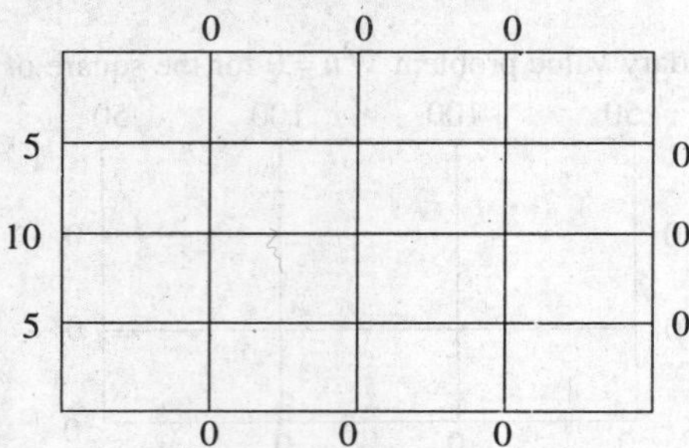


**6.** Solve: $\nabla^2 u = 0$ in the square region bounded by $x = 0$, $x = 4$, $y = 0$, $y = 4$ and with boundary conditions,

$$u(0, y) = 0,\ u(4, y) = 8 + 2y,\ u(x, 0) = \frac{1}{2}x^2 \text{ and } u(x, 4) = x^2 \text{ taking } h = k = 1$$

**7.** Solve $u_{xx} + u_{yy} = 0$ for the following square mesh with given boundary conditions:

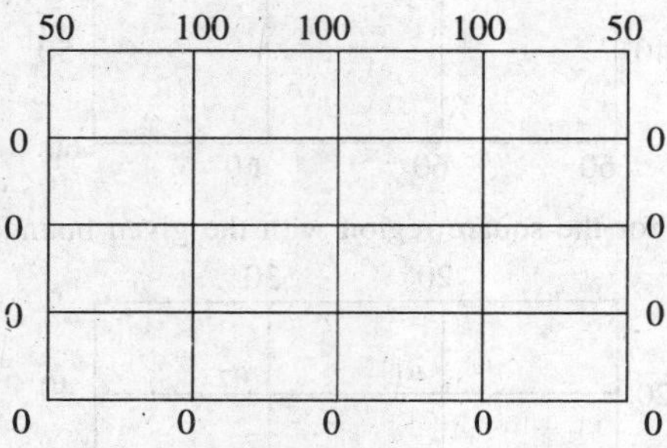


**8.** Solve $\nabla^2 u = 0$ in the following square region with the boundary conditions as shown below in the figures.

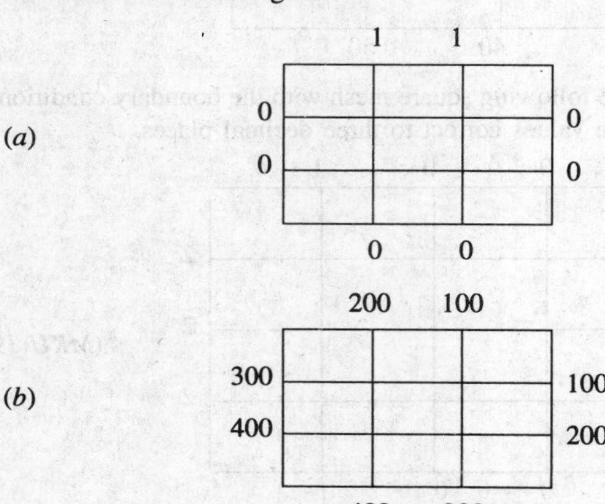

## PARABOLIC EQUATIONS

### 12·8. Bender-Schmidt Method

The one-dimensional heat equation, namely,

$\frac{\partial u}{\partial t} = \alpha^2 \frac{\partial^2 u}{\partial x^2}$ where $\alpha^2 = \frac{k}{\rho c}$ is an example of parabolic equation.

Setting $\alpha^2 = \frac{1}{a}$, the equation becomes, $\frac{\partial^2 u}{\partial x^2} - a \frac{\partial u}{\partial t} = 0$.

Here $A = 1$, $B = 0$, $C = 0$ $\therefore$ $B^2 - 4AC = 0$. Therefore, it is parabolic at all points.

**AIM :** Our aim is to solve this by the method of finite differences.

*To solve* : $$u_{xx} = au_t \quad ...(1)$$

with boundary conditions,

$$u(0, t) = T_0 \quad ...(2)$$

$$u(l, t) = T_l \quad ...(3)$$

and with initial condition $$u(x, 0) = f(x), 0 < x < l \quad ...(4)$$

We select a spacing $h$ for the variable $x$ and a spacing $k$ for the time variable $t$.

$$u_{xx} = \frac{u_{i+1,j} - 2u_{i,j} + u_{i-1,j}}{h^2}$$

and $$u_t = \frac{u_{i,j+1} - u_{i,j}}{k}$$

Hence (1) becomes,

$$\frac{u_{i+1,j} - 2u_{i,j} + u_{i-1,j}}{h^2} = \frac{a}{k}(u_{i,j+1} - u_{i,j})$$

$$\therefore \quad u_{i,j+1} - u_{i,j} = \frac{k}{ah^2}(u_{i+1,j} - 2u_{i,j} + u_{i-1,j})$$

$$= \lambda(u_{i+1,j} - 2u_{i,j} + u_{i-1,j})$$

where $$\lambda = \frac{k}{ah^2}.$$

*i.e.*, $$\boxed{\mathbf{u_{i,j+1} = \lambda u_{i+1,j} + (1 - 2\lambda)\, u_{i,j} + \lambda u_{i-1,j}}} \quad ...(5)$$

Writing the boundary condition as $u_{0,j} = T_0$ ...(6)

$$u_{n,j} = T_l \quad ...(7)$$

where $$nh = l.$$

and initial condition as

$$u_{i,0} = f(ih),\ i = 1, 2, \ldots \quad \ldots(8)$$

$u$ is known at $t = 0$.

Equation (5) facilitates to get the value of $u$ at $x = ih$ and time $t_{j+k}$.

Equation (5) is called EXPLICIT FORMULA. It is valid if $0 < \lambda \leq \frac{1}{2}$.

If we take, $\lambda = \frac{1}{2}$, the coefficient of $u_{i,j}$ vanishes.

Hence Equation (5) becomes,

$$\boxed{\mathbf{u_{i,j+1} = \frac{1}{2}[u_{i-1,j} + u_{i+1,j}]}} \quad \ldots(9)$$

when $\lambda = \frac{1}{2} = \frac{k}{ah^2}$; *i.e.*, $k = \frac{a}{2}h^2$

*i.e.*, the value of $u$ at $x = x_i$ at $t = t_{j+1}$ is equal to the average of the values of $u$ the surrounding points $x_{i-1}$ and $x_{i+1}$ at the previous time $t_j$.

Equation (9) is called **Bender-Schmidt recurrence equation.**

This is valid only if $k = \frac{a}{2}h^2$ (so, select $k$ like this)

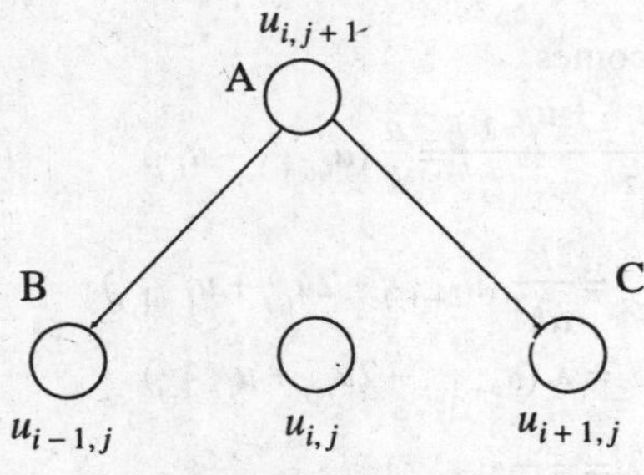


Schematic diagram

Value of $u$ at $A = \frac{1}{2}$ [Value of $u$ at $B$ + value of $u$ at $C$]

**Example 11.** *Solve* $\frac{\partial^2 u}{\partial x^2} - 2\frac{\partial u}{\partial t} = 0$ *given*

$u(0, t) = 0$, $u(4, t) = 0$, $u(x, 0) = x(4 - x)$. *Assume* $h = 1$. *Find the values of* $u$ *upto* $t = 5$. *(MKU 1975)*

**Solution.** $u_{xx} = au_t \quad \therefore \quad a = 2$

To use Bender-Schmidt's equation, $k = \frac{a}{2} h^2 = 1$

Step-size in time = $k$ = 1. The values of $u_{i,j}$ are tabulated below.

$x$-direction →

| $j$ \ $i$ | 0 | 1 | 2 | 3 | 4 | |
|---|---|---|---|---|---|---|
| 0 | 0 | 3 | 4 | 3 | 0 | ← $u(x, 0) = x(4 - x)$ |
| 1 | 0 | 2 | 3 | 2 | 0 | |
| 2 | 0 | 1·5 | 2 | 1·5 | 0 | |
| 3 | 0 | 1 | 1·5 | 1 | 0 | |
| 4 | 0 | 0·75 | 1 | 0·75 | 0 | |
| 5 | 0 | 0·5 | 0·75 | 0·5 | 0 | |

↓ $t$-direction

*Analysis*: Range for $x$ : (0, 4); for $t$ : (0, 5)

$u(x, 0) = x(4 - x)$. This gives $u(0, 0) = 0$, $u(1, 0) = 3$,

$u(2, 0) = 4$, $u(3, 0) = 3$, $u(4, 0) = 0$.

For all , at $x = 0$, $u = 0$ and for all $t$ at $x = 4$, $u = 0$.

Using these values we fill up column under $x = 0$, $x = 4$ and row against $t = 0$.

a b

c

This means $c = \frac{a+b}{2}$

The values of $u$ at $t$ = 1 are written by seeing the values of $u$ at $t$ = 0 and using the average formula.

**Example 12.** *Solve* $\frac{\partial^2 u}{\partial x^2} = \frac{\partial u}{\partial t}$ *given* $u(0, t) = 0$, $u(4, t) = 0$, $u(x, 0) = x(4 - x)$ *assuming* $h = k = 1$.

*Find the values of u upto t = 5.* (*U.Q.*)

**Solution.** If we want to use Bender-Schmidt formula, we should have $k = \frac{a}{2} h^2$.

Here, $k = h = 1, a = 1$. These values do not satisfy the condition. Hence we cannot employ Bender-Schmidt formula.

Hence we go to the basic equation in Article 12·8, namely,

$$u_{i,j+1} = \lambda u_{i+1,j} + (1 - 2\lambda) u_{i,j} + \lambda u_{i-1,j} \quad ...(1)$$

Now $\lambda = \dfrac{k}{ah^2} = \dfrac{1}{1 \times 1} = 1$

Hence, (1) reduces to,

$$u_{i,j+1} = u_{i+1,j} - u_{i,j} + u_{i-1,j}$$

That is,

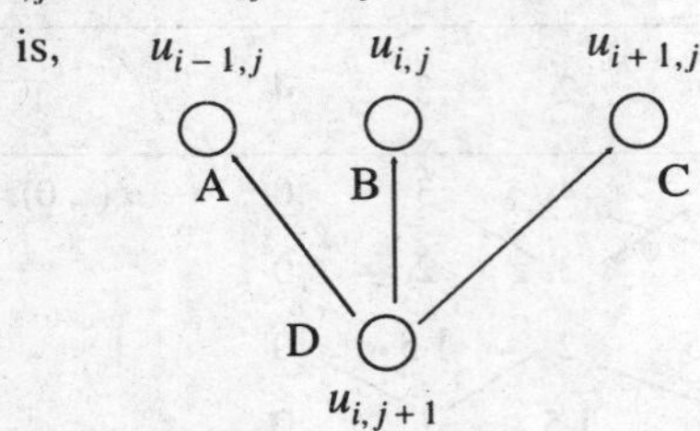


Value of $u$ at D = value of $u$ at A + value of $u$ at C – value of $u$ at B.

Now we are ready to create the table values.

→$x$ direction

| $j$ \ $i$ | 0 | 1 | 2 | 3 | 4 |
|---|---|---|---|---|---|
| 0 | 0 | 3 | 4 | 3 | 0 |
| 1 | 0 | 1 | 2 | 1 | 0 |
| 2 | 0 | 1 | 0 | 1 | 0 |
| 3 | 0 | – 1 | 2 | – 1 | 0 |
| 4 | 0 | 3 | – 4 | 3 | 0 |
| 5 | 0 | – 7 | 10 | – 7 | 0 |

↓ $t$ direction

Here,

$a$ $b$ $c$
O O O

This figure means O
$d$

$$d = a + c - b$$

**Note:** Since $\lambda = 1$ is used in the working, it violates the condition for use of *Explicit formula.* So the solution is not stable and it is not a practical problem. Such questions should be avoided, since unstable solutions do not exist.

**Example 13.** *Solve* $u_t = u_{xx}$ *subject to* $u\ (0,\ t) = 0$, $u\ (1,\ t) = 0$ *and* $u\ (x,\ 0) = \sin \pi x$, $0 < x < 1$. *(MS. N. 1991)*

**Solution.** Since $h$, and $k$ are not given we will select them properly and use Bender-Schmidt method.

$$k = \frac{a}{2}h^2 = \frac{1}{2}h^2 \because a = 1.$$

Since range of $x$ is (0, 1), take $h = 0{\cdot}2$.

Hence $k = \dfrac{(0{\cdot}2)^2}{2} = 0{\cdot}02$.

The formula is $u_{i,\,j+1} = \dfrac{1}{2}(u_{i-1,j} + u_{i+1,j})$

$$u(0, 0) = 0, \ u(0{\cdot}2, 0) = \sin\frac{\pi}{5} = 0{\cdot}5878$$

$$u(0{\cdot}4, 0) = \sin\frac{2\pi}{5} = 0{\cdot}9511; \sin(0{\cdot}6, 0) = \sin\frac{3\pi}{5} = 0{\cdot}9511$$

$$\sin(0{\cdot}8, 0) = \sin\frac{4\pi}{5} = 0{\cdot}5878 \qquad \sin(1, 0) = 0$$

We form the table.

$x \rightarrow$ direction $h = 0{\cdot}2$

| $j$ \ $i$ | 0 | 0·2 | 0·4 | 0·6 | 0·8 | 1·0 |
|---|---|---|---|---|---|---|
| 0 | 0 | 0·5878 | 0·9511 | 0·9511 | 0·5878 | 0 |
| 0·02 | 0 | 0·4756 | 0·7695 | 0·7695 | 0·4756 | 0 |
| 0·04 | 0 | 0·3848 | 0·6225 | 0·6225 | 0·3848 | 0 |
| 0·06 | 0 | 0·3113 | 0·5036 | 0·5036 | 0·3113 | 0 |
| 0·08 | 0 | 0·2518 | 0·4074 | 0·4074 | 0·2518 | 0 |
| 0·1 | 0 | 0·2037 | 0·3296 | 0·3296 | 0·2037 | 0 |

$\downarrow$ *t*-direction $k = 0{\cdot}02$

**Example 14.** *Given* $\dfrac{\partial^2 f}{\partial x^2} = \dfrac{\partial f}{\partial t}$, $f(0, t) = f(5, t) = 0$, $f(x, 0) = x^2(25 - x^2)$, *find f in the range taking h = 1 and upto 5 seconds.*

**Solution.** To use Schmidt method, $k = \dfrac{a}{2}h^2$.

Here, $a = 1, h = 1 \quad \therefore \quad k = 1/2$

Step-size of time = 1/2

Step-size of $x$ = 1.

$f(0, 0) = 0, f(1, 0) = 24, f(2, 0) = 84, f(3, 0) = 144, f(4, 0) = 144$, $f(5, 0) = 0$.

We have, $u_{i,\,j+1} = \dfrac{1}{2}(u_{i-1,j} + u_{i+1,j})$

→ $x$ direction

| $j$ \ $i$ | 0 | 1 | 2 | 3 | 4 | 5 |
|---|---|---|---|---|---|---|
| 0 | 0 | 24 | 84 | 144 | 144 | 0 |
| ½ | 0 | 42 | 84 | 114 | 72 | 0 |
| 1 | 0 | 42 | 78 | 78 | 57 | 0 |
| 1·5 | 0 | 39 | 60 | 67·5 | 39 | 0 |
| 2 | 0 | 30 | 53·25 | 49·5 | 33·75 | 0 |
| 2·5 | 0 | 26·625 | 39·75 | 43·5 | 24·75 | 0 |
| 3 | 0 | 19·875 | 35·0625 | 32·25 | 21·75 | 0 |
| 3·5 | 0 | 17·5312 | 26·0625 | 28·4062 | 16·125 | 0 |
| 4 | 0 | 13·0312 | 22·9687 | 21·0938 | 14·2031 | 0 |
| 4·5 | 0 | 11·4843 | 17·0625 | 18·5859 | 10·5469 | 0 |
| 5 | 0 | 8·5312 | 15·0351 | 13·8047 | 9·2929 | 0 |

↓ $t$-direction

**Example 15.** *Solve $u_{xx} = 32u_t$, taking $h = 0{\cdot}25$ for $t > 0$, $0 < x < 1$ and $u(x, 0) = 0$, $u(0, t) = 0$, $u(1, t) = t$.* *(Ap. 1992)*

**Solution.** The range for $x$ is (0, 1); $h = 0{\cdot}25$

$$k = \frac{a}{2}h^2 = \frac{32}{2}\left(\frac{1}{4}\right)^2 = 1$$

Step-size of time $t$ is 1;

direction of $x$

| $j$ \ $i$ | 0 | 0·25 | 0·5 | 0·75 | 1 |
|---|---|---|---|---|---|
| 0 | 0 | 0 | 0 | 0 | 0 |
| 1 | 0 | 0 | 0 | 0 | 1 |
| 2 | 0 | 0 | 0 | 0·5 | 2 |
| 3 | 0 | 0 | 0·25 | 1 | 3 |
| 4 | 0 | 0·125 | 0·5 | 1·625 | 4 |
| 5 | 0 | 0·25 | 0·875 | 2·25 | 5 |

$t$ ↓

Values of $u$

## 12·9. Crank-Nicholson Difference Method

**AIM:** To solve the parabolic equation

$u_{xx} = au_t$ with boundary conditions

$u(0, t) = T_0$, $u(l, t) = T_l$ and the initial condition $u(x, 0) = f(x)$.

The equation to be solved is $u_{xx} = au_t$ ...(1)

At $u_{i,j}$,

$$u_{xx} = \frac{u_{i+1,j} - 2u_{i,j} + u_{i-1,j}}{h^2}$$

and at $u_{i,j+1}$,

$$u_{xx} = \frac{u_{i+1,j+1} - 2\,u_{i,\,j+1} + u_{i-1,j+1}}{h^2}$$

Taking the average of these two values,

$$u_{xx} \approx \frac{u_{i+1,j+1} - 2u_{i,j+1} + u_{i-1,j+1} + u_{i+1,j} - 2u_{i,j} + u_{i-1,j}}{2h^2}$$

Using $u_t = \dfrac{u_{i,j+1} - u_{i,j}}{k}$, equation (1) reduces to

$$\frac{u_{i+1,j+1} - 2u_{i,j+1} + u_{i-1,j+1} + u_{i+1,j} - 2u_{i,j} + u_{i-1,j}}{2h^2} = a\,\frac{u_{i,j+1} - u_{i,j}}{k}$$

Setting $\dfrac{k}{ah^2} = \lambda$, the above equation reduces to

$$\frac{1}{2}\lambda\,\mathbf{u}_{i+1,j+1} + \frac{1}{2}\lambda\,\mathbf{u}_{i-1,j+1} - (\lambda+1)\,\mathbf{u}_{i,j+1} = -\frac{1}{2}\lambda\,\mathbf{u}_{i+1,j} - \frac{1}{2}\lambda\,\mathbf{u}_{i-1,j} + (\lambda-1)\,\mathbf{u}_{i,j} \quad \text{...(I)}$$

This can be rewritten as,

$$\lambda\,(u_{i+1,j+1} + u_{i-1,j+1}) - 2\,(\lambda+1)\,u_{i,j+1} = 2\,(\lambda-1)\,u_{i,j} - \lambda\,(u_{i+1,j} + u_{i-1,j}) \quad \text{...(I)}$$

Equation I is called **Crank-Nicholson difference scheme or method.**

**Note 1.** The six points in the above formula (or scheme) are shown below:

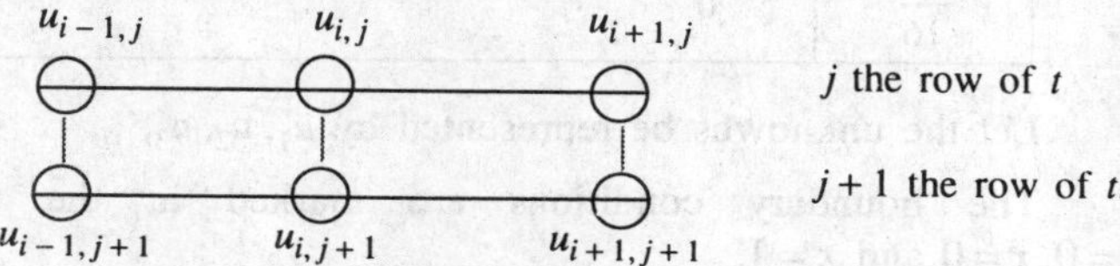


**Note 2.** A convenient choice of $\lambda$ makes the scheme simple. Setting $\lambda = 1$ *i.e.,* $\boxed{\mathbf{k = ah^2}}$ The Crank-Nicholson formula reduces to

$$\mathbf{u}_{i,j+1} = \frac{1}{4}\,[\mathbf{u}_{i-1,j+1} + \mathbf{u}_{i+1,j+1} + \mathbf{u}_{i-1,j} + \mathbf{u}_{i+1,j}] \quad \text{...(II)}$$

In problems, we will use this simplified formula subject to $k = ah^2$.

*Scheme*

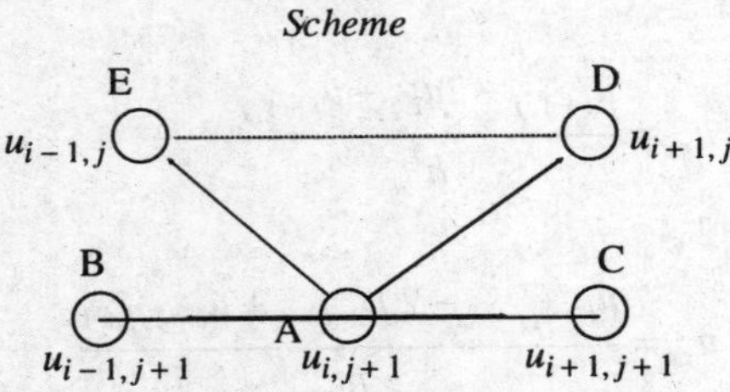


The value of $u$ at A = average of the values at B, C, D, E.

**Note 3.** The Crank-Nicholson scheme converges for all values of $\lambda$.

**Example 16.** *Solve by Crank-Nicholson method the equation* $u_{xx} = u_t$ *subject to* $u(x, 0) = 0$, $u(0, t) = 0$ *and* $u(1, t) = t$, *for two time steps.*

**Solution.** $x$ ranges from 0 to 1. Take $h = \frac{1}{4}$; here $a = 1$

$\therefore$ $k = ah^2$ to use simple form

$$k = 1\left(\frac{1}{4}\right)^2 = \frac{1}{16}.$$

We use $u_{i,j+1} = \frac{1}{4}[u_{i+1,j+1} + u_{i-1,j+1} + u_{i-1,j} + u_{i+1,j}]$ ...(1)

$x \rightarrow$ direction

| $t \downarrow$ | | 0 | 0·25 | 0·5 | 0·75 | 1 |
|---|---|---|---|---|---|---|
| | 0 | 0 | 0 | 0 | 0 | 0 |
| | $\frac{1}{16}$ | 0 | $u_1$ | $u_2$ | $u_3$ | $\frac{1}{16}$ |
| | $\frac{2}{16}$ | 0 | $u_4$ | $u_5$ | $u_6$ | $\frac{2}{16}$ |
| | $\frac{3}{16}$ | 0 | | | | $\frac{3}{16}$ |

Let the unknowns be represented by $u_1, u_2, u_3, \ldots$

The boundary conditions are marked in the table against $t = 0, x = 0$ and $x = 1$.

Using the scheme (1),

$u_1 = \frac{1}{4}(0 + 0 + 0 + u_2)$ | *i.e.,* $u_1 = \frac{1}{4}u_2$ ...(2)

$u_2 = \frac{1}{4}(0 + 0 + u_1 + u_3)$ | $u_2 = \frac{1}{4}(u_1 + u_3)$ ...(3)

$u_3 = \frac{1}{4}\left(0 + 0 + u_2 + \frac{1}{16}\right)$ | $u_3 = \frac{1}{4}\left(u_2 + \frac{1}{16}\right)$ ...(4)

Solving the three equations given by (2), (3), (4) we get $u_1, u_2, u_3$. Substitute $u_3, u_1$ values in (3).

$$u_2 = \frac{1}{4}\left[\frac{1}{4}u_2 + \frac{1}{4}\left(u_2 + \frac{1}{16}\right)\right]$$

$$u_2 = \frac{1}{224}\mathbf{0{\cdot}0045},\ u_1 = \frac{1}{896} = \mathbf{0{\cdot}0011},\ u_3 = \mathbf{0{\cdot}0168}.$$

Similarly $u_4, u_5, u_6$ can be got again getting 3 equations in 3 unknowns $u_4, u_5, u_6$.

We get $u_4 = \mathbf{0{\cdot}005899}$, $u_5 = \mathbf{0{\cdot}01913}$, $u_6 = \mathbf{0{\cdot}05277}$.

**Note:** In solving the three equations (2), (3), (4) we could have used Gauss-Seidel method also. The iterated values are noted below.

| | | | | | | | | |
|---|---|---|---|---|---|---|---|---|
| $u_1$ | – | 0·125 | 0·0391 | 0·0059 | 0·0017 | 0·0012 | 0·0011 | 0·0011 |
| $u_2$ | 0·5 | 0·1563 | 0·0235 | 0·0069 | 0·0048 | 0·0045 | 0·0045 | 0·0045 |
| $u_3$ | 0·5 | 0·0547 | 0·0215 | 0·0174 | 0·0168 | 0·0168 | 0·0168 | 0·0168 |

**Example 17.** *Using Crank-Nicholson's scheme, solve*

$u_{xx} = 16u_t$, $0 < x < 1$, $t > 0$ *given*

$u(x, 0) = 0$, $u(0, t) = 0$, $u(1, t) = 100t$.

*Compute u for one step in t direction taking* $h = \frac{1}{4}\cdot$

**Solution.** Here $a = 16, h = \frac{1}{4}\cdot \quad \therefore \quad k = ah^2 = 16\left(\frac{1}{16}\right) = 1;$

$$u_{i,j+1} = \frac{1}{4}[u_{i+1,j+1} + u_{i-1,j+1} + u_{i+1,j} + u_{i-1,j}]$$

$\rightarrow x$ increasing

| | j \ i | 0 | 0·25 | 0·5 | 0·75 | 1 |
|---|---|---|---|---|---|---|
| ↓ t | 0 | 0 | 0 | 0 | 0 | 0 |
| | 1 | 0 | $u_1$ | $u_2$ | $u_3$ | 100 |

$$u_1 = \frac{1}{4}(0 + 0 + 0 + u_2) \quad \therefore \quad u_1 = \frac{1}{4}u_2 \qquad ...(2)$$

$$u_2 = \frac{1}{4}(0 + 0 + u_1 + u_3) \quad \therefore \quad u_2 = \frac{1}{4}(u_1 + u_3) \qquad ...(3)$$

$$u_3 = \frac{1}{4}(0 + 0 + u_2 + 100) \quad \therefore \quad u_3 = \frac{1}{4}(u_2 + 100) \qquad ...(4)$$

Substitute $u_1, u_3$ values in (3),

$$u_2 = \frac{1}{4}\left[\frac{1}{4}(2u_2 + 100)\right] = \frac{1}{8}u_2 + \frac{25}{4} \quad \therefore \quad u_2 = \frac{50}{7} = 7{\cdot}1429$$

$u_1 = 1{\cdot}7857$ ; $u_3 = 26{\cdot}7857$.

The values are

$$\boxed{\mathbf{u_1 = 1{\cdot}7857,\ u_2 = 7{\cdot}1429,\ u_3 = 26{\cdot}7857.}}$$

**Example 18.** *Using Crank-Nicholson method, solve* $\dfrac{\partial u}{\partial t} = \dfrac{\partial^2 u}{\partial x^2}$, *subject to* $u(x, 0) = 0$, $u(0, t) = 0$ *and* $u(1, t) = t$, *(i) taking* $h = 0{\cdot}5$ *and* $k = \frac{1}{8}$ *and (ii)* $h = 1/4$ *and* $k = 1/8$.

**Solution.** Here, $a = 1$; $\therefore \quad \lambda = \dfrac{k}{ah^2} = \dfrac{\frac{1}{8}}{1 \times \frac{1}{4}} = 1/2$

Since $\lambda = 1/2$, we cannot use simplified formula.

We use Equation I in Article 12·9. Putting $\lambda = 1/2$ the formula becomes,

$$u_{i+1,j+1} + u_{i-1,j+1} - 6\,u_{i,j+1} = -2\,u_{i,j} - (u_{i-1,j} + u_{i+1,j}) \qquad ...(1)$$

$x \rightarrow$ increasing

| $t$ \ $x$ | 0 | 0·5 | 1 | |
|---|---|---|---|---|
| 0 | 0 | 0 $(u_{i,j})$ | 0 | $\leftarrow j$th |
| $\frac{1}{8}$ | 0 | $u_1$ $(u_{i,j+1})$ | $\frac{1}{8}$ | $\leftarrow j+1$th |
| $\frac{1}{4}$ | 0 | | $\frac{1}{4}$ | |

$t \downarrow$

Now, using (1)

$$\frac{1}{8} + 0 - 6\,u_1 = -2\,(0) - (0 + 0)$$

$$\therefore \quad u_1 = \frac{1}{48} = 0{\cdot}0208333$$

*(ii)* If $h = \dfrac{1}{4}$, $k = \dfrac{1}{8}$, $\lambda = \dfrac{k}{ah^2} = \dfrac{1/8}{1 \times \frac{1}{16}} = 2.$

Using in general Crank-Nicholson formula, I of Article 12·9, we get,

$$u_{i+1,j+1} + u_{i-1,j+1} - 3\,u_{i,j+1} = u_{i,j} - u_{i+1,j} - u_{i-1,j}$$

$x \rightarrow$

| $t \downarrow$ | | 0 | 0·25 | 0·5 | 0·75 | 1 |
|---|---|---|---|---|---|---|
| | 0 | 0 | 0 | 0 | 0 | 0 |
| | $\frac{1}{8}$ | 0 | $u_1$ | $u_2$ | $u_3$ | $\frac{1}{8}$ |

$$\therefore \quad 0 + u_2 - 3u_1 = 0 \quad \therefore \quad u_2 = 3u_1 \qquad \text{...(2)}$$

$$u_1 + u_3 - 3u_2 = 0 \quad \therefore \quad 3u_2 = u_1 + u_3 \qquad \text{...(3)}$$

$$\text{Also, } u_2 + \frac{1}{8} - 3u_3 = 0 \quad \therefore \quad 3u_3 = u_2 + \frac{1}{8} \qquad \text{...(4)}$$

$$\text{Adding (2) and (4), } 3(u_1 + u_3) = 2u_2 + \frac{1}{8} \qquad \text{...(5)}$$

From (3) and (5), we get

$$9u_2 = 2u_2 + \frac{1}{8}$$

$$\therefore \quad \mathbf{u_2 = \frac{1}{56} = 0{\cdot}01786}$$

$$\mathbf{u_1 = \frac{1}{168} = 0{\cdot}00595}$$

$$\mathbf{u_3 = \frac{8}{168} = 0{\cdot}04762}$$

## EXERCISE 12.3

**1.** Find $u(x, t)$ satisfying $u_t = 4u_{xx}$, and the boundary condition, $u(0, t) = 0 = u(8, t)$ and $u(x, 0) = 4x - \frac{1}{2}x^2$ for points $x = 0, 1, 2, 3, 4, 5, 6, 7, 8$, $t = \frac{1}{8}j$, $j = 0, 1, 2, 3, 4, 5$.

**2.** Solve $u_t = u_{xx}$, given $u(0, t) = 0$, $u(x, 0) = x(1 - x)$, $u(1, t) = 0$. Assume $h = 0{\cdot}1$ and, choose suitable $k$, so that $u(i, j)$ is found out for $i = 0, 0{\cdot}1, \ldots 1$ and $j = k, 2k, 3k$. *(Ap. 1992)*

**3.** Solve $u_{xx} = 2u_t$, $0 \le x < 12$, $0 \le t < 12$ with conditions $u(x, 0) = \frac{1}{4}x(15 - x)$, $0 \le x \le 12$, $u(0, t) = 0$, $u(12, t) = 9$, $0 < t < 12$ using Schmidt process.

**4.** Solve $u_t = 5u_{xx}$ with $u(0, t) = 0$, $u(5, t) = 60$

and $u(x, 0) = \begin{cases} 20x & \text{for } 0 < x \le 3 \\ 60 & \text{for } 3 < x \le 5 \end{cases}$ *(Nov. '89)*

for 5 time steps having $h = 1$, by Schmidt method.

**5.** Solve $2u_t = u_{xx}$, $0 < x < 4$, $t > 0$ with the condition $u(0, t) = 0$, $u(4, t) = 0$, $u(x, 0) = x(4 - x)$, taking $h = 1$ and using Schmidt method. Get the solution through 10 time steps. *(MS. Ap. '92)*

**6.** Solve $25u_{xx} = u_t, 0 < x < 1, t > 0,$ with boundary conditions $u(0, t) = u(10, t) = 0$ and $u(x, 0) = \frac{1}{25}x(10 - x)$ choosing $h = 1, k$ suitably, find $u_{ij}$ for $i = 1, 2, \ldots 9$ and $j = 1, 2, 3, 4.$ *(MS. Ap. '90)*

**7.** Apply Crank-Nicholson method with $h = 0{\cdot}2$ and $\lambda = 1$ and find $u(x, t)$ in the rod by considering two time steps of the heat equation $u_{xx} = u_t$ given $u(x, 0) = \sin \pi x$ and $u(x, 0) = 0, u(1, t) = 0.$

**8.** Solve the equation $u_t = u_{xx}, 0 \le x \le 1, t > 0$ under condition $u(0, t) = u(1, t) = 0$

$$\text{and } u(x, 0) = \begin{cases} 2x & \text{for } 0 \le x \le x\,1/2 \\ 2(1 - x) & \text{for } \frac{1}{2} \le x \le 1. \end{cases}$$

Using Crank-Nicholson method, $h = \frac{1}{10}, \; k = \frac{1}{100}; \; \lambda = 1.$

**9.** Using Crank-Nicholson method, solve *(Anna Ap. 2005)*

$u_t = u_{xx}, 0 < x < 5, t > 0, u(x, 0) = 20$

$u(0, t) = 0, u(5, t) = 100,$ for one time step by Nicholson method.

**10.** Solve by Nicholson's method,

$$u_t = u_{xx}, 0 < x < 1, t > 0$$

$u(x, 0) = 100\,x(1 - x), u(0, t) = 0 = u(1, t) = 0,$ taking $h = 0{\cdot}25$ for one-time step. *(BR. 1996 A)*

## 12·10. Hyperbolic Equations

The wave equation in one dimension (vibration of strings) is

$$a^2 \frac{\partial^2 u}{\partial x^2} - \frac{\partial^2 u}{\partial t^2} = 0 \; ; \; \text{ i.e., } \; a^2 u_{xx} - u_{tt} = 0.$$

Here, $A = a^2, B = 0, C = -1 \quad \therefore \quad B^2 - 4AC = 4a^2 = +ve.$

Therefore, the equation is hyperbolic.

Let us solve this equation by reducing it to difference equation.

**AIM:** Solve $a^2 u_{xx} - u_{tt} = 0$ ...(1)

together with the boundary conditions

$$u(0, t) = 0 \quad \text{...(2)}$$

$$u(l, t) = 0 \quad \text{...(3)}$$

and the initial conditions

$$u(x, 0) = f(x) \quad \text{...(4)}$$

$$u_t(x, 0) = 0 \quad \text{...(5)}$$

Assuming $\Delta x = h, \; \Delta t = k,$ we have

$$u_{xx} = \frac{u_{i+1,j} - 2\,u_{i,j} + u_{i-1,j}}{h^2}$$

$$u_{tt} = \frac{u_{i,j+1} - 2\,u_{i,j} + u_{i,j-1}}{k^2}$$

Substituting these values in (1),

$$\frac{a^2}{h^2}(u_{i+1,j} - 2\,u_{i,j} + u_{i-1,j}) - \frac{1}{k^2}(u_{i,j+1} - 2\,u_{i,j} + u_{i,j-1}) = 0$$

*i.e.*, $\lambda^2 a^2 (u_{i+1,j} - 2\,u_{i,j} + u_{i-1,j}) - u_{i,j+1} + 2\,u_{i,j} - u_{i,j-1} = 0$

where $\lambda = \dfrac{k}{h}$.

$$\mathbf{u_{i,j+1} = 2\,(1 - \lambda^2 a^2)\,u_{i,j} + \lambda^2 a^2\,(u_{i-1,j} + u_{i+1,j}) - u_{i,j-1}} \qquad \text{...(6)}$$

To make the equation simpler, select $\lambda$ such that

$$1 - \lambda^2 a^2 = 0 \quad i.e., \quad \lambda^2 = \frac{1}{a^2} = \frac{k^2}{h^2} \quad i.e., \quad k = \frac{h}{a}$$

under this selection of $\lambda^2 = \dfrac{1}{a^2}$ ; *i.e.*, $k = \dfrac{h}{a}$, the equation (6) reduces to the simplest form

$$\mathbf{u_{i,j+1} = u_{i-1,j} + u_{i+1,j} - u_{i,j-1}} \qquad \text{...(7)}$$

Equation (6) is called an **Explicit scheme or Explicit formula** to solve the wave equation.

Equation (7) gives a simpler form under the condition $k = \dfrac{h}{a}$.

Formula (7) enables us to find $u$ at the $(j+1)$th row only if we know the values of $u$ at the $j$th and $(j-1)$th row

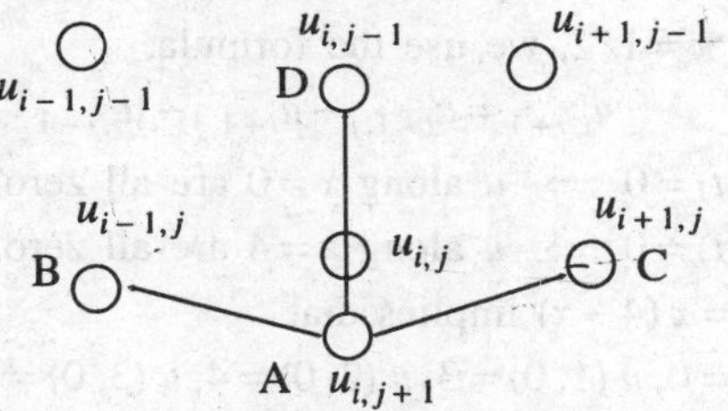


The value of $u$ at $A$ = value of $u$ at $B$ + value of $u$ at $C$ – value of $u$ at $D$.

**Note 1.** The boundary condition $u(0, t) = 0$ *i.e.*, $u_{0,j} = 0$ gives the values of $u$ along the line $x = 0$; that all $u = 0$.

The boundary condition $u(l, t) = 0$ or $u_{n,j} = 0$ gives the values of $u$ along the line $x = l$, *i.e.*, all $u = 0$ along this line.

**Note 2.** Initial condition $u(x, 0) = f(x)$ becomes

$$\boxed{\mathbf{u(i, 0) = f(ih), i = 1, 2, 3, \ldots}}$$

This gives the value of $u$ along $t = 0$ for various values of $i$.

$$\boxed{\mathbf{u(i, 0) = f(ih) = f_i}} \qquad \ldots(8)$$

**Note 3.** The initial condition $u_t(x, 0) = 0$ gives $\dfrac{u_{i, j+1} - u_{i, j-1}}{2k} = 0$ when $j = 0$ (central difference approximation)

$$\therefore \qquad \boxed{\mathbf{u_{i, 1} = u_{i, -1}}} \qquad \ldots(9)$$

Setting $j = 0$ in (7),

$$u_{i, 1} = u_{i+1, 0} + u_{i-1, 0} - u_{i, -1}$$

$$u_{i, 1} = u_{i+1, 0} + u_{i-1, 0} - u_{i, 1}, \text{ using (9),}$$

$$\boxed{\therefore \quad \mathbf{u_{i, 1} = \frac{1}{2}(u_{i-1, 0} + u_{i+1, 0})}} \qquad \ldots(10)$$

**Note 4.** If $1 - \lambda^2 a^2 < 0$, *i.e.*, $\lambda a > 1$, *i.e.*, $\dfrac{ak}{h} > 1$, the solution is unstable. If $\dfrac{ka}{h} = 1$, it is stable and if $\dfrac{ka}{h} < 1$, it is stable but the accuracy of the solution decreases as $\dfrac{ak}{h}$ decreases.

That is, for $\lambda = \dfrac{1}{a}$ the solution is stable.

**Example 19.** *Solve numerically, $4\, u_{xx} = u_{tt}$ with the boundary conditions $u(0, t) = 0$, $u(4, t) = 0$ and the initial conditions $u_t(x, 0) = 0$ and $u(x, 0) = x(4 - x)$, taking $h = 1$. (for 4 time steps)*

*(MS. Ap. '92) (BR. 1995 N)*

**Solution.** Since $a^2 = 4, h = 1, k = \dfrac{h}{a} = \dfrac{1}{2}$ ...(1)

$\therefore$ Taking $k = 1/2$, we use the formula,

$$u_{i, j+1} = u_{i-1, j} + u_{i+1, j} - u_{i, j-1} \qquad \ldots(2)$$

From $u(0, t) = 0 \Rightarrow u$ along $x = 0$ are all zero.

From $u(4, t) = 0 \Rightarrow u$ along $x = 4$ are all zero.

$u(x, 0) = x(4 - x)$ implies that

$u(0, 0) = 0, u(1, 0) = 3, u(2, 0) = 4, u(3, 0) = 3.$

Now, we fill up the row $t = 0$ using the above values,

$$u_t(x, 0) = 0, \text{ implies } u_{i, 1} = \frac{u_{i+1, 0} + u_{i-1, 0}}{2} \qquad \ldots(3)$$

Now we draw the table; for that we require

$$u_{1, 1} = \frac{u_{2, 0} + u_{0, 0}}{2} = \frac{4 + 0}{2} = 2$$

$$u_{2,1} = \frac{u_{3,0} + u_{1,0}}{2} = \frac{3+3}{2} = 3$$

$$u_{3,1} = \frac{u_{4,0} + u_{2,0}}{2} = 2$$

$$u_{4,1} = 0.$$

**Table**

| t \ x | 0 | 1 | 2 | 3 | 4 | |
|---|---|---|---|---|---|---|
| 0 | 0 | 3 | 4 | 3 | 0 | $u(x, 0) = x(4-x)$ |
| 0·5 | 0 | 2 | 3 | 2 | 0 | |
| 1 | 0 | 0<br>(3 + 0 − 3) | 0<br>(2 + 2 − 4) | 0<br>(3 + 0 − 3) | 0 | |
| 1·5 | 0 | − 2 | − 3 | − 2 | 0 | |
| 2 | 0 | − 3 | − 4 | − 3 | 0 | |
| 2·5 | 0 | − 2 | − 3 | − 2 | 0 | |
| 3 | 0 | 0 | 0 | 0 | 0 | |
| 3·5 | 0 | 2 | 3 | 2 | 0 | |
| 4 | 0 | 3 | 4 | 3 | 0 | |

Period is 4 seconds or $8(k) = 8\left(\frac{1}{2}\right) = 4$ secs.

**Example 20.** *Solve* $25\,u_{xx} - u_{tt} = 0$ *for* $u$ *at the pivotal points, given* $u(0, t) = u(5, t) = 0$, $u_t(x, 0) = 0$ *and* $u(x, 0) = 2x$ *for* $0 \le x \le 2{\cdot}5$

$= 10 - 2x$

*for* $2{\cdot}5 \le x \le 5$. (*MS. Ap. 1989*)

*for one half period of vibration.*

**Solution.** Here, $a^2 = 25 \quad \therefore \quad a = 5$;

Period of vibration $= \dfrac{2l}{a} = \dfrac{2 \times 5}{5} = 2$ seconds.

half period = 1 second.

Therefore we want values upto $t = 1$ second

$$k = \frac{h}{a} = \frac{1}{5}, \text{ taking } h = 1$$

Step-size in $t$-direction $= \dfrac{1}{5}$.

The Explicit scheme is

$$u_{i,j+1} = u_{i-1,j} + u_{i+1,j} - u_{i,j-1} \qquad \text{...(1)}$$

Boundary conditions are $u(0, t) = 0$ or $u_{0,j} = 0$, $u(5, t) = 0$ or $u_{5,j} = 0$ } for all $j$

$$u_t(x, 0) = 0 \Rightarrow u_{i,1} = \frac{u_{i+1,0} + u_{i-1,0}}{2} \qquad ...(2)$$

$$u(x, 0) = 2x \text{ for } 0 \leq x \leq 2{\cdot}5$$
$$= 10 - 2x \text{ for } 2{\cdot}5 \leq x \leq 5$$

$\therefore$ $u(0, 0) = 0;\ u(1, 0) = 2,\ u(2, 0) = 4,$
$u(3, 0) = 4,\ u(4, 0) = 2,\ u(5, 0) = 0.$

$$u_{1,1} = \frac{u_{2,0} + u_{0,0}}{2} = \frac{4+0}{2} = 2 \qquad \text{Here, } u(x, 0) = u(i, 0)$$

$$u_{2,1} = \frac{u_{3,0} + u_{1,0}}{2} = 3$$

$$u_{3,1} = \frac{u_{4,0} + u_{2,0}}{2} = 3$$

$$u_{4,1} = \frac{u_{5,0} + u_{3,0}}{2} = 2$$

We form the table.

| $t \backslash x$ | 0 | 1 | 2 | 3 | 4 | 5 |
|---|---|---|---|---|---|---|
| 0 ($j = 0$) | 0 | 2 | 4 | 4 | 2 | 0 |
| $t = \frac{1}{5}$ ($j = 1$) | 0 | 2 | 3 | 3 | 2 | 0 |
| $t = \frac{2}{5}$ ($j = 2$) | 0 | 1 | 1 | 1 | 1 | 0 |
| $t = \frac{3}{5}$ ($j = 3$) | 0 | – 1 | – 1 | – 1 | – 1 | 0 |
| $t = \frac{4}{5}$ ($j = 4$) | 0 | – 2 | – 3 | – 3 | – 2 | 0 |
| $t = 1$ ($j = 5$) | 0 | – 2 | – 4 | – 4 | – 2 | 0 |

**Note 1.** First fill up all value against $j = 0$ and $j = 1$ and then go for filling up other rows using formula (1).

**Note 2.** In using $u_t(x, 0) = 0$ we used central difference approximation for first derivative

$$u_t = \frac{u_{i,j+1} - u_{i,j-1}}{2k}$$

But instead, we could also use

$$u_t = \frac{u_{i,j+1} - u_{i,j}}{k} \text{ in which case}$$

$$u_t(x, 0) = 0 \Rightarrow u_{i,1} = u_{i,0}$$

In other words, the values of $u$ corresponding to $j = 0$ and $j = 1$ are same.

If this is adopted, then the values of $u$ against $t = 0$ and $t = 0{\cdot}5$ in the table of worked Example 19 will be same. That is

| $t$ \ $x$ | 0 | 1 | 2 | 3 | 4 |
|---|---|---|---|---|---|
| 0 | 0 | 3 | 4 | 3 | 0 |
| 0·5 | 0 | 3 | 4 | 3 | 0 |

This will make all the entries of the table different from the one given under worked Example 19.

(This is also applicable to worked Example 20).

This assumption of $u_t(x, 0) = 0$ makes the values of $u$ same at $t = 0$; and $t = 0.5$ which is *not acceptable* in practice.

Hence, we do not adopt this definition of $u_t(x, 0)$ and so we accepted the central difference approximation which is more *reasonable*.

**This is the reason why the same problem gives two different answers by two different authors.**

**Example 21.** *Evaluate the pivotal values of the following equation taking h = 1 and upto one half of the period of the oscillation* $16u_{xx} = u_{tt}$ *given* $u(0, t) = u(5, t) = 0$, $u(x, 0) = x^2(5 - x)$ *and* $u_t(x, 0) = 0$.

*(MS. Nov. 1988)*

**Solution.** Here $a^2 = 16 \quad \therefore \quad a = 4$

Period of oscillation $= \frac{2l}{a} = \frac{2 \times 5}{4} = \frac{5}{2}$ seconds.

$\therefore$ One half of period $= \frac{5}{4}$ seconds.

$$k = \frac{h}{a} = \frac{1}{4}$$

Step-size of time $= \frac{1}{4}$

$$\left.\begin{aligned} u(0, t) = 0 &\Rightarrow u_{0,j} = 0 \\ u(5, t) = 0 &\Rightarrow u_{5,j} = 0 \end{aligned}\right\} \text{ for all } j$$

$$u(x, 0) = x^2(5 - x)$$

$\Rightarrow u(0, 0) = 0, u(1, 0) = 4, u(2, 0) = 12, u(3, 0) = 18, u(4, 0) = 16$

$$u(5, 0) = 0$$

$$u_t(x, 0) = 0 \Rightarrow u_{i,1} = \frac{u_{i+1,0} + u_{i-1,0}}{2}$$

$$\therefore \quad u_{1,1} = \frac{u_{2,0} + u_{0,0}}{2} = 6$$

$$u_{2,1} = \frac{u_{3,0} + u_{1,0}}{2} = 11$$

$$u_{3,1} = \frac{u_{4,0} + u_{2,0}}{2} = 14$$

$$u_{4,1} = \frac{u_{5,0} + u_{3,0}}{2} = 9$$

*Now we form the table* $(t \neq j)$

| $t$ \ $x = i$ | 0 | 1 | 2 | 3 | 4 | 5 |
|---|---|---|---|---|---|---|
| 0 $(j = 0)$ | 0 | 4 | 12 | 18 | 16 | 0 |
| 0·25 $(j = 1)$ | 0 | 6 | 11 | 14 | 9 | 0 |
| 0·5 $(j = 2)$ | 0 | 7 | 8 | 2 | – 2 | 0 |
| 0·75 $(j = 3)$ | 0 | 2 | – 2 | – 8 | – 7 | 0 |
| 1·0 $(j = 4)$ | 0 | – 9 | – 14 | – 11 | – 6 | 0 |
| 1·25 $(j = 5)$ | 0 | – 16 | – 18 | – 12 | – 4 | 0 |

**Example 22.** *Solve* $\frac{\partial^2 u}{\partial t^2} = \frac{\partial^2 u}{\partial x^2}$, $0 < x < 1, t > 0,$ *given* $u(x, 0) = u_t(x, 0) = u(0, t) = 0$ *and* $u(1, t) = 100 \sin \pi t$. *Compute u for 4 times steps with* $h = 0{\cdot}25$. *(U.Q. Ap. 1992)*

**Solution.** Note that this problem is different from all those mentioned earlier. Here, the two ends are not fixed $\therefore$ $x = 1$ is a free end with displacement not equal to zero.

Since the differential equation is same, we have

$$u_{i,j+1} = u_{i-1,j} + u_{i+1,j} - u_{i,j-1} \qquad \text{...(1)}$$

if $$k = \frac{h}{a} = \frac{0{\cdot}25}{1} = 0{\cdot}25 \text{ since } a = 1.$$

Step-size is 0·25 in both variable.

Range of $x$ is (0, 1).

At $t = 0$, all $u$'s are zero.

At $x = 0$, all $u$'s are zero; since $u(1, t) = 100 \sin \pi t$, $u(1, 0) = 0$,

$$u(1, 0{\cdot}25) = 100 \sin \frac{\pi}{4} = 70{\cdot}7106$$

$$u(1, 0{\cdot}5) = 100 \sin \frac{\pi}{2} = 100$$

$$u(1, 0{\cdot}75) = 100 \sin \frac{3\pi}{4} = 70{\cdot}7106$$

$$u(1, 1) = 0$$

$$u_t(x, 0) = 0 \Rightarrow u_{i,1} = \frac{u_{i+1,0} + u_{i-1,0}}{2}$$

$$u_{1,1} = \frac{u_{2,0} + u_{0,0}}{2} = 0$$

$$u_{2,1} = 0$$

$$u_{3,1} = 0$$

$$u_{4,1} = 70{\cdot}7106 = u(4, 0{\cdot}25)$$

(Please note $u(x, t) \neq u(i, j)$)

Since $x = ih$, $t = jk$.

| $t$ \ $x$ | | $i = 0$<br>$x = 0$ | 1<br>0·25 | 2<br>0·5 | 3<br>0·75 | 4<br>1·0 |
|---|---|---|---|---|---|---|
| $t$ | $j$ | | | | | |
| 0 | 0 | 0 | 0 | 0 | 0 | 0 |
| 0·25 | 1 | 0 | 0 | 0 | 0 | 70·7106 |
| 0·50 | 2 | 0 | 0 | 0 | 70·7106 | 100 |
| 0·75 | 3 | 0 | 0 | 70·7106 | 100 | 70·7106 |
| 1·0 | 4 | 0 | 70·7106 | 100 | 70·7106 | 0 |

## EXERCISE 12.4

**1.** Solve $u_{tt} = u_{xx}$, given $u(0, t) = u(4, t) = 0$, $u(x, 0) = \frac{1}{2} x(4 - x)$, and $u_t(x, 0) = 0$. Take $h = 1$. Find the solutions upto 5 steps in $t$-direction. (*Nov. '92*)

**2.** Solve $u_{xx} = u_{tt}$ upto $t = 0{\cdot}5$ with spacing of 0·1, given $u(0, t) = u(1, t) = 0$, $u(x, 0) = 10x(10 - x)$, $u_t(x, 0) = 0$. (Take $h = 0{\cdot}1 = k$).

**3.** Solve numerically, $25u_{xx} = u_{tt}$, given, $u_t(x, 0) = 0$, $u(0, t) = u(5, t) = 0$ and $u(x, 0) = 20x$ for $0 \le x \le 1$
$= 5(5 - x)$ for $1 \le x \le 5$.

**4.** Show by suitable transformation of variables, the equation $u_{xx} - a^2 u_{tt} = 0$ can be transformed into the normalised form of the wave equation $u_{xx} - u_{tt} = 0$. (*MS. 1974*)

**5.** Solve $u_{xx} = u_{tt}$ upto $t = 0{\cdot}5$ with spacing of 0·1 given $u(0, t) = 0$, $u(1, t) = 0$, $u_t(x, 0) = 0$ and $u(x, 0) = 10 + x(1 - x)$. (*MS. Ap. '90*)
(**Hint.** Take $h = k = 0{\cdot}1$; $a = 1$)

## 12·11. Solution of Partial Differential Equations by the Method of Relaxation

We have already studied the method of relaxation in an earlier chapter. Now we shall use that technique in solving an elliptic equation.

We consider the Laplace equation $\nabla^2 u = 0$. ...(1)

We have to solve $\nabla^2 u = 0$ in a square region of step-size $h$, given the boundary values of $u$.

We have seen

$$4\, u_{i,j} \approx u_{i-1,j} + u_{i+1,j} + u_{i,j-1} + u_{i,j+1} \qquad ...(2)$$

This is only an approximate formula.

If the actual values of $u$ at these five pivots are substituted the equation (2) may not be satisfied. This means that $r = u_{i-1,j} + u_{i+1,j} + u_{i,j-1} + u_{i,j+1} - 4\, u_{i,j}$ has a non-zero value and this is the residual at $(i, j)$ node.

Corresponding to each node, there will be a residual.

Our object of the relaxation process is to reduce all these residuals to zero or to reduce them as small as possible.

Take a specific case at $u_0$ (at A) as in figure.

$r_0 = u_1 + u_2 + u_3 + u_4 - 4\, u_0$ ...(3)

Similarly,

$r_1 = u_0 + u_4 + u_5 + u_6 - 4\, u_1$ ...(4)

$r_2 = \cdots$

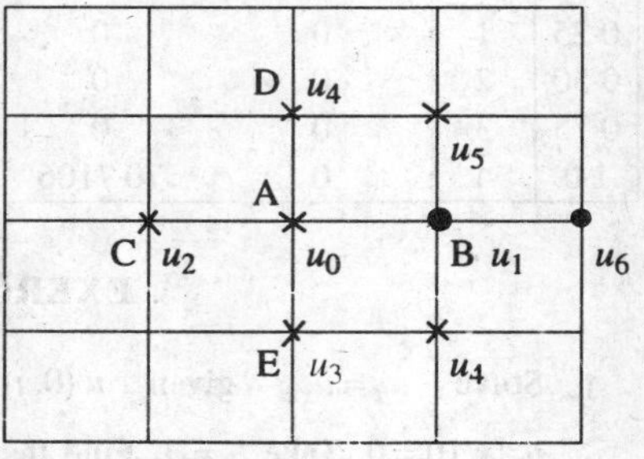


When the value of $u$ is changed at $u_0$, the values of the residuals at the adjacent points also get changed. An increase of 1 unit in $u_0$, increases the residual $r_0$ by – 4 where $r_1$ gets increased by 1 unit.

That is, if the value of the function $u$ is increased at *a* mesh point by 1 unit, the residual at that point is increased by – 4 while the residuals at the adjacent interior points get increased each by the same quantity of 1 unit. We have the relaxation operator, $R_0$ (See figure).

At each step, we take mesh point with the numerically largest residual and apply to it a suitable multiple of $R_0$ so as to liquidate the residual as small as possible, if not to zero.

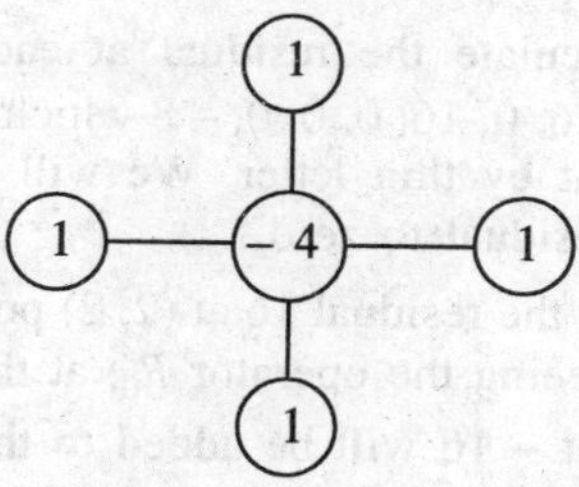


Operator $R_0$.

We see the technique in the following example.

**Example 23.** *Solve the Laplace equation $\nabla^2 u = 0$ inside the square region bounded by the lines $x = 0$, $x = 4$, $y = 0$ and $y = 4$ given that $u = x^2y^2$ on the boundary, by using relaxation method.*

**Solution.** Take $h = k = 1$ with 16 sub-squares, we mark the boundary values using $u = x^2y^2$ at each boundary mesh point.

y 16 64 144 y = 4
0 256
– 2
0
– 2
24 0 4 – 4 0
– 8 **56** 0 **104** – 16
0 144
**A** **B** **C**
– 2
2 0
4 **4** 0 4
**16** 0 **32** 16 **56** 0
0 64 x = 4
**C′** **D** **E**
2
x = 0 4 – 2 0
**8** 0 **16** 0 **24** – 8
0 16
**F** **G** **H**
0 0 0 0 0 x
y = 0

Using either SFPF or DFPF we get the rough values of $u$ at the 9 interior grid points. Doing this, we get them as 24, 56, 104, 16, 32, 56, 8, 16, 24 as marked in the figure by **clarendon type (thick letter)** on the left side of each point.

The residual at $A = 0 + 16 + 16 + 56 - 4\,(24) = 88 - 96 = -8$

The residual at $B = 64 + 32 + 24 + 104 - 4\,(56) = 0$

Similarly we calculate the residual at each interior node. These residuals are – 8, 0, – 16, 0, 16, 0, 0, 0, – 8 which, are marked on the right side of each grid point by thin letter. We will do relaxation to reduce numerically greatest residual to zero.

We will start with the residual 16 at (2, 2) point. To liquidate to zero, we should add – 16, seeing the operator $R_0$, at this node we increase the value of $u$ by 4 so that – 16 will be added to the residual.

The residuals in the neighbouring nodes will get increased by 4. We mark 4 on the left side of $D$ above 32 and mark the new residuals on the right side of the 5 points $B$, $C$, $D$, $E$, $G$. Now among the latest residuals the numerically maximum is – 16 at (3, 3). Thus, residual at this point will reduce to zero if we apply $-4\,R_0$.

After this operation, the residue at $C$ is 0, and the value of $u$ at this node increases by – 4. The residuals at the neighbouring nodes will increase by – 4.

Mark these new values of $u$ and residuals in the figure.

Now the maximum (numerically) residual is – 8 at (1, 3). Now apply $-2\,R_0$ to make this residual to zero. The residual at this point increases by 8 and it is zero at this point.

The value of $u$ at this point is increased by – 2 while the residuals in the neighbouring points are changed by – 2. Mark these in the figure.

Now apply $-2\,R_0$ at $H$ (3, 1). The residual at $H$ becomes zero. The value of $u$ at this node is increased by –2 and the residuals at the neighbouring points are increased by –2.

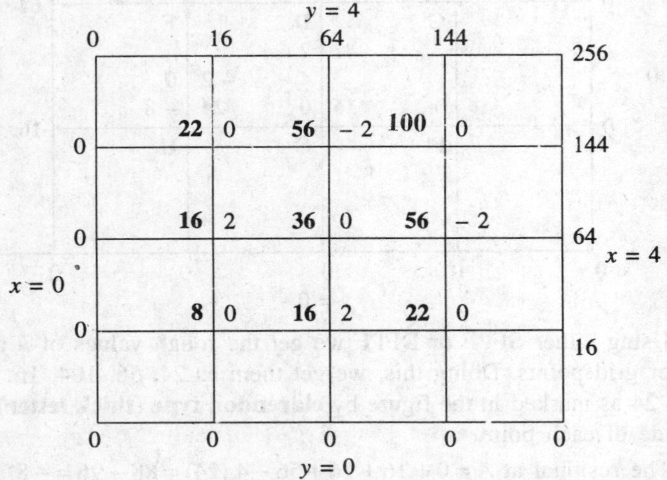


At each node, the right hand side top most value is the residual at that point while the value of $u$ at each grid point is the sum of the values on the left side of that point.

Now maximum value of residual is only 2.

Hence we stop here. The final answers with values of $u$ on the left side and the residuals on the right of the points are marked in the figure on the previous page.

**Example 24.** *Solve, by relaxation method, the Laplace equation* $\frac{\partial^2 u}{\partial x^2}+\frac{\partial^2 u}{\partial y^2}=0$ *in the following square region for the values of u at each interior node given the rough estimates of u at A, B, C, D to be 1.*

(*MS. 1977*)

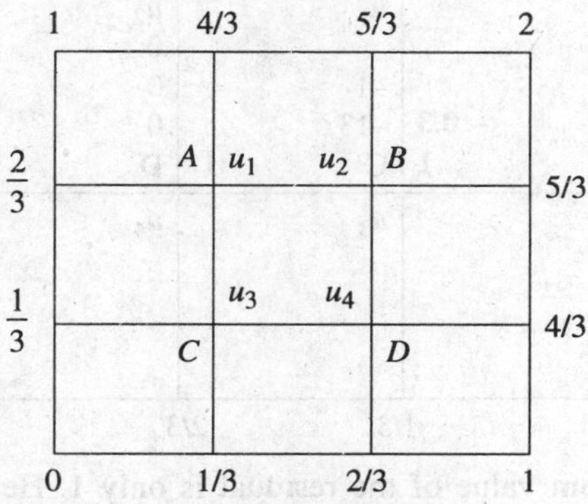


**Solution.** Let $r_A$ denote the residual at the point $A$. Assume the rough estimates of $u_1=u_2=u_3=u_4=1$.

$$\text{Then } r_A=1+1+\frac{2}{3}+\frac{4}{3}-4=0$$

$$r_B=\frac{5}{3}+\frac{5}{3}+1+1-4=\frac{4}{3}\approx 1{\cdot}3333\approx 1{\cdot}3$$

$$r_C=\frac{1}{3}+\frac{1}{3}+1+1-4=-\frac{4}{3}\approx -1{\cdot}3333\approx -1{\cdot}3$$

$$r_D=\frac{2}{3}+\frac{4}{3}+1+1-4=0$$

Since the residuals are in decimals, we multiply the values by 10 and proceed to relax the values. The values of $u$ will be altered in the first decimal place.

The maximum residual is 13 and it is at $B$.

So apply $3\,R_0$ and hence the residue at this point is changed to $13+(-12)=1$. The value of $u_2$ increases by 0·3 and the residuals at the neighbouring points increase by 3.

Again apply $-3R_0$ at $C$. The residuals at $C$ is increased by 12 and new residual is –1. The value of $u$ at $u_3$ is increased by – 0·3 and the residuals at the neighbouring nodes are increased by –3.

The latest residuals and the values of $u$ at the nodes are marked in the figure.

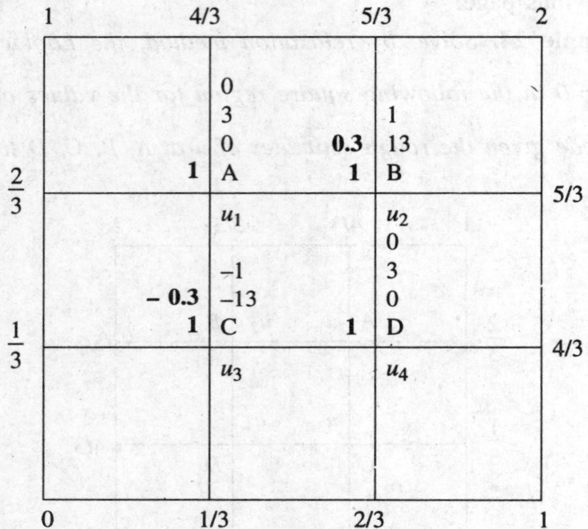


The maximum value of the residual is only 1. Hence we stop here.

Therefore $u_1 = 1, u_2 = 1 + 0{\cdot}3 = 1{\cdot}3, u_3 = 1 - 0{\cdot}3 = 0{\cdot}7, u_4 = 1.$

## EXERCISE 12.5

**1.** Solve $\nabla^2 u = 0$ given $\left.\begin{array}{l} u(0, y) = 0, \\ u(4, y) = 16y \end{array}\right\}$ for $0 < y < 4$

$\left.\begin{array}{l} u(x, 0) = 0 \\ u(x, 4) = x^3 \end{array}\right\}$ for $0 < x < 4$

by relaxation method dividing the square plate with 16 square meshes of side 1 unit. *(B.E. 1977)*

**2.** Solve $\nabla^2 f = 0$ given $f(0, y) = 0,$

$$f(4, y) = 8 + 2y, \;\; f(x, 0) = \frac{1}{2}x^2 \;\text{ and } f(x, 4) = x^2$$

in the square region $0 \le x \le 4, 0 \le y \le 4$, by the relaxation method at the nodal points with spacing $h = k = 1$. *(B.E. 1975)*

**3.** Work out the worked examples 3 to 7 of this chapter by relaxation method.

# ANSWERS

## EXERCISE 12.1 Page 419

**1.** hyperbolic **2.** elliptic **4.** hyperbolic **3, 5.** Parabolic

## EXERCISE 12.2 Page 439

**1.** 37·5, 37·5, 12·5, 12·5 **2.** 26·65, 33·33, 43·32, 46·66

**3.** 27·5, 34·999, 42·5 **4.** 0·1875, 0·5, 1·1875, 0·25, 0·6250, 1·2500

**6.** 1·567, 3·705, 6·56, 8·06, 4·68, 2·06, 8·99, 4·91, 1·99

**7.** 7·17, 9·86, 7·16, 18·78, 25·04, 18·77, 42·88, 52·70, 42·87

**8.** (*a*) 0·126, 0·126, 0·376, 0·376

(*b*) 250, 175, 325

## EXERCISE 12.3 Page 451

**1.**

| $t$ \ $x$ | 0 | 1 | 2 | 3 | 4 | 5 | 6 | 7 | 8 |
|---|---|---|---|---|---|---|---|---|---|
| 0 | 0 | 3·5 | 6 | 7·5 | 8 | 7·5 | 6 | 3·5 | 0 |
| $\frac{1}{8}$ | 0 | 3 | 5·5 | 7 | 7·5 | 7 | 5·5 | 3 | 0 |
| $\frac{2}{8}$ | 0 | 2·75 | 5 | 6·5 | 7 | 6·5 | 5 | 2·75 | 0 |
| $\frac{3}{8}$ | 0 | 2·5 | 4·625 | 6 | 6·5 | 6 | 4·625 | 2·5 | 0 |
| $\frac{4}{8}$ | 0 | 2·3125 | 4·25 | 5·5525 | 6 | 5·5625 | 4·25 | 2·125 | 0 |
| $\frac{5}{8}$ | 0 | 2·125 | 3·9875 | 5·125 | 5·5625 | 5·125 | 3·9875 | 2·125 | 0 |

**2.**

| $j$ \ $i$ | 0 | 1 | 2 | 3 | 4 | 5 | 6 | 7 | 8 | 9 | 10 |
|---|---|---|---|---|---|---|---|---|---|---|---|
| 0 | 0 | 0·09 | 0·16 | 0·21 | 0·24 | 0·25 | 0·24 | 0·21 | 0·16 | 0·09 | 0 |
| 1 | 0 | 0·08 | 0·15 | 0·20 | 0·23 | 0·24 | 0·23 | 0·20 | 0·15 | 0·08 | 0 |
| 2 | 0 | 0·075 | 0·14 | 0·19 | 0·22 | 0·23 | 0·22 | 0·19 | 0·14 | 0·075 | 0 |
| 3 | 0 | 0·07 | 0·1325 | 0·18 | 0·21 | 0·22 | 0·21 | 0·18 | 0·1325 | 0·07 | 0 |

**3.** $\rightarrow x$ $h = 3$

↓ $t$ $k = 3$

| $t$ \ $x$ | 0 | 3 | 6 | 9 | 12 |
|---|---|---|---|---|---|
| 0 | 0 | 9 | 13·5 | 13·5 | 9 |
| 3 | 0 | 8·25 | 12·75 | 12·75 | 9 |
| 6 | 0 | 7·625 | 12 | 12·125 | 9 |
| 9 | 0 | 7·083 | 11·292 | 11·583 | 9 |
| 12 | 0 | 6·604 | 10·639 | 11·104 | 9 |

**4.**

| $t$ \ $x$ | 0 | 1 | 2 | 3 | 4 | 5 |
|---|---|---|---|---|---|---|
| 0 | 0 | 20 | 40 | 60 | 60 | 60 |
| 0·1 | 0 | 20 | 40 | 50 | 60 | 60 |
| 0·2 | 0 | 20 | 35 | 50 | 55 | 60 |
| 0·3 | 0 | 17·5 | 35 | 45 | 55 | 60 |
| 0·4 | 0 | 17·5 | 31·25 | 45 | 52·5 | 60 |
| 0·5 | 0 | 15·625 | 31·25 | 41·875 | 52·5 | 60 |

**5.**

| $x$ \ $t$ | 0 | 1 | 2 | 3 | 4 | 5 | 6 | 7 | 8 | 9 | 10 |
|---|---|---|---|---|---|---|---|---|---|---|---|
| 0 | 0 | 0 | 0 | 0 | 0 | 0 | 0 | 0 | 0 | 0 | 0 |
| 1 | 0 | 2 | 1·5 | 1 | 0·75 | 0·5 | 0·375 | 0·25 | 0·1875 | 0·125 | 0·094 |
| 2 | 0 | 3 | 2 | 1·5 | 1·0 | 0·75 | 0·5 | 0·375 | 0·25 | 0·1875 | 0·125 |
| 3 | 0 | 2 | 1·5 | 1 | 0·75 | 0·5 | 0·375 | 0·25 | 0·1875 | 0·125 | 0·094 |
| 4 | 0 | 0 | 0 | 0 | 0 | 0 | 0 | 0 | 0 | 0 | 0 |

**6.**

| $t$ \ $x$ | 0 | 1 | 2 | 3 | 4 | 5 | 6 | 7 | 8 | 9 | 10 |
|---|---|---|---|---|---|---|---|---|---|---|---|
| 0 | 0 | 0 | 0 | 0 | 0 | 0 | 0 | 0 | 0 | 0 | 0 |
| 1 | 0 | 0·32 | 0·6 | 0·8 | 0·92 | 0·96 | 0·92 | 0·8 | 0·6 | 0·32 | 0 |
| 2 | 0 | 0·3 | 0·56 | 0·76 | 0·88 | 0·92 | 0·88 | 0·76 | 0·64 | 0·3 | 0 |
| 3 | 0 | 0·28 | 0·53 | 0·72 | 0·84 | 0·88 | 0·84 | 0·76 | 0·53 | 0·32 | 0 |
| 4 | 0 | 0·265 | 0·5 | 0·685 | 0·8 | 0·84 | 0·82 | 0·685 | 0·54 | 0·265 | 0 |

**7.**

| $t$ \ $x$ | 0 | 0·588 | 0·951 | 0·951 | 0·588 | 0 |
|---|---|---|---|---|---|---|
| 0 | 0 | 0·399 | 0·646 | 0·646 | 0·399 | 0 |
| $t_1$ | 0 | 0·271 | 0·439 | 0·439 | 0·271 | 0 |

**9.**

$\rightarrow x$

$\downarrow t$

| $t$ \ $x$ | 0 | 1 | 2 | 3 | 4 | 5 |
|---|---|---|---|---|---|---|
| 0 | 0 | 20 | 20 | 20 | 20 | 100 |
| 1 | 0 | 9·80 | 20·19 | 30·72 | 59·92 | 100 |

**10.**

$x \rightarrow$

$t \downarrow$

| $t$ \ $x$ | 0 | 0·25 | 0·5 | 0·75 | 1 |
|---|---|---|---|---|---|
| 0 | 0 | 18·75 | 25·00 | 18·75 | 0 |
| $\frac{1}{16}$ | 0 | 9·82 | 14·29 | 9·82 | 0 |

## EXERCISE 12.4 Page 459

**1.**

| $t$ \ $x$ | 0 | 1 | 2 | 3 | 4 |
|---|---|---|---|---|---|
| 0 | 0 | 1·5 | 2 | 1·5 | 0 |
| 1 | 0 | 1 | 1·5 | 1 | 0 |
| 2 | 0 | 0 | 0 | 0 | 0 |
| 3 | 0 | − 1 | − 1·5 | − 1 | 0 |
| 4 | 0 | − 1·5 | − 2 | − 1·5 | 0 |
| 5 | 0 | − 1 | − 1·5 | − 1 | 0 |

**3.** $\rightarrow x$

| $j$ \ $x = i$ ($\downarrow t$) | 0 | 1 | 2 | 3 | 4 | 5 |
|---|---|---|---|---|---|---|
| 0 | 0 | 20 | 15 | 10 | 5 | 0 |
| 1 | 0 | 7·5 | 15 | 10 | 5 | 0 |
| 2 | 0 | − 5 | 2·5 | 10 | 5 | 0 |
| 3 | 0 | − 5 | − 10 | − 2·5 | 5 | 0 |
| 4 | 0 | − 5 | − 10 | − 15 | − 7·5 | 0 |
| 5 | 0 | − 5 | − 10 | − 15 | − 20 | 0 |

**5.** $\rightarrow x$

| $t$ \ $x$ ($\downarrow t$) | 0 | 0·1 | 0·2 | 0·3 | 0·4 | 0·5 | 0·6 | 0·7 | 0·8 | 0·9 | 1·0 |
|---|---|---|---|---|---|---|---|---|---|---|---|
| 0 | 0 | 10·09 | 10·16 | 10·21 | 10·24 | 10·25 | 10·24 | 10·21 | 10·16 | 10·09 | 10·0 |
| 0·1 | 0 | 5·08 | 10·15 | 10·20 | 10·23 | 10·24 | 10·23 | 10·20 | 10·15 | 10·08 | 0·0 |
| 0·2 | 0 | 0·06 | 5·12 | 10·17 | 10·20 | 10·21 | 10·20 | 10·17 | 10·12 | 0·06 | 0·0 |
| 0·3 | 0 | 0·04 | 0·08 | 5·12 | 10·15 | 10·16 | 10·15 | 10·12 | 10·08 | 0·04 | 0·0 |
| 0·4 | 0 | 0·02 | 0·04 | 0·06 | 5·08 | 10·09 | 10·08 | 10·06 | 10·04 | 0·02 | 0·0 |
| 0·5 | 0 | 0 | 0 | 0 | 0 | 0 | 0 | 0 | 0 | 10 | 0 |

## EXERCISE 12.5 Page 464

**1.** 4·5, 12·75, 27·5, 4·25, 11, 20·25, 2·5, 5·75, 10·5

**2.** 1·9, 4·9, 9·1, 2·1, 4·7, 8·4, 1·6, 3·9, 6·7.

# 13

# *Iterative Method For Eigen Values**

## 13·1. Power Method

Power method is used to determine numerically largest eigen value and the corresponding eigen vector of a matrix $A$.

Let A be a $n \times n$ square matrix and let $\lambda_1, \lambda_2, \ldots \lambda_n$ be the distinct eigen values of $A$ so that

$$|\lambda_1| > |\lambda_2| > |\lambda_3| > \cdots |\lambda_n| \quad \text{...(1)}$$

Let $\upsilon_1, \upsilon_2, .. \upsilon_n$ be their corresponding eigen vectors

$$\therefore \quad A\upsilon_i = \lambda_i \upsilon_i, \ i = 1, 2, ..... n \quad \text{...(2)}$$

This method is applicable only if the vectors $\upsilon_1, \upsilon_2, \ldots \upsilon_n$ are linearly independent. This may be true even if the eigen values $\lambda_1, \lambda_2, \ldots \lambda_n$ are not distinct.

These $n$ vectors constitute a vector space of which these vectors form a basis.

Let $Y_0$ be any vector of this space.

Then $Y_0 = C_1\, \upsilon_1 + C_2\, \upsilon_2 + C_3\, \upsilon_3 + \cdots + C_n\, \upsilon_n$

where $C_i$'s are constants (scalars).

Pre-multiplying by $A$, we get

$$Y_1 = AY_0 = C_1 A\upsilon_1 + C_2 A\upsilon_2 + \cdots + C_n A\upsilon_n$$
$$= C_1\lambda_1\upsilon_1 + C_2\lambda_2\upsilon_2 + \cdots + C_n\lambda_n\upsilon_n$$

Similarly $Y_2 = AY_1 = C_1\lambda_1^2\upsilon_1 + C_2\lambda_2^2\upsilon_2 + \cdots + C_n\lambda_n^2\upsilon_n$

continuing this process

$$Y_r = AY_{r-1} = A^r Y_0 = C_1\lambda_1^r\upsilon_1 + C_2\lambda_2^r\upsilon_2 + \cdots + C_n\lambda_n^r\upsilon_n$$

$$= \lambda_1^r \left[ C_1\upsilon_1 + C_2 \left(\frac{\lambda_2}{\lambda_1}\right)^r \upsilon_2 + \cdots + C_n \left(\frac{\lambda_n}{\lambda_1}\right)^r \upsilon_n \right] \quad \text{...(3)}$$

Similarly,

$$Y_{r+1} = A^{r+1} Y_0 = \lambda_1^{r+1}\left[C_1 \upsilon_1 + C_2\left(\frac{\lambda_2}{\lambda_1}\right)^{r+1} \upsilon_2 + \cdots + C_n\left(\frac{\lambda_n}{\lambda_1}\right)^{r+1} \upsilon_n\right] \quad ...(4)$$

As $r \to \infty$, $\left(\frac{\lambda_i}{\lambda_1}\right)^r \to 0, i = 2, 3, .. n$

In the limit as $r \to \infty$

$$Y_r \to \lambda_1^r C_1 \upsilon_1$$

$$Y_{r+1} \to \lambda_1^{r+1} C_1 \upsilon_1$$

$$\therefore \quad \lambda_i = \underset{r \to \infty}{\text{Lt}} \frac{\left(A^{r+1} Y_0\right)_i}{\left(A^r Y_0\right)_i}, \quad i = 1, 2, \ldots n,$$

where the suffix $i$ denotes the $i$th component of the vector.

To get the convergence quicker, we normalize the vector before multiplication by $A$.

**Method:** Let $\upsilon_0$ be an arbitrary vector and find

$$Y_{k+1} = A\, \upsilon_k$$

$$\upsilon_{k+1} = \frac{Y_{k+1}}{m_{k+1}},$$ where $m_{k+1}$ is the numerically largest element of $Y_{k+1}$.

Then

$$\lambda_1 = \underset{k \to \infty}{\text{Lt}} \frac{\left(Y_{k+1}\right)_i}{\left(\upsilon_k\right)_i}, \quad i = 1, 2, \ldots.. n,$$

and $\upsilon_{k+1}$ is the required vector.

**Note:** $\lambda_1$ is dominant if $|\lambda_1| > |\lambda_2| \geq |\lambda_3| \geq \cdots |\lambda_n|$.

**Note 1.** To find the numerically smallest eigen value of $A$, obtain the numerically greatest eigen value of $A^{-1}$ and then take its reciprocal.

**2.** The eigen values of $A - KI$ are $\lambda_i - K$ where $\lambda_i$ are the eigen values of $A$.

**3.** Sum of the eigen values of a matrix is equal to the sum of the diagonal elements of the matrix. (= Trace of the matrix).

**Note:** To find the numerically smallest eigen value of $A$, obtain the dominant eigen value $\lambda_1$ of $A$ and then find $B = A - \lambda_1 I$ and find the dominant eigen value of $B$. Then, the smallest eigen value of $A$ is equal to the dominant eigen value of $B + \lambda_1$.

**Example 1.** *Find the dominant eigen value of* $A = \begin{bmatrix} 1 & 2 \\ 3 & 4 \end{bmatrix}$ *by power method and hence find the other eigen value also. Verify your results by any other matrix theory.*

**Solution.** Let an initial arbitrary vector be $X_1 = \begin{pmatrix} 0 \\ 1 \end{pmatrix}$

$$A\,X_1 = \begin{pmatrix} 1 & 2 \\ 3 & 4 \end{pmatrix}\begin{pmatrix} 0 \\ 1 \end{pmatrix} = \begin{pmatrix} 2 \\ 4 \end{pmatrix} = 4\begin{pmatrix} 0{\cdot}5 \\ 1 \end{pmatrix} = 4\,X_2$$

$$A\,X_2 = \begin{pmatrix} 1 & 2 \\ 3 & 4 \end{pmatrix}\begin{pmatrix} 0{\cdot}5 \\ 1 \end{pmatrix} = \begin{pmatrix} 2{\cdot}5 \\ 7{\cdot}5 \end{pmatrix} = 7{\cdot}5\begin{pmatrix} \frac{1}{3} \\ 1 \end{pmatrix} = 7{\cdot}5\,X_3$$

$$A\,X_3 = \begin{pmatrix} 1 & 2 \\ 3 & 4 \end{pmatrix}\begin{pmatrix} \frac{1}{3} \\ 1 \end{pmatrix} = \begin{pmatrix} \frac{7}{3} \\ 5 \end{pmatrix} = 5\begin{pmatrix} \frac{7}{15} \\ 1 \end{pmatrix} = 5\,(X_4)$$

$$A\,X_4 = \begin{pmatrix} 1 & 2 \\ 3 & 4 \end{pmatrix}\begin{pmatrix} \frac{7}{15} \\ 1 \end{pmatrix} = \begin{pmatrix} \frac{37}{15} \\ \frac{81}{15} \end{pmatrix} = \frac{81}{15}\begin{pmatrix} \frac{37}{81} \\ 1 \end{pmatrix} = \frac{81}{15}\,X_5$$

$$A\,X_5 = \begin{pmatrix} 1 & 2 \\ 3 & 4 \end{pmatrix}\begin{pmatrix} 0{\cdot}4568 \\ 1 \end{pmatrix} = \begin{pmatrix} 2{\cdot}4568 \\ 5{\cdot}3704 \end{pmatrix} = 5{\cdot}3704\begin{pmatrix} 0{\cdot}4575 \\ 1 \end{pmatrix} = 5{\cdot}3704\,X_6$$

$$A\,X_6 = \begin{pmatrix} 1 & 2 \\ 3 & 4 \end{pmatrix}\begin{pmatrix} 0{\cdot}4575 \\ 1 \end{pmatrix} = \begin{pmatrix} 2{\cdot}4575 \\ 5{\cdot}3724 \end{pmatrix} = 5{\cdot}3724\begin{pmatrix} 0{\cdot}4574 \\ 1 \end{pmatrix} = 5{\cdot}3724\,X_7$$

$$A\,X_7 = \begin{pmatrix} 1 & 2 \\ 3 & 4 \end{pmatrix}\begin{pmatrix} 0{\cdot}4574 \\ 1 \end{pmatrix} = \begin{pmatrix} 2{\cdot}4574 \\ 5{\cdot}3723 \end{pmatrix} = 5{\cdot}3723\begin{pmatrix} 0{\cdot}4574 \\ 1 \end{pmatrix}$$

$$A\,X_8 = \begin{pmatrix} 1 & 2 \\ 3 & 4 \end{pmatrix}\begin{pmatrix} 0{\cdot}4574 \\ 1 \end{pmatrix} = \begin{pmatrix} 2{\cdot}4574 \\ 5{\cdot}3723 \end{pmatrix} = 5{\cdot}3723\begin{pmatrix} 0{\cdot}4574 \\ 1 \end{pmatrix}$$

Hence $\lambda_1 = 5{\cdot}3723$ and eigen vector $X_1 = \begin{pmatrix} 0{\cdot}4574 \\ 1 \end{pmatrix}$

Since $\lambda_1 + \lambda_2 = \text{Trace of } A = 1 + 4 = 5$

Second eigen value $= \lambda_2 = -\,0{\cdot}3723$.

(*ii*) Characteristic equation is $\lambda^2 - (1+4)\,\lambda + \begin{vmatrix} 1 & 2 \\ 3 & 4 \end{vmatrix} = 0$

*i.e.,* $\quad \lambda^2 - 5\lambda - 2 = 0$

$$\therefore \quad \lambda = \frac{5 \pm \sqrt{25+8}}{2} = \frac{5 \pm \sqrt{33}}{2} = 5{\cdot}3723,\ -\,0{\cdot}3723.$$

The values got by power method exactly coincide with the solutions from analytical method.

**Example 2.** *Find the numerically largest eigen value of*

$A = \begin{pmatrix} 25 & 1 & 2 \\ 1 & 3 & 0 \\ 2 & 0 & -4 \end{pmatrix}$ *and the corresponding eigen vector.*

(*BR. Ap. 1992*)

**Solution.** Let $X_1 = \begin{pmatrix} 1 \\ 0 \\ 0 \end{pmatrix}$ be an arbitrary initial eigen vector.

$$A\,X_1 = \begin{pmatrix} 25 & 1 & 2 \\ 1 & 3 & 0 \\ 2 & 0 & -4 \end{pmatrix}\begin{pmatrix} 1 \\ 0 \\ 0 \end{pmatrix} = \begin{pmatrix} 25 \\ 1 \\ 2 \end{pmatrix} = 25\begin{pmatrix} 1 \\ 0{\cdot}04 \\ 0{\cdot}08 \end{pmatrix} = 25\,X_2$$

$$A\,X_2 = \begin{pmatrix} 25 & 1 & 2 \\ 1 & 3 & 0 \\ 2 & 0 & -4 \end{pmatrix}\begin{pmatrix} 1 \\ 0{\cdot}04 \\ 0{\cdot}08 \end{pmatrix} = \begin{pmatrix} 25{\cdot}2 \\ 1{\cdot}12 \\ 1{\cdot}68 \end{pmatrix} = 25{\cdot}2\begin{pmatrix} 1 \\ 0{\cdot}0444 \\ 0{\cdot}0667 \end{pmatrix} = 25{\cdot}2\,X_3$$

$$A\,X_3 = \begin{pmatrix} 25 & 1 & 2 \\ 1 & 3 & 0 \\ 2 & 0 & -4 \end{pmatrix}\begin{pmatrix} 1 \\ 0{\cdot}0444 \\ 0{\cdot}0667 \end{pmatrix} = \begin{pmatrix} 25{\cdot}1778 \\ 1{\cdot}1332 \\ 1{\cdot}7337 \end{pmatrix} = 25{\cdot}1778\begin{pmatrix} 1 \\ 0{\cdot}0450 \\ 0{\cdot}0688 \end{pmatrix}$$

$$= 25{\cdot}1778\,X_4$$

$$A\,X_4 = \begin{pmatrix} 25{\cdot}1826 \\ 1{\cdot}135 \\ 1{\cdot}7248 \end{pmatrix} = 25{\cdot}1826\begin{pmatrix} 1 \\ 0{\cdot}0451 \\ 0{\cdot}0685 \end{pmatrix} = 25{\cdot}1826\,X_5$$

$$A\,X_5 = \begin{pmatrix} 25{\cdot}1821 \\ 1{\cdot}1353 \\ 1{\cdot}7260 \end{pmatrix} = 25{\cdot}1821\begin{pmatrix} 1 \\ 0{\cdot}0451 \\ 0{\cdot}0685 \end{pmatrix} = 25{\cdot}1821\,X_6$$

We have reached the limit.

$\therefore\ \lambda_1 = 25{\cdot}1821$ and the corresponding eigen vector is $\begin{pmatrix} 1 \\ 0{\cdot}0451 \\ 0.0685 \end{pmatrix}$.

**Example 3.** *Find the dominant eigen value and the corresponding eigen vector of* $A = \begin{pmatrix} 1 & 6 & 1 \\ 1 & 2 & 0 \\ 0 & 0 & 3 \end{pmatrix}$.

*Find also the least latent root and hence the third eigen value also.*

**Solution.** Let $X_1 = \begin{pmatrix} 1 \\ 0 \\ 0 \end{pmatrix}$ be an approximate eigen value.

$$A\,X_1 = \begin{bmatrix} 1 & 6 & 1 \\ 1 & 2 & 0 \\ 0 & 0 & 3 \end{bmatrix}\begin{bmatrix} 1 \\ 0 \\ 0 \end{bmatrix} = \begin{bmatrix} 1 \\ 1 \\ 0 \end{bmatrix} = 1\begin{bmatrix} 1 \\ 1 \\ 0 \end{bmatrix} = 1{\cdot}X_2$$

$$A\,X_2 = \begin{bmatrix} 1 & 6 & 1 \\ 1 & 2 & 0 \\ 0 & 0 & 3 \end{bmatrix}\begin{bmatrix} 1 \\ 1 \\ 0 \end{bmatrix} = \begin{bmatrix} 7 \\ 3 \\ 0 \end{bmatrix} = 7\begin{bmatrix} 1 \\ 0{\cdot}4286 \\ 0 \end{bmatrix} = 7\,X_3$$

$$A\,X_3 = \begin{bmatrix} 1 & 6 & 1 \\ 1 & 2 & 0 \\ 0 & 0 & 3 \end{bmatrix} \begin{bmatrix} 1 \\ 0{\cdot}4286 \\ 0 \end{bmatrix} = \begin{bmatrix} 3{\cdot}5714 \\ 1{\cdot}8572 \\ 0 \end{bmatrix} = 3{\cdot}5714 \begin{bmatrix} 1 \\ 0{\cdot}52 \\ 0 \end{bmatrix} = 3{\cdot}5714\,X_4$$

$$A\,X_4 = \begin{bmatrix} 1 & 6 & 1 \\ 1 & 2 & 0 \\ 0 & 0 & 3 \end{bmatrix} \begin{bmatrix} 1 \\ 0{\cdot}52 \\ 0 \end{bmatrix} = \begin{bmatrix} 4{\cdot}12 \\ 2{\cdot}04 \\ 0 \end{bmatrix} = 4{\cdot}12 \begin{bmatrix} 1 \\ 0{\cdot}4951 \\ 0 \end{bmatrix} = 4{\cdot}12 X_5$$

$$A\,X_5 = \begin{bmatrix} 1 & 6 & 1 \\ 1 & 2 & 0 \\ 0 & 0 & 3 \end{bmatrix} \begin{bmatrix} 1 \\ 0{\cdot}4951 \\ 0 \end{bmatrix} = \begin{bmatrix} 3{\cdot}9706 \\ 1{\cdot}9902 \\ 0 \end{bmatrix} = 3{\cdot}9706 \begin{bmatrix} 1 \\ 0{\cdot}5012 \\ 0 \end{bmatrix} = 3{\cdot}9706\,X_6$$

$$A\,X_6 = \begin{bmatrix} 1 & 6 & 1 \\ 1 & 2 & 0 \\ 0 & 0 & 3 \end{bmatrix} \begin{bmatrix} 1 \\ 0{\cdot}5012 \\ 0 \end{bmatrix} = \begin{bmatrix} 4{\cdot}0072 \\ 2{\cdot}0024 \\ 0 \end{bmatrix} = 4{\cdot}0072 \begin{bmatrix} 1 \\ 0{\cdot}4997 \\ 0 \end{bmatrix} = 4{\cdot}0072\,X_7$$

$$A\,X_7 = \begin{bmatrix} 1 & 6 & 1 \\ 1 & 2 & 0 \\ 0 & 0 & 3 \end{bmatrix} \begin{bmatrix} 1 \\ 0{\cdot}4997 \\ 0 \end{bmatrix} = \begin{bmatrix} 3{\cdot}9982 \\ 1{\cdot}9994 \\ 0 \end{bmatrix} = 3{\cdot}9982 \begin{bmatrix} 1 \\ 0{\cdot}5000 \\ 0 \end{bmatrix} = 3{\cdot}9982\,X_8$$

$$A\,X_8 = \begin{bmatrix} 1 & 6 & 1 \\ 1 & 2 & 0 \\ 0 & 0 & 3 \end{bmatrix} \begin{bmatrix} 1 \\ 0{\cdot}5 \\ 0 \end{bmatrix} = \begin{bmatrix} 4 \\ 2 \\ 0 \end{bmatrix} = 4 \begin{bmatrix} 1 \\ 0{\cdot}5 \\ 0 \end{bmatrix} = 4\,X_9$$

$\therefore$ Dominant eigen value = 4; corresponding eigen vector is $(1, 0{\cdot}5, 0)$.

To find the least eigen value, let $B = A - 4\,I$ since $\lambda_1 = 4$

$$\therefore\; B = \begin{bmatrix} 1 & 6 & 1 \\ 1 & 2 & 0 \\ 0 & 0 & 2 \end{bmatrix} - \begin{bmatrix} 4 & 0 & 0 \\ 0 & 4 & 0 \\ 0 & 0 & 4 \end{bmatrix} = \begin{bmatrix} -3 & 6 & 1 \\ 1 & -2 & 2 \\ 0 & 0 & -2 \end{bmatrix}$$

We will find the dominant eigen value of $B$.

Let $Y_1 = \begin{bmatrix} 1 \\ 0 \\ 0 \end{bmatrix}$ be the initial vector.

$$BY_1 = \begin{bmatrix} -3 & 6 & 1 \\ 1 & -2 & 0 \\ 0 & 0 & -2 \end{bmatrix} \begin{bmatrix} 1 \\ 0 \\ 0 \end{bmatrix} = \begin{bmatrix} -3 \\ 1 \\ 0 \end{bmatrix} = -3 \begin{bmatrix} 1 \\ -0{\cdot}3333 \\ 0 \end{bmatrix} = -3\,Y_2$$

$$BY_2 = \begin{bmatrix} -3 & 6 & 1 \\ 1 & -2 & 0 \\ 0 & 0 & -2 \end{bmatrix} \begin{bmatrix} 1 \\ -0{\cdot}3333 \\ 0 \end{bmatrix} = \begin{bmatrix} -5 \\ 1{\cdot}6666 \\ 0 \end{bmatrix} = -5 \begin{bmatrix} 1 \\ -0{\cdot}3333 \\ 0 \end{bmatrix} = -5\,Y_3$$

$$\therefore\quad BY_3 = \begin{bmatrix} -3 & 6 & 1 \\ 1 & -2 & 0 \\ 0 & 0 & -2 \end{bmatrix} \begin{bmatrix} 1 \\ -0{\cdot}3333 \\ 0 \end{bmatrix} = \begin{bmatrix} -5 \\ 1{\cdot}6666 \\ 0 \end{bmatrix} = -5 \begin{bmatrix} 1 \\ -0{\cdot}3333 \\ 0 \end{bmatrix}$$

$\therefore$ Dominant eigen value of $B$ is $= -5$.

Adding 4, smallest eigen value of $A = -5 + 4 = -1$

Sum of eigen values = Trace of $A = 1 + 2 + 3 = 6$

$$4 + (-1) + \lambda_3 = 6 \quad \therefore \quad \lambda_3 = 3.$$

All the three eigen values are 4, 3, –1.

**Example 4.** *Using power method, find all the eigen values of* $A = \begin{bmatrix} 5 & 0 & 1 \\ 0 & -2 & 0 \\ 1 & 0 & 5 \end{bmatrix}$.

**Solution.** Let $X_1 = \begin{bmatrix} 1 \\ 0 \\ 0 \end{bmatrix}$ be an approximate eigen vector.

$$A X_1 = \begin{bmatrix} 5 & 0 & 1 \\ 0 & -2 & 0 \\ 1 & 0 & 5 \end{bmatrix} \begin{bmatrix} 1 \\ 0 \\ 0 \end{bmatrix} = \begin{bmatrix} 5 \\ 0 \\ 1 \end{bmatrix} = 5 \begin{bmatrix} 1 \\ 0 \\ 0{\cdot}2 \end{bmatrix} = 5 X_2$$

$$A X_2 = \begin{bmatrix} 5 & 0 & 1 \\ 0 & -2 & 0 \\ 1 & 0 & 5 \end{bmatrix} \begin{bmatrix} 1 \\ 0 \\ 0{\cdot}2 \end{bmatrix} = \begin{bmatrix} 5{\cdot}2 \\ 0 \\ 2 \end{bmatrix} = 5{\cdot}2 \begin{bmatrix} 1 \\ 0 \\ 0{\cdot}3846 \end{bmatrix} = 5{\cdot}2 X_3$$

$$A X_3 = \begin{bmatrix} 5 & 0 & 1 \\ 0 & -2 & 0 \\ 1 & 0 & 5 \end{bmatrix} \begin{bmatrix} 1 \\ 0 \\ 0{\cdot}3846 \end{bmatrix} = \begin{bmatrix} 5{\cdot}3846 \\ 0 \\ 2{\cdot}9231 \end{bmatrix} = 5{\cdot}3846 \begin{bmatrix} 1 \\ 0 \\ 0{\cdot}5429 \end{bmatrix} = 5{\cdot}3846 X_4$$

$$A X_4 = \begin{bmatrix} 5 & 0 & 1 \\ 0 & -2 & 0 \\ 1 & 0 & 5 \end{bmatrix} \begin{bmatrix} 1 \\ 0 \\ 0{\cdot}5429 \end{bmatrix} = \begin{bmatrix} 5{\cdot}5429 \\ 0 \\ 3{\cdot}7143 \end{bmatrix} = 5{\cdot}5429 \begin{bmatrix} 1 \\ 0 \\ 0{\cdot}6701 \end{bmatrix} = 5{\cdot}5429 X_5$$

$$A X_5 = \begin{bmatrix} 5 & 0 & 1 \\ 0 & -2 & 0 \\ 1 & 0 & 5 \end{bmatrix} \begin{bmatrix} 1 \\ 0 \\ 0{\cdot}6701 \end{bmatrix} = \begin{bmatrix} 5{\cdot}6701 \\ 0 \\ 4{\cdot}3505 \end{bmatrix} = 5{\cdot}6701 \begin{bmatrix} 1 \\ 0 \\ 0{\cdot}7672 \end{bmatrix} = 5{\cdot}6701 X_6$$

$$A X_6 = \begin{bmatrix} 5 & 0 & 1 \\ 0 & -2 & 0 \\ 1 & 0 & 5 \end{bmatrix} \begin{bmatrix} 1 \\ 0 \\ 0{\cdot}7672 \end{bmatrix} = \begin{bmatrix} 5{\cdot}7642 \\ 0 \\ 4{\cdot}8360 \end{bmatrix} = 5{\cdot}7672 \begin{bmatrix} 1 \\ 0 \\ 0{\cdot}8385 \end{bmatrix} = 5{\cdot}7672 X_7$$

$$A X_7 = \begin{bmatrix} 5 & 0 & 1 \\ 0 & -2 & 0 \\ 1 & 0 & 5 \end{bmatrix} \begin{bmatrix} 1 \\ 0 \\ 0{\cdot}8385 \end{bmatrix} = \begin{bmatrix} 5{\cdot}8385 \\ 0 \\ 5{\cdot}1927 \end{bmatrix} = 5{\cdot}8385 \begin{bmatrix} 1 \\ 0 \\ 0{\cdot}8894 \end{bmatrix} = 5{\cdot}8385 X_8$$

$$A X_8 = \begin{bmatrix} 5 & 0 & 1 \\ 0 & -2 & 0 \\ 1 & 0 & 5 \end{bmatrix} \begin{bmatrix} 1 \\ 0 \\ 0{\cdot}8894 \end{bmatrix} = \begin{bmatrix} 5{\cdot}8894 \\ 0 \\ 5{\cdot}4470 \end{bmatrix} = 5{\cdot}8894 \begin{bmatrix} 1 \\ 0 \\ 0{\cdot}9249 \end{bmatrix} = 5{\cdot}8894 X_9$$

$$A X_9 = \begin{bmatrix} 5 & 0 & 1 \\ 0 & -2 & 0 \\ 1 & 0 & 5 \end{bmatrix} \begin{bmatrix} 1 \\ 0 \\ 0{\cdot}9249 \end{bmatrix} = \begin{bmatrix} 5{\cdot}9249 \\ 0 \\ 5{\cdot}6244 \end{bmatrix} = 5{\cdot}9249 \begin{bmatrix} 1 \\ 0 \\ 0{\cdot}9493 \end{bmatrix}$$

$$A X_{10} = \begin{bmatrix} 5 & 0 & 1 \\ 0 & -2 & 0 \\ 1 & 0 & 5 \end{bmatrix} \begin{bmatrix} 1 \\ 0 \\ 0.9493 \end{bmatrix} = \begin{bmatrix} 5.9493 \\ 0 \\ 5.7465 \end{bmatrix} = 5.9493 \begin{bmatrix} 1 \\ 0 \\ 0.9659 \end{bmatrix} = 5.9493 X_{11}$$

$$A X_{11} = \begin{bmatrix} 5 & 0 & 1 \\ 0 & -2 & 0 \\ 1 & 0 & 5 \end{bmatrix} \begin{bmatrix} 1 \\ 0 \\ 0.9659 \end{bmatrix} = \begin{bmatrix} 5.9659 \\ 0 \\ 5.8296 \end{bmatrix} = 5.9659 \begin{bmatrix} 1 \\ 0 \\ 0.9771 \end{bmatrix} = 5.9659 X_{12}$$

$$A X_{12} = \begin{bmatrix} 5 & 0 & 1 \\ 0 & -2 & 0 \\ 1 & 0 & 5 \end{bmatrix} \begin{bmatrix} 1 \\ 0 \\ 0.9771 \end{bmatrix} = \begin{bmatrix} 5.9771 \\ 0 \\ 5.8857 \end{bmatrix} = 5.9771 \begin{bmatrix} 1 \\ 0 \\ 0.9847 \end{bmatrix} = 5.9771 X_{13}$$

$$A X_{13} = \begin{bmatrix} 5 & 0 & 1 \\ 0 & -2 & 0 \\ 1 & 0 & 5 \end{bmatrix} \begin{bmatrix} 1 \\ 0 \\ 0.9847 \end{bmatrix} = \begin{bmatrix} 5.9847 \\ 0 \\ 5.9236 \end{bmatrix} = 5.9847 \begin{bmatrix} 1 \\ 0 \\ 0.9898 \end{bmatrix} = 5.9847 X_{14}$$

$$A X_{14} = \begin{bmatrix} 5 & 0 & 1 \\ 0 & -2 & 0 \\ 1 & 0 & 5 \end{bmatrix} \begin{bmatrix} 1 \\ 0 \\ 0.9898 \end{bmatrix} = \begin{bmatrix} 5.9898 \\ 0 \\ 5.9489 \end{bmatrix} = 5.9898 \begin{bmatrix} 1 \\ 0 \\ 0.9932 \end{bmatrix} = 5.9898 X_{15}$$

$$A X_{15} = \begin{bmatrix} 5 & 0 & 1 \\ 0 & -2 & 0 \\ 1 & 0 & 5 \end{bmatrix} \begin{bmatrix} 1 \\ 0 \\ 0.9932 \end{bmatrix} = \begin{bmatrix} 5.9932 \\ 0 \\ 5.9659 \end{bmatrix} = 5.9932 \begin{bmatrix} 1 \\ 0 \\ 0.9954 \end{bmatrix} = 5.9932 X_{16}$$

$$A X_{16} = \begin{bmatrix} 5 & 0 & 1 \\ 0 & -2 & 0 \\ 1 & 0 & 5 \end{bmatrix} \begin{bmatrix} 1 \\ 0 \\ 0.9954 \end{bmatrix} = \begin{bmatrix} 5.9954 \\ 0 \\ 5.9772 \end{bmatrix} = 5.9954 \begin{bmatrix} 1 \\ 0 \\ 0.9970 \end{bmatrix} = 5.9954 X_{17}$$

$$A X_{17} = \begin{bmatrix} 5.9970 \\ 1 \\ 5.9848 \end{bmatrix} = 5.9970 \begin{bmatrix} 1 \\ 0 \\ 0.9980 \end{bmatrix}$$

$\therefore \quad \lambda_1 = 6$; eigen vector $= \begin{pmatrix} 1 \\ 0 \\ 1 \end{pmatrix}$.

$B = A - 6I = \begin{bmatrix} -1 & 0 & 1 \\ 0 & -8 & 0 \\ 1 & 0 & -1 \end{bmatrix}$. Take $Y_1 = \begin{bmatrix} 1 \\ 0 \\ 0 \end{bmatrix}$

$$B Y_1 = \begin{bmatrix} -1 \\ 0 \\ 1 \end{bmatrix} = -1 \begin{bmatrix} 1 \\ 0 \\ -1 \end{bmatrix} = -1\, Y_2$$

$$B Y_2 = \begin{bmatrix} -1 & 0 & 1 \\ 0 & -8 & 0 \\ 1 & 0 & -1 \end{bmatrix} \begin{bmatrix} 1 \\ 0 \\ -1 \end{bmatrix} = \begin{bmatrix} -2 \\ 0 \\ 2 \end{bmatrix} = -2 \begin{bmatrix} 1 \\ 0 \\ -1 \end{bmatrix} = -2\, Y_3$$

$$B Y_3 = \begin{bmatrix} -1 & 0 & 1 \\ 0 & -8 & 0 \\ 1 & 0 & -1 \end{bmatrix} \begin{bmatrix} 1 \\ 0 \\ -1 \end{bmatrix} = -2 \begin{bmatrix} 1 \\ 0 \\ -1 \end{bmatrix}$$

Greater eigen value of $B = -2$

$\therefore$ Smallest eigen value of $A = -2 + 6 = 4$

$\lambda_1 + \lambda_2 + \lambda_3$ Trace $= 5 - 2 + 5 = 8$

$6 + 4 + \lambda_3 = 8 \quad \therefore \quad \lambda_3 = -2$

$\therefore$ Eigen values are 6, 4, –2.

## EXERCISES 13.1

Using power method, calculate the dominant eigen values of the following matrices; if possible find the corresponding eigen vector and also the other eigen values of the matrix.

**1.** $\begin{bmatrix} -4 & -5 \\ 1 & 2 \end{bmatrix}$ **2.** $\begin{bmatrix} 2 & -1 & 0 \\ -1 & 2 & -1 \\ 0 & -1 & 2 \end{bmatrix}$ **3.** $\begin{bmatrix} -15 & 4 & 3 \\ 10 & -12 & 6 \\ 20 & -4 & 2 \end{bmatrix}$

**4.** $\begin{bmatrix} 1 & 3 & -1 \\ 3 & 2 & 4 \\ -1 & 4 & 10 \end{bmatrix}$ **5.** $\begin{bmatrix} 10 & 2 & 1 \\ 2 & 10 & 1 \\ 2 & 1 & 10 \end{bmatrix}$ **6.** $\begin{bmatrix} -0.5 & 1.5 & 0.17 \\ 0.25 & -0.25 & -0.08 \\ 0 & 0 & 0.33 \end{bmatrix}$

**7.** $\begin{bmatrix} 4 & 1 \\ 1 & 3 \end{bmatrix}$ **8.** $\begin{bmatrix} 3 & 2 & 4 \\ 2 & 0 & 2 \\ 4 & 2 & 3 \end{bmatrix}$ **9.** $\begin{bmatrix} 1 & -3 & 2 \\ 4 & 4 & -1 \\ 6 & 3 & 5 \end{bmatrix}$ (*Anna Ap. 2005*

**10.** $\begin{bmatrix} 8 & -6 & 2 \\ -6 & 7 & -4 \\ 2 & -4 & 3 \end{bmatrix}$ **11.** $\begin{bmatrix} 3 & 2 & 4 \\ -1 & 4 & 10 \\ 1 & 3 & -1 \end{bmatrix}$

## ANSWERS
## EXERCISES 13.1

**1.** – 3 ; (1, – 0.2)′ **2.** 3.414; (– 0.707, 1, 0.707)′
**3.** – 20, (1, – 0.5, – 1)′ **4.** 11.66; (0.025, 0.422, 1)′
**5.** 13; (1, 1, 1)′ **6.** – 1, (1, – 0.33, 0)′]
**7.** 4.6179, (1, 0.618)′] **8.** 8; (1, $\frac{1}{2}$, 1)′ **9.** 7 : (4.5, 1, 15)′
**10.** 15, 3, 0 **11.** 7.4; (0.8, 1, 0.4)′.

## JACOBI METHOD FOR FINDING EIGEN VALUES

We use Jacobi's method to find the eigen values of a real symmetric matrix. By this method we can find all eigen values and eigen vectors of a symmetric matrix. The basic principle involved in this method is to find a sequence of similarity transformations which reduce the given matrix into another whose eigen values can be found easily. If a matrix of higher order is given, we have to use only computers to solve the problem. Hence we will resort only to matrices of orders two and three in this chapter.

We recall some of the following theorems that we studied in the previous semesters in the theory of matrices.

1. Two square matrices $A$ and $B$ are said to be similar if there exists a non-singular matrix $S$ such that $B = S^{-1}$ AS or A = $S^{-1}$ BS.

2. Two similar matrices have the same eigen values

3. A square matrix A is said to be orthogonal

   if $AA' = I$ or $A'A = I$ or $A^{-1} = A'$.

4. For an orthogonal matrix $A$, det $A = |A| = \pm 1$

5. A matrix A is symmetrix if $A' = A$ i.e. $a_{ij} = a_{ji}$

6. For a real symmetric matrix. $A$,

   (*i*) all eigen values are real

   (*ii*) eigen vectors corresponding to distinct eigen values are orthogonal

   (*iii*) A is diagonalisable.

7. The diagonal elements of a diagonal matrix $D$ are its eigen values.

**Theorem:** If $A$ is a real symmetric matrix and $R$ is an orthogonal matrix then the transformation given by

$$B = R^1 AR = R^{-1} AR \quad (\because R^1 = R^{-1})$$

transforms $A$ into $B$ and this transformation preserves the symmetry and the eigen values of $B$. That is, $B$ is also symmetric and the eigen values of $B$ are also those of A. If X is the eigen vector corresponding to $\lambda$ of $A$, then the eigen vector of $B$ corresponding to $\lambda$ is $R^1 X = R^{-1} X$. The proof of this can be seen in the chapter on matrices. Further if $B$ happens to be the diagonal matrix, the eigen values of $B$ and hence of $A$ are the diagonal elements of $B$.

**Rotation matrix**

If $P(x, y)$ is any point in the $xy$ plane and if $OP$ is rotated ($O$ is the origin) in the clockwise direction through an angle $\theta$, then the new position of $P(x', y')$ is given by

$$\begin{pmatrix} x' \\ y' \end{pmatrix} = \begin{pmatrix} \cos\theta & -\sin\theta \\ \sin\theta & \cos\theta \end{pmatrix} \begin{pmatrix} x \\ y \end{pmatrix}.$$

*i.e.,* $$\begin{pmatrix} x' \\ y' \end{pmatrix} = R \begin{pmatrix} x \\ y \end{pmatrix} \text{where } R = \begin{pmatrix} \cos\theta & -\sin\theta \\ \sin\theta & \cos\theta \end{pmatrix}$$

Hence R is called a **Rotation matrix** in the xy plane. Here R is also an orthogonal matrix since $RR' = I$

**In general**

$$R = \begin{pmatrix} 1\ 0\ 0\ \ldots\ldots\ldots\ 0\ \ldots\ldots\ 0\ \ldots\ldots\ 0 \\ 0\ 1\ 0\ \ldots\ldots\ldots\ldots\ldots\ldots\ldots\ldots\ldots\ 0 \\ 0\ 0\ 1\ \ldots\ldots\cos\phi\ \ldots\ldots -\sin\phi\ \ldots\ldots\ 0 \\ 0\ 0\ 0\ 1\ \ldots\ldots\ldots\ldots\ldots\ldots\ldots\ldots\ 0 \\ \ldots\ldots\ldots\ldots\ldots\ldots\ldots\ldots\ldots\ldots\ldots \\ 0\ 0\ 0\ 0\ \ldots\ldots\sin\phi\ \ldots\ldots\cos\phi\ \ldots\ldots\ldots\ 0 \\ \ldots\ldots\ldots\ldots\ldots\ldots\ldots\ldots\ldots\ldots\ldots \\ 0\ 0\ 0\ \ldots\ldots\ldots\ldots\ldots\ldots\ldots\ldots\ldots\ 1 \end{pmatrix}$$

(columns marked: $i^{\text{th}}$ col, $j^{\text{th}}$ col; rows marked: → $i$th row, → $j$th row)

is an *orthogonal Rotation matrix* where all diagonal elements are 1 and all off diagonal elements are zero except

$$a_{ii} = \cos\phi,\ a_{ij} = -\sin\phi,\ a_{ji} = \sin\phi \text{ and } a_{jj} = \cos\phi$$

If $\quad X = (x_1, x_2, \ldots x_n)',\ Y = (y_1, y_2 \ldots y_n)'$

then $\quad Y = RX$ gives the transformation where

$$y_p = x_p \text{ where } p \neq i \text{ and } p \neq j$$

$$y_i = x_i \cos\phi - x_j \sin\phi$$

$y_j = x_i \sin\phi + y_i \cos\phi$ where $\phi$ is the angle of rotation in the $x_i x_j$ plane.

**Finding eigen values of 2 × 2 matrix by Jacobi method**

Let $A = \begin{pmatrix} a_{11} & a_{12} \\ a_{21} & a_{22} \end{pmatrix}$ be a symmetrix 2 × 2 matrix

where $\quad a_{12} = a_{21}$. The most general orthogonal

Rotation 2 × 2 matrix is $\begin{pmatrix} \cos\theta & -\sin\theta \\ \sin\theta & \cos\theta \end{pmatrix} = R$

Let $B = R'AR$ be the similar transformation. $B$ is also symmetric.

Hence, $\begin{pmatrix} b_{11} & b_{12} \\ b_{21} & b_{22} \end{pmatrix} = \begin{pmatrix} \cos\theta & \sin\theta \\ -\sin\theta & \cos\theta \end{pmatrix} \begin{pmatrix} a_{11} & a_{12} \\ a_{21} & a_{22} \end{pmatrix} \begin{pmatrix} \cos\theta & -\sin\theta \\ \sin\theta & \cos\theta \end{pmatrix}$ gives

$$b_{11} = a_{11}\cos^2\theta + a_{12}\sin 2\theta + a_{22}\sin^2\theta \quad \ldots (1)$$

$$b_{12} = b_{21} = \frac{1}{2}(a_{22} - a_{11})\sin 2\theta + a_{12}\cos 2\theta \quad \ldots (2)$$

$$b_{22} = a_{11}\sin^2\theta - a_{12}\sin 2\theta + a_{22}\cos^2\theta \quad \ldots (3)$$

(Please note: $b_{11} + b_{22} = a_{11} + a_{22}$)

Now our aim is to make B as a diagonal matrix

Therefore, select $\theta$ so that $b_{12} = b_{21} = 0$

*i.e.* $$\frac{1}{2}(a_{22} - a_{11})\sin 2\theta = -a_{12}\cos 2\theta$$

$\therefore$ $$\cot 2\theta = \frac{a_{11} - a_{22}}{2a_{12}} \quad \text{... (4)}$$

From (4), we can get $\theta$ and hence using (1) and (3) we get $b_{11}$ and $b_{22}$.

Hence, eigen values of B and A are $b_{11}$ and $b_{22}$.

From (4), $$\theta = \frac{1}{2}\tan^{-1}\left(\frac{2a_{12}}{a_{11} - a_{22}}\right) \text{ if } a_{11} \neq a_{22}$$

$$= \begin{cases} \pi/4 \text{ if } a_{11} = a_{22} \text{ and } a_{12} > 0 \\ -\pi/4 \text{ if } a_{11} = a_{22} \text{ and } a_{12} < 0 \end{cases}$$

From (4) cot $2\theta$ is known: let cot $2\theta = \alpha$

Then, using $\cot^2\theta - 1 = 2\alpha\cot\theta$, we get

$$\cot\theta = \beta = \alpha \pm \sqrt{\alpha^2 + 1}$$

Then $\sin\theta = \dfrac{\text{sgn}(\beta)}{\sqrt{1+\beta^2}}$ where sgn ($\beta$) is signum function and it is + 1 or – 1 according as $\beta$ is positive or negative.

$\therefore$ $$\sin\theta = \frac{1}{\sqrt{1+\beta^2}} \text{ and } \cos\theta = \frac{\beta}{\sqrt{1+\beta^2}} \text{ if } \beta \text{ is positive}$$

and $$\sin\theta = \frac{-1}{\sqrt{1+\beta^2}} \text{ and } \cos\theta = \frac{-\beta}{\sqrt{1+\beta^2}} \text{ if } \beta \text{ is negative.}$$

Then $b_{11}$, $b_{22}$ are found out from (1) and (3)

**Working Rule**

**1.** Assume the rotation matrix $R = \begin{pmatrix} \cos\theta & -\sin\theta \\ \sin\theta & \cos\theta \end{pmatrix}$ and find

$$\cot\ 2\theta = \alpha = \frac{a_{11} - a_{22}}{2a_{12}}$$

**2.** Find $\cot\theta = \beta = \alpha \pm \sqrt{\alpha^2 + 1}$

**3.** Then find $\sin\theta = \dfrac{1}{\sqrt{1+\beta^2}}$, $\cos\theta = \dfrac{\beta}{\sqrt{1+\beta^2}}$ if $\beta > 0$

$$\sin\theta = \frac{1}{\sqrt{1+\beta^2}}, \; \cos\theta = \frac{\beta}{\sqrt{1+\beta^2}} \text{ if } \beta > 0$$

**4.** Then calculate the eigen values of $A$ as

$$\boxed{b_{11} = a_{11}\cos^2\theta + a_{12}\sin 2\theta + a_{22}\sin^2\theta}$$

$$b_{22} = a_{11}\sin^2\theta - a_{12}\sin 2\theta + a_{22}\cos^2\theta$$

$$\boxed{b_{22} = a_{11} + a_{22} - b_{11}}$$

OR

**1.** Use $\theta = \frac{1}{2}\tan^{-1}\left(\frac{2a_{12}}{a_{11} - a_{22}}\right)$ if $a_{11} \neq a_{22}$

$= \pi/4$ if $a_{11} = a_{22}$ and $a_{12} > 0$

$= -\pi/4$ if $a_{11} = a_{22}$ and $a_{12} < 0$.

**2.** Write down $R = \begin{pmatrix} \cos\theta & -\sin\theta \\ \sin\theta & \cos\theta \end{pmatrix}$ using the value of $\theta$.

**3.** Get $B = R'AR$.

**4.** The diagonal elements of $B$ are the eigen values.

**5.** The columns of $R$ are the corresponding eigen vectors.

**Example 1.** *Using Jacobi method, find eigen values of*

(*i*) $A = \begin{pmatrix} 6 & \sqrt{3} \\ \sqrt{3} & 4 \end{pmatrix}$ (*ii*) $A = \begin{pmatrix} 1 & \sqrt{2} \\ \sqrt{2} & 0 \end{pmatrix}$

**Solution.** Evidently the given matrix in both problems is symmetric.

Let $R = \begin{pmatrix} \cos\theta & -\sin\theta \\ \sin\theta & \cos\theta \end{pmatrix}$ and $B = R'AR$

(*i*) $\cot 2\theta = \alpha = \dfrac{a_{11} - a_{22}}{2a_{12}} = \dfrac{6-4}{2\sqrt{3}} = \dfrac{1}{\sqrt{3}}$

$$\cot\theta = \beta = \alpha \pm \sqrt{1+\alpha^2} = \frac{1}{\sqrt{3}} \pm \sqrt{1+\frac{1}{3}} = \sqrt{3} \text{ or } -\frac{1}{\sqrt{3}}$$

Take $\beta = \sqrt{3}$

$$\sin\theta = \frac{1}{\sqrt{1+\beta^2}} = \frac{1}{2} \text{ and } \cos\theta = \frac{\beta}{\sqrt{1+\beta^2}} = \frac{\sqrt{3}}{2}$$

*i.e.* $\theta = \pi/6$

$$b_{11} = a_{11}\cos^2\theta + a_{12}\sin 2\theta + a_{22}\sin^2\theta$$

$$= 6\left(\frac{3}{4}\right)+\sqrt{3}\left[2.\frac{1}{2}.\frac{\sqrt{3}}{2}\right]+4\left(\frac{1}{4}\right)$$

$$= \frac{9}{2}+\frac{3}{2}+1=7$$

$$b_{22} = a_{11}+a_{22}-b_{11} = 6+4-7=3$$

$\therefore$ Hence eigen values of $B$ and $A$ are, 7, 3.

Here $$B = D = \begin{pmatrix} 7 & 0 \\ 0 & 3 \end{pmatrix}$$

and Rotation matrix $$R = \begin{pmatrix} \cos\pi/6 & -\sin\pi/6 \\ \sin\pi/6 & \cos\pi/6 \end{pmatrix} = \begin{pmatrix} \frac{\sqrt{3}}{2} & -\frac{1}{2} \\ \frac{1}{2} & \sqrt{3}/2 \end{pmatrix}$$

The eigen vectors are the columns of $R$ namely

$$X_1 = \begin{pmatrix} \sqrt{3} \\ 1 \end{pmatrix} \text{ and } X_2 = \begin{pmatrix} -1 \\ \sqrt{3} \end{pmatrix}$$

(*ii*) Here $$\cot 2\theta = \alpha = \frac{1-0}{2\sqrt{2}} = \frac{1}{2\sqrt{2}}$$

$$\cot\theta = \beta = \alpha \pm \sqrt{1+\alpha^2} = \frac{1}{2\sqrt{2}} \pm \sqrt{1+\frac{1}{8}} = \sqrt{2}, -\frac{1}{\sqrt{2}}$$

Take $$\beta = \sqrt{2};\ \sin\theta = \frac{1}{\sqrt{1+2}} = \frac{1}{\sqrt{3}}$$

$$\cos\theta = \sqrt{2/3}$$

$$b_{11} = 1\left(\frac{2}{3}\right)+\sqrt{2}\left(2.\frac{1}{\sqrt{3}}.\sqrt{\frac{2}{3}}\right)+0\left(\frac{1}{3}\right)$$

$$= 2$$

$$b_{22} = a_{11}+a_{22}-b_{11} = 1+0-2=-1$$

Hence eigen values of $B$ and $A$ are 2 and – 1. The eigen vectors of $A$ are the columns of $R$, namely $\begin{pmatrix} \sqrt{2} \\ 1 \end{pmatrix}$ and $\begin{pmatrix} -1 \\ \sqrt{2} \end{pmatrix}$

The corresponding Rotation matrix $$R = \begin{pmatrix} \sqrt{\frac{2}{3}} & -\frac{1}{\sqrt{3}} \\ \frac{1}{\sqrt{3}} & \sqrt{\frac{2}{3}} \end{pmatrix}$$

**Example 2.** *Using Jacobi method, find eigen values of*

(*i*) $A=\begin{pmatrix} 1 & 3 \\ 3 & 4 \end{pmatrix}$ (*ii*) $A=\begin{pmatrix} 2 & 1 \\ 1 & 2 \end{pmatrix}$

**Solution.**

(*i*) $$\cot 2\theta = \alpha = \frac{a_{11}-a_{22}}{2a_{12}} = \frac{1-4}{6} = -\frac{1}{2}$$

$$\beta = \alpha \pm \sqrt{1+\alpha^2} = -\frac{1}{2} \pm \sqrt{1+\frac{1}{4}} = \frac{-1\pm\sqrt{5}}{2}$$

Take $$\beta = \frac{\sqrt{5}-1}{2} > 0;\ 1+\beta^2 = 1+\left(\frac{\sqrt{5}-1}{2}\right)^2 = \frac{10-2\sqrt{5}}{4}$$

$$\sin\ \theta = \frac{1}{\sqrt{1+\beta^2}} = \frac{2}{\sqrt{10-2\sqrt{5}}}$$

$$\cos\theta = \frac{\beta}{(1+\beta^2)} = \frac{\sqrt{5}-1}{\sqrt{10-2\sqrt{5}}}$$

$\therefore$ $$b_{11} = a_{11}\cos^2\theta + a_{12}(2\sin\theta\cos\theta) = a_{22}\sin^2\theta$$

$$= 1\left[\frac{(\sqrt{5}-1)^2}{10-2\sqrt{5}}\right] + \frac{3\times 2\times 2(\sqrt{5}-1)}{10-2\sqrt{5}} + 4\times\frac{4}{10-2\sqrt{5}}$$

$$b_{11} = \frac{10+10\sqrt{5}}{10-2\sqrt{5}} = \frac{5+5\sqrt{5}}{5-\sqrt{5}} = \frac{\sqrt{5}(\sqrt{5}+1)}{(\sqrt{5}-1)} = \sqrt{5}\,\frac{(\sqrt{5}+1)^2}{(5-1)} = \frac{5+3\sqrt{5}}{2}$$

$$b_{22} = a_{11}+a_{22}-b_{11} = 1+4-\left(\frac{5+3\sqrt{5}}{2}\right) = \frac{5-3\sqrt{5}}{2}$$

The eigen values are $\frac{5\pm3\sqrt{5}}{2}$. The corresponding eigen vectors are the columns of $R$ namely $\begin{pmatrix}\cos\theta \\ \sin\theta\end{pmatrix}$ and $\begin{pmatrix}-\sin\theta \\ \cos\theta\end{pmatrix}$ or their proportional values

Hence $X_1 = \begin{pmatrix}\sqrt{5}-1 \\ 2\end{pmatrix}$ and $\begin{pmatrix}-2 \\ \sqrt{5}-1\end{pmatrix}$

[OR] We can write down $R'AR$ and get eigen values

(*ii*) Here $a_{11} = a_{22} = 2$

$$\therefore\ \tan 2\theta = \frac{2a_{12}}{a_{11}-a_{22}} = \frac{2}{2-2} = \infty \therefore 2\theta = \pi/2 \text{ and } \theta = \pi/4$$

$\therefore \quad \cos\theta = \cos\frac{\pi}{4} = \frac{1}{\sqrt{2}}; \ \sin\theta = \frac{1}{\sqrt{2}}$

$\therefore \quad b_{11} = a_{11}\cos^2\theta + a_{12}(\sin 2\theta) + a_{22}\sin^2\theta$

$$= 2\left(\frac{1}{2}\right) + (1)\,(1) + 2\left(\frac{1}{2}\right) = 3$$

$$b_{22} = a_{11} + a_{22} - b_{11} = 2 + 2 - 3 = 1$$

Hence the eigen values are 3, 1.

The corresponding eigen vectors are $\begin{pmatrix}\cos\theta\\ \sin\theta\end{pmatrix}$ and $\begin{pmatrix}-\sin\theta\\ \cos\theta\end{pmatrix}$

That is $\begin{pmatrix}1\\ 1\end{pmatrix}$ and $\begin{pmatrix}-1\\ 1\end{pmatrix}$.

**Example 3.** *Find the eigen values and eigen vectors of*

*(i)* $A = \begin{pmatrix}2 & 2\\ 2 & -1\end{pmatrix}$ *(ii)* $\begin{pmatrix}2 & 3\\ 3 & 2\end{pmatrix}$

**Solution.** (*i*) Here $a_{11} = 2,\ a_{22} = -1,\ a_{12} = 2 > 0$

$$\tan 2\theta = \frac{2a_{12}}{a_{11} - a_{22}} = \frac{4}{3}; \ \cot 2\theta = \frac{3}{4} = \alpha$$

$$\beta = \alpha \pm \sqrt{1 + \alpha^2} = \frac{3}{4} \pm \sqrt{1 + \frac{9}{16}} = 2, -1/2; \text{ Take } \beta = 2$$

$$\therefore \quad \sin\theta = \frac{1}{\sqrt{1+\beta^2}} = \frac{1}{\sqrt{5}}; \cos\theta = \frac{\beta}{\sqrt{1+\beta^2}} = \frac{2}{\sqrt{5}}$$

$$\therefore \quad b_{11} = a_{11}\cos^2\theta + a_{12}(2\sin.\cos\theta) + a_{22}\sin^2\theta$$

$$= 2\left(\frac{4}{5}\right) + 2\left(\frac{4}{5}\right) + (-1)\frac{1}{5} = 3$$

$$b_{22} = a_{11} + a_{22} - b_{11} = 2 - 1 - 3 = -2$$

$\therefore$ The eigen values are 3, – 2

The eigen vectors are $\begin{pmatrix}\cos\theta\\ \sin\theta\end{pmatrix}$ and $\begin{pmatrix}-\sin\theta\\ \cos\theta\end{pmatrix}$ i.e. $\begin{pmatrix}2\\ 1\end{pmatrix}$ and $\begin{pmatrix}-1\\ 2\end{pmatrix}$

(*ii*) $A = \begin{pmatrix}2 & 3\\ 3 & 2\end{pmatrix}$ Since $a_{11} = a_{22} = 2$, tan $2\theta = \infty$

$\therefore \quad \theta = \pi/4$

Here, $R = \begin{pmatrix} \cos\theta & -\sin\theta \\ \sin\theta & \cos\theta \end{pmatrix} = \begin{pmatrix} \frac{1}{\sqrt{2}} & -\frac{1}{\sqrt{2}} \\ \frac{1}{\sqrt{2}} & \frac{1}{\sqrt{2}} \end{pmatrix}$

$$\therefore \quad R'AR = \begin{pmatrix} \frac{1}{\sqrt{2}} & \frac{1}{\sqrt{2}} \\ -\frac{1}{\sqrt{2}} & \frac{1}{\sqrt{2}} \end{pmatrix} \begin{pmatrix} 2 & 3 \\ 3 & 2 \end{pmatrix} \begin{pmatrix} \frac{1}{\sqrt{2}} & -\frac{1}{\sqrt{2}} \\ \frac{1}{\sqrt{2}} & \frac{1}{\sqrt{2}} \end{pmatrix}$$

$$= \frac{1}{2}\begin{pmatrix} 1 & 1 \\ -1 & 1 \end{pmatrix} \begin{pmatrix} 2 & 3 \\ 3 & 2 \end{pmatrix} \begin{pmatrix} 1 & -1 \\ 1 & 1 \end{pmatrix}$$

$$= \frac{1}{2}\begin{pmatrix} 1 & 1 \\ -1 & 1 \end{pmatrix} \begin{pmatrix} 5 & +1 \\ 5 & -1 \end{pmatrix}$$

$$= \begin{pmatrix} 5 & 0 \\ 0 & -1 \end{pmatrix}$$

The eigen values are 5 and – 1 and the eigen vectors are columns of $R$ namely $\begin{pmatrix} 1 \\ 1 \end{pmatrix}$ and $\begin{pmatrix} -1 \\ 1 \end{pmatrix}$.

**Extension to Higher order Symmetric Matrices.**

Jacobi method can be extended to higher order symmetric matrices by similarity transformation. Jacobi method of finding the eigen values of a real symmetric matrix is to apply repeatedly the plane rotations R until the sum of the squares of the off-diagonal elements is smaller than some specified tolerance value. At that point, the elements of the diagonal values are taken as approximate eigen values. To annihilate the off-diagonal element every time is a time consuming job and we require the help of a computer to do the job and that too expensive. Hence, for this course, we stop with second and third order symmetric matrices; However, we give below a general approach to an $n$th order symmetric matrix.

Suppose we want to annihilate the off-diagonal numerically largest element $a_{ij}$ in $(a_{ij})_{n\times n}$ matrix.

First we select the Rotation matrix $S_1$ where

$$S_1 = \begin{bmatrix} 1 & 0 & \ldots\ldots\ldots\ldots\ldots\ldots & 0 \\ 0 & 1 & 0 \ldots\ldots\ldots\ldots\ldots & 0 \\ 0 \ldots & \cos\theta & \ldots\ldots -\sin\theta \ldots\ldots & 0 \\ 0 \ldots\ldots & \sin\theta & \ldots\ldots \cos\theta \ldots\ldots & 0 \\ 0 \ldots\ldots & \ldots\ldots & \ldots\ldots\ldots\ldots & 1 \end{bmatrix} \begin{matrix} \\ \\ \rightarrow i\text{th row} \\ \rightarrow j\text{th row} \\ \\ \end{matrix}$$

$\downarrow$ $i$th col $\quad$ $\downarrow$ $j$th col

$S_1$ is a $n \times n$ matrix in which diagonal elements are 1 and all off-diagonal elements are zero except

$$a_{ii} = \cos\theta,\ \ a_{jj} = \cos\theta,\ a_{ij} = -\sin\theta,\ a_{ji} = \sin\theta$$

Now $S_1$ is orthogonal.

Perform $S_1^{-1}AS_1 = S_1'AS_1 = B_1$ since $S_1^{-1} = S_1'$

annihilating $b_{ij} = 0$ in $B_1$.

In the next step, take the largest off-diagonal element $b_{kl}$ in $B_1$ and annihilate to get

$$B_2 = S_2^{-1}B_1S_2$$

Performing series of such rotation by $S_1$, $S_2$, $S_3$ ......
after $K$ operations, we get

$$B_k = S_k^{-1}S_{k-1}^{-1}....S_1^{-1}AS_1S_2...S_k$$

$$= (S_1S_2...S_k)^{-1}A(S_1S_2..S_k) = S^{-1}AS$$

where $\quad S = S_1S_2...S_k$.

If $B_k$ is diagonal matrix, we get immediately eigen values of $B_k$ and hence of A.

Since an element annihilated by one plane rotation may not necessarily remain zero during subsequent transformations, the operations may continue so that $k \to \infty$. As $k \to \infty$, $B_k$ will approach a diagonal matrix. The eigen vectors of A are the columns of the matrix $S = S_1S_2...S_k$. That is why in the case of $2 \times 2$ matrix in which case only one operation was necessary, the columns of $S_1$ are the eigen vectors of A. The minimum number of rotations required to bring A to a diagonal form is $n(n-1)/2$.

Now, we will apply the above procedure to get the eigen values and eigen vectors of a third order matrix.

Note: If $\tan 2\theta = \dfrac{2a_{ij}}{a_{ii} - a_{jj}}$, then

$$\tan\theta = \frac{-2a_{ij}}{(a_{jj} - a_{ii}) + \sqrt{(a_{ii} - a_{jj})^2 + 4a_{ij}^2}} \text{ if } a_{ii} < a_{jj}$$

and
$$\tan\theta = \frac{2a_{ij}}{(a_{ii} - a_{jj}) + \sqrt{(a_{ii} - a_{jj})^2 + 4a_{ij}^2}} \text{ if } a_{ii} > a_{jj}$$

and
$$\cos\theta = \frac{1}{\sqrt{1 + \tan^2\theta}}$$

$$\sin\theta = \cos\theta\tan\theta.$$

**Example 4.** *Find the eigen values and eigen vectors of the matrix*

$$A = \begin{pmatrix} 1 & \sqrt{2} & 2 \\ \sqrt{2} & 3 & \sqrt{2} \\ 2 & \sqrt{2} & 1 \end{pmatrix}.$$

**Solution.** Here the largest off-diagonal element is $a_{13} = a_{31} = 2$ and $a_{11} = 1$, $a_{33} = 1$.

Hence take the rotation matrix

$$S_1 = \begin{pmatrix} \cos\theta & 0 & -\sin\theta \\ 0 & 1 & 0 \\ \sin\theta & 0 & \cos\theta \end{pmatrix}$$

Select $\theta$ so that $\cot 2\theta = \dfrac{a_{11} - a_{33}}{2a_{13}} = \dfrac{2-2}{4} = 0$

$\therefore \quad 2\theta = \pi/2;\ \theta = \pi/4$

$$\therefore \quad S_1 = \begin{pmatrix} \frac{1}{\sqrt{2}} & 0 & -\frac{1}{\sqrt{2}} \\ 0 & 1 & 0 \\ \frac{1}{\sqrt{2}} & 0 & \frac{1}{\sqrt{2}} \end{pmatrix}$$

$$B_1 = S_1^{-1} A S_1 = S_1' A S_1$$

$$= \begin{pmatrix} \frac{1}{\sqrt{2}} & 0 & \frac{1}{\sqrt{2}} \\ 0 & 1 & 0 \\ -\frac{1}{\sqrt{2}} & 0 & \frac{1}{\sqrt{2}} \end{pmatrix} \begin{pmatrix} 1 & \sqrt{2} & 2 \\ \sqrt{2} & 3 & \sqrt{2} \\ 2 & \sqrt{2} & 1 \end{pmatrix} \begin{pmatrix} \frac{1}{\sqrt{2}} & 0 & -\frac{1}{\sqrt{2}} \\ 0 & 1 & 0 \\ \frac{1}{\sqrt{2}} & 0 & \frac{1}{\sqrt{2}} \end{pmatrix}$$

$$= \frac{1}{2} \begin{pmatrix} 1 & 0 & 1 \\ 0 & \sqrt{2} & 0 \\ -1 & 0 & 1 \end{pmatrix} \begin{pmatrix} 1 & \sqrt{2} & 2 \\ \sqrt{2} & 3 & \sqrt{2} \\ 2 & \sqrt{2} & 1 \end{pmatrix} \begin{pmatrix} 1 & 0 & -1 \\ 0 & \sqrt{2} & 0 \\ 1 & 0 & 1 \end{pmatrix}$$

$$= \frac{1}{2} \begin{pmatrix} 1 & 0 & 1 \\ 0 & \sqrt{2} & 0 \\ -1 & 0 & 1 \end{pmatrix} \begin{pmatrix} 3 & 2 & 1 \\ 2\sqrt{2} & 3\sqrt{2} & 0 \\ 3 & 2 & -1 \end{pmatrix}$$

$$= \begin{pmatrix} 3 & 2 & 0 \\ 2 & 3 & 0 \\ 0 & 0 & -1 \end{pmatrix}$$

Again annihilate the largest off-diagonal element $a_{12} = a_{21} = 2 \text{ in } B_1$

Also, $\quad a_{11} = 3,\ a_{22} = 3$

Take

$$S_2 = \begin{pmatrix} \cos\theta & -\sin\theta & 0 \\ \sin\theta & \cos\theta & 0 \\ 0 & 0 & 1 \end{pmatrix}$$

Select $\theta$ so that $\cot 2\theta = \dfrac{a_{11} - a_{22}}{2a_{12}} = \dfrac{3-3}{4} = 0$

$$\therefore \quad \theta = \pi / 4$$

$$\therefore \quad S_2 = \begin{pmatrix} \frac{1}{\sqrt{2}} & -\frac{1}{\sqrt{2}} & 0 \\ \frac{1}{\sqrt{2}} & \frac{1}{\sqrt{2}} & 0 \\ 0 & 0 & 1 \end{pmatrix}$$

$$\text{Now } B_2 = S_2^1 B_1 S_2 = \begin{pmatrix} \frac{1}{\sqrt{2}} & \frac{1}{\sqrt{2}} & 0 \\ -\frac{1}{\sqrt{2}} & \frac{1}{\sqrt{2}} & 0 \\ 0 & 0 & 1 \end{pmatrix} \begin{pmatrix} 3 & 2 & 0 \\ 2 & 3 & 0 \\ 0 & 0 & -1 \end{pmatrix} \begin{pmatrix} \frac{1}{\sqrt{2}} & -\frac{1}{\sqrt{2}} & 0 \\ \frac{1}{\sqrt{2}} & \frac{1}{\sqrt{2}} & 0 \\ 0 & 0 & 1 \end{pmatrix}$$

$$= \frac{1}{2} \begin{pmatrix} 1 & 1 & 0 \\ -1 & 1 & 0 \\ 0 & 0 & \sqrt{2} \end{pmatrix} \begin{pmatrix} 3 & 2 & 0 \\ 2 & 3 & 0 \\ 0 & 0 & -1 \end{pmatrix} \begin{pmatrix} 1 & -1 & 0 \\ 1 & 1 & 0 \\ 0 & 0 & \sqrt{2} \end{pmatrix}$$

$$= \frac{1}{2} \begin{pmatrix} 1 & 1 & 0 \\ -1 & 1 & 0 \\ 0 & 0 & \sqrt{2} \end{pmatrix} \begin{pmatrix} 5 & -1 & 0 \\ 5 & 1 & 0 \\ 0 & 0 & -\sqrt{2} \end{pmatrix}$$

$$= \begin{pmatrix} 5 & 0 & 0 \\ 0 & 1 & 0 \\ 0 & 0 & -1 \end{pmatrix}$$

After 2 rotations, A is reduced to the diagonal matrix $B_2$. Hence the eigen values of A are 5, 1, – 1

$$S = S_1 S_2 = \begin{pmatrix} \frac{1}{\sqrt{2}} & 0 & -\frac{1}{\sqrt{2}} \\ 0 & 1 & 0 \\ \frac{1}{\sqrt{2}} & 0 & \frac{1}{\sqrt{2}} \end{pmatrix} \begin{pmatrix} \frac{1}{\sqrt{2}} & -\frac{1}{\sqrt{2}} & 0 \\ \frac{1}{\sqrt{2}} & \frac{1}{\sqrt{2}} & 0 \\ 0 & 0 & 1 \end{pmatrix}$$

$$= \frac{1}{2} \begin{pmatrix} 1 & 0 & -1 \\ 0 & \sqrt{2} & 0 \\ 1 & 0 & 1 \end{pmatrix} \begin{pmatrix} 1 & -1 & 0 \\ 1 & 1 & 0 \\ 0 & 0 & \sqrt{2} \end{pmatrix}$$

$$= \begin{pmatrix} \frac{1}{2} & -\frac{1}{2} & -\frac{1}{\sqrt{2}} \\ \frac{1}{\sqrt{2}} & \frac{1}{\sqrt{2}} & 0 \\ \frac{1}{2} & -\frac{1}{2} & \frac{1}{\sqrt{2}} \end{pmatrix}$$

Hence the corresponding eigen vectors are $\begin{pmatrix} 1 \\ \sqrt{2} \\ 1 \end{pmatrix}, \begin{pmatrix} -1 \\ \sqrt{2} \\ -1 \end{pmatrix}$ and $\begin{pmatrix} -1 \\ 0 \\ 1 \end{pmatrix}$

**Example 5.** *Find the eigen values and eigen vectors of* $A = \begin{pmatrix} 2 & 0 & 1 \\ 0 & 2 & 0 \\ 1 & 0 & 2 \end{pmatrix}$.

**Solution.** Hence, the largest off diagonal element is $a_{13} = 1$
Let us annihilate this element.

Take $$S_1 = \begin{pmatrix} \cos\theta & 0 & -\sin\theta \\ 0 & 1 & 0 \\ \sin\theta & 0 & \cos\theta \end{pmatrix}$$

$$\therefore \quad \tan 2\theta = \frac{2a_{13}}{a_{11} - a_{33}} = \frac{2}{2-2} = \infty \quad \therefore \theta = \pi/4$$

$$\therefore \quad S_1 = \begin{pmatrix} \frac{1}{\sqrt{2}} & 0 & -\frac{1}{\sqrt{2}} \\ 0 & 1 & 0 \\ \frac{1}{\sqrt{2}} & 0 & \frac{1}{\sqrt{2}} \end{pmatrix}$$

$$B_1 = S_1' A S_1 = \begin{pmatrix} \frac{1}{\sqrt{2}} & 0 & \frac{1}{\sqrt{2}} \\ 0 & 1 & 0 \\ -\frac{1}{\sqrt{2}} & 0 & \frac{1}{\sqrt{2}} \end{pmatrix} \begin{pmatrix} 2 & 0 & 1 \\ 0 & 2 & 0 \\ 1 & 0 & 2 \end{pmatrix} \begin{pmatrix} \frac{1}{\sqrt{2}} & 0 & -\frac{1}{\sqrt{2}} \\ 0 & 1 & 0 \\ \frac{1}{\sqrt{2}} & 0 & \frac{1}{\sqrt{2}} \end{pmatrix}$$

$$= \frac{1}{2} \begin{pmatrix} 1 & 0 & 1 \\ 0 & \sqrt{2} & 0 \\ -1 & 0 & 1 \end{pmatrix} \begin{pmatrix} 2 & 0 & 1 \\ 0 & 2 & 0 \\ 1 & 0 & 2 \end{pmatrix} \begin{pmatrix} 1 & 0 & -1 \\ 0 & \sqrt{2} & 0 \\ 1 & 0 & 1 \end{pmatrix}$$

$$= \frac{1}{2} \begin{pmatrix} 1 & 0 & 1 \\ 0 & \sqrt{2} & 0 \\ -1 & 0 & 1 \end{pmatrix} \begin{pmatrix} 3 & 0 & -1 \\ 0 & 2\sqrt{2} & 0 \\ 3 & 0 & 1 \end{pmatrix}$$

$$= \begin{pmatrix} 3 & 0 & 0 \\ 0 & 2 & 0 \\ 0 & 0 & 1 \end{pmatrix}$$

Though it is a 3 × 3 matrix, we are lucky to get the diagonal matrix in one rotation because $a_{12} = 0$, $a_{23} = 0$.

∴ The eigen values of A are 3, 2, 1.

The corresponding eigen vectors of A are the columns of $S_1$

namely $\begin{pmatrix}1\\0\\1\end{pmatrix}, \begin{pmatrix}0\\1\\0\end{pmatrix}$ and $\begin{pmatrix}-1\\0\\1\end{pmatrix}$

**Example 6.** *Find eigen values and eigen vectors of*

$$A = \begin{pmatrix}1 & 0 & 0\\0 & 3 & -1\\0 & -1 & 3\end{pmatrix}$$

**Solution.** The element $|a_{23}| = 1$ is to be annihilated.

Take $$S_1 = \begin{pmatrix}1 & 0 & 0\\0 & \cos\theta & -\sin\theta\\0 & \sin\theta & \cos\theta\end{pmatrix}$$

$$\tan 2\theta = \frac{2a_{23}}{a_{22} - a_{33}} = \frac{-2}{0} = \infty \;\therefore\; \theta = \pi/4$$

$$S_1 = \begin{pmatrix}1 & 0 & 0\\0 & \frac{1}{\sqrt{2}} & -\frac{1}{\sqrt{2}}\\0 & \frac{1}{\sqrt{2}} & \frac{1}{\sqrt{2}}\end{pmatrix}$$

$$B_1 = S_1' A S_1$$

$$= \begin{pmatrix}1 & 0 & 0\\0 & \frac{1}{\sqrt{2}} & \frac{1}{\sqrt{2}}\\0 & -\frac{1}{\sqrt{2}} & \frac{1}{\sqrt{2}}\end{pmatrix}\begin{pmatrix}1 & 0 & 0\\0 & 3 & -1\\0 & -1 & 3\end{pmatrix}\begin{pmatrix}1 & 0 & 0\\0 & \frac{1}{\sqrt{2}} & -\frac{1}{\sqrt{2}}\\0 & \frac{1}{\sqrt{2}} & \frac{1}{\sqrt{2}}\end{pmatrix}$$

$$= \frac{1}{2}\begin{pmatrix}\sqrt{2} & 0 & 0\\0 & 1 & 1\\0 & -1 & 1\end{pmatrix}\begin{pmatrix}1 & 0 & 0\\0 & 3 & -1\\0 & -1 & 3\end{pmatrix}\begin{pmatrix}\sqrt{2} & 0 & 0\\0 & 1 & -1\\0 & 1 & 1\end{pmatrix}$$

$$= \frac{1}{2}\begin{pmatrix} \sqrt{2} & 0 & 0 \\ 0 & 1 & 1 \\ 0 & -1 & 1 \end{pmatrix}\begin{pmatrix} \sqrt{2} & 0 & 0 \\ 0 & 2 & -4 \\ 0 & 2 & 4 \end{pmatrix}$$

$$= \begin{pmatrix} 1 & 0 & 0 \\ 0 & 2 & 0 \\ 0 & 0 & 4 \end{pmatrix}$$

$\therefore$ The eigen values of A are 1, 2, 4

The corresponding eigen vectors are columns of $S_1$, namely

$$\begin{pmatrix} 1 \\ 0 \\ 0 \end{pmatrix}, \begin{pmatrix} 0 \\ 1 \\ 1 \end{pmatrix} \text{ and } \begin{pmatrix} 0 \\ -1 \\ 1 \end{pmatrix}$$

## EXERCISES 13.2

Find the eigen values and eigen vectors of the following matrices, using Jacobi method.

**1.** $\begin{pmatrix} 2 & -1 \\ -1 & 2 \end{pmatrix}$ **2.** $\begin{pmatrix} 3 & 2\sqrt{3} \\ 2\sqrt{3} & 2 \end{pmatrix}$ **3.** $\begin{pmatrix} 4 & 1 \\ 1 & 4 \end{pmatrix}$ **4.** $\begin{pmatrix} 0 & 1 \\ 1 & 0 \end{pmatrix}$

**5.** $\begin{pmatrix} 7 & 6 \\ 6 & -2 \end{pmatrix}$ **6.** $\begin{pmatrix} 3 & 1 \\ 1 & 3 \end{pmatrix}$ **7.** $\begin{pmatrix} 3 & -1 & 1 \\ -1 & 5 & -1 \\ 1 & -1 & 3 \end{pmatrix}$

**8.** $\begin{pmatrix} 6 & -2 & 2 \\ -2 & 3 & -1 \\ 2 & -1 & 3 \end{pmatrix}$ **9.** $\begin{pmatrix} 2 & 0 & -1 \\ 0 & 2 & 0 \\ -1 & 0 & 2 \end{pmatrix}$

## ANSWERS

**1.** 1, 3, $(1, 1)^T, (1, -1)^T$ **2.** 6, – 1; $(2, \sqrt{3})^T, (3, -2\sqrt{3})^T$

**3.** 5, 3; $(1,1)^T, (1,-1)^T$ **4.** 1, – 1; $(1, 1)^T, (1, -1)^T$

**5.** 10, – 5; $(2, 1)^T; (1, -2)^T$ **6.** 2, 4; $(-1, 1)^T; (1, 1)^T$

**7.** 2, 3, 6; $(1, 0, -1)^T, (1, 1, 1)^T; (1, -2, 1)^T$

**8.** 8, 2, 2; $(2, -1, 1)^T, (0, 1, 1)^T; (1, 1, -1)^T$

**9.** 1, 2, 3; $(1, 0, 1)^T, (0, 1, 0)^T; (1, 0, -1)^T$.

## SHORT ANSWER QUESTIONS (2 marks questions)

1. What is the principle on which the method of group averages is based ?
2. What is principle of least squares ?
3. What are the normal equations in fitting a straight line or a parabola ?
4. In fitting a straight line $y = ax + b$, what is the formula to find the sum of the squares of the residuals ?
5. In fitting a parabola $y = ax^2 + bx + c$, what is the formula for finding the sum of the squares of the residuals ?

6. What are observation equations in fitting a curve by the method of moments ?
7. In fitting a straight line to the data what are the normal equations ?

| $x$ | 0 | 1 | 2 | 3 |
|---|---|---|---|---|
| $y$ | 0 | 1·1 | 2·1 | 3·1 |

8. The product and the sum of the roots of the equation $x^5 = 2$ are_____ and_____ .
9. If $\alpha, \beta, \gamma$ are the roots of $x^3 = 7$, then $\Sigma\alpha^3$ is______and $\Sigma\alpha$ is_____ .
10. If $\alpha, \beta, \gamma$ are the roots of $x^3 + qx + k = 0$ then the value of $\Sigma\alpha^3 - 3\alpha\beta\gamma$ is______ .
11. If $\alpha, \beta, \gamma$ are the roots of $x^3 + px + q = 0$ then find the values of $\Sigma\alpha^2, \Sigma\frac{1}{\alpha}, \Sigma\alpha^3$.
12. If $\alpha_1, \alpha_2, \ldots \alpha_n$ are the roots of $(a_1 - x)(a_2 - x) \cdots (a_n - x) + b = 0$ show that $a_1, a_2, \ldots a_n$ are the roots of $(\alpha_1 - x)(\alpha_2 - x) \cdots (\alpha_n - x) = b$.
13. Increase the roots of $x^3 = 3x - 1$ by 2.
14. Diminish the roots of $x^4 - x^3 - 10x^2 + 4x + 24 = 0$ by 3.
15. State Descarte's rule of signs.
16. $\sqrt{3}$ and $1 + 2i$ are the roots of a biquadratic equation; find it
17. Classify the equation $x^5 - 5x^4 + 10x^3 - 10x^2 + 5x - 1 = 0$.
18. Transform $x^4 - 8x^3 + 7x^2 - 5x + 1 = 0$ into one in which $x^3$ is missing.
19. If $f(x) = 0$ has a double root $\alpha$, then $f'(x) = 0$ has a root______ .
20. If $\alpha, \beta, \gamma$ are the roots of $x^3 = 14x - 8$, then find $\Sigma\alpha^2$, and $\Sigma\alpha^3$.
21. If $\alpha, \beta, \gamma$ are the roots of $x^3 + x^2 + x + 1 = 0$, then the equation whose roots are, $\frac{1}{\alpha}, \frac{1}{\beta}, \frac{1}{\gamma}$ is______ .
22. Find the third degree equation two of whose roots are $1 - i$ and 2.
23. Find the roots of $x^3 - 15x^2 + 71x = 105$ if they are in A.P.
24. If $6x^6 - 25x^5 + 31x^4 + ax^3 - 31x^2 + 25x - 6 = 0$ is a reciprocal equation then the value of $a$ is
25. Write down two roots of $x^6 + 2x^5 + 2x^4 - 2x^2 - 2x - 1 = 0$.
26. Find the number of complex roots of the equation $x^5 + x^3 + x + 1 = 0$.
27. Solve $4x^3 + 16x^2 - 9x - 36 = 0$ if sum of two roots is zero.
28. If $\alpha, \beta, \gamma$ are the roots $x^3 + 3x + 4 = 0$ form the equation whose roots are $\alpha + \beta, \beta + \gamma, \gamma + \alpha$.
29. What is the number of positive roots of $x^6 + x^5 + 7x^3 + 11x^2 + 7x + 1 = 0$ ?
30. $y = f(x)$ is a polynomial curve and $f(1), f(2)$ are positive; then there can never be a root of $f(x) = 0$ between 1 and 2 – say true or false.
31. $f(x) = 0$ is a second degree polynomial equation such that $f(0) = -1, f(1) = 1$, $f(2) = 4$. Then a root of it is (*a*) 0·35, (*b*) 0·44, (*c*) 0·56, (*d*) 0·62.
32. In fitting a straight line $y = ax + b$, $\Sigma x = -6, \Sigma y = 12, \Sigma x^2 = 54, \Sigma xy = 12$, find the straight line.

**33.** A straight line (best fitting) was got for the following data.

| $x$ | : | 0 | 1 | 2 | 3 | 4 |
|---|---|---|---|---|---|---|
| $y$ | : | 1 | 1·8 | 1·3 | 2·5 | 6·3 |

What is the error made in this ?

**34.** Say true or false: In fitting the best fitting straight line, the line must pass through two paired data.

**35.** You are given $(x_i, y_i)$, $i = 1, 2, \ldots n$ and a parabola is fitted to them. It is possible that no point of the system may lie on the parabola – say true or false.

**36.** Define a reciprocal equation.

**37.** If $\alpha, \beta, \gamma$ are the roots of $x^3 + px + q = 0$, evaluate $\sum \frac{1}{\alpha}, \sum \frac{1}{\alpha\beta}$.

**38.** If $\alpha, \beta, \gamma$ are the roots of $x^3 = 2$, then $\Sigma \alpha^4 =$——— and $\Sigma \alpha^6 =$———.

**39.** Find a root of $ax^3 + bx^2 + cx + d = 0$ if the roots are in A.P.

**40.** In a reciprocal equation of third degree, two roots are 1, 2. What is the third root ? Reason out.

**41.** If $f(x)$ is continuous in $(a, b)$ and if $f(a) \cdot f(b) < 0$ then $f(x) = 0$ will have at least_______ .

**42.** In the case of bisection method, the convergence is

(*a*) linear (*b*) quadratic (*c*) very rapid (*d*) is $h^2$.

**43.** What is the condition for the convergence of the iteration method for solving $x = \varphi(x)$ ?

**44.** State Newton-Raphson formula for iteration.

**45.** The order of convergence of Newton-Raphson method is_______ .

**46.** In Newton-Raphson method, the error at any stage is proportional to the_______of the error in the previous stage.

**47.** In calculating $\sqrt{N}$, the iterative formula is $x_{n+1} = \frac{1}{2}\left(x_n + \frac{N}{x_n}\right)\cdot$ Is it correct ?

**48.** Gauss-Seidel method always converges—say true or false.

**49.** Does a root of $x^3 - 3x^2 + 2{\cdot}5 = 0$ lie between 1·1 and 1·2 ?

**50.** The equation whose roots are ten times the roots of $x^3 - 3x^2 + 2{\cdot}5 = 0$ is_______ .

**51.** By Gauss-elimination, solve $x + y = 2$; $2x + 3y = 5$.

**52.** The numerical methods of solving linear equations are of two types; one is direct and the other is_______ .

**53.** Gauss-elimination and Gauss-Jordan are direct methods while_______ and_______are iterative methods.

**54.** State the condition for convergence of Gauss-Seidel method.

**55.** If the relaxation method is to succeed, the diagonal elements of the coefficient matrix must *dominate* the other coefficients in the corresponding row—true or false ?

**56.** Define $\Delta, \nabla, \delta, E$.

**57.** Define $\mu$ and $\delta$.

**58.** What is $\Delta [f(x) \cdot g(x)]$ ?

**59.** What is $\Delta \left[ \dfrac{f(x)}{g(x)} \right]$ ?

**60.** Prove $\Delta^3 y_0 = y_3 - 3y_2 + 3y_1 - y_0$.

**61.** Prove $y_3 = y_2 + \Delta y_1 + \Delta^2 y_0 + \Delta^3 y_0$.

**62.** Which one is wrong ?

(*a*) $\Delta (f_1 + f_2) = \Delta f_1 + \Delta f_2$ (*b*) $E = 1 + \Delta$

(*c*) $\Delta [f(x) \cdot g(x)] = \Delta f(x) \cdot \Delta g(x)$ (*d*) $\Delta (5) = 0$.

**63.** Find the *n*th difference of $e^x$.

**64.** Prove $\Delta \tan^{-1} x = \tan^{-1} \left( \dfrac{h}{1 + hx + x^2} \right)$.

**65.** *n*th difference of a polynomial of degree *n* is

(*a*) zero (*b*) +ve (*c*) –ve (*d*) constant.

**66.** $y_k$ is equal to (*a*) $\Delta^k y_0$ (*b*) $\nabla^k y_0$ (*c*) $(1 + \Delta)^k y_0$ (*d*) $(1 + \nabla)^k y_0$.

**67.** Express $x^3 + x^2 + x + 1$ in factorial polynomial.

**68.** If $\Delta f(x) = x^3 + x + 2$ find $f(x)$.

**69.** Find the value of $\Delta^{20} [(2x^{10} - 1)(x^5 - 1)(x^3 - 1)(x^2 - 1)]$ if the interval of differencing is 3.

**70.** Prove $E = e^{hD}$, $\nabla = 1 - e^{-hD}$.

**71.** Prove $\Delta^3 y_2 - \nabla^3 y_5 = 0$.

**72.** Prove $\Delta\nabla = \Delta - \nabla$ and $\Delta\nabla = \nabla\Delta$.

**73.** If $u_1 + u_2 + u_3 + \cdots + u_n = \left( \Delta^{-1} u_x \right)_a^b$, what are the limit values *a* and *b* ?

**74.** Using finite integration, sum the series $1 + 2 + 3 + \cdots + n$.

**75.** Prove $\sum_{k=0}^{n-1} \Delta^2 f_k = \Delta f_n - \Delta f_0$.

**76.** Find $\Delta (\sin x)$ and $\Delta (\cos x)$.

**77.** Prove $\Delta \tan^{-1} \left( \dfrac{x-1}{x} \right) = \tan^{-1} \left( \dfrac{1}{2x^2} \right)$.

**78.** Which one is correct ?

(*i*) $\Delta x^r = r x^{r-1}$ (*ii*) $\Delta x^{(r)} = r x^{(r-1)}$ (*iii*) $\Delta^n e^x = e^x$ (*iv*) $\Delta \sin x = \cos x$.

**79.** $E^{-2} f(x)$ is (*i*) $f(x + 2h)$ (*ii*) $f(x - h)$ (*iii*) $f(x + h)$ (*iv*) $f(x - 2h)$.

**80.** Central difference operation $\delta$ is

(*i*) $E^{1/2} + E^{-1/2}$ (*ii*) $\dfrac{1}{2}(E^{1/2} + E^{-1/2})$ (*iii*) $E^{1/2} - E^{-1/2}$

(*vi*) $\dfrac{1}{2}(E^{1/2} - E^{-1/2})$.

**81.** State Gregory-Newton forward difference interpolation formula.

**82.** State Newton's backward difference interpolation formula.

**83.** A third degree polynomial passes through (0, – 1), (1, 1), (2, 1) and (3, – 2), find its value at $x = 4$.

**84.** State Gauss' forward interpolation formula.

**85.** State Gauss' backward interpolation formula.

**86.** State Bessel's formula of interpolation.

**87.** State Everett's interpolation formula.

**88.** Bessel's formula truncated after third differences is equivalent to Everett's formula truncated after second differences – true or false ?

**89.** Define $\underset{x_1}{\Delta} f(x)$.

**90.** Given the three points $(x_i, y_i)$, $i = 1, 2, 3$, we find a parabola by curve fitting and also by interpolation technique. Will the two functions be equal in general ?

**91.** Write the divided difference table given

| $x$ : | 1 | 2 | 4 | 7 |
|---|---|---|---|---|
| $y$ : | 22 | 30 | 82 | 106 |

**92.** State Newton's divided difference interpolation formula.

**93.** State Lagrange's interpolation formula.

**94.** Can you use Lagrange's interpolation formula when the intervals are equal ?

**95.** Find the second divided differences with arguments $a$, $b$, $c$, if $f(x) = \frac{1}{x}$.

**96.** The $n$th divided differences of a polynomial of the $n$th degree are________ .

*(BR 1996 A)*

**97.** If $f(x) = \frac{1}{x^2}$ then the divided difference $f(a, b)$ is________ .

**98.** State Stirling's formula of interpolation.

**99.** Stirling's formula is just the average of the Gauss formulae—true or false ?

**100.** Write the formula that we use to get $\left(\frac{dy}{dx}\right)_{x=x_0}$ using Newton's forward difference interpolation formula.

**101.** Also write the formula for $(y'')_{x=x_0}$.

**102.** Write down formula for $(y')_{x=x_n}$ using Newton's backward difference formula.

**103.** State trapezoidal rule.

**104.** State Simpson's 1/3 and 3/8 rule.

**105.** Error in the trapezoidal rule is of order________ .

**106.** Error in Simpson's rule is of order________ .

**107.** A curve passes through (0, 1), (0·25, 0·9412), (0·5, 0·8) (0·75, 0·64) and (1, 0·5). Find the area between the curve, $x$-axis and $x$ = 0 and 1, by trapezoidal rule.

**108.** For the following data, find the area bounded by $y = f(x)$ $x$-axis and $x = 7{\cdot}47$ to $7{\cdot}52$ using trapezoidal rule.

| $x$ : | 7·47 | 7·48 | 7·49 | 7·50 | 7·51 | 7·52 |
|---|---|---|---|---|---|---|
| $f(x)$ : | 1·93 | 1·95 | 1·98 | 2·01 | 2·03 | 2·06 |

**109.** Can you use Simpson's rule in question 108. Why ?

**110.** Which one is more reliable, Simpson's rule or trapezoidal rule ?

**111.** What is the order of $u_{x+2}+u_{x+1}=2^x$ ?

**112.** If $E^2 u_x = x^2$, what is $u_x$ if $h = 1$ ?

**113.** Find the order and degree of $y_x y_{x+1}^2 - y_{x+2} y_x + 5y_x = 7$.

**114.** Form the difference equation by eliminating $a$, $b$ from $y=(a+bx)\,2^x$.

**115.** The difference equation which satisfies $y_x = A{\cdot}2^x + B{\cdot}3^x$ is_______ .

**116.** Solve $y_{n+2} - 4y_{n+1} + 3y_n = 0$.

**117.** Solve : $(\Delta^2 + 2\Delta + 1)\,u_x = 3x + 2$.

**118.** Solve : $y_{x+3} - 2\,y_{x+2} + 2y_x - y_{x+1} = 0$.

**119.** Solve : $y_{x+2} - 6y_{x+1} + 8y_x = 4^x$.

**120.** Solve : $\Delta\,u_x + \Delta^2 u_x = 0$.

**121.** Given $y_3 = 2, y_4 = -6, y_5 = 8, y_6 = 9, y_7 = 17$, calculate $\Delta^4 y_3$.

**122.** Find $\Delta^{-1}\,[x\,(x+1)(x+2)]$.

**123.** The particular integral of $u_{x+2} - 6u_{x+1} + 9u_x = 3^x$ is_______ .

**124.** $\dfrac{a^x}{(E-a)^3}$ is_______

**125.** Find the particular solution of $\Delta^2 u_x - 2\,\Delta u_x + u_x = 3x + 2$.

**126.** In solving $\dfrac{dy}{dx} = f(x, y), y\,(x_0) = y_0$.

Write down Taylor series for $y\,(x_1)$.

**127.** In solving $\dfrac{dy}{dx} = f(x, y), y\,(x_0) = y_0$, write down the algorithm used in

(*i*) Euler's method (*ii*) Improved Euler's method (*iii*) Modified Euler's method (*iv*) Runge-Kutta methods of 2nd, 3rd and 4th order.

**128.** Write down iteration formula for $y$ in solving $y' = f(x, y), y\,(x_0) = y_0$ due to Picard.

**129.** By Taylor series, find $y\,(1{\cdot}1)$ given $y' = x + y$, $y\,(1) = 0$.

**130.** Using Euler's method find $y\,(0{\cdot}2)$ given $y' = x + y$, $y\,(0) = 1$.

**131.** Using Runge-Kutta method of second order, find $y\,(0{\cdot}1)$ given $y' = -y$, $y\,(0) = 1$.

**132.** A particular case of Runge-Kutta method of second order is (*i*) Taylor's method (*ii*) Picard's method (*iii*) Modified Euler's method (*iv*) Milne's method.

**133.** Define a difference quotient.

**134.** Write the formulae for $u_x, u_{xx}, y_y, y_{yy}$ in terms of difference quotients.

**135.** Define elliptic, parabolic and hyperbolic type of partial differential equations.

**136.** Give examples of the above three types of equations.

**137.** Classify the equation: $u_{xx} + 2u_{xy} + 4u_{yy} = 0$.

**138.** Write down standard five point formula in solving Laplace equation over a region.

**139.** Write down diagonal five point formula in solving Laplace equation over a region.

**140.** What is the purpose of Liebmann's process ?

**141.** If $u$ is harmonic, will it satisfy $\nabla^2 u = 0$ ?

**142.** The boundary conditions in solving $u_{xx} + u_{yy} = 0$ are

(*i*) $u(0, y) = 0$ for $0 \le y \le 4$

(*ii*) $u(4, y) = 12 + y$ for $0 \le y \le 4$

(*iii*) $u(x, 0) = 3x$ for $0 \le x < 4$

(*iv*) $u(x, 4) = x + 2$ for $0 \le x \le 4$.

Plot the values of $u$ on the boundary at the grid points taking $h = k = 1$.

**143.** Express $\frac{\partial u}{\partial t} = \alpha^2 \frac{\partial^2 u}{\partial x^2}$ in difference equation.

**144.** What is Bender-Schmidt recurrence equation ? For what purpose you use it ?

**145.** Write down Crank-Nicholson difference method ?

**146.** What is the purpose of the above method ?

**147.** Name two methods that you use to solve one dimensional heat equation.

**148.** Express $\frac{\partial^2 u}{\partial x^2} = \frac{\partial u}{\partial t}$ in terms of difference quotients.

**149.** Express $a^2 u_{xx} = u_{tt}$ in terms of difference quotients.

**150.** Write down the explicit scheme to solve one dimensional wave equation.

**151.** In solving the wave equation how will you express the initial condition $u_t(x, 0) = 0$.

**152.** In the explicit formula got in connection with solving wave equation, if we take $\lambda^2 = \frac{1}{a^2}$, what is the simple form to which it reduces.

**153.** What is the relaxation operator that we have in solving $\nabla^2 u = 0$ by relaxation method?

**154.** To get the simple explicit difference formula for parabolic equation $u_t = \alpha^2 u_{xx}$, we should take $\frac{(\Delta x)^2}{\alpha^2 \Delta t}$ as

(1) 1/2 (2) 2 (3) 1 (4) 0.

**155.** In solving equation $u_t = \alpha^2 u_{xx}$, by the Crank-Nicholson method, to simplify method we take $\frac{(\Delta x)^2}{\alpha^2 k}$ as (*i*) 1/2 (*ii*) 2 (*iii*) 1 (*iv*) 0.

## ANSWERS TO SHORT ANSWER QUESTIONS

**4.** $E = \Sigma y^2 - a\,\Sigma xy - b\Sigma y$ **5.** $E = \Sigma y^2 - a\Sigma x^2 y - b\,\Sigma xy - c\,\Sigma y$

**7.** $6a + 4b = 6{\cdot}3;\ 14a + 6b = 14{\cdot}6$ **8.** 2, 0 **9.** 21, 0

**10.** 0 **11.** $-2p, -\dfrac{p}{q}, -3q$ **13.** $y^3 - 6y^2 + 9y - 1 = 0$

**14.** $x^4 + 11x^3 + 35x^2 + 25 = 0$ **16.** $x^4 - 2x^3 + 2x^2 + 6x - 15 = 0$

**17.** Reciprocal of odd degree with unlike signs

**18.** $x^4 - 17x^2 - 41x - 29 = 0$ **19.** $\alpha$ **20.** 28, – 24

**21.** $x^3 + x^2 + x + 1 = 0$ **22.** $x^3 - 4x^2 + 6x = 4$

**23.** 3, 5, 7 **24.** 0 **25.** $\pm 1$ **26.** 4 complex roots

**27.** $-4, \pm 3/2$ **28.** $x^3 + 3x - 4 = 0$ **29.** No positive root

**30.** False **31.** 0·56 **32.** $y = 0{\cdot}4242x + 0{\cdot}1818$

**33.** – 1·6 **34.** False **35.** True **37.** $-\dfrac{p}{q}, 0$ **38.** 0, 12

**39.** $-\dfrac{b}{3a}$ **40.** $\dfrac{1}{2}$ **41.** One real root between $a$ and $b$ **42.** Linear

**43.** $|\varphi'(x)| < 1$ in the range. **45.** 2 **46.** Square **47.** Yes **48.** No

**49.** Yes **50.** $x^3 - 30x^2 + 2500 = 0$ **51.** 1, 1 **52.** Iterative

**53.** Gauss-Jacobi and Gauss-Seidel **55.** True.

**58.** $f(x)\,\Delta\,g(x) + g(x+1)\,\Delta f(x)$ **59.** $\dfrac{g(x)\,\Delta f(x) - f(x)\,\Delta\,g(x)}{g(x)\,g(x+1)}$ **62.** (*c*)

**63.** $\Delta^n e^x = e^x (e^h - 1)^n$ **65.** Constant **66.** $c$

**67.** $x^{(3)} + 4x^{(2)} + 3x^{(1)} + 1$ **68.** $\dfrac{x^{(4)}}{4} + 3\,\dfrac{x^{(3)}}{3} + x^{(2)} + 2x + c$ **69.** $2\,(3^{20})(20!)$

**73.** 1 and $n+1$ **78.** (*ii*) **79.** (*iv*)

**80.** (*iii*) **83.** – 9 **88.** True **90.** No

**91.**

| | | | |
|---|---|---|---|
| 1 | | | |
| | 8 | | |
| 2 | | 6 | |
| | 26 | | – 1·6 |
| 4 | | – 3·6 | |
| | 8 | | |
| 7 | | | |

**94.** Yes **95.** $\dfrac{1}{abc}$ **96.** Constant **97.** $\dfrac{-(a+b)}{a^2 b^2}$ **99.** Yes.

**105.** $h^2$ **106.** $h^4$ **107.** 0·7828 **108.** 0·09965

**109.** No since number of ordinates is six **110.** Simpson's rule

**111.** 1 **112.** $(x-2)^2$ **113.** 2, 2 **114.** $y_{x+2} - 4y_{x+1} + 4y_x = 0$

**115.** $y_{x+2} - 5y_{x+1} + 6y_x = 0$ **116.** $y_n = A + B3^n$ **117.** $u_x = 3x - 4$

**118.** $y_x = A + B\,(-1)^x + C{\cdot}2^x$ **119.** $y_x = A.4^n + B2^n + \dfrac{1}{2}\,x\,4^{x-1}$

**120.** $u_x = A$ **121.** 55 **122.** $(x+2)(x+1)(x)(x-1)/4 + c\,(x)$

**123.** $\dfrac{x^{(2)}}{2} \cdot 3^{x-2}$ **124.** $\dfrac{a^{x-3}x^{(3)}}{3!}$ **125.** $3x+8$ **129.** 0·110338

**130.** 1·2 **131.** 0·905 **132.** (*iii*) **137.** elliptic **141.** Yes

**155.** (2) 2 **155.** (*iii*) 1.

# 14

# Numerical Methods For Double Integrals

The integral $\int_1^2 \int_0^3 e^{-(x^2+y^2)} dxdy$ cannot be integrated since we fail to integrate $\int_0^3 e^{-x^2} dx$. In such cases, we resort to numerical integration though the value is only approximate by applying either Trapezoidal rule or Simpson's rule.

**Trapezoidal rule**

Now, consider the double integral

$$I = \int_{y_j}^{y_{j+1}} \int_{x_i}^{x_{i+1}} f(x, y) dxdy \qquad \text{... (1)}$$

where $\quad x_{i+1} = x_i + h$ and $y_{j+1} = y_j + k$

Now we will apply trapezoidal rule repeatedly to get the value of $I$.

$$I = \int_{y_j}^{y_{j+1}} \left[ \int_{x_i}^{x_{i+1}} f(x, y) dx \right] dy$$

Apply trapezoidal rule to the inner integral, when $y$ is a constant and $x$ varies.

$$\therefore \qquad I = \int_{y_j}^{y_{j+1}} \frac{h}{2} [f(x_i, y) + f(x_{i+1}, y)] dy$$

$$= \frac{h}{2} \left[ \int_{y_j}^{y_{j+1}} f(x_i, y) dy + \int_{y_j}^{y_{j+1}} f(x_{i+1}, y) dy \right]$$

Now, apply trapezoidal rule to the two integrals, keeping in mind that $y$ varies and $x_i$, $x_{i+1}$ are constants

$$\therefore I = \frac{h}{2} \left[ \frac{k}{2} \{ f(x_i, y_{j+1}) + f(x_i, y_j) \} + \frac{k}{2} \{ f(x_{i+1}, y_{j+1}) + f(x_{i+1}, y_j) \} \right]$$

$$i.e., \; I = \frac{hk}{4} \left[ f(x_i, y_j) + f(x_i, y_{j+1}) + f(x_{i+1}, y_j) + f(x_{i+1}, y_{j+1}) \right]$$

*i.e.,* $$I = \frac{hk}{4}\left[f_{i,j} + f_{i,\,j+1} + f_{i+1,\,j} + f_{i+1,j+1}\right] \qquad \text{... (2)}$$

Where $f_{i,j} = f(x_i, y_j)$

Using the figure,

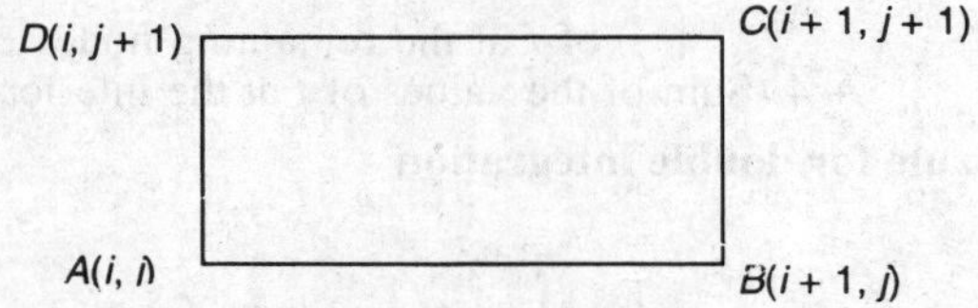


$$I = \frac{hk}{4} \text{ [Sum of the values of } f(x, y) \text{ at the four corner points}$$

$$= \frac{hk}{4}[f_A + f_B + f_c + f_D] \qquad \text{... (3)}$$

**Extension to general form of trapezoidal rule**

Suppose we want to evaluate $\int_c^d \int_a^b f(x, y)dxdy$ where $a$, $b$, $c$, $d$ are constants. The area of integration is the rectangle in the $xy$ plane as shown below

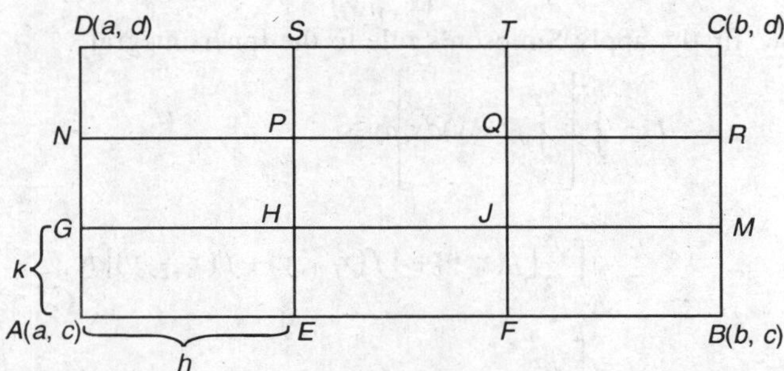


Divide the area of integration (rectangle $ABCD$) into meshes by dividing $AB$ into 3 equal parts (in general into $m$ equal parts) each part length being $h$, and $AD$ into 3 equal parts, (in general $n$ equal parts) each part length being $k$.

Now, the integral over the whole rectangle is equal to sum of the integrals over each mesh. So, extending the formula given by (3),

$$I = \int_c^d \int_a^b f(x, y)dxdy = \frac{hk}{4}\left[(f_A + f_E + f_H + f_G) + (f_E + f_F + f_J + f_H) + .....\right]$$

$$= \frac{hk}{4}\left[(f_A + f_B + f_C + f_D) + 2(f_G + f_N + f_S + f_T + f_R + f_M + f_F + f_E)\right.$$
$$\left. + 4(f_P + f_Q + f_H + f_J)\right] \quad \dots (4)$$

$I = \frac{hk}{4}$ [(Sum of values of $f$ at the four corners + 2 (Sum of the values of $f$ at the remaining nodes on the boundary) + 4 (Sum of the values of $f$ at the interior nodes)] ... (5)

**Simpson's rule for double integration**

Consider the integral $I = \int_{y_j}^{y_{j+2}} \int_{x_i}^{x_{i+2}} f(x, y)dxdy$

Where $x_{i+1} = x_i + h$

$y_{i+1} = y_j + k$

The corresponding area of integration is given below

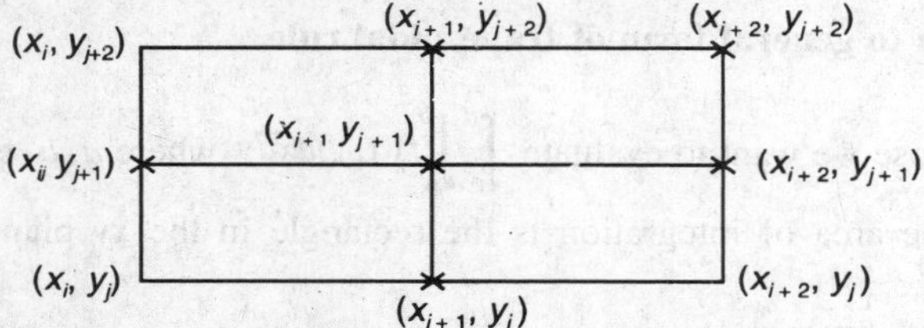


Now, firstly, apply Simpson's rule to the inner integral.

$$I = \int_{y_j}^{y_{j+2}} \left[ \int_{x_i}^{x_{i+2}} f(x, y)dx \right] dy$$

$$= \int_{y_j}^{y_{j+2}} \frac{h}{3}[f(x_i, y) + 4f(x_{i+1}, y) + f(x_{i+2}, y)]dy$$

$$= \frac{h}{3}\left[ \int_{y_j}^{y_{j+2}} f(x_i, y)dy + 4\int_{y_j}^{y_{j+2}} f(x_{i+1}, y)dy + \int_{y_j}^{y_{j+2}} f(x_{i+2}, y)\,dy \right]$$

$$= \frac{h}{3}\cdot\frac{k}{3}\left[\{f(x_i, y_j) + 4f(x_i, y_{j+1}) + f(x_i, y_{j+2})\} + 4\{f(x_{i+1}, y_j) + 4f(x_{i+1}, y_{j+1})\right.$$
$$\left. + f(x_{i+1}, y_{j+2})\} + \{f(x_{i+2}, y_j) + 4f(x_{i+2}, y_{j+1}) + f(x_{i+2}, y_{j+2})\}\right]$$

using Simpson's rule for each integral in $y$ direction.

$$= \frac{hk}{9}\left[(f_{i,j} + f_{i,j+2} + f_{i+2,j} + f_{i+2,j+2}) + 4(f_{i,j+1} + f_{i+1,j}\right.$$
$$\left. + f_{i+1,j+2} + f_{i+2,j+1}) + 16 f_{i+1,j+1}\right] \quad \dots (6)$$

$$I = \frac{hk}{9} \text{ [Sum of the values of } f \text{ at the 4 corners)}$$

$$+ 4 \text{ (Sum of the values of } f \text{ at the remaining nodes in the boundary)}$$

$$+ 16 \text{ (value of } f \text{ at the central point)]} \quad \text{... (7)}$$

**Extension to general form of simpson's rule**

Suppose we want to evaluate $I = \int_c^d \int_a^b f(x, y)dxdy$

where the limits are constants.

The area of integration is shown below

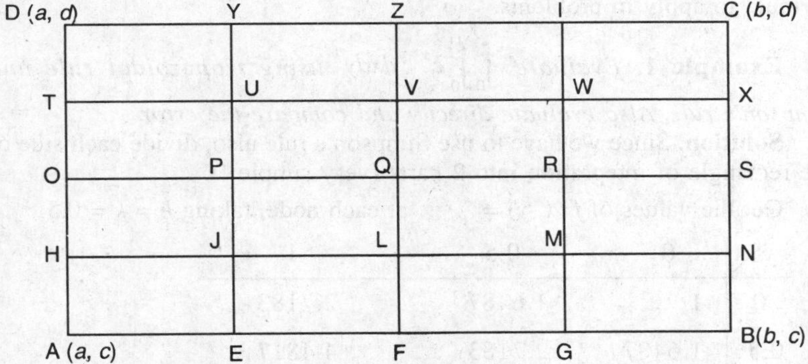


Divide the interval $(a, b)$ into even number of equal parts (each part equals $h$) and the interval $(c, d)$ into even number of equal parts (each part-equals $k$)

In the figure, $(a, b)$ and $(c, d)$ are divided into 4 equal parts.

Now apply the result given by (7) to the 4 rectangles *AF QO*, *FBSQ*, *OQZD* and *QSCZ*. Hence

$$I = \frac{hk}{9}\Big[\big(f_A + f_F + f_Q + f_O\big) + 4\big(f_E + f_L + f_P + f_H\big) + 16 f_J\Big]$$

$$+ \big\{(f_F + f_B + f_S + f_Q) + 4(f_G + f_N + f_R + f_L) + 16 f_M\big\}$$

$$+ \{(f_O + f_Q + f_z + f_D) + 4(f_P + f_V + f_Y + f_T) + 16 f_U\}$$

$$+ \{(f_Q + f_S + f_C + f_Z) + 4(f_R + f_X + f_I + f_V) + 16 f_W\}]$$

$$= \frac{hk}{9}[(f_A + f_B + f_C + f_D) + 2(f_O + f_Z + f_S + f_F)$$

$$+4(f_H + f_T + f_I + f_Y + f_X + f_N + f_G + f_E) + 4(f_Q) + 8(f_p + f_R))]$$

$$+ 8(f_L + f_V) + 16(f_J + f_M + f_U + f_W)]$$

$I = \frac{hk}{9}$ [(Sum of the values of $f$ at the four corners)

+ 2 (Sum of the values of $f$ at the odd positions on the boundary except the corners)

+ 4 (Sum of the values of $f$ at the even positions on the boundary)

+ {4 (Sum of values of $f$ at odd positions)

+ 8 (sum of values of f at even positions) on the odd row of the matrix except boundary rows}

+ {8 (Sum of values of $f$ at the odd positions)

+ 16 (Sum of values of $f$ at the even positions) on the even rows of the matrix}] (8)

**Note:** Equation (8) is written in a particular format to remember the formula to apply in problems.

**Example 1.** *Evaluate* $\int_0^1\int_0^1 e^{x+y}dxdy$ *using trapezoidal rule and simpson's rule. Also evaluate directly and compare the error.*

**Solution.** Since we have to use Simpson's rule also, divide each side of the rectangle of integration into 2 parts (very simple !).

Get the values of $f(x, y) = e^{x+y}$ at each node, taking $h = k = 0.5$

| y \ x | 0 | 0.5 | 1 |
|---|---|---|---|
| 0 | 1 | 1.6487 | 2.7183 |
| 0.5 | 1.6487 | 2.7183 | 4.4817 |
| 1 | 2.7183 | 4.4817 | 7.3891 |

**Case 1.** Using Trapezoidal rule, equation (5), we get

$$\int_0^1\int_0^1 e^{x+y}dxdy = I = \frac{hk}{4}[(1+2.7183+2.7183+7.3891)+2(1.6487$$

$$+1.6487+4.4817+4.4817)+4(2.7183)]$$

$$= \frac{(0.5)(0.5)}{4}\ [49.2205]$$

$$= 3.0763$$

**Case 2.** Using Simpson's rule, equation (8), we get,

$$I = \frac{hk}{9}[(1+2.7183+2.7183+7.3851)+2(0)+4(1.6487$$

$$+1.6487+4.4817+4.4817)\ +\{4(0)+8(0)\}+\{8(0)+16(2.7183)]$$

$$= \frac{0.25}{9}\ (106.3577)$$

$$= 2.9545$$

**Case 3.** By integrating directly, $I = (\int_0^1 e^x dx)(\int_0^1 e^y dy)$

$$= (e^x)_0^1 \times (e^y)_0^1 = (e-1)^2 = 2.9525$$

This shows that the value of Simpson's rule is close to the exact value.

**Example 2.** *Evaluate* $\int_1^{1.4}\int_2^{2.4} \frac{1}{xy} dxdy$ *using Trapezoidal rule and simpson's rule Verify your result by actual integration.*

**Solution.** Divide the range of $x$ and $y$ into 4 equal parts.

$$h = \frac{2.4-2}{4} = 0.1 \text{ and } k = \frac{1.4-1}{4} = 0.1$$

We will calculate the values $f(x, y) = \frac{1}{xy}$ at nodal points.

| y \ x | 2 | 2.1 | 2.2 | 2.3 | 2.4 |
|---|---|---|---|---|---|
| 1 | 0.5 | 0.4762 | 0.4545 | 0.4348 | 0.4167 |
| 1.1 | 0.4545 | 0.4329 | 0.4132 | 0.3953 | 0.3788 |
| 1.2 | 0.4167 | 0.3968 | 0.3788 | 0.3623 | 0.3472 |
| 1.3 | 0.3846 | 0.3663 | 0.3497 | 0.3344 | 0.3205 |
| 1.4 | 0.3571 | 0.3401 | 0.3247 | 0.3106 | 0.2976 |

**Case 1.** By **trapezoidal rule** using equation (5), we get

$$I = \frac{(0.1)(0.1)}{4} [(0.5 + 0.4167 + 0.3571 + 0.2976) + 2\,(0.3846 + 0.4167 + 0.4545 + 0.4762 + 0.4545 + 0.4348 + 0.3788 + 0.3472 + 0.3205 + 0.3106 + 0.3247 + 0.3401) + 4\,(0.4329 + 0.4132 + 0.3953 + 0.3968 + 0.3788 + 0.36223 + 0.3663 + 0.3497 + 0.3344)]$$

$$= \frac{0.01}{4} [1.5714 + 9.2864 + 13.7188]$$

$$= 0.0614$$

**Case 2.** By Simpson's rule, (**Note:** There are even number of intervals in each direction), using equation (8), we get

$$I = \frac{(0.1)(0.1)}{9} [(0.5 + 0.4167 + 0.3571 + 0.2976) + 2\,(0.4167 + 0.4545 + 0.3472 + 0.3247) + 4\,(0.3846 + 0.4545 + 0.4762 + 0.4348 + 0.3788 + 0.3205 + 0.3106 + 0.3401) + 4\,(0.3788) + 8\,(0.3968 + 0.3623) + 8\,(0.3497 + 0.4132) + 16\,(0.3663 + 0.3344 + 0.4329 + 0.3953)]$$

$$= \frac{0.01}{9}[55.2116]$$
$$= 0.0613$$

**Case 3.** By actual integration,

$$\int_1^{1.4}\int_2^{2.4}\frac{1}{xy}dxdy = (\int_1^{1.4}\frac{1}{y}dy)(\int_2^{2.4}\frac{1}{x}dx)$$
$$= (\log y)_1^{1.4}(\log x)_2^{2.4}$$
$$= (\log 1.4)\ (\log 1.2)$$
$$= 0.0613$$

We see here, that the actual value and the value by Simpson's rule are equal while the value by trapezoidal rule differs only by 0.0001.

**Example 3.** *Evaluate* $\int_0^{\pi/2}\int_0^{\pi/2}\sin(x+y)dxdy$ *by using trapezoidal rule, Simpson's rule and also by actual integration.*

**Solution.** Divide the range on $x$ and $y$ direction in 2 equal parts and obtain the values of $f = \sin(x + y)$ at each node.

Here $$h = \frac{\pi}{4} = k$$

| y \ x | 0 | π / 4 | π / 2 |
|---|---|---|---|
| 0 | 0 | 0.7071 | 1 |
| π / 4 | 0.7071 | 1 | 0.7071 |
| π / 2 | 0 | 0.7071 | 0 |

**Case 1.** By trapezoidal rule,

$$I = \frac{\frac{\pi}{4}\times\frac{\pi}{4}}{4}\ [(0 + 1 + 1 + 0) + 2\ (0.7071 + 0.707)$$
$$+ 0.7071 + 0.7071) + 4\ (1)]$$
$$= 0.1542\ (11.6568)$$
$$= 1.7975$$

**Case 2.** By Simpson's rule,

$$I = \frac{\frac{\pi}{4}\times\frac{\pi}{4}}{9}\ [(0 + 1 + 1 + 0) + 2\ (0) + 4\ (0.7071$$
$$+ 0.7071 + 0.7071 + 0.7071) + 16\ (1)]$$

$= 0.0685 \times 29.3136$

$= 2.0080$

**Case 3.** By actual integration,

$$\int_0^{\pi/2}\int_0^{\pi/2} \sin(x+y)\,dxdy = \int_0^{\pi/2}\int_0^{\pi/2}(\sin x\cos y + \cos x \sin y)dxdy$$

$$= \left(\int_0^{\pi/2}\sin x dx\right)\left(\int_0^{\pi/2}\cos y dy\right) + \left(\int_0^{\pi/2}\cos x dx\right)\left(\int_0^{\pi/2}\sin y dy\right)$$

$$= (-\cos x)_0^{\pi/2}(\sin y)_0^{\pi/2} + (\sin x)_0^{\pi/2}(-\cos y)_0^{\pi/2}$$

$$= 1 \times 1 + 1 \times 1 = 2$$

The value got by Simpson's rule differs from the exact value only by 0.008 while the error in the trapezoidal rule is 0.2125

**Example 4.** *Evaluate* $\int_1^{1.2}\int_1^{1.4} \frac{1}{x+y}dxdy$ *by trapezoidal rule and simpson's rule.*

**Solution.** Range for $x$ is (1, 1.4) and range for $y$ is (1, 1.2)

$\therefore$ Divide the $x$-range into 4 equal parts ($h = 0.1$) and $y$ range into 2 equal parts ($k = 0.1$)

Values of $f(x, y) = \frac{1}{x+y}$ are noted down in the table.

| $y$ \ $x$ | 1 | 1.1 | 1.2 | 1.3 | 1.4 |
|---|---|---|---|---|---|
| 1 | 0.5000 | .4762 | 0.4545 | 0.4348 | 0.4167 |
| 1.1 | 0.4762 | 0.4545 | 0.4348 | 0.4167 | 0.4000 |
| 1.2 | 0.4545 | 0.4348 | 0.4167 | 0.4000 | 0.3846 |

**Case 1.** By Trapezoidal rule

$$I = \int_1^{1.2}\int_1^{1.4}\frac{1}{x+y}dxdy$$

$$= \frac{(0.1)(0.1)}{4}\ [(0.5 + 0.4167 + 0.4545 + 0.3846)$$
$$+ 2(0.4545 + 0.4762 + 0.4348 + 0.4 + 0.4 + 0.4167$$
$$+ 0.4348 + 0.4762) + 4\ (0.4545 + 0.4348 + 0.4167)]$$

$$= \frac{0.01}{4}\ [1.7558 + 6.9864 + 5.224]$$

$$= 0.0349$$

**Case 2.** By Simpson's rule, using equation 8,

$$I = \frac{hk}{9}\ [(0.5 + 0.4167 + 0.4545 + 0.3846) + 2\ (0.4545 + 0.4167)$$

$$+ 4\ (0.4762 + 0.4762 + 0.4348 + 0.4 + 0.4 + 0.4348)$$
$$+ \{8\ (0.4348) + 16\ (0.4545 + 0.4167)]$$

$$= \frac{0.01}{9}\ [1.7558 + 1.7424 + 10.4880 + 3.4784 + 13.9392]$$

$= 0.0349$ .

**Note.** In this problem, the values by both methods are equal.

**Example 5.** *Evaluate* $\int_1^2 \int_3^4 \frac{1}{(x+y)^2} dxdy$ *taking* $h = k = 0.5$ *by both trapezoidal rule and simpson's rule.*

**Solution.** $f(x, y) = \frac{1}{(x+y)^2}$ ; range for $x$ is (3, 4)

| y \ x | 3 | 3.5 | 4 |
|---|---|---|---|
| 1 | 0.0625 | 0.0494 | 0.04 |
| 1.5 | 0.0494 | 0.04 | 0.0331 |
| 2 | 0.04 | 0.0331 | 0.0278 |

**Case1.** By Trapezoidal rule

$$\int_1^2 \int_3^4 \frac{1}{(x+y)^2} dxdy = \frac{hk}{4}\ [(0.0625 + 0.04 + 0.04 + 0.0278)$$

$$+ 2\ (0.0494 + 0.0494 + 0.0331 + 0.0331) + 4\ (0.04)]$$

$$= \frac{0.25}{4}\ [0.1703 + 0.3300 + 0.16]$$

$= 0.0413.$

**Case 2.** By Simpson's rule, $I = \frac{0.25}{9}\ [(0.0625 + 0.04 + 0.04 + 0.0278)$

$$+ 2\ (0) + 4\ (0.0494 + 0.0494 + 0.0331 + 0.0331) + 16\ (0.04)]$$

$$= \frac{0.25}{9}\ [0.1703 + 0.6600 + 0.64]$$

$= 0.0408$

## EXERCISES

Using the trapezoidal rule and Simpson's rule for multiple integrals, evaluate the following integrals. Where ever possible check your answer by direct integration and obtain the percentage of error.

(*i*) $\int_1^2 \int_2^3 \sqrt{(x+y)}\, dxdy$ (*ii*) $\int_0^1 \int_0^1 e^{2x+3y} dxdy$

(*iii*) $\int_0^{\pi/2} \int_0^{\pi/2} \cos(x-y) dxdy$ (*iv*) $\int_4^{4.2} \int_2^{2.3} \frac{1}{xy} dydx$

(*v*) $\int_1^{1.4} \int_2^{2.4} \frac{1}{(x+y)^2} dxdy$ taking $h = k = 0.1$

(*vi*) $\int_1^{1.8} \int_2^{2.8} (x^2+y^2) dxdy$ taking $h = k = 0.2$

(*vii*) $\int_1^2 \int_2^3 \log(x+y)\, dxdy$ (take $h = k = 0.5$)

(*viii*) $\int_2^{2.4} \int_4^{4.} xydxdy$ taking $h = k = 0.1$

(*ix*) $\int_4^{4.8} \int_3^{3.8} \frac{1}{x^2+y^2} dx\, dy$ taking $h = k = 0.2$

(*x*) $\int_0^1 \int_0^1 e^{-(x+y)} dxdy$.

(*xi*) $\int_{1.4}^{2} \int_1^{1.5} \log(x+2y) dx\, dy$, taking

$\Delta x = 0.15, \Delta y = 0.25$

(Ans : 0.4292 by trapezoidal rule 0.4296 by simpsonis rule)

(*xii*) Evaluate $\int_0^1 \int_1^2 \frac{2xy\, dxdy}{(1+x^2)(1+y^2)}$ by trapezoidal rule with $h = k = 0.25$

*(Anna Nov. 2004)*

# Appendix – A

## *Inverse of a matrix by Gauss-Jordan Method*

**Elementary row operations E :** The following operations on the rows of a matrix are called Elementary row operations on a matrix.

1. Multiplication of the elements of any row by a non-zero constant— $R_i(k)$ denotes for the multiplication of the elements of the $i$th row by the non-zero constant $k$.

2. Interchange of any two rows. $R_{ij}$ denotes the inter change of $i$th and $j$th rows.

3. Addition to the elements of any row of a multiple of elements of any other row.

$R_{ij}(k)$ denotes for the addition of $k$ times the elements of the $j$th row to the corresponding elements of the $i$th row.

We know that the elementary operations do not alter the rank of a matrix.

**Theorem :** If a sequence of elementary row operations transform a non-singular matrix $A$ into the identity matrix $I$, then the same sequence of elementary operations will transform $I$ into the inverse of $A$, that is, $A^{-1}$.

**Proof ·** Consider the linear transformation $Y = AX$. This can be written a.

$$AX = IY \quad ...(1)$$

If the sequence of the elementary row operations $E_1, E_2, E_3, ....E_n$ transform $A$ into $I$, then $(E_1\ E_2 ....E_n A)\ X = (E_1, E_2 ....E_n I)Y$

i.e., $\quad IX = (E_1\ E_2 ....E_n I)Y$

$\therefore \quad X = (E_1\ E_2 ....E_n I)Y \quad ...(2)$

From $AX = Y$ we have $X = A^{-1}Y \quad ...(3)$

Hence, from (2) and (3), $\quad A^{-1} = E_1\ E_2 ....E_n I$

**Note :** While reducing $A$ to $I$, we take the diagonal elements of $A$ as the **pivots**.

**Example 1.** *Using Gauss-Jordan method, find the inverse of*

$(a)\ \begin{pmatrix} 1 & 3 & 3 \\ 1 & 4 & 3 \\ 1 & 3 & 4 \end{pmatrix} \quad (b)\ \begin{pmatrix} 2 & 0 & 1 \\ 3 & 2 & 5 \\ 1 & -1 & 0 \end{pmatrix} \quad (c)\ \begin{pmatrix} 2 & 1 & 1 \\ 1 & -1 & 1 \\ 4 & 2 & -3 \end{pmatrix} \quad (d)\ \begin{pmatrix} 0 & 1 & 2 \\ 1 & 2 & 3 \\ 3 & 1 & 1 \end{pmatrix}$

**Solution :** *(a)* We will form a table writing $A$. $I$ as below.

**Computation of inverse of $A$**

| $A$ | | | $I$ | | | *Operations and Remarks* |
|---|---|---|---|---|---|---|
| 1 | 3 | 3 | 1 | 0 | 0 | |
| 1 | 4 | 3 | 0 | 1 | 0 | nothing |
| 1 | 3 | 4 | 0 | 0 | 1 | |

| | | |
|---|---|---|
| $\begin{matrix} 1 & 3 & 3 \\ 0 & 1 & 0 \\ 0 & 0 & 1 \end{matrix}$ | $\begin{matrix} 1 & 0 & 0 \\ -1 & 1 & 0 \\ -1 & 0 & 1 \end{matrix}$ | Taking $a_{11}$ as the pivot make all elements below that as zeros by operations, $R_{21}(-1)$, $R_{31}(-1)$ |
| $\begin{matrix} 1 & 0 & 3 \\ 0 & 1 & 0 \\ 0 & 0 & 1 \end{matrix}$ | $\begin{matrix} 4 & -3 & 0 \\ -1 & 1 & 0 \\ -1 & 0 & 1 \end{matrix}$ | Taking $a_{22}$ as the pivot make all elements above $a_{22}$ as zeros by $R_{12}(-3)$ |
| $\begin{matrix} 1 & 0 & 0 \\ 0 & 1 & 0 \\ 0 & 0 & 1 \end{matrix}$ | $\begin{matrix} 7 & -3 & -3 \\ -1 & 1 & 0 \\ -1 & 0 & 1 \end{matrix}$ | Taking $a_{33}$ as the pivot all elements above $a_{33}$ are made to zero by $R_{13}(-3)$ |

$$\therefore \qquad A^{-1} = \begin{pmatrix} 7 & -3 & -3 \\ -1 & 1 & 0 \\ -1 & 0 & 1 \end{pmatrix}$$

(*b*) We write the augmented matrix (*A*, *I*) as

$$\begin{array}{c} \quad A \qquad\qquad I \\ \left[\begin{array}{ccc|ccc} 2 & 0 & 1 & 1 & 0 & 0 \\ 3 & 2 & 5 & 0 & 1 & 0 \\ 1 & -1 & 0 & 0 & 0 & 1 \end{array}\right] \end{array}$$

**Step 1.** We will bring 1 in the place of $a_{11}$ by $R_{13}$ (interchange of row 1 and row 3)

$$\left[\begin{array}{ccc|ccc} 1 & -1 & 0 & 0 & 0 & 1 \\ 3 & 2 & 5 & 0 & 1 & 0 \\ 2 & 0 & 1 & 1 & 0 & 0 \end{array}\right]$$

**Step 2.** Make all elements below $a_{11}$ zeros by $R_{21}(-3)$, $R_{31}(-2)$

$$\left[\begin{array}{ccc|ccc} 1 & -1 & 0 & 0 & 0 & 1 \\ 0 & 5 & 5 & 0 & 1 & -3 \\ 0 & 2 & 1 & 1 & 0 & -2 \end{array}\right]$$

**Step 3.** Make $a_{22}=1$, *by* $R_2\left(\frac{1}{5}\right)$

$$\left[\begin{array}{ccc|ccc} 1 & -1 & 0 & 0 & 0 & 1 \\ 0 & 1 & 1 & 0 & \frac{1}{5} & -\frac{3}{5} \\ 0 & 2 & 1 & 1 & 0 & -2 \end{array}\right]$$

**Step 4.** Taking $a_{22}=1$ as pivot, make all elements below and above $a_{22}$ as zeros by $R_{12}(1)$, $R_{32}(-2)$

$$\left[\begin{array}{ccc|ccc} 1 & 0 & 1 & 0 & \frac{1}{5} & \frac{2}{5} \\ 0 & 1 & 1 & 0 & \frac{1}{5} & -\frac{3}{5} \\ 0 & 0 & -1 & 1 & -\frac{2}{5} & -\frac{4}{5} \end{array}\right]$$

**Step 5.** Make $a_{33}=1$ by $R_3(-1)$

$$\left[\begin{array}{ccc|ccc} 1 & 0 & 1 & 0 & 0.2 & 0.4 \\ 0 & 1 & 1 & 0 & 0.2 & -0.6 \\ 0 & 0 & 1 & -1 & 0.4 & 0.8 \end{array}\right]$$

**Step 6.** Make all elements above $a_{33}$ as zeros by $R_{13}(-1)$, $R_{23}(-1)$

$$\left[\begin{array}{ccc|ccc} 1 & 0 & 0 & 1 & -0.2 & -0.4 \\ 0 & 1 & 0 & 1 & -0.2 & -1.4 \\ 0 & 0 & 1 & -1 & 0.4 & 0.8 \end{array}\right]$$

$$\therefore \quad A^{-1}=\begin{bmatrix} 1 & -0.2 & -0.4 \\ 1 & -0.2 & -1.4 \\ -1 & 0.4 & 0.8 \end{bmatrix}$$

(*c*) Augmented matrix $(A, I)$ is

$$\left[\begin{array}{ccc|ccc} 2 & 1 & 1 & 1 & 0 & 0 \\ 1 & -1 & 1 & 0 & 1 & 0 \\ 4 & 2 & -3 & 0 & 0 & 1 \end{array}\right]$$

$$\left[\begin{array}{ccc|ccc} 1 & -1 & 1 & 0 & 1 & 0 \\ 2 & 1 & 1 & 1 & 0 & 0 \\ 4 & 2 & -3 & 0 & 0 & 1 \end{array}\right] \textit{by } R_{21}$$

$$\left[\begin{array}{ccc|ccc} 1 & -1 & 1 & 0 & 1 & 0 \\ 0 & 3 & -1 & 1 & -2 & 0 \\ 0 & 6 & -7 & 0 & -4 & 1 \end{array}\right] \text{ by } R_{21}(-2),\ R_{21}(-4)$$

$$\left[\begin{array}{ccc|ccc} 1 & -1 & 1 & 0 & 1 & 0 \\ 0 & 1 & -\frac{1}{3} & \frac{1}{3} & -\frac{2}{3} & 0 \\ 0 & 6 & -7 & 0 & -4 & 1 \end{array}\right] \text{ by } R_2\left(\frac{1}{3}\right) \text{ to make } a_{22} = 1$$

$$\left[\begin{array}{ccc|ccc} 1 & 0 & \frac{2}{3} & \frac{1}{3} & \frac{1}{3} & 0 \\ 0 & 1 & -\frac{1}{3} & \frac{1}{3} & -\frac{2}{3} & 0 \\ 0 & 0 & -5 & -2 & 0 & 1 \end{array}\right] \text{ by } R_{21}(1) \text{ and } R_{23}(-6)$$

$$\left[\begin{array}{ccc|ccc} 1 & 0 & \frac{2}{3} & \frac{1}{3} & \frac{1}{3} & 0 \\ 0 & 1 & -\frac{1}{3} & \frac{1}{3} & -\frac{2}{3} & 0 \\ 0 & 0 & 1 & \frac{2}{5} & 0 & -\frac{1}{5} \end{array}\right] \text{ by } R_3\left(-\frac{1}{5}\right) \text{ to make } a_{33}(1)$$

$$\left[\begin{array}{ccc|ccc} 1 & 0 & 0 & \frac{1}{15} & \frac{1}{3} & \frac{2}{15} \\ 0 & 1 & 0 & \frac{7}{15} & -\frac{2}{3} & -\frac{1}{15} \\ 0 & 0 & 1 & \frac{2}{5} & 0 & -\frac{1}{5} \end{array}\right] \text{ by } R_{13}\left(-\frac{2}{3}\right) \text{ and } R_{23}\left(\frac{1}{3}\right)$$

$$\therefore \quad A^{-1} = \begin{bmatrix} \frac{1}{15} & \frac{1}{3} & \frac{2}{15} \\ \frac{7}{15} & -\frac{2}{3} & -\frac{1}{15} \\ \frac{2}{5} & 0 & -\frac{1}{5} \end{bmatrix}$$

(*d*) Writing the augmented matrix

$$\left[\begin{array}{ccc|ccc} 0 & 1 & 2 & 1 & 0 & 0 \\ 1 & 2 & 3 & 0 & 1 & 0 \\ 3 & 1 & 1 & 0 & 0 & 1 \end{array}\right]$$

Perform $R_{21}$; then

$$\left[\begin{array}{ccc|ccc} 1 & 2 & 3 & 0 & 1 & 0 \\ 0 & 1 & 2 & 1 & 0 & 0 \\ 3 & 1 & 1 & 0 & 0 & 1 \end{array}\right]$$

Perform $R_{31}(-3)$

$$\left[\begin{array}{ccc|ccc} 1 & 2 & 3 & 0 & 1 & 0 \\ 0 & 1 & 2 & 1 & 0 & 0 \\ 0 & -5 & -8 & 0 & -3 & 1 \end{array}\right]$$

Perform $R_{12}(-2)$, $R_{32}(5)$

$$\left[\begin{array}{ccc|ccc} 1 & 0 & -1 & -2 & 1 & 0 \\ 0 & 1 & 2 & 1 & 0 & 0 \\ 0 & 0 & 2 & 5 & -3 & 1 \end{array}\right]$$

Perform $R_3\left(\frac{1}{2}\right)$

$$\left[\begin{array}{ccc|ccc} 1 & 0 & -1 & -2 & 1 & 0 \\ 0 & 1 & 2 & 1 & 0 & 0 \\ 0 & 0 & 1 & \frac{5}{2} & -\frac{3}{2} & \frac{1}{2} \end{array}\right]$$

Perform $R_{13}(1)$, $R_{23}(-2)$

then,
$$\left[\begin{array}{ccc|ccc} 1 & 0 & 0 & \frac{1}{2} & -\frac{1}{2} & \frac{1}{2} \\ 0 & 1 & 0 & -4 & 3 & -1 \\ 0 & 0 & 1 & \frac{5}{2} & -\frac{3}{2} & \frac{1}{2} \end{array}\right]$$

Hence $A^{-1} = \begin{bmatrix} \frac{1}{2} & -\frac{1}{2} & \frac{1}{2} \\ -4 & 3 & -1 \\ \frac{5}{2} & -\frac{3}{2} & \frac{1}{2} \end{bmatrix}$

## EXERCISES

By Using Gauss-Jordan method, find the inverse of

**1.** $\begin{bmatrix} 3 & -1 & 1 \\ -15 & 6 & -5 \\ 5 & -2 & 2 \end{bmatrix}$ **2.** $\begin{bmatrix} 0 & 1 & 1 \\ 1 & 2 & 0 \\ 3 & -1 & -4 \end{bmatrix}$ **3.** $\begin{pmatrix} 4 & 1 & 2 \\ 2 & 3 & -1 \\ 1 & -2 & 2 \end{pmatrix}$ **4.** $\begin{bmatrix} 1 & 0 & -4 \\ 0 & -1 & 2 \\ -1 & 2 & 1 \end{bmatrix}$

**5.** $\begin{pmatrix} 1 & 1 & 1 \\ 0 & 1 & -2 \\ -1 & 1 & 1 \end{pmatrix}$ **6.** $\begin{pmatrix} 1 & 2 & 3 \\ 2 & -1 & 4 \\ 3 & 1 & -1 \end{pmatrix}$ **7.** $\begin{pmatrix} 2 & 1 & 1 \\ 3 & 2 & 3 \\ 1 & 4 & 9 \end{pmatrix}$ **8.** $\begin{pmatrix} 3 & -3 & 4 \\ 2 & -3 & 4 \\ 0 & -1 & 1 \end{pmatrix}$

**9.** $\begin{pmatrix} 3 & 2 & 4 \\ 2 & 1 & 1 \\ 1 & 3 & 5 \end{pmatrix}$ **10.** $\begin{pmatrix} 3 & 1 & 2 \\ 2 & -3 & -1 \\ 1 & 2 & 1 \end{pmatrix}$ **11.** $\begin{pmatrix} 1 & 1 & 1 \\ 4 & 3 & -1 \\ 3 & 5 & 3 \end{pmatrix}$ **12.** $\begin{pmatrix} -1 & 1 & 1 \\ 0 & -1 & 2 \\ 1 & 1 & 1 \end{pmatrix}$

## ANSWERS

**1.** $\begin{pmatrix} 2 & 0 & -1 \\ 5 & 1 & 0 \\ 0 & 1 & 3 \end{pmatrix}$ **2.** $\begin{pmatrix} \frac{8}{3} & -1 & \frac{2}{3} \\ -\frac{4}{3} & 1 & -\frac{1}{3} \\ \frac{7}{3} & -1 & \frac{1}{3} \end{pmatrix}$ **3.** $\begin{bmatrix} -\frac{4}{3} & 2 & \frac{7}{3} \\ \frac{5}{3} & -2 & -\frac{8}{3} \\ \frac{7}{3} & -3 & \frac{10}{3} \end{bmatrix}$ **4.** $\begin{bmatrix} 5 & 8 & 4 \\ 2 & 3 & 2 \\ 1 & 2 & 1 \end{bmatrix}$

**5.** $\frac{1}{6}\begin{pmatrix} 3 & 0 & -3 \\ 2 & 2 & 2 \\ 1 & -2 & 1 \end{pmatrix}$ **6.** $\frac{1}{40}\begin{pmatrix} -3 & 5 & 11 \\ 14 & -10 & 2 \\ 5 & 5 & -5 \end{pmatrix}$ **7.** $\frac{1}{2}\begin{pmatrix} -6 & 5 & -1 \\ 24 & -17 & 3 \\ -10 & 7 & -1 \end{pmatrix}$

**8.** $\begin{pmatrix} 1 & -1 & 0 \\ -2 & 3 & -4 \\ -2 & 3 & -3 \end{pmatrix}$ **9.** $\frac{1}{8}\begin{pmatrix} 2 & 2 & -2 \\ -9 & 11 & 5 \\ 5 & -7 & -1 \end{pmatrix}$ **10.** $\begin{pmatrix} -1 & 3 & 5 \\ -3 & 1 & 7 \\ 7 & -5 & -11 \end{pmatrix}$

**11.** $\begin{pmatrix} 1.4 & 0.2 & -0.4 \\ -1.5 & 0 & 0.5 \\ 1.1 & -0.2 & -0.1 \end{pmatrix}$ **12.** $\frac{1}{6}\begin{pmatrix} -3 & 0 & 3 \\ 2 & -2 & 2 \\ 1 & 2 & 1 \end{pmatrix}$

# Appendix–B

## *Hermite's Interpolation formula*

So far, we considered Interpolation Formulae which make use of a certain number of function values only. Now, we will see an interpolation formula in which both the function values and its first derivative values at certain arguments will be made use of. In other words, given the values $f(x_i)$ and $f'(x_i)$ at $x = x_i$ of $f(x)$ and $f'(x)$ for $i = 0, 1, 2...n,$ we want to determine the interpolating polynomial or collocation polynomial of at most degree $P_{2n+1}(x)$ such that

$$\left.\begin{aligned} P_{2n+1}(x_i) &= f(x_i) = y_i \\ \text{and} \quad P'_{2n+1}(x_i) &= f'(x_i) = y'_i \end{aligned}\right\} \quad ...(1)$$

for $i = 0, 1, 2 ... n$

Since there are $(2n + 2)$ conditions given by (1), we can get a unique polynomial of degree $(2n + 1)$ at most.

Let $P(x) = P_{2n+1}(x) = \sum_{i=0}^{n} A_i(x) f(x_i) + \sum_{i=0}^{n} B_i(x) f'(x_i)$ ...(2)

be the required interpolating polynomial

where $A_i(x)$ and $B_i(x)$ are polynomials of degree $\leq (2n + 1)$ and satisfy

$$A_i(x_j) = \delta_i^j = \begin{cases} 1 \text{ if } i = j \\ 0 \text{ if } i \neq j \end{cases} \quad \text{(kronecker delta)} \quad ...(3)$$

$$A_i'(x_j) = 0 \text{ for all } i \text{ and } j \quad ...(4)$$

$$B_i(x_j) = 0 \text{ for all } i \text{ and } j \quad ...(5)$$

$$B_i'(x_j) = \delta_i^j = \begin{cases} 1 \text{ for } i = j \\ 0 \text{ for } i \neq j \end{cases} \quad ...(6)$$

The above four conditions on $A_i$ and $B_i$ are got by using the $(2n + 2)$ conditions given by (1)

The Lagrange's fundamental polynomial of degree $n$ based on $(n + 1)$ distinct points $a \leq x_0 \leq x_1 ... < x_n \leq b$ can be written as

$$l_i(x) = \frac{(x - x_0)(x - x_1)...(x - x_{i-1})(x - x_{i+1})...(x - x_n)}{(x_i - x_0)(x_i - x_1)...(x_i - x_{i-1})(x_i - x_{i+1})...(x_i - x_n)}$$

where $i = 0, 1, 2...n.$ and $l_i(x_j) = \delta_i^j$

Using $l_i(x),$ we can write

$$A_i(x) = a_i(x)[l_i(x)]^2 \quad (7.1)$$

$$B_i(x) = b_i(x)\left[l_i(x)\right]^2 \qquad (7.2)$$

Since $[l_i(x)]^2$ is a polynomial of degree $2n$,

$a_i(x)$ and $b_i(x)$ are linear polynomials.

So, let
$$\left.\begin{aligned} a_i(x) &= p_i x + q_i \\ \text{and} \quad b_i(x) &= c_i x + d_i \end{aligned}\right\} \qquad ...(8)$$

Using (7.1) $A_i(x_i) = a_i(x_i)\left[l_i(x_i)\right]^2 = a_i(x_i)$ since $l_i(x_i) = 1$

$\therefore \quad a_i(x_i) = 1$ since $A_i(x_i) = 1$

From (7.1)

$$A_i'(x) = a'_i(x)\left[l_i(x)\right]^2 + 2a_i(x)\left[l_i(x)\right].\, l_i'(x)$$

$\therefore \quad A_i'(x_i) = a_i'(x_i) + 2\times 1\times l_i'(x_i) = 0$ gives

$$a_i'(x_i) = -2l_i'(x_i) = p_i$$

Using (7.2)

$$B_i(x_i) = b_i(x_i)\left[l_i(x_i)\right]^2 = b_i(x_i) = 0$$

$\therefore \quad b_i(x_i) = c_i x_i + d_i = 0$

From (7.2)

$$B_i'(x) = b_i'(x)\left[l_i(x)\right]^2 + |\, l_i(x).\, 2\left[l_i(x)\right]l_i'(x)$$

$\therefore \quad B_i'(x_i) = b_i'(x_i)1 + 0$

$\therefore \quad b_i'(x_i) = 1 = c_i$

Using (8), we get;

$$\left.\begin{aligned} a_i(x) &= 1 - 2l_i'(x_i)(x - x_i) \\ b_i(x) &= x - x_i \end{aligned}\right\} \qquad ...(9)$$

Hence, using (9), (7.1), (7.2) in (2), we get

$$P(x) = \sum_{i=0}^{n}\left[\left\{1 - 2l_i'(x_i)(x - x_i)\right\}\left\{l_i(x)\right\}^2 f(x_i)\right]$$

$$+\sum_{i=0}^{n}\left[(x - x_i)\left\{l_i(x)\right\}^2 f'(x_i)\right] \qquad ...(10)$$

Equation (10) is called **Hermite's interpolation formula**

**Example 1.** *From the following table values of* $f(x)$ *and* $f'(x)$, *obtain* $f(-0.5)$ *and* $f(0.5)$

| $x$ | $-1$ | $0$ | $1$ |
|---|---|---|---|
| $f(x)$ | 1 | 1 | 3 |
| $f'(x)$ | $-5$ | 1 | 7 |

**Solution** : In the problem, $x_0 = -1,\ x_1 = 0,\ x_2 = 1$ and $n = 2$ therefore, the polynomial is of degree $2 \times 2 + 1 = 5$.

Let $P_5(x) = \sum_{i=0}^{2} A_i(x) f(x_i) + \sum_{i=0}^{2} B_i(x) f'(x_i)$ ...(1)

Let us Calculate $A_i$ and $B_i$

$$A_i(x) = [1 - 2l_i'(x_i)(x - x_i)][l_i(x)]^2$$

$$B_i(x) = (x - x_i)[l_i(x)]^2$$

$$\therefore \quad A_0(x) = [1 - 2l_0'(x_0)(x - x_0)][l_0(x)]^2$$

$$A_1(x) = [1 - 2l_1'(x_1)(x - x_1)][l_1(x)]^2$$

$$A_2(x) = [1 - 2l_2'(x_2)(x - x_2)][l_2(x)]^2$$

$$B_0(x) = (x - x_0)[l_0(x)]^2$$

$$B_1(x) = (x - x_1)[l_1(x)]^2$$

$$B_2(x) = (x - x_2)[l_2(x)]^2$$

Now we will calculate $l_i(x)$ and $l_1'(x),\ i = 0, 1, 2$

$$l_0(x) = \frac{(x-0)(x-1)}{(-1-0)(-1-1)} = \frac{1}{2}x(x-1);\ l_0'(x_0) = l_0'(-1) = -\frac{3}{2}$$

$$l_1(x) = \frac{(x+1)(x-1)}{(0+1)(0-1)} = 1 - x^2;\ l_1'(x_1) = l_1'(0) = 0$$

$$l_2(x) = \frac{(x+1)(x-0)}{(1+1)(1-0)} = \frac{1}{2}x(x+1);\ l_2'(x_2) = l_2'(1) = \frac{3}{2}$$

$$\therefore \quad A_0(x) = [1 - 2(-3/2)(x+1)]\frac{x^2(x-1)^2}{4} = [4 + 3x]\frac{x^2(x-1)^2}{4}$$

$$= \frac{1}{4}\left[3x^5 - 2x^4 - 5x^3 + 4x^2\right]$$

$$A_1(x) = [1 - 2(0)(x-0)](1-x^2)^2 = 1 - 2x^2 + x^4$$

$$A_2(x) = \left[1 - 2\left(\frac{3}{2}\right)(x-1)\right]\frac{x^2(x+1)^2}{4}$$

$$= \frac{1}{4}\left[-3x^5 - 2x^4 + 5x^3 + 4x^2\right]$$

$$B_0(x) = (x+1).\frac{x^2(x-1)^2}{4} = \frac{1}{4}\left[x^5 - x^4 - x^3 + x^2\right]$$

$$B_1(x) = (x-0)(1-x^2)^2 = x^5 - 2x^3 + x$$

$$B_2(x) = (x-1).\frac{x^2(x+1)^2}{4} = \frac{1}{4}\left[x^5 + x^4 - x^3 - x^2\right]$$

Using equation (1), we get

$$P_5(x) = \frac{1}{4}\left[3x^5 - 2x^4 - 5x^3 + 4x^2\right](1) + (1 - 2x^2 + x^4)(1)$$

$$+\frac{1}{4}\left[-3x^5 - 2x^4 + 5x^3 + 4x^2\right](3) + \frac{1}{4}\left[x^5 - x^4 - x^3 + x^2\right](-5)$$

$$+(x^5 - 2x^3 + x)(1) + \frac{1}{4}\left[x^5 + x^4 - x^3 - x^2\right](7) = 2x^4 - x^2 + x + 1$$

Putting $x = 0.5$ and $x = -0.5$ in $P_5(x)$, we get

$$P(0.5) \approx f(0.5) \approx 2\left(\frac{1}{2}\right)^4 - \left(\frac{1}{2}\right)^2 + \frac{1}{2} + 1 = \frac{11}{8}$$

$$P(-0.5) \approx f(-0.5) \approx 2\left(-\frac{1}{2}\right)^4 - \left(-\frac{1}{2}\right)^2 - \frac{1}{2} + 1 = \frac{3}{8}$$

**Note :** Even for $n = 0$, if takes more time for calculation. For higher values of *n*, the work is tedious, no doubt.

**Example 2.** *From the following data, find* $P_5(x)$ *using Hermite's interpolation formula and hence get* $P_5(0.5)$.

| $x$ | $f(x)$ | $f'(x)$ |
|---|---|---|
| –1 | 1 | –1 |
| 0 | 0 | 1 |
| 1 | 1 | 0 |

**Solution.** Since the values of *x* given are same as in the previous problem, there is no change in $A_0$, $A_1$, $A_2$ and $B_0$, $B_1$, $B_2$.

Hence

$$P_5(x) = \frac{1}{4}\left[3x^5 - 2x^4 - 5x^3 + 4x^2\right](1) + \left(1 - 2x^2 + x^4\right)(0)$$

$$+\frac{1}{4}\left[-3x^5 - 2x^4 + 5x^3 + 4x^2\right](1) + \frac{1}{4}\left[x^5 - x^4 - x^3 + x^2\right](-1)$$

$$+\left(x^5 - 2x^3 + x\right)(1) + \frac{1}{4}\left(x^5 + x^4 - x^3 - x^2\right)(0)$$

$$= \frac{1}{4}\left[3x^5 - 3x^4 - 7x^3 + 7x^2 + 4x\right]$$

$$P_5(0.5) = \frac{1}{4}\left[\frac{89}{32}\right] = 0.6953125$$

**Example 3.** *Using Hermite's interpolation formula, find interpolating polynomial* $P_5(x) \approx f(x)$ *from the data given below. Also find* $f(0.5)$.

| $x$ | 0 | 1 | 2 |
|---|---|---|---|
| $f(x)$ | 0 | 4 | 0 |
| $f'(x)$ | 0 | 0 | 0 |

**Solution.** Let $P_5(x) = \sum_{i=0}^{2} A_i(x) f(x_i) + \sum_{i=0}^{2} B_i(x) f'(x_i)$ ...(1)

Since $f'(x_i) = 0$ for $i = 0, 1, 2$ and $f'(x) = 0$ for $i = 0$ and $2$, from the table, all terms on the R.H.S. of $P_5(x)$ vanish except the only term in $f(x_1)$. So, we need to calculate only $A_1(x)$.

$$A_1(x) = [1 - 2l_1'(x_1)(x - x_1)][l_1(x)]^2 \qquad ...(2)$$

where $$l_1(x) = \frac{(x-0)(x-2)}{(1-0)(1-2)} = -x(x-2)$$

$$l_1'(x) = 2 - 2x$$

$$l_1'(x_1) = l_1'(1) = 2 - 2 = 0$$

Putting in (2),

$$A_1(x) = [l_1(x)]^2 = (2x - x^2)^2$$

Substituting in (1),

$$P_5(x) \approx f(x) \approx (2x - x^2)^2 f(1) = (2x - x^2)^2 \times 4$$

$$\therefore \quad P_5(0.5) \approx f(0.5) = 4\left(1 - \frac{1}{4}\right)^2 = \frac{9}{4}$$

**Example 4.** *Using Hermite's interpolation, find* $f(1.05)$ *given* $f(1) = 0.84147$, $f'(1) = 0.54030$, $f(1.10) = 0.89121$ *and* $f'(1.10) = 0.45360$.

**Solution.** Here only 2 values of $x$ are given; $x_0 = 1$, $x_1 = 1.10$. Hence we get only third degree $P_3(x)$ polynomial.

Let $P_3(x) = A_0(x)f(x_0) + A_1(x)f(x_1) + B_0(x)f'(x_0) + B_1(x)f'(x_1)$ ...(1)

$$l_0(x) = \frac{x - x_1}{x_0 - x_1} = \frac{x - 1.10}{1 - 1.10} = \frac{x - 1.1}{-0.1} = 11 - 10x$$

$$l_1(x) = \frac{x - x_0}{x_1 - x_0} = \frac{x - 1}{1.1 - 1} = 10x - 10$$

$$l_0'(x) = -10;\ l_1'(x) = 10 \ \therefore\ l_0'(x_0) = -10,\ l_1'(x_1) = 10$$

$$f(x_0) = 0.84147,\ f(x_1) = 0.89121$$

$$f'(x_0) = 0.54030,\ f'(x_1) = 0.45360$$

$$A_0(x) = [1 - 2l_0'(x_0)(x - x_0)][l_0(x)]^2 = [1 + 20(x - 1)][11 - 10x]^2$$

$$A_0(1.05) = [1 + 20(0.50)][0.5]^2 = 0.5$$

$$A_1(x) = [1 - 2l_1'(x_1)(x - x_1)][l_1(x)]^2 = [1 - 20(x - 1.1)](10x - 10)^2$$

$$A_1(1.05) = [1 - 20(-0.05)](10.5 - 10)^2 = 0.5$$

$$B_0(x) = (x - x_0)[l_0(x)]^2 = (x - 1)[11 - 10x]^2$$

$$B_0(1.05) = (0.05)[11 - 10.5]^2 = 0.0125$$

$$B_1(x) = (x - x_1)[l_1(x)]^2 = (x - 1.1)(10x - 10)^2$$

$$B_1(1.05) = (-0.05)(0.5)^2 = -0.0125$$

Using (1),

$$P_3(1.05) = A_0(1.05)f(1) + A_1(1.05)f(1.1) + B_0(1.05)f'(1) + B_1(1.05)f'(1.1)$$

$$= (0.5)(0.84147) + 0.5(0.89121) + (0.0125)(0.54030) - 0.0125(0.45360)$$

$$= (0.5)(1.73268) + (0.0125)(0.08670)$$

$$P_3(1.05) \approx f(1.05) = 0.86742375$$

## EXERCISES

**1.** From the following table values of $\log x$, using Hermite's interpolation formula, obtain log (0.6).

| $x$ | $f(x) = \log x$ | $f'(x) = \dfrac{1}{x}$ |
|---|---|---|
| 0.4 | –0.91629 | 2.50 |
| 0.5 | –0.69315 | 2.00 |
| 0.7 | –0.35667 | 1.43 |
| 0.8 | –0.22314 | 1.25 |

(**Ans.** –0.51069)

**2.** Using Hermitian interpolation, find $f(x)$ and $f(0.5)$ from the table below.

| $x$ | –1 | 0 | 1 |
|---|---|---|---|
| $f(x)$ | 1 | 0 | 1 |
| $f'(x)$ | 0 | 0 | 0 |

*(Anna Ap. 2005)*

(**Ans.** $f(x) = 2x^2 - x^4; f(0.5) = 7/16$)

**3.** Using Hermite's interpolation, find a cubic polynomial from the data below. Also find $f(0.5)$.

| $x$ | 0 | 1 |
|---|---|---|
| $f(x)$ | 0 | 1 |
| $f'(x)$ | 0 | 1 |

(**Ans.** $f(x) = 2x^2 - x^3; f(0.5) = 3/8$)

**4.** Using Hermite's interpolation, find $f(x)$ given the table below. Obtain $f(2)$.

| $x$ | $f(x)$ | $f'(x)$ |
|---|---|---|
| 0 | 0 | 0 |
| 4 | 2 | 0 |

(**Ans.** $f(x) = (6x^2 - x^3)/16; f(2) = 1$)

**5.** Obtain $f(0.5)$, using Hermite's formula of interpolation, from the table below.

| $x$ | $f(x)$ | $f'(x)$ |
|---|---|---|
| 0 | 1.00 | 0 |
| 1 | 2.00 | 5 |
| 1.5 | 8.59 | 25.31 |

(**Ans.** 1.03)

**6.** Find $f(1.8)$ given the table below, by Hermite's formula.

| $x$ | 1.7 | 1.9 | 2.0 |
|---|---|---|---|
| $f(x)$ | 5.47 | 6.686 | 7.389 |
| $f'(x)$ | 5.474 | 6.686 | 7.389 |

(**Ans.** 6.049)

**7.** Given $f(x) = e^x$, obtain $f(x), f'(x)$ at $x = 0, 0.2, 0.3$. Hence, using Hermite's interpolation formula, get the value of $f(0.1)$ and find the error by actual calculation.

**(Ans.** 1.105)

**8.** Find $f(x)$ by Hermite's formula given

| $x$ | −1 | 0 | 1 |
|---|---|---|---|
| $f(x)$ | −1 | 1 | 1 |
| $f'(x)$ | 9 | 0 | 1 |

**(Ans.** $f(x) = x^5 - x^4 + 1$)

**9.** Find $f(0.5)$ from the data below, by Hermite's formula.

| $x$ | 0 | 1 |
|---|---|---|
| $f(x)$ | 1 | 1 |
| $f'(x)$ | 0 | 1 |

**(Ans.** 7/8)

**10.** Find $f(0.25)$ by Hermite's method given

| $x$ | 0 | 1 | 2 |
|---|---|---|---|
| $f(x)$ | 0 | 0 | 0 |
| $f'(x)$ | 2 | −1 | 2 |

**(Ans.** $21/64$)

# Appendix–C

## *Gaussian Quadrature*

In numerical integration, so far seen, such as Newton—Cotes formula, Trapezoidal rule or simpson's rule, the range (a, b) of the integration was divided into $n$ equal parts by points at $x_1, x_2, x_3 ... x_{n-1}$. Thus the x-values were predetermined and $x_i - x_{i-1} = h =$ constant.

By Trapezoidal rule,

$$\int_{x_0}^{x_n} f(x)dx = h\left[\frac{1}{2}f_0 + f_1 + f_2 + f_{n-1} + \frac{1}{2}f_n\right]$$

$$= h\sum_{i=0}^{n} w_i f_i$$

By Simpson's rule,

$$\int_{x_0}^{x_n} f(x)dx = h\left[\frac{1}{3}f_0 + \frac{4}{3}f_1 + \frac{2}{3}f_2 + \frac{4}{3}f_3 + .... + \frac{1}{3}f_n\right]$$

$$= h\sum_{i=0}^{n} w_i f_i$$

Gauss developed a procedure in which both positions of the sampling points $x_i$, and weights $w_i$ have been optimized. Gauss realized that by treating both the $n$ sample points $x_i$ and the n weights $w_i$ as variables, we can make the formula exact and accurate for polynomials with $2n$ coefficients (*i.e.*, polynomials of degree $(2n - 1)$ or less). Formula got by using this idea is called Gauss-Legendre (or simply Gauss) quadrature formula. This is an open quadrature formula and the function values at the end points need not be known.

In general $\int_{x_0}^{x_n} f(x)dx = \sum w_i f(x_i) + R_n$

where $x_i's$ are sampling points and $w_i$'s are the weights at these points.

Gauss-Legendre integration formula can be expressed as

$$\int_{-1}^{1} f(x)dx = \sum_{i=1}^{n} w_i f(x_i)$$

where the arguments or sampling points $x_i$ are the zeros of $P_n(x)$ (Legendre polynomial) and the coefficients $w_i$ are given by

$$w_i = \frac{2(1-x_i^2)}{n^2\left[P_{n-1}(x_i)\right]^2}$$

For $n = 2$, $P_2(x) = \frac{1}{2}(3x^2 - 1) = 0$ gives, $x = \pm\frac{1}{\sqrt{3}} = \pm 0.57735$ and $w_1 = w_2 = 1$.

For $n = 3$, $P_3(x) = \frac{1}{2}(5x^3 - 3x) = 0$ gives

$$x = 0,\ x = \pm\sqrt{\frac{3}{5}} = \pm 0.77459$$

and $$w_1 = w_3 = 0.55555 \text{ and } w_2 = 0.88888$$

For different values of *n*, the table values for $x_i$ and $w_i$ can be seen in Treatise on this subject.

## TWO POINTS GAUSSIAN QUADRATURE

For $n = 2$, we can also get sampling points and weights as follows.

Let $$\int_{-1}^{1} f(x)dx = af(x_1) + bf(x_2) \qquad ...(1)$$

This formula will be exact for $2n - 1 = 2 \times 2 - 1 = 3$ degrees that is, it is exact when $f(x) = 1, x, x^2$ and $x^3$.

$\therefore$ $$\int_{-1}^{1} 1dx = a + b = 2 \qquad ...(2)$$

$$\int_{-1}^{1} xdx = ax_1 + bx_2 = 0 \qquad ...(3)$$

$$\int_{-1}^{1} x^2dx = ax_1^2 + bx_2^2 = \frac{2}{3} \qquad ...(4)$$

$$\int_{-1}^{1} x^3dx = ax_1^3 + bx_2^3 = 0 \qquad ...(5)$$

Solving these four equation, we get $x_1 = -x_2 = \frac{1}{\sqrt{3}}$ and $a = b = 1$

Hence $$\int_{-1}^{1} f(x)dx = f\left(-\frac{1}{\sqrt{3}}\right) + f\left(\frac{1}{\sqrt{3}}\right) \qquad ...(6)$$

This is called **TWO POINTS GAUSSIAN QUADRATURE FORMULA.** This formula is exact for polynomials upto degree 3.

## THREE POINTS GAUSSIAN QUADRATURE

Assuming $\int_{-1}^{1} f(x)dx = af(x_1) + bf(x_2) + cf(x_3)$ and this formula is exact for $2 \times 3 - 1 = 5$ degrees of polynomials, that is for $1, x, x^2, x^3, x^4, x^5$, we can get $x_1, x_2, x_3, a, b, c$ from six equations. These three sampling points are nothing but the roots of $P_3(x) = 0$.

Hence
$$x_1 = -\sqrt{\frac{3}{5}} = -0.77459 = -\sqrt{0.6}$$
$$x_2 = 0$$
$$x_3 = +\sqrt{\frac{3}{5}} = 0.77459 = +\sqrt{0.6}$$
$$a = c = 0.55555 \text{ and } b = 0.88888$$

Hence THREE POINTS GAUSSIAN QUADRATURE FORMULA is

$$\int_{-1}^{1} f(x)dx = \frac{5}{9}[f(-0.77459) + f(0.77459)] + \frac{8}{9} f(0)$$

i.e.,
$$\int_{-1}^{1} f(x)dx = 0.55555[f(-0.77459) + f(0.77459)] + 0.88888.f(0) \quad ....(7)$$

This formula is exact for polynomials upto degree 5.

**Weights and the Sampling points of Quadrature formula**

| No. of terms $n$ | Sampling points $x_i$ | Weights $w_i$ |
|---|---|---|
| 1. | 0 | 2.00000 |
| 2. | $\pm\frac{1}{\sqrt{3}} = \pm 0.57735$ | 1.00000 |
| 3. | $0 = 0.00000$<br>$\pm\sqrt{\frac{3}{5}} = \pm 0.77459$ | $0.88888 = \frac{8}{9}$<br>$0.55555 = \frac{5}{9}$ |
| 4. | $\pm 0.861136$<br>$\pm 0.339981$ | 0.347854<br>0.652145 |
| 5. | 0.00000<br>$\pm 0.538469$<br>$\pm 0.906179$ | 0.568888<br>0.478628<br>0.236926 |

## FOR GENERAL RANGE (A, B)

Suppose we require $\int_a^b f(x)dx.$ By proper linear transformation, the range $(a,b)$ is mapped into $(-1, 1)$.

Let $$x = \alpha z + \beta$$

When $x = a, z = -1$ and $x = b, z = 1$.

$$a = \beta - \alpha, \text{ and } b = \alpha + \beta$$

$$\therefore \quad \alpha = \frac{b-a}{2} \text{ and } \beta = \frac{b+a}{2}$$

Hence $$x = \frac{1}{2}[(b-a)z + (b+a)]$$

When range for $x$ is $(a, b)$, range for $z$ is $(-1, 1)$

$$dx = \frac{1}{2}(b-a)dz$$

$$\therefore \quad \int_a^b f(x)dx = \frac{1}{2}(b-a)\int_{-1}^{1} f\left[\frac{1}{2}(b-a)z + \frac{1}{2}(b+a)\right]dz$$

$$= \frac{1}{2}(b-a)\int_{-1}^{1}\phi(z)dz$$

Now $\int_{-1}^{1}\phi(z)dz$ can be evaluated using Two points or three points Gaussian quadrature formulae.

**Example 1.** *Apply Gauss two-point formula to evaluate*

(i) $\int_{-1}^{1}\frac{1}{1+x^2}dx$ (ii) $\int_0^1 \frac{dx}{1+x^2}$ *(Anna Ap. 2005)*

**Solution.** (*i*) Here $f(x) = \frac{1}{1+x^2};\ f\left(\frac{1}{\sqrt{3}}\right) = f\left(-\frac{1}{\sqrt{3}}\right) = \frac{3}{4}$

Hence $\int_{-1}^{1}\frac{1}{1+x^2}dx = f\left(-\frac{1}{\sqrt{3}}\right) + f\left(\frac{1}{\sqrt{3}}\right) = \frac{3}{2} = 1.5$

But $\int_{-1}^{1}\frac{1}{1+x^2} = 2\left(\tan^{-1}x\right)_0^1 = \pi/2 = 1.5708$

Here, the error due to two-point formula is 0.0708

(*ii*) $\int_0^1 \frac{dx}{1+x^2} = \frac{1}{2}\int_{-1}^{1}\frac{dx}{1+x^2} = 0.75$

**Example 2.** *Using Gaussian three-point formula evaluate*

*(i)* $\int_{-1}^{1}(3x^2+5x^4)dx$ *(ii)* $\int_{0}^{1}(3x^2+5x^4)dx$

*Also compare with exact values.*

**Solution.**

(*i*) Let $f(x)=3x^2+5x^4;\ f\left(-\sqrt{0.6}\right)=f\left(\sqrt{0.6}\right)=3(0.6)+5(0.6)^2$

$$=3.6 \text{ and } f(0)=0$$

$$\therefore \quad \int_{-1}^{1} f(x)dx=\frac{5}{9}\left[f\left(-\sqrt{0.6}\right)+f\left(\sqrt{0.6}\right)\right]+\frac{8}{9}f(0)$$

$$=\frac{5}{9}(3.6+3.6)+0=4$$

Exact value of the integral in also 4 by direct integration.

(*ii*) $\int_{0}^{1}(3x^2+5x^4)dx=\frac{1}{2}\int_{-1}^{1}(3x^2+5x^4)dx=\frac{1}{2}\times 4=2$ .

**Example 3.** *Use Gaussian three-point formula and evaluate*

$$I=\int_{1}^{5}\frac{dz}{z}.$$

**Solution.** By actual integration I = log 5 = 1.609438

Here the range is not (–1, 1). Therefore

put $\quad z=\frac{b-a}{2}x+\frac{b+a}{2}=2x+3;\ dz=2dx$

when $\quad x=-1,\ z=1, \text{ and } x=1,\ z=5$

$$\therefore \quad I=\int_{1}^{5}\frac{dz}{z}=2\int_{-1}^{1}\frac{1}{2x+3}dx$$

Now, let $\quad f(x)=\frac{2}{2x+3}$

$$\therefore \quad f\left(-\sqrt{0.6}\right)=\frac{2}{3-2\sqrt{0.6}} \text{ and } f\left(\sqrt{0.6}\right)=\frac{2}{3+2\sqrt{0.6}} \text{ and } f(0)=\frac{2}{3}$$

$$\therefore \quad I=\frac{5}{9}\left[\frac{2}{3-2\sqrt{0.6}}+\frac{2}{3+2\sqrt{0.6}}\right]+\frac{8}{9}\left(\frac{2}{3}\right)=\frac{10}{9}\left[\frac{6}{9-4(0.6)}\right]+\frac{16}{27}$$

$$=\frac{20}{3\times 6.6}+\frac{16}{27}=\frac{20}{19.8}+\frac{16}{27}=1.602693$$

The error is only 0.006745.

**Example 4.** *Evaluate* $\int_{-2}^{2} e^{-\frac{x}{2}}dx$ *by Gauss two point formula.*

**Solution.** Here, Let $x = \frac{b-a}{2}z + \frac{b+a}{2} = 2z;\ dx = 2\,dz$

$$\therefore \qquad I = 2\int_{-1}^{1} e^{-z}dz = 2\left[f\left(-\frac{1}{\sqrt{3}}\right) + f\left(\frac{1}{\sqrt{3}}\right)\right]$$

$$= 2\left[e^{-0.57735} + e^{0.57735}\right]$$

$$= 2[0.5614 + 1.7813] = 4.6854$$

**Example 5.** *Evaluate* $\int_0^{\pi/2} \sin t\,dt$ *by Gaussian two-point formula.*

**Solution.** Let $t = \frac{\pi}{4}x + \frac{\pi}{4} = \frac{\pi}{4}(x+1);\ \therefore dt = \frac{\pi}{4}dx.$

$$I = \int_0^{\pi/2} \sin t\ dt$$

$$= \frac{\pi}{4}\int_{-1}^{1} \sin\left(\frac{\pi x + \pi}{4}\right)dx$$

$$= \frac{\pi}{4}\left[\sin\frac{\pi}{4}(1.57735) + \sin\frac{\pi}{4}(0.42265)\right]$$

$$= \frac{\pi}{4}[\sin(0.39434\pi) + \sin(0.10566\pi)]$$

$$= 0.99847$$

Exact value of I is 1. Therefore, the error is 0.00153.

**Example 6.** *Using three point Gaussian formula find* $\int_{0.2}^{1.5} e^{-t^2}\,dt$.

**Solution.** Let $\quad t = \left(\frac{1.5-0.2}{2}\right)x + \frac{1.5+0.2}{2} = 0.65x + 0.85$

$$dt = 0.65dx$$

$$\therefore \qquad I = 0.65\int_{-1}^{1} e^{-(0.65x+0.85)^2}\,dx$$

$$= 0.65\left[\begin{array}{l} 0.5555e^{-[0.65(-0.77459)+0.85]^2} \\ \qquad + 0.5555e^{-[0.65(0.77459)+0.85]^2} \\ \qquad\qquad + 0.888e^{-[0.85]^2} \end{array}\right]$$

$$= 0.65860$$

**Example 7.** *By Gaussian formulae evaluate* $\int_2^3 \frac{dt}{1+t}$.

**Solution.** Let $t = \frac{b-a}{2}x + \frac{b+a}{2} = \frac{x}{2} + \frac{5}{2};\ dt = \frac{1}{2}dx$

$$\int_2^3 \frac{dt}{1+t} = \frac{1}{2}\int_{-1}^{1} \frac{2dx}{7+x} = \int_{-1}^{1} \frac{dx}{7+x}$$

By Two point formula, $I = f\left(-\frac{1}{\sqrt{3}}\right) + f\left(\frac{1}{\sqrt{3}}\right)$

$$= \frac{1}{7-\frac{1}{\sqrt{3}}} + \frac{1}{7+\frac{1}{\sqrt{3}}} = \frac{42}{149} = 0.28188$$

By Three point formula $I = \frac{5}{9}\left[\frac{1}{7-0.77459} + \frac{1}{7+0.77459}\right] + \frac{8}{9}\left(\frac{1}{7}\right)$

$$= \frac{5}{9}[0.16063 + 0.12862] + 0.12698$$

$$= 0.28767$$

## EXERCISES *(Gaussian Quadrature)*

By using Gaussian two-points or three points formula, evaluate.

**1.** $\int_0^1 e^x dx$ (2 points)

**2.** $\int_2^4 (2x^4 + 2)dx$ (3 points)

**3.** $\int_0^1 \frac{dx}{1+x}$ (3 points)

**4.** $\int_0^3 x^2 \cos x\, dx$ (3 points)

**5.** $\int_0^{\pi/2} \log(1+x)dx$ (2 points)

**6.** $\int_0^{\pi/2} \frac{d\theta}{\sqrt{1+\sin^2\theta}}$ (2 points)

**7.** $\int_0^1 \frac{dt}{\sqrt{1-t^4}}$ (2 points)

**8.** $\int_5^{12} \frac{dx}{x}$ (3 points)

**9.** $\int_1^2 e^x dx$ (3 points)

## ANSWERS

**1.** 2.342696
**2.** 400.8028
**3.** 0.693122
**4.** –4.936
**5.** 0.858
**6.** 1,311028
**7.** 311028
**8.** 0.87534
**9.** 4.67077

# Appendix D
## *Solution of Systems of Nonlinear Equations*

### NEWTON-RAPHSON METHOD

**Method 1**

Consider the system of two nonlinear equations in two variables

Let $$f(x, y) = 0 \qquad \text{... (1)}$$

and $$g(x, y) = 0$$

be two non linear equations in $x$ and $y$. Knowing that $(x_0, y_0)$ is an approximate solution of (1), we have to find a better approximate solution of the system (1).

Let $(x_0 + h, y_0 + k)$ be the exact solution of the system. (1).

Therefore, $f(x_0 + h, y_0 + k) = 0$ and $g(x_0 + h, y_0 + k) = 0$

By Taylor series,

$$f(x_0 + h,\ y_0 + k) \approx f(x_0,\ y_0) = \left[h\frac{\partial f}{\partial x} + k\frac{\partial f}{\partial y}\right]_{(x_0,\ y_0)} = 0 \qquad \text{... (2)}$$

and $$g(x_0 + h,\ y_0 + k) \approx g(x_0,\ y_0) + \left[h\frac{\partial g}{\partial x} + k\frac{\partial g}{\partial y}\right]_{(x_0,\ y_0)} = 0 \qquad \text{... (3)}$$

Solving for $h$ and $k$ from,

$$f(x_0,\ y_0) + \left[h\frac{\partial f}{\partial x} + k\frac{\partial f}{\partial y}\right]_{(x_0,\ y_0)} = 0$$

and $$g(x_0,\ y_0) + \left[h\frac{\partial g}{\partial x} + k\frac{\partial g}{\partial y}\right]_{(x_0,\ y_0)} = 0$$

we get,

$$h = \left(\frac{g\dfrac{\partial f}{\partial y} - f\dfrac{\partial g}{\partial y}}{\dfrac{\partial f}{\partial x}\dfrac{\partial g}{\partial y} - \dfrac{\partial f}{\partial y}\cdot\dfrac{\partial g}{\partial x}}\right)_{(x_0,\ y_0)} = \left(\frac{gf_y - fg_y}{J}\right)_{(x_0,\ y_0)} \qquad \text{... (4)}$$

and $$K = \left( \frac{f\dfrac{\partial g}{\partial x} - g\dfrac{\partial f}{\partial x}}{\dfrac{\partial f}{\partial x}\dfrac{\partial g}{\partial y} - \dfrac{\partial f}{\partial y}\dfrac{\partial g}{\partial x}} \right)_{(x_0,\, y_0)} = \left( \frac{fg_x - gf_x}{J} \right)_{(x_0,\, y_0)} \quad \text{... (5)}$$

where $$J = \begin{vmatrix} \dfrac{\partial f}{\partial x} & \dfrac{\partial f}{\partial y} \\ \dfrac{\partial g}{\partial x} & \dfrac{\partial g}{\partial y} \end{vmatrix} = \frac{\partial(f, g)}{\partial\,(x, y)}$$

We can also write in the form

$$h = \frac{\begin{vmatrix} -f & f_y \\ -g & g_y \end{vmatrix}}{\begin{vmatrix} f_x & f_y \\ g_x & g_y \end{vmatrix}} \text{ at } (x_0, y_0) \quad \text{and} \quad K = \frac{-\begin{vmatrix} -f & f_x \\ -g & g_x \end{vmatrix}}{\begin{vmatrix} f_x & f_y \\ g_x & g_y \end{vmatrix}} \text{ at } (x_0, y_0)$$

Since $h$ and $k$ are only approximate values (since terms are neglected in Taylor expansion) the first better approximate values of $x$ and $y$ are

$x_1 = x_0 + h$ and $y_1 = y_0 + k$ where $h$ and $k$ are given by (4) and (5)

Again starting from $(x_1, y_1)$ we can get the second approximate value $(x_2, y_2)$ such that $x_2 = x_1 + h$ and $y_2 = y_1 + k$, $h$ and $k$ being calculated from (4) and (5) at $(x_1, y_1)$. This process can be continued until we get the described accuracy.

**Note.** The initial values $(x_0, y_0)$ must be so chosen that the sequences $x_1, x_2, x_3$ ... and $y_1, y_2, y_3$, ... converge.

**Method 2.** *Another simple form of Newton-Raphson method*

Consider the system of equations

$$f(x, y) = 0 \quad \text{... (6)}$$

and $g\,(x, y) = 0$ in two unknowns $x$ and $y$.

Treating each equation in one variable, Newton's method for one variable can be applied and the iterative formulae are

$$x_{i+1} = x_i - \frac{f(x_i, y_i)}{\dfrac{\partial f}{\partial x}(x_i, y_i)} = x_i - \frac{f(x_i, y_i)}{f_x(x_i, y_i)}$$

and $$y_{i+1} = y_i - \frac{g(x_{i+1}, y_i)}{\dfrac{\partial g}{\partial y}(x_{i+1}, y_i)} = y_i - \frac{g(x_{i+1}, y_i)}{g_y(x_{i+1}, y_i)}$$

where $$f_x = \frac{\partial f}{\partial x} \text{ and } g_y = \frac{\partial g}{\partial y} \text{ and } i = 0, 1, 2, \ldots$$

till we get $\quad | x_{i+1} - x_i | + | y_{i+1} - y_i | < \in$

where $\in$ is the given accuracy.

**Note 1.** This scheme can be extended to $n$ simultaneous equations in $n$ variables.

2. In the iteration scheme, only the current values (latest known values) of independent variables are used as in the case of Gauss-Seidel interation method.

3. This scheme requires only one derivative computation to get $x_{i+1}$ or $y_{i+1}$.

4. When $x_{i+1}$ is computed $y_i$ is kept fixed and when $y_{i+1}$ is computed $x_i$ is kept fixed.

**Example 1.** *Solve the equations (for a root) $x^2 + y^2 = 16$ and $x^2 - y^2 = 4$ given that the starting approximate solution is* $(2\sqrt{2},\ 2\sqrt{2})$.

**Solution.** Let $x_0 = y_0 = 2\sqrt{2}$ and $x_1 = x_0 + h,\ y_1 = y_0 + k$ we will use method 1 here

Let $\quad f = x^2 + y^2 - 16 \quad$ and $\quad g = x^2 - y^2 - 4$

$$\frac{\partial f}{\partial x} = f_x = 2x; \quad \frac{\partial f}{\partial y} = f_y = 2y$$

$$\frac{\partial g}{\partial x} = g_x = 2x\ ; \quad \frac{\partial g}{\partial y} = g_y = -2y$$

$$f(x_0,\ y_0) = f(2\sqrt{2},\ 2\sqrt{2}) = 0$$

$$g(x_0,\ y_0) = g(2\sqrt{2},\ 2\sqrt{2}) = -4$$

$$g_x(x_0,\ y_0) = 4\sqrt{2},\ g_y(x_0,\ y_0) = -4\sqrt{2}$$

$$f_x(x_0,\ y_0) = 4\sqrt{2}\ ;\ f_y(x_0,\ y_0) = 4\sqrt{2}$$

$$J = \begin{vmatrix} f_x & f_y \\ g_x & g_y \end{vmatrix}_{(x_0,\ y_0)} = \begin{vmatrix} 4\sqrt{2} & 4\sqrt{2} \\ 4\sqrt{2} & -4\sqrt{2} \end{vmatrix} = -64 \neq 0$$

$$\therefore \quad h = \left( \frac{gf_y - fg_y}{J} \right)_{(x_0,\ y_0)}$$

$$= \frac{(-4)\ (4\sqrt{2}) - (0)(-4\sqrt{2})}{(-64)} = \frac{\sqrt{2}}{4} = 0.354$$

$$K = \left( \frac{fg_x - gf_x}{J} \right)_{(x_0, y_0)}$$

$$= \frac{(0)\,(4\sqrt{2})-(-4)\,(4\sqrt{2})}{(-64)} = -\frac{\sqrt{2}}{4} = -0.354$$

Hence $\quad x_1 = x_0 + h = 2\sqrt{2} + 0.354 = 3.182$

$\quad y_1 = y_0 + k = 2\sqrt{2} - 0.354 = 2.474$

Again start with these values as the initial approximation and proceed as before.

Let $\quad x_2 = x_1 + h\,,\ y_2 = y_1 + k$

$f\,(x_1, y_1) = f\,(3.182, 2.474) = 10.125 + 6.121 - 16 = 0.246$

$g\,(x_1, y_1) = g\,(3.182, 2.474) = 10.125 - 6.121 - 4 = 0.004$

$f_x\,(x_1, y_1) = f\,(3.182, 2.474) = 2\,(3.182) = 6.364$

$f_y\,(x_1, y_1) = f_y\,(3.182, 2.474) = 2\,(2.474) = 4.948$

$g_x\,(x_1, y_1) = g_x\,\ (3.182, 2.474) = 6.364$

$g_y\,(x_1, y_1) = g_y\,(3.182, 2.474) = -\,2\,(2.474) = -\,4.948$

$$J = \begin{vmatrix} 6.364 & 4.948 \\ 6.364 & -4.948 \end{vmatrix} = -62.978$$

$$h = \left(\frac{gf_y - fg_y}{J}\right)_{(x_1,\,y_1)}$$

$$= \frac{(0.004)(4.948)-(0.246)(-4.948)}{(-62.978)} = -0.0196$$

$$k = \left(\frac{fg_x - gf_x}{J}\right)_{(x_1,\,y_1)}$$

$$= \frac{(0.246)\,(6.364)-(0.004)\,(6.364)}{(-62.978)} = -0.025$$

$\therefore \quad x_2 = x_1 + h = 3.182 - 0.0196 = 3.162$

$\quad y_2 = y_1 + k = 2.474 - 0.025 = 2.449$

Hence the second iteration yields,

$x_2 = 3.162$ and $y_2 = 2.449$.

We can proceed in the same way and get

$(x_3, y_3), (x_4, y_4)$ etc.

**Note.** Even by two iterations, we have not got the result correct to two decimals.

**Example 2.** *Solve the equations* $x^2 + y - 11 = 0$ *and* $y^2 + x - 7 = 0$ *starting with the initial values* $x_0 = 3.5$ *and* $y_0 = -\,1.5$ *(2 iterations)*

**Solution.** Here $x_0 = 3.5$, $y_0 = -1.5$

Let $$f = x^2 + y - 11 \text{ and } g = y^2 + x - 7$$

$$f_x = 2x;\ f_y = 1;\ g_x = 1 \text{ and } g_y = 2y$$

$$f(x_0, y_0) = f(3.5, -1.5) = 12.25 - 1.5 - 11 = -0.25$$

$$g(x_0, y_0) = g(3.5, -1.5) = -0.25$$

$$f_x(x_0, y_0) = 2x_0 = 7;\ f_y(x_0, y_0) = 1;\ g_x(x_0, y_0) = 1$$

and $$g_y(x_0, y_0) = 2y_0 = -3$$

$$J = \begin{vmatrix} f_x & f_y \\ g_x & g_y \end{vmatrix}_{(x_0, y_0)} = \begin{vmatrix} 7 & 1 \\ 1 & -3 \end{vmatrix} = -22 \neq 0$$

$$\therefore \quad h = \left(\frac{hf_y - fg_y}{J}\right)_{(x_0, y_0)} = \frac{(-0.25)(1) + (0.25)(-3)}{(-22)} = 0.0454$$

$$K = \left(\frac{fg_x - gf_x}{J}\right)_{(x_0, y_0)}$$

$$= \frac{(-0.25)(1) + (0.25)\ (7)}{(-22)} = -0.0682$$

Hence $$x_1 = x_0 + h = 3.5 + 0.0454 = 3.5454$$

and $$y_1 = y_0 + k = -1.5 - 0.0682 = -1.568$$

The first iteration result is $x_1 = 3.545$, and $y_1 = -1.568$

Again, let $x_2 = x_1 + h$ and $y_2 = y + k$.

$$\therefore \quad f(x_1, y_1) = x_1^2 + y_1 - 11 = (3.545)^2 - 1.5682 - 11 = -0.001$$

$$g(x_1, y_1) = (-1.568)^2 + 3.545 - 7 = -0.996$$

$$f_x(x_1, y_1) = 2x_1 = 7.090;\ f_y(x_1, y_1) = 1$$

$$g_x(x_1, y_1) = 1 \text{ and } g_y(x_1, y_1) = 2y_1 = -3.136$$

$$\therefore \quad J = \begin{vmatrix} 7.090 & 1 \\ 1 & -3.136 \end{vmatrix} = -23.234$$

$$\therefore \quad h = \left(\frac{gf_y - fg_y}{J}\right)_{(x_1, y_1)}$$

$$= \frac{(-0.996)(1) + (0.001)\ (-3.136)}{(-23.234)} = 0.043$$

$$K = \left(\frac{fg_x - gf_x}{J}\right)_{(x_1, y_1)}$$

$$= \frac{(-0.001)(1) + (0.996)(7.090)}{(-23.234)} = -0.304$$

$$\therefore \qquad x_2 = x_1 + h = 3.545 + 0.043 = 3.588$$

$$y_2 = y_1 + k = -1.568 - 0.304 = -1.872$$

Hence $x_2 = 3.588$, $y_2 = -1.872$ give the second iteration values.

Since $f(x_2, y_2) = 0.0017$, $g(x_2, y_2) = 0.0923$,
perhaps we can stop here. We can proceed further if we require further accuracy.

**Note:** $x = 3$, $y = 2$ is an exact solution and we did not get this solution from our starting solution.

**Example 3.** *Solve for x and y the equations*

$$f(x, y) = x^2 + y - 11 = 0 \text{ and } g(x, y) = y^2 + x - 7 = 0$$

*assuming initial approximations $x_0 = 3.5$, $y_0 = -1.8$ by using Newton–Raphson method.*

**Solution.** Let $x_1 = x_0 + h,\ y_1 = y_0 + k$

$$f_x = 2x; \quad f_y = 1; \quad g_x = 1; \quad g_y = 2y$$

$$f(x_0, y_0) = 12.25 - 1.8 - 11 = -0.55$$

$$g(x_0, y_0) = 3.24 + 3.5 - 7 = -0.26$$

$$\left(\frac{\partial f}{\partial x}\right)_{(x_0, y_0)} = 7; \quad \left(\frac{\partial f}{\partial y}\right)_{(x_0, y_0)} = 1; \quad \left(\frac{\partial g}{\partial x}\right)_{(x_0, y_0)} = 1$$

and $$\left(\frac{\partial g}{\partial y}\right)_{(x_0, y_0)} = -3.6$$

$$J = \begin{vmatrix} 7 & 1 \\ 1 & -3.6 \end{vmatrix} = -26.2$$

$$h = \left(\frac{gf_y - fg_y}{J}\right)_{(x_0, y_0)}$$

$$= \frac{(-0.26)(1) - (-0.55)(-3.6)}{(-26.2)} = 0.0855$$

$$K = \left(\frac{fg_x - gf_x}{J}\right)_{(x_0, y_0)}$$

$$= \frac{(-0.55)(1) - (-0.26)(7)}{(-26.2)} = -0.0485$$

$\therefore \quad x_1 = x_0 + h = 3.5855$

$y_1 = y_0 + k = -1.8485$

Again starting from $(x_1, y_1)$, and repeating the process, $x_2 = 3.5844$, $y_2 = -1.8482$

We proceed further if we require more accuracy.

**Example 4.** *Solve* $x^3 - 3xy^2 + 1 = 0$ *and* $3x^2y - y^3 = 0$ *starting with the approximate solution (0.5, 0.5) by Newton–Raphson method.*

**Solution.** Let $f(x, y) = x^3 - 3xy^2 + 1;\; g(x, y) = 3x^2y - y^3$

$$f_x = 3x^2 - 3y^2; \quad f_y = -6xy; \quad g_x = 6xy; \quad g_y = 3x^2 - 3y^2$$

Let $x_0 = 0.5, y_0 = 0.5$

$$f(x_0, y_0) = \frac{1}{8} - \frac{3}{8} + 1 = 3/4\,; \quad g(x_0, y_0) = \frac{3}{8} - \frac{1}{8} = 1/4$$

$$f_x(x_0, y_0) = 0, \quad f_y(x_0, y_0) = -3/2$$

$$g_x(x_0, y_0) = 3/2; \quad g_y(x_0, y_0) = 0$$

$$J = \begin{vmatrix} 0 & -3/2 \\ 3/2 & 0 \end{vmatrix} = 9/4$$

$$\therefore \quad h = \left(\frac{gf_y - fg_y}{J}\right)_{(x_0, y_0)} = \frac{\frac{1}{4}(-3/2)}{9/4} = -\frac{1}{6}$$

$$K = \left(\frac{fg_x - gf_x}{J}\right)_{(x_0, y_0)} = \frac{(3/4)(3/2)}{(9/4)} = 1/2$$

Hence $x_1 = x_0 + h = \frac{1}{2} - \frac{1}{6} = 1/3$

$$y_1 = y_0 + k = \frac{1}{2} + \frac{1}{2} = 1$$

Again, starting from these values as the initial approximate values, we proceed.

Let $x_2 = x_1 + h; \quad y_2 = y_1 + k$

$$f(x_1, y_1) = \left(\frac{1}{3}\right)^3 - 1 + 1 = \frac{1}{27}$$

$$g(x_1, y_1) = -2/3$$

$$f_x(x_1, y_1) = \frac{1}{3} - 3 = \frac{-8}{3};\ f_y(x_1, y_1) = -2$$

$$g_x(x_1, y_1) = 2;\ g_y(x_1, y_1) = \frac{1}{3} - 3 = -8/3$$

$$J = \begin{vmatrix} -8/3 & -2 \\ 2 & -8/3 \end{vmatrix} = \frac{100}{9}$$

$$\therefore \quad h = \left(\frac{gf_y - fg_y}{J}\right)_{(x_1,\, y_1)}$$

$$= \frac{(-2/3)\,(-2) - \left(\frac{1}{27}\right)(-8/3)}{\left(\frac{100}{9}\right)} = 0.1288$$

$$K = \left(\frac{fg_x - gf_x}{J}\right)_{(x_1,\, y_1)}$$

$$= \frac{\left(\frac{1}{27}\right)(2) - (-2/3)\,(-8/3)}{\left(\frac{100}{9}\right)} = -0.1533$$

$$\therefore \quad x_2 = x_1 + h = \frac{1}{3} + 0.1288 = 0.4621$$

$$y_2 = y_1 + k = 1 - 0.1533 = 0.8467$$

Proceeding like this, after a few iterations, we get closer to the exact solution

$$x = 0.5 \text{ and } y = \frac{\sqrt{3}}{2} = 0.866$$

**Note.** Perhaps, if we have started with a different $(x_0, y_0)$, we may have a quicker convergence.

**Example 5.** *Solve* $f(x, y) = x^2 + y^2 - 4 = 0$ *and* $g(x, y) = y + e^x - 1 = 0$ *starting with an approximate solution (1, – 1.7) by Newton's method.*

**Solution.** Here, $f_x = 2x; f_y = 2y; g_x = e^x; g_y = 1$

$$f(x_0, y_0) = 1 + 2.89 - 4 = -0.11$$

$$g(x_0, y_0) = -1.7 + 2.718 - 1 = 0.018$$

$$f_x(x_0, y_0) = 2, f_y(x_0, y_0) = -3.4, g_x(x_0, y_0) = 2.718$$

and $\quad g_y(x_0, y_0) = 1$

$$J = \begin{vmatrix} 2 & -3.4 \\ 2.718 & 1 \end{vmatrix} = 11.242 \neq 0$$

$$h = \left(\frac{gf_y - fg_y}{J}\right)_{(x_0,\, y_0)}$$

$$= \frac{(0.018)\,(-3.4) + (0.11)\,(1)}{11.242} = 0.0043$$

$$K = \left(\frac{fg_x - gf_x}{J}\right)_{(x_0,\, y_0)}$$

$$= \frac{(-0.11)(2.718) - (0.018)\,(2)}{11.242} = -\,0.0298$$

$\therefore \quad x_1 = x_0 + h = 1.0043$

and $\quad y_1 = y_0 + k = -1.7298$

Proceeding again in the same way, we get $(x_2, y_2)$, $(x_3, y_3)$ and so on.

(In this p·oblem, the first iteration itself gives a better solution which is close to the exact value).

**Example 6.** *Using simple form of Newton's method solve the equations*

$$f(x, y) = y^2 + 4x^2 + 2xy - y - 2 = 0$$

*and* $\quad g(x, y) = y^2 + 2x^2 + 3xy - 3 = 0$

*starting with* $\quad x_0 = 0.4$ *and* $y_0 = 0.9$

**Solution.** Here, $\quad f_x = 8x + 2y; \quad g_y = 2y + 3x$

Also, $$x_{i+1} = x_i - \frac{f(x_i,\, y_i)}{f_x(x_i,\, y_i)} \qquad \text{... (1)}$$

$$y_{i+1} = y_i - \frac{g(x_{i+1},\ y_i)}{g_y\ (x_{i+1},\, y_i)} \qquad \text{... (2)}$$

$$f(x_0,\, y_0) = (0.9)^2 + 4(0.4)^2 + 2(0.4)(0.9) - 0.9 - 2 = -0.73$$

$$f_x(x_0,\, y_0) = 8(0.4) + 2(0.9) = 5$$

$$x_1 = x_0 - \frac{f(x_0,\ y_0)}{f_x(x_0,\, y_0)} = 0.4 + \frac{0.73}{5} = 0.546$$

$$g(x_1,\, y_0) = (0.9)^2 + 2(0.546)^2 + 3(0.546)\;(0.9) - 3 = -\,0.1196$$

$$g_y(x_1, y_0) = 2(0.9) + 3(0.546) = 3.438$$

Hence, $$y_1 = y_0 - \frac{g(x_1, y_0)}{g_y(x_1, y_0)} = 0.9 + \frac{0.1196}{3.438} = 0.9347$$

$\therefore$ $\boldsymbol{x_1 = 0.546; y_1 = 0.9347}$

$$f(x_1, y_1) = (0.9347)^2 + 4(0.5460)^2 + 2(0.9347)\,(0.5460) - 0.9347 - 2$$
$$= 0.1522$$
$$g\,(x_1, y_1) = (0.9347)^2 + 2\,(0.5460)^2 + 3\,(0.9347)\,(0.5460) - 3$$
$$= 0.0009$$

Now, starting with $x_1 = 0.5460$ and $y_1 = 0.9347$ and proceeding as before we get $\boldsymbol{x_2 = 0.5216, y_2 = 0.9694}$

Here,

$$f(x_2, y_2) = (0.9694)^2 + 4(0.5216)^2 + 2(0.9694)\,(0.5216) - (0.9694) - 2$$
$$= 0.0699$$

$$g(x_2, y_2) = (0.9694)^2 + 2(0.5216)^2 + 3(0.9694)(0.5216) - 3 = 0.0008$$

Again proceeding from $x_2, y_2$ we obtain $x_3, y_3$ and so on. Calculations can be made easily using computer programs for the iterations.

$$x_{i+1} = x_i - \frac{4x_i^2 + y_i^2 + 2x_i y_i - y_i - 2}{8x_i + 2y_i}$$

and $$y_{i+1} = y_i - \frac{2x_{i+1}^2 + 3x_{i+1}y_i + y_i^2 - 3}{3x_{i+1} + 2y_i}$$

We tabulate below the values.

| iteration | $x_i$ | $y_i$ | $f\,(x_i, y_i)$ | $g\,(x_i, y_i)$ |
|---|---|---|---|---|
| 0 | 0.4 | 0.9 | – 0.73 | – |
| 1 | 0.5460 | 0.9347 | 0.1522 | 0.0009 |
| 2 | 0.5216 | 0.9694 | 0.0699 | 0.0008 |

and so on

**Note 1.** An exact solution of the problem is $x = 0.5$; $y = 1$

2. Since there are more than one solution for the problem, different starting values may lead to different solutions.

**Example 7.** *Find a complex root of the equation $z^3 - 2z + 2 = 0$, using Newton's method.*

**Solution.** Let $z = x + iy$

$$z^3 - 2z + 2 = 0 \Rightarrow (x + iy)^3 - 2\,(x + iy) + 2 = 0$$

*i.e.* $$(x^3 - 3x\;\;y^2 - 2x + 2) + i\,(3x^2 y - y^3 - 2y) = 0$$

*i.e.,* $f(x, y) = x^3 - 3xy^2 - 2x + 2 = 0$ ... (1)

and $g(x, y) = 3x^2 y - y^3 - 2y = 0$ ... (2)

Now we have to solve (1) and (2).

Choose $x_0 = 1$, $y_0 = 1$ and use the iterations,

$$x_{i+1} = x_i - \frac{x_i^3 - 3x_i y_i^2 - 2x_i + 2}{3x_i^2 - 3y_i^2 - 2}$$

and
$$y_{i+1} = y_i - \frac{3x_{x+1}^2 y_i - y_i^3 - 2y_i}{3x_{i+1}^2 - 3y_i^2 - 2}$$

We get the values of $x_i$, $y_i$ and tabulate below by using a computer: $z = x + iy$ gives the complex root.

| *iteration* | *x* | *y* | *f* | *g* |
|---|---|---|---|---|
| 0 | 1 | 1 | –2 | 0 |
| 1 | 0.00000 | 0.400000 | – 2.000000 | – 3.000000 |
| 2 | 0.806452 | 0.242008 | 2.000000 | – 0.083563 |
| 3 | 4.234091 | – 0.000549 | 0.769887 | 12.517641 |
| 4 | 2.893126 | 0.000000 | 69.438580 | – 0.012695 |
| 5 | 2.009126 | 0.000000 | 20.429739 | 0.000000 |
| 6 | 1.406564 | 0.000000 | 6.091757 | 0.000000 |
| 7 | 0.906051 | 0.000000 | 1.969648 | 0.000000 |
| 8 | – 1.107192 | 0.000000 | 0.931701 | 0.000000 |
| 9 | – 2.810260 | 0.000000 | 2.857106 | 0.000000 |
| 10 | – 2.138435 | 0.000000 | – 14.573686 | 0.000000 |
| 11 | – 1.839598 | 0.000000 | – 3.501994 | 0.000000 |
| 12 | – 1.772596 | 0.000000 | – 0.546225 | 0.000000 |
| 13 | – 1.769300 | 0.000000 | – 0.024475 | 0.000000 |
| 14 | – 1.769292 | 0.000000 | – 0.000058 | 0.000000 |
| 15 | – 1.769292 | – 0.000000 | – 0.000000 | – 0.000000 |

Hence $x_{15} = -1.7\ 69292$; $y_{15} = 0$

$\therefore$ $z = x + iy = -1.769292 + i(0)$

**Note.** Since the work is tedious, such problems cannot be done using calculator in the examination hall within a short time.

## EXERCISES

Using Newton-Raphson method, solve for a root of the following equations starting from the initial approximations using method 1. (or method 2)

1. $x^3 - 3xy^2 + 1 = 0$; $3x^2y - y^3 = 0$; given $x_0 = y_0 = 1$ (**Ans.** 0.5, 0.866)
2. $x^3 - 3xy^2 + 35 = 0$, $x^4 + y^4 = 67$; $x_0 = 2$, $y_0 = 3$
3. $x = \sin x \cosh y$; $y = \cos x \sinh y$; $x_0 = 2$, $y_0 = 3$
4. $x^2 + y^2 - 4 = 0$; $x^2 + y^2 - 4x - 3 = 0$, $x_0 = 1.5$, $y_0 = 2.5$

   (exact root 1.5, $\frac{\sqrt{7}}{3}$)
5. $x^2 + y^2 - 4 = 0$, $xy - 2 = 0$, $x_0 = y_0 = 1.3$
6. $x^2 - y^2 = y$; $x^2 + y^2 = x$, $x_0 = 0.8$, $y_0 = 0.4$

   (**Ans.** 0.7974, 0.4006)
7. $y^2 - 3xy + 7 = 0$, $x - 2y - 2 = 0$, $x_0 = 3.5$, $y_0 = 0.7$

   (**Ans.** 3.453, 0.727)
8. $y^3 - 3xy + 7 = 0$, $x - 2y - 2 = 0$, $x_0 = y_0 = -1.8$

   (**Ans.** – 1.853, – 1.927)
9. $y - e^x = 0$, $e^x - xy = 0$ (exact root: 1, $e$)
10. Solve $\sin z = z - 2$ where $z = x + iy$ reducing to two simultaneous equations in $x$ and $y$ given $x_0 = 2$, $y_0 = 0$.
11. Given $(x_0, y_0) = (2, 0.25)$ compute $(x_1, y_1)$, $(x_2, y_2)$ and $(x_3, y_3)$ by solving. $x^2 - 2x - y + 0.5 = 0$, $x^2 + 4y^2 = 4$. *(Anna Ap. 2003)*

# Appendix E

## *Numerical solution of Ordinary differential equation by finite difference method*

When the closed form solution is not possible in solving an ordinary differential equation, we transform it to an approximate difference equation and solve for the unknown for different values of the independent variable.

By Taylor series,

$$y(x+h) = y(x) + hy'(x) + \frac{h^2}{2!}y''(x) + \ldots \qquad \ldots (1)$$

$$\frac{y(x+h)-y(x)}{h} = y'(x) + \frac{h}{2}y''(x) + \ldots$$

Hence, $$y'(x) = \frac{y(x+h)-y(x)}{h} - \frac{h}{2}y''(x) + \ldots$$

*i.e.,* $$y'(x) = \frac{y(x+h)-y(x)}{h} + O(h) \qquad \ldots (2)$$

(2) is forward difference approximation for $y'(x)$.

Also, $$y(x-h) = y(x) - hy'(x) + \frac{h^2}{2!}y''(x) \qquad \ldots (3)$$

$\therefore$ $$y'(x) = \frac{y(x)-y(x-h)}{h} + O(h) \qquad \ldots (4)$$

(4) is backward difference approximation for $y'(x)$

A central difference approximation for $y'(x)$ can be got as follows. Subtract (3) from (1) and divide by $2h$. We get

$$\frac{y(x+h)-y(x-h)}{2h} = y'(x) + O(h^2) \qquad \ldots (5)$$

(5) gives a better approximation for $y'(x)$ than what is given in (2) or (4)

Adding (3) and (1), we get,

$$y(x+h) + y(x-h) = 2y(x) + h^2 y''(x) + \frac{h^4}{24}y''''(x) + \ldots$$

$$\therefore \quad y''(x) = \frac{y(x+h)+y(x-h)-2y(x)}{h^2} + O(h^2) \quad \text{.... (6)}$$

(6) is taken as a difference approximation for $y''(x)$

Therefore, at $x = x_i$, from (5) and (6), we get

$$y_i' \approx \frac{y_{i+1} - y_{i-1}}{2h} \quad \text{... (7)}$$

and
$$y_i'' \approx \frac{y_{i-1} + y_{i+1} - 2y_i}{h^2} \quad \text{... (8)}$$

neglecting O ($h^2$), if $h$ is small.

Suppose a boundary value problem

$y'' + a(x)y' + b(x)y(x) = c(x)$, together with the boundary conditions $y(x_0) = \alpha$, $y(x_n) = \beta$ is given when $x \in (x_0, x_n)$.

We replace $y'(x)$ and $y''(x)$ by the difference formulae given by (7) and (8) and reduce to

$$\frac{y_{i+1} + y_{i-1} - 2y_i}{h^2} + a(x_i)\frac{y_{i+1} - y_{i-1}}{2h} + b(x_i).y_i = c(x_i)$$

Simplifying, we get

$$y_{i+1}\left(1 + \frac{h}{2}a_i\right) + y_i(h^2 b_i - 2) + y_{i-1}\left(1 - \frac{h}{2}a_i\right) = a_i\ h^2 \quad \text{... (9)}$$

where $\qquad i = 1, 2, \ldots n-1$ and $y_0 = \alpha$, $y_n = \beta$,

$$a_i = a(x_i),\ b_i = b(x_i),\ c_i = c(x_i)$$

Equation (9) will give $(n-1)$ equations for $i = 1, 2, 3, \ldots (n-1)$ which is a tridiagonal system and together with $y_0 = \alpha$, $y_n = \beta$ we get $(n+1)$ equations in the $(n+1)$ unknowns

$$y_0, y_1, y_2, \ldots, y_n$$

Solving from these $(n+1)$ equations, we get $y_0, y_1, y_2, \ldots, y_n$ values, *i..e*, the values of $y$ at $x = x_0, x_1, \ldots, x_n$.

**Example 1.** *Using finite difference method, solve for y given the differential equation* $\frac{d^2y}{dx^2} + y + 1 = 0$, $x \in (0, 1)$ *and the boundary conditions* $y(0) = y(1) = 0$, *taking (i)* $h = \frac{1}{2}$ *(ii)* $h = 1/4$

**Solution.** Let the interval of $x$, that is, (0, 1) be divided into $n$ equal parts, each part being equal to $h$, so that $nh = 1$.

**Case 1.** Suppose $n = 2$ (*i.e.*, divide the range into 2 equal parts); hence $h = 1/2$

Using $y_i'' = \dfrac{y_{i+1} + y_{i-1} - 2y_i}{h^2}$ in the differential equation, we get

$$\frac{y_{i+1} + y_{i-1} - 2y_i}{h^2} + y_i + 1 = 0$$

*i.e.*, $$y_{i+1} + y_i(h^2 - 2) + y_{i-1} + h^2 = 0 \quad \ldots (1)$$

where $i = 1$ and $h = 1/2$

Hence $y_2 - \frac{7}{4}y_1 + y_0 = -1/4$ where $y_0 = y(0) = 0$

and $y_2 = y(1) = 0$

$\therefore$ $y_1 = 1/7$

That is, $y_1 = y(0.5) = 1/7 = 0.1428$.

Tabulating the values of $y$; we get, for $h = 1/2$,

| $x$ | 0 | 0.5 | 1 |
|---|---|---|---|
| | 0 | $\frac{1}{7} = 0.1428$ | 0 |

Solving analytically the given differential equation we get $y\ (0.5) = 0.1395$. Hence the error is only 0.0133

**Case 2.** Taking $n = 4$ or $h = 1/4$

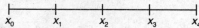

$x_0 \quad x_1 \quad x_2 \quad x_3 \quad x_4$

equation (1) reduces to

$$y_{i+1} - \frac{31}{16}y_i + y_{i-1} = -\frac{1}{16} \quad \ldots (2)$$

Setting $i = 1, 2, 3$, we get

$$y_2 - \frac{31}{16}y_1 + y_0 = -\frac{1}{16}$$

$$y_3 - \frac{31}{16}y_2 + y_1 = -\frac{1}{16}$$

$$y_4 - \frac{31}{16}y_3 + y_2 = -\frac{1}{16}$$

subject to $y_0 = y_4 = 0$

Therefore, $y_2 - \frac{31}{16}y_1 = -\frac{1}{16} \quad \ldots (3)$

$$y_3 - \frac{31}{16} y_2 + y_1 = -\frac{1}{16} \qquad \text{... (4)}$$

$$\frac{-31}{16} y_3 + y_2 = -\frac{1}{16} \qquad \text{... (5)}$$

(3) – (4) gives, $\frac{-31}{16}(y_1 - y_3) = 0$

$\therefore \qquad y_1 = y_3$

(4) becomes, $\quad 2y_1 - \frac{31}{16} y_2 = \frac{-1}{16} \qquad \text{... (6)}$

$$\frac{-31}{16} y_1 + y_2 = -\frac{1}{16} \qquad \text{... (7)}$$

Solving from (6) and (7), $y_1 = \frac{47}{449}$, $y_2 = \frac{63}{449}$

Tabulating the values of $y$, we get,

| $x$ | 0 | 0.25 | 0.5 | 0.75 | 1 |
|---|---|---|---|---|---|
| $y$ | 0 | $\frac{47}{449}$ | $\frac{63}{449}$ | $\frac{47}{449}$ | 0 |

$y_2 = \frac{63}{449} = 0.1403$. The error is only 0.0008 when compared to the exact value.

**Note.** From the above result, we infer that the accuracy by finite difference method depends upon

(1) The number of subintervals (or width of the subinterval) chosen and

(2) also on the order of the approximation. By increasing $n$, though the accuracy of the result increases, the number of equations to be solved also increases resulting more expenditure of time and energy.

**Example 2.** *Using finite difference method, solve* $\frac{d^2 y}{dx^2} = y$ *in (0, 2) given y (0) = 0, y (2) = 3.63*
*subdividing the range of x into 4 equal parts.*

**Solution.** $nh = b - a \Rightarrow 4h = 2 \therefore h = 1/2$

Replacing the derivative $y''$ by differences, we get

$$\frac{y_{i+1} + y_{i-1} - 2y_i}{h^2} = y_i$$

*i.e.* $$y_{i+1} - (2+h^2)y_i + y_{i-1} = 0, \; i = 1, 2, 3.$$

Putting $h = 1/2$, we get

$$y_{i+1} - \frac{9}{4}y_i + y_{i-1} = 0 \qquad \text{... (1)}$$

where $i = 1, 2, 3$

Hence the equations to be solved are

$$y_2 - \frac{9}{4}y_1 + y_0 = 0 \qquad \text{... (2)}$$

$$y_3 - \frac{9}{4}y_2 + y_1 = 0 \qquad \text{... (3)}$$

$$y_4 - \frac{9}{4}y_3 + y_2 = 0 \qquad \text{... (4)}$$

Using $y_0 = 0$, $y(2) = y_4 = 3.63$, we have

$$y_2 - \frac{9}{4}y_1 = 0 \qquad \text{... (5)}$$

$$y_3 - \frac{9}{4}y_2 + y_1 = 0 \qquad \text{... (6)}$$

$$3.63 - \frac{9}{4}y_3 + y_2 = 0 \qquad \text{... (7)}$$

Eliminating $y_1$ from (5) and (6),

$$\frac{9}{4}y_3 - \frac{81}{16}y_2 + y_2 = 0$$

*i.e.,* $$\frac{9}{4}y_3 - \frac{65}{16}y_2 = 0 \qquad \text{... (8)}$$

From (7) and (8), we get

$$\left(1 - \frac{65}{16}\right)y_2 = -3.63$$

$$\therefore \qquad y_2 = 1.1853$$

Putting this value of $y_2$ in (8), we get

$$y_3 = 2.1401$$

From (5), $$y_1 = \frac{4}{9}y_2 = 0.5268$$

Tabulating the values, the solution is,

| $x$ | 0 | 0.5 | 1 | 1.5 | 2 |
|---|---|---|---|---|---|
| $y$ | 0 | 0.5268 | 1.1853 | 2.1401 | 3.63 |

**Example 3.** *Using finite difference method, solve* $y'' - 64y + 10 = 0$, $x \in (0, 1)$ *given* $y(0) = y(1) = 0$, *subdividing the interval into (i) 4 equal parts (ii) two equal parts.* **[Madras 1987]**

**Solution.** Since $n = 4$ and $nh = 1$, $h = 1/4$

Converting the differential equation into difference equation, we have,

$$\frac{y_{i+1} + y_{i-1} - 2y_i}{h^2} - 64y_i + 10 = 0$$

*i.e.,* $$y_{i+1} + y_{i-1} - (2 + 64h^2)y_i + 10h^2 = 0$$

Putting $h = 1/4$, this becomes,

$$y_{i+1} - 6y_i + y_{i-1} = \frac{-5}{8} \quad \text{... (1)}$$

where $i = 1, 2, 3, y(0) = y(1) = 0$

Hence using, $y_0 = 0$, $y_4 = 0$, we get

$$y_2 - 6y_1 = -5/8 \quad \text{... (2)}$$

$$y_3 - 6y_2 + y_1 = -5/8 \quad \text{... (3)}$$

$$-6y_3 + y_2 = -5/8 \quad \text{... (4)}$$

(2) – (4) gives,

$$6(y_3 - y_1) = 0$$

$$\therefore \quad y_1 = y_3$$

(3) becomes,

$$2y_3 - 6y_2 = -5/8$$

$$-6y_3 + y_2 = -5/8 \quad \text{... (5)}$$

Eliminating $y_3$, we have,

$$-17y_2 = -5/2$$

$$\therefore \quad y(0.5) = y_2 = 5/34 = 0.1471$$

Hence (2) reduces to

$$6y_1 = 5/34 + 5/8 = \frac{105}{36}$$

$$\therefore \quad y_3 = y_1 = \frac{35}{272} = 0.1287$$

Exact value of $y_2$ is 0.1505

When $n = 2$, $y_2$ is 0.1389.

**Example 4.** *Solve* $y'' - y = x$, $x \in (0, 1)$ *given* $y(0) = y(1) = 0$ *using finite differences dividing the interval into 4 equal parts.*

**Solution.** Since $nh = b - a = 1$, $h = 1/4$.

The nodal points are $x = 0, 1/4, 1/2, 3/4, 1$.

Converting the differential equations into difference equation, we get,

$$\frac{y_{i+1} + y_{i-1} - 2y_i}{h^2} - y_i = x_i$$

*i.e.,* $$y_{i+1}-(2+h^2)y_i+y_{i-1}=h^2x_i \text{ where } h=1/4$$

$\therefore$ $$16y_{i+1}-33y_i+16y_{i-1}=x_i \text{ where } i=1, 2, 3$$

Setting $i = 1, 2, 3$ and using $y_0 = y(0) = 0$, $y_4 = y(1) = 0$
We get,

$$16y_2-33y_1=1/4 \text{ since } x_1=1/4 \quad \text{... (1)}$$

$$16y_3-33y_2+16y_1=1/2 \text{ since } x_2=1/2 \quad \text{... (2)}$$

$$-33y_3+16y_2=3/4 \text{ since } x_3=3/4 \quad \text{... (3)}$$

(1) – (3) gives $$y_1-y_3=\frac{1}{66} \quad \text{... (4)}$$

Eliminating $y_2$ from (1) and (2), we get,

$$256y_3-833y_1=\frac{65}{4} \quad \text{... (5)}$$

Eliminating $y_3$ from (4) and (5) we get,

$$y_1=-0.03488$$

$\therefore$ $$y_3=\left(833y_1+\frac{65}{4}\right)/256$$

*i.e.,* $$y_3=-0.05002$$

$$y_2=\frac{33y_1+1/4}{16}=-0.05632$$

Tabulating, we have

| $x$ | 0 | 0.25 | 0.5 | 0.75 | 1 |
|---|---|---|---|---|---|
| $y$ | 0 | – 0.03488 | – 0.05632 | – 0.05002 | 0 |

**Note:** Exact solution of the differential equation is

$$y=\frac{\sinh x}{\sinh 1}-x$$

The exact values at the nodal points are

0, – 0.03505, –0.05659, – 0.05028, 0

and hence the errors are

0, 0.00017, 0.00027, 0.00026, 0

**Example 5.** *Solve* $y''-xy=0$ *given* $y(0) = -1$, $y(1) = 2$ *by finite difference method taking* $n = 2$

**Solution.** If $n = 2$, then $h = 1/2$ since range is (0, 1).
The nodal points are $x_0 = 0$, $x_1 = 0.5$, $x_2 = 1$
The differential equation reduces to,

$$\frac{y_{i+1}+y_{i-1}-2y_i}{h^2}-x_iy_i=0$$

*i.e.*, $y_{i+1}-(2+h^2x_i)y_i+y_{i-1}=0$

where $i = 1$, $h = 1/2$, $x_i = 0.5$, $y_0 = -1$, $y_2 = 2$

$$\therefore \quad y_2-\left(2+\frac{1}{8}\right)y_1+y_0=0$$

$$2-\frac{17}{8}y_1-1=0$$

$$\therefore \quad y_1=\frac{8}{17}=0.4706$$

Tabulating, we get,

| $x$ | 0 | 0.5 | 1 |
|---|---|---|---|
| $y$ | − 1 | 0.4706 | 2 |

## EXERCISES

***Using finite differences, solve the following equations :***

**1.** $y''-xy=0$ given $y(0) = -1$, $y(1) = 2$ where $h = 1/4$

**2.** $xy''+y=0$ given $y(1) = 1$, $y(2) = 2$, $h = 1/4$

**3.** $y''+xy'+y=2+3x^2$ given $y(0) = y(1) = 1$; $n = 4$

**4.** $\dfrac{d^2y}{dx^2}-y=0$, $x\in(0,\ 1)$ given $y(0) = 0$, $y(1) = 1$, $n = 2$

**5.** $\dfrac{d^2y}{dx^2}+y=0$, $x\in(0,\ 1)$ given $y(0) = 0$, $y(1) = 1$

**6.** $y''+2y'+y=0$, $x\in(0,1)$ given $y(0) = 0$, $y(1) = 1$

**7.** $y''+y'-2y=0$ given $y(0) = 2$, $y(1) = 2.85$

**8.** $y''-3y'+2y=0$ given $y(0) = 2$, $y(1) = 10.1$

**9.** $y''+6y'+9y=3$ given $y(0) = 4/3$, $y(1) = 0.38$

## ANSWERS

**2.** $y(1.25) = 1.3513$, $y(1.5) = 1.635$, $y(1.75) = 1.8505$

**3.** $y(0.25) = 0.062$, $y(0.5) = 0.25$, $y(0.75) = 0.562$

**4.** exact value $y(0.5) = 0.4434$

**5.** exact value $y=\dfrac{\sin x}{\sin 1}$

**6.** exact value $y(0.5) = 0.824$

**7.** exact value $y(0.5) = 2.0165$

**8.** exact value $y(.5) = 4.367$

**9.** exact value $y(0.5) = 0.55646$

# APPENDIX F

## CUBIC SPLINE INTERPOLATION

In the recent past, this topic finds important applications in the numerical solution of differential and integral equations. But, we will restrict our study to the derivation of an interpolatory *cubic spline* only.

We are given the $(n + 1)$ data points $(x_i, y_i)$ $i = 0, 1, 2, \ldots n$. Our aim is to find the value of $y$ corresponding to $x$ where $x_i < x < x_{i+1}$, $i = 0, 1, \ldots (n - 1)$, by using a smooth polynomial curve. We have already seen many methods. A recent one which is becoming important is the *Spline – fitting*. The name was derived from a draftman's device to draw a curve through these $(n + 1)$ points in such a way that not only the collocation polynomial but also its slope and the curvature as well are continuous functions.

We define a cubic spline, $S(x)$ as follows.

(*i*) $S(x)$ is a polynomial of degree one for $x < x_0$ and $x > x_n$

(*ii*) $S(x)$ is at most a cubic polynomial in each interval $(x_{i-1}, x_i)$, $i = 1, 2, \ldots n$

(*iii*) $S(x)$, $S'(x)$ and $S''(x)$ are continuous at each point $(x_i, y_i)$, $i = 0, 1, \ldots n$, and

(*iv*) $S(x_i) = y_i$, $i = 0, 1, 2, \ldots n$.

### Method 1

For convenience, we assume equal intervals, *i.e.*, $x_i - x_{i-1} = h$, $i = 1, 2, 3, \ldots n$. Since there are $n$ equal intervals, we have to find $n$ cubic polynomials totally. Hence, if the number of intervals is large, it is not easy to find all these polynomials – cubic splines.

Since $S(x)$ is a cubic polynomial, $S''(x)$ is linear in each interval. In the interval $(x_{i-1}, x_i)$,

Let us assume

$$S''(x) = \frac{1}{h}\left[(x_i - x)\, S''(x_{i-1}) + (x - x_{i-1})\, S''(x_i)\right] \quad \ldots (1)$$

You can easily check that this equation is valid when we put $x = x_{i-1}$ and $x = x_i$.

Integrating twice,

$$S(x) = \frac{1}{h}\left[\frac{(x_i - x)^3}{3!}S''(x_{i-1}) + \frac{(x - x_{i-1})^3}{3!}S''(x_i)\right] + a_i(x_i - x) + b_i(x - x_{i-1}) \quad \ldots (2)$$

where $a_i$, $b_i$ are constants to be found out by using the conditions,

$$S(x_i) = y_i \text{ (given)}, \; i = 0, 1, 2, \ldots n \quad \ldots (3)$$

Put $x = x_{i-1}$ in (2), we get

$$y_{i-1} = \frac{1}{h}\left[\frac{h^3}{3!}S''(x_{i-1})\right] + h\,a_i$$

$$\therefore \quad a_i = \frac{1}{h}\left[y_{i-1} - \frac{h^2}{3!}s''(x_{i-1})\right] \quad \ldots (4)$$

Put $x = x_i$ in (2); we get

$$b_i = \frac{1}{h}\left[y_i - \frac{h^2}{3!}S''(x_i)\right] \quad \ldots (5)$$

Hence the equation (2) reduces to

$$S(x) = \frac{1}{h}\left[\frac{(x_i - x)^3}{3!}S''(x_{i-1}) + \frac{(x - x_{i-1})^3}{3!}S''(x_i)\right]$$

$$+ \frac{1}{h}(x_i - x)\left[y_{i-1} - \frac{h^2}{3!}S''(x_{i-1})\right] + \frac{1}{h}(x - x_{i-1})\left[y_i - \frac{h^2}{3!}S''(x_i)\right]$$

Writing $S''(x_i) = M_i$, the above equation becomes,

$$S(x) = \frac{1}{6h}\left[(x_i - x)^3 M_{i-1} + (x - x_{i-1})^3 M_i\right]$$

$$+ \frac{1}{h}(x_i - x)\left[y_{i-1} - \frac{h^2}{6}M_{i-1}\right] + \frac{1}{h}(x - x_{i-1})\left[y_i - \frac{h^2}{6}M_i\right] \quad \ldots (6)$$

for $i = 1, 2, 3, \ldots n$

The quantities $M_i$ which are the spline second derivatives are not yet known. Now we will impose the continuity of $S'(x)$

From (6), $$S'(x) = \frac{1}{6h}\left[3(x_i - x)^2(-M_{i-1}) + 3(x - x_{i-1})^2 M_i\right]$$

$$+ \frac{1}{h}\left[-y_{i-1} + \frac{h^2}{6}M_{i-1}\right] + \frac{1}{h}\left[y_i - \frac{h^2}{6}M_i\right]$$

$$\therefore \quad S'(x_i-) = \frac{h}{3}M_i + \frac{h}{6}M_{i-1} + \frac{1}{h}(y_i - y_{i-1}) \quad \ldots (7)$$

Similarly, $S'(x_i+) = -\frac{h}{3}M_i - \frac{h}{6}M_{i+1} + \frac{1}{h}(y_{i+1} - y_i)$ ... (8)

Equating (7) and (8), we get

$$M_{i-1} + 4M_i + M_{i+1} = \frac{6}{h^2}[y_{i-1} - 2y_i + y_{i+1}] \quad \text{... (9)}$$

for $i = 1, 2, 3, \ldots (n-1)$

Further, in view of the first condition, that

$S(x)$ is linear for $x < x_0$ and $x > x_n$, we have $S''(x) = 0$ at $x = x_0$ and $x = x_n$.

Hence $\quad M_0 = 0, \ M_n = 0$ ... (10)

Equations (9) and (10) give $(n + 1)$ equations in $(n + 1)$ unknowns, $M_0, M_1, M_2, \cdots M_n$. Hence, we can solve for $M_0, M_1, M_2, \cdots M_n$.

Substituting in (6), we get the cubic spline in each interval.

**Note :** Some authors do not assume linearity of $S(x)$ for $x < x_0$ and $x > x_n$. In that case $M_0$, $M_n$ will not be zero.

**Method 2**

In $(x_{i-1}, x_i)$ let $S(x)$ be such that

$$S(x) = P_i(x) = a_i x^3 + b_i x^2 + c_i x + d_i, \ i = 1, 2, \ldots n \quad \text{... (11)}$$

Now, we have $4n$ unknowns, $a_i, b_i, c_i, d_i, i = 1, 2, \ldots n$.

Using continuity of $S(x)$, $S'(x)$ and $S''(x)$, we get

$$\left.\begin{aligned} P_i(x_i) &= y_i = a_i x_i^3 + b_i x_i^2 + c_i x_i + d_i \\ P_{i+1}(x_i) &= y_i = a_{i+1} x_i^3 + b_{i+1} x_i^2 + c_{i+1} x_i + d_{i+1} \end{aligned}\right\} \quad \text{... (12)}$$

for $i = 1, 2, \ldots (n-1)$

Equations (12) give $2(n - 1)$ conditions.

$$\left.\begin{aligned} 3a_i x_i^2 + 2b_i x_i + c_i &= 3a_{i+1} x_i^2 + 2b_{i+1} x_i + c_{i+1} \\ 6a_i x_i + 2b_i &= 6a_{i+1} x_i + 2b_{i+1} \end{aligned}\right\} \quad \text{...(13)}$$

for $i = 1, 2, 3, \ldots (n-1)$

Equations (13) give $2(n - 1)$ conditions

Further $\quad y_0 = a_1 x_0^3 + b_1 x_0^2 + c_1 x_0 + d_1$

and $\quad y_n = a_n x_n^3 + b_n x_n^2 + c_n x_n + d_n$

Hence, totally we have $4n - 2$ conditions.

Further, $S''(x_0) = M_0, \ S''(x_n) = M_n$

Now, we have $4n$ conditions to solve for the $4n$ unknowns. This will give the cubic spline in each subinterval.

If $M_0 = 0$ and $M_n = 0$, we call this cubic spline as *natural spline*.

**Example 1.** *From the following table*

| $x$ | 1 | 2 | 3 |
|---|---|---|---|
| $y$ | –8 | –1 | 18 |

*Compute y (1.5) = and y′(1), using cubic spline.*

**Solution.** Here $h = 1$, and $n = 2$. Also assume $M_0 = 0$ and $M_2 = 0$

We have

$$M_{i-1} + 4M_i + M_{i+1} = \frac{6}{h^2}\left[y_{i-1} - 2y_i + y_{i+1}\right]$$

for $i = 1, 2, \ldots (n-1)$

From this,

$$M_0 + 4M_1 + M_2 = 6\left[y_0 - 2y_1 + y_2\right]$$

$$\therefore \quad 4M_1 = 6\left[-8 - 2(-1) + 18\right] = 72$$

$$\therefore \quad M_1 = 18$$

From equation (6), for $1 \le x \le 2$, putting $i = 1$, we get

$$S(x) = \frac{1}{6}\left[18(x-1)^3\right] + (2-x)(-8) - 4(x-1)$$

$$= 3(x-1)^3 + 4x - 12 = 3x^3 - 9x^2 + 13x - 15$$

$$y(1.5) \approx S(1.5) = 3(0.5)^3 + 4(1.5) - 12 = -\frac{45}{8}$$

$$y' \approx S'(x) = 9(x-1)^2 + 4$$

$$\therefore \quad y'(1) = 4$$

**Note 1.** We can also find $S(x)$ in the interval (2, 3) using the equation (6) for $i = 2$.

**Note 2.** Since $y(1.5)$ is required, we have not cared to find $S(x)$ in (2, 3)

**Note 3.** Please note that $y = x^3 - 9$ also gives the above table values in the range (1, 3).

**Method 2 :** We will use the second method and work out the above problem.

Let the cubic splines be

$$P_1(x) = a_1x^3 + b_1x^2 + c_1x + d_1 \text{ in } [1, 2]$$

$$P_2(x) = a_2x^3 + b_2x^2 + c_2x + d_2 \text{ in } [2, 3]$$

$$P_1(1) = a_1 + b_1 + c_1 + d_1 = -8 \qquad \ldots (1)$$

$$P_1(2) = 8a_1 + 4b_1 + 2c_1 + d_1 = -1 \qquad \ldots (2)$$

$$P_2(2) = 8a_2 + 4b_2 + 2c_2 + d_2 = -1 \quad \text{... (3)}$$

$$P_2(3) = 27a_2 + 9b_2 + 3c_2 + d_2 = 18 \quad \text{... (4)}$$

$$P_1'(x_1) = P_2'(x_1) \text{ gives}$$

$$3a_1(4) + 2b_1(2) + c_1 = 3a_2(4) + 2b_2(2) + c_2 \quad \text{... (5)}$$

$$P_1''(x_1) = P_2''(x_1) \text{ gives}$$

$$6a_1(2) + 2b_1 = 6a_2(2) + 2b_2 \quad \text{... (6)}$$

$$P_1''(x_0) = S''(x_0) = 0 \text{ gives}$$

$$6a_1(1) + 2b_1 = 0 \quad \text{... (7)}$$

$$P_2''(x_2) = S''(x_2) = 0 \text{ gives}$$

$$6a_2(3) + 2b_2 = 0 \quad \text{... (8)}$$

Solving equations (1) to (8), we get

$$a_1 = 3, \quad b_1 = -9, \quad c_1 = 13, \quad d_1 = -15$$
$$a_2 = -3, \quad b_2 = 27, \quad c_2 = -59 \quad \text{and} \quad d_2 = 33$$

Hence $P_1(x) = 3x^3 - 9x^2 + 13x - 15$ in [1, 2]

$$P_2(x) = -3x^3 + 27x^2 - 59x + 33 \text{ in } [2, 3]$$

$$\therefore \quad P_1(1.5) = 3\left(\frac{3}{2}\right)^3 - 9\left(\frac{3}{2}\right)^2 + 13\left(\frac{3}{2}\right) - 15$$

$$= \frac{81}{8} - \frac{81}{4} + \frac{39}{2} - 15 = -\frac{45}{8}$$

$$P_1'(x) = 9x^2 - 18x + 13$$

$$\therefore \quad P_1'(1) = 9 - 18 + 13 = 4$$

**Note 4.** The above 8 equations can be solved by matrix inversion method, if we use the computer. Otherwise by elimination method, they can be solved slowly.

**Note 5.** Even with 3 paired data, solving 8 equations becomes tedious.

**Note 6.** The cubic spline in both methods in (1, 2) is the same function

$$3^{x^2} - 9x^2 + 13x - 15$$

**Note 7.** If we require $S(1.5)$ only, it is not necessary to find the cubic spline in the other interval (2, 3)

**Note 8.** Using $P_1(x)$,

$$P_1(1) = 3 - 9 + 13 - 15 = -8$$

$$P_1(2) = 24 - 36 + 26 - 15 = -1$$

Using $P_2(x)$,

$$P_2(2) = -3(8) + 27(4) - 59(2) + 33 = -1$$
$$= P_1(2)$$
$$P_2(3) = -3(27) + 27(9) - 59(3) + 33$$
$$= 276 - 258 = 18$$

All these values tally with tabular values as $x = 1, 2, 3$.

**Example 2.** *Using cubic spline, find y(0.5) and* $y'(1)$ *given* $M_0 = M_2 = 0$ *and the table*

| $x$ | 0 | 1 | 2 |
|---|---|---|---|
| $y$ | –5 | – 4 | 3 |

**Solution.** Here also, $h = 1$, and $n = 2$

We have

$$M_{i-1} + 4M_i + M_{i+1} = \frac{6}{h^2}[y_{i-1} - 2y_i + y_{i+1}]$$
$$\text{for} \quad i = 1, \quad 2, \ldots (n-1)$$

Putting $i = 1$,

$$M_0 + 4M_1 + M_2 = 6[-5 - 2(-4) + 3] = 36$$
$$\therefore \quad 4M_1 = 36; \quad M_1 = 9$$

We will derive the cubic spline in [0, 1] using (6).

Put $i = 1$ in (6)

$$S(x) = \frac{1}{6}\left[(1-x)^3(0) + (x-0)^3(9)\right]$$
$$+ (1-x)\left[-5 - \frac{1}{6}(0)\right] + (x-0)\left[-4 - \frac{9}{6}\right]$$
$$= \frac{3}{2}x^3 - 5(1-x) - \frac{33}{6}(x)$$
$$= \frac{3}{2}x^3 - \frac{x}{2} - 5, \text{ where } 0 \le x \le 1$$
$$S(0.5) = \frac{3}{2}\left(\frac{1}{8}\right) - \frac{1}{4} - 5 = -\frac{81}{16}$$
$$S'(x) = \frac{9}{2}x^2 - \frac{1}{2}$$
$$\therefore \quad S'(1) \approx y'(1) = \frac{9}{2} - \frac{1}{2} = 4$$

**Note 1.** In the question, the cubic spline is not asked. But only $S(0.5)$ is required. Hence, $S(x)$ in the interval [1, 2] is not found out.

**Note 2.** The function $y = x^3 - 5$ gives the tabular values in the entire range [0, 2]. $y$ (0.5) from this curve is $-\frac{39}{8}$

**Example 3.** *Find the cubic spline approximaton for the function given below.*

| $x$ | 0 | 1 | 2 | 3 |
|---|---|---|---|---|
| $y = f(x)$ | ! | 2 | 33 | 244 |

Assume $M(0) = M(3) = 0$. Also find $y(2.5)$.

**Solution.** Here also $h = 1$, and $n = 3$

We have $$M_{i-1} + 4M_i + M_{i+1} = \frac{6}{h^2}\left[y_{i-1} - 2y_i + y_{i+1}\right] \text{ for } i = 1, 2$$

$$\therefore \quad M_0 + 4M_1 + M_2 = 6\left[y_0 - 2y_1 + y_2\right]$$

and $$M_1 + 4M_2 + M_3 = 6\left[y_1 - 2y_2 + y_3\right]$$

These reduces to, (taking $M_0 = 0, \ M_3 = 0$)

$$4M_1 + M_2 = 6\,(1 - 4 + 33) = 180$$

$$M_1 + 4M_2 = 6(2 - 66 + 244) = 1080$$

Solving $$M_1 = -24, M_2 = 276$$

Now we use equation (6) for every subinterval.

In [0, 1], (Put $i = 1$ in (6))

$$S(x) = \frac{1}{6}\left[(1-x)^3(0) + (x-0)^3(-24)\right] + (1-x)\left[1 - \frac{1}{6}(0)\right] + (x-0)\left[2 - \frac{(-24)}{6}\right]$$

$$= -4x^3 + (1-x) + 6x$$

$$= -4x^3 + 5x + 1 \qquad \text{... (1)}$$

In [1, 2], [Put $i = 2$ in (6)],

$$S(x) = \frac{1}{6}\left[(2-x)^3(-24) + (x-1)^3(276)\right] + (2-x)\left[2 - \frac{(-24)}{6}\right] + (x-1)\left[33 - \frac{276}{6}\right]$$

$$= 50x^3 - 162x^2 + 167x - 53 \qquad \text{... (2)}$$

In [2, 3], [Put $i = 3$ in (6)],

$$S(x) = \frac{1}{6}\left[(3-x)^3 M_2\right] + (3-x)\left[33 - \frac{M_2}{6}\right] + (x-2)\,(244-0)$$

$$= \frac{1}{6}\left[(3-x)^3 (276)\right] + (3-x)\,(33-46) + (x-2)\,(244)$$

$$= 46(3-x)^3 - 13(3-x) + 244\,(x-2)$$

$$= 46\left[27 - 27x + 9x^2 - x^3\right] - 39 + 13x + 244x - 488$$

$$= -46x^3 + 414x^2 - 985x + 715 \qquad \ldots (3)$$

Equations (1), (2), (3) give the cubic spline in each sub-interval.

$$y(2.5) = -46(2.5)^3 + 414(2.5)^2 - 985(2.5) + 715$$
$$= 121.25$$

**Note :** Since $x = 2.5$ lies in the range [2, 3], we substitute $x$ in the cubic spline given by equation (3).

**Example 4.** *Test whether the following functions are cubic splines or not.*

(1) $P_1(x) = x^2 - x + 1, \qquad 1 \le x \le 2$

$P_2(x) = 3x - 3, \qquad 2 \le x \le 3$

(2) $P_1(x) = -2x^2 + x^3 \qquad -1 \le x \le 0$

$P_2(x) = x^2 - 2x^3 \qquad 0 \le x \le 1$

**Solution.** Each polynomial is at most of degree three in each sub-interval.

(*i*) $P_1(2) = 3 = P_2(2)$

$P_1'(2) = 3 = P_2'(2)$

$P_1''(2) = 2; \; P_2''(2) = 0$

$\therefore$ Not a cubic spline since $S''(x)$ is not continuous as $x = 2$

(*ii*) $P_1(0) = 0 = P_2(0)$

$P_1'(0) = 0 = P_2'(0)$

$P_1''(0) = -4; \; P_2'' = 2$

$\therefore$ Not a cubic spline since $S''(x)$ is not continuous at $x = 0$.

**Example 5.** *Find the cubic spline given the table*

| $x$ | 0 | 2 | 4 | 6 |
|---|---|---|---|---|
| $y$ | 1 | 9 | 41 | 41 |

and $M_0 = 0, M_3 = -12$

**Solution.** Here $h = 2$

$$\therefore \quad M_0 + 4M_1 + M_2 = \frac{6}{4}(y_0 - 2y_1 + y_2)$$

$$= \frac{3}{2}(1 - 18 + 41) = 36$$

$$M_1 + 4M_2 + M_3 = \frac{6}{4}(y_1 - 2y_2 + y_3)$$

$$= \frac{3}{2}(9 - 82 + 41) = -48$$

Using $M_0 = 0$, $M_3 = -12$, we get,

$$4M_1 + M_2 = 36, \text{ and } M_1 + 4M_2 = -36$$

Solving $M_1 = 12, \quad M_2 = -12$

$$\therefore \quad S(x) = \frac{1}{12}\left[(2-x)^3(0) + (x-0)^3(12)\right]$$

$$S(x) = \frac{1}{12}\left[(2-x)^3(0) + (x-0)^3(12)\right]$$

$$+ \frac{1}{2}(2-x)\left[1 - \frac{2}{3}(0)\right] + \frac{1}{2}(x-0)\left[9 - \frac{2}{3}(12)\right]$$

$$= \frac{1}{12}(12x^3) + 1 - \frac{x}{2} + \frac{x}{2} = 1 + x^3$$

$$\therefore \quad S(x) = 1 + x^3, \qquad 0 \le x \le 2$$

Similarly, $S(x) = 25 - 36x + 18x^2 - 2x^3, \qquad 2 \le x \le 4$

and $S(x) = -103 + 60x - 6x^2, \qquad 4 \le x \le 6$

### Clamped Conditions

The natural or free conditions $S''(x_0) = M_0 = 0$ and $S''(x_n) = M_n = 0$ give the natural cubic spline.

Suppose the clamped conditions $S'(x_0) = f'(x_0) = k_0$ and $S'(x_n) = f'(x_n) = k_n$ are given. That is the tangent directions $f'(x_0) = k_0$ and $f'(x_n) = k_n$ are given at the ends.

We have to find the cubic spline under these conditions.

For equidistant intervals, $x_{i+1} - x_i = h$

We have the relation

$$K_{j-1} + 4K_j + K_{j+1} = \frac{3}{h}(f_{j+1} - f_{j-1})$$

*i.e.* $$K_{j-1} + 4K_j + K_{j+1} = \frac{3}{h}(y_{j+1} - y_{j-1}) \quad \text{... (1)}$$

for $j = 1, 2, \ldots (n-1)$

If in the interval $x_j < x < x_{j+1}$,

$P_j(x)$ is the cubic spline then

$$P_j(x) = a_{j0} + a_{j1}(x - x_j) + a_{j2}(x - x_j)^2 + a_{j3}(x - x_j)^3 \quad \text{... (2)}$$

for $j = 0, 1, 2, \ldots (n-1)$

where $$a_{j0} = P_j(x_j) = f_j = y_j \quad \text{... (3)}$$

$$a_{j1} = P_j'(x_j) = K_j \quad \text{... (4)}$$

$$a_{j2} = \frac{1}{2}P_j''(x_j) = \frac{3}{h^2}(y_{j+1} - y_j) - \frac{1}{h}\left(k_{j+1} + 2k_j\right) \quad \text{... (5)}$$

$$a_{j3} = \frac{1}{6}p_j'''(x_j) = \frac{2}{h^3}(y_j - y_{j+1}) + \frac{1}{h^2}(k_{j+1} + k_j) \quad \text{... (6)}$$

**Note :** For proofs of derivation of equations (1) to (6), the reader can refer to treatise on the subject.

**Example 6.** *Obtain the cubic spline given the following data*

| $x$ | $-1$ | $0$ | $1$ |
|---|---|---|---|
| $y$ | $1$ | $0$ | $1$ |

$$S'(-1) = k_0 = -4$$

and $S'(1) = k_2 = 4$. Also find $y(0.5)$, $y(-0.5)$

**Solution.** Here $n = 2$ and $h = 1$

We have $k_{j-1} + 4k_j + k_{j+1} = \frac{3}{h}(y_{j+1} - y_{j-1})$ for $j = 1, 2$

$$\therefore \quad k_0 + 4k_1 + k_2 = 3(1-1) = 0$$

$$\therefore \quad -4 + 4k_1 + 4 = 0$$

$$\therefore \quad k_1 = 0$$

$$a_{j0} = y_j \qquad \therefore\ a_{00} = 1 \quad \text{and} \quad a_{10} = y_1 = 0$$

$$a_{j1} = k_j \qquad \therefore\ a_{01} = k_0 = -4; \quad a_{11} = k_1 = 0$$

$$a_{j2} = \frac{3}{h^2}(y_{j+1} - y_j) - \frac{1}{h}(k_{j+1} + 2k_j)$$

$$\therefore \quad a_{02} = 3(0-1) - 1(0 + 2(-4)) = 5$$

$$a_{12} = 3(1-0) - (4 + 2(0)) = -1$$

$$a_{j3} = \frac{2}{h^3}(y_i - y_{i+1}) + \frac{1}{h^2}(k_{j+1} + k_j)$$

$$a_{03} = 2(1-0) + 1[0 + (-4)] = -2$$

$$a_{13} = 2(0-1) + (4+0) = 2$$

$$P_j(x) = a_{j0} + a_{j1}(x - x_j) + a_{j2}(x - x_j)^2 + a_{j3}(x - x_j)^3$$

$j = 0, 1$

$$\therefore P_0(x) = a_{00} + a_{01}(x - x_0) + a_{02}(x - x_0)^2 + a_{03}(x - x_0)^3$$

$$= 1 - 4(x+1) + 5(x+1)^2 - 2(x+1)^3$$

$$= -2x^3 - x^2$$

$$P_1(x) = a_{10} + a_{11}(x - x_1) + a_{12}(x - x_1)^2 + a_{13}(x - x_1)^3$$

$$= 0 + 0(x-0) + (-1)(x)^2 + 2(x)^3$$

$$= 2x^3 - x^2$$

$$\therefore P_0(x) = -2x^3 - x^2 \quad \text{in} \quad -1 \le x \le 0$$

$$P_1(x) = 2x^3 - x^2 \quad \text{in} \quad 0 \le x \le 1$$

$x = 0.5$ lies in $(0, 1)$

$$\therefore y(0.5) = P_1(0.5) = 2(0.5)^3 - (0.5)^2 = \frac{2}{8} - \frac{1}{4} = 0$$

$$y(-0.5) = -2(-0.5)^3 - (-0.5)^2 = \frac{2}{8} - \frac{1}{4} = 0$$

**Example 7.** *Find the cubic spline in [0, 2] given* $S'(0) = k_0 = 0$, $S'(6) = k_3 = -12$ *for the following data.*

| $x$ | 0 | 2 | 4 | 6 |
|---|---|---|---|---|
| $y$ | 1 | 9 | 41 | 41 |

*Also find y(1) and* $y'(1)$.

**Solution.** This problem is same as example 5. But, here the end conditions are given in terms of first derivatives whereas in example 5, the end conditions are given in terms of second derivatives.

Here $h = 2, n = 3.$

$$k_0 + 4k_1 + k_2 = \frac{3}{2}(y_2 - y_0) = \frac{3}{2}(41-1) = 60$$

Since, $k_0 = 0,$

$$4k_1 + k_2 = 60 \qquad \text{... (1)}$$

$$k_1 + 4k_2 + k_3 = \frac{3}{2}(y_3 - y_1) = \frac{3}{2}(41-9) = 48$$

$$\therefore \quad k_1 + 4k_2 - 12 = 48$$

$$k_1 + 4k_2 = 60 \qquad \text{... (2)}$$

From (1) and (2), $k_1 = k_2 = 12$

$$a_{j0} = y_j \qquad \therefore \quad a_{00} = 1$$

$$a_{j1} = k_j \qquad \therefore \quad a_{01} = k_0 = 0$$

$$a_{j2} = \frac{3}{h^2}(y_{j+1} - y_j) - \frac{1}{h}(k_{j+1} + 2k_j)$$

$$a_{02} = \frac{3}{4}(9-1) - \frac{1}{2}(12+0) = 0$$

$$a_{j3} = \frac{2}{h^3}(y_j - y_{j+1}) + \frac{1}{h^2}(k_{j+1} + k_j)$$

$$a_{03} = \frac{2}{8}(1-9) + \frac{1}{4}(12+0) = 1$$

$$\therefore \quad P_j(x) = a_{j0} + a_{j1}(x-x_j) + a_{j2}(x-x_j)^2 + a_{j3}(x-x_j)^3$$

$$\therefore \quad P_0(x) = 1 + 0(x-0) + 0(x-0)^2 + 1(x-0)^3$$

$$P_0(x) = 1 + x^3 \quad \text{in } [0, 2]$$

Similarly, we can find

$$P_1(x) = 25 - 36x + 18x^2 - 2x^3 \quad \text{in } [2, 4]$$

and

$$P_2(x) = -103 + 60x - 6x^2 \quad \text{in } [4, 6]$$

$$y(1) = P_0(1) = 1 + 1 = 2$$

$$y'(x) = P_0'(x) = 3x^2$$

$$y'(1) = P_0'(1) = 3$$

## EXERCISES 1

**1.** Find the cubic spline valid in the interval [3, 4] for the function given by the following table under the conditions $M(1) = 0$, $M(4) = 0$

| $x$ | 1 | 2 | 3 | 4 |
|---|---|---|---|---|
| $y$ | 3 | 10 | 29 | 65 |

**2.** Find the cubic spline for the data given below under the conditions $M(0) = 0 = M(3)$ and valid in the sub-interval [1, 2]. Hence find $f(1.5)$

| $x$ | 0 | 1 | 2 | 3 |
|---|---|---|---|---|
| $y$ | 1 | 4 | 10 | 8 |

**3.** For the following data, get the cubic spline in the range [2, 3] and also get $y(2.5)$ and $y'(2)$.

| $x$ | 2 | 3 | 4 |
|---|---|---|---|
| $y$ | 11 | 49 | 123 |

**4.** Obtain the natural cubic spline curve for the points (1, 1), (2, 5) and (3, 11).

**5.** Find the natural cubic spline for the data

| $x$ | 0 | 1 | 2 |
|---|---|---|---|
| $y$ | 0 | 1 | 0 |

Also find $y(0.5)$, $y'(1)$.

**6.** Find the natural cubic spline to fit the data

| $x$ | 1 | 2 | 3 | 4 |
|---|---|---|---|---|
| $y$ | 0 | 1 | 0 | 0 |

**7.** Find the natural cubic spline for the data in [1, 2]

| $x$ | 1 | 2 | 3 | 4 |
|---|---|---|---|---|
| $y$ | 1 | 5 | 11 | 8 |

Hence obtain $y(1.5)$.

**8.** Find the natural cubic spline in [0, 1] for the following data.

| $x$ | 0 | 1 | 2 |
|---|---|---|---|
| $y$ | 0 | 2 | 6 |

Also find $y(0.5)$ and $y'(1)$.

**9.** Find the natural cubic spline in the range [0, 6] for the following data.

| $x$ | 0 | 6 | 12 |
|---|---|---|---|
| $y$ | 1 | 3 | 11 |

Also find $y(3)$ and $y'(3)$.

**10.** Test whether the following functions are cubic splines or not.

$$P_1(x) = -x^2 + 20x^3, \qquad -1 \le x \le 0$$

$$P_2(x) = -x^2 + 6x^3 \qquad 0 \le x \le 1$$

**11.** Find the cubic spline for the following data with $M_0 = 10$, $M_2 = 10$.

| $x$ | $-1$ | 0 | 1 |
|---|---|---|---|
| $y$ | 1 | 0 | 1 |

**12.** Obtain the cubic spline given $f(-1) = 0, f(0) = 4, f(1) = 0$ and $M_0 = 24$, $M_2 = 24$

**13.** Find the cubic spline $S(x)$ given $f(0) = 3, f(2) = 5, f(4) = 31$, $k_0 = 1$ and $k_2 = 21$. Also find $f(1)$ and $f(3)$.

**14.** Find the cubic spline for the following data

| $x$ | 0 | 1 | 2 | 3 |
|---|---|---|---|---|
| $y$ | 1 | 0 | $-1$ | 0 |

given $S'(0) = k_0 = 0$, $S'(3) = k_3 = -6$.
Also find $y(0.5)$.

**15.** If $f(-1) = 0$, $f(0) = 4$, $f(1) = 0$ find the cubic spline assuming $S'(-1) = k_0 = 0$, $S'(1) = k_2 = 0$.
Also obtain $y(0.5)$.

## Answers (Cubic Spline)

**1.** $M_1 = 62/5$, $M_2 = 112/5$.

In [3, 4], $P_3(x) = \dfrac{1}{15}(-56x^3 + 672x^2 - 2092x + 2175)$

**2.** $M_1 = 8$, $M_2 = -14$; In [1, 2],

$$P_2(x) = \frac{1}{3}(-11x^3 + 45x^2 - 40x + 18)$$

**3.** In [2, 3], $P_1(x) = 9(x-2)^3 + 29x - 47$; $M_1 = 54$

$y(2.5) \approx 26.625$; $y'(2) = 29$

**4.** In [1, 2], $P_1(x) = \dfrac{1}{2}\left[(x-1)^3 + 7x - 5\right]$; $M_1 = 3$

In [2, 3], $P_2(x) = \dfrac{1}{2}\left[(3-x)^3 + 13x - 17\right]$

**5.** In [0, 1], $M_1 = -3$; $P_1(x) = \frac{1}{2}\left[3x - x^3\right]$

$y(0.5) = 11/6$; $y'(1) = 0$

In [1, 2], $P_2(x) = \frac{1}{2}\left[3(2-x)-(2-x)^3\right]$

**6.** $M_1 = -18/5$, $M_2 = 12/5$.

$P_1(x) = \frac{1}{5}(-3x^3 + 9x^2 - x - 5)$ in [1, 2]

$P_2 x = \frac{1}{5}\left[5x^3 - 39x^2 + 95x - 69\right]$ in [2, 3]

$P_3(x) = \frac{1}{5}\left[-2x^3 + 24x^2 - 94x + 120\right]$ in [3, 4]

**7.** $M_1 = 34/5$, $M_2 = -76/5$

$P_1(x) = \frac{1}{15}(17x^3 - 51x^2 + 94x - 45)$ in [1, 2]

$y(1.5) = 2.575$

**8.** $M_1 = 3$; In [0, 1], $P_1(x) = \frac{1}{2}(3x + x^3)$

$y'(1) = 3$, $y(0.5) = 13/16$

**9.** $M_1 = \frac{1}{4}$. In [0, 6], $P_1(x) = \frac{1}{144}\left[x^3 + 12x + 144\right]$

$y(3) = \frac{207}{144}$; $y'(3) = \frac{39}{144}$.

**10.** Yes; it is a cubic spline.

**11.** $P_1(x) = -x^2 - 2x^3$, $\quad -1 \le x \le 0$

$P_2(x) = -x^2 + 2x^3$ $\quad 0 \le x \le 1$

**12.** $P_1(x) = 4 - 12x^2 - 8x^3$, $\quad -1 \le x \le 0$

$P_2(x) = 4 - 12x^2 + 8x^3$, $\quad 0 \le x \le 1$

**13.** $P_0(x) = 3 + x - 2x^2 + x^3$, in $0 \le x \le 2$

$P_1(x) = 5 + 5(x-2) + 4(x-2)^2$ in $2 \le x \le 4$

$y(1) = f(1) = 3$, $y(3) = 14$.

**14.** $P_0(x) = 1 - x^2$ in $0 \le x \le 1$

$P_1(x) = -2(x-1) - (x-1)^2 + 2(x-1)^3$, $\quad 1 \le x \le 2$

$P_2(x) = -1 + 2(x-2) + 5(x-2)^2 - 6(x-2)^3$ in $2 \le x \le 3$

$y(0.5) = 1 - \frac{1}{4} = \frac{3}{4}$

**15.** Same as question 12; $y(0.5) = 2$.

# MODEL QUESTION PAPER I

## NUMERICAL METHODS

*Max : 100 marks* *Time : 3 Hrs.*

*Answer all Questions*

**PART A** — (*20 × 2 = 40 marks*)

State true or false.

**1.** By the method of least square, a curve of the form $y = ax^2 + bx + c$ is fitted to the data $(x_i, y_i)$, $i = 1, 2, \dots n$. This curve will pass through all the points.

**2.** Iteration method is a self-correcting method.

**3.** The $n$th differences of a polynomial of degree $n$ are zeros.

**4.** Liebmann's iteration process is used to solve one directional heat equation.

**5.** If $\alpha, \beta, \gamma$ are the roots of $x^3 - x + 1 = 0$ then $\Sigma\,\alpha^3$ is_______.

**6.** The order of convergence of Newton-Raphson method is_______.

**7.** "Whenever Trapezoidal rule is applicable, Simpson's rule can be applied." This is_______.

**8.** The particular integral of $u_{x+2} + 2u_{x+1} + u_x = 2^x$ is_______.

**9.** Write down the normal equations in the case of fitting a parabola $y = ax^2 + bx + c$.

**10.** Find the values of $\Sigma\,\alpha^3$ and $\Sigma\,\alpha^6$ if $\alpha, \beta, \gamma$ are the roots of $x^3 - 4 = 0$.

**11.** If $\Delta f(x) = x^3 + 2x^2 + x - 1$, find $f(x)$.

**12.** Define $\Delta, \nabla, \delta, \mu$.

**13.** State Simpson's 1/3 rule and $\frac{3}{8}$ rule.

**14.** Solve $y_{x+2} + y_{x+1} - 2\,y_x = 2^x + 7$

**15.** What are the methods you use to solve one dimensional wave equation?

**16.** Write down the algorithm of Runge-Kutta method of fourth order.

**17.** In solving $u_t = \alpha^2 u_{xx}$ by Crank-Nicholson method, to simplify the equation we take $\frac{(\Delta x)^2}{\alpha^2 k}$ as

(*i*) 1/2 (*ii*) 2 (*iii*) 1 (*iv*) –1.

**18.** Express $a^2 u_{xx} = u_{tt}$ in terms of difference quotients.

**19.** Using Euler's method find $y(0{\cdot}1)$ given $y' = -y,\ y(0) = 1$.

**20.** State Bessel's and Everett's formulae.

**PART B — (*5 × 12 = 60 marks*)**

**21.** (*a*) Fit a straight to the data by the method of least squares.

| $x$ : | 0 | 5 | 10 | 15 | 20 |
|---|---|---|---|---|---|
| $y$ : | 7 | 10 | 15 | 21 | 25 |

(*b*) Solve $6x^5 + x^4 - 43x^3 - 43x^2 + x + 6 = 0$

**OR**

(*c*) Fit a straight line to the data by the method of moments.

| $x$ : | 1 | 2 | 3 | 4 |
|---|---|---|---|---|
| $y$ : | 16 | 19 | 23 | 26 |

(*d*) If $\alpha, \beta, \gamma$ are the roots of $x^3 + 2x^2 + x - 1 = 0$, form the equation whose roots are $\alpha + \beta - \gamma,\ \beta + \gamma - \alpha,\ \gamma + \alpha - \beta$.

**22.** (*a*) Find the positive root of $x^3 + x - 1 = 0$ correct to 2 decimals by Horner's method.

(*b*) Using Gauss-Seidel method, solve:

$$28x + 4y - z = 32$$
$$x + 3y + 10z = 24$$
$$2x + 17y + 4z = 35$$

**OR**

(*c*) Solve by Crout's method

$2x - 6y + 8z = 24,\ 3x + y + 2z = 6,\ 5x + 4y - 3z = 2$

(*d*) Find the inverse of $\begin{bmatrix} 2 & 1 & -1 \\ 0 & 2 & 1 \\ 5 & 2 & -3 \end{bmatrix}$ by Gauss method.

**23.** (*a*) Sum the series $1{\cdot}2{\cdot}3 + 2{\cdot}3{\cdot}4 + 3{\cdot}4{\cdot}5 + \cdots$ to $n$ terms by finite integration.

(*b*) Find the missing value from the table

| $x$ : | 2 | 4 | 6 | 8 | 10 |
|---|---|---|---|---|---|
| $y$ : | 5·6 | 8·6 | 13·9 | – | 35·6 |

**OR**

(*c*) If $u_x = x^3 + 3x^2 - 5x + 1$, find $\Delta u_x, \Delta^2 u_x, \Delta^3 u_x$ and $\Delta^{-1} u_x$.

(*d*) Apply Gauss's forward formula to find $y\,(3{\cdot}75)$ from the table

| $x$ : | 2·5 | 3·0 | 3·5 | 4·0 | 4·5 | 5·0 |
|---|---|---|---|---|---|---|
| $y$ : | 24·14 | 22·04 | 20·22 | 18·64 | 17·26 | 16·04 |

**24.** (*a*) Given the table

| $x$ : | 14 | 17 | 31 | 35 |
|---|---|---|---|---|
| $f(x)$ : | 68·7 | 64·1 | 44·2 | 39·6 |

find $f(27)$.

(*b*) Using the table below, find $f'(0)$ and $\int_0^9 f(x)\,dx$.

| $x$ : | 0 | 2 | 3 | 4 | 7 | 9 |
|---|---|---|---|---|---|---|
| $f(x)$ : | 4 | 26 | 58 | 110 | 460 | 920 |

**OR**

(*c*) Solve $u_{x+2} + 6u_{x+1} + 9u_x = 3^x + x.2^x + 7$.

(*d*) By means of Newton's divided difference formula, find $f(8)$.

| $x$ : | 4 | 5 | 7 | 10 | 11 | 13 |
|---|---|---|---|---|---|---|
| $f(x)$ : | 46 | 100 | 290 | 900 | 1200 | 2020 |

**25.** (*a*) If $y' = \dfrac{y-x}{y+x}$, $y(0) = 1$, find $y(0{\cdot}1)$ by Picard's method.

(*b*) Solve the elliptic equation $u_{xx} + u_{yy} = 0$ for the following square mesh.

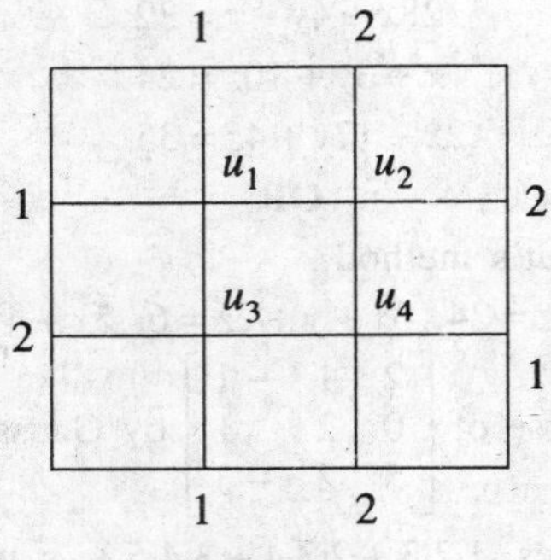


**OR**

(*c*) Apply Runge-Kutta method of fourth order to calculate $y(0{\cdot}2)$ given $y' = x + y$, $y(0) = 1$ taking $h = 0{\cdot}1$.

(*d*) Evaluate the pivotal values of the equation $25\,u_{xx} = u_{tt}$ for one-half period of oscillation given

$$u(0, t) = u(5, t) = 0$$

$$u(x, 0) = 2x \text{ for } 0 \le x \le 2{\cdot}5$$

$$= 10 - 2x \text{ for } 2{\cdot}5 \le x \le 5$$

and $$\frac{\partial u}{\partial t}(x, 0) = 0.$$

# MODEL PAPER II

*Answer all Questions*

*Max : 100 marks* *Time : 3 Hrs.*

**1.** What is the principle of least squares'?

**2.** If $1+i$ and $2+\sqrt{3}$ are two roots of a biquadratic equation, find the equation.

**3.** If $x^4+ax^3+bx^2-x-1=0$ is a reciprocal equation, then values of $a$ and $b$ are________and________.

**4.** If $\alpha, \beta, \gamma$ are the roots $x^3+x^2-2x+1=0$ find the value of $\frac{1}{\alpha}+\frac{1}{\beta}+\frac{1}{\gamma}$.

**5.** State Simpson's $\frac{1}{3}$ and $\frac{3}{8}$ rule.

**6.** State Newton-Raphson iteration formula.

**7.** The order of convergence of Newton-Raphson methods is ________.

**8.** Write down the values of $\Delta, \nabla, \delta, \mu$ in terms of $E$.

**9.** Find the sum to $n$ terms of $= 1\cdot 2+2\cdot 3+3\cdot 4+\cdots$

**10.** Find $y'(x=1)$ given

| $x$ : | 1 | 2 | 3 | 4 | 5 |
|---|---|---|---|---|---|
| $y$ : | 1 | $-1$ | 1 | $-1$ | 1 |

**11.** Also find $\int_1^5 y\,dx$ in question 10.

**12.** State Laplace-Everett's formula and Lagrange's interpolation formula.

**13.** Solve $u_{x+2}+5u_{x+1}+6u_x=2^x+7$.

**14.** If $f(x)=\frac{1}{x}$, find the divided differences $f(a, b)$ and $f(a, b, c)$.

**15.** Given $y'=x+y$, $y(0)=1$ find $y(0\cdot 1)$ by Taylor series.

**16.** Write down the Milne' predictor and corrector algorithm.

**17.** State Bender-Schmidt recurrence formula.

**18.** For the following mesh in solving $\nabla^2 u=0$, find one set of rough values of $u$ at interior mesh points.

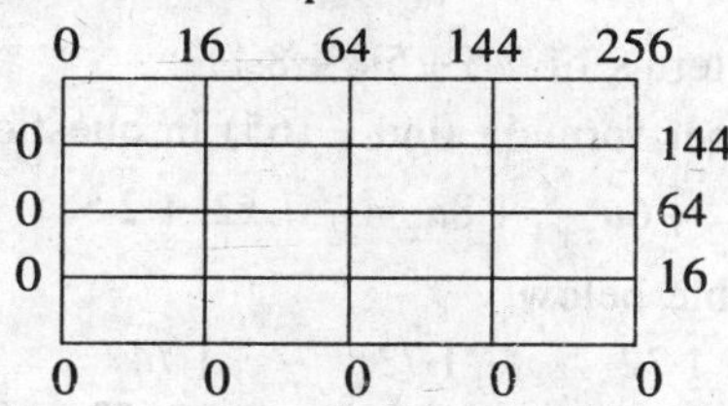

**19.** Write down Runge-Kutta algorithm (4th order).

**20.** Find $y\,(0\cdot1)$ given $y' = \frac{1}{2}(x+y),\ y\,(0) = 1$ by modified Euler method.

**PART B** *(5 × 12 = 60)*

**21.** (*a*) Find a curve $y = ae^{bx}$ to the data

| $x$ | 0 | 2 | 4 |
|---|---|---|---|
| $y$ | 5·1 | 10 | 31·1 |

(*b*) If $\alpha, \beta, \gamma$ are the roots of $x^3 + x + 5 = 0$, find the values of $\Sigma\alpha^2, \Sigma\alpha^3, \Sigma\alpha^5$.

**OR**

(*c*) Find a parabola $y = ax^2 + bx + c$ given

| $x$ : | 1 | 2 | 3 | 4 | 5 |
|---|---|---|---|---|---|
| $y$ : | 10 | 12 | 8 | 10 | 14 |

(*d*) Solve $x^4 - 4x^3 + 8x + 35 = 0$ given $2 + \sqrt{3}\ i$ is a root.

**22.** (*a*) Find the positive root of $x^3 + 2x - 5 = 0$ correct to 2 decimal places by Newton-Raphson method.

(*b*) By Gaussion elimination find $A^{-1}$ if $A = \begin{bmatrix} 4 & 1 & 2 \\ 2 & 3 & -1 \\ 1 & -2 & 2 \end{bmatrix}$.

(*c*) By relaxation method, solve

$$10x - 2y - 2z = 6$$
$$x - 10y + 2z = -7$$
$$x + y - 10z = -8$$

(*d*) Solve the equation in (*c*) by Gauss Seidel method.

**23.** (*a*) Prove $\left(\frac{\Delta^2}{E}\right)e^x \neq \frac{\Delta^2\,e^x}{E\,e^x}$.

(*b*) From the following data, find $y$ (42) and $y$ (85).

| $x$ : | 40 | 50 | 60 | 70 | 80 | 90 |
|---|---|---|---|---|---|---|
| $y$ : | 184 | 204 | 226 | 250 | 276 | 304 |

**OR**

(*c*) Sum to $n$ terms of $2{\cdot}5 + 5{\cdot}8 + 8{\cdot}11 + \cdots$

(*d*) Using proper formula find $y$ (65) in question 23(*b*).

**24.** (*a*) Solve $u_{x+2} - 6u_{x+1} + 8u_x = 2^x + x2^x + 2{\cdot}5$

(*b*) For the table below:

| $x$ : | 1·72 | 1·73 | 1·74 | 1·75 | 1·76 |
|---|---|---|---|---|---|
| $f(x)$ : | 0·17907 | 0·17728 | 0·17552 | 0·17377 | 0·17204 |

find $f'(1{\cdot}76)$ and $f'(1{\cdot}72)$.

**OR**

(*c*) Find a polynomial of least degree to fit the data by Lagrange's formula

| $x$ : | 0 | 1 | 3 | 4 |
|---|---|---|---|---|
| $y$ : | $-4$ | 1 | 29 | 52 |

(*d*) Find $f'(5)$ if

| $x$ : | 0 | 2 | 3 | 4 | 5 | 9 |
|---|---|---|---|---|---|---|
| $f(x)$ : | 5 | 25 | 55 | 100 | 460 | 900 |

**25.** (*a*) Using modified Euler method find $y(0{\cdot}2)$ given $y' = \log(x+y)$, $y(0) = 1$ if $h = 0{\cdot}2$.

(*b*) Solve: $\nabla^2 u = 0$ in the region $0 \le x \le 4,\ 0 \le y \le 4$ under the conditions $(h = 1,\ k = 1)$

$u(0, y) = 0,\ u(4, y) = 12 + y$ for $0 \le y \le 4$

$u(x, 0) = 3x,\ u(x, 4) = x^2$ for $0 \le x \le 4$.

**OR**

(*c*) Derive Bender-Schmidt formula for one dimensional heat equation.

(*d*) Solve $4u_{xx} = u_{tt}$ given $u(0, t) = 0 = u(4, t),\ u_t(x, 0) = 0$ and $u(x, 0) = x(4 - x)$, taking $h = 1, k = 1/2$.

# BHARATHIAR UNIVERSITY

## B.E. DEGREE EXAMINATION, NOVEMBER 1995

*Fifth Semester*

**Common to all Branches**

## NUMERICAL METHODS

*Time : Three hours* *Maximum : 100 marks*

Answer ALL questions.

**PART A** — *(20 × 2 = 40 marks)*

*State True or False:*

**1.** A non-linear relation between $x$ and $y$ cannot be transformed to a linear relation always.

**2.** To solve the equation $f(x) = 0$ by the simple method of iteration, the equation can be rewritten in the form $x = \phi(x)$ in only one way.

**3.** $\sum_{r=1}^{n} y_r = (\Delta^{-1} y_r)_1^n$.

**4.** To find the interpolating polynomial for the given data $(x_r, y_r)$, $r = 1, 2, \ldots n$, Lagrange's method can be applied only when the $x_r$'s are not equally spaced.

**5.** Euler's formulas for the solution of $\frac{dy}{dx} = f(x, y), y(x_0) = y_0$ provide a pair of predictor-corrector formulas.

*Fill in the blanks:*

**6.** If $\alpha, \beta, \gamma, \delta, \in$ are the roots of $ax^5 + bx^4 + cx + d = 0$, the equation whose roots are $-\alpha, -\beta, -\gamma, -\delta, -\in$ is_______.

**7.** If we start with zero values for $x, y, z$ while solving the equations $10x + y + z = 12, x + 10y + z = 12, x + y + 10z = 12$ by Gauss-Seidel iteration, the values for $x, y, z$ after one iteration will be_______.

**8.** The particular integral of the solution of the difference equation $y_{n+2} - 6y_{n+1} + 9y_n = 3^n$ is_______.

**9.** To compute $\nabla^3 u_5$, we require, apart from $u_5$, the value of_______.

**10.** To get the simplest explicit difference formula for the parabolic equation $u_t = \alpha^2 u_{xx}$, we should take $\frac{\Delta x^2}{\alpha^2 \Delta t} =$_______.

*Choose the correct answer :*

**11.** If $\alpha, \beta, \gamma$ are the roots of the equation $x^3 + px^2 + qx + 1 = 0$, the equation whose roots are $-\frac{1}{\alpha}, -\frac{1}{\beta}, -\frac{1}{\gamma}$ is (*a*) $x^3 + qx^2 - px - 1 = 0$

(*b*) $x^3 + qx^2 - px + 1 = 0$

(*c*) $x^3 - qx^2 + px - 1 = 0$

(*d*) $x^3 - qx^2 + px + 1 = 0$.

**12.** If an approximate value of the root of the equation $x^x = 1000$ is 4·5, a better approximation of the root got by Newton-Raphson method is

(*a*) 4·44 (*b*) 4·56 (*c*) 5·17 (*d*) None of the above.

**13.** If $u_1 = 1, u_3 = 17, u_4 = 43$ and $u_5 = 89$, the value of $u_2$ is

(*a*) 5 (*b*) 10 (*c*) 12 (*d*) 15.

**14.** Given $f(0) = -1, f(1) = 1$ and $f(2) = 4$, the root of the polynomial equation $f(x) = 0$ is

(*a*) 0·35 (*b*) 0·44 (*c*) 0·56 (*d*) 0·62.

**15.** Which of the following formulas is a particular case of Runge-Kutta formula of the second order?

(*a*) Taylor series formula

(*b*) Picard's formula

(*c*) Euler's modified formula

(*d*) Milne's predictor formula.

*Answer the following short-answer equations:*

**16.** Write down the normal equations to be used for finding *a* and *b*, when fitting a straight line $y = ax + b$ by the method of moments.

**17.** Under what conditions are the group and block relaxations not necessary for solving a set of simultaneous algebraic equations?

**18.** State Laplace-Everett interpolation formula.

**19.** State Simpson's $\frac{1}{3}$ and $\frac{3}{8}$ rules of numerical integration.

**20.** Write down the general and the simplest forms of the difference equation corresponding to the hyperbolic equation $u_{tt} = c^2 u_{xx}$.

**PART B** — (*5 × 12 = 60 marks*)

**21.** (*a*) (*i*) Fit the least square straight lines $y = a + bx$ to the following data:

| $x$ : | –5 | –3 | –1 | 0 | 1 | 2 | 4 |
|---|---|---|---|---|---|---|---|
| $y$ : | 0·4 | –0·1 | –0·2 | –0·3 | –0·3 | 0·1 | 0·4 |

(*ii*) Solve $x^4 - 2x^3 + 4x^2 + 6x - 21 = 0$, given that the sum of two of its roots is zero.

**OR**

(*b*) (*i*) Find *a* and *b* so that $y = ab^x$ best fits the following data :

| $x$ : | 0·2 | 0·3 | 0·4 | 0·5 | 0·6 | 0·7 |
|---|---|---|---|---|---|---|
| $y$ : | 3·16 | 2·38 | 1·75 | 1·34 | 1·00 | 0·74 |

(*ii*) Solve the equation $x^5 - 5x^4 + 9x^3 - 9x^2 + 5x - 1 = 0$.

**22.** (*a*) (*i*) Find the root of the equations $x^3 - 2x - 5 = 0$ lying between 2 and 3, correct to 3 places of decimals, using Regula Falsi method.

(*ii*) Using Gauss elimination method, find the inverse of the matrix $\begin{pmatrix} 2 & 1 & 1 \\ 1 & 0 & -1 \\ 2 & -1 & 2 \end{pmatrix}$.

**OR**

(*b*) (*i*) Compute the positive root of the equation $x - \cos x = 0$, correct to 2 places of decimals, using the bisection method.

(*ii*) Solve the following set of equations, correct to 3 places of decimals, using relaxation method

$28x + 4y - z = 32,\ x + 3y + 10z = 24,\ 2x + 17y + 4z = 35.$

**23.** (*a*) (*i*) Express $x^3 - 2x + 1$ in terms of factorial polynomials:

(*ii*) Obtain the missing term in the following table:

| $x$ : | 1 | 2 | 3 | 4 | 5 |
|---|---|---|---|---|---|
| $f(x)$ : | 0 | 7 | – | 63 | 124 |

**OR**

(*b*) (*i*) Show that $\sum_{n=1}^{\infty} \frac{1}{n(n+3)} = \frac{11}{18}$.

(*ii*) Find $f(2{\cdot}36)$ from the following table:

| $x$ : | 1·6 | 1·8 | 2·0 | 2·2 | 2·4 | 2·6 |
|---|---|---|---|---|---|---|
| $f(x)$ : | 4·95 | 6·05 | 7·39 | 9·03 | 11·02 | 13·46 |

**24.** (*a*) (*i*) Find $f(2)$, if $f(-1) = 2, f(0) = 1, f(1) = 0$ and $f(3) = -1$.

(*ii*) Solve $y_{n+2} - 5y_{n+1} + 6y_n = 2^n + 1$.

**OR**

(*b*) (*i*) Evaluate $\int_0^{0\cdot8} e^{-x^2} dx$, by Romberg's method with $h = 0{\cdot}1$ and 0·2.

(*ii*) Solve $y_{n+2} - 2y_{n+1} + 2y_n = 2^n + n^2$.

**25.** (*a*) (*i*) Solve $y' = y - x^2$, $y(0) = 1$, by Picard's method, upto the third approximation.

(*ii*) Using Liebmann's method, solve the equation $\nabla^2 u = 0$ for the following square mesh with boundary values as shown in the figure:

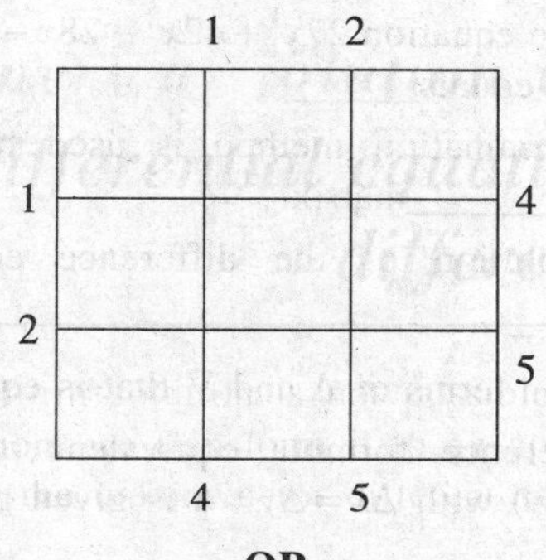


**OR**

(*b*) (*i*) Compute $y$ at $x = 0{\cdot}25$ by Modified Euler's method given that $y' = 2xy$, $y(0) = 1$.

(*ii*) Compute $u$ for 4 time steps with $h = 1$, given that $u_{tt} = 4u_{xx}$; $u(0, t) = 0$, $u(4, t) = 0$, $u_t(x, 0) = 0$ and $u(x, 0) = x(4 - x)$.

# BHARATHIAR UNIVERSITY

## B.E. DEGREE EXAMINATION, APRIL 1996

*Fifth Semester*

**Common to all Branches**

## NUMERICAL METHODS

*Time : Three hours* *Maximum marks: 100*

Answer ALL questions.

**PART A** — *(20 × 2 = 40 marks)*

*State True or False*:

**1.** To fit a straight line for the given data $(x_r, y_r)$, $r = 1, 2, \ldots n$, by the method of least squares, the values of $x_r$ must be equally spaced.

**2.** Newton-Raphson's iterative formula for

$$\frac{1}{N} \text{ is } x_{n+1} = x_n (2 - Nx_n)$$

**3.** $\Delta^{10} \{(1 - ax)(1 - bx^2)(1 - cx^3)(1 - dx^4)\} = abcd.$

**4.** The $n$th divided differences of a polynomial of the $n$th degree are not constant.

**5.** Euler's improved formula $y_{m+1} = y_m = \frac{h}{2}(y'_m + y'_{m+1})$ can be treated as a corrector formula.

*Fill in the banks*:

**6.** If the roots of the equation $27x^3 + 42x^2 - 28x - 8 = 0$ are in G.P. then one of the roots equals______ .

**7.** When Gauss elimination method is used to solve $AX = B, A$ is transferred in a_______matrix.

**8.** The general solution of the difference equation $y_{n+2} - 4y_{n+1} + 4y_n = 0$ is______ .

**9.** The expression in terms of $\Delta$ and $\nabla$ that is equal to $2\mu\delta$ is______ .

**10.** The finite difference formula equivalent to Poisson's equation $u_{xx} + u_{yy} = -f(x, y)$ with $\Delta x = \Delta y = h$ is given by $u_{ij} =$ —— .

*Choose the correct answer*:

**11.** If the roots of the equation $x^3 - 18x^2 + 92x - 120 = 0$ are in A.P. then the product of the two extreme roots equals

(*a*) 20 (*b*) 32 (*c*) 35 (*d*) 36

**12.** To find the smallest positive root of the equation $x^3 - x - 1 = 0$ by the method of simple iteration the equation should be rewritten as

(*a*) $x = x^3 - 1$ (*b*) $x = (x + 1)^{1/3}$ (*c*) $x = \frac{1}{x^2 - 1}$ (*d*) $x = \frac{x + 1}{x^2}$.

**13.** If $\Delta y = 1 + 2x + 3x^3$, which of the following is not true?

(*a*) $a^2 y = 6x + 5$ (*b*) $\Delta^3 y = 6$

(*c*) $\Delta^4 y = 0$ (*d*) $y = Hx + x^2 + x^3$.

**14.** The area bounded by the curve passing through the points (0, 1), (1, 7), (2, 23), (3, 55) and (4, 109), the $x$-axis and the ordinates $x = 0$ and $x = 4$, as computed by Simpson's 1/3 rule is nearly equal to

(*a*) 115 (*b*) 130 (*c*) 135 (*d*) 145

**15.** For solving numerically the hyperbolic equation $u_{tt} = c^2 u_{xx}$, the starting solution is provided by the boundary condition

(*a*) $u\,(0, t) = 0$ (*b*) $u\,(l, t) = 0$

(*c*) $u_t\,(x, 0) = 0$ (*d*) $u\,(x, 0) = f(x)$

*Answer the following short-answer questions*:

**16.** Write down the normal equations to be used for finding and $a$ and $b$, when fitting a parabola $y = a + bx + cx^2$ by the method of least squares.

**17.** State the condition for convergence of Jacobi's iteration method, for solving a system of simultaneous algebraic equations.

**18.** State Bessel's interpolation formula.

**19.** Show that $y_n = 1 - \frac{2}{n}$ is a solution of the difference equation $(n+1)\, y_{n+1} + n y_n = 2n - 3$.

**20.** Derive Picard's formula for the solution of the equation $\frac{dy}{dx} = f(x, y),\ y(x_0) = y_0$.

**PART B — (5 × 12 = 60 marks)**

**21.** (*a*) (*i*) Fit a parabola of the form $y = a + bx + cx^2$ to the following data by the method of least squares:

| $x$ | : | 1 | 2 | 3 | 4 | 5 | 6 |
|---|---|---|---|---|---|---|---|
| $y$ | : | 3·13 | 3·76 | 6·94 | 12·62 | 20·86 | 31·53 |

(*ii*) Solve the equation $6x^6 - 25x^5 + 31x^4 - 31x^2 + 25x - 6 = 0$.

**OR**

(*b*) (*i*) Determine $a$ and $b$ so that $y = ae^{bx}$ best fits the following data:

| $x$ | : | 1 | 2 | 3 | 4 |
|---|---|---|---|---|---|
| $y$ | : | 7 | 11 | 17 | 27 |

(*ii*) Increase the roots of the equation $x^4 - x^3 - 10x^2 + 4x + 24 = 0$ by 2 and hence solve it.

**22.** (*a*) (*i*) Find the root of the equation $2x^3 + 3x - 10 = 0$ lying between 1 and 2, correct to two places of decimals using Horner's method.

(*ii*) Solve the following set of equations by Crout's reduction:

$2x - 2y - 4z = 1,\ 2x + 3y + 2z = 9,\ -x + y + z = 0{\cdot}5$

**OR**

(*b*) (*i*) Find the positive root of the equation $xe^x - \cos x = 0$, correct to 4 places of decimals, using Newton-Raphson method.

(*ii*) Solve the following set of equations by Gauss-Seidel iteration, correct to 3 places of decimals:

$10x - 5y - 2z(le) = 3,\ 4x - 10y + 3z = -3,\ x + 6y + 10z = -3.$

**23.** (*a*) (*i*) Show that (1) $\Delta - \nabla = \Delta\nabla$; (2) $\frac{\Delta}{\nabla} - \frac{\nabla}{\Delta} = \Delta + \nabla$.

(*ii*) Prove that $\sum_{n=2}^{\infty} \frac{1}{n^2 - 1} = \frac{3}{4}$.

(*iii*) Find $f(x)$ at $x = 1{\cdot}5$ from the following data:

| $x$ | : | 0 | 1 | 2 | 3 | 4 | 5 |
|---|---|---|---|---|---|---|---|
| $f(x)$ | : | − 1 | 0 | 7 | 26 | 63 | 124 |

**OR**

(*b*) (*i*) Prove that $E = e^{hD}$.

(*ii*) If $C_n = 2^{n/2} \cos \frac{\pi n}{4}$, $S_n = 2^{n/2} \sin \frac{\pi n}{4}$, prove that $\Delta C_n = S_n$ and $\Delta S_n = C_n$.

(*iii*) Obtain the missing terms in the following table:

| $x$ | : | 1 | 2 | 3 | 4 | 5 | 6 | 7 | 8 |
|---|---|---|---|---|---|---|---|---|---|
| $y$ | : | 10 | 18 | – | 74 | 135 | – | 353 | 522 |

**24.** (*a*) (*i*) Find $f(1)$ from the following table:

| $x$ | : | – 1 | 0 | 2 | 5 | 10 |
|---|---|---|---|---|---|---|
| $f(x)$ | : | – 2 | – 1 | 7 | 124 | 999 |

(*ii*) Solve the difference equation

$$y_{n+2} - 2y_{n+1} + 2y_n = \cos \frac{\pi n}{2}.$$

**OR**

(*b*) (*i*) Compute the value of π by evaluating $\int_0^1 \frac{dx}{1+x^2}$, using Simpson's 1/3 rule with 10 divisions.

(*ii*) Solve $y_{n+2} - y_{n+1} - y_n = 0, y_0 = 0, y_1 = 1$.

**25.** (*a*) (*i*) Given that $yy' = y^2 - 2x$, $y(0) = 1$, compute $y(0{\cdot}2)$ and $y(0{\cdot}4)$, using Runge-Kutta method of the fourth order with $h = 0{\cdot}2$.

(*ii*) With step size $h = 1/2 = K$, solve the equation

$\nabla^2 u = -100, \ |x| < 1, \ |y| < 1; \ u(\pm 1, y) = u(x, \pm 1) = 0.$

**OR**

(*b*) (*i*) Solve the equation $y' = x^2 + y^2$, $y(0) = 1$, by Taylor series (with the first five terms) method for $y(\cdot 1)$ and $y(\cdot 2)$.

(*ii*) Compute $u$ for 4 time steps with $h = 0{\cdot}25$, given that $u_t = u_{xx}$, $0 < x < 1, t > 0$; $u(0, t) = u(1, t) = 0$ and $u(x, 0) = 100x(1 - x)$.

# MADRAS UNIVERSITY

## B.E. Degree Examination, October 1996

### Fifth Semester

### Numerical Methods

**Time : Three hours** **Maximum : 100 marks**

Answer All Questions

Part A — (20 × 2 = 40 marks)

1. Write down the normal equations to fit a quadratic curve by least square method.

2. Write the distributive, commutative and Index laws of operator $\Delta$.

3. Show that $(1 + \Delta)(1 - \nabla) = 1$ with usual notation.

4. Evaluate $\frac{\Delta^2}{E} x^3$.

5. State Newton's formula on interpolation.

6. State Simpson's rule.

7. From the difference equation by eliminating $a$ and $b$ from the relation $y_m = a2^x + b(-2)^x$.

8. Solve $U_{x+2} - 6U_{x+1} + 9u_x = 0$.

9. Explain the terms : Round off error, Truncation error.

10. Explain briefly Gauss Jordon iteration to solve simultaneous equation.

11. Show that Newton-Raphson formula to find $\sqrt{a}$ can be expressed in the form $x_{n+1} = \frac{1}{2}\left(x_n + \frac{a}{x_n}\right)$ $n = 0, 1, 2$.

12. Explain convergency of the relaxation method.

13. State the algorithm of Runge-Kutta method of order two to solve $y' = f(x, y), y(x_0) = y_0$ at $x = x_0 + h$.

14. State Milne's predictor formula.

15. Write the merits and demerits of the Taylor method of solution.

16. State the Adams-Bashforth predictor-corrector formula.

17. State the finite differences scheme of $u_{xx} + u_{yy} = 0$.

18. Identify the equation $f_{xx} + 2f_{xy} + f_{yy} = 0$

19. Write the Crank Nicholson difference scheme to solve $u_{xx} = au_t$ with $u(0, t) = T_0$, $u(l, t) = T_l$ and the initial condition as $u(x, 0) = f(x)$.

20. Write down the finite difference form of the equation $\nabla^2 u = f(x, y)$

PART B – ($5 \times 12 = 60$ marks)

Answer (*a*) or (*b*) in each question.

21. (*a*) Fit a second degree parabola to the following :

| $x = 0$ | 1 | 2 | 3 | 4 |
|---|---|---|---|---|
| y = 1 | 1.8 | 1.3 | 2.5 | 6.3 |

Or

(*b*) (*i*) Evaluate $\Delta^2 (\cos 2x)$.
(*ii*) Explain the difference between $\left(\frac{\Delta^2}{E}\right) u_x$ and $\frac{\Delta^2 u_x}{EU_x}$ and find the values of these when $u_x = x^3$.

22. (*a*) The following are data from the stream table :

| temp C° | 140 | 150 | 160 | 170 | 180 |
|---|---|---|---|---|---|
| pressure kgf/cm$^2$ | 3.685 | 4.854 | 6.302 | 8,076 | 10.225 |

Using Newtons formula, find the pressure of the stream for a temp of 142°.

Or

(*b*) Dividing the range into 10 equal parts, find the approximate value of $\int_0^{\pi} \sin x \, dx$ by (i) Trapezoidal rule (ii) Simpson's rule.

23. (*a*) (*i*) Use Newton Raphson method to find the roots of the following equation $e^x = 2x + 21$.

(ii) By Gauss-Seidal method solve $4x_1 + x_2 + 2x_3 = 4$, $3x_1 + 5x_2 + x_3 = 7$ and $x_1 + x_2 + 3x_3 + 3$.

Or

(*b*) (*i*) Solve $9x - y + 2z = 9$, $x + 10y - 2z = 15$ $2x - 2y - 13z - 17$ to three decimal places by relaxation method.

(*ii*) Solve $x^3 - 8x^2 + 17x - 10 = 0$ by Graffe's method.

24. (*a*) Using Euler's modified method solve $\frac{dy}{dx} = x + y$ and $y(0) = 1$ at $x = 0.05$ to $0.20$

(*b*) Solve $y' = x^2 + y^2 - 2$ using Milne's predictor corrector method for $x = 0.3$ given the initial value $x = 0$, $y = 1$ the values of $y$ for $x = -0.1$, $0.1$ and $0.2$ should be computed by a Taylor series expansion.

25. (*a*) Given the values of $u(x, y)$ on the boundary of the square given in the figure, evaluate the function $u(x, y)$ satisfying Laplace's equation $\nabla^2 u - 0$ at the pivotal points of this figure.

1000 1000
1000
2000
1000
500
1
2
2000
0
3
4
1000
0
500 0

(*b*) solve by Crank-Nicolson's method

$$\frac{\partial u}{\partial t} = \frac{1}{16}\frac{\partial^2 u}{\partial x^2} \quad 0 < x < 1,\ t > 0$$

$$u(x, 0) = 0,\ u(0, t) = 0,\ u(1, t) = 100\,t$$

Compute $u$ for one step with $h = 1/4$

# BHARATHIAR UNIVERSITY

## B.E. Degree Examination, November 1996

## Fifth Semester

## (Common to all Branches)

## Numerical Methods

**Time : Three hours** **Maximum : 100 marks**

Answer All Questions

Part A — (20 × 2 = 40 Marks)

State True o' False :

I. The number of real roots of an odd degree algebraic equation with real coefficient is odd.

II. If a curve is fit to the points $(x_1, y_1)$, $i = 1, 2, \ldots n$ by least square method, then the curve passes through the point $(\overline{x}, \overline{y})$, i.e.,

$$\left(\frac{\sum x_1}{n}, \frac{\sum y_1}{n}\right)$$

III. Gauss-Seidel iteration converges only if the coefficient matrix is diagonally dominant.

IV. For any root the order of convergence of Newton-Raphson method is two.

V. Crank-Nicholson's difference formula is used to solve wave equation.

Fill in the blanks :

VI. The sum of the roots of the equation $x^2 - |x| - 12 = 0$ is ...........

VII. $\Delta^m f_n = \nabla^m f_p$ where $p$ is .........

VIII. The solution of the difference equation $Y_{n+1} - 2y_n = 1$, $y_0 = 1$ is $y_n =$ .................

IX. The number of real roots of $x^4 + x^3 + x^2 + x + 1 = 0$ is .......

X. In terms of factorial powers, $\frac{1}{x^2 - 1}$ is .............

XI. If the roots of $x^3 - px + q = 0$ are in A.P., then

(a) $p = 0$ (b) $q = 0$ (c) $p = q$ (d) $d + q = 0$

XII. $\frac{1}{\Delta} - \frac{1}{\nabla}$ is equal to

(a) 1 (b) −1 (c) Δ (d) ∇

XIII. $\frac{\Delta}{\nabla} - \frac{\nabla}{\Delta}$ is equal to

(a) 0 (b) $\Delta - \nabla$ (c) $\nabla - \Delta$ (d) $\nabla + \Delta$..

XIV. If α, β γ are the roots of $x^3 - 2x - 3 = 0$, then $\alpha^2 + \beta^2 + \gamma^2$ is

(a) 1 (b) 2 (c) 3 (d) 4

XV. Simpson's rule of integration is exact for all polynomials of degree not exceeding

(a) 2 (b) 3 (c) 4 (d) 5

Answer the following short answer questions :

XVI. If α, β, γ are the roots of $x^3 + 2x - 1 = 0$, what is the value of $\alpha^3 + \beta^3 + \gamma^3$?

XVII. What is the solution of the difference equation $y_{n+2} - 2y_{n+1} - 24y_n = 0$ ?

XVIII. What is the equation whose roots are $\pm 1, \pm i, 1 \pm i$ ?

XIX. State Schmidt's explicit formula for solving heat equation.

XX. State a difference formula for solving wave equation.

PART B — $(5 \times 12 = 50$ marks)

XXI. (*a*) (*i*) Fit the least square straight line $y = a + bx$ to the data : $f(0) = 6, f(1) = 5, f(2) = 3, f(4) = 0, f(5) = -3$.

(*ii*) Solve the reciprocal equation

$$4x^4 - 20x^3 + 33x^2 - 20x + 4 = 0$$

OR

(*b*)(*i*) Fit the least square parabola $y = a + bx + cx^2$ to the data $f(-1) = -2, f(0) = 1, f(1) = 2, f(2) = 4$

(*ii*) Solve $x^3 - 19x^2 + 114x - 216 = 0$ given that the roots are in G.P.

XXII. (*a*) (*i*) Compute the positive root of $x^4 - x - 10 = 0$ correct to 2 decimal places.

(*ii*) By Gauss elimination method invert the matrix

$$\begin{pmatrix} 10 & 1 & 0 \\ 1 & 0 & 0 \\ 0 & 0 & 1 \end{pmatrix}$$

OR

(*b*) (*i*) Compute the root $4x = e^x$ near 2 correct to 2 decimal places.

(*ii*) Solve by Crout'smethod : $2x + 5y - z = 10$, $8x - y + 3z = 12$, $x + 3y + 6z = -1$.

XXIII. (*a*) (*i*) Compute the missing value :

| $x$ : | 1 | 2 | 3 | 4 | 5 |
|---|---|---|---|---|---|
| $f$ : | 0 | 7 | 26 | — | 124 |

(*ii*) Find the sum $\sum_{x=1}^{\infty} \frac{1}{x(x+2)}$

OR

(*b*) (*i*) Express $x^3$ in factorial powers.

(*ii*) Compute the missing value :

| $x$ : | −1 | 0 | 1 | 2 | 3 |
|---|---|---|---|---|---|
| $f$ : | 5 | 2 | — | 0 | 1 |

XXIV. (*a*) (*i*) If $f(-1) = -2$, $f(0) = -1$, $f(2) = 7$, $f(5) = 124$, compute $f(1)$

(*ii*) Compute $\int_0^4 e^x dx$ by Simpson's 1/3 rule with 10 subdivisions.

OR

(*b*) (*i*) Compute $f'(1)$ using the data :

| $x$ : | 10 | 1.5 | 2.0 | 2.5 | 3.0 |
|---|---|---|---|---|---|
| $f$ : | 27.00 | 106.75 | 324.00 | 783.75 | 1621.00 |

(*ii*) Compute $\int_0^4 \frac{dx}{1+x^2}$ by Simpson's 1/3 rule with six subdivisions.

XXV. (*a*) (*i*) Given that $y' = y$, $y(0) = 1$, express $y(h)$ as a polynomial in $h$ by Runge-Kutta method.

(*ii*) Obtain the five-point formula for solving Laplace equation.

OR

(*b*) (*i*) Compute $y(0, 2)$ correct to 4 decimal places from the Taylor series solution of the equation $yy' = y^2 - 2x$, $y(0) = 1$.

(*ii*) Solve the Poisson's equation

$$\frac{\partial^2 u}{\partial x^2} + \frac{\partial^2 u}{\partial y^2} = -100 \qquad |x| \le 1, \ |y| = 1$$

given that $u = 0$ on the boundary of the square. Take $h = 1/2$

# BHARATHIAR UNIVERSITY

## B.E. Degree Examination, April 1997

## Fifth Semester

## (Common to all Branches)

## Numerical Methods

**Time : Three hours** **Maximum : 100 marks**

Answer All Questions

Part A — (20 × 2 = 40 marks)

State True of False :

I. By the method of least square, a curve of the form $y = ax^2 + bx + c$ is fitted to the data $(x_1, y_1)$, $i = 1, 2, \ldots n$. This curve will pass through all the points.

II. Iteration method is a self-correction method.

III. The third differences of a polynomial of degree 4 are zeros.

IV. Liebmann's iteration process is used to solve two dimensional heat equation.

V. Milne's corrector formula is given by

$$y_{n+1} = y_{n-1} + \frac{h}{3}(y'_{n-1} + 2y'_n + y'_n + y'_{n+1})$$

Fill in the blanks :

VI. If $\alpha, \beta, \gamma$ are the roots of $x^3 + x^2 + x + 1 = 0$, than the equation whose roots are $\frac{1}{\alpha}, \frac{1}{\beta}, \frac{1}{\gamma}$ is ____________.

VII. Gauss-elimination and Gauss-Jordan are direct methods while ________ and __________ are iterative methods.

VIII. The difference equation which satisfies $y_x = A \,.\, 2^x + B.3^x$ is __________

IX. $E - \Delta =$ ____________.

X. The finite difference formula equivalent to Laplaces' equation $u_{xx} + u_{yy} = 0$ with $\Delta x = \Delta y = h$ is given by $u_{ij} =$ ____________.

Choose the correct answer.

XI. If the roots of the equation $x^3 - 19x^2 + 114x - 216 = 0$ are in G.P., then the product of the two extreme roots equals

(a) 24 (b) 54 (c) 36 (d) 35

XII. Which of the following is true?

(a) $\Delta x^r = rx^{r-1}$ (b) $\Delta x^{(r)} = rx^{(r-1)}$

(c) $\Delta^n e^x = e^x$ (d) $\Delta \sin x = \cos x$

XIII. If $u_1 = 1$, $u_3 = 17$, $u_4 = 43$ and $u_5 = 89$, the value of $u_2$ is

(a) 12 (b) 15 (c) 5 (d) 10

XIV. By evaluating $\int_0^1 \frac{dx}{1+x^2}$ by a numerical integration method, we can obtain an approximate value of

(a) $\log_e 2$ (b) $\pi$ (c) e (d) $\log_{10} 2$

XV. In solving equation $u_t = \alpha^2 u_{xx}$, by Crank-Nicholson method, to simplify method we take $\frac{(\Delta x)^2}{\alpha^2 K}$ as

(a) $\frac{1}{2}$ (b) 2 (c) 1 (d) 0

Answer the following short answer questions :

XVI. Write down the normal equations to be used for finding *a, b* and *c* when fitting a parabola $y = ax^2 + bx + c$ by the method of least squares.

XVII. State the condition for convergence of Gauss-Seidel method.

XVIII. Define $\mu$ and $\delta$.

XIX. State Lagrange's interpolation formula.

XX. Define a difference quotient.

PART B — ($5 \times 12 = 60$ marks)

XXI. (*a*) (*i*) Fit a straight line to the data by the method of least squares:

| $x$ : | 0 | 5 | 10 | 15 | 20 |
|---|---|---|---|---|---|
| $y$ : | 7 | 10 | 15 | 21 | 25 |

(*ii*) Solve : $6x^5 + x^4 - 43x^3 - 43x^3 + x + 6 = 0$

OR

(*b*) (*i*) Fit a curve $y = ae^{bx}$ to the data :

| $x$ : | 0 | 2 | 4 |
|---|---|---|---|
| $y$ : | 5.1 | 10 | 31.1 |

(*ii*) Diminish the roots of the equation

$$x^4 - 4x^3 - 7x^2 + 22x + 24 = 0$$

by 1 and hence solve it.

XXII. (*a*) (*i*) Find the positive root of $x^3 + x - 1 = 0$ correct to 2 decimals by Horner's method.

(*ii*) Using Gauses-Seidel method, solve

$$28x + 4y - z = 35$$
$$x + 3y + 10z = 24$$
$$2x + 17y + 4z = 35$$

OR

(*b*) (*i*) Solve by Crout's method

$$2x - 6y + 8z = 24$$
$$3x + y + 2z = 6$$
$$5x + 4y - 3z = 2$$

(*ii*) Find the inverse of $\begin{bmatrix} 2 & 1 & -1 \\ 0 & 2 & 1 \\ 5 & 2 & -3 \end{bmatrix}$ by Gauss method.

XXIII. (*a*) Sum the series 1.2.3 + 2.3.4 + 3.4.5 + ... to *n* terms by finite integration.

(*ii*) Find the missing value from the table :

| $x$ : | 0 | 1 | 2 | 3 | 4 |
|---|---|---|---|---|---|
| $y$ : | 1 | 3 | 9 | | 81 |

(*b*) (*i*) If $u_x = x^3 + 3x^2 - 5x + 1$, find $\Delta u_x$, $\Delta^2 u_x$, $\Delta^3 u_x$ and $\Delta^{-1} u_x$.

(*ii*) Apply Gauss's forward formula to find *y* (3.75) from the table

| $x$ : | 2.5 | 3.0 | 3.5 | 4.0 | 4.5 | 5.0 |
|---|---|---|---|---|---|---|
| $y$ : | 24.14 | 22.04 | 20.22 | 18.64 | 17.26 | 16.04 |

XXIV. (*a*) Given the table

| $x$: | 14 | 17 | 31 | 35 |
|---|---|---|---|---|
| $f(x)$ | 68.7 | 64.1 | 44.2 | 39.6 |

find $f(27)$.

(ii) Find $f'(5)$ if

| $x$ : | 0 | 2 | 3 | 4 | 5 | 9 |
|---|---|---|---|---|---|---|
| $f(x)$ : | 5 | 25 | 55 | 100 | 460 | 900 |

OR

(*b*) (*i*) Solve : $u_{x+2} + 6u_{x+1} + 9u_x = 3^x + x.2^x + 7.$

(*ii*) Fit a polynomial of least degree to fit the data by Lagrange's formula

| $x$ : | 0 | 1 | 3 | 4 |
|---|---|---|---|---|
| $y$ : | –4 | 1 | 29 | 52 |

XXV. (*a*) (*i*) Apply Runge-Kutta method of fourth order to calculate

$$y(0, 2) \text{ given } \frac{dy}{dx} = x + y, \; y(0) = 1 \text{ taking } h = 0.1.$$

(*ii*) Solve $\nabla^2 u = 0$ in the region $0 \le x \le 4$, $0 \le y \le 4$ under the conditions $(h = 1, \; k = 1)$ $u(0, y) = 0$, $u(4, y) = 12 + y$, $0 \le y \le 4$ $u(x, 0) = 3x$, $u(x, 4) = x^2$, $0 \le x \le 4$

OR

**(*b*) (*i*) Derive Bender-Schmidt formula for one dimensional heat** equation.

(*ii*) Evaluate the pivotal values of the equation $25u_{xx} = u_{tt}$ for one-half period oscillation given

$$u(0, t) = u(5, t) = 0$$

$$u(x, 0) = 2x, \; 0 \le x \le 2.5$$

$$= 10 - 2x, \; 2.5 \le x \le 5$$

# BHARTHIAR UNIVERSITY

## B.E. DEGREE EXAMINATION, NOVEMBER 1997

*Fifth Semester*

**(Common to All Branches)**

## NUMERICAL METHODS

**Time : Three hours** **Maximum : 100 marks**

**Answer All Questions**

**PART A — ($20 \times 2 = 40$ marks)**

**State True or False:**

I. By the method of least square, a curve of the form $y = ax^2 + bx + c$ is fitted to the data $(x_k, y_k)$, $k = 1, 2, \ldots n$. This curve will pass through all the points.

II. The root of the transcendental equation can be obtained by Horner's method.

III. $\Delta + \nabla = \Delta \nabla$.

IV. Lagrange's interpolation formula can be used whether the arguments are equally spaced or not.

V. Liebmann's iteration process is used to solve one-dimensional heat flow equation.

**Fill in the blanks:**

VI. When the roots of the equation $x^3 - 15x^2 + 71x - 105 = 0$ are in A.P., one of the roots equal to ........... .

VII. When Gauss–Jordan elimination method is used to solve $AX = B$, $A$ is transferred into a .......... matrix.

VIII. The particular integral of $u_{n+2} + 2u_{n+1} + u_n = 2^n$ is ........... .

IX. If $h = 1$, $\Delta^3(1 - x)(1 - 2x)(1 - 3x) =$ .............. .

X. The simplest form of the explicit formula to solve $a^2 u_{xx} = u_{tt}$, can be got if we select $\lambda$ as ............ .

**Choose the correct answer :**

XI If 1, 1, 3 are the roots of $x^3 + ax^2 + bx + c + 0$ then $ab - c$equals

(*a*) 32 (*b*) – 32 (*c*) – 18 (*d*) 18.

XII. Under the conditions $f(a)$ and $f(b)$ having opposite signs and $a < b$, the first approximation of one of the roots of $f(x) = 0$, by Regula Falsi method, is given by

(*a*) $\dfrac{af(b) + bf(a)}{f(b) + f(a)}$ (*b*) $\dfrac{af(a) - bf(b)}{f(a) - f(b)}$

(*c*) $\dfrac{af(b) - bf(a)}{f(b) - f(a)}$ (*d*) $\dfrac{af(a) + bf(b)}{f(a) + f(b)}$

XIII. The sixth term of the sequence 8, 12, 19, 29, 42, ........ is
(*a*) 48 (*b*) 58 (*c*) 49 (*d*) 57.

XIV. By Trapezoidal rule, the value of $\int_0^6 \frac{1}{1+x} dx$, by dividing the range into six equal parts is
(*a*) 1.94591015 (*b*) 1.95873016
(*c*) 1.96607143 (*d*) 2.02142857

XV. Bender-Schmidt recurrence equation is given by

(*a*) $U_{i,j} = \frac{1}{4}(U_{i-1,j-1} + U_{i-1,j+1} + U_{i+1,j-1} + U_{i+1,j+1})$

(*b*) $U_{i,j} = \frac{1}{4}(U_{i-1,j} + U_{i+1,j} + U_{i,j-1} + U_{i,j+1})$

(*c*) $U_{i,j+1} = U_{i-1,j} + U_{i+1,j} - U_{i,j+1}$

(*d*) $U_{i,j+1} = \frac{1}{2}(U_{i-1,j} + U_{i+1,j})$.

**Answer the following short-answer questions:**

XVI. Define a reciprocal equation.

XVII. By Gauss elimination method, solve
$$x + y = 2,\ 2x + 3y = 5.$$

XVIII. State Everette's interpolution formula.

XIX. Evaluate $\dfrac{1}{(E-a)^3} a^x$.

XX. In solving $\dfrac{dy}{dx} = f(x, y)$, $y(x_0) = y_0$ write down Taylor' series for $y(x_1)$.

**PART B — (5 × 12 = 60 marks)**

XXI.(*a*) (*i*) Use the method of moments to fit a straight line to the data given below:

| $x$ : | 1 | 3 | 5 | 7 | 9 |
|---|---|---|---|---|---|
| $y$ : | 1.5 | 2.8 | 4.0 | 4.7 | 6.0 |

(*ii*) Solve the equation
$$x^5 - 5x^4 + 9x^3 - 9x^2 + 5x - 1 = 0.$$

Or

(*b*) (*i*) From the table given below, find the best value of $a$ and $b$ in the law $y = ae^{bx}$ by the method of least squares:

| $x$ : | 0 | 2 | 4 |
|---|---|---|---|
| $y$ : | 5.012 | 10 | 31.62 |

(*ii*) Remove the second term in $x^4 - 12x^3 + 48x^2 - 72x + 35 = 0$ and hence solve it.

XXII. (*a*) (*i*) Find the positive root of $x - \cos x = 0$ by bisection method.

(*ii*) Solve, by Crout's method, the following:

$x + y + z = 3,\ 2x - y + 3z = 16,\ 3x + y - z = -3.$

Or

(*b*) (*i*) Find the cube root of 24, by Newton's method.

(*ii*) Solve the following system of equations by Gauss–Seidel method:

$30x - 2y + 3z = 75,\ 2x + 2y + 18z = 30,\ x + 17y - 2z = 48$

XXIII. (*a*) (*i*) Prove that $\Delta = \mu\delta + \frac{1}{2}\delta^2$.

(*ii*) Sum the series:

$1 . 2 + 2 . 3x + 3 . 4x^2 + \ldots\ldots$ to $\infty$.

(*iii*) From the following table, find the value of tan 45°15′.

| $x°$ : | 45 | 46 | 47 |
|---|---|---|---|
| $\tan x°$ : | 1.00000 | 1.03553 | 1.07237 |
| $x°$ : | 48 | 49 | 50 |
| $\tan x°$ : | 1.11061 | 1.15037 | 1.19175 |

Or

(*b*) (*i*) Prove that $\mu + \frac{1}{2}\delta = E^{1/2}$.

(*ii*) Find the missing value from the table:

| $x$ : | 2 | 4 | 6 | 8 | 10 |
|---|---|---|---|---|---|
| $y$ : | 5.6 | 8.6 | 13.9 | — | 35.6 |

(*iii*) If $U_x = x^3 + 3x^2 - 5x + 1$, find $\Delta U_x$, $\Delta^2 U_x$, $\Delta^3 U_x$ and $\Delta^{-1} U_x$.

XXIV. (*a*) (*i*) Using Lagrange's formula, fit a polynomial to the data:

| $x$ : | 0 | 1 | 3 | 4 |
|---|---|---|---|---|
| $y$ : | − 12 | 0 | 6 | 12 |

Also find $y$ at $x = 2$.

(*ii*) Find the first and second derivative of the function tabulated below at $x = 0.6$.

| $x$ : | 0.4 | 0.5 | 0.6 | 0.7 | 0.8 |
|---|---|---|---|---|---|
| $y$ : | 1.5836 | 1.7974 | 2.0442 | 2.3275 | 2.6511 |

Or

(*b*) (*i*) Find the value of $\log 2^{1/3}$ from $\int_0^1 \frac{x^2}{1+x^3}\,dx$ using Simpson's one-third rule with $h = 0.25$.

(*ii*) Solve $y_{x+2} - y_{x+1} + y_x = 0$ given $y_0 = 1$, $y_1 = \frac{\sqrt{3}+1}{2}$.

XXV.(*a*) (*i*) If $\frac{dy}{dx} = \frac{y-x}{y+x}$, $y(0) = 1$, find $y(0.1)$ by Picard's method.

(*ii*) Solve $\nabla^2 u = 0$ in the square region bounded by $x = 0$, $x = 4$, $y = 0$, $y = 4$ and with boundary conditions, $u(0, y) = 0$, $u(4, y) = 8 + 2y$, $u(x, 0) = \frac{1}{2}x^2$, and $u(x, 0) = 2$ taking $h = k = 1$.

Or

(*b*) (*i*) Obtain the values of $y$ at $x = 0.1, 0.2$ using R.K. method of fourth order for the differential equation $y' = -y$, given $y(0) = 1$.

(*ii*) Solve $U_{xx} = 32\,U_t$, taking $h = 0.25$ for $t > 0$, $0 < x < 1$ and $u(x, 0) = 0$, $u(0, t) = 0$. $u(1, t) = t$.

# BHARTHIAR UNIVERSITY

## B.E. DEGREE EXAMINATION, APRIL 1998

*Fifth Semester*

**(Common to all Branches)**

## NUMERICAL METHODS

**Time: Three hours** **Maximum: 100 marks**

**Answer All questions.**

**Part A — (20 x 2 = 40 marks)**

**State True or False:**

I. The cubic equation with real coefficients always has atleast one real root.

II. Gausss-Jacobi method coverages faster than Gauss-Seidel method.

III. $\left[\frac{\Delta^2}{E}\right]U_x = \frac{\Delta^2 U_x}{EU_x}$.

IV. The solution of the difference equation $Y_{x+2} - 5y_{x+1} + 6y_x = 0$ is $Y_x = Ae^{2x} + Be^{3x}$.

V. Adam-Bashforth predictor formula is given by

$$Y_{n+1,p} = Y_n + \frac{h}{24}\left[55y_n + 59y_{n-1} - 37y_{n-2} + 9y_{n-3}\right]$$

**Fill up the blanks:**

VI. To fit a straight line by least square method, the normal equations are ______________

VII. In Gauss elimination method the coefficient matrix is transformed to ________ form.

VIII. $\Delta + E^{-1} =$ ___________ .

IX. Newton's divided difference formula is ____________ .

X. The type of the partial differential equation

$$\frac{\partial^2 f}{\partial x^2} + 2\frac{\partial^2 f}{\partial x \partial y} + 4\frac{\partial^2 f}{\partial y^2} = 0 \text{ is}$$ _____________ .

**Choose the correct answer :**

XI. If the roots of the equation $x^3 + px^2 + qx + r = 0$ are in A.P., then the condition is

(a) $2q^3 - 9pqr + 27r^2 = 0$ (b) $p^3 r = q^3$

(c) $2p^3 - 9pq + 27r = 0$ (d) None.

XII. Newton's formula converges if

(a) $|f'(x) . f''(x)| < \{f(x)\}^2$ (b) $|f(x) . f''(x)| < \{f'(x)\}^2$

(c) $|f(x) . f'(x)| < \{f'(x)\}^2$ (d) None.

XIII. $\Delta\left\{\frac{1}{f(x)}\right\}$ is equal to

(a) $\frac{\Delta f(x)}{f(x) f(x+1)}$ (b) $\frac{\Delta f(x+1)}{f(x+1) f(x)}$

(c) $-\frac{\Delta f(x)}{f(x) f(x+1)}$ (d) None.

XIV. The error in the trapezoidal rule is of the order

(a) $h^3$ (b) $h$ (c) $h^2$ (d) None.

XV. The partial differential equation $\frac{\partial^2 u}{\partial x^2} + \frac{\partial^2 u}{\partial y^2} = f(x, y)$ is called

(a) Heat equation (b) Wave equation

(c) Laplace equation (d) Poisson's equation.

**Answer the following short answer questions:**

XVI. If $\alpha, \beta, \gamma$ are the roots of $x^3 + qx + r = 0$ from the equation whose roots are $\frac{1}{\alpha}, \frac{1}{\beta}, \frac{1}{\gamma}$.

XVII. Compare Gauss elimination and Gauss–Seidal methods.

XVIII. Write the formula for $\frac{dy}{dx}$ at $x = x_n$ using backward difference operator.

XIX. State Simpson's three-eighths rule.

XX. State Milne's predictor formula.

**PART B — ($5 \times 12 = 60$ marks)**

XXI. (a) (i) Fit a straight line by the method of moments for the following data:

| $x$ : | 1 | 3 | 5 | 7 | 9 |
|---|---|---|---|---|---|
| $y$ : | 8 | 14 | 20 | 26 | 32. |

(ii) Solve: $6x^4 + 5x^3 - 38x^2 + 5x + 6 = 0$.

Or

(b) (i) Fit a curve of the form $y = ax^b$ for the following data by the method of least squares.

| $x$ : | 10 | 20 | 30 | 40 | 50 |
|---|---|---|---|---|---|
| $y$ : | 1.581 | 2.236 | 2.739 | 3.162 | 3.536 |

XXII. (a) (i) Using Newton–Raphson method, find a positive root of $xe^x = 1$.

(*ii*) Using Gauss–Seidel method, solve

$$4x + 2y + z = 14$$
$$x + 5y - z = 10$$
$$x + y + 8z = 20,$$

Correct to three decimals.

Or

(*b*) (*i*) Find the positive root of $x^3 - 3x + 1 = 0$ correct to 2 decimals by Horner's method.

(*ii*) Solve by Crout's method

$$x + y + 2z = 7$$
$$3x + 2y + 4z = 13$$
$$4x + 3y + 2z = 8.$$

XXIII.(*a*) (*i*) By finite integration, sum to *n* terms of the series

$$\frac{1}{1\,.\,2\,.\,3} + \frac{1}{2\,.\,3\,.\,4} + \frac{1}{3\,.\,4\,.\,5} + \ldots\ldots$$

(*ii*) The following are data from the steam table:

| temp. C° | 140 | 150 | 160 | 170 | 180 |
|---|---|---|---|---|---|
| pressure kgf/cm$^2$ | 3.685 | 4.854 | 6.302 | 8.076 | 10.225 |

Using Newton's formula, find the pressure of the steam for a temp. of 142°.

Or

(*b*) (*i*) Express $f(x) = 2x^3 - 3x^2 + 3x - 10$ in factorial notation and hence find $\Delta^3 f(x)$.

(*ii*) Given the values

| $x$ : | 20 | 23 | 26 | 29 |
|---|---|---|---|---|
| $y$ : | 0.3420 | 0.3907 | 0.4384 | 0.4848 |

Find $y$ at $x = 28$.

XXIV.(*a*) (*i*) Using Lagrange interpolation find $y$ (2) from the following data:

| $x$ : | 0 | 1 | 3 | 4 |
|---|---|---|---|---|
| $y$ : | 0 | 1 | 81 | 256 |

(*ii*) Find $y$ (1.05) if

| $x$ : | 1 | 1.05 | 1.1 | 1.15 | 1.2 | 1.25 | 1.3 |
|---|---|---|---|---|---|---|---|
| $y$ : | 1 | 1.025 | 1.049 | 1.072 | 1.095 | 1.118 | 1.14. |

Or

(*b*) (*i*) Find the value of $\log 2^{1/3}$ from $\int_0^1 \frac{x^2}{1 + x^3}\,dx$ using Simpson's one-third rule with $h = 0.25$.

(*ii*) Solve $y_{x+2} - 5y_{x+1} - 8y_x = x(x-1)\,2^x$.

XXV. (*a*) (*i*) Solve $\frac{dy}{dx} = \frac{3x+y}{x+2y}$, $y(1) = 1$ at $x = 1.1$ using Runge-Kutta fourth order method.

(*ii*) Solve $U_{xx} + U_{yy} = 0$; $0 \leq x,\ y \leq 1$ with $u(0, y) = 10 = u(1, y)$ and $u(x, 0) = 20 = u(x, 1)$.

Take $h = 0.25$ and apply Liebmann method to 3 decimal accuracy.

(*b*) (*i*) Compute at $x = 0.25$ by Modified Euler method given $\frac{dy}{dx} = 2xy$, $y(0) = 1$.

(*ii*) Using Crank–Nicholson's sceneme solve $U_{xx} = 16U_t$, $0 < x < 1$, $t > 0$ given $u(x, 0) = 0$, $u(0, t) = 0$, $u(1, t) = 100t$. Compute $u$ for one step in $t$ direction taking $h = \frac{1}{4}$.

# BHARATHIAR UNIVERSITY

## B.E. Degree Examination, November 1999

## Fifth Semester

**Time : Three hours** **Maximum : 100 marks**

Answer all the questions

**Part A — (20 × 2 = 40 marks)**

1. Write the observation equations when the equation y = ax + b is fit by the method of moments.

2. State true or false :
If a curve is fit to the points $(x_i, y_i)$, i = 1, 2, ..... n by least square method, then the curve passes through the point $\left(\frac{\Sigma x_i}{n}, \frac{\Sigma y_i}{n}\right)$,

3. Fill in the blanks :
If α, β, γ, are the roots of $x^3 + x^2 + x + 1 = 0$, then the equation whose roots are $\frac{1}{\alpha}, \frac{1}{\beta}, \frac{1}{\gamma}$ is . . . . . .

4. Choose the correct answer :
If the roots of the equation $x^3 - 19x^2 + 114x - 216 = 0$ are in G.P., then product of the two extreme roots equals
(a) 24 (b) 54 (c) 36 (d) 35.

5. What is the condition for the convergence of Gauss–Seidel iterative method ?

6. State the condition for convergence of Jacobi's iteration method for solving a system of simultaneous algebraic equations.

7. When does relaxation method succeed in solving a set of simultaneous equations ?

8. How to reduce the number of iterations while finding the root of an equation by Regula–Falsi method ?

9. Solve the difference equation
$u_{x+2} - 6u_{x+1} + 9u_x = 0.$

10. Write the difference table for

| x : | 3 | 5 | 7 | 9 |
|---|---|---|---|---|
| y : | 6 | 24 | 58 | 108 |

**11.** What is the Largrange's formula to find y if three sets of values $(x_o, y_0)$, $(x_1, y_1)$ and $(x_2, y_2)$ are given ?

**12.** Prove that $\frac{D}{\nabla} - \frac{\nabla}{D} = E - E^{-1}$

**13.** State Newton's forward interpolation formula.

**14.** Fill in the blanks :

To compute $\nabla^3 u_5$, we require, apart from $u_5$, the value of ....

**15.** Choose the correct answer :

Simpson's rule of integration is exact for all polynomials of degree not exceeding :

(a) 1 (b) 3 (c) 4 (d) 5.

**16.** Give the Newton's divided difference interpolation formula.

**17.** What is the disadvantage in Taylor series method ?

**18.** What is a predictor–corrector method of solving a differential equation ?

**19.** Is Euler's modified formula, a particular case of second order Runge–Kutta method ?

**20.** Give the Crank Nicolson difference scheme formula to solve the equation $u_t = \alpha^2 u_{xx}$.

**Part B – (5 × 12 = 60 marks)**

**21.** Fit a straight line to the data by the method of least squares :

| $x$ : | 0 | 5 | 10 | 15 | 20 |
|---|---|---|---|---|---|
| $y$ : | 7 | 10 | 15 | 21 | 25 |

Or

**22.** Diminish the roots of the equation $x^4 - 4x^3 - 7x^2 + 22x + 24 = 0$ by 1 and hence solve it.

**23.** Find the positive root of $x^3 + x - 1 = 0$ correct to 2 decimals by Horner's method.

Or

**24.** Solve by Crout's method :

$$2x - 6y + 8z = 24$$
$$3x + y + 2z = 6$$
$$5x + 4y - 3z = 2$$

**25.** Explain the difference between $\left(\frac{\Delta^2}{E}\right)u_x$ and $\frac{\Delta^2 u_x}{Eu_x}$, and find the values of these when $u_x = x^3$.

Or

**26.** Find the cubic polynomial which takes the following set of values (0, 1), (1,2), (2, 1) and (3, 10).

**27.** Compute $\int_0^4 e^x \, dx$ by Simpson's $\frac{1}{3}$ rule with 10 subdivisions.

Or

**28.** Solve : $u_{x+2} + 6u_{x+1} + 9u_x = 3^x + x2^x + 7$.

**29.** Apply Runge–Kutta method of fourth order to calculate y(0.2) given $\frac{dy}{dx} = x + y,\ y(0) = 1$ taking $h = 0.1$.

Or

**30.** Solve : $\frac{\partial^2 u}{\partial x^2} + \frac{\partial^2 u}{\partial y^2} = 0$, subject to

(a) $u(0, y) = 0$, for $0 \le y \le 4$

(b) $u(4, y) = 12 + y$, for $0 \le y \le 4$

(c) $u(x, 0) = 3x$, for $0 \le x \le 4$

(d) $u(x, 4) = x^2$, for $0 \le x \le 4$

by dividing the square into 16 square meshes of side 1.

# BHARATHIAR UNIVERSITY

## B.E. Degree Examination, November 1999
## Fifth Semester

**Time : Three hours** **Maximum : 100 marks**

**Part A — (20 × 1 = 20 marks)**

State True or False :

**1.** A cubic equation may have two real roots and one complex root

**2.** Crout's method is an iterauve method.

**3.** $1 + \Delta = (1 - \nabla)^{-1}$.

**4.** Lagrange's interpolation formula cannot be used when the base points are equally spaced.

**5.** Modified Euler's method is a Runge–Kutta method of seocnd roder.

Fill in the blanks :

**6.** The number of normal equations to fit a parabola $y = ax^2 + bx + c$ is

**7.** In Crout's method the coefficient matrix is expressed as a product of a lower triangular matrix and a ____________ matrix.

**8.** $\delta$ is given in terms of E as __________.

**9.** Newton's divided difference formula for equal intervals is called _____.

**10.** Euler's method is a Taylor's series method of __________ order.

Choose the correct answer :

**11.** If $-1 + i$ is a root of a polynomial equation then there is another root of the form

(a) $1 - i$ (b) 0

(c) $-1 - i$ (d) $1 + i$.

**12.** Newton–Raphson method is convergent

(a) Linearly (b) Quadratically

(c) Cubically (d) Biquadratically.

**13.** The central difference $\delta$ is equivalent to

(a) $2 \sin \dfrac{hD}{2}$ (b) E $\Delta$

(c) E $\nabla$ (d) $\nabla \Delta$.

**14.** If $u_1 = 1, u_3 = 17, u_4 = 43, u_5 = 89$, then $u_2$ is

(a) 5 (b) 10

(c) 12 (d) 15

**15.** $\dfrac{\partial^2 u}{\partial + 2} = \dfrac{d^2 u}{dx^2}$ is

(a) Elliptic (b) Parabolic

(c) Hyperbolic (d) Poisson.

**16.** What are the normal equation to fit a curve of type $y = ae^{bx}$ to the date $(x_i, y_i), i = 1, 2, .... n$ ?

**17.** Derive Newton's algorithm to find cube root of a number.

**18.** If $E^2 u_n = n^2$, what is $u_n$ when $h = 1$.

**19.** Evaluate $y(1)$ from

| x : | 0 | 2 | 3 |
|---|---|---|---|
| y : | –1 | 3 | 5 |

**20.** What is the geometrical meaning of Euler's algorithm ?

**Part B — (5 × 12 = 60 marks)**

**21.** (a) Fit a curve of the form $y = ax^b$ to the following date using the method of group averages :

| $x$: | 10 | 20 | 30 | 40 | 50 | 60 | 70 | 80 |
|---|---|---|---|---|---|---|---|---|
| $y$: | 1.06 | 1.33 | 1.52 | 1.68 | 1.81 | 1.91 | 2.01 | 2.11 |

Or

(b) If $\alpha$, $\beta$, $\gamma$ are the roots of $x^3 + px + q = 0$, from the equation whose roots are $(\alpha - \beta)^2$, $(\beta - \gamma)^2$, $(\gamma - \alpha)^2$ and hence evaluate $(\alpha - \beta)^2 (\beta - \gamma)^2 (\gamma - \alpha)^2$.

**22.** (a) Find a root of $xe^x = 2$ using method of false position.

(b) Evaluate $\sqrt[3]{7}$ using Newton method.

Or

(c) Solve :

$$2x + 3y + z = -1$$
$$5x + y + z = 9$$
$$3x + 2y + 4z = 11$$

using Crout's method.

23. (a) Sum the series upto $n$ terms

$$\frac{1}{1.\,2.\,3} + \frac{1}{2.\,3.4} + \frac{1}{3.\,4.\,5}$$

(b) Find the missing term in the table :

| $x$ : | 2 | 4 | 6 | 8 | 10 |
|---|---|---|---|---|---|
| $y$ : | 5.6 | 8.6 | 13.9 | — | 35.6 |

Or

(c) Obtain y (3.75) from

| $x$ : | 2.5 | 3.0 | 3.5 | 4.0 | 4.5 | 5.0 |
|---|---|---|---|---|---|---|
| $y$ : | 24.14 | 22.04 | 20.22 | 18.64 | 17.26 | 16.04 |

Using Gauss formula.

(d) Write short notes on different kinds of differences

24. (a) Use Lagrange's formula to fit a polynomial for the data :

| $x$: | 0 | 1 | 3 | 4 |
|---|---|---|---|---|
| $y$: | –12 | 0 | 6 | 12 |

and hence evaluate $y$ (2)

Or

(b) Evaluate $\int_1^2 \frac{dx}{1+x}$ using Simpson's rule with $h = 0.1$.

(c) Solve $y_{n+2} - 5y_{n+1} + 6y_n = x^2 + x + 1$.

25. (a) solve $\frac{dy}{dx} = xy - y^2$, . $y(0) = 1$ to find y, sing Milne's P–C method. Evaluate the intermediate values using R–K method.

Or

(b) Solve $u_{tt} = u_{xx}$, $0 \le x \le 1$, $t \ge 0$ with

$$u(x, 0) = x(1 - x), \quad 0 \le x \le 1$$
$$u_t, (x, 0) = 0 \quad 0 \le x \le 1$$
$$u(0, t) = u(1, t) = 0, \ \forall\, t = 0$$

for 5 time steps ith h = 0.2.

# B.E. DEGREE EXAMINAITON, APRIL 2001

**Fourth Semester**

**Common to CSE/Information Technology**

**MATHEMATICS — IV**

(Numerical Methods)

Time : Three hours Maximum : 80 marks

Answer All questions

All questions carry equal marks

PART A — ($20 \times 1 = 20$ MARKS)

State True or False :

1. The normal equations to fit the line $y = a + ax$ and $y = ax + b$ are same.
2. Bisection method is an iterative method.
3. Eighth order difference of a polynomial of degree five is always zero.
4. The order of the truncation error of Simpson's 1/3 rule is higher than that of Trapezoidal rule.
5. Crank-Nicolson formula is an explicit formula.

**Fill in the blanks :**

6. Crout's method is a ____________ (direct/iterative) method.
7. The number of normal equations required to fit a curve of the form $y = a\, x^b$ is __________ .
8. The $n$th order difference of the polynomial $p = a_0x^n + a_1x^{n-1} + ... + a_n$ is ____________ .
9. Stirling's formula is based on ________ and ________ formulae.
10. Laplace equation is $a\ (n)$ __________ partial differential equation.

**Choose the correct answer :**

11. The rational root of $x^3 - 11x^2 + 37x - 35 = 0$, given that $(3+\sqrt{2})$ is a root, is

    (*a*) – 17 (*b*) 7 (*c*) 5 (*d*) –5.

12. Horner's method is based on

    (*i*) diminishing of roots (*ii*) multiplication of roots.

    (*a*) (i) (*b*) (ii)

    (*c*) (i) or (ii) (*d*) (i) and (ii)

13. The function whose first order difference is $3x^{(2)} - 2x^{(1)}$ is

    (*a*) $x^{(3)} - x^{(2)}$ (b) $\dfrac{x^{(3)}}{3} - x^{(2)}$

    (*c*) $3x^{(3)} - 2x^{(2)}$ (*d*) $3x^{(3)} - x^{(1)}$

14. The solution of $u_{n+2} - 5u_{n+1} + 6u_n = 0$ is

(*a*) $A(3)^n + B(2)^n$ (*b*) $A(-3)^n + B(-2)^n$

(*c*) $A(-3)^n + B(2)^n$ (*d*) $A(3)^n + B(-2)^n$

15. The equation $u_t = \alpha^2 u_{xx}$ is

(*a*) Elliptic (*b*) Hyperbolic

(*c*) Parabolic (*d*) Poisson.

16. Find the sum of the squares of the roots of $x^3 - x = 0$.

17. What is the other name for Regula-falsi method?

18. Write Everett's formula.

19. Solve : $u_{n+1} - 3u_n = 0$ given $u_0 = 2$.

20. Whether Picard's method can be applied to any first order differential equation with an initial value? Explain.

Part B – (5 × 12 = 60 marks)

21. (*a*) (*i*) Fit a curve of the form $I = a\,D^n$ for the data

| $D$: | 1720 | 2300 | 3200 | 4100 |
|---|---|---|---|---|
| $I$: | 655 | 789 | 1000 | 1164 |

(*ii*) Explain the method of moments.

Or

(*b*) (*i*) Solve $3x^3 + 8x^2 + 8x + 12 = 0$ by diminishing its roots by 4.

(ii) Show that the condition that $x^3 + 3px + q = 0$ should have repeated roots is $4p^3 + q^2 = 0$.

22. (*a*) Solve by Crout's method

$$2x + y + 3z = 13,\ 3x + y + 4z = 17,$$
$$x + 5y + z = 14.$$

Or

(b) (*i*) Solve, to find a real root of, $x^3 - x - 2 = 0$ using Newton-Raphson method.

(*ii*) Use Gauss-Seidal method to solve

$$x + 5y - z = 10,\ 4x + 2y + z = 14,\ x + y + 8z = 20.$$

23. (*a*) (*i*) Prove that $u_0 + u_1 x + u_2 x^2 + \dots \infty =$

$$\frac{u_0}{1-x} + \frac{x\,\Delta^2 u_0}{(1-x)^2} + \frac{x^2 \Delta u_0}{(1-x)^3} + \dots,$$

(*ii*) Prove that $\Delta \tan^{-1}\left(\frac{x-1}{x}\right) = \tan^{-1}\left(\frac{1}{2x^2}\right)$.

(*b*) Find y corresponding to $x = 0.644$ using Bessel's formula given

| $x$: | 0.61 | 0.62 | 0.63 | 0.64 | 0.65 | 0.66 |
|---|---|---|---|---|---|---|
| $y$: | 1.840431 | 1.858928 | 1.877610 | 1.896481 | 1.915541 | 1.934792 |

24. (*a*) (i) Derive Newton's divided difference formula.

(ii) Fit a Lagrangian polynomial of degree two

| $x$: | 1 | 2 | –4 |
|---|---|---|---|
| $f(x)$: | 3 | –5 | 4 |

Or

(*b*) (i) Solve $u_{n+2} - 5u_{n+1} + 3u_n = n\, 2^n$.

(ii) Evaluate $\int_0^2 \frac{1}{1+x^3}\, dx$ using Simpson's 1/3 rule choosing $h = 0.5$.

25. (*a*) Find $y(1.1)$ using Euler method and $y(1.2)$ using R-K method of order four, satisfying $10y' = x^2 + y^2, y(0) = 1$.

Or

(*b*) (*i*) Solve $u_t = 2u_{xx}$ by finite difference method subject to the conditions u (0. $t$) = 0

$u(1, t) = 0, u(x, 0) = \sin \pi x$.

(*ii*) Derive standard five point formula to solve Laplace equation, stating the assumptions you make.

# ANNA UNIVERSITY

## B.E./B.TECH. DEGREE EXAMINATION,

## APRIL/MAY 2003

## Fourth Semester

## CIVIL ENGINEERING

## MA-038 — NUMERICAL METHODS

(Common to Mechanical, Production, Mechatronics, Aeronautical, Automobile, Instrumentation and Control Engineering and Instrumentation Engineering )

Time : Three Hours Maximum Marks : 100

Answer ALL questions.

**PART A — (10 × 2 = 20 marks)**

1. If $g(x)$ is continuous in $[a, b]$, then under what condition the interative method $x = g(x)$ has a unique solution in $[a, b]$?
2. Compare Gauss–Jacobi and Gauss–Seidel methods for solving linear systems of the form $AX = B$.
3. Construct a linear interpolating polynomial given the points $(x_0, y_0)$ and $(x_1, y_1)$.
4. Write down the range for $p$ for which Stirling's formula gives most accurate result.
5. Find the error in the derivative of $f(x) = \cos x$ by computing directly and using the approximation $f'(x) = \dfrac{f(x+h)-f(x-h)}{2h}$ at $x = 0.8$ choosing $h = 0.01$.
6. What are the errors in Trapezoidal and Simpson's rules of numerical integration?
7. What is a predictor-corrector method?
8. What do we mean by saying that a method is self-starting? Not self-starting?
9. What is the truncation error of the central difference approximation of $y'(x)$ ?
10. For what value of $\lambda$, the explicit, method of solving the hyperbolic equation $\dfrac{\partial^2 u}{\partial x^2} = \dfrac{1}{C^2}\dfrac{\partial^2 u}{\partial t^2}$ is stable, where $\lambda = \dfrac{C\,\Delta t}{\Delta x}$ ?

**PART B – (5 × 16 = 80 marks)**

11. (*i*) Consider the non linear system $x^2 - 2x - y + 0.5 = 0$ and $x^2 - 4y^2 - 4 = 0$. Use Newton-Raphson method with the starting

value $(x_0, y_0) = (2.00, 0.25)$ and compute $(x_1, y_1)$ $(x_2, y_2)$ and $(x_3, y_3)$.

(*ii*) Find all eigen values of the matrix $\begin{bmatrix} 2 & -1 & 0 \\ -1 & 2 & -1 \\ 0 & -1 & 2 \end{bmatrix}$ by Jacobi method (Apply only 3 iterations).

**12.** (*a*) Find an approximate polynomial for $f(x)$ which agrees with the data:

| $k$ | $x_k$ | $f(x_k)$ | $f'(x_k)$ |
|---|---|---|---|
| 0 | 1.3 | 0.62009 | – 0.52202 |
| 1 | 1.6 | 0.45540 | – 0.56990 |
| 2 | 1.9 | 0.28182 | – 0.58116 |

using Hermite's interpolation. Hence find the approximate value of $f(1.5)$.

*Or*

(*b*) (*i*) Use Newton's backward difference formula to construct an interpolating polynomial of degree 3 for the data : $f(-0.75) = -0.07181250$, $f(-0.5) = -0.024750$, $f(-0.25) = 0.33493750$ and $f(0) = 1.10100$. Hence find $f(-1/3)$.

(*ii*) Given :

| $x$ (in degrees) | : | 0° | 5° | 10° | 15° | 20° | 25° | 30° |
|---|---|---|---|---|---|---|---|---|
| $f(x)$ | : | 0 | 0.0875 | 0.1763 | 0.2679 | 0.3640 | 0.4663 | 0.5774 |

Using Stirling's formula, find $f(16°)$.

**13.** (*a*) (*i*) Consider the following table of data :

| $x$ | : | 0.2 | 0.4 | 0.6 | 0.8 | 1.0 |
|---|---|---|---|---|---|---|
| $f(x)$ | : | 0.9798652 | 0.9177710 | 0.8080348 | 0.6386093 | 0.3843735 |

Find $f'(0.25)$ using Newton's forward difference approximation, $f'(0.6)$ using Stirling's approximation and $f'(0.95)$ using Newton's backward difference approximation.

(*ii*) For the given data :

| $x$ | : | 0.7 | 0.9 | 1.1 | 1.3 |
|---|---|---|---|---|---|
| $f(x)$ | : | 0.64835 | 0.91360 | 1.16092 | 1.36178 |
| $x$ | : | 1.5 | 1.7 | 1.9 | 2.1 |
| $f(x)$ | : | 1.49500 | 1.55007 | 1.52882 | 1.44573 |

Using Simpson's $\frac{1}{3}$ rule for the first six intervals and trapezoidal rule for the last interval to evaluate $\int_{0.7}^{2.1} f(x)\,dx$

Also use trapezoidal rule for the first interval and Simpson's $\frac{1}{3}$ rule for the rest of the intervals to evaluate $\int_{0.7}^{2.1} f(x)\,dx$

Comment on the obtained values by comparing with the exact value of the integral which is equal to 1.81759.

Or

(*b*) (*i*) Evaluate $\int_{0.2}^{1.5} e^{-x^2}\,dx$ using the three point Gaussian quadrature.

(*ii*) Using trapezoidal rule evaluate $\int_{1.4}^{2.0}\int_{1.0}^{1.5} \ln(x+2y)\,d\,y\,d\,x$ choosing $\Delta x = 0.15$ and $\Delta y = 0.25$.

**14.** (*a*) Consider the initial value problem $\frac{dy}{dx} = y - x^2 + 1$, $y(0) = 0.5$.

(*i*) Using the modified Euler method, find $y(0.2)$.

(*ii*) Using 4th order Runge-Kutta method, find $y(0.4)$ and $y(0.6)$.

(*iii*) Using Adam-Bashforth Predictor-Corrector method, find $y(0.8)$.

*Or*

(*b*) Consider the second order initial value problem $y'' - 2y' + 2y = e^{2t}\sin t$, with $y(0) = -0.4$ and $y'(0) = -0.6$.

(*i*) Using Taylor series approximation, find $y(0.1)$.

(*ii*) Using 4th Order Runge-Kutta method, find $y(0.2)$.

**15.** (*a*) Solve $\frac{\partial^2 u}{\partial x^2} = \frac{\partial u}{\partial t}$, $0 < x < 2$, $t > 0$, $u(0, t) = u(2,t) = 0$, $t > 0$

and $u(x,0) = \sin\frac{\pi x}{2}, 0 \le x \le 2$ using $\Delta x = 0.5$ and $\Delta t = 0.25$ for two times steps by Crank-Nicholson implicit finite difference method.

*Or*

(*b*) Approximate the solution to the wave equation $\frac{\partial^2 u}{\partial x^2} = \frac{\partial^2 u}{\partial t^2}$, $0 < x < 1$, $t > 0$, $u(0, t) = u(1, t) = 0$, $t > 0$, $u(x, 0) = \sin 2\pi x$, $0 \le x \le 1$ and $\frac{\partial u}{\partial t}(x,0) = 0$, $0 \le x \le 1$ with $\Delta x = 0.25$ and $\Delta t = 0.25$ for 3 time steps.

## B.E./B.TECH. DEGREE EXAMINATION, NOVERMBER/DECEMBER 2004

**Fourth Semester**

Aeronautical Engineering

MA 038 – NUMERICAL METHODS

[Common to Civil Engineering, Automobile Engineering, Instrumentation Engineering, Instrumentation and Control Engineering, Mechanical Engineering, Mechatronics Engineering, and Production Engineering]

Time : Three hours | Maximum : 100 marks

Answer ALL questions

PART A – (10 × 2 = 20 marks)

1. State the order of convergence and convergence condition for Newton's Raphson method.

2. Find the dominant eigen value of $A = \begin{pmatrix} 1 & 2 \\ 3 & 4 \end{pmatrix}$ by power method.

3. If $u = \dfrac{x - x_0}{h}$, then specify the range for $u$ to obtain better result using Stirling's formula and Bessel's formula.

4. Show that $\underset{bcd}{\overset{3}{\Delta}}\left(\dfrac{1}{a}\right) = -\dfrac{1}{abcd}$

5. State three point Gaussian quadrature formula.

6. Using Trapezoidal rule evaluate $\int_0^{\pi} \sin x dx$ by dividing the range into 6 equal parts.

7. Using modified Euler's method, find $y$ (0.1) if $\dfrac{dy}{dx} = x^2 + y^2$, $y$ (0) = 1.

8. Write down the formula to solve 2nd order differential equation using Runge-Kutta method of 4th order.

9. Write down the diagonal five point formula to solve the equation $u_{xx} + u_{yy} = 0$.

10. Write down the Implicit formula to solve one dimensional heat flow equation $u_{xx} = \dfrac{1}{c^2} u_t$.

**PART B — (5 × 16 = 80 marks)**

11. (*i*) Derive explicit scheme to solve parabolic equation $u_{xx} = \dfrac{1}{c^2} u_t$. (4)

(ii) Solve $y_{tt} = y_{xx}$ upto $t = 0.5$ with a spacing of 0.1 subject to $y(0, t) = 0, y(1, t) = 0,\ y_t(x, 0) = 0$ and $y(x, 0) = 10 + x(1 - x)$. (12)

**12.** (a) (i) Find a root of $x\log_{10}^{x} - 1.2 = 0$ by Newton's method correct to three decimal places. (8)

(ii) Solve $10x + y + z = 12$, $2x + 10y + z = 13$, $x + y + 5z = 7$ by Gauss-Jordan method. (8)

Or

(b) (i) Find all the eigen values and eigen vectors of $A = \begin{pmatrix} 2 & 3 & 1 \\ 3 & 2 & 2 \\ 1 & 2 & 1 \end{pmatrix}$ by Jacobi method. (10)

(ii) Using Gauss-Jordan method, find the inverse of $A = \begin{bmatrix} 1 & 1 & 3 \\ 1 & 3 & -3 \\ -2 & -4 & -4 \end{bmatrix}$. (6)

**13.** (a) (i) Obtain the root of $f(x) = 0$ by Lagrange Inverse Interpolation given that $f(30) = -30$, $f(34) = -13$, $f(38) = 3$, $f(42) = 18$. (8)

(ii) find $e^{0.644}$ from the following data, using Bessel's formula

| $x$ : | 0.61 | 0.62 | 0.63 | 0.64 | 0.65 | 0.66 | 0.67 |
|---|---|---|---|---|---|---|---|
| $e^x$ : | 1.8404 | 1.8589 | 1.8776 | 1.8965 | 1.9155 | 1.9348 | 1.9542 |

(8)

Or

(b) (i) Find $f(x)$ as a polynomial in $x$ for the following data by Newton's divided difference formula. (8)

| $x$ : | –4 | –1 | 0 | 2 | 5 |
|---|---|---|---|---|---|
| $f(x)$ : | 1245 | 33 | 5 | 9 | 1335 |

(ii) Find $y(35)$ by Stirling's formula from the following data : (8)

| $x$ : | 20 | 30 | 40 | 50 |
|---|---|---|---|---|
| $y$ : | 512 | 439 | 346 | 243 |

**14.** (a) (i) Evaluate $\int_0^1\int_1^2 \frac{2xy\,dxdy}{(1+x^2)(1+y^2)}$ by Trapezoidal rule with $h = k = 0.25$. (10)

(*ii*) Find the value of sec 31° from the following data : (6)

| $\theta$(deg) : | 31° | 32° | 33° | 34° |
|---|---|---|---|---|
| tan $\theta$ : | 0.6008 | 0.6249 | 0.6494 | 0.6745 |

Or

(*b*) (*i*) Using Simpson's $\frac{3}{8}$th rule evaluate $\int_0^6 \frac{dx}{1+x^2}$, by dividing the range into 6 equal parts. (6)

(*ii*) Find the maximum and minimum value of *y* tabulated below : (10)

| $x$ : | –2 | –1 | 0 | 1 | 2 | 3 | 4 |
|---|---|---|---|---|---|---|---|
| $y$ : | 2 | –0.25 | 0 | –0.25 | 2 | 15.75 | 56 |

**15.** (*a*) (*i*) Using Taylor series method find *y* at $x = 0.1$ if $\frac{dy}{dx} = x^2 y - 1$. (8)

(*ii*) Given $\frac{dy}{dx} = x^2(1+y)$, $y(1) = 1$, $y(1.1) = 1.233$, $y(1.2) = 1.548$, $y(1.3) = 1.979$, evaluate $y$ (1.4) by Adams–Bashforth method. (8)

Or

(*b*) (*i*) Using Runge–Kutta method of 4th order, solve $\frac{dy}{dx} = \frac{y^2 - x^2}{y^2 + x^2}$ with $y(0) = 1$ at $x = 0.2$. (8)

(*ii*) Using Milne's method to find $y(4.4)$ given that $5xy + y^2 - 2 = 0$ given $y(4) = 1$, $y(4.1) = 1.0049$, $y(4.2) = 1.0097$, $y(4.3) = 1.0143$. (8)

## B.E./B.Tech. DEGREE EXAMINATION, APRIL/MAY 2005

Fourth Semester

## MA 038 — NUMERICAL METHODS

(Common to : Civil Engineering, Automobile Engineering, Instrumentation Engineering, Instrumentation and Control Engineering, Mechanical Engineering, Mechatronics Engineering and Production Engineering)

Time : Three hours | Maximum : 100 marks

Answer ALL questions.

**PART A – (10 × 2 = 20 marks)**

1. What is the order of convergence of Newton-Raphson method?
2. State the principle used in Gauss-Jordan method.
3. State Stirling's central difference formula.
4. If the Hermite's polynomial is $P(x) = \sum_{1}^{n} A_i f(x_i) + \sum_{1}^{n} B_i f'(x_i)$, write down the values of $B_1$ and $B_2$ given that $f(0) = 0$, $f(1) = 1$; $f'(0) = 0$, $f'(1) = 0$.
5. Evaluate $\int_{-1}^{1} \frac{dx}{1+x^2}$ by Gaussian two point formula.
6. Write down the Trapezoidal rule to evaluate $\int_{1}^{6} f(x)dx$ with $h = 0.5$.
7. Write down Adam-Bashforth predictor and corrector formulae.
8. What are the values of $k_1$ and $l_1$ to solve $y'' + xy' + y = 0$; $y(0) = 1$, $y'(0) = 0$ by Runge-Kutta method of fourth order.
9. Write down the standard five point formula to solve Laplace equation

$$\frac{\partial^2 u}{\partial x^2} + \frac{\partial^2 u}{\partial y^2} = 0.$$

10. What is the value of $k$ to solve $\frac{\partial u}{\partial t} = \frac{1}{2} u_{xx}$ by Bender-Schmidt method with $h = 1$ if $h$ and $k$ are the increments of $x$ and $t$ respectively?

**PART B — (5 × 16 = 80 marks)**

**11.** (*i*) Solve the Poisson equation $u_{xx} + u_{yy} = -81xy$, $0 < x < 1$; $0 < y < 1$ given that $u(0, y) = 0$; $u(x, 0) = 0$; $u(1, y) = 100$; $u(x, 1) = 100$ and $h = \frac{1}{3}$. (8)

(*ii*) Solve $\frac{\partial u}{\partial t} = \frac{\partial^2 u}{\partial x^2}$ in $0 < x < 5$; $t > 0$ given that $u(x, 0) = 20$ $u(0, t) = 0$; $u(5, t) = 100$. Compute $u$ for one time-step with $h = 1$ by Crank-Nicholson method. (8)

**12.** (*a*) (*i*) Solve the following equations by Gauss-Seidel method $4x + 2y + z = 14$; $x + 5y - z = 10$; $x + y + 8x = 20$. (8)

(*ii*) Solve $x^2 + y^2 = 1$; $xy = x + y$ given that $x_0 = 0.5$, $y_0 = -1$ by Newton-Raphson method (2 iterations). (8)

Or

(*b*) (*i*) Solve $x + 3y + 3z = 16$; $x + 4y + 3z = 18$; $x + 3y + 4z = 19$ by Gauss-Jordan method. (8)

(*ii*) Find the numerically largest eigen value of

$$A = \begin{bmatrix} 1 & -3 & 2 \\ 4 & 4 & -1 \\ 6 & 3 & 5 \end{bmatrix}$$ by power method. (8)

**13.** (*a*) (*i*) Find $f(8)$ by Newton's divided difference formula for the data : (8)

| $x$ : | 4 | 5 | 7 | 10 | 11 | 13 |
|---|---|---|---|---|---|---|
| $f(x)$ : | 48 | 100 | 294 | 900 | 1210 | 2028 |

(*ii*) By using Bessel's formula find the value of $y_{25}$ if

| $x$ : | 20 | 24 | 28 | 32 |
|---|---|---|---|---|
| $y$ : | 2854 | 3162 | 3544 | 3992 |

(8)

Or

(*b*) (*i*) Find the polynomial $f(x)$ by using Lagrange's formula and hence find $f(3)$ for

| $x$ : | 0 | 1 | 2 | 5 |
|---|---|---|---|---|
| $f(x)$ : | 2 | 3 | 12 | 147 |

(8)

(*ii*) Find the Hermite's polynomial for

| $x$ : | $-1$ | 0 | 1 |
|---|---|---|---|
| $f(x)$ : | 1 | 0 | 1 |
| $f'(x)$ : | 0 | 0 | 0 |

(8)

**14.** (*a*) (*i*) Find $f'(3)$ and $f''(3)$ for the following data :

| $x$ : | 3.0 | 3.2 | 3.4 | 3.6 | 3.8 | 4.0 |
|---|---|---|---|---|---|---|
| $f(x)$ : | $-14$ | $-10.032$ | $-5.296$ | $-0.256$ | 6.672 | 14 |

(*ii*) Evaluate $\int_0^5 \frac{dx}{4x+5}$ by Simpson's one-third rule and hence find the value of $\log_e 4$ ($n = 10$). (8)

Or

(*b*) (*i*) Evaluate $\int_0^2\int_0^2 f(x, y)dxdy$ by Trapezoidal rule for the following data : (8)

| $x/y$ | 0 | 0.5 | 1 | 1.5 | 2 |
|---|---|---|---|---|---|
| 0 | 2 | 3 | 4 | 5 | 5 |
| 1 | 3 | 4 | 6 | 9 | 11 |
| 2 | 4 | 6 | 8 | 11 | 14 |

(*ii*) Evaluate $\int_0^2 \frac{x^2+2x+1}{1+(x+1)^4}dx$ by Gaussian three point formulae. (8)

**15.** (*a*) (*i*) Solve $y' = x+y$; $y(0) = 1$ by Taylor's series method. Find the values of $y$ at $x = 0.1$ and $x = 0.2$. (8)

(*ii*) Solve $y' = \frac{y^2-x^2}{y^2+x^2}$; $y(0) = 1$ by Runge-Kutta method of fourth order to find $y(0.2)$. (8)

Or

(*b*) (*i*) Solve $y' = x-y^2$, $0 \le x \le 1$, $y(0) = 0$, $y(0.2) = 0.02$; $y(0.4) = 0.0795$; $y(0.6) = 0.1762$ by Milne's method to find $y(0.8)$ and $y(1)$. (10)

(*ii*) Solve $y' = 1-y$; $y(0) = 0$ by modified Euler's method. (6)

**ANNA UNIVERSITY**

# B.E./B.TECH. DEGREE EXAMINATION, NOVEMBER/DECEMBER 2005

**Fourth Semester**

**AERONAUTICAL ENGINEERING**

**MA-038 — NUMERICAL METHODS**

(Common to Auto, Civil, Instrumentation, Instrumentation and Control Engineering, Mechanical Engineering, Mechatronics and Production Engineering,)

Time : Three Hours  Maximum Marks : 100

Answer ALL questions.

**PART A — (10 × 2 = 20 marks)**

**1.** Solve $3x + y = 2$, $x + 3y = -2$, by Gauss Seidel iteration method.

**2.** Explain power method of finding the eigen values of a matrix.

**3.** Find the quadratic polynomial that fits $y(x) = x^4$ at $x = 0, 1, 2$.

**4.** Use Lagrange's formula, to find the quadratic polynomial that takes these values.

| $x$ : | 0 | 1 | 3 |
|---|---|---|---|
| $y$ : | 0 | 1 | 0 |

Then find $y(2)$.

**5.** By differentiating Newton's backward difference formula, find the first derivative of the function $f(x)$.

**6.** What are the errors involved in Simpson's $\frac{1}{3}$ and $\frac{3}{8}$ rules for the evaluation of a definite integral of the form $\int_a^b f(x)dx$?

**7.** Solve the differential equation $\frac{dy}{dx} = x + y + xy, y(0) = 1$ by Taylor series method to get the value of $y$ at $x = h$.

**8.** Compare the Milne's predictor-corrector and Adam-Bashforth predictor-corrector methods for solving ordinary differential equations.

**9.** Derive a difference scheme for the one dimensional heat equation using backward difference for the time derivative.

**10.** Set up a finite difference scheme for the boundary value problem $u'' = u, u'(1) = a$ and $u'(3) = b$ with $h = 0.5$ central differences.

**PART B – (5 × 16 = 80 marks)**

**11.** (*i*) Solve the system $e^x - y = 0$ and $xy - e^x = 0$ by Newton-Raphson method to obtain the solution near (0.95, 2.7). Perform only 3 iterations. (8)

(*ii*) Find the inverse of the matrix

$$\begin{pmatrix} 2 & 0 & 1 \\ 3 & 2 & 5 \\ 1 & -1 & 0 \end{pmatrix}$$

by Gauss-Jordan method. (8)

**12.** (*a*) (*i*) Using Newton's divided differences method find $f(1.5)$ using the data $f(1.0) = 0.7651977$, $f(1.3) = 0.6200860$ $f(1.6) = 0.4554022$, $f(1.9) = 0.2818186$ and $f(2.2) = 0.1103623$. (8)

(*ii*) Construct an approximating polynomial for the following data : (8)

| $x$ | $f(x)$ | $f'(x)$ |
|---|---|---|
| 0.8 | 0.22363 | 2.16918 |
| 1.0 | 0.65810 | 2.04670 |

*Or*

(*b*) (*i*) Compute cosh 0.56 from the data cosh 0.5 = 1.127626, cosh 0.6 = 1.185465, cosh 0.7 = 1.255169 and cosh 0.8 = 1.337435. (8)

(*ii*) Using Bessel's approximation, find the value of $p(1.2)$ from the data : (8)

| $x$ : | 0.2 | 0.6 | 1.0 | 1.4 | 1.8 |
|---|---|---|---|---|---|
| $p(x)$: | 0.39104 | 0.33322 | 0.24197 | 0.14973 | 0.07895 |

**13.** (*a*) (i) Find the first and second derivatives at $x = 1.6$ for the function represented by the following tabular data : (10)

| $x$ : | 1 | 1.5 | 2.0 | 3.0 |
|---|---|---|---|---|
| $y$ : | 0 | 0.40547 | 0.69315 | 1.09861 |

(*ii*) Using three point Gaussian quadrature, evaluate $\int_0^1 \frac{dx}{\sqrt{1+x^4}}$. (6)

*Or*

(*b*) Evaluate $\int_0^1 \left\{ \int_1^2 \frac{2xydy}{(1+x^2)(1+y^2)} \right\} dx$ using Simpson's $\frac{1}{3}$ rd method with step length $h = k = 0.25$. (16)

**14.** (*a*) Compute the first 3 steps of the initial value problem $\frac{dy}{dx} = \frac{x-y}{2}$, $y(0) = 1.0$ by Taylor series method and next step by Milne's method with step length $h = 0.1$. (16)

*Or*

(*b*) Consider the second order initial value problem $x''(t)+4x'(t)+5x(t)=0$, with $x(0) = 3$ and $x'(0) = -5$.

(*i*) Write down the equivalent system of two first order equations. (1)

(*ii*) Given $x(0.1) = 2.5257$, $x'(0.1) = -4.820$, $x(0.2) = 2.1040$ and $x'(0.2) = -3.9506$, find $x(0.3)$ and $x'(0.3)$ using 4th order Runge-Kutta method. (6)

(*iii*) Find $x(0.4)$ and $x'(0.4)$ using Adam-Bashforth method. (9)

**15.** (*a*) Approximate the solution to the wave equation $\frac{\partial^2 u}{\partial x^2} - \frac{\partial^2 u}{\partial t^2} = 0$, $0 < x < 1$, $t > 0$, $u(0,t) = u(1,t) = 0, t > 0, u(x,0) = \begin{cases} 1, 0 \le x \le 1/2 \\ -1, 1/2 < x \le 1 \end{cases}$ and $\frac{\partial u}{\partial t}(x,0) = x$ using $h = k = 0.1$ for 3 time steps. (16)

*Or*

(*b*) Approximate the solution to the following elliptic partial differential equation $\frac{\partial^2 u}{\partial x^2} + \frac{\partial^2 u}{\partial y^2} = e^{xy}(x^2 + y^2), 0 < x < 1,\ 0 < y < 1$, $u(0, y) = 1$, $u(1, y) = e^y$, $0 \le y \le 1$, , *and* $u(x, 0) = 1$, $u(x, 1) = e^x$, $0 \le x \le 1$, using $h = k = \frac{1}{3}$. (16)

# B.E./B.TECH. DEGREE EXAMINATION, NOVEMBER/DECEMBER 2005

**Sixth Semester**

## ELECTRONICS AND INSTRUMENTATION ENGINEERING

## MA-038 — NUMERICAL METHODS

(Common to Textile Technology, Chemical Engineering, Leather Technology)

Time : Three Hours Maximum Marks : 100

Answer ALL questions.

**PART A — (10 × 2 = 20 marks)**

1. What is the condition for the convergence of the iterative method for solving $x = \phi(x)$?
2. Solve by Gauss method $x + y = 2$ $2x - y = 1$.
3. State Lagranges Interpolation formula.
4. State Bessel's formula of Interpolation.
5. What is the order of error in (a) Trapezoidal rule (b) Simpson's rule.
6. Apply Gauss two point formula to evaluate $\int_{-1}^{1} \frac{dx}{1+x^2}$.
7. Using Euler's method find $y(z)$ given $y' = x + y$ $y(0) = 1$.
8. State Adam-Bashforth predictor-corrector formulae.
9. Write down the finite difference scheme to solve $\nabla^2 u = f(x, y)$.
10. State Crank-Nicholson scheme to solve $U_{xx} = aUt$ when $k = ah^2$.

**PART B – (5 × 16 = 80 Marks)**

11. (*i*) Solve $y'' = xy$ $y(0) = -1$ $y(1) = 2$ by finite difference method taking $n = 2$. (8)

(*ii*) Solve $U_{xx} = U_t$ given u $(0, t) = 0$ u$(4, t) = 0$ $u(x, 0) = x(4 - x)$ assuming $h = k = 1$ upto $t = 5$. (8)

12. (*a*) (*i*) Solve $f(x, y) = x^2 + y^2 - 4 = 0$ $g(x, y) = y + e^x - 1 = 0$ starting with $(1, -1.7)$ by Newton's method. (8)

(*ii*) Find the dominant. Eigen value of $A = \begin{pmatrix} 1 & 2 \\ 3 & 4 \end{pmatrix}$ by power method and the corresponding Eigen vector starting with initial vector $X_1 = \begin{pmatrix} 0 \\ 1 \end{pmatrix}$. (8)

*Or*

(*b*) (*i*) Using Gauss Jordan method solve $x + 2y + z = 3$ $2x + 3y + 3z = 10$ $3x - y + 2z = 13$. (8)

(*ii*) Solve by Gauss Seidel method

$28x + 4y - z = 32$, $2x + 17y + 4z = 35$, $x + 3y + 10z = 24$. (8)

**13.** (*a*) (*i*) From the following table find $f(x)$ and $f(6)$ using Newton's interpolation formula. (8)

| $x$ | : | 1 | 2 | 7 | 7 |
|---|---|---|---|---|---|
| $f(x)$ | : | 1 | 5 | 5 | 4 |

(*ii*) Using Stirling's formula find $y(1.22)$ given (8)

| $x$ | : | 1.0 | 1.1 | 1.2 | 1.3 | 1.4 |
|---|---|---|---|---|---|---|
| $y$ | : | .84147 | .89121 | .93204 | .96356 | 0.98545 |

*Or*

(*b*) From the following table find the Hermite's interpolating polynomial and hence find $f(.5)$. (16)

| $x$ | : | –1 | 0 | 1 |
|---|---|---|---|---|
| $f(x)$ | : | 1 | 1 | 3 |
| $f'(x)$ | : | –5 | 1 | 7 |

**14.** (*a*) (*i*) Find $f'(x), f''(x)$ at $x = 1.5$ given.

| $x$ | : | 1.5 | 2.0 | 2.5 | 3.0 | 3.5 | 4.0 |
|---|---|---|---|---|---|---|---|
| $f(x)$ | : | 3.375 | 7.0 | 13.625 | 24.0 | 38.875 | 59.0 |

(*ii*) Evaluate $\int_0^1 e^{-x^2} dx$ by dividing the range into 4 equal parts using Simpson's rule. (8)

*Or*

(*b*) (*i*) Evaluate $\int_0^1 \int_0^1 e^{x+y} dx\, dy$ by using Trapezoidal rule. (8)

(*ii*) Obtain $f'(.04)$ using Bessel's formula given (8)

| $x$ | : | .01 | .02 | .03 | .04 | .05 | .06 |
|---|---|---|---|---|---|---|---|
| $f(x)$ | : | .1023 | .1047 | .1071 | .1096 | .1122 | .1148 |

**15.** (*a*) (*i*) Using Taylor series method compute $y(.2)$, omitting $0(h^6)$

$\frac{dy}{dx} = 1 - 2xy$ $y(0) = 0$. (8)

(*ii*) Using R-K method find $y(.7)$ given $y' = y - x^2$ $y(.6) = 1.7379$. (8)

*Or*

(*b*) Given $y' = \dfrac{(1+x^2)y^2}{2}$, $y(0) = 1$ $y(.1) = 1.06$ $y(.2) = 1.12$ $y(.3) = 1.21$, evaluate $y(.4)$ by Milne's predictor corrector method. (16)

# ANNA UNIVERSITY

## B.E./B.TECH. DEGREE EXAMINATION, MAY/JUNE 2006

### Sixth Semester

### Electronics and Instrumentation Engineering

### MA 038 – NUMERICAL METHODS

(Common to Chemical Engineering Textile Technology and Leather Technology)

Time : Three hours　　　　　　　　Maximum : 100 marks

Answer All questions.

**PART A – (10 × 2 = 20 marks)**

1. Solve by iterative method to determine the real root of $x^3 - 9x + 1 = 0$ correct to three decimal places.
2. If $A$ is the largest eigen value of the matrix $A$, write the suitable method mathematically which will yield the smallest eigen value.
3. Write the divided difference table for the data given below :

| $x$ : | 1 | 2 | 4 | 7 |
|---|---|---|---|---|
| $y(x)$ : | 22 | 30 | 82 | 106 |

4. State Stirling's formula of interpolation.
5. Write the Newton's formula for $\frac{dy}{dx}$ at $x = x_0$ and Newton's backward difference formula for $\frac{d^2y}{dx^2}$ at $x = x_n$.
6. A curve passes through (0, 1), (0.25, 0.9412), (0.5, 0.8), 0.75, 0,64) and (1.0, 0.5). Find the area between the curve, $x$–axis and $x = 0$, $x = 1$ by trapezoidal rule.
7. In solving $\frac{dy}{dx} = f(x, y), y(x_0) = y_0$; write down the algorithm used in Euler's method.
8. State Adam's predictor and corrector formulae.
9. Name the two methods that you can solve one dimensional heat equation.
10. Write down the different formulae for $\frac{\partial u}{\partial x}$ in terms of difference quotients.

**PART B – (5 × 16 - 80 marks)**

**11.** (*i*) Evaluate the pivotal values of the equation $\frac{\partial^2 u}{\partial t^2} = 16\frac{\partial^2 u}{\partial x^2}$, taking $\Delta x = 1$ upto $t = 1.00$. The boundary conditions are $u(0,t) = u(5,t)$ $= 0$, $\frac{\partial u}{\partial t}(x,0) = 0$ and $u(x,0) = x^2(5-x)$. (8)

(*ii*) Solve $y^n = xy$, $y(0) = -1$, $y(1) = 2$ by finite difference method taking $n = 2$. (8)

**12.** (*a*) (*i*) By using Newton-Raphson's method, find the root of $x^4 - x - 10 = 0$ which is nearer to $x = 2$, correct up to three decimal places. (8)

(ii) Find the inverse of the matrix $\begin{bmatrix} 1 & 1 & 3 \\ 1 & 3 & -3 \\ -2 & -4 & -4 \end{bmatrix}$ using Gauss-Jordan method. (8)

**Or**

(b) (*i*) Solve the following system by Gauss-Jacobi method :

$10x - 5y - 2z = 3,\ 4x - 10y + 3z = -3,\ x + 6y + 10z = -3.$ (8)

(*ii*) Determine the largest eigen value and the corresponding eigen vector of the matrix $\begin{bmatrix} 1 & 3 & -1 \\ 3 & 2 & 4 \\ -1 & 4 & 10 \end{bmatrix}$ with $[1\ 1\ 0]^T$ upto eight iterations. (8)

**13.** (*a*) (*i*) Find $f(x)$ as a polynomial in $x$, using Newton's divided difference interpolation formula from the following data : (8)

| $x$ : | −1 | 0 | 3 | 6 | 7 |
|---|---|---|---|---|---|
| $f(x)$ : | 5 | −4 | 41 | 824 | 1613 |

(*ii*) Given the following data : (8)

| $x$ : | 20 | 30 | 40 | 50 |
|---|---|---|---|---|
| $y(x)$ : | 512 | 439 | 346 | 243 |

Find $y(35)$ using Bessel's formula.

**Or**

(*b*) (*i*) From the following table, estimate the number of students who obtained marks between 40 and 45. (6)

| Marks : | 30–40 | 40–50 | 50–60 | 60–70 | 70–80 |
|---|---|---|---|---|---|
| No. of students : | 31 | 42 | 51 | 35 | 31 |

(*ii*) Determine the Hermite polynomial of degree 5 which fits the following data: (10)

| $x$ : | 2.0 | 2.5 | 3.0 |
|---|---|---|---|
| $y(x)$ : | 0.69315 | 0.91629 | 1.09861 |
| $y'(x)$ : | 0.5 | 0.4000 | 0.33333 |

**14.** (*a*) (*i*) Using Bessel's formula, find $f(7.5)$ from the following data : (8)

| $x$ : | 7.47 | 7.48 | 7.49 | 7.50 | 7.51 | 7.52 | 7.53 |
|---|---|---|---|---|---|---|---|
| $f(x)$ : | 0.193 | 0.195 | 0.198 | 0.201 | 0.203 | 0.206 | 0.208 |

(*ii*) Evaluate $I = \int_0^1 \int_0^1 e^{x+y}\, dx\, dy$ using Simpson's rule and compare with the exact value of the double integral. (8)

**Or**

(b) (i) A slider in a machine moves along a fixed straight rod. Its distance $x$ cm. along the rod is given below for various values of the time $t$ seconds. Find the velocity of the slider when $t = 0.3$ seconds. (6)

| $t$ : | 0 | 0.1 | 0.2 | 0.3 | 0.4 | 0.5 | 0.6 |
|---|---|---|---|---|---|---|---|
| $x$ : | 30.13 | 31.62 | 32.87 | 33.64 | 33.95 | 33.81 | 33.24 |

(ii) The table below gives the velocity $\upsilon$ of a moving particle at time $t$ seconds. Find the distance covered by the particle in 12 seconds and also the acceleration at $t = 2$ seconds. (10)

| $t$ : | 0 | 2 | 4 | 6 | 8 | 10 | 12 |
|---|---|---|---|---|---|---|---|
| $\upsilon$ : | 4 | 6 | 16 | 34 | 60 | 94 | 136 |

**15.** (*a*) (*i*) Given $\frac{dy}{dx} = y - x;\ y(0) = 2,$ find $y$ (0.1), $y$ (0.2) $y$(0.3) and $y$(0.4) by Runge-Kutta method of second order, correct upto four decimal places. (8)

(*ii*) Find the Taylor series for $y(x)$, find $y(0.1)$, $y(0.2)$, $y(0.3)$ correct to four decimal places if $y(x)$ satisfies $\frac{dy}{dx} = x - y^2,\ y(0) = 1.$ (8)

**Or**

(*b*) Using Runge-Kutta method of order four, find $y$ for $x = 0.1$, 0.2, 0.3 given that $\frac{dy}{dx} = xy + y^2,\ y(0) = 1.$ Also continue to get the solution at $x = 0.4$ by Milne's method. (16)

# ANNA UNIVERSITY

## B.E./B.TECH. DEGREE EXAMINATION, MAY/JUNE 2006

## Fourth Semester

## Aeronautical Engineering

## MA 038 – NUMERICAL METHODS

(Common to Automobile Engineering, Civil Engineering, Instrumentation Engineering, Instrumentation and Control Engineering, Mechanical Engineering, Mechatronics Engineering and Production Engineering)

Time : Three hours Maximum : 100 marks

Answer All questions.

**PART A – (10 × 2 = 20 marks)**

**1.** State the following statement is 'true or false' and justify.

The convergence in the Guass-Seidel method is thrice as fast as in Jacobi's method.

**2.** Show that the iterative formula for finding the reciprocal of $N$ is $x_{n+1} = x_n(2 - Nx_n)$.

**3.** Write down the Newton's forward difference formula.

**4.** Distinguish between interpolation and extrapolation.

**5.** Evaluate $\int_{\frac{1}{2}}^{1} \frac{1}{x}\,dx$ by Trapezoidal rule, dividing the range into 4 equal parts.

**6.** When does Simpson's rule give exact result ?

**7.** How many prior values are required to predict the next value in Adam's method ?

**8.** Write down the Euler's algorithm to solve the ordinary differential equation of the first order.

**9.** Write the finite difference scheme of the differential equation $y^n + 2y = 0$.

**10.** Derive the five point formula for solving Laplace equation using finite differences.

**PART B – (5 × 16 = 80 marks)**

**11.** (*i*) Using Newton-Raphson method, establish the formula

$$x_{n+1} = \frac{1}{2}\left( x_n + \frac{N}{x_n} \right)$$ to calculate the square root of $N$. Hence find the square root of 5 correct to four places of decimals. (8)

(*ii*) Find by Gaussian elimination, the inverse of the matrix

$$\begin{bmatrix} 4 & 1 & 2 \\ 2 & 3 & -1 \\ 1 & -2 & 2 \end{bmatrix}$$ (8)

**12.** (a) (i) Construct Newton's forward interpolation polynomial for the following data: (8)

| $x$ : | 4 | 6 | 8 | 10 |
|---|---|---|---|---|
| $y$ : | 1 | 3 | 8 | 16 |

Use it to find the value of $y$ for $x = 5$.

(ii) Given $u_0 = -4$, $u_1 = -2$, $u_4 = 220$, $u_5 = 546$, $u_6 = 1148$, find $u_2$ and $u_3$.

**Or**

(*b*) (*i*) Probability distribution function values of a normal distribution are given as follows :

| $x$ : | 0.2 | 0.6 | 1.0 | 1.4 | 1.8 |
|---|---|---|---|---|---|
| $p(x)$ | 0.39104 | 0.33322 | 0.24197 | 0.14973 | 0.07895 |

Using a suitable interpolation formula, find $p(1.2)$ (8)

| $x$ : | 14 | 17 | 31 | 35 |
|---|---|---|---|---|
| $f(x)$ : | 68.7 | 64.0 | 44.0 | 39.1 |

find the value of $f(x)$ when $x = 27$.
(8)

**13.** (*a*) (*i*) From the following table, find the value of $x$ for which $y$ is minimum and find this value of $y$.

| $x$ : | –2 | –1 | 0 | 1 | 2 | 3 | 4 |
|---|---|---|---|---|---|---|---|
| $y$ : | 2 | –0.25 | 0 | –0.25 | 2 | 15.75 | 56 |

(*ii*) Using the following data, find $f'(5)$.

| $x$ : | 0 | 2 | 3 | 4 | 7 | 9 |
|---|---|---|---|---|---|---|
| $f(x)$ : | 4 | 26 | 58 | 112 | 466 | 922 |

**Or**

(*b*) (*i*) Dividing the range into 10 equal parts, find the approximate value of $\int_0^{\pi} \sin x\, dx$ by trapezoidal rule.

(*ii*) Evaluate $\int_0^1 \int_0^1 e^{x+y}\, dx dy$ using Simpson's rule.

**14.** (*a*) Solve $\frac{dy}{dx} = 1 - y$ with the initial condition $x = 0$, $y = 0$, using Euler's algorithm and tabulate the solutions at $x = 0.1, 0.2, 0.3, 0.4$. Using these remits find $y(0.5)$ using Adams-Bashforth predictor and corrector method.

**Or**

(*b*) Apply the fourth order Runge-Kutta method, to find an approximate value of $y$ when $x = 0.2$ and $x = 0.4$ given that $y' = x + y$, $y(0) = 1$ with $h = 0.2$.

**15.** (*a*) Solve $\frac{\partial^2 u}{\partial t^2} = \frac{\partial^2 u}{\partial x^2}$ subject to the following conditions

$$\left.\begin{aligned} u(0,t) &= 0 \\ u(1,t) &= 0 \end{aligned}\right\} t > 0$$

and $$\left.\begin{aligned} \frac{\partial u}{\partial t}(x,0) &= 0 \\ u(x,0) &= \sin^3 \pi x \end{aligned}\right\} \text{for all } x \text{ in } 0 \le x \le 1.$$

taking $h = \frac{1}{4}$, compute $u$ for 4 time steps.

**Or**

(*b*) Solve $\frac{\partial u}{\partial t} = \frac{\partial^2 u}{\partial x^2}$ in $0 < x < 5$; $t > 0$ given that $u(x,0) = 20$, $u(0,t) = 0$, $u(5,t) = 100$, compute $u$ for one time step with $h = 1$, by Crank-Nicholson method.

# ANNA UNIVERSITY

## B.E./B.Tech. DEGREE EXAMINATION, MAY/JUNE 2007

### Fourth Semester

### NUMERICAL METHODS

Time : Three Hours　　　　　　　　　　　　Maximum Marks : 100

Answer ALL questions.

### PART A – (10 × 2 = 20 Marks)

1. What is the criterion for the convergence of Newton-Raphson method?
2. Write down the condition for the convergence of Gauss-Seidel iteration scheme.
3. If $f(x) = \frac{1}{x^2}$, find $f(a, b)$ and $f(a, b, c)$ by using divided differences.
4. Using Lagrange's interpolation, find the polynomial through (0, 0), (1, 1) and (2, 2).
5. State the formula of Simpson's $\frac{3}{8}$th rule.
6. Write Newton's forward difference formula to find the derivatives

   $$\left(\frac{dy}{dx}\right)_{x=x_0} \text{ and } \left(\frac{d^2y}{dx^2}\right)_{x=x_0}$$

7. Write Runge-Kutta's 4th order formula to solve $\frac{dy}{dx} = f(x, y)$ with $y(x_0) = y_0$.
8. Write Taylor's series formula to solve $y' = f(x, y)$ with $y(x_0) = y_0$.
9. Write down one dimensional wave equation and its boundary conditions.
10. State the explicit formula for the one dimensional wave equation with $1 - \lambda^2 a^2 = 0$ where $\lambda = \frac{k}{h}$ and $a^2 = T/m$.

### PART B – (5 × 16 = 80 Marks)

11. (*a*) (*i*) Obtain the positive root of $2x^3 - 3x - 6 = 0$ that lies between 1 and 2 by using Newton-Raphson method. (8)

(*ii*) Find the inverse of the matrix $\begin{bmatrix} 1 & 2 & -1 \\ 4 & 1 & 0 \\ 2 & -1 & 3 \end{bmatrix}$ by Gauss-Jordan method. (8)

**Or**

(*b*) (*i*) By using Gauss-Seidel method, solve the following system of equations $6x + 3y + 12z = 35$, $8x - 3y + 2z = 20$, $4x + 11y - z = 33$. (8)

(*ii*) Find, by power method, the largest eigen value and the eigen vector of the matrix $\begin{bmatrix} 25 & 1 & 2 \\ 1 & 3 & 0 \\ 2 & 0 & -4 \end{bmatrix}$. (8)

**12.** (*a*) (*i*) Using Newton's divided difference forumla find $f(x)$ and $f(6)$ from the following data : (8)

| $x$ | : | 1 | 2 | 7 | 8 |
|---|---|---|---|---|---|
| $f(x)$ | : | 1 | 5 | 5 | 4 |

(*ii*) From the following table, find the value of tan 45°15′ by Newton's forward interpolation formula. (8)

| $x^0$ | : | 45 | 46 | 47 | 48 | 49 | 50 |
|---|---|---|---|---|---|---|---|
| $\tan x^0$ | : | 1.00000 | 1.03553 | 1.07237 | 1.11061 | 1.15037 | 1.19175 |

**Or**

(*b*) Fit the cubic spline for the data : (16)

| $x$ | : | 0 | 1 | 2 | 3 |
|---|---|---|---|---|---|
| $f(x)$ | : | 1 | 2 | 9 | 28 |

**13.** (*a*) (*i*) Evaluate $\int_1^2 \int_1^2 \frac{dx\,dy}{x+y}$ with $h = k = 0.2$ by using trapezoidal rule. (8)

(*ii*) From the following table, find the value of $x$ for which $f(x)$ is maximum. Also find the maximum value. (8)

| $x$ | : | 60 | 75 | 90 | 105 | 120 |
|---|---|---|---|---|---|---|
| $f(x)$ | : | 28.2 | 38.2 | 43.2 | 40.9 | 37.7 |

**Or**

(*b*) (*i*) Using Romberg's rule, evaluate $\int_0^1 \frac{dx}{1+x}$ correct to three decimal places by taking $h = 0.5$, 0.25 and 0.125. (8)

(*ii*) By dividing the range into ten equal parts, evaluate $\int_0^{\pi} \sin x dx$ by using Simpson's $\frac{1}{3}$rd rule. Is it possible to evaluate the same by Simpson's $\frac{3}{8}$th rule . Justify your answer. (8)

**14.** (*a*) (*i*) Using Taylor's series method, find $y$ when $x = 1.1$ and $1.2$ from $\frac{dy}{dx} = xy^{1/3}$, $y(1) = 1$. (4 decimal places). (8)

(*ii*) By using Adam's pc method find $y$ when $x = 0.4$, given $\frac{dy}{dx} = \frac{xy}{2}$, $y(0) = 1, y(0.1) = 1.01, y(0.2) = 1.022, y(0.3) = 1.023$. (8)

**Or**

(*b*) (*i*) Using Runge-Kutta method of 4th order, solve $\frac{dy}{dx} = \frac{y^2 - x^2}{y^2 + x^2}$, given $y(0) = 1$ at $x = 0.2$. Take $h = 0.2$. (8)

(*ii*) Find the value of $y$ when $x = 0.1$ and $0.2$, given $\frac{dy}{dx} = x^2 + y^2$ with $y = 1$ when $x = 0$. Use modified Euler's method. (8)

**15.** (*a*) Solve the Laplace's equation over the square mesh of side 4 units, satisfying the boundary conditions : (16)

$u(0, y) = 0,\ 0 \le y \le 4;\ u(4, y) = 12 + y, 0 \le y \le 4;$

$u(x, 0) = 3x,\ 0 \le x \le 4;\ u(x, 4) = x^2,\ 0 \le x \le 4.$

**Or**

(*b*) (*i*) Derive Bender-Schmidt for solving $u_{xx} - au_t = 0$ with the b.cs. $u(0, t) = T_0$; $u(l, t) = T_l$ and $u(x, 0) = f(x)$ for $0 < x < l$. Also find corresponding recurrence equation. (8)

(*ii*) By finite difference method, solve $\frac{d^2 y}{dx^2} + x^2 y = 0$ with the b.cs $y(0) = 0$ and $y(1) = 1$, $h = 0.25$. (8)

# INDEX